THE THEORY OF HEAT

MACMILLAN AND CO., Limited
LONDON · BOMBAY · CALCUTTA · MADRAS
MELBOURNE

THE MACMILLAN COMPANY
NEW YORK · BOSTON · CHICAGO
DALLAS · SAN FRANCISCO

THE MACMILLAN COMPANY
OF CANADA, LIMITED
TORONTO

THE

THEORY OF HEAT

BY

THOMAS PRESTON

M.A. (Dub.), D.Sc. (R.U.I.), F.R.S.

FELLOW OF THE ROYAL UNIVERSITY OF IRELAND
PROFESSOR OF NATURAL PHILOSOPHY, UNIVERSITY COLLEGE, DUBLIN
INSPECTOR OF SCIENCE SCHOOLS UNDER THE SCIENCE AND ART DEPARTMENT

FOURTH EDITION

EDITED BY

J. ROGERSON COTTER

M.A. (Dub.)

LECTURER IN THE SCHOOL OF ENGINEERING, TRINITY COLLEGE, DUBLIN

MACMILLAN AND CO., LIMITED
ST. MARTIN'S STREET, LONDON

1929

PRINTED IN GREAT BRITAIN
BY R. & R. CLARK, LIMITED, EDINBURGH

PREFACE TO THE FIRST EDITION

In preparing this volume my object has been to treat the science of heat in a comprehensive manner, so as to produce a tolerably complete account of the whole subject in its experimental as well as its theoretical aspect. I have consequently enjoyed a freedom in my choice of subject-matter, and mode of exposition, which would not have been possible in a work designed to meet the requirements of some particular class of persons preparing for examinations or engaged in practical pursuits.

It is but a short time since the pursuit of experimental research was regarded merely as a matter of individual curiosity; but owing to the high commercial value and important bearings of many of the recent discoveries in the fields of science, the public mind has now become awakened to the conviction that knowledge is wealth, and that the scientific education of the people is a matter of national importance.

In the struggle for place it is not surprising that the nobler aspect of science, as an instrument of education and culture, should be lost sight of in the popular desire for a mere acquaintance with the facts demanded by the exigencies of the moment. It cannot, however, be too soon or too often impressed upon the beginner that an acquaintance with a number of facts does not constitute a scientific education, and that there is no royal road to learning other than that by which it is pursued for its own sake.

The great lessons of history are not to be found in the records of battles or in the details of infamous amours and massacres, nor in the memory of the dates, but rather in the full knowledge of the inner meaning of events, and a due appreciation of their general bearing on the social development of mankind. So also in science, that knowledge which is power is not the mere memory of facts, but the comprehension of their whole meaning in the story of nature.

It is in the pursuit of this knowledge that scientific theories are formed. Without a theory all our knowledge of nature would be reduced to a mere inventory of the results of observation. Every scientific theory must be regarded as an effort of the human mind to grasp the truth, and as long as it is consistent with the facts, it forms a chain by which they are linked together and woven into harmony.

The fact that any theory, however plausible, may ultimately become untenable, demands its constant comparison with the results of experiments, and the closest scrutiny at every step of its development. In this respect, and also from an educational point of view, the historical method of treatment possesses many advantages in the exposition of any scientific subject. When this method is combined with that detail in description and explanation which is necessary to secure instruction, and also with such suggestion and criticism as may excite intellectual life and independent thought on the part of the student, it does not lend itself readily to the production of a pocket edition of the sciences. It must be remembered, however, that the most fruitful method of exposition is not necessarily that by which a given number of facts may be recorded in the smallest space, but rather that by which they may be most easily assimilated by the mind, and most comprehensively grasped in their general bearings and mutual relations ; and this is the method which is most calculated to advance knowledge and raise the intellectual character of the individual.

I have now to express my obligations to the many sources of information which I have laid under contribution during the comparatively short time allotted to the preparation of this work. Due reference is given to these throughout the text, and it is hoped this may increase the usefulness of the book to those who desire fuller information on any particular point. I have given in detail what may be called the classical experiments of the subject, and in addition I have noticed such other investigations as will give the student a general idea of the character of the work that has been done in each department up to the present time. The diagrams with which these descriptions are illustrated have all been prepared by Mr. J. D. Cooper (188 Strand, London) with exceptional attention and despatch.,

Such subjects as the steam-engine and the theory of solutions have been omitted, as they demand, and have already obtained, separate treatment in special works. The kinetic theory of gases has only been entered into so far as to meet the immediate requirements of the subject in hand; and it would be desirable to treat this, and some other subjects usually dealt with in treatises on Heat, in a separate volume.

In conclusion, I beg to offer my best thanks to Mr. Charles J. Joly, M.A., of Trinity College, Dublin, and Professor Alex. Anderson of Queen's College, Galway, for their kind assistance in reading the proofs. To Professor G. F. FitzGerald I am indebted for much valuable criticism and suggestion while the work was passing through the press, and also for the continuance of that generous assistance and advice with which he favoured me during the preparation of my work on the *Theory of Light*.

THOMAS PRESTON.

DUBLIN, *January* 1894.

PREFACE TO THE FOURTH EDITION

SINCE the publication of the last edition of this treatise very few of the advances made in theoretical physics have been concerned with the subject of heat, except in the domain of quantum theory, which is beyond the scope of the book. In the preparation of the present edition I have accordingly devoted my attention almost exclusively to an endeavour to bring the book up to date in the department of experimental determinations of thermal data. With this object in view, I have read a large number of original papers published in a great variety of scientific journals. Owing to limitations of space I have been compelled to restrict myself rigorously in the use of this material, but I venture to hope that little of importance or interest has escaped my notice.

In order to obtain room for new additions I have omitted considerable portions of the last edition and condensed others. The omitted parts consist mainly of descriptions of experiments and discussions about disputed points which possess little interest at the present day. Some readers may perhaps think that the process of condensation might have been carried further, but besides feeling a natural reluctance to interfere with the work of the author more than is strictly necessary, I find it difficult to condense a description already written without producing a patchy effect. Some discussions relating to methods which may be regarded as obsolete have been deliberately retained on the ground that they are both interesting and instructive and not likely to be found elsewhere.

In the second and third editions new additions were distinguished by enclosing them in square brackets. These have now become so numerous that they would have rendered the book unsightly, and I have consequently omitted them altogether. As the first edition appeared in 1894, additions to the work of the original author may generally be recognised by the dates given in the footnotes. These additions include descriptions of modern methods of thermometry and calorimetry, the parts relating to black-body radiation, and the chapter on the kinetic theory of gases. The size of the book is about the same as in the last edition.

I have made some use of Glazebrook's *Dictionary of Applied Physics* as a work of reference, but in the description of experimental methods, etc., I have invariably consulted the original sources.

I have to thank Dr. W. E. Forsythe of Cleveland, Ohio; Professor Henning of Berlin; and Professor Keesom of Leyden, for copies of original papers, some of which I could not obtain in the Dublin libraries.

J. R. COTTER.

40 Trinity College, Dublin,
    13th *November* 1928.

CONTENTS

CHAPTER I

PRELIMINARY SKETCH

CHAPTER II

THERMOMETRY

CHAPTER III

DILATATION

CHAPTER IV

CALORIMETRY

CHAPTER V

CHANGE OF STATE

CHAPTER VI

RADIATION AND ABSORPTION

CHAPTER VII

CONDUCTION

CHAPTER VIII

THERMODYNAMICS

CHAPTER IX

KINETIC THEORY OF GASES

CHAPTER I

PRELIMINARY SKETCH

SECTION I

INTRODUCTORY

1. THERE is, perhaps, no scientific inquiry more full of human interest than the study of the nature of heat, and the manner in which matter in general is affected by it. No branch of physical science is so intimately connected with the everyday occupations of life, and, consequently, none of them interests mankind more closely.

The influence of heat is manifestly so universal, and its actions so important and necessary to the progress of all the operations of nature, that, to those who first considered it with some attention, it must have at once appeared to be the general principle of all life and activity on this globe. With its return in springtime the bud breaks into blossom, and new life animates the vegetable kingdom. By its agency the incubation of the egg progresses, a living thing is brought into the world, and heat is still necessary to its support. Finally, to the power which man has acquired over it is due that supernatural strength which has made him superior to all other animals, and master of land and sea.

It is not surprising, therefore, that an agent at once so powerful and so serviceable, so beneficent and yet sometimes so terrible, should have become a subject of adoration and worship among the inhabitants of the earth, but at first sight it may seem more than surprising that its study in early times should have been so much neglected.

2. This indifference can only be attributed to that lack of attention with which men always regard those things which they are accustomed to use instinctively for their needs, and which they have before them at all times. The first instinct of man is to direct and use the forces of nature for the purposes of life. Theorising follows

1   B

9145

afterwards. The early acquisition of this practical knowledge is proved by mighty monuments which were raised by the workmen of the earliest historic times. The magnificent temples of India, the vast pyramids of Egypt, the noble architecture and sculpture of Greece and Rome, prove that the engineers of those days had acquired a knowledge of some of the methods of transporting cyclopean masses. Various hydraulic and pneumatic apparatus were certainly in vogue, and many engines were invented by Ctesibus and his pupil Hero.

The ancient philosophers were, however, strongly disinclined to impart their learning to the public, and each in general communicated it only to his special disciples. They all esteemed it an essential part of learning to be able to conceal their knowledge from the uninitiated, and even those who were most celebrated for their inventions were so infected by this superstition that they refrained from leaving any written account of their discoveries,—a practice which was certainly detrimental to the advancement of posterity.

3. The question, "What is heat?" must, however, have been proposed and pondered over by all inquiring minds from the earliest times. Man could not go on for ever using fire to cook his food and warm his body without seeking to know something of the source and nature of this agent. The inquiring mind cannot rest satisfied with the mere observation of the facts of nature, but is irresistibly led to investigate their origin and cause. The fact of highest interest and importance is that the sun illuminates and warms the earth, and the questions which must have presented themselves earliest to the attention of philosophers were, "What is light?" and "What is heat?" A question of a much simpler order is, "What is sound?" and that any satisfactory answer has been obtained to the two former is probably owing to the proposition and solution of the latter. Amid the phenomena of sound we deal with a medium which we can subject to experiment, and whose properties we can thoroughly examine, but in the phenomena of heat and light we step at once into the sanctuary of the unknown. From the domain of the visible and tangible we pass into that of the invisible and intangible. The known process, however, gives direction to the line of thought, and, reasoning by analogy, the imagination expands from the domains of the senses and embraces in thought the regions which lie beyond it. By observation and experiment the human mind becomes acquainted with a knowledge of the properties and relations of things, and, reasoning upon the information thus supplied, we rise to the explanation of the unknown and intangible by means of the ideas which we have gained from what is known and tangible.

The reverse and less philosophic process—the explanation of the visible by means of the invisible—seems to have been the general habit of those who first speculated in physical science. In all the pursuits which required refined taste and the native powers of the intellect, the ancient Greeks were pre-eminent. They possessed, as if instinctively, the perception of everything that is sublime and beautiful. They were keen observers of men, but as physical philosophers they failed, not perhaps from want of genius or application, but because they pursued a false path; because they reasoned more upon an imaginary system of nature than upon an accurate knowledge of the facts; and tried to explain physical phenomena by resorting to speculation more than to observation and experiment. The general tendency was to explain the seen by means of the unseen, and to appeal to the imagination rather than to observe facts. Thus, the general effects of heat were *explained* by the invention of *fire atoms*, which drove furiously through the pores of bodies, and loosened their molecules asunder, reducing solids to liquids, and liquids to vapours.

4. The systematic study of heat, as a distinct branch of experimental science, commenced little more than half a century ago. Previously the nature and effects of heat (or fire) were investigated only by the chemist, whose most powerful agent and ally it has always proved. One of the earliest attempts at theorising in chemistry originated in the explanation of the nature of combustion, and, consequently, in tracing the origin and growth of our subject we are led back to the early study and growth of the science of chemistry, and of experimental inquiry in general.

Although the practice of alchemy seems to have been common among the Egyptians in very remote ages, yet the origin of experimental inquiry cannot be dated farther back than the seventh or eighth century of the Christian era. Its inception seems to have been coeval with the short period during which cultivation and scientific learning were promoted by the Arabians. Actuated by the desire for wealth, the alchemists ardently prosecuted the search after the artificial production of the noble metals, and visionary as may have been their hopes, yet they made experiments, and the experiments of the alchemists were more calculated to extend the bounds of human knowledge than the speculations of the Greeks.

While Greece and Italy sank into barbarism, the early Mohammedans, who had previously destroyed almost all the records of the progress of the human mind, rekindled the light of learning, and became the cultivators of a new science. From Egypt, where they became acquainted with the Aristotelian philosophy and chemistry, they penetrated through northern Africa, and crossed over into Spain, and here arts and sciences flourished under their dominion. The academies of Spain were soon thronged with students from all parts of the Christian world, the knowledge of alchemy spread, and in the thirteenth century alchemists of the Arabian school were established in all the chief countries of Europe.

5. Amongst a people of conquerors disposed to sensuality and luxury, even from the very spirit of their religion, and who were romantic and magnificent in their views of power, it was not to be expected that any new science would be pursued in a rational and philosophic manner. As a consequence the early discoveries in chemistry led to the practice of alchemy, the objects of which were to produce a substance (*the philosopher's stone*) capable of converting all the other metals into gold, and to discover *the elixir of life*—a universal remedy against old age, calculated to preserve youth and prolong indefinitely the period of human life.

The processes relating to the discovery of the philosopher's stone and the elixir of life were probably widely diffused by means of the Crusades, for many of the warriors who, animated with visionary plans of conquest, fought the battles of their religion in Palestine, seem to have returned to their native lands under the influence of a new delusion.

At this time the public spirit of the West was calculated to assist the progress of all pursuits that carried with them the air of mysticism. Burning with the ardour of a rapidly extending and exalted religion, men were much more disposed to believe than to reason. In all times, however, the love of knowledge and power has been instinctive to the human mind; in darkness it desires light, and follows it with ardent enthusiasm, even when appearing in delusive glimmerings.

6. The Middle Ages consequently constitute what may be regarded as the heroic, or fabulous, epoch in experimental physics, and, as might be expected, their records contain a great variety of anecdotes relating to the transmutation of metals, and the views or pretensions of persons considered as adepts in alchemy.

Some of these alchemists were low impostors, whose object was to delude and defraud the credulous and ignorant. Others seem to have deceived themselves with vain hopes, but all followed the pursuit as a secret and mysterious study. The processes were communicated only to a few chosen disciples, and, being veiled in the most obscure and enigmatic language, their importance was enhanced by their ambiguity.

In all ages men have been governed more by what they desire or fear than by what they know, and in this age it was particularly easy to deceive, but difficult to enlighten, the public mind.[1] Truths, however, were discovered, but they were so blended with the false and marvellous that another era was required to separate them from concomitant absurdity, and to demonstrate their true importance and uses.

The alchemists in chemistry have been somewhat like the perpetual motionists in natural philosophy. Both, by seeking after the impossible, have led up to discoveries of the greatest importance and practical value. Both, like the fabled husbandmen of old, by seeking after brilliant impossibilities, sometimes discovered useful realities.

7. Even in these times, however, progress was made, and there were some who essayed to form scientific views. Men of exceptional intellectual power were found differentiating themselves from the crowd, and seeking to connect natural phenomena with their physical principles. By the early alchemists the elements had been placed under the dominion of spiritual beings, and their followers in Europe conceived gnomes and nymphs, sylphs and salamanders, genii and fairies, capable of being governed and enslaved by man. These spiritual agents seem to have originated with the alchemists, who all professed to believe in supernatural powers, in an art above experiment, and a system of knowledge not derived from the senses. In addition, the systems of logic adopted in the schools were founded rather upon the analogies of words than upon the relations of things, and they were consequently more calculated to conceal error than to discover the truth.

8. With the revival of literature in Europe came the desire for philosophic discussion in the sciences. The diffusion of letters gradually brought the opinions of men to the standard of truth and nature. Failures in the experimental arts produced caution, and the frequent detection of imposture created rational scepticism. Science demanded the extirpation of the gods and demons which haunted its domains, and called for absolute reliance upon law in nature. The supernatural was swept from the field, and gave place to a rational basis for natural phenomena, and the problems previously attacked from above were now approached from below.

In the beginning of the thirteenth century Roger Bacon of Oxford applied himself to observation and experiment with characteristic

---

[1] That the delusions of alchemy were ardently pursued may be learned from the public acts of these times. In 1316 the alchemists were openly condemned by Pope John XXII. as impostors, who promised what they did not perform, and in England an Act of Parliament was passed in the fifth year of the reign of Henry IV., prohibiting attempts at transmutation, and rendering them felonious.

talent and sagacity. A man of truly philosophic turn, desirous of
investigating nature, and of extending the resources of art, his
inquiries offered some very extraordinary combinations, but neither
his labours nor those of Albert of Cologne (a contemporary genius of
kindred spirit) seem to have had any considerable influence on the
improvement of his age. The wonders performed by the experimental
art were attributed by the vulgar to magic, and at a time when knowledge resided only in the cloister any new philosophy was regarded by
the learned with a jealous eye.

9. Before the time of Lord Bacon there had been no distinct views
concerning the art of experimental inquiry. It was left for him to
point out how little could be effected by the unassisted human powers.
He directed the attention of inquirers to artificial resources and the
use of instruments for assisting the senses, and for examining bodies
under new relations. He taught that man was but the servant and
interpreter of nature, capable of discovering truth in no way but by
observing and imitating her operations ; that facts were to be collected
before speculations were formed ; and that the materials for the
foundations of true systems of knowledge were not to be discovered
in the books of the ancients, nor in metaphysical theories, nor in the
fancies of men, but by observation of the visible and tangible in the
external world.

Facts are independent of taste and fashion, and are subject to
no code of criticism. They are perhaps more useful when they contradict than when they support received doctrines, for our theories
at best are only imperfect approximations to the real knowledge of
things, and in all physical research doubt is usually an incentive to
new labours, and tends continually to the development of truth. The
thoughts and questionings of man turn towards the sources of natural
phenomena and seek a knowledge of the actions which underlie them.
By a process of abstraction from experience physical theories are
formed which lie outside the pale of experience, but which satisfy the
desire of the mind to see every event in nature resting upon a cause.
Natural philosophy is an *experimental* and not an *intuitive* science, and
a priori reasoning cannot alone conduct us to a physical truth. We
must endeavour to discover what it is, and not speculate on what it
might be, or decide on what ought to have been, and the causes and
connections of the phenomena of nature have escaped the apprehension
of man for ages by the wilful ignoring of this fact.[1]

10. About the middle of the seventeenth century mathematical
and physical investigations were pursued in every part of the civilised

[1] See Tait's *Sketch of Thermodynamics*. Edinburgh : David Douglas.

world with an enthusiasm before unknown. The new mode of improving knowledge by collecting facts associated together a number of labourers in the same pursuit. It was felt that the whole of nature was yet to be investigated, and that there were distinct subjects connected with utility and glory, sufficient to employ all inquirers, yet tending to the common end of promoting the progress of the human mind.

Learned bodies were formed in Italy, England, and France, for the purpose of the interchange of opinions, the combination of labour, the division of expense in performing new experiments, and the accumulation and diffusion of knowledge. The Academy del Cimento was established in 1651, under the patronage of the Duke of Tuscany ; the Royal Society of London in 1660 ; and the Royal Academy of Sciences of Paris in 1666. A number of celebrated men, who have been the great luminaries of the different departments of science, were brought together or arose in these noble establishments. The ardour of scientific investigation was excited and kept alive by sympathy. Taste was improved by discussion, and by a comparison of opinions. The conviction that useful discoveries would be appreciated and rewarded was a constant stimulus to industry, and every field of inquiry was open to the free and unbiassed exercise of the powers of genius.

11. Chemistry had scarcely begun to assume the form of a science when the attention of all the most brilliant intellects became directed to another object of research. The Newtonian philosophy sprang into full life at a single bound, and its objects were calculated by their grandeur to monopolise the attention of the most gifted men of the age. The effect occasioned on the scientific minds of the time has been compared to that which the new sensations of vision produce on the blind receiving sight. The highest interest and most enthusiastic admiration were awakened, and for nearly half a century the new study engrossed the thoughts of the most eminent philosophers of Europe.

At length the current of scientific thought began to flow in other channels, and in the latter half of the eighteenth century the foundations of a systematic inquiry into the nature of heat were laid by Black, Wilcke, Crawford, Irvine, and Lavoisier, followed by Rumford, Pictet, Herschel, Leslie, Dalton, Davy, Gay-Lussac, and many others. On the basis thus firmly laid a noble edifice has since been raised, a lasting monument to the genius of the nineteenth century ; and from base to highest battlement may be traced the work of our illustrious countrymen—Rankine, Joule, and Thomson.

12. A review of the opinions of the ancients, and of their speculations in physical science, may prove amusing in some parts, but everywhere it is a most instructive task.   Their writings on every branch
partake more of the character of a record of ingenious speculation
than of experimental inquiry.   Hypotheses of a mystical character
were framed to explain the phenomena of nature, and physical results
were based on meaningless dogmas.   Men were told that the planets
move in circles *because* circular motion is perfect, and systems of
physics were founded on the assertion that "nature abhors a vacuum"
and the Latin dogma, "causa equat effectum."   While this lasted
progress in the physical sciences was impossible.   Dogma was handed
down from generation to generation, and free thought found no place
in the schools of the Middle Ages.

It is, however, unfair to boast of the progress of the nineteenth
century as compared with that of the generations which have preceded
it.   At a time when little is known men grope after knowledge in the
dark, and though the gateway may be near at hand, the entrance may
not be effected, until happily some one stumbles in by accident.   Once
entered, the passage becomes easy for those who follow, and future
progress is enormously assisted by the history of the failures and
successes of those who have gone before.   Difference of native intellectual power in different ages is not so much the cause of the varying success attending the labours of men as the peculiar nature of
the artificial resources and means in their possession.   At all times
progress is retarded by absolute reliance on the work of great masters.
The first function of the human mind is to doubt, and to free itself
from prejudice and from all testimony which may deceive the senses.
Emancipation from the slavery of superstition and the influences of
early education is a very slow process.   Sentiment is constitutional
to mankind, and the strongest intellects find it hard to break away
from the teaching of those whom they have early learned to reverence,
even when its errors are clearly and conclusively pointed out to them.
Throughout this long period the spirit of free inquiry was growing
and gathering strength for a brave struggle against the superstition
and mysticism in which it was entangled.   The germ of true scientific
inquiry finally took root and flourished.   Intellectual health ensued,
and resulted in scientific progress.   The abominations of the alchemists
were swept away, the spirits of the air disappeared, and the pursuit of
science became the free inquiry after truth.

The history of such a period is therefore not merely a matter of
curiosity.   It is a great lesson to all subsequent ages.   It shows that
truth in physical science is not to be sought for in dogma, nor can a

system of nature be built up from our inner consciousness, but that it must be sought for earnestly and honestly by patient observation and skilled experiment.

It is sometimes asserted that metaphysical speculation is a thing of the past, and that physical science has extirpated it. But as long as the mind of man is fresh, speculation will continue as fascinating as it was in the days of Thales. Perhaps at no time has the scientific atmosphere been more pregnant with speculation than at present. Almost every day fresh discoveries are made and new theories formulated and advanced on doubtful or entirely hypothetical foundations. At the same time the germs of all kinds of mental disorders are rife. Perpetual motionists and believers that the earth is flat have not yet become extinct. Spiritualists and quack scientists increase at an amazing pace, and the patent-medicine man grows wealthy, while the spirit of true scientific inquiry sickens in the fierce struggle for existence.

SECTION II

13. The Sense of Heat.—The terms hot and cold are primitive
words of the language referring to a certain class of sensations which
we experience through the *sense of heat.* The sense of touch is regarded
by some as a double sense, embracing that of heat as well as that of
force or resistance. When a body is touched with the hand two very
distinct sensations are in general experienced, one a feeling of resistance or force, and the other of warmth or coldness derived through
what is termed our sense of heat. The latter class of sensation is also
experienced when we sit in the sun or before the fire, or in the neighbourhood of any hot body, and consequently to excite it actual contact
with matter is not necessary. It is therefore not at all obvious that
the sense of heat is part of, or in any way related to, the sense of
touch. On the contrary, it appears to be much more closely related
to the sense of sight. A hot body is to be regarded as the source of
an influence which affects the sense of heat just as a luminous body is
regarded as the source of an influence affecting the sense of sight.
The name given to the active agent in the former case is *heat* and in
the latter *light,* and we shall see as the subject progresses that these
two influences are of the same character, and that the nature of the
active agent in one case is the same as in the other. The sense of
heat, therefore, is quite as distinct as the sense of sight, and is certainly
less related to the sense of touch than is the sense of taste or smell,
which both depend upon contact with some form of matter (see
further, p. 31).

14. Definition of Temperature.—The words hot and cold, or hotness and coldness, refer to the state of a body as judged by the sense
of heat. By means of this sense we say that one body is hot and that
another is cold, or that one body is hotter than another. If several
pieces of the *same* substance be given, we can by means of the sense of

10

heat alone arrange them in order so that each shall be hotter than all that precede it in the series and colder than all that come after. We are hence led to the idea of a *scale of hotness*, and to inquire how much one body is hotter than another.

The estimation of the hotness of a body must of course be relative to some scale or standard of measurement. When this standard is chosen we may speak scientifically of the hotness of a body, and for this purpose the word *temperature* is employed. The word temperature thus means simply the degree of hotness of a body measured according to some arbitrarily chosen scale. It is a *scientific* term, and contains all the meaning of the primitive word hotness, as well as the idea of a measure of the hotness. It embraces two conceptions— first, the idea of equality of hotness, or that condition of two pieces of matter when they are said to have the same temperature; and secondly, the idea of difference of hotness and of its mode of measurement.

Scientific term.

By means of the sense of heat alone a series of pieces of the *same* substance might be arranged in order of temperature, or the equality of temperature of two pieces of the same substance might be fairly accurately judged, and if the impressions could be distinctly remembered a system of measurement of temperature might be founded on the sense of heat alone. Accuracy by this method would be practically impossible, for the recollection of even a single temperature can be only roughly retained by those who specially cultivate the sense of heat for this purpose, such as bath attendants or hospital nurses. For scientific purposes it is therefore highly desirable to estimate temperature by some property of matter which varies continuously with the hotness, and which always remains the same at the same hotness.

Intervals of hotness cannot, however, be *measured* in the proper sense of the word. They may be indicated in a thoroughly definite manner, according to some chosen scale or standard, but one hotness cannot be expressed in terms of another in the same sense that one length or mass may be expressed in terms of another. In order to *measure* any magnitude we must compare it with some other magnitude of the same order which is taken as the unit. Thus a measuring tape is constructed by adding together any number of units of length, but we possess no means of adding together in the same way units of hotness. When, however, the scale of temperature is laid down and graduated by arbitrary definition, we may say that the interval between two temperatures is equal to the interval between two other temperatures, meaning thereby merely that each interval contains the same number of scale-units on our chosen system.

15. Expansion.—One of the most general effects of change of

temperature or hotness in any body is change of bulk, or expansion
by heat. The bulk of every body, with few exceptions, is found to
increase continuously with its hotness, and consequently this change
has been selected as the basis of a method of measuring temperature.
The mode by which the change of temperature is indicated by the
change of volume of course remains a matter of choice, as well as the
particular substance employed.

General
effects.
There are many ways of exhibiting the expansion of solids by
heat, and several of these are so common that almost every one must
be familiar with them. Thus the metal rails on a railway track are
laid not with their ends in contact, but with a short space between to
allow for expansion in summer, and for the same reason in large
structures, such as metal bridges, the girders are not fixed rigidly at
both ends, but a certain play is allowed so that they may expand
without warping or rupturing the structure. This expansion is also
made use of in the shoeing of cart wheels, the tyre being slipped on
while hot, and as it cools it contracts and clasps the wooden frame
within. A similar application occurs in the bracing together of the
walls of a building which suffer from an outward lean. Strong bars
of iron are thrust through the building and secured on the outside
while hot, and on cooling the bars contract and pull the walls
together. To expansion also is to be attributed the ventilation of
mines and houses, as well as the general circulation of water and air
on the earth's surface, and the effect of these great ocean streams and
air currents is to produce a more uniform distribution of temperature.

A familiar class illustration is that known as Gravesande's ring.
A metal sphere which just passes through a ring when cool, when heated
over a lamp will no longer pass through. Its diameter is now larger
than that of the ring, but in cooling it contracts and again passes freely
through. In the same manner a metal bar which fits into a tube
when cold cannot when heated be passed into the same tube. It is
for this reason that a glass stopper tightly jammed in the neck of a
bottle may be easily removed by heating the neck. The heat of the
hand placed around the neck of the bottle is often sufficient for this
purpose. If the stopper happens to be colder than the neck of the
bottle when it is inserted in it, then, as the neck cools, it contracts
and grasps the stopper tightly. In the same manner ordinary
tumblers often become wedged within one another, and in such
cases, if the inner is initially much colder than the outer, the contraction of the latter or expansion of the former may lead to the
fracture of one or both.

One of the most interesting illustrations of expansion, however, is presented in the gradual creeping of a sheet of metal down a slope. Take the case of a long bar of metal lying lengthwise down an inclined plane. When the temperature increases the bar expands and pushes forward its lower end rather than its upper, on account of the action of gravity which facilitates motion down the plane rather than up it. In the same way, when the bar cools it contracts and draws in its upper end, and this process goes on with every variation of temperature, the result being that the bar gradually creeps down the incline worm-wise by alternately pushing forward its lower, and pulling in its upper end. The gradual creeping in this manner of the sheet lead covering the choir of Bristol Cathedral is cited by Professor Tyndall,[1] the rate of motion being about 9 inches per annum.

Similarly, by placing a metal bar on wheels capable of rotation Creepers. in one direction only, the system will creep forward in this direction with every variation of temperature, so that the ordinary variations of temperature by day and night will cause this apparatus to move in any desired direction, up hill or down, and during this motion it might be loaded in any way, and perform the part of a heat engine. The motion, of course, would be very slow unless special means were devised to increase it. Thus, for example, the bar might be replaced by a highly expansive liquid enclosed in a large bulb furnished with a cylindrical tube in which a piston is fitted. When the temperature rises, the liquid in the bulb will expand and push the piston forward, and when the temperature falls, the liquid will contract, leaving a vacuum behind the piston, and for this reason the bulb will move forward, since on account of the construction of the wheels on which the instrument is supported the piston cannot move back. Similar apparatus may be constructed by supporting on wheels bent tubes filled with some expansive liquid or a bent strip of two or more metals welded together, such as those employed in metallic thermometers (see Art. 77). In principle, however, all such forms of apparatus are the same as the curiosity known as Stevenson's Creeper.[2]

In the case of solids, the volume may be measured directly, and Apparent the absolute expansion determined, but in the case of liquids, which expansion. must be enclosed in some solid envelope, the expansion of the liquid is complicated by that of the vessel which contains it, and the result observed is the relative or apparent expansion of the liquid in the envelope. Thus, for example, if a large bulb furnished with a narrow stem, or a flask with a narrow neck, be filled with a liquid, and

[1] Tyndall, *Heat a Mode of Motion*, p. 95, 6th edition.
[2] Described in Tait's *Heat*, p. 116.

then heated over a lamp, the liquid will at first be observed to descend in the neck as if it contracted when heated. Soon, however, the apparent contraction ceases, and the liquid begins to rise in the stem, and continues to do so as the temperature becomes more and more elevated. The first effect is due to the sudden expansion of the flask before the general mass of the liquid becomes warm. For this reason the internal volume of the flask is increased while the volume of the liquid is scarcely altered. Soon, however, the liquid grows warm and expands accordingly. If the expansion of the liquid be greater than that of the envelope, the level of the liquid will rise in the neck, but if it be less, the level of the liquid will fall. The level would neither rise nor fall if the expansion of the liquid were the same as that of the envelope. The movement of the liquid in the stem, therefore, does not indicate its absolute expansion, but only its apparent expansion, or its expansion relative to that of the material of the envelope.

16. Change of State.—Another general effect of heat on matter is change of physical state. By sufficiently increasing the temperature, solids are converted into liquids, and liquids into vapours. While either change is taking place the temperature of the mass is found to remain constant till the change is completely effected. Thus, if a vessel full of broken ice be placed over a lamp, the ice will gradually melt, but the temperature of the whole mass will not alter till the melting is completed. The heat received is employed in changing the state of the substance, in converting it from solid ice to liquid water. If the supply of heat be still continued, the liquid will rise in temperature and ultimately begin to boil. When this point is reached, the temperature again remains stationary. The liquid simply passes into vapour, and the heat supplied during this process is used up in changing the state of the substance from that of liquid to that of vapour.

The change of physical state of any substance thus furnishes us with two fixed temperatures when the conditions under which the change takes place are given. Such changes are often very abrupt, and are consequently not suited to the estimation of temperatures which vary continuously or rapidly. They serve rather to indicate particular temperatures. For this reason the property made use of most commonly in practice is the change of volume of some liquid contained in a glass envelope, such as the ordinary mercurial thermometer.

17. The Mercury Thermometer.—For the better understanding of the subsequent matter of this chapter, it may be well here to describe briefly the ordinary mercury thermometer,[1] which is the instrument most commonly employed in the measurement of temperature. The property made use of in this instrument for the measurement of temperature is the expansion of mercury enclosed in a glass measuring flask, or volume indicator. This consists of a glass bulb, generally cylindrical or spherical, furnished with a stem of capillary bore (Fig. 1). The bulb and part of the stem are filled with mercury, and, as already explained, the level of the mercury in the stem will vary with the temperature, unless the glass and the mercury expand equally when heated. As a matter of fact, the mercury is much more expansible than the glass, and the level of the mercury rises in the stem as the instrument grows warmer.

Here, then, we have an instrument, the indications of which vary continuously with its hotness, and which will always show the same indications under the same conditions, and which, therefore, supplies a mode of measuring temperature, and enables us to define degrees of temperature, so that it shall in some way indicate the hotness of a body, and thus replace our sense of heat.

In order to obtain a numerical measure of temperature the instrument must be graduated, and for this purpose two fixed temperatures are chosen. The points of the stem at which the mercury stands at these two temperatures are marked, and the portion of the stem between them is divided into any desirable number of parts of equal capacity. The two

Fig. 1.

fixed points correspond to the temperature of melting ice and the temperature of the vapour of water boiling under the pressure of a standard atmosphere, it having been found that when the instrument is placed in melting ice or snow, the mercury always stands at the same point, and this, according to our chosen measure, means that ice always melts at the same temperature under the atmospheric pressure, and for the same reason the steam of boiling water is used to determine the second fixed point.

We have now a definite standard of reference for all other temperatures. For example, if the mercury stands below the lower fixed point, then we say that the temperature is below the freezing point of water, or what is the same thing, the melting point of ice, and if it stands above the upper fixed point we say the temperature is higher than the boiling point of water under the pressure of one atmosphere, while for intermediate points we have intermediate

---

[1] The general subject of Thermometry is considered in Chap. II.

temperatures. In order to refer to these temperatures conveniently, the interval between the two fixed points on the stem is divided into a number of equal parts. Let us suppose that it is divided after the manner of Celsius into 100 parts, the lower fixed point reading 0° and the upper 100°; and let the same process of division be continued on the stem above the upper and below the lower fixed point.[1] Then if the mercury stands at 20°, we refer to this as the temperature 20°, meaning thereby that the temperature is such that when the thermometer attains it, the mercury stands in the stem at the division 20°. We do not imply, however, that when the mercury stands at 40° the temperature is twice as high (in the sense of the hotness being twice as intense) as when the mercury stands at 20°, or that when it stands at 100° it is four times as hot as when it stands at 25°. It is only in this sense that we have said we cannot *measure* hotness. The thermometer is an indicator which enables us to determine equality of temperatures, and tells us how much one body is hotter or colder than another, in terms of our chosen scale. It indicates degrees of hotness, and ought always to show the same reading when at the same hotness. By making the bore of the stem very fine and the bulb large, the instrument can be rendered very sensitive, so that small changes of temperature which would otherwise escape notice can be registered.

In this method of estimating temperature some particular substance is chosen, and then by definition the change of temperature is taken proportional to the change of volume of the thermometric substance, or rather to the change in the reading of the thermometer. Once a substance is chosen, and a thermometer constructed, this may be Standard regarded as the standard instrument by means of which all others can instrument. be standardised, so that all thermometers will agree in their indications. If this plan were adopted, we should be furnished with a definite and consistent method of estimating temperature. All thermometers would be copies of a standard instrument, just as our weights and measures are copies of arbitrarily chosen originals, kept for the sake of reference. This plan, however, as will be seen afterwards, is not absolutely necessary, for instruments can be constructed which will agree sufficiently well in their indications without previous comparison. Such agreement is not found, however, among instruments which are not constructed of the same materials. Thus a mercury thermometer which agrees with an alcohol thermometer at the points 0° and 60° will in general disagree with it at the other parts of the scale. Some standard of comparison must therefore be chosen, by means

---

[1] This is usually called the centigrade scale and is indicated by the letter C, thus, —20° C.

of which all thermometers are to be graduated, and for this purpose the gas thermometer possesses special advantages (see Chap. II.).

18. Expansion of the Thermometric Substance—Coefficient of Expansion.—We shall now consider the relation between the volume and temperature of the thermometric substance, that is, the substance by the expansion of which temperature is measured. This relation is determined entirely by the method chosen for measuring temperature, and is not to be regarded as a new result connecting volume and temperature.

Let it be supposed that equal changes of temperature are measured by equal changes of volume of some substance. Then if V_o be the volume at the zero of the scale, and V the volume at any temperature θ, we have

$$V - V_o = v\theta,$$

where v is the increase of volume for one degree, or what may be called a degree measure, and is by definition the same all along the scale. This formula is merely the algebraic method of stating the definition, or the mode of measuring temperature, and may be written in the form

$$V = V_o\left(1 + \frac{v}{V_o}\theta\right) = V_o(1 + a\theta).$$

The quantity $a = v/V_o$ is obviously the expansion per unit volume of the substance in changing its temperature from $0°$ to $1°$. This quantity is called its *coefficient of expansion* at zero. In general, the coefficient of expansion of a substance is measured by the change in bulk of a unit volume of the substance per degree of temperature. If V and V' denote the volumes at temperatures θ and θ' respectively, then the change in bulk of a unit volume is

$$\frac{V' - V}{V},$$

and the average change in bulk per degree of temperature between θ and θ' will be

$$\frac{V - V'}{V(\theta - \theta')}.$$

This is termed the *mean coefficient of expansion* between the temperatures θ and θ'. In the case of the thermometric substance, the mean coefficient of expansion between zero and any temperature θ is constant and equal to v/V_o, for we have by definition

$$a = \frac{v}{V_o} = \frac{V - V_o}{V_o\theta}.$$

C

It is to be carefully observed that this formula holds only for the thermometric substance, and is true for it as a result of our definition of temperature, whereby equal increments of temperature are measured by equal absolute increments of volume of this substance. In the case of the thermometer just described the expansion of the mercury is measured by the rise of the column in a capillary glass tube. The expansion thus observed is not the *absolute* expansion of the mercury, but only its *apparent* expansion in a glass envelope. If the stem is originally divided into parts of equal capacity, these will increase as the temperature rises, owing to the expansion of the glass. Hence, if temperature is measured by the absolute expansion of mercury, the expansion of the glass must be taken into account in graduating the stem of a thermometer. Correction in this respect will render the degree intervals shorter and shorter as we proceed up the scale. If the divisions were to be equidistant along the stem its bore would have to be conical, or the substance of the envelope would require to be non-expansible. It follows, then, that if a denotes the zero coefficient of absolute expansion of the thermometric substance, the foregoing formula applies only to that substance. In the case of any other substance the volume at any temperature θ° will be some complicated function of the temperature, and we may assume that it can be expressed in the form

$$V = V_o(1 + a\theta + b\theta^2 + c\theta^3 + \ \ldots),$$

where V_o is the volume at zero.

19. Temperature Equilibrium.—If, when a thermometer is placed in contact with several bodies, or dipped into different liquids, it shows the same reading in each case, we say that all these substances are at the same temperature. If now any pair of these substances be placed in contact, or mixed together, it is found by experiment that they still continue at the same temperature (provided no chemical action occurs). It is thus found that when there is equality of temperature before contact (or mixture), this equality remains after contact. In this case there is said to be equilibrium of temperature, and we are furnished with the *experimental fact* that bodies which are in temperature equilibrium with the same body are also in temperature equilibrium with each other.

If, however, two bodies at different temperatures are placed in contact it is found that in general the temperature of the warmer falls while that of the colder rises, and this process continues till equilibrium is established. There are cases, however, in which the temperature of one changes while that of the other remains fixed.

This process takes place when one of the bodies is changing state, as when a mass of ice is placed in a basin of hot water. Here the ice gradually melts, but its temperature remains the same, while that of the water gradually falls, till the melting is completed, or equality of temperature is established. A similar process occurs when a liquid is being converted into vapour.

20. Quantity of Heat.—In order to account for the sensation experienced in presence of a hot body an active agent is postulated, and the name given to this agent is heat. A hot body is regarded as a source of heat just as a luminous body is regarded as a source of light. In the same way, when two bodies at different temperatures are placed in contact, the temperature of the warmer falls while that of the other rises. To account for this we say that *heat* passes from one to the other, that the warmer loses heat and the colder gains it. In this sense heat is regarded as something which may be added to or taken away from matter; something which can be communicated to matter, and which can be handed on from one piece of matter to another. Heat thus possesses the rank of a *quantity*, and we are led to seek *how much* heat a body gains or loses when its temperature changes. On the other hand, temperature is regarded rather as a quality which varies from one body to another, or from one part to another of the same body, when heat is being communicated to or abstracted from it, or which may vary, as we shall subsequently see, in consequence of actions taking place within the body itself, or performed on it from without.

It must, however, be distinctly remembered that what we directly *observe* is temperature and changes of temperature, and when the temperature of a body (free from other actions) rises we *say* it has received heat. The effect observed is the change of temperature, and the postulated cause is addition or subtraction of heat.

The use of the term *force* in dynamics is somewhat of the same nature ; what we really observe is motion and changes of motion, or changes in the relative positions of bodies. To account for change of motion the idea of force is introduced, and a measure is adopted.[1] Once a definite system of measurement is laid down the vagueness of the term disappears, and the meaning of the force on a body becomes perfectly clear and distinct. So to account for changes of temperature the idea of heat as something which can be added to or taken away from a body is introduced, and a measure of heat as a quantity must also be adopted. For this purpose a unit is essential, just as in the measurement of length or weight. This unit is

---

[1] The idea of force is probably chiefly due to the sense of muscular effort.

more or less arbitrary, and for the purpose of definite measurement may be chosen in connection with any one of the effects attributed to heat.

In popular language the word heat has a somewhat lax usage. It is sometimes used to denote a high temperature, as in the phrases, "white heat," "tropical heat," and "blood heat." Commonly, however, it is used either to express the sensations experienced in presence of hot bodies, or else the ultimate cause of those sensations, and in this latter sense it is used in such phrases as "the theory of heat" and "the science of heat." In the theory of heat we inquire into the nature of the process by which the various effects attributed to heat are brought about, and seek to determine the mechanism by which one body becomes warmer while another becomes colder, or, as we say, the process in operation when heat enters or leaves a body.

In saying that the heat of a body increases with its temperature, or that a body loses heat in cooling, we tacitly attribute to heat a positive character, so that its presence produces warmth and its absence cold. The word cold, then, has a negative character, and merely refers to the absence of heat. As the ideas of heat and cold are derived from the sensations, the positive value of either might be regarded as the negative value of the other, and the presence of one might be regarded as the absence of the other. As far, then, as the sensations alone direct us, either or both might possess a positive character. We have no more experience of the total absence of heat, or greatest possible coldness, than we have of the greatest possible accumulation of heat or greatest possible hotness. The general opinion has long been that the sensation of coldness is due to loss of heat and that of warmth to the gain of heat. In early times, however, this did not appear so evident. When the hand is placed on a piece of ice, instead of heat being given by the hand to the ice, some philosophers supposed that in such a case the cold body possessed minute "particles of frost" or "frigorific particles," which passed from cold bodies into those which are warmer, and these spiculæ or little darts were supposed to account for the acutely painful sensation, and some other effects, due to intense cold.

21. Unit of Quantity.—The unit of heat generally employed is the quantity of heat necessary to raise the temperature of one gramme of pure water one degree centigrade. The same quantity of heat will be given out by one gramme in cooling 1° C. This, however, is not *a priori* evident. It is not a truism, but a truth established by experiment.

In the case of a uniformly heated mass of water it is legitimate to assert that the quantity of heat contained in any one gramme of it is the same as that contained in any other, and that the quantity of heat required to raise any one cubic centimetre of it, from any one definite temperature to any other, will be the same, under the same conditions, as for any other cubic centimetre. Thus, if the quantity of heat necessary to raise the temperature of a gramme of water, or any other substance, through a given interval of temperature, be denoted by q, then the quantity required to raise m grammes through the same range of temperature will be mq.

We cannot, however, assert that the quantity of heat necessary to raise the temperature of a body $1°$ is the same at all parts of the scale, or that the quantity given out by a body in cooling from $50°$ to $40°$ is equal to that given out by the same body in cooling from $25°$ to $15°$. We have no reason to expect *a priori* that the quantity of heat is proportional to the interval of temperature. In defining the unit of heat above we have only stated that it is the quantity of heat necessary to raise one gramme of water $1°$ C. We have not stated at what part of the scale the degree is to be taken, whether it is the interval from $0°$ to $1°$, or from $4°$ to $5°$, or any other. In strictness this ought to be done, but in practice it is found that there is scarcely any appreciable difference, whatever be the degree chosen. Experiment proves that very approximately the same quantity of heat is required to raise a given mass of water $1°$ in temperature at any part of the scale between the freezing point and the boiling point (see Art. 171). It is well, however, to be accurate, and to fix a particular degree, say from $19°·5$ to $20°·5$. According to this system a quantity Q of heat means the quantity which will raise Q grammes of water from $19°·5$ to $20°·5$ C., and not the quantity which will raise one gramme of water $Q°$ C. The latter happens, however, as we have already said, to be very approximately equal to the former.

Other units of heat might be, and actually have been, chosen depending on other effects of heat on matter, such, for example, as the change of state. These will be noticed later on.

It is important to remark that we can now speak definitely of the quantity of heat required to raise a body from one temperature to another, but that the "quantity of heat in a body" is still without meaning. So far the quantity of heat in a body is as indefinite as the quantity of sound in a bell, or the height of an object above an unknown plane.

22. Sensible Heat and Latent Heat.—As already noticed, when two bodies at different temperatures are placed in contact, heat is supposed to pass from the hotter to the colder, but either of two

things may happen.   Either the temperature of the colder may rise,
while that of the warmer falls, or a change of state may occur in one
while the temperature of the other alone varies.   In the former case,
that is, when the heat which leaves one enters the other and increases
its temperature, the heat which enters it exhibits itself in the corresponding rise of temperature, and is said to be *sensible* heat.   That
is, it can be detected by the thermometer.   In the second case,
however, the warmer body is continually losing heat, but the
temperature of the colder remains fixed.   Its state merely changes.
The heat which it receives does not exhibit itself by any rise of
temperature, and cannot be detected by the thermometer.   It becomes, as Black said, latent, and is consequently termed *latent heat*.
In illustration of this point it may be well to describe here the
experiment by which Black [1] was led to his doctrine of latent heat.

Black's ex-   Having exposed a mass (5 oz.) of ice-cold water in a vessel
periment.   suspended in a large hall, he noticed that the temperature rose very
nearly 4° C. (7° F.) in half an hour.   He also exposed an equal mass
of ice in the same room under the same conditions and found that it
required ten hours to melt.   Now the ice receives heat from the
room, and the quantity received during ten hours was only sufficient
to melt it.   This quantity may be calculated from the experiment on
the ice-cold water, which received as much heat in half an hour as
raised its temperature almost 4° C.   Assuming that the melting ice
received heat at the same rate, the total quantity required to melt it
will be nearly twenty times that required to raise an equal weight
of water 4° C., or almost as much as would raise eighty times its
weight of water one degree centigrade.[2]   This shows roughly that
about eighty units of heat are required to convert a gramme of ice
into a gramme of ice-cold water, without changing the temperature.
That is, eighty units of heat have disappeared or become latent in
effecting the change of state from solid to liquid.   For this reason
eighty is said to be the latent heat of ice, meaning that eighty units
of heat are necessary for the liquefaction of ice per gramme.

Black also determined the latent heat of ice by mixing warm
water and ice in known quantities and noting the change of
temperature.   Allowing for the influence of the containing vessel he
found by this method 79·4—a number remarkably near that given
by the best recent determinations.

[1] Black, *Elements of Chemistry*, vol. i. p. 116.   Published by John Robison,
Edinburgh, 1803.

[2] Black used a Fahrenheit thermometer, a description of which will be found in
Chap. II.

Before the time of Black it was universally considered that when a solid changed into a liquid, or a liquid into a vapour, no continued supply of heat was necessary for the transformation, and that all the heat supplied exhibited itself in a corresponding rise of temperature. In other words, heat was always sensible, and could be detected by the thermometer. Black [1] says : "This was the universal opinion on this subject so far as I know when I began to read my lectures in the University of Glasgow, in the year 1757. . . . The opinion I formed from attentive observation of the facts and phenomena is as follows. When ice, for example, or any other solid substance, is changing into a fluid by heat, I am of opinion that it receives a much greater quantity of heat than what is perceptible in it immediately after by the thermometer. A great quantity of heat enters into it on this occasion without making it apparently warmer when tried by this instrument. This heat, however, must be thrown into it, in order to give it the form of a fluid ; and I affirm that this great addition of heat is the principal and most immediate cause of the fluidity induced."

" And on the other hand, when we deprive such a body of its fluidity again, by a diminution of its heat, a very great quantity of heat comes out of it, while it is assuming the solid form, the loss of which heat is not to be perceived by the common manner of using the thermometer."

Sensible and latent heats are thus very analogous to kinetic and potential energies. When work is spent in increasing the velocity of, or generating motion in, any body, the work so spent becomes visible, or sensible, in the motion of the body, and it is analogous to sensible heat. When, on the other hand, work is spent in raising a weight from the surface of the earth, or in changing the distances between the parts of a mutually attracting system, the work so spent is not visible as any motion of the system, but has as it were become latent, or potential, as it is termed. That some real relation here exists, and not merely an analogy, will probably appear as a knowledge of the facts accumulates.

23. Specific Heat and Thermal Capacity.—Having laid down a system of measurement of quantities of heat, the question which immediately presents itself is whether equal quantities of heat raise the temperatures of equal masses of different substances by the same amount, or if any relation exists between the quantities of heat given to equal masses, or equal volumes, of different substances, and the corresponding changes of temperature. If equal weights of the same

---

[1] Black, *loc. cit.*

substance (water, for example) at different temperatures be mixed, the temperature of the mixture is the arithmetic mean of the temperatures of the two components before mixture (or very approximately so). The quantity of heat given out by the warmer mass in falling through a certain range of temperature raises the colder mass through an equal range. The case is very different if two dissimilar substances are mixed together. The change of temperature of a body is not alone sufficient to determine the quantity of heat it has gained or lost. This quantity depends not only on the change of temperature but also on the nature of the substance, and for this reason different substances are said to have different *thermal capacities* or *specific heats*. This is strikingly illustrated in the case of mercury and water. Thus, if a pound of mercury at 80° C. be mixed with a pound of water at 20° C., the temperature of the mixture will be only about 22° C. This shows that the heat lost by the mercury in cooling through 58° will raise an equal weight of water through only 2°. In other words, the quantity of heat which will raise the temperature of a given weight of water 1° will raise the temperature of an equal weight of mercury nearly 30°, or the thermal capacity of water is about thirty times that of mercury.

The thermal capacity of a body is defined as the quantity of heat necessary to raise the temperature of the body 1° C., and the thermal capacity of a substance is the quantity of heat required to raise unit weight (one gramme) of the substance 1° C.

The specific heat of a substance is its thermal capacity compared with that of water; in other words, it is the ratio of the quantity of heat required to raise the temperature of a given weight of the substance 1°, to the quantity of heat which will raise the temperature of an equal weight of water 1°. When the unit of heat is that required to raise the temperature of unit weight of water 1°, the thermal capacity and the specific heat of a substance are expressed by the same number.

Before the time of Black it was commonly supposed that the quantities of heat required to change the temperatures of different bodies by the same amount were directly proportional to the quantities of matter in them, or that all substances had the same thermal capacity.

Black's opinion. "But very soon (1760) after I began to think on this subject," says Black,[1] "I perceived that this opinion was a mistake, and that the quantities of heat which different kinds of matter must receive, to reduce them to equilibrium with one another, or to raise their

[1] *Lectures on the Elements of Chemistry,* p. 79.

temperatures by an equal number of degrees, are not in proportion to the quantity of matter in each, but in proportions widely different from this. . . . This opinion was first suggested to me by an experiment described by Dr. Boerhaave (*Elements of Chemistry*). After relating the experiment which Fahrenheit made at his desire, by mixing hot and cold water, he also tells us that Fahrenheit agitated together quicksilver and water unequally heated. From the Doctor's account it is quite plain that quicksilver, though it has more than thirteen times the density of water, produced less effect in heating or cooling water to which it was applied than an equal measure of water would have produced. He says expressly that the quicksilver never produced more effect in heating or cooling an equal measure of water than would have been produced by water equally hot or cold with the quicksilver and only two-thirds of its bulk."

Black concluded, therefore, that quicksilver has a much less capacity for heat than water, and that different substances have different thermal capacities. The inference made by Dr. Boerhaave from the same experiment is very surprising. Seeing that the heat obviously was not distributed among different bodies at the same temperature in proportion to their masses, he concluded that it was distributed in proportion to their volumes, or that equal volumes of all substances have the same thermal capacity. This conclusion, as Black remarks, was contradicted by the very experiment on which it was founded, yet in it Boerhaave was followed and supported by Muschenbroeck.

The small capacity for heat of a dense body like mercury was considered by Black as a strong objection against the dynamical theory of heat, for if heat be motion, then in his opinion a dense body should contain much more of it than a rare one at the same temperature.

24. Thermometry by Quantities of Heat.—A perfectly scientific though inconvenient system of thermometry might be founded on the measurement of quantities of heat rather than on changes of volume. Thus, if we lay down any two definite temperatures, such as the melting point of ice and the boiling point of water under a definite pressure, or the melting point of any other solid, these temperatures will correspond to certain fixed marks on the stem of an instrument, such as the mercurial thermometer already described. If now the unit of heat be taken as the quantity of heat necessary to raise one gramme of water from one of these temperatures to the other, then n units of heat will raise n grammes of water through the same interval of temperature. It will be convenient to take the lower fixed temperature as that of melting ice, as ice-cold water is easily procurable, and the other fixed temperature may be taken as corresponding to any fixed mark on the stem of the mercurial thermometer, say the division marked 1°.

If now we wish to compare the temperatures of two pieces of the *same* substance in the same physical state, it will be only necessary to find how many grammes of water [1] a gramme of each (or equal weights of each) will raise from 0° to 1° (our chosen fixed temperatures)—that is, the number of units of heat each will give out per unit mass in falling from their original temperatures to the upper fixed temperature. Equal differences of temperature will thus correspond to equal increments of heat, or the temperatures of two pieces of the same substance will be in the ratio of the quantities of heat required to raise unit mass of each from the lower fixed point to its present condition. For temperatures below the lower fixed point it will be necessary to find the weight of water which, in cooling from the upper to the lower fixed point, will raise unit mass of the substance from its present temperature to that of the lower fixed point. This point consequently becomes the zero of our new scale, and temperatures expressed by this system will be so much above or below the lower fixed point.

So far we have only compared the temperatures by this system of different pieces of the *same* substance. This restriction was necessary because it is found that equal masses of different substances heated uniformly in the same enclosure or bath will give out very different quantities of heat in falling from their common initial temperature to that of the upper fixed point. This is expressed by saying that different substances have different thermal capacities per unit mass, or different *specific heats*. If, therefore, it is desired to make this system of thermometry generally applicable, a small carrier body, say a small metallic disc supported by a silk thread, may be employed, just as a proof plane is employed in the measurement of electrical potentials. If this small carrier be brought into contact with any body it will rapidly assume the temperature of the body ; errors arising from the finite mass of the carrier and initial temperature difference between it and the body being neglected. The carrier may now be removed to the vessel containing the ice-cold water and the weight of water which it raises from zero to the upper fixed point estimated. By this means we can compare, or as it were weigh, the temperatures of different bodies.

In order that this system of thermometry should agree with that

---

[1] Perhaps it would be better to work with the quantity of ice melted.

which measures equal increments of temperature by equal increments of volume, it is necessary that equal expansions of the thermometric substance, should correspond to equal increments of heat, or that the dilatation should be proportional to the quantity of heat received. Air and the permanent gases seem to be the only substances which satisfy this condition very closely, but between 0° and 100° C., and for some distance beyond these points, mercury, expanding in an ordinary glass envelope, also possesses this property. In general the dilatation of a body increases for equal additions of heat as the temperature becomes more elevated. Dulong and Petit [1] executed a series of experiments on this point. They measured the quantities of heat absorbed by various substances, and also the consequent dilatation, and they found that the expansion was not simply proportional to the quantity of heat, but that between the dilatation and the quantity of heat absorbed some complicated relation exists which depends on the nature of the substance. In the case of the permanent gases, however, Regnault [2] found that the change of volume under constant pressure was simply proportional to the quantity of heat received, and hence the system of thermometry here considered will agree with that registered by an air thermometer.

Expansion of gases.

For this and many other reasons the air (or rather perfect gas) thermometer is the only strictly scientific measurer of temperature, and all other thermometers ought to be standardised by direct comparison with it.

25. Thermometry by the Sense of Heat.—The sense of heat is a somewhat delicate test of the equality of temperature in the case of similar bodies, that is, of portions of the same sort of matter. Thus by the hand alone a very small difference in the temperatures of two water baths may be detected, especially by persons who have cultivated the sense of heat for this purpose. It is very different, however, when we touch in succession objects which are of dissimilar natures. Let us take the case of a room without a fire on a cold frosty day. All the objects in such a room will be at the same temperature. This may be tested by means of a thermometer. A metal paper weight will, however, when touched feel much colder than the paper on which it rests, and the wooden table will feel colder than the woollen table-cloth. In explanation of this, we regard the sensation of coldness as due to the loss of heat by the hand, and this is not simply dependent on the temperature of the body touched, but depends rather on the

---

[1] *Ann. de Chimie et de Phys.*, 2ᵉ série, tom. ii. p. 240, 1816.
[2] *Relation des expériences*, tom. i. p. 163 ; *Mémoires de l'Académie des Sciences*, tom. xxi.

rate of loss of heat.   The hand loses heat much more rapidly to the
metal paper weight than to the paper, and more rapidly to the wooden
floor than to the carpet.   The rate at which one body communicates
heat to another at a lower temperature depends, as we shall see later
on, not only on the difference of temperature, but also on the nature
of the materials of which they are composed, and on their surfaces.
The properties involved are specific heat, and internal and external
conductivities for heat.

It is rather surprising at first to find on touching some bodies,
which we know to be at or below the freezing point, that they actually
feel warm ; a moment's reflection, however, leads to an explanation.
Our bodies part with heat to all other bodies at a lower temperature,
and on a cold day we are constantly giving out heat to the air.   If,
then, we touch any body which draws off heat more rapidly than the
air it appears cold, but if it draws away the heat less rapidly than
the air from the hand it will feel warm by comparison.   It is for a
similar reason that we feel much warmer when clothed than when naked,
and that woollen stuffs are employed for bedcovers.

The estimation of temperature by the sense of heat depends upon
so many variable conditions, the state of the observer included, that it
cannot be used with any certainty.   In illustration of this a well-
known experiment is often cited.   Thus if one hand be placed in a
basin of hot water, while the other is placed in a basin of cold water,
and then the two are simultaneously placed in a basin of tepid water,
this latter will appear cold to the hand which was in the hot water
and hot to that which was placed in the cold.   This arises from the
fact that the tepid water is colder than the surface of the hand which
was in the hot water, and warmer than that which was placed in
the cold water.   The result is that one hand gives up heat to the
tepid water, while the other receives heat; the former accordingly
becomes chilled, while the latter is heated.   When cultivated, however, not only can very small differences of temperature be detected
in similar substances by the sense of heat, but a memory of certain
definite temperatures can be permanently acquired.   This happens in
the case of bath attendants and hospital attendants, and those engaged
with hot liquids in various manufactories, such as dyeworks.   Such
persons can tell to within less than a degree centigrade whether a bath
or a poultice is at " blood heat," or " fever heat," or some other definite
temperature to which they are accustomed.[1]

26. Remarks on the Definition of Temperature.—In concluding
this section it may be well to call attention to the great importance of

[1] Sir William Thomson, *Math. and Phys. Papers*, vol. iii. p. 130.

a clear definition and a thorough understanding of the exact meaning of each term used in any branch of science.   Without this progress is hopeless, and all reasoning on the subject becomes a meaningless tangle of words, more calculated to confuse than enlighten.

Attention has already been directed to the method of explaining the seen by means of the unseen, and the known by means of the unknown.   A similar and perhaps more pernicious habit which still lingers is the definition of scientific terms by means of other words to which no distinct meaning can be assigned.   As an example take the following definition : " The temperature of a body is the energy with which the heat in a body acts in the way of transferring or communicating a portion of itself to other bodies."   In this definition two new words, energy and heat, are introduced, and the idea of " the energy with which the heat in a body acts," as well as the conception of the transference of heat from one body to another.   Until the new words, as well as the ideas involved, are thoroughly explained, such a definition can give no distinct idea of what the word temperature means. The student would be better without any definition than with such a one.   A mystifying string of words can only addle and discourage him at the outset of a new and difficult subject.

Other and no less objectionable forms of definition ordinarily met with are " the power of a body to communicate heat to other bodies," or, " the greater or less extent to which it tends to impart sensible heat to other bodies."   The first essays to explain the word temperature by the introduction of the word power.   Now the word power with reference to engines has a perfectly definite meaning, but in ordinary language it seems to enjoy an almost universal application. It is so thoroughly indefinite that it does not attract the attention of the student, especially when mixed up with scientific words, and he passes on without seeing that such a sentence really has no meaning. If we take " the power of a body " referred to above as meaning the quantity of heat it will give to other bodies, we see at once that this will depend not only on the hotness of the body, but on its mass and the thermal capacity of its material as well as on the " other bodies." If we take the power as the rate of giving out heat, we are again in similar difficulties, for the rate of loss of heat will depend upon the nature of the surface as well as that of the material, and by no means on the hotness alone of the body.   Similar remarks apply to the second definition.   It perhaps excels the first in indistinctness.   The " greater or less tendency of a body " seems to contain an idea, but it is not easy to understand its precise meaning !

The last form of definition which we shall consider is much

superior to the others. Here temperature is laid down as "the thermal state of a body considered with reference to its power of communicating heat to other bodies." The "power of communicating heat," as has been already pointed out, either means nothing or is entirely incorrect. The thermal state of a body, if it means anything, means the hotness of a body, and the definition implies that the temperature is the hotness considered in a certain aspect.

Another strange inversion of ideas is also generally met with. It occurs in the consideration of difference of temperatures. Thus it is stated that two bodies are said to be at different temperatures when, if placed in contact, heat passes from one to the other. Now it is in the reverse order that the ideas are actually obtained. What we directly *observe* is temperature and change of temperature (see Art. 20). When the temperature of a body changes we account for it by supposing that heat has left or entered it. We do not *observe* the heat passing from one body to another, and find that as a consequence the temperature changes. In order to find out which of two bodies is at the higher temperature we do not place them in thermal communication, and observe if "heat" flows from one to the other. The flow of heat is an assumed phenomenon arising from the observed change of temperature, and is asserted merely because we say that when the temperature of a body is changing it is gaining or losing heat, or that increase of temperature is accompanied or caused by a gain, and fall of temperature by a loss of heat.

A theory may be wrong, but it certainly ought to be clear and distinct, and should be expressed in language which can be easily understood. The definitions sometimes met with often escape the merit of being false by being expressed in words which have no assignable meaning. In the theory of heat ambiguity in this respect probably arises from the fact that during the present century a new theory has been built up while the old doctrine lingered on. Terms which were distinct in the latter have been retained with a very different signification in the former, and an imperfect apprehension of their exact meaning perplexes the student.

SECTION III

27. Two Theories prevalent.—From the dawn of science to the present century two rival hypotheses regarding the nature of heat were generally entertained, neither of them, however, being founded on any sufficiently established basis. According to one, known as the caloric theory, heat was supposed to be a subtle elastic fluid which permeated the pores of bodies, and filled the interstices between the molecules of matter. The other doctrine, which is as old as the ancient Greeks, and contains the germ of the modern theory, supposed heat to be due to a rapid vibration of the molecules of a body, and consequently attributed heat to motion. The supporters of this theory seem to have been long in a miserable minority.

28. Lord Bacon.—The first philosophic attempt at the formation of a theory founded on observation seems to have been made by Lord Bacon [1] in a treatise which he offered as a model of the proper manner of prosecuting investigations in Natural Philosophy. In this treatise he sums up all the principal facts then known relating to heat, or to the production of heat, and after a cautious and mature consideration of these he endeavours to form a well-founded opinion of their cause. On deliberating over the various ways in which heat is produced by friction and percussion, the only conclusion he could draw from the whole facts was the very general one that " heat is motion."

The opinion of Lord Bacon was adopted very generally, but with two different modifications. The greater number of his followers in England supposed that the motion or tremor which constituted heat was in the small particles of the body, while the majority of continental philosophers supposed that the vibration was not that of the particles of the body itself, but rather of the particles of a subtle and highly elastic fluid, penetrating the pores of bodies, and interposed between their particles. This fluid they imagined to be diffused through the

---

[1] *De forma Calidi.*

31

whole universe, pervading with ease the densest bodies, and in the
opinion of some, when modified in certain ways, produced the phenomena of light and electricity.[1]

29. The Caloric Theory.—The other school of philosophers, however, was in power till the beginning of the nineteenth century.
They held that heat was not due to motion, but to the action of a
highly elastic and self-repellent fluid, which was all-pervading and
universal. At first the only properties postulated were that it was
highly elastic, and that its particles repelled each other very strongly.
It was by this latter property of caloric, as the heat fluid was called
later on, that bodies in combustion threw off heat and light. Subsequently Dr. Cleghorn introduced another property which was
strongly favoured by Black, namely, that the particles of the caloric,
though self-repellent, were yet strongly attracted by the particles of
ordinary matter, and that different kinds of matter attracted the
caloric with different degrees of force. Thus, among any system of
bodies, an equilibrium would be established between the self-repulsion
of the caloric and the attractive influence exerted on it by the matter,
and caloric would pass from one body to another until this equilibrium
was established.

The fundamental quality demanded for the heat fluid was that it
was indestructible and uncreatable by any process. Bodies became
warmer when caloric was added to them, and grew colder as it left
them. In this respect it possessed the essential property of ordinary
matter—a property also attributed to energy, which replaces it in the
dynamical theory.

As to the possession of the other property of matter—namely,
weight—a great diversity of opinion existed. Some philosophers held
that caloric had weight, while others held that it had not. Experiments on this point were difficult and doubtful, and contradictory
results were often obtained. At the close of the eighteenth century,
however, the general opinion in the best informed circles was that the
heat fluid was imponderable, and in this respect it differed from
ordinary matter. Count Rumford[2] finally settled the point by a set
of delicate and most instructive experiments, from which he concluded
that "all attempts to discover any effect of heat upon the apparent
weights of bodies will be fruitless."

That equal weights of different substances require different amounts
of caloric to raise their temperature through the same interval was

[1] See Black's *Lectures on the Elements of Chemistry*, vol. i. p. 33.
[2] Rumford, "An Inquiry concerning the Weight of Heat," *Phil. Trans.*, 1799 ;
and *Complete Works*, vol. ii. p. 2.

easily explained by the calorists on Cleghorn's supposition, that different kinds of matter attract the caloric differently, and consequently it was reasonable to suppose that some substances would absorb greater quantities of caloric than others in rising through the same range of temperature. Other very plausible explanations of physical phenomena were arrived at by the partisans of this theory. Thus the general expansion of bodies by heat followed as a natural consequence, for, the caloric being a self-repellent fluid, when the quantity in any body increased it was to be expected that the self-repulsion of this fluid would cause an increase of volume. Even when heating caused contraction, it was not difficult to find analogies in support of the theory. Thus contraction occurs when water and alcohol are mixed, and in alloys of copper and tin, and in some chemical combinations the volume of the combination may be less than that of either constituent.

To explain his doctrine of latent heat, Black supposed that caloric could not only exist in the free state, that is as sensible heat, but also in combination with matter, in which case it became latent and inactive. It could not then be detected by the thermometer. From this point of view water is the result of a combination of the substance of ice with a certain proportion of caloric, and steam is a combination of water with a further quantity of caloric. This doctrine, proposed by Black, was not, however, generally accepted. There were many who thought that liquefaction was not attributable to heat alone. They considered, for example, that water was a fluid from an essential quality, depending upon the supposed spherical shape of its particles, and that the freezing of it depended upon the introduction of some extraneous substance, such as frigorific particles, etc., and this view was supported in the case of water by the increase of bulk in freezing.[1]

The conduction of heat—that is, its transference from one body to another in contact with it, or from one part to another of the same body—also presented no difficulty, for the caloric was supposed to flow from places of higher to places of lower temperature, as a liquid flows from places of higher to places of lower level. The flow of the caloric from higher to lower temperatures was a consequence of the supposed mutual repulsion of its particles.

So far the explanations of the calorists were certainly satisfactory, although in some cases they were cumbrous and difficult of application. We shall, however, see immediately, as facts accumulate, that cases will come to hand which cannot be explained by the caloric doctrine, at least without radical changes in its fundamental postulates.

[1] This view was defended by Prof. Muschenbroeck, *Phys. de Aqua.*

D

SECTION IV

THE DYNAMICAL GENERATION OF HEAT

30. Heat developed by Friction.—That heat may be freely developed by friction seems to have been well known to all classes of men from the earliest times. Every schoolboy is well acquainted with the fact that a brass nail may be heated to a painful degree by rubbing it on a wooden seat. Friction, indeed, is the ordinary resource of the savage in lighting his fire.[1]

It is on account of the great heat developed by friction that such precautions are taken to keep the axles of railway carriages well greased, and even with the utmost provision against it the axles and axle-boxes of express trains become so warm that a stoppage or slackening of speed becomes necessary. Outbreaks of fire arising from the heat developed by friction between the wheel and axle of a rapidly driven carriage have not infrequently occurred. An analogous development of heat is produced by percussion. A soft iron rod rapidly hammered on an anvil may be heated by an experienced hand to the point of incandescence, while a few strokes will warm it sufficiently to light a match. In like manner a bullet is found to be considerably heated after striking a target. The flash of light often seen when an iron shot strikes a target shows that the heat developed by the impact is sufficient to raise to incandescence the scattered dust and particles abraded by the collision.

In like manner there is a development of heat by friction in

---

[1] The Gaucho of the Pampas presses the blunt end of a flexible rod about 18 inches long against his breast, and the other end, which is pointed, he places in a hole drilled in a piece of dry wood. Bending the rod by the pressure of his body, he seizes the curved part and turns it rapidly round, till the heat developed by the friction of the rod against the block of wood is sufficient to produce ignition. In Australia and Tasmania ignition is produced by the rapid twirling of the pointed stick between the palms of the hands, and among the Esquimaux one person presses the end of the rod against the piece of wood, while another produces a rapid rotation to and fro by means of a thong.

liquids. In the ordinary process of churning there is a considerable rise in the temperature of the milk before the operation is completed. Water, or any other liquid, may be heated in the same manner, and it was by an experiment of this kind that Joule first determined the dynamical equivalent of heat, that is, the relation between the quantity of work spent in churning and the quantity of heat developed by the process.

31. The Fire Syringe.—One of the most interesting illustrations of the dynamical generation of heat is furnished by the fire syringe. This instrument consists of a stout cylindrical glass tube, accurately bored and quite smooth within. An air-tight piston is fitted into it, so that by forcing the piston forward the air in the tube is compressed. When the air is thus forcibly compressed, heat is suddenly generated, and the rise of temperature thus developed may be sufficient to ignite a piece of tinder attached to the inner end of the piston.

If a pellet of cotton wool, moistened with bisulphide of carbon, be thrown into the tube and then immediately ejected, so that a mixture of its vapour and air fills the tube, a flash of light will be seen on suddenly compressing the contents. The heat developed by the compression has been sufficient to ignite the vapour.

The converse operation—the development of cold or destruction of heat—may be also illustrated by means of this or some similar apparatus.[1] Thus if the gas be compressed, and after attaining a fixed temperature be allowed to expand, pushing the piston before it, so that work is done against the external pressure, a noticeable fall in the temperature of the gas will occur.

That the temperature of a gas is elevated by sudden compression and reduced by expansion seems to have been first noticed by Dr. Cullen and Dr. Darwin.[2] This fact being once noticed would naturally lead to an inquiry as to the quantity of heat developed by a given compression, or the relation between the amount of compression and the change of temperature or quantity of heat developed. Dalton[3] was the first to estimate this change of temperature with some degree of accuracy, and from his experiment he concluded that when air is compressed to one-half its bulk a heating of $50°$ F. occurs, with a similar cooling when a corresponding rarefaction takes place.

[1] For example, by allowing air to escape from a vessel in which it has been compressed. The cooling effect when small may be registered by some sensitive thermo-electric apparatus. The cooling produced by the expansion of carbonic acid gas when escaping under high pressure into the atmosphere, is so great that the escaping gas becomes not merely liquefied but actually solidified.

[2] Joule, *Phil. Mag.*, May 1845.

[3] Dalton, *Memoirs of Lit. and Phil. Soc. of Manchester*, vol. v. pt. 2, pp. 251-255.

Subsequently Dulong[1] showed that equal volumes of all gases taken at the same temperature and pressure evolved (or absorbed) the same quantity of heat when suddenly compressed (or dilated) by the same amount.

32. Explanation of the Calorists.—That heat is developed by friction and percussion was well known to the supporters of the caloric theory, and accounted for by well-framed hypotheses. Thus any body in its normal state possessed a certain capacity for heat, and contained a certain quantity of caloric at a definite temperature. Percussion altered the condition of the substance and lessened its capacity for heat. Some of the caloric was squeezed out of it, and, being thus set free, manifested its presence by the rise of temperature. Similarly, in the hammering of a nail, the caloric was simply hammered out of the pores of the iron. The molecules of the matter were driven closer together, and the caloric was ejected. In the case of friction, however, part of the material was abraded or rubbed into powder, and the calorists postulated that the capacity for heat of the powder was smaller than that of the solid from which it was abraded ; there was thus an evolution of heat.

This reasoning is strictly philosophical if the assumptions on which it is based be true, viz. that the capacity for heat is less in the state of powder than in the solid state ; and further, that heat is indestructible, or that the quantity of heat fluid in the universe remains permanently the same. The calorists did not, however, appeal to experiment to prove that the capacity of a body for heat was less in the state of dust than in the block. If they had done so, they would have found their postulate overthrown, and would have been forced to abandon their theory, or devise some other explanation of the heat developed by friction. The production of heat by the friction of liquids, as in the process of churning, could scarcely be explained on the same lines. Here there is no abrasion, no apparent change of state or powdering of the material, and consequently no room for the postulate that its heat capacity is diminished by the process which generates the heat.

The peculiarity of the heat supply obtainable by friction is that it appears to be inexhaustible, so that the quantity of heat obtainable by rubbing together two bodies which do not abrade would be infinite. This cannot possibly be explained by the supposition that the heat capacity of the substance is less in the powdered or compressed than in the original state, but its explanation must be looked for in the action or agent which causes the rubbing. From this point of view

[1] Dulong, *Ann. de Chimie*, 2ᵉ série, tom. xli. p. 156, 1828.

the heat developed is the result of the work done by the agent producing the rubbing.

33. Rumford's Experiment.—The first experimental investigation
into the true nature of heat was made by Count Rumford [1] in 1798.

While engaged in the boring of brass cannon at the military
arsenal in Munich, he was struck by the high temperature of the
metallic chips thrown off, and by the excessive development of heat
during the process.   In order to investigate the matter thoroughly he
prepared a hollow gun-metal cylinder, formed in the waste head [2] of a
cannon, and mounted it so that it could be rotated by horse-power on
a horizontal axis, while a blunt steel borer pressed against its bottom.
The cylinder was covered with a thick coating of flannel to prevent
loss of heat, and a small radial hole to contain a thermometer was
drilled into the bottom, and terminated at its centre.   The bulb of
the thermometer was thus at the middle point of the thick bottom of
the cylinder,[3] and the stem projected from its side.

At the beginning of the experiment the thermometer stood at
60° F., and after half an hour, when the cylinder had made 960
revolutions, the temperature was found to be 130° F., which fairly
represented the mean temperature of the cylinder.

He now removed the metallic dust or scaly matter abraded by the
friction from the bottom of the cylinder, and found it weighed only
837 grains troy.   "Is it possible," he exclaims, "that the very considerable quantity of heat produced in this experiment—(a quantity
which actually raised the temperature of above 113 lbs. of gun-metal
at least 70 degrees of the Fahrenheit thermometer, and which, of
course, would have been capable of melting $6\frac{1}{2}$ lbs. of ice, or of causing
near 5 lbs. of ice-cold water to boil)—could have been furnished by

---

[1] Rumford, *Phil. Trans.*, 1798.   Count Rumford's name was Benjamin Thomson.
He was born in 1753 at Woburn, near Boston, and was driven to Europe for his
loyalty during the rebellion of the British colonies in America.   He effected various
important reforms in Bavaria, and chose the title by which he is generally known
(and which was conferred on him for his services) from a village in New Hampshire,
now called Concord, where he was obliged to leave his wife and infant daughter.

[2] The *verlorener Kopf*, or waste head, was a solid mass about 2 feet long, projecting beyond the muzzle of the gun.   This was cut off before boring.   It was cast
with the gun in order that its weight on the lower parts might make them compact.
Without this precaution the metal in the neighbourhood of the muzzle would be
more or less porous.

[3] The external diameter of the cylinder was $7\frac{3}{4}$ in., and its length 9·8 in.   The
diameter of the internal cavity (which was drilled out) was 3·7 in., and its depth
7·2 in., so that the bottom was 2·6 in. thick.   The borer was a flat piece of hardened
steel 4 in. long, 0·63 in. thick, and nearly as wide as the cavity, viz. 3·5 in.   It
was kept fixed and pressed against the bottom of the cylinder by means of a strong
screw with a pressure of 10,000 lbs.

so inconsiderable a quantity of metallic dust, and this merely in consequence of *a change* in its capacity for heat ? . . . But without insisting on the improbability of this supposition, we have only to recollect that from the results of actual and decisive experiments, made for the express purpose of ascertaining that fact, the capacity for heat of the metal of which great guns are cast is *not sensibly changed* by being reduced to the form of metallic chips in the operation of boring cannon, and there does not seem to be any reason to think that it can be much changed, if it be changed at all, in being reduced to much smaller pieces by a borer that is less sharp."

This test was not, however, conclusive to the calorists. It was not sufficient to prove, as Rumford did prove, that the capacity for heat of the solid metal was the same as that of the chips. It was still necessary to prove that equal masses of the solid metal and the abraded dust always contain the *same quantity* of heat when at the same temperature. A calorist might say that although metal and the dust possess the same thermal capacity at the same temperature, yet the solid metal contains a greater quantity of heat than the dust, the difference having been evolved during abrasion. It has been stated that this point might have been settled by melting equal weights of the two, and observing the quantity of heat necessary to change equal weights of the solid and abraded dust into fused metal. If these are equal, and if it be allowed that the fused mass is exactly the same in all respects in one case as in the other, then the dust and the solid metal will contain equal quantities of heat per unit weight when at the same temperature. A similar test would be by solution in an acid, and observation of the heat of combination. Rumford, however, did not stake his opinion on such experiments as these. He adhered firmly to the one main point and feature of the experiment, namely, that the supply of heat is inexhaustible. If the heat were rubbed out of the material, a stage would be reached at which all its heat would be exhausted. No such stage was ever observed. The supply was as free and copious at the end of the experiment as at the beginning. All that was necessary was the continued working of the machinery. The quantity of heat obtained depended in no way on the amount of rubbing or hammering the brass had previously received ; it depended only on the work spent in friction during the experiment (see further, p. 41).

Rumford also proceeded to determine if the exclusion of the air from the cylinder had any effect. For this purpose he closed the end of the cylinder with a tight-fitting collar so that the air had no access to the interior during the experiment, but he found no observable difference in the result.   He also placed the cylinder in a wooden box filled with water in such a manner that it could revolve either water-tight or open, while the borer pressed against its bottom as before. At the beginning of the experiment the temperature of the water was 60° F.   One hour after the machinery had been set in motion the temperature of the water, which weighed 18·77 lbs., was 107° F., or had been raised 47° F.   In thirty minutes more the temperature was 142° F., and at the end of two hours from the beginning of the experiment the temperature was 178° F., while in 2½ hours the water actually boiled!

He then proceeded to calculate the quantity of heat possessed by each part of the apparatus at the conclusion of the experiment, and found that the total was sufficient to raise 26·58 lbs. of ice-cold water to the boiling point.   This, together with the duration of the experiment, gave the rate at which the heat was generated to be "greater than that produced in the combustion of nine wax candles, each three quarters of an inch in diameter, all burning together with clear bright flames."

"One horse," he adds, "would have been equal to the work performed, though two were actually employed.   Heat may thus be produced merely by the strength of a horse, and in a case of necessity this might be used in cooking victuals.   But no circumstance could be imagined in which this method of procuring heat would be advantageous; for more heat might be obtained by using the fodder necessary for the support of the horse as fuel."

"In meditating over the results of all these experiments, we are naturally brought to the great question which has so often been the subject of speculation among philosophers, namely—

"What is Heat?—is there any such thing as an *igneous fluid*?   Is there anything that can with propriety be called *caloric*?"

"We have seen that a very considerable quantity of heat may be excited by the friction of two metallic surfaces, and given off in a constant stream or flux *in all directions*, without interruption or intermission, and without any signs of diminution or exhaustion. . . ."

"In reasoning on this subject we must not forget that most remarkable circumstance, that the source of the heat generated by friction in these experiments appeared evidently to be *inexhaustible*."

"It is hardly necessary to add that anything which any *insulated* body or system of bodies can continue to furnish without *limitation* cannot possibly be a *material substance*; and it appears to me to be extremely difficult, if not quite impossible, to form any distinct idea of anything capable of being excited and communicated in the manner the heat was excited and communicated in these experiments except it be MOTION."

34. Davy's Experiment.—The fatal blow to the caloric theory was delivered by Humphry Davy, who first showed that two pieces of ice may be melted by simply rubbing them together. Davy reasoned that if ice can be liquefied by friction, a substance (water) will be produced, which is allowed by all parties to contain a far greater amount of heat than the ice. Liquefaction will then conclusively demonstrate the generation of new heat. He tried the experiment and succeeded. He says:[1] "I procured two parallelepipedons of ice (the result of the experiment is the same if wax, tallow, resin, or any substance fusible at a low temperature be used) of the temperature 29° F., 6 inches long, 2 wide, and $\frac{2}{3}$ of an inch thick; they were fastened by wires to two bars of iron. By a peculiar mechanism their surfaces were placed in contact, and kept in a continued and violent friction for some minutes. They were almost entirely converted into water, which water was collected and its temperature ascertained to be 35° F., after remaining in an atmosphere of a lower temperature for some minutes. The fusion took place only at the plane of contact of the two pieces of ice, and no bodies were in friction but ice. From this experiment it is evident that ice by friction is converted into water, and according to the supposition of the calorists its capacity is diminished; but it is a well-known fact that the capacity of water for heat is much greater than that of ice, and ice must have an absolute quantity of heat added to it before it can be converted into water. Friction consequently does not diminish the capacities of bodies for heat."

Davy then proceeded to determine if the heat which produced the liquefaction could have been derived from the air or bodies in contact with the ice. For this purpose he caused the experiment to be performed by clock-work under the exhausted receiver of an air-pump surrounded with ice; but in this case also liquefaction was produced as before. He consequently concluded that heat is *produced* by friction, and that caloric, or the matter of heat, does not exist; that "a motion or vibration of the corpuscles of bodies must be necessarily generated by friction and percussion. Therefore we may reasonably conclude that this motion or vibration is heat. . . . Heat then . . . may be defined as a peculiar motion, probably a vibration of the corpuscles of bodies tending to separate them."

[1] Davy, "Essay on Heat and Light and Combinations of Light," *Complete Works*, vol. ii. p. 11. This was his first contribution to science, and was published in 1799 in the *Contributions to Physical and Medical Knowledge*, principally from the west of England. Collected by Thomas Beddoes, M.D.

The minds of scientists were, however, so imbued with the caloric doctrine that the experiments and arguments of Davy attracted but little attention. They were even treated by some as wild and extravagant speculations. Even Davy himself did not seem to be confident. His subsequent writings do not bear the mark of complete conviction which characterises so unmistakably those of Rumford, and it was not until 1812 that he distinctly laid down [1] that—

"The immediate cause of the phenomena of heat is motion, and the laws of its communication are precisely the same as the laws of the communication of motion."

Both Rumford and Davy might, however, have been successfully met by any calorist who was willing to abandon some of the less essential parts of the doctrine. When heat is generated by friction or compression, the calorists accounted for it by asserting that the capacity of the material for heat is diminished, or that the heat is rubbed or squeezed out of it. Now let us suppose that it is proved beyond doubt that this is not the case. How then is a calorist to explain the evolution of heat in Rumford's experiment ? By the fundamental tenets of his doctrine he is bound to consider heat as indestructible and uncreatable ; but in this experiment a constant stream of heat flows from the parts in friction as long as the motion continues, and no equivalent loss of heat can be detected elsewhere. Any competent reasoner will therefore turn to the agent which keeps the machinery in motion. The calorist will be forced to state that the heat evolved in Rumford's experiment comes from the horse, and in making this assertion his position will be as strong, but scarcely so acceptable or rational, as that of his opponent. Briefly stated, the position of the calorist would be that heat is an imponderable fluid which cannot be created or destroyed, and therefore if heat appears to be generated in any mechanical process it must be derived from the agents or sources which maintain that process. The opponents of the caloric theory, on the other hand, assert that heat is not a fluid, but may be developed by the expenditure of work or energy. While one party might say that the caloric (or heat) is derived from the horse in Rumford's experiment, the other party maintains that energy is derived from the horse, and the heat which is evolved is the equivalent of it. The fundamental postulate of modern science concerning energy is that it cannot be created or destroyed, and this is exactly the property demanded for caloric. The horse in Rumford's experiment supplies something to the machinery which possesses exactly the same fundamental quality of permanence according to both schools.

Position of the calorists.

[1] Davy, *Elements of Chemical Philosophy*, p. 94.

35. The Dynamical Equivalent of Heat—Joule's Experiments.
—That some relation existed between the work spent in driving the
apparatus and the heat developed in Count Rumford's experiment
had doubtless floated before the minds of many philosophers before
either the correct enunciation or the exact experimental determination
of this relation was made.   A rough estimation indeed of this relation
may be obtained from the experiment actually performed by Rumford.[1]
The accurate investigation of the whole subject was taken up by Dr.
Joule of Manchester in the year 1840, and continued for a long period
with the highest experimental skill in several distinct investigations.
The object of Joule's inquiry was to determine exactly the quantity
of heat developed by the expenditure of a known amount of work
when this work is spent solely in producing heat by friction.

The method employed was practically a modification of that used
by Rumford in showing that heat is developed when work is spent in
friction.   The modification consisted in the adoption of accurate
methods for estimating the work spent and the heat generated.   The
heat was produced by friction of a brass paddle revolving in water
contained in a specially constructed brass vessel, so that the water was
heated by a kind of revolving-churn process, and the temperature was
registered by means of a delicate mercurial thermometer.   The paddle
was driven by two leaden weights attached to a doubled cord passing
over two pulleys, and the work spent in turning it was estimated from
a knowledge of the mass of the weights and the height through which
they descended.

After all corrections [2] were made, Joule decided that his mean
result was 772 foot-pounds per degree Fahrenheit between the
temperatures 55° and 60° F.   That is, the work done in raising a
weight of one pound through 772 feet in the latitude of Manchester
will, if spent in friction (between brass and water), raise the temperature of one pound of water one degree Fahrenheit.   The unit of
heat being the quantity which will raise unit mass of water one degree
Unreduced Fahrenheit on the mercury thermometer, and the unit of work being
value of J.
that spent in elevating unit mass one foot, the general relation between
heat and work will be $H = W/772$, or $W = 772H$.

If the unit of heat be that required to raise unit mass of water

---

[1] Thus Rumford estimated the thermal capacity of the water and apparatus as
equivalent to that of 26·58 lbs. of water.   Further, one horse was sufficient to turn
the machinery and change the temperature of this mass from 33° to 212° F. in two
and a half hours, the rate of increase of temperature being about 1°·3 per minute.
This gives 847 foot-pounds as the dynamical equivalent, a number which is only
about 10 per cent in excess of Joule's estimate.

[2] Except reduction to the air thermometer, see Chap. VIII. section i.

one degree centigrade, the work equivalent will be the $\frac{9}{5}$ of 772, that is 1390, the unit of work being the same as before.   But if the unit of work be that spent in raising unit mass one metre, the value of the mechanical equivalent will be 424.   This is expressed by saying that the mechanical equivalent of heat is 424 grammetres, or the work spent in raising a weight of one gramme to a height of 424 metres will, if spent in friction, produce as much heat as will raise the temperature of one gramme of water one degree centigrade. Denoting the value of the mechanical equivalent by J in any system of units, we shall have between the work spent and the heat produced the general equation

$$W = JH.$$

The symbol J represents the number of units of work necessary to the generation of one unit of heat, when the work is all spent in generating heat.   It ought to be remembered that in the experiments devised by Rumford and Joule, the work may not all be spent in generating heat.   There may be electric or magnetic actions developed, or other actions may take place which we have as yet no means of detecting. If any such actions take place, the values of J derived by different methods and with different materials would not be expected to be equal, and if they are found to be equal it does not prove that such actions do not occur, but only that the ratio of the part of the work spent in producing heat to that spent in these other actions is the same in all the methods employed, or that the same definite fraction of the work is spent in all the methods in producing heat.

Joule was quite clear on the point that if the work is really all spent in producing heat, then with every form of apparatus we must obtain the same amount of heat for the expenditure of the same amount of work.   He consequently determined the dynamical equivalent by the friction of other liquids than water, and by other methods than friction.   The results of three series of experiments gave—

(1) Friction of water contained in a brass vessel with a brass paddle J = 772·695.
(2) Friction of mercury contained in an iron vessel with iron paddle J = 774·083.
(3) Friction of two iron rings rubbing against each other in mercury J = 774·987.

In 1878 Joule repeated his experiments, and found the number 773·369 for the dynamical equivalent in the latitude of Manchester.   This, reduced to the sea-level and the latitude of Greenwich, becomes 773·492, the unit of heat being that which raised the temperature of 1 lb. of water from 60° to 61° F., the weighing being made with brass weights when the barometer stood at 30 in.   When the weighing is made in vacuo this becomes reduced to 772·55.   In 1879 Joule made a careful comparison of his thermometer with one which had been standardised by Rowland.   The results were published as an appendix to Rowland's paper in the

Proceedings of the American Academy for March 1880. A considerable correction
was then found to be necessary in the values obtained by Joule. Again, Joule had
assumed Regnault's expression for the specific heat of water, and a correction for the
capacity for heat of the calorimeter was also rendered necessary by the changes in
the thermometry. Joule's result is given in the above-mentioned paper as 774·6,
which, when all corrections are applied, becomes (for temp. 12°·7 C. and latitude of
Baltimore) 778·5 (E. H. Griffiths, *Phil. Trans.*, A, 1893, p. 499).

Later experiments on this subject have been carried out by
Professor H. A. Rowlands and several others. The experiments of
Rowland are remarkable for their range and consistency, as well as
for the skill and completeness with which they were executed. They
were conducted at temperatures varying between 39°·1 F. and 96°·8
F. (a much wider range than that employed by Joule), and gave
results varying from 774·7 to 778·3 on the mercurial thermometer,
and from 775·9 to 783·4 on the air thermometer, the higher results being
obtained at the lower temperatures (see further, Chap. IV. sec. ix.).

When the gas thermometer is taken as the standard, and the unit
of heat as the quantity required to raise the temperature of unit
mass of water 1° at a temperature of 20° C. on the gas thermometer,
the foregoing results may be replaced by the numbers—

Corrected
value at
20° C.

$$J = \quad 427\cdot5 \text{ (grammetres degree C.)}$$
$$= \quad 779 \quad \text{(foot-pounds degree F.)}$$
$$= 1402 \quad \text{(foot-pounds degree C.)}.$$

36. Transformation of Heat into Work.—We have seen how
Rumford, Davy, and Joule proved that the work done by animals or
falling weights may be converted into heat, and we shall now consider
the converse operation—the transformation of heat into work, or the
derivation of mechanical effect from thermal agencies.

This process is exhibited in the steam-engine and all other heat
engines. Thus in the steam-engine fuel is consumed and heat
generated in the furnace, and at the expense of this heat the engine
is set in motion, and work is performed. The kinetic energy of the
particles of a hot body, which, according to the dynamical theory,
constitutes its heat, is thus transformed into the visible motion of the
parts of the engine, and this in turn is transformed partly into
external work, or mechanical effect, such as the raising of weights, or
communicating motion to or altering the configuration or state of
other bodies, or systems of bodies, and it is partly frittered down
again into heat developed by the friction of the parts of the engine
itself, or of other bodies which it may set in motion.

Thus in a locomotive the heat drawn from the furnace passes first
into heat motion or energy of the particles of water and steam ; this

in turn passes into the motion of the machinery. All the visible motion of the engine and its parts is thus derived from the invisible motions of the molecules of the water vapour, which in turn comes from the furnace, and this invisible motion or agitation of the molecules of a body we regard as the source of its sensible heat, and the performance of work by a heat engine we regard merely as a transformation of the kinetic energy of the particles of the hot body, or source of heat, into the visible energy of motion of large masses, or into that energy of position which we call potential energy. When a train is propelled by steam-power, part of the energy derived from the furnace is converted into energy of motion of parts of the apparatus, and part of this energy of motion will, if the train is ascending an incline, be converted into energy of position or potential energy, and part will be re-converted into heat developed by friction in the rails, air, and parts of the train. If the train moves uniformly, the moving parts are giving out as much energy as they receive from the furnace; if its speed is being accelerated, they are receiving more energy than they give out; and if its speed is diminishing, they are receiving less. The potential energy might be recovered again as motion (in part at least) by allowing the train to fall to its original level. The engine thus acts the part of a still, in converting energy which first exists as heat motion in the furnace into visible motion of the machine, and this again into heat motion developed by friction. In all heat engines, however, by far the greater part of the heat energy is given out as such, without being converted into mechanical energy at all.

If the engine be employed in merely producing motion in itself or other bodies without altering their relative positions or state, and if these motions finally subside through friction, as in the case of a train coming to rest at the same level as that from which it started, then on the whole there will be no external work done, there will be no mechanical advantage gained, and all the heat derived from the furnace will be frittered down, and reappear again as heat developed by the friction which brings the mass to rest. If, however, work has been done by the engine in raising its mass, or any other masses, to a higher level, an equivalent of the heat drawn from the furnace will disappear; this will have been used up in doing work, viz. the work necessary to raise the masses to the higher level; the remainder of the heat drawn from the furnace will reappear as heat developed by friction, so that the heat thus developed is not now the complete equivalent of that drawn from the furnace, but is less by an amount W/J where W is the work done in raising the masses.

The direct verification that heat disappears when work is done by a steam-engine was first experimentally demonstrated by Hirn in 1857, but as early as 1839 an essay was made by Séguin in the same direction.

Hirn's experiments. Hirn actually measured in an ordinary working steam-engine the quantity of heat which was carried from the boiler in a given time, and also the quantity which reached the condenser during the same interval. He also calculated the quantity lost by radiation and conduction over all parts of the machine, and found that when the engine was at work, turning other machinery, the difference between the quantity of heat which left the boiler and that which entered the condenser was much greater than when the engine performed no external work, and the steam merely passed through the engine from the boiler to the condenser.

Hirn also pushed the experimental inquiry further, and actually deduced a fair estimate of the dynamical equivalent of heat from his observations of the work done by the engine, and the quantity of heat used up in performing it. The work W performed in any time can be deduced from the area of the Watt's indicator diagram (see Art. 66) and the number of strokes of the piston. To determine the quantity of heat converted into work, the weight of water that passes from the boiler to the condenser must be estimated. Knowing the latent heat of vaporisation at the temperature of the boiler (see Art. 198), the quantity of heat Q drawn from the boiler in any time becomes known. But this quantity is not all converted into work. Part of it q is carried into the condenser, and a part R is lost by radiation in the transit. Hence the quantity of heat converted into work is $Q - q - R$, and the value of J is found from the equation

$$W = J(Q - q - R).$$

By this means Hirn obtained the numbers 413 and 420·4 (gramme-metres), which, considering the difficulty of the investigation, must be regarded as exceedingly good approximations.

37. The Two Laws of Thermodynamics—Meaning of the Term Law in Physical Science.—It has been shown that heat may be generated by the expenditure of work, and conversely that work may be performed by the expenditure of an equivalent quantity of heat. A certain equivalence has been shown, by the experiments of Joule, to exist between the work done and the heat generated (or spent) in First law. such cases, and this equivalence is known as the first law of thermodynamics. This law is algebraically stated in the equation

$$W = JH,$$

which means that when work is spent in generating heat, or heat spent in performing work, then J units of work are equivalent to one unit of heat.

In the general case a quantity of work W is spent in driving a machine, and a smaller quantity of work w is performed by the machine—for example, in raising weights or moving certain masses. The balance $W - w$ is spent, partly at least, and perhaps wholly, in overcoming the friction of the parts of the machinery, and an equivalent quantity of heat is developed. It must not, however, be assumed that the heat thus developed is the complete equivalent of the difference $W - w$. Other processes besides the development of heat may be in operation. Electrical phenomena may occur, and generally do occur, when dissimilar substances rub together. Magnetic and electro-magnetic actions may also take place, and energy may be radiated into space or dissipated, during the motion or collision of masses, in modes which we are as yet unable to detect. The expenditure of the work in Joule's experiment may not be quite so simple as it appears at first sight, and until it is proved that in all such cases the work is wholly spent in producing heat, it is not clear that the value of J, determined by the friction of one pair of substances, should be the same as that determined in the same manner by another pair. That other actions do take place can scarcely be doubted, and perhaps it is to these that the differences in the determinations of J by different methods are to be partly attributed. The corrected equation would in this case be

$$W = JH + w,$$

where w represents the quantity of work spent in developing other phenomena hitherto unnoticed.

The second law of thermodynamics was introduced by Clausius Second and Thomson, and these two laws form the basis of the modern law. science of thermodynamics. This law, as stated by Clausius, asserts that heat cannot be conveyed from one body to another at a higher temperature without the expenditure of work, or some equivalent process. Thus of a system of bodies at different temperatures any pair may be converted into a heat engine, that at the higher temperature acting as the source, or furnace, and the other playing the part of the condenser. When such an engine performs work the heat used up is always that of the source or body of highest temperature. A certain quantity of heat is drawn from the source, and part of this is converted into work, while the remainder passes into the condenser or body of lower temperature. If the process were reversed work would be spent in driving the engine, while a certain quantity of heat would be drawn from the condenser and a certain quantity would be restored to the source. Thus in the direct process heat is drawn from the warmer and given in part to the colder of two bodies, while external work is performed by the engine. In this process the tendency is to equilibrate the temperatures of the two bodies. In the reverse process, however, work is spent in driving the engine, while heat is drawn from the colder and given to the warmer of the two bodies, and the tendency is to exaggerate their difference of temperature. It is from this point of view that Thomson regarded the matter, and proposed the principle that the method by which work is obtained from heat is by allowing it to pass from bodies of higher to bodies of lower temperature, or that work may be done by using up the heat of the warmer of two bodies but not by using the heat of the colder. In Thomson's statement the direct process of obtaining mechanical effect by thermal agencies is kept in view, and the impossibility of obtaining work by using up the heat of the coldest of a system of bodies is insisted on. In order that heat may be drawn from the coldest body the engine must be reversed, and work must be spent in effecting the process. This is the statement of Clausius, and the two are therefore equivalent.

An apparent violation of the second law of thermodynamics, possible but for our inability to deal with individual molecules, has been ingeniously pointed out by Maxwell. The fuller consideration of this and other matters, together with the applications of the law, will be taken up again in the sequel (Chap. VIII.). At present it will only be necessary to call attention to the meaning of the word *law* in physics.

Physical laws.

A law in physical science usually means a relation between the numerical magnitudes of certain physical quantities which has been experimentally found to hold, when these quantities are caused to vary, subject to given conditions. For instance, Boyle's law states that the volume of a given mass of gas varies inversely as the pressure, when the temperature is kept constant. Again, the laws of reflection and refraction of light state general relations between the directions of two rays which under certain conditions are always found to hold. The title of a law is also frequently given to some general principle which cannot be directly proved by experiment, but which, when used as the basis of a theory, has been found to account satisfactorily for a number of known facts and perhaps has suggested other facts which have been subsequently verified by experiment. Newton's laws of motion, the law of the conservation of energy, and the second law of thermodynamics, belong to this category. These laws may not be absolutely true, but they are stated as laws because, so far as our experience goes, they have not yet been found to be false, *i.e.* to lead to contradictory results. Such laws are not mere logical conceptions, but are evolved from the consideration of long series of observations, and are tested by repeated experiment under ever-varying circumstances. In proportion only as they are found to bear such tests does our confidence in their trustworthiness increase. They are for the most part working hypotheses of the greatest utility in systematising our knowledge and cataloguing facts. To find the true law of any class of phenomena requires a complete knowledge of the processes by which they are brought about; and before we can say that our knowledge of any one law of nature is complete we must have ascertained that it holds good without exception. Only so far as it has been tested can it be trusted, and when we say that any law is established by a series of experiments the *range* of the series must be stated, and it is only asserted that within this range the law is in accordance with the facts.

It is often necessary to distinguish carefully between a law which expresses an ascertained physical fact, and a relation between physical quantities which follows necessarily from our definition of the mode in which some quantity is to be measured. Thus, Gay-Lussac's law states, in effect, that when the pressure of a given mass of a gas is kept constant, and the temperature is varied, the change of volume is proportional to the change of temperature measured in degrees. Now, if the accepted scale of temperature were based on the expansion of a particular gas, *e.g.* hydrogen, in a constant pressure gas thermometer, the statement of Gay-Lussac's law would be a mere truism as far as hydrogen is concerned, because it would follow necessarily from the mode of definition of temperature measurement. Further, if the accepted scale of temperature were based on the measurement of the pressure of hydrogen in a constant volume hydrogen thermometer (see Chap. II. sec. ii.), then Gay-Lussac's law for hydrogen would be an immediate deduction from Boyle's law, and would not correspond to any new property of the gas. The modern fundamental scale of temperature, on which all theoretical reasoning is based, does not, however, depend on any property of hydrogen or any other substance, but is Lord Kelvin's absolute scale, founded on the second law of thermodynamics (see Chap. VIII. sec. viii.). Gay-Lussac's law has, in fact, been found to be very approximately true for hydrogen as well as for other gases.[1]

[1] The further statement contained in Gay-Lussac's law, viz. that the coefficient of expansion is the same for all gases, is one with which we are not here concerned.

SECTION V

THE WAVE THEORY OF RADIANT HEAT

38. Antiquity of the Dynamical Theory.—Having learned that heat may be generated by the expenditure of work, and *vice versa*, we shall now consider the theory which has been founded on these facts.

The first notions of the dynamical theory of heat date from such a remote epoch that their origin cannot be attributed with precision to any single person or period. Thus some of the Greek philosophers, from mere observation of the destructive effects of heat, considered it as a movement of the ultimate particles of matter. So also at the time of the scientific renaissance inaugurated by Bacon, and continued by Descartes, we find the claims of the dynamical theory freely advocated. These statements of the doctrine, however, can only be regarded as more or less acute speculations, as no sure basis for the theory was laid till Rumford and Davy executed their experiments, nor indeed was the theory generally accepted until a considerably later period. The calorist, in fact, had not become extinct in the middle of the nineteenth century! While the majority of scientists were convinced that light was due to wave motion in the ether, they still adhered with the greatest pertinacity to their heat fluid or caloric.

39. The Ether.—Although we are forced to regard space itself as unlimited, yet there is no mental necessity compelling us to regard it either as filled throughout, or in part, with a medium, or as entirely empty. When, however, we endeavour to explain the phenomena of heat and light we are forced to the conclusion that all space, at least as far as the farthest visible star, is filled with a fundamental medium, which we may call the ether. This hypothesis is forced upon us by the fact that heat and light travel through space with a definite velocity, and we find it impossible to conceive of more than two methods by which an influence, travelling in time, may be propagated from one body to another situated at a distance.

Take, for example, the case of two ships at sea. One of these may disturb the other in either of two ways—either by firing bullets against Two it or by exciting waves in the water (medium between them) which, methods of explana- diverging from the centre of disturbance, break upon the other ship tion. and disturb it. In the first case one emits a substance which impinges against the other, and in the second it is the source of a disturbance which travels through a medium existing between the two. The former method is the basis of the emission theories of heat and light, and on the latter is founded the wave theory. According to the emission theory, a hot or luminous body emits a fluid or a shower of fine particles, travelling through space with the velocity of light (300,000,000 metres per second). This theory has been altogether abandoned, and the supposition that the light and heat which we receive from the sun are due to wave motion in a medium filling all space has been universally adopted. The medium is of course hypo-thetical, in so far as what we term the *direct* evidence of our senses is concerned. It is not visible or tangible; yet its existence is advocated by the phenomena of electricity and magnetism, and, in fact, by all the operations of nature. When we speak of the direct evidence of our senses, how do we circumscribe the term? what exactly do we mean ? what fixed line of demarcation have we to tell us where this evidence begins and where it ceases ?

The notion of such a medium is neither new nor fanciful, nor is it to be regarded as a vague speculation on the part of scientists. The hypothesis has been admitted on accumulated evidence, and in con-sequence of the demand for a rational and consistent explanation of all the phenomena of nature. It is certainly as easy to conceive of space as filled with a medium, capable of carrying energy from one region to another, as to believe that the interstellar spaces are entirely empty ; and if the question be impartially considered it will perhaps be conceded that we have really as much reason for believing in the existence of a universal ether as in that of anything else.[1]

It is to be remembered, however, that we do not postulate density, Postulates. or compressibility, or molecular structure, or necessarily any property of matter, for this ether, except that it can contain and propagate energy. It is merely assumed as a fundamental medium, by means of which the properties of all substances, and all the phenomena of nature, are to be explained. It is certainly unscientific to postulate elasticity and density, or any structure, for this medium, if by means of it we are to account for the elasticity, density, and structure of

---

[1] The ancients certainly appear to have had no difficulty in admitting the simul-taneous existence of several ethers and imponderable fluids, and at the present time the vast majority of people think of electricity as a fluid, or two fluids !

matter. Such a procedure does not even push the inquiry one stage farther back.

40. Heat and Light Reducible to the same Agency.—The idea that heat is ultimately due to a motion of some sort has been long entertained. By friction and collision the sensible motion of bodies disappears and heat is generated. The supposition has been that the motion in such cases is not really lost, but is merely transferred from the body as a whole to its individual particles. Thus when a moving body is brought to rest by friction, or collision, the energy of the original visible motion of the body is not annihilated, but passes over into the invisible atoms of the substances taking part in the friction or collision.

Now we have evidence in favour of the supposition that light is due to wave motion in the ether, and we have exactly the same evidence in favour of the same supposition with regard to radiant heat. Radiant heat (for example, the heat emitted by hot-water pipes or a blackened stove) and light behave in exactly the same way in a variety of experiments—in fact the only difference that can be detected is that light, as well as possessing all the characteristic qualities of the radiant heat, is also able to affect the sense of sight.

Radiant heat then, like light, is supposed to be due to wave motion in the ether.[1] We say that the molecules of a hot body are in a state of very rapid vibration, or are the centres of rapid periodic disturbances

[1] Among the contemporaries of Rumford and Davy, Dr. Thomas Young seems to have been the only man who comprehended the full bearing of their experiments. He called in question the principle assumed by the calorists, that the heat absorbed in any process is precisely the same as that evolved when the body passes back again to its initial condition, and points out that this assumption had not been proved in a single case (" Lecture on the Nature of Heat"). That Young had thoroughly grasped the idea of the wave theory is proved by the following passage :—" If heat be not a substance it must be a quality, and this quality can only be motion. It was Newton's opinion that heat consists in a minute vibratory motion of the particles of bodies, and that this motion is communicated through an apparent vacuum by the undulations of an elastic medium, which is also concerned in the phenomena of light. If the arguments which have been lately advanced in favour of the undulatory nature of light be deemed valid, there will be still stronger reasons for admitting this doctrine respecting heat, and it will only be necessary to suppose the vibrations and undulations principally constituting it to be larger and stronger than those of light, while at the same time the smaller vibrations of light, and even the blackening rays, derived from still more minute vibrations, may perhaps, when sufficiently condensed, concur in producing the effects of heat. These effects, beginning from the blackening rays, which are invisible, are a little more perceptible in the violet, which still possess but a faint illuminating power ; the yellow-green afford the most light ; the red gives less light, but much more heat ; while the still larger and less frequent vibrations, which have no effect on the sense of sight, may be supposed to give rise to the least refrangible rays, and to constitute invisible heat."

of some sort, that they thus excite waves in the ambient ether, that these waves travel through the ether between us and the body with the velocity of light, and that when they fall upon us they are more or less absorbed by, and cause corresponding motions in, the molecules of our bodies, and thus arises the feeling of hotness. The sense of heat in us is thus excited by the ethereal waves diverging from the hot body, just as the eye is excited by the waves diverging from a luminous body, or as the ear, in an analogous manner, is affected by the aerial waves originated by a sounding body.

The question now arises, Are there two distinct sets of waves in the ether ? Are there heat waves and light waves, or are these waves of the same nature and type ? That a light wave also possesses heating power at once leads us to suspect that there is no essential difference in character between the wave motion which affects our sense of heat and that which affects our sense of vision. To explain how this may be we revert to the more easily comprehended case of sound.

If a sounding bell vibrates one hundred times per second it generates waves in the air which are about 11 feet in length, and if it vibrates eleven hundred times per second the corresponding waves are about 1 foot long, while fifty vibrations per second will give rise to waves about 7 yards in length, and so on. The impression upon the ear depends on the number of waves which fall upon it per second —that is, upon the rate of vibration of the sounding body—and as a consequence we derive the idea of pitch. That is, we say a note is high or low according as the number of vibrations per second is comparatively large or small. Further, the range of the ear is limited, and the rate of vibration may be so high that the ear fails to respond to the demand upon it, and the rate of vibration may, on the other hand, be so low as to cause no distinct impression. In other words, the aerial waves may be too short or too long to cause the impression of sound.[1] There are certain limits of length between which the waves must lie—from about 12 or 13 yards to about $\frac{1}{3}$ of an inch. These limits are determined by the construction and constitution of the ear, and vary slightly from individual to individual. The very long waves and the very short waves which do not affect the ear are, however, waves of exactly the same character as those which cause the impression of sound ; the only difference is one of

Effect of frequency.

---

[1] The rapidity of vibration or frequency is the main point to be kept in view rather than the length of the wave, and in what follows, a short wave is to be taken as meaning one of high rate of vibration, while a long wave is one of low rate. For the same rate of vibration the actual length of the wave will depend upon the nature of the medium.

rapidity. The fault lies with the ear and not with the waves. We do not say that there are two distinct classes of aerial waves, those which give rise to sound and those which do not. We prefer to look upon all the waves as of the same class—that is, the physical process in action during the propagation of all is the same. The difference is merely one of rapidity, and, as the range of the ear is limited, it cannot meet the demands upon it in both directions to an unlimited extent.

In the same manner every body in space is regarded as a source of incessant ethereal commotion. Every molecule of matter is in vibration, and generates waves in the ether. The clouds may shut off the light and heat of the sun, but they are warm bodies themselves, and radiate waves of heat. The earth itself is warm, and on the coldest night the dark space embraced by its shadow is traversed by incessant streams of radiated waves. We are thus bathed day and night in the midst of never-ceasing change. The ether is never still.

It is, however, to be distinctly remembered that we do not make any assumption as to the nature of the vibration or the process going on in the ether. We merely call it a vibration, because we believe it to be a periodic variation of some sort. This never-ending tremor affects us in two distinct ways. To it we owe the sensation of vision as well as that of heat. If an ethereal wave lies between certain limits of frequency it affects the eye, and we call it light. Such a wave falling upon our bodies may also set up commotions among our molecules, and give rise to the feeling of warmth. The same wave may thus cause two distinct impressions, that of light and also that of heat, just as if a sound wave could not only affect the ear but could also cause our bodies to tingle and develop a sensation of warmth. Thus while we have only one sense to tell us directly that the air is vibrating, we have two by which we can examine the ether. In this aspect, then, the sense of heat may be regarded as an extension of the sense of sight (see Art. 13).

41. Existence of Waves beyond the Limits of the Senses.—The eye, like the ear, is, however, limited in range. An ethereal wave may be either too slow or too quick to affect it. Outside these limits waves of any power might fall upon us, and yet we should be enveloped in perpetual night. Our sense of heat would, however, come to the rescue. Waves which are too slow to affect the eye can warm our bodies. Thus these two senses overlap and extend each other. The waves, however, which most powerfully affect the eye are not generally those which most excite the sense of heat. While some

waves are of such a length that they can be easily detected by either
sense, still some are so long that the eye fails to cope with them, yet
they are easily responded to by the sense of heat; and, on the other
hand, some are so short that although they may affect the eye, yet
they are with difficulty, if at all, detected by the sense of heat.

We are now left with those waves which undoubtedly exist in
myriads, and which are too short or too long to be detected by either
the sense of sight or the sense of heat.   Such waves might fall upon
us for all time, and still by means of our unaided senses we could
never become aware of their presence.   An ether might exist and be
continually troubled by such waves, and yet we could have no direct
evidence of their existence or of the medium which carried them.
The suggestion of such a medium by any one would probably be
looked upon as strong evidence of insanity.   Even with the double
evidence of our senses which we now have in favour of a space-filling
ether, there are many who would rather doubt such evidence than
believe in a thing which they cannot directly perceive by the senses.
However, considering the medium as only hypothetical, the fact that
it might certainly exist and fill important functions in the life of the
universe and still never be detected or suspected by us is a strong
reason why the postulation of such a medium for the explanation of
natural phenomena should not be branded as irrational or un-
philosophic.

The ingenuity of man has not allowed these long waves, nor even
the very short waves, to escape.   Those which are too short to be
directly detected by the eye can be placed in evidence by means of
their chemical action, while those which are too long to affect our
sense of heat (it is only waves in the neighbourhood of $\frac{1}{2000}$ part
of a millimetre that act directly on our senses) have been recently
subjected to the power of man by the celebrated experiments of
Professor Hertz.   Previous to 1889 we were confined in our observations to waves about $\frac{1}{50000}$ part of an inch in length, now we can
work with ether waves a foot or a yard or a mile long if desired.[1]

42. Restriction of the term Heat.—As long as the waves which
constitute radiant heat are travelling through free space or transparent
bodies they obey the same laws as those of light.   When, however,
they fall on bodies which are opaque to them, both heat and light
waves are absorbed, a conversion of ethereal into molecular energy
takes place, and the bodies are warmed.   In the study of heat we are
chiefly concerned, not with the laws of the ethereal waves, but with
the manifestations of the molecular energy of material bodies to which

[1] See the author's *Theory of Light*, chap. xxi.

they give rise.   Hence it is generally convenient to treat of the energy of ethereal waves, whether visible or not, as light energy, and to restrict the term heat to the molecular energy of matter.   If it should, however, be necessary to make special mention of the invisible heat-producing waves, they may be referred to as *radiant heat*.

Before we proceed to the study of the effects of heat it may be of advantage to glance at some considerations in relation to matter and motion, and the ether as the vehicle of energy, for before any theory of heat can be worked out in full detail some satisfactory theory of matter must be first formulated, and this appears to be a task of no ordinary difficulty.   We shall, therefore, consider briefly the evidence we have regarding the structure of matter and the causes which determine its composition and physical state.   A full knowledge of the ultimate constitution of matter may possibly lie beyond the grasp of the human intellect, for this can only be traced with certainty as far as our senses, combined with physical apparatus, enable us to observe it.   The essential differences, however, between the three typical forms—solids, liquids, and gases—and their modes of inter-action, form a legitimate subject of inquiry.

SECTION VI

ON MATTER

43. Definitions.—Various, and very diverse, definitions of the term matter have been proposed from time to time. The experimental physicist, however, uses the word merely to denote the substance or stuff contained in the objects around him, and which constitute what is termed the external or material universe. These objects we recognise and distinguish by means of their properties—that is, by the impressions, direct or indirect, which they make on our organs of sense, and by means of which we perceive their presence and consequently say they exist. Two general properties have been usually attributed to matter, namely, *extension* and *impenetrability*, the former term being used to signify that any portion of matter occupies space, or has volume, and the latter to denote that two bodies, or portions of matter, cannot occupy the same portion of space at the same time.

The term impenetrability thus appears to mean pretty much the same thing as extension, for if we say a body occupies a certain space, we ought to mean that it occupies that space to the exclusion of all other bodies. So that in addition to referring to no new property, and being therefore unnecessary, the name seems to be ill chosen, as it is undoubtedly misleading in its signification.

We distinguish different kinds of matter by such properties as compressibility, greater or less rigidity, colour, taste, smell, but the one property which characterises all forms of matter, as we know it, is *weight*. We measure matter by weight, and we say that two bodies of equal weight have equal masses—that is, contain equal quantities of matter. The term " conservation of matter " might, therefore, with advantage be replaced by the term " *conservation of weight,*" as it would keep the mind in closer touch with the property that really is conserved throughout chemical processes, namely weight. Thus there is no mental necessity compelling us to believe that the weight of two

57

or more atoms in chemical combination should be the same as the sum
of their separate weights before combination, even though the quantity
of matter (measured in the same way) remained the same as before.
Thus if matter be regarded as an objective reality independent of man
and his ideas, then we could easily imagine that matter should remain
permanent in quantity throughout any chemical change, and yet the
weight in the same case might be very different at the end of the
reaction from that at the beginning. It is, therefore, better to adhere
strictly to the main fact, namely, that the weight is conserved so far
as our experience has yet gone.

The property of extension, however, does not sufficiently circumscribe the term matter for our purpose, for this property belongs to
anything conceivable by the human mind as existing in space. We
do not wish to call the ether matter, or if we adopted the fluid theory
of heat or electricity, or the corpuscular theory of light, we should
avoid calling these media matter, for they have all been supposed to
be devoid of weight, which is the characteristic of all matter as we
know it. We might speak of ether, or caloric, or electricity as fluids
or fluid media, or simply as media, but never as matter. It must now
be clear that when we speak of matter we use the term for the sake of
convenience to denote that stuff which constitutes the bodies around
us, and that the property common to all kinds of matter, as we know
it, is weight.

What we constantly *observe*, however, is change ; and in matter we
observe both change of quality or state, and change of position or
motion. Thus wine when exposed to the air turns into vinegar,
and water when heated turns into vapour. The former is a change
in quality and is termed a *chemical* change or process, while the latter
is a change of the state of aggregation of the matter and is referred
to shortly as a change of state.

44. Divisibility of Matter.—Much futile discussion has been
engaged in by metaphysicians and physicists as to the infinite
divisibility of matter. A block of wood may be split in two by a
hatchet, and each of these portions may be again divided, and so on.
The question then arises, Can this process of subdivision be carried
on indefinitely ? Divisibility in the abstract can certainly be carried
on indefinitely, for here it only depends on the imagination ; but in
practice it is quite a different question. If any body can be divided
into two portions it is a matter to be tested by experiment alone if
each of these portions can be divided into two others, and so on
indefinitely. The question of the *infinite* divisibility of matter is,
however, beyond the scope of experiment, since the infinite, from the

very meaning of the word, cannot be the subject of experience. The question is therefore an objectless one for experimental science.

If by experiment, however, it were found that the process of division could not be pushed beyond a certain limit, that we finally came to parts which we could not further break up, we still would not be justified in saying that further division is impossible, but should rest satisfied with stating that we did not yet possess the means of pushing the division any further.

45. Antiquity of the Idea of Atoms and Molecules.—The idea that all bodies are composed of a multitude of very small particles seems to have been entertained since the earliest times of civilisation. The *hard* atom was conceived 2400 years ago by the Greek philosophers Democritus and Leucippus, and was subsequently glorified in the poetry of Lucretius. An argument urged by the latter in favour of the hypothesis is the facility with which it lends itself to the explanation of the mobility of fluids such as air and water. This arises, according to the poet, because there are vacant spaces between the perfectly solid particles, and hence, although the particles are hard, yet the substance as a whole may be soft and yielding.

The idea of a perfectly hard atom seems to be refuted by all those modern researches, such as spectroscopic work, which lead us to reflect on the molecular structure of matter. The behaviour of matter in regard to radiant heat and light leads us irresistibly to conclude that an atom is not simply a hard, structureless particle, but that it is a more or less complicated system capable of internal vibrations of several distinct periods.

The atomic theory, however, only acquired a definite form at the beginning of last century, when it was revived by Dalton to explain the fact that in chemical combinations the elements unite in certain definite proportions. Since that time the hypothesis has grown in strength, and has been a fruitful instrument of progress in many branches of physical science, so that it now claims the rank of a well-tested theory.

46. Value of a Theory.—Such a theory, however, claims not the truth of an abstract law. The human mind deals much less easily with abstract truths by themselves than by aid of well-conceived analogies and illustrative imagery. The value of any hypothesis depends upon its convenience in systematising observed facts, and by the extent to which it embraces all known phenomena must its utility be estimated. Such an hypothesis cannot be proved. It may be true, but it must, nevertheless, be regarded merely as a tool to be used for the sake of convenience as long as it is consistent with observation, and which must be rejected, or modified to suit our wants, when found to be no longer applicable. A well-chosen hypothesis not only concatenates the observed facts, and gives a clear and connected idea of the general laws to which they are subject, but may often lead to the discovery of new relations, and thus place in our hands the means of anticipating phenomena previously unobserved. The process of scientific inquiry may be thus advanced from the stage of blind groping to that of well-planned and conscious investigation.

47. Molecules considered as Groups of Atoms.—According to the molecular theory all bodies consist of very small parts termed molecules. Every molecule is supposed to be similar to every other molecule of the same substance, and to possess all the mass properties of the substance.[1] In other words, it is the smallest part of the body which can be separated from it and still possess all the characteristics which distinguish the substance. The necessity for this limitation arises from the fact that substances which are apparently homogeneous can be decomposed into two or more other substances which are very dissimilar in their properties. Thus water can be decomposed into hydrogen and oxygen, the volume of the former being twice that of the latter. For this reason a molecule of water is said to consist of two atoms of hydrogen united to (or in chemical union with) one atom of oxygen. It must, however, be admitted that we have no right to assert that two atoms of hydrogen united in this way to one atom of oxygen—that is, a molecule of water—would, if we could deal with it, possess all the mass properties of water. Any portion of a substance that we can subject to experiment contains an enormous number of molecules, and its properties may be, and probably are, very different from those of a single molecule. The chemical definitions, therefore, require modification.

It is also found that such substances as hydrogen and oxygen cannot be further decomposed by any process at our command, and they are consequently said to be simple substances. An atom is the smallest portion of a simple substance which can enter into chemical combination. A molecule, on the other hand, may consist of two or more atoms associated together in a manner which we do not as yet understand, and to denote this manner of association we say they are in chemical union. A molecule of a compound substance is thus a little society of atoms of what we call the elementary substances. Thus if we suppose the solar system to dwindle down till the masses forming it attained the size of atoms, then the whole

---

[1] See, however, Art. 49.

system thus associated might be taken to represent what we call a molecule, the different planets and their satellites forming its constituent atoms.

48. Evidence in Favour of the Atomic Theory.—The atomic theory involves the supposition that there is a practical limit to the divisibility of matter. In fact, it is only on this supposition that any definite meaning can be attached to the existence of elements in chemical combination according to Dalton's law of multiple proportions. An atom as a whole enters into or passes out of chemical combination ; a portion of it cannot be removed from a molecule leaving the rest in combination, and this is what the name signifies.

All chemical experience harmonises with the atomic theory, and finds in it an easy and intelligible mode of expression. The hypothesis is also strongly corroborated by spectroscopic researches, and by observations in the other domains of physical science ; yet, as to the ultimate nature of matter, and as to the question whether in going on dividing a portion of matter we should finally arrive at an atom, or portion which could not be further divided, man is still quite as ignorant as he was in the days of Lucretius. The solution of this problem appears to recede from our grasp as fast as we approach it, and this, perhaps, is as yet a matter of indifference in chemical investigation.

49. Idea of a Fundamental Substance—The Protyle Theory.— Any substance, such as oxygen or hydrogen, which cannot be further decomposed, is called an element or simple substance. It must be carefully remembered, however, that an element in the chemical sense is an undecomposed, not necessarily an undecomposable, substance. Attempts to draw general conclusions as to the constitution of the various elementary substances, from the values of their atomic weights, have been made in two directions. The first line, started by Prout in 1815, was based upon the philosophic assumption of a fundamental substance, or "protyle." This substance was supposed to be hydrogen, and all the other elementary substances were supposed to be made up of it, so that if weight be conserved throughout chemical combination, or such combination as would yield the various elements out of hydrogen, then the atomic weights of all the elements, and in fact of all substances, simple or compound, should be multiples of that of hydrogen. In other words, if the weight of an atom of hydrogen be taken as unit of weight, then the weight of an atom of any other element, or of a molecule of any chemical compound, should be expressible as a whole number, provided the weight of a molecule be equal to the sum of the weights of its constituent atoms.

This, however, is not the case, for the atomic weights in many cases differ from those required by the theory by quantities much larger than the probable errors of experiment. There is, however, a surprising approximation to the multiples of hydrogen in the atomic weights of many elements.

The explanation of this anomaly has only recently been arrived at. In 1906 Boltwood [1] discovered ionium, a disintegration product of uranium, and found that it was chemically indistinguishable from thorium, although it differs from the latter element in atomic weight and in radioactive properties. Other similar discoveries followed, and finally Aston [2] showed that many of the chemical elements are mixtures of two or more kinds of atoms differing in atomic weight, although identical in chemical and spectroscopic properties. In such cases the atomic weights of the constituents are represented by whole numbers, but the mean atomic weight of the mixture cannot be so represented. For example, chlorine, whose atomic weight is 35·46, consists of two kinds of atoms whose atomic weights are 35 and 37 respectively. Later, Sir E. Rutherford [3] showed that the nuclei (see Art. 58) of the atoms of several light elements, e.g. nitrogen, could be disintegrated by bombardment with swift α particles.

50. The Periodic System.—The second line of consideration, introduced in 1864 by Newlands in England, and Lothar Meyer in Germany, might be termed the periodic system. In the hands of Lothar Meyer and Mendeléeff it has yielded a considerable harvest, and they have shown that in a fairly general way the properties of the elementary substances are periodic functions of their atomic weights. Thus if all the elements be arranged in the order of their atomic weights their chemical properties will vary from member to member till a certain number of elements have been passed, and then these properties, or very similar ones, will be repeated again in order as we pass up the series of elements. This system is by no means perfect. Many incongruities still remain to be eliminated by new facts, or fresh considerations, and so far it can only be regarded as the commencement of what promises to be a fruitful method of investigation.

51. Continuity Possible.—The supposition of atoms and molecules is, however, by no means absolutely necessary. Matter might also be regarded as continuous and structureless, not composed of discrete particles, but completely filling the space enclosed by the surface of the body. It is difficult, from this point of view, to explain com-

---

[1] Boltwood, *Amer. Journ. Science*, xxii. p. 537, 1906.
[2] *Isotopes*, by F. W. Aston, 2nd ed., 1924.
[3] *Phil. Mag.* xxxvii. p. 581, 1919.

pressibility, unless we postulate it as a primary quality of every element of matter, yet the theory need not be discarded at once on this account. Our powers of forming conceptions are limited by our experience, and to say that a supposition is inconceivable is merely to assert that it has not yet come within the bounds of our experience. Every explanation in physical science is but a reduction of a complex problem to its simpler elements, and there is probably a limit to such reduction beyond which the mind of man may never pass. Our explanations, in all cases, are made in terms of ideas which arise out of our experience. Beyond this we cannot go, but we attempt to fathom the unknown by means of analogies derived from the known.

52. Heterogeneity Possible.—Chemical combination might result from the mixture of different substances which penetrate each other so intimately that we cannot find in the compound the properties of any of the separate substances of which it is composed. The smallest portion which we can examine is apparently homogeneous with the whole mass. The mass, however, may still be intensely heterogeneous, and in fact such heterogeneity is indicated in apparently homogeneous bodies, such as water and mercury, by different lines of reasoning based on experimental facts. Lord Kelvin[1] has shown that with such a constitution of matter gravitation alone would sufficiently explain the greater part of the phenomena which have been ascribed to the so-called molecular forces. That such heterogeneity might actually exist in the apparently most homogeneous substances and still escape notice is clear, for its detection will depend on our powers of observation. Thus, if we consider a cubic mile of pudding-stone forming a practically continuous mass, made up of blocks of various sorts of stones varying in volume from a cubic foot to a cubic inch, then one cubic foot of such a conglomerate might differ entirely from another cubic foot, and we should say the mass was intensely heterogeneous. If, however, we suppose the whole mass to be reduced according to a uniform scale, so that the cubic mile becomes a cubic foot, the heterogeneity will now fairly escape observation, and we should say that of such a mass any cubic foot was the same as any other cubic foot. In fact, we should say the mass was homogeneous. Thus, in a liquid the molecules may be clustered at some points and uniformly distributed at others, so that at some points the molecular aggregation may approximate to that of the solid state, while at others it may resemble that belonging to the vapour.

This idea of ultimate heterogeneity in masses which are apparently homogeneous will be found very useful in dealing with some pheno-

[1] W. Thomson, *Proc. Roy. Soc. Edin.*, 1862.

mena which at first sight appear difficult to explain, such, for example, as variations of specific or latent heat. Thus in the fluid state the molecules at some points may be arranged in that condition which characterises the solid state. It is not at all likely that a system of molecules which mutually attract each other would travel for ever singly (as they are ordinarily supposed to do in a permanent gas) as if they were a system of hard spheres. It is much more likely that at some points they will get into clusters, so that here and there in the gaseous mass an element of the substance partakes more of the properties of a liquid than of a gas, and as the gas approaches its condensing point more closely it is likely that these clusters rapidly increase in number until condensation sets in. So also when a liquid approaches the freezing point, the state of aggregation which appertains to the solid state may be regarded as coming more and more into prominence until solidification actually sets in. The whole idea, then, comes to this, that we shall be probably near the truth in regarding as ordinary gas a mixture of what we call a perfect gas with the liquid, and a liquid may in the same way contain a portion of the solid in solution.

53. Three States of Matter—Molecular Theory.—The three states of matter—viz. solid, liquid, and gas—must now be considered with reference to the molecular theory. In general, any substance may take each of the three states—the state in which it happens to exist being determined by its temperature and pressure. Thus, water substance at the ordinary atmospheric pressure may exist either as solid ice, liquid water, or be altogether converted into vapour, according to the temperature.

To explain this, the theory supposes that the molecules of every body are in a state of perpetual agitation, and this may consist in the motion of the molecule as a whole, or as a vibration or rotation of its constituent parts, or both. This molecular motion is supposed to depend upon the temperature; the hotter a body is, the greater the intensity of its molecular agitation. In a solid the molecules are supposed to oscillate round mean positions. Each is confined to a very small space, which it never leaves.[1] As the temperature rises the molecular agitation increases, and at length becomes so violent that

[1] The experiments of Sir W. C. Roberts-Austen on the diffusion of solid metals into each other show, however, that this view can only be approximately true (see *Proc. Roy. Soc.*, Feb. 1896). W. H. and W. L. Bragg, by studying the diffraction effects due to X-rays in crystals, have determined the mode of arrangement of the atoms in a number of crystals. A crystal cannot be regarded (in many cases at any rate) as composed of distinct molecules; the constitution is atomic (*X-rays and Atomic Structure*, by W. H. and W. L. Bragg, 1915).

the molecules break away from their imprisonment and wander about indiscriminately amongst each other. In this state the substance is said to be in the liquid form.

In a liquid, then, the molecules as well as being in a state of vibration have also a motion of translation whereby they continually move in and out amongst each other, so that any molecule in one part can pay a visit to another in any other part of the liquid. Such a visit, however, is quite accidental. Each molecule is so jostled by the others in its wanderings that its path is almost entirely fortuitous. In order to endow the molecules with this extra motion, and also to overcome the forces which held the molecules confined in the solid state, work must be done, and this work is the equivalent of what is known as the latent heat of fusion. This continual interchange of position and gliding through each other of the molecules of a liquid is suggested by the phenomenon of diffusion, which takes place even in opposition to the force of gravity.

If we now consider a liquid to be gradually heated the molecular energy will increase, and when a molecule approaches the surface it may possess a velocity sufficient to project it completely from the liquid into the space above against the attraction of the neighbouring molecules in the surface layer. There will thus be a continuous stream of projected molecules leaving the liquid, and this is what we know as evaporation, and when the molecules all attain velocities sufficient to carry them through the surface layer, the liquid will all pass into the state of vapour or become a gas.

The essential difference between a liquid and a gas according to our theory is, that while in a liquid the molecules move about amongst each other, each can travel no appreciable distance before it encounters another, and has its direction of motion altered by impact or mutual influence. In a liquid there is nothing of the nature of a free path ; each molecule is constantly under the influence of its neighbours. In the case of a gas, however, each molecule between two consecutive collisions is free from the influence of the others.[1] There is a free path, and this path is rectilinear but very short. In the passage from the liquid to the gaseous state, the molecules must be separated from each other in opposition to their mutual attraction, and the work thus spent represents part, at least, of what is known as the latent heat of vaporisation.

54. **Encounter and Free Path.**—When two approaching molecules come within a certain limiting distance of each other, their relative velocity in the direction of the line joining their centres is supposed

---

[1] The reasons for this supposition will be given afterwards, see Art. 247.

F

to diminish gradually, and become finally reversed. This mutual action is referred to as an *encounter* between two molecules, and in a permanent gas the time spent during an encounter must be much less than that occupied in the free path. As the density of a gas increases the length of the free path diminishes, and the encounters become more frequent. The proportion of time spent in collision becomes comparable with that of free motion, and the properties of the substance become considerably modified by the mutual influence of the molecules on each other. The effect of compression is to bring the molecules more within the sphere of each other's attraction, so that the substance gradually loses the characteristic properties of a perfect gas and acquires gradually the properties appertaining to the liquid state. In liquids there is no free path. The molecules are continually within the sphere of each other's attraction, and the behaviour of the substance with regard to pressure and temperature will be determined by the nature of the molecules and their mutual action. On the other hand, the mutual influence of the molecules is practically negligible in gases, and the behaviour of such substances with respect to pressure and temperature will, within certain limits, be independent of the nature of the molecular attraction, and the law connecting volume, pressure, and temperature will be the same for all gases.[1] It ought to be kept in mind, however, that when two molecules approach each other the encounter may not always be accompanied by a rebound, for the two may start rotating about each other, and thus form the nucleus of condensation which leads to the heterogeneity spoken of in Art. 52.

55. The Dynamical Theory of Gases.—In order to account for the pressure of gases against the walls of the enclosing vessel, as well as their power of expanding to fill any space, their molecules were endowed by many philosophers with mutually repelling forces.[2] The idea that the molecules of a gas repel each other does not seem to be yet quite extinct, although it was shown by Daniel Bernoulli[3] as early as 1738 that the pressure and expansive power of gases could be satisfactorily explained by the supposition of molecular motion.

[1] Sir Wm. Crookes regarded the ultra-gaseous condition in which the molecules are so far apart that collision is rare as a *fourth* state of matter ("Radiant State of Matter," *Proc. Roy. Soc.* vol. xxx. p. 469, 1880).

[2] The assumption of such a mutual repulsion between the molecules of a gas is contrary to all experience, except the term be restricted to such forces as those which come into operation during impact and rebound. For if the molecules repelled each other, their kinetic energies would increase as their distances from each other increased, that is as the volume of the gas increases. Consequently, if a gas expanded without doing external work, its temperature would rise, that is if the temperature is determined by the energy of motion of the molecules.

[3] Bernoulli, *Hydrodynamica*, Strasbourg, 1738.

Let us, for the sake of clearness, consider the molecules of a gas as small equal masses, and let us inquire into the effect of a number of such molecules when enclosed in a vessel, and each in rapid motion. Let the vessel be a horizontal tube closed at one end, and having a movable piston fitting into the other, so as to slide freely in it. We shall consider the bombardment of the molecules against the piston. Each molecule as it strikes the piston communicates a certain impulse to it which would set it in motion outwards if not held at rest. Here, then, at once we find that a certain force will be necessary to hold the piston in position, or, in other words, the enclosed gas exerts a pressure in virtue of the motion of its molecules. The force necessary to hold the piston in position will depend on the number of molecules which strike it per second, and for molecules of a given kind moving with a given velocity this will be proportional to the number of molecules per unit volume, that is, to the density of the gas. The pressure then will be proportional to the density, that is, inversely as the volume when the mass is given. If the temperature of a gas depends only on the motion of its molecules, it will follow, then, that at constant temperature the product of the volume and pressure will be constant. Thus we have deduced Boyle's law as an immediate consequence of the dynamical theory.

We shall now examine the matter a little more closely. If a molecule of mass m approaches a wall with a velocity u, and rebounds with the same velocity, the momentum or impulse given to the wall by the impact will be twice the momentum of the molecule, that is

$$2mu.$$

For simplicity let us consider a single molecule moving perpendicularly to a pair of opposite sides of a cubical box of unit volume. If the molecule moves backwards and forwards with velocity u impinging on the two sides alternately, it will strike each side $\frac{1}{2}u$ times per second (since the space traversed between two consecutive impacts on the same wall is twice the edge of the cube or two units of length), hence the impulsive pressure caused by a single molecule will be

$$2mu \times \frac{u}{2} = mu^2,$$

and if n molecules be enclosed, the pressure will be the sum of the partial pressures due to the individual molecules (that is, if they are so sparsely distributed that their mutual influence may be neglected), and the pressure will be

$$p = \Sigma mu^2 = m\Sigma u^2.$$

If, however, $\overline{u^2}$ be taken to represent the mean of all the values of u^2 for the various molecules, then if there be n molecules in the unit volume we shall have $n\overline{u^2} = \Sigma u^2$, and

$$p = mn\overline{u^2}.$$

Now, in the general case a molecule may be moving in any direction with a velocity V, the rectangular components of which perpendicular to the faces of the cube are u, u', u'', so that

$$V^2 = u^2 + u'^2 + u''^2,$$

and if $\overline{V^2}$ denotes the mean of all the values of V^2 for the various molecules, with corresponding meanings for $\bar{u}$, $\bar{u}'$, $\bar{u}''$, we shall have

$$\overline{V^2} = \overline{u^2} + \overline{u'^2} + \overline{u''^2},$$

and since the molecules do not tend to accumulate in any part of the vessel there will be, on the whole, as many passing across any plane per second in any one direction as in the opposite, or, in other words, the pressure will be equal in all directions, and

$$\overline{u^2} = \overline{u'^2} = \overline{u''^2} = \tfrac{1}{3}\overline{V^2}.$$

Consequently in the general case, when the molecules are moving indiscriminately through the cube with a velocity whose mean square is $\overline{V^2}$, the pressure per unit area will be

$$p = \tfrac{1}{3}mn\overline{V^2},$$

where n is the number of molecules per unit volume. Now mn is the mass per unit volume, or the density ρ of the gas, consequently [1]

$$p = \tfrac{1}{3}\rho\overline{V^2}.$$

If a given mass M of gas be enclosed in a vessel of volume v, then $M = \rho v$ and the equation becomes

$$pv = \tfrac{1}{3}M\overline{V^2}.$$

---

[1] This equation enables us to calculate the velocity of mean square for any gas, as was shown by Joule. (Paper read before *Manch. Lit. and Phil. Soc.*, 1848. Republished in *Phil. Mag.* vol. xiv. p. 211, 1857.) Thus at atmospheric pressure $p = 1033$ grammes per square centimetre, and at 0° C. the density of hydrogen is $0\cdot00008957$ (gr. per c.c.), hence taking $g = 981$, we have for hydrogen at 0° C.—

vel. of mean square $= 1842$ metres per second.

[Clausius (*Pogg. Ann.* c. 1857, p. 377) has given the following values for velocities of mean square of gases at 0° C. :—

Oxygen	.	.	.	.	461 metres per second
Nitrogen	.	.	.	.	492 ,,
Hydrogen	.	.	.	.	1844 ,,

It is to be observed that the velocity of mean square (*i.e.* the square root of $\overline{V^2}$, the mean value of the squares of molecular velocities) is not the same as the mean velocity of the molecules. The former is somewhat greater than the latter, see Art. 375.]

Hence if the mean square of the velocities of the molecules remains constant the product of the pressure and volume will be constant. For unit mass we have therefore for all gases the equation

$$pv = \tfrac{1}{3}\overline{V^2}.$$

It is thus proved that the pressure of a gas may be explained by the motion of its molecules, and that the supposition of repulsive forces between the molecules is quite unnecessary, as well as being unscientific, molecules being already endowed with the property of mutual attraction. There is one point, however, which should be noticed. By Boyle's law we know that the product pv is constant at constant temperature, and, therefore, the right-hand member of the above equation must be a function of the temperature. The temperature, then, must be measured in some way by $\overline{V^2}$, the mean square of the velocities of the molecules, or by their mean kinetic energy. Hence the heat of a gas must be in some way related to the kinetic energy of its molecules, and the same conclusion may be legitimately extended to all other bodies.

COR. If several gases be mixed in the same vessel, and if their molecular masses are m_1, m_2, m_3, etc., while the number per unit volume of each is n_1, n_2, n_3, etc., then as before, if their mean squares of velocities are $\overline{V_1^2}$, $\overline{V_2^2}$, $\overline{V_3^2}$, etc.,

$$p = \tfrac{1}{3}m_1 n_1 \overline{V_1^2} + \tfrac{1}{3}m_2 n_2 \overline{V_2^2} + \tfrac{1}{3}m_3 n_3 \overline{V_3^2} + \text{etc.},$$

or

$$p = p_1 + p_2 + p_3 + \text{etc.}$$

That is, the pressure of the mixture is equal to the sum of the pressures which the gases would exert if they occupied the whole space separately. This result was discovered experimentally by Dalton, and is true of course only so long as the molecules do not sensibly obstruct each other.

56. Structure of Atoms—Rankine's Hypothesis.—The hard atom of the Grecian philosophers, although at present in disrepute and out of touch with the more modern scientific conceptions, still survives in a certain sense unrefuted. Rival theories have been developed which are perhaps just as improbable, and perhaps not less illusory. The most inconceivable of these is that of Boscovich, who by mathematical refinement got rid of the material atom altogether, and replaced it by a mere point, or centre of force towards, or from, which certain forces were directed. This view was supported on the assertion that matter can only be known by its effects, and if these can be explained otherwise the assumption of a substance is not necessary. The phenomena of nature were thus to be explained by a mathematical fiction similar to that which in the hands of Gauss and Poisson formed the foundation of the theory of statical electricity.

The first step towards a rational theory was made by Rankine,[1] who about 1842 endeavoured to derive the laws of pressure and expansion of gases from what he termed the *hypothesis of molecular vortices*.

This hypothesis assumes "that each atom of matter consists of a nucleus or central point enveloped by an elastic atmosphere, which is retained in its position by attractive forces, and that the elasticity due to heat arises from the centrifugal force of those atmospheres, revolving or oscillating about their nuclei or central points." No definite supposition is made as to whether the elastic atmospheres are continuous or consist of discrete particles—that is, whether the elasticity of these atmospheres is a primary quality or entirely due to the "repulsion" of discrete molecules. Further, the nucleus at the centre of each molecule may or may not be distinct in nature from the elastic envelope. It may be a portion of the atmosphere in a condensed state, or merely a centre of condensation of the atmosphere. The word nucleus signifies merely the atomic centre, and its volume, if any, is assumed to be inappreciably small compared with that of the envelope. The supposition peculiar to the inquiry is "that the vibration which, according to the wave theory, constitutes radiant heat and light, is a motion of the atomic nuclei or centres, and is propagated by means of their mutual attractions and repulsions." The absorption and emission of heat and light consist in a transference of motion from the nuclei to their atmospheres, and *vice versa*, and this hypothesis Rankine considered as possessing immense advantages in explaining the propagation of transverse vibrations, the immense velocity of light, and its dispersion as well as its mode of propagation through crystalline media. According to this theory, in the case of perfect fluidity each atomic atmosphere possesses uniform density throughout each spherical layer described round the central nucleus. In other words, the density at any point of the atmosphere is considered as a function of the distance from the centre of the atom. The quantity of heat in a body is measured by the kinetic energy of its molecular revolutions or oscillations. These molecular motions might either be an oscillation of the spherical layers of the atomic atmospheres to and from their centres, or else a vortex motion of the elements of the atmospheres round the radii of the spherical atoms, so that each spherical layer is filled with radial vortices.

Such is Rankine's attempt to explain dynamically the increase of pressure of gases caused by heat, and although it is merely a first trial, and probably is far from the truth, yet in its very name it contains the germs of suggestion which render it not unworthy of its author.[2]

57. Preliminary Considerations on the Possibility of Matter being due to Motion in a Medium.—The question which now presents itself is, What is an atom of matter? By assuming the existence of atoms

[1] *Trans. Roy. Soc. Edin.*, 4th Feb. 1850 ; *Phil. Mag.*, Dec. 1851 ; *Scientific Papers*, p. 16.

[2] A germ of Rankine's theory seems to be contained in the older opinion regarding the heat fluid. According to Becher and Stahl the *terra inflammabilis*, or phlogiston, was affected with a rapid whirling motion, *motus vorticillaris*, and when the particles of any body were agitated with this motion it exhibited the phenomenon of heat, or ignition or inflammability, according to the violence of the motion.

and molecules, and endowing them with certain qualities, many of the properties of bodies may be plausibly explained, but, granting the existence of atoms, the problem which still remains, and which probably ever will remain, for speculation is, What is an atom? The existence of a fundamental medium, the ether, has already been postulated for many reasons. Being furnished with this medium and motion in it, the problem before us, broadly stated, is "construct the physical universe."

In attacking a problem of this nature we may with profit consider the case of a person furnished with ordinary faculties, and placed in a uniform medium. For the sake of clearness let us take a being capable of moving through a homogeneous ocean, and having no knowledge of its boundaries, or of what is called the top and bottom. The ocean being supposed perfectly uniform in all directions, the supposed person can detect no differences in its properties as he moves through it, and he will consequently be ignorant of his own motion, as well as of the existence of the medium in which he moves. Let us now suppose that at a certain place in the ocean there is a whirlpool, or what is termed a rectilinear vortex. When the being approaches this part of the ocean he will experience certain actions, or sensations, arising from the motion of the medium, and on reflection he will consider that there is something at this place, and will give it a name. This whirlpool will be something to him, and all the rest of the ocean will be void. If other whirls exist at other places he will also regard them as objects, and he will be able to determine their positions with respect to each other, as well as his own position and motion with respect to them, so that he is now furnished with the ideas of distance, relative position, and motion. For the sake of distinctness we may assume that by some means he is able to see these whirlpools. For example, they may be in a state of vibration, and may propagate waves in the medium, and these waves may excite a sense appertaining to the being, which for the present we shall call the sense of sight. Thus, even though at a distance, he can now detect the whirls by their effect on his senses. The same waves may also affect other senses, for example the sense of heat, or they may not affect either sense, for they may be too long or too short, just as sound waves may be too long or too short to affect the sense of hearing.

Thus a person situated in a homogeneous medium might not be aware of the existence of the medium, but he might be aware of certain parts of it which are in a certain state of motion, and on account of this motion these parts might appear luminous and hot, and possess many other properties which would be discovered through

Being in an infinite ocean.

his other senses, and on account of which he would say that these parts were objects, or bodies, or matter, while he fails to recognise the parts of the medium which do not possess this kind of motion. Thus to him certain parts of space would appear occupied by bodies and the remainder would seem to be empty, although all space might in reality be filled with a medium, one part of which differed from another only in the nature of its motion.

The motion of one part or whirl might also be influenced by that of the others, and as a consequence each will exert certain forces on the others, causing them to move towards it or farther away. That is, these whirls might attract or repel each other according to some law determined by the nature of the whirl. By the very motion, then, which constitutes these objects, they would be endowed with a property analogous to gravitation.

Attraction and repulsion.

In connection with this part of the subject it may be well to consider the terms attraction and repulsion which are so freely used in natural philosophy. If two objects which are free move towards each other they are ordinarily said to attract each other, but if they move away from each other they are said to repel each other. When we say the earth attracts a stone, we only mean that a stone will move towards the earth when let go at any point above its surface. When we say that the earth attracts the stone, we do not explain the motion or its ultimate causes, we merely describe it. The introduction of a new word is very satisfying to a certain class of mind, and often stops further inquiry. There are many who are quite satisfied that a phenomenon is explained when it has received a name.

To exemplify this, let us consider the case of a person situated in an ocean of water on the earth's surface, and ignorant of the top and bottom, and let this person be furnished with a number of pieces of cork and also a number of pieces of stone. Then if he at first takes a piece of cork and a piece of stone simultaneously in his hand and lets them go, he observes that the cork flies in one direction and the stone in the opposite. His first inference is probably that the cork and stone repel each other. He now takes a piece of cork by itself, and he finds that it moves in the same direction as the other piece of cork, and similarly any piece of stone will descend after the other without a piece of cork being near it. He now will probably begin to doubt the truth of his first surmise, that cork and stone repel each other. For he has found that the cork rises just as rapidly whether the stone be near it or not. The force on a piece of either material is the same at all distances from the other, so that the law of force on each of them is independent of the distance or magnitude of the other body. He will probably look beyond his immediate surroundings and begin to speculate in the wildest manner, till by chance he becomes acquainted with the bottom of the ocean. He will now assert that the bottom is the *vera causa* of the motion, and that it repels cork and attracts stone. If, however, he had first become acquainted with the top he would have been quite satisfied that the top attracted the cork and repelled the stone, and when he knows both top and bottom he is furnished with a variety of alternatives. He may say that the top attracts the cork and the bottom attracts the stone, or that the top repels the stone and the bottom repels the cork. Probably the last thing which will strike him will be that the top and bottom may be without influence on both pieces of matter, and that these bodies may also be without direct action on each other, but that their motion in all cases arises from the immediate action of a medium in which they are immersed.

58. The Vortex Atom.—The idea that motion is in some way the basis of what we call matter is an old one, but no distinct conceptions on the subject were formed till Helmholtz[1] (1858) developed his investigations in fluid motion. In this celebrated paper it was shown

that the rotating parts of a perfect, incompressible fluid, in which there is no slipping, maintain their identity for ever, and are thus eternally differentiated from the non-rotating parts. Also that these rotating parts are arranged either in endless filaments forming closed curves, or are terminated only at the boundaries of the fluid ; and these vortex filaments, as they are called, may be knotted or linked together

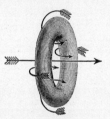

Fig. 2.—Vortex ring.

in a variety of ways. Thus if we treat the ether as a perfect fluid, then any portion of it in vortex motion must for ever remain so. Such motion can never be created or destroyed, and a portion of the ether possessing it must for ever remain differentiated from the rest. A vortex filament in the ether will thus at once possess the character of permanence demanded for matter. It will be an atom in the true sense, for it can never be severed. The ends of such a filament cannot exist except at the boundaries of the ether, which is supposed to fill all space.

The vortex atom theory of matter was originated by Sir William Thomson,[2] soon after the appearance of Helmholtz's paper—in fact,

---

[1] Helmholtz, *Crelle*, 1858 ; *Phil. Mag.*, 1867.
[2] Sir William Thomson, *Proc. Roy. Soc. Edin.*, 1867.

while witnessing Professor P. G. Tait's beautiful experiments on vortex rings.[1]

Vortex rings are formed when air is puffed through a circular aperture in the side of a box. The smoke rings which some smokers are expert in making are also fairly good examples.

Professor Tait conducted his experiments with the simple apparatus represented in Fig. 3. It consists of a plain wooden box with a circular aperture, 6 or 8 inches in diameter, in one end. The opposite end of the box is removed and replaced by a tightly stretched cloth or sheet of india-rubber. In order to render the rings visible the air in the box must be impregnated with smoke or fine particles of some floating matter which are distinctly visible. For this purpose the bottom of the box is first sprinkled with a strong solution of ammonia, so that the interior becomes filled with ammonia gas. Hydrochloric acid gas is then generated in the box by simply pouring some sul-

Fig. 3.—Vortex rings in pursuit.

phuric acid into a saucer containing common salt. The hydrochloric acid gas unites with the ammonia and forms a dense cloud of small crystals of sal-ammoniac in the air within the box. If now a sudden blow is given to the membrane covering the end of the box, a vortex ring issues from the aperture in the other end and moves forward through the room like a solid projectile. When two such rings collide they rebound and vibrate, in consequence of the shock, like bands of solid india-rubber. Vortex rings may, however, be caused to vibrate without impinging on one another. When the hole is circular the rings are circular, and this is the stable form. If the rings deviate from the circular form they will vibrate about that form as a position of equilibrium. Hence to obtain vibrating rings it is only necessary to make the aperture through which they are discharged elliptical, or oval, or even square.

Another curious result deduced by Helmholtz in his paper may also be shown experimentally. If two vortex rings be moving in the

[1] *Recent Advances in Physical Science*, p. 290. Some interesting experiments on vortex rings are also described by Sir R. Ball, *Phil. Mag.* vol. xxxvi. p. 12, 1868.

same direction with their planes perpendicular to the line joining their centres, the pursuer contracts and accelerates its speed, as A and B, Fig. 3, while the pursued expands in diameter and diminishes in speed, so that the hinder one ultimately overtakes, passes through the other, and takes the lead (shown at A'B'). The same process occurs again, and a system of alternate threading is kept up. If, however, they approach each other from opposite directions, both decrease in velocity and expand indefinitely in diameter, but never reach each other. One behaves to the other as its image in a plane mirror, and the same thing happens when a vortex ring moves up directly towards a plane wall.

As any ring sails through the room it is not only the particles of sal-ammoniac or smoke (which merely render it visible) that remain permanently in it. The air forming its core remains the same, and is the very ring of air which left the aperture of the box. In fact, if there were no fluid friction the ring would not only remain permanently constituted of the same particles of air, but would go on rotating for ever. Once created, it would remain eternal. Vortex rings in a perfect non-viscous fluid thus possess the essential property of indestructibility demanded for matter by chemistry, and in such a fluid it would be equally impossible to create such rings. Theoretically a vortex filament may have a variety of different shapes, and may be knotted or looped about in any manner. In practice, however, it seems possible only to form rings of the simple circular type. An aperture has not yet been devised which will allow the smoke rings to escape in a knotted or looped form.

The motion of the air in the ring is a rotation round the core or central line. If the ring be looked at when approaching the observer from the box, then the particles of air on the inner edge are moving forward, and those on the outside edge are moving backward, from the observer, as shown in Fig. 2.

The vortex atom has at first sight very strong recommendations in its favour. It possesses at once many of the essential qualities of matter. It is indestructible and indivisible while its strength and volume remain constant, although its diameter may vary, and if two rings be linked or knotted they must remain so for ever. Again, a vortex ring, when free from the influence of others, moves rapidly forward in a right line, and thus possesses kinetic energy, while it may also vibrate about a form of equilibrium, and in this way give rise to such wave motions in the ether as are supposed to constitute light and radiant heat. The theory is consequently much more fundamental in character than any other, since it merely makes use of a postulated

Claims of the vortex atom.

medium, the ether, and the principles of hydrodynamics to explain
the properties of matter, and consequently all the phenomena of
nature. It does not posit hard atoms endowed with powers of
attraction and repulsion, but it endeavours to follow the mechanism
by which one molecule influences another, and thus gives a mental
representation of the actual processes in action. The development
of the subject is seriously impeded by very formidable mathematical difficulties, and only some of the simpler problems have been
worked out.[1]

The properties of radioactive substances discovered in recent
years, together with the laws relating to the spectral lines and other
physical properties of the chemical elements, point strongly to the
conclusion that the true atom is the atom of electricity, of which
two kinds exist, positive and negative. The researches of Sir J. J.
Thomson have shown that the unit of negative electricity, now
usually called an *electron*, possesses a mass less than one-thousandth
that of a hydrogen atom, this mass being probably entirely due to its
electromagnetic inertia and consequently dependent on the velocity of
the electron. The unit of positive electricity, or *proton*, possesses a
much greater mass than the electron. A neutral chemical atom is
regarded as being made up of an equal number of units of positive
and negative electricity, bound together by their mutual attraction.
Lord Kelvin proposed the view that an atom of matter consists of
a sphere of positive electricity containing within it a number of
electrons whose total charge is equal to that of the positive sphere.
This theory has been elaborated by Sir J. J. Thomson, who has
shown that the stability of the system can be accounted for on
mechanical principles if the electrons rotate in concentric rings. If the
electrons are less than five in number, a stable arrangement is possible without rotation. Five electrons will form a stable system if
rotating in a single ring round the centre of the positive sphere. If
there are more than five, there must be more than one ring. A
positively charged atom is one which has lost one or more electrons,
and a negatively charged electron is one which has acquired one or more
electrons in excess. This theory accounts successfully for a number
of chemical facts, such as the valency of elements and the periodic
system. It has, however, been shown by Sir E. Rutherford that
it is necessary to assign a very small positive nucleus to the atom
in order to account for the scattering of α particles by matter. On
this view, a remarkable theory of the atom has been put forward by

---

[1] J. J. Thomson on Vortex Rings : Macmillan and Co., 1883.

N. Bohr.[1] According to Bohr's theory the atom of hydrogen, for instance, consists of a very small nucleus of positive electricity with a single electron rotating round it in an orbit which is probably circular. A positively electrified hydrogen atom is one which has lost its electron, and is therefore simply a unit of positive electricity. The mass of the atom is practically all resident in the positive nucleus. The atom of helium consists of a double charge of positive electricity in the nucleus with two electrons revolving round it in the same orbit, but situated at opposite ends of a diameter. Thus the α particle of radioactive processes is a helium atom without its electrons. The lithium atom has a triple positive charge at the centre with three electrons rotating round it, two in an inner and one in an outer orbit, and so on for successive elements. To account for the stability of the systems and the homogeneity of their spectral lines, Bohr abandons the ordinary Newtonian mechanics and invokes the aid of Planck's quantum theory (see Art. 285). The orbit in which the electron of a hydrogen atom revolves may be any one of an infinite series determined by the quantum theory. When the atom is ionised, as in a Geissler tube, and recombination takes place, then the energy emitted during recombination is given out as a homogeneous radiation whose period is determined by the particular orbit into which the electron settles down, no radiation being emitted while the electron continues in any orbit. The innermost orbit, corresponding to the greatest emission of energy during recombination, is the most stable. In this way Bohr is able to account for the series of spectral lines, known as the Balmer series, for hydrogen and helium. The constant (Rydberg's constant) occurring as a coefficient in the formula for spectral lines is given correctly in numerical value by the theory, and striking confirmation is afforded by its agreement with many other physical and chemical facts. The order of the chemical elements appears to depend solely on the positive charge of the nucleus, which is roughly equal to half the atomic weight. This was pointed out by Rutherford, and is supported by Moseley's experiments on the X-ray spectra of the elements.[2] If the vortex-atom theory of this Article should ever be revived, it will doubtless be in a different form, and designed to account for the constitution of the electrical atom.

[1] *Phil. Mag.*, 1913, pp. 1, 476, 857 ; 1914, p. 506 ; 1915, p. 394.
[2] *Ibid.* Dec. 1913, p. 1024.

SECTION VII

ON ENERGY

59. Motion the Primary Basis of all Phenomena.—If we admit the belief which lies at the foundations of chemical science, namely, that all material substances are built up of simpler substances or elements, which may combine in various manners, but which are unchangeable, and ever retain their distinctive properties, we are led to regard all changes in the universe as ultimately due to changes in the local distribution, or state of aggregation, of elementary matter, and therefore eventually brought about through motion. If, therefore, motion be the primary change which lies at the basis of all other changes, the final aim of physical science must be to determine those movements which give rise to all other phenomena, and trace their origin and progress. The problem thus merges itself into one of dynamics, and all the various so-called forces of nature must be estimated by the same standard, namely, mechanical force, and this, in fact, is expressed in the law of the conservation of energy.

60. All Motion and Energy Relative.—In speaking of motion it must always be borne in mind that all estimation of it is necessarily relative, and for this reason no body considered by itself can be said to be either at rest or in motion. When we say a body is at rest, or moves uniformly in a right line, the estimation is made relatively to some system which we arbitrarily choose as fixed. Force, then, which is measured by the rate of change of motion (the word here meaning momentum, or mass multiplied by velocity) is also relative, and kinetic energy which is measured by half the product of the mass and the square of the velocity is also relative to the same system. Energy, then, in its estimation is relative, simply because velocity is relative.

When we speak of the kinetic energy of a body or system, we always mean the energy with respect to some other chosen system, or else we mean nothing at all. This relativity of energy is sometimes lost sight of, and it is not uncommon to find the kinetic energy of a body spoken of as something quite independent of all modes of calculation —in fact as an objective reality, a thing existing outside our senses, as the mass of a body is commonly regarded to be.

Energy is again often stated to be only associated with matter, so that matter has been defined as the vehicle of energy ; this, however, does not hold according to our limitation of the word matter, for we know that energy in immense quantities is perpetually passing through space with the velocity of light in the form of radiant heat and light, and that it exists also in the so-called potential state. The former exists in the ether, and probably also the latter.

The ether, then, is the great vehicle of energy ; and, indeed, it is chiefly on this account that the ether has been postulated. For the sake of distinctness we have agreed not to regard the ether as matter, or a material substance, or as necessarily possessing the distinctive properties of matter, but choose rather to take it as a fundamental medium, and to endeavour to explain all phenomena, matter included, by means of it. If the law of conservation be true, however, the energy in an isolated system is objective like the matter of the system in so far as it is measured relative to a being in the system. To this being the quantity of energy will be definite and constant. It cannot increase or diminish, except by communication from or to the regions outside. To a being outside the system, the energy of the system will depend altogether on the standard of reference, and the question then arises if the matter of the system also varies to that being in a similar manner.

It will consequently be of prime importance to examine the meaning and foundation of the law of conservation of energy, on which all modern physical science has been built.

61. Measure of Energy and the Law of Conservation.—We approach the subject of energy through our ideas of work, or sense of effort. When a weight is raised from the surface of the earth, work is said to have been performed or energy spent. The work done is proportional to the weight and to the height through which it is raised conjointly, and the *measure* of the amount of work done or energy spent is accordingly taken equal to the product of the weight w and height h, or wh. Now if any mass falls under the action of gravity through a height h, the square of its terminal velocity will be $v^2 = 2gh$, so that $\frac{1}{2}mv^2 = wh$, where m is the mass of the body and w is equal to mg. In the same way,[1] if the mass m be

___

[1] It should be carefully noticed that the equation $wh = \frac{1}{2}mv^2$ is not a new relation containing a new physical law, but arises entirely from our definitions of work and

projected vertically upwards with a velocity v, it will rise to a height h given by the foregoing equation, so that the initial velocity v possessed by the mass m will perform the work necessary to raise it to a height h. For this reason we say that a body in virtue of its velocity can do work, and the measure of this work is $\frac{1}{2}mv^2$. We consequently say it possesses energy of motion or kinetic energy.

Conversely, the body in descending through a height h could draw an equal mass up to an equal height, or any other weight w' to a height h' given by the equation $wh = w'h'$, so that a body in virtue of its position can do work, and this we call energy of position or potential energy. As thus measured, the two energies are exactly complementary. In the case of a body falling freely, as the potential energy diminishes the kinetic increases, and their sum remains constant. This is the simplest case of conservation, and is beautifully illustrated in the common pendulum. At the highest point of the swing the velocity is zero, and the kinetic energy vanishes. Here the potential energy is greatest, but as the pendulum falls the potential diminishes and the kinetic increases. The speed of the falling bob increases as it descends, and at the lowest point it possesses a velocity sufficient to raise it to its original level ; here the energy is all kinetic and the potential vanishes. At any other point the energy is partly kinetic and partly potential, but their sum has always the same value. If h be the height above the lowest point at any instant, and v the velocity of the bob, then $wh + \frac{1}{2}mv^2$ is the same at all points of the swing.

The same oscillation from kinetic to potential and back again occurs in the planetary system. When the earth is farthest from the sun, her velocity and consequently her kinetic energy is least, but in this position she possesses a balancing store of potential. As she rounds the farthest point of her orbit and begins to approach the sun, she acquires increase of kinetic at the expense of her potential energy. When nearest the sun her velocity is greatest and her potential energy least. As she rounds this nearest point, and begins to retreat

---

force, and their mode of measurement. Thus force is measured by the rate of change of momentum, or for a body of given mass m

$$F = \frac{d(mv)}{dt} = m\frac{dv}{dt},$$

and work is defined as force multiplied by distance worked through, that is the space integral of the force. Hence

$$W = \int F ds = \int m\frac{dv}{dt}ds = \int m\frac{ds}{dt}dv = \int mv dv = \frac{1}{2}mv^2 + C.$$

The work done, therefore, in changing the velocity of a body from v_0 to v is $\frac{1}{2}mv^2 - \frac{1}{2}mv_0^2$, and this follows from the mode of measuring force and work.

from the sun, her kinetic energy begins to diminish; it is used up in doing the work necessary to withdraw the earth against the powerful attraction of the sun, but an equivalent is always stored up ready for use, full tale, without loss, but still without gain. Such is the ebb and flow throughout all nature of the visible energy of the universe. At one place increasing and exhibiting itself, like new life in the motion of her matter; at another diminishing, disappearing, becoming latent, or, as we say, potential, leaving the matter, at least as visible motion, oscillating throughout all the regions of space from potential to kinetic, and from kinetic to potential, but without increase or diminution of the total stock.

Other examples of stored-up or potential energy occur in a wound-up clock, a bent cross-bow or spring, etc. The work done in winding up a clock or watch is stored up as this so-called potential energy, and, being paid out gradually to the machinery, keeps it in motion. The energy spent in drawing a bow reappears again in the kinetic energy of the shaft which flies from it, and perhaps it is in some very similar manner that the vast stores of potential energy are pent up in explosives.

Illustrations of the principle of conservation occur in all the ordinary working engines and mechanical contrivances to facilitate labour. A great weight may be raised to a house-top by a single man through the means of a system of pulleys, or a large mass may be moved by a lever; but in all such cases the work done by the man is undiminished by the use of the engine. It merely enables one man to do a piece of work which it might have required ten to do without the engine, but the work done by the one man, measured in the ordinary way, is always equal in quantity to that done by the ten without the engine. This general principle is usually stated for machines in the form, " What is gained in power is lost in speed." *Illustrations of the principle.*

The output of energy of an engine is, however, in practice always less than the supply. Thus a pendulum once started to swing should go on swinging for ever, but in practice this is not the case. The amplitude of the swing gradually decreases, and finally the pendulum comes to rest. It gradually loses its energy. The kinetic energy it possesses at the lowest point of its swing does not raise it to quite so high a level as that from which it fell. One cause of this will be found in the air in which the pendulum moves. During its oscillation the pendulum is continually beating the air away in front. It is setting the air around in motion, and consequently losing a part of its own motion, so that the kinetic energy at the lowest point becomes less and less every swing, till it is finally all frittered away. If there were no

G

air around the pendulum, the motion would still gradually subside from another cause. This arises in the friction at the supports. In the same way a fly-wheel turning on an axle gradually loses its motion through friction. Heat, we know, is generated by friction, and the heat produced is, by Joule's experiment, equivalent to a certain amôunt of work. When heat is produced a certain amount of energy must be spent somewhere, so that if friction occurs in any part of a machine there is a loss of energy there. For this reason, then, the fly-wheel comes to rest. Even though heat were not produced, electrification may be produced, and this would use up part of the energy, and the system would come to rest. If, however, neither heat nor electricity be produced, the energy of the system might be spent in processes of which we have no cognisance. It might be gradually radiated into space, so that, although by experiment we would be unable to account for the dissipation of the energy of the system, yet the principle of conservation might be true. In the same way the machinery might receive energy from the vast store in the ether,[1] and of this we might have no cognisance, so that friction might occur and still the machinery go on for ever. We should then have a kind of perpetual motion, but not necessarily a violation of the doctrine of conservation of energy. From this point of view, the principle can be neither proved nor disproved ; it must for ever rest on accumulated evidence.

62. Recapitulation.—In recapitulation, then, we see that an elevated mass can do work by sinking to a lower level, and that it loses its capacity for doing such work as it sinks, that is, in proportion as the work is actually performed. The same applies to springs and elastic bodies in a state of compression or extension, as well as to moving masses. Heat may be employed to do work, but in this process an equivalent quantity of heat is destroyed. Electric currents may be used to do work, but to maintain the current an equivalent amount of work must be spent. Chemical compounds may be decomposed by the expenditure of energy, and the energy may be regained by recombination of the elements. Thus the universal characteristic of equivalence and convertibility prevails in all mechanical, electrical, thermal, and chemical forms of energy. When a quantity of any form is spent, an equivalent of some other form, or forms, is produced.

According to the law of conservation, the universe is endowed with a store of energy which, through all the varied changes of natural processes, can be neither increased nor diminished, but which, though pass-

---

[1] Take, for example, the storage of energy by plants and motion of the radiometer. These operations might also be effected by waves which we could not detect otherwise.

ing through ever-varying phases of transformation, is, like the matter
of the universe, unchanging in quantity from eternity to eternity. All
changes and phenomena are due simply to variations in its mode of
appearance. Here we find one portion of it as the *vis viva* of masses
moving as a whole, or as the vibration of their parts, and there we
detect another in the ethereal waves which produce light and radiant
heat ; while, on the other hand, we locate vast quantities of it in the
energy of position of large masses, or of their constituent molecules,
under the names potential and chemical energies. This probably is
engaged in the process by which one body attracts another and one molecule another, while in perhaps some similar way a portion is distributed
in the ether around magnets, or engaged in electrical processes. The
principle, as it now stands, has come to be by far the most fruitful
generalisation of modern physics, and its truth is supported by every
experiment and application of physical principles. There is no department of physical science with which it does not deal and furnish the
investigator with an engine of attack of the most powerful character.

  63. **Historical.**—The first clear and distinct statement of the law
of the conservation of energy in its general form was published in
1842 by Dr. Julius Robert Mayer [1] of Heilbronn. For a small group
of phenomena it had been already stated by Galileo and Newton, and
afterwards more definitely by D. Bernoulli, and so continued recognised as applicable to the then known mechanical processes. Certain
amplifications were from time to time introduced by such men as
Rumford, Davy, Carnot, Séguin, and Montgolfier, and it is probable
that more than one of these philosophers had a strong feeling of its
perfect generality, but feared to state it without sufficient experimental evidence. This evidence did not exist when Mayer first
published his general statement,[2] but still remained to be deduced in
that department where the applicability of the law appeared most
doubtful, viz. the production of heat from work, and of work from
heat. While Joule and Colding independently laboured to establish

  [1] Liebig's *Annalen*, May 1842.
  [2] Joule says : "Neither in Séguin's writings, nor in Mayer's paper of 1842, were
there such proofs of the hypothesis advanced as were sufficient to cause it to be
admitted into science without further inquiry. I believe that the experiment
attributed to Gay-Lussac was not referred to by Mayer previously to the year 1845:
Mayer appears to have hastened to publish his views for the express purpose of
securing priority. He did not wait till he had the opportunity of supporting them
by facts. My course, on the contrary, was to publish only such theories as I had
established by experiments calculated to commend them to the scientific public,
being well convinced of Sir J. Herschel's remark that ' hasty generalisation is the
bane of science '" (Joule, *Phil. Mag.*, 1864, part ii. p. 151 ; see also 1862, part ii.
p. 121). Joule's experiments were commenced in 1840.

the law, Mayer was led to it by physiological questions, and with the greatest clearness grasped the principle in its widest generality. He also pointed out that the dynamical equivalent of heat was a fundamental constant to be determined by experiment, and assuming that the work done in compressing a gas is the equivalent of the heat generated, he deduced the number 367 gr. met. from the values of the two specific heats of air available at the time (see Art. 152). With regard to this method, which will be described elsewhere (Art. 159), it may be remarked that the substance operated on does not pass through a complete cycle of changes ; it is not in the same condition at the end of the operation as at the beginning, and consequently it is not legitimate to assume that the heat evolved is the sole effect of the work spent in compressing the gas. The volume is changed, and it is quite impossible to say *a priori* whether this change may not involve an expenditure of work such as is employed in winding up a spring. Three years previously (1839) Séguin had given expression to the same ideas regarding the equivalence of heat and work, and had obtained the value 369 by a similar method, and it appears from the last edition of Carnot's works that at least before 1832 (the date of his death) this distinguished scientist had not only embraced the dynamical theory of heat, but had planned many of those very experiments by which Joule subsequently established the equivalence of heat and work. He also gave an estimation of this equivalent (370), probably deduced from the same data as those employed by Mayer. It thus appears that the principle of equivalence was harboured by nearly all the great scientific thinkers of the early part of this century, and that the general doctrine of the conservation of energy grew in a more or less gradual manner as experience became more and more extended. Great service was undoubtedly rendered to science by Mayer's distinct and comprehensive statements, but at the time he made these statements, Joule was conducting his experiments on the dynamical equivalent of heat, and Colding was presenting important papers on the same subject to the Royal Scientific Society of Copenhagen. It does not seem just, therefore, to assign to any particular person the credit of establishing the general principle, or to regard any particular man as the father of the doctrine of the conservation of energy, but one thing is certain, namely, that Joule was the first to make an accurate determination of the dynamical equivalent of heat, and that the final development of the methods of applying the doctrine in detail to the problems which occur in the science of heat was mainly due to the simultaneous work of Clausius, Rankine, and William Thomson between 1849 and 1851.

Much about the same time Helmholtz independently set himself
to work out the principle from a mathematical point of view, and
showed [1] that the energy of any system must be conserved by starting
with Newton's laws of motion, and the supposition that matter consists
of particles which act on each other with forces directed along the lines
joining them, and which depend only on the distance.

The general principle of the conservation of energy is not, how- No abso-
ever, to be proved by mathematical formulæ.   A law of nature must lute proof.
be founded on experiment and observation, and the general agreement
of the law with facts leads to a general belief in its probable truth.
Further, the conservation of energy cannot be absolutely *proved* even
by experiment, for the proof of a law requires a universal experience.
On the other hand, the law cannot be said to be untrue, even though
it may seem to be contradicted by certain experiments, for in these
cases energy may be dissipated in modes of which we are as yet
unaware.

64. On Potential Energy—all Energy probably Kinetic.—It
may not be out of place to examine here the meaning of the term
potential energy.   When a body is projected vertically upwards its
velocity gradually decreases, the kinetic energy which it possessed at
the beginning of the flight gradually leaves it as it rises, and when the
body reaches its highest point all its initial energy of motion has disappeared.   The question then arises, what has become of the energy
of motion of the body ?   We say it has become potential, that it has
become latent or has disappeared, or ceased to exist as visible motion,
or that it has been used up in raising the body from the earth.   This,
however, is by no means an explanation of what has happened.   It
teaches us nothing further as to the process in operation during
motion.   Observation shows us that the body possesses motion
initially, that as it rises the motion is gradually lost, and that it is
gradually regained as the body returns to earth.   The word potential
energy here is only a name for the difference between the initial
kinetic energy of the body when starting in its upward flight, and that
possessed at any other point of the path.   This, we have seen, may
be represented by the expression wh, where w is the weight of the
body and h the height it has ascended.   In the same way the potential
energy of an isolated system of masses in any configuration merely
denotes the difference between the kinetic energy of the system in that
configuration, and the kinetic energy in some other chosen configuration (generally chosen as that of maximum kinetic energy).

The question still remains, what becomes of the motion when the

[1] Helmholtz, *Erhaltung der Kraft*, 1847.

kinetic energy of a system diminishes ?　Can motion ever be changed into anything else than motion ?　If we assume a fundamental medium whereby to explain all the phenomena of nature, then the properties of this medium ought to remain unchanged, and all other changes must be explained by motion of the medium.　Such an assumption is quite philosophic, and the method of procedure is certainly scientific.　An evident reply to the question of what becomes of the motion of a projectile rising upwards is that it passes into the ether.　The first assumed property of the ether is that it can contain and convey energy. There is no *a priori* reason, then, why the energy of motion of a projectile as it rises upwards should not be stored up as energy of motion of the ether between the body and the earth, or elsewhere.　The

Kinetic energy in the ether.

oscillation from kinetic to potential, and from potential to kinetic, in the case of the pendulum is then, from this point of view, merely an interchange of energy of motion going on between the mass of the pendulum and the ether around it.　According to this view all energy is energy of motion, and must be measured by the ordinary mechanical standard.　The work we do in lifting a body from the earth is spent in generating motion in the ether, and as the body falls this motion passes from the ether to the body, which thus acquires velocity.　In the same way, the work spent in generating electric currents and electrifying conductors must be represented as spent in generating motion of the ether around the electric circuits and conductors.　On the vortex-atom theory of matter this view is quite intelligible, for here we have nothing but ether and motion in the universe, so that all change must be interchange of motion.　If motion passes from one body it must either pass into other bodies or else into the ether, so that all energy is kinetic, and what we call potential energy, or energy of position of a system, is energy of motion in the ether, which has left the system and become located in the ether, and which may be regained by the system from the ether.　The oscillation of energy, then, is from ether to matter, and from matter to ether, and on this oscillation all the physical life of the universe depends.

A rough mental picture of the process might be obtained as follows.　We might suppose a body connected to the earth by vortex filaments in the ether, which would replace the lines of force.　The ether is spinning round these lines, and when the body is lifted from the earth the work done is expended in increasing the length of the vortex filaments.　The work is thus being stored up as energy of motion of the ether, and when the body falls to earth the vortex lines diminish in length, and their energy of motion passes into the body and is represented by the kinetic energy of the mass.

65. Perpetual Motion—Indestructibility of Matter.—The object of the perpetual-motionists was to construct an engine which would work continually without the aid of any external driving force—an engine which would do work without fuel or any other supply of energy. The solution of this problem promised enormous gains, and bid fair to replace the gold-hunting operations of the alchemists. Work is wealth, and a machine which could work without fuel would prove as profitable a possession as the philosopher's stone. The possibility of perpetual motion in this sense, viz. the creation of energy, is opposed to the law of conservation of energy, which is now universally accepted as the foundation of physical science. Still it would be quite consistent with this law to construct an engine which would go on working without expense to the owner, other than the wear and tear of the machinery. An actual example of such an engine is a water-wheel. Here the driving power costs nothing, except there be a river tax; it comes indirectly from our great reservoir, the sun. In the same way, on a small scale, Crookes's Radiometer is more directly driven by the heat of the sun, and there is no *a priori* reason why the ingenuity of man should not utilise the vast stores of energy which are located in the ether, and ever traversing it, to drive his engines.

So also, if matter be vortex motion in the ether, it is not impossible that the constitution of the ether may be such that the very motion which constitutes matter may in time be used to serve the purposes of man. Matter, in fact, may not be indestructible or uncreatable, and man may yet discover the means of so directing the motions already existing in the ether, that any one kind of motion may be converted into any other at will, and still the law of conservation may hold throughout. Such speculations are, perhaps, visionary, but still they are not out of place, for they tend to overthrow dogma as to what must or must not happen. If the ether fills the universe, and if it contains energy throughout, then the store is infinite; and with this infinite store at our disposal what may not be possible when we discover the means of using it?

INDICATOR DIAGRAMS

66. Graphic Representation of the State of a Substance.— An exceedingly fertile and lucid method of treating many physical problems was introduced by Watt, the celebrated improver of the steam-engine, and is known as the graphic method. This consists in representing the pressure and volume of a substance by the co-ordinates of a point, so that each point in the plane of the figure corresponds to a definite pressure and volume, and therefore represents a definite condition of the substance. The state of the substance may, therefore, be said to be determined or represented by the position of the corresponding point in the diagram. The method was devised by Watt for the purpose of determining the work done by a steam-engine, and it is still employed for that and similar purposes. Subsequently Clapeyron employed it to interpret the work of Carnot, and it has since been adopted and used with great advantage in every branch of science, especially in the domain of thermodynamics, where it often proves itself easily intelligible to those who cannot follow the more complicated analytical investigations.

Let OX and OY (Fig. 4) be two fixed rectangular lines chosen as axes of reference ; then the distances OA′ and AA′ of any point A

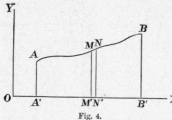

Fig. 4.

from these lines completely determine the position of A. These distances are termed the co-ordinates of the point, and when they are known the point A can be found.

Hence, if pressures are measured parallel to OY and volumes parallel to OX, so that AA′ represents the pressure of a substance and OA′ its volume (per unit mass), then the position of A on the figure represents the state of the substance as regards pressure and volume. Every position of A corresponds to a definite condition of the substance, for when the pressure and volume are known the temperature is in general completely determined. Sometimes, however, two or more different temperatures may be possible at the same pressure and volume, as happens in the case of water for an interval above 4° C., between 4° and 0°, and below 0° C. To represent the state of the substance completely then, it is only necessary to erect a perpendicular at A to the plane of the figure, and to measure off along this perpendicular a length representing the temperature (or lengths representing the temperatures) corresponding to A, and as A moves about over the plane the extremity of the perpendicular will describe a surface in space which will represent the characteristics of the substance, every point on the surface corresponding to a definite condition of the substance. Thus, if the characteristic equation connecting the pressure, volume, and temperature be $f(p,\ v,\ \theta) = 0$, then this will be the equation of the foregoing surface, and $p,\ v,\ \theta$ will be the rectangular co-ordinates of any point on it.

Returning, however, to the case of two rectangular axes : if we

Characteristic surface.

suppose A to move along any curve AB, this will represent that the substance passes from A to B through a perfectly definite series of conditions, the pressure and volume in each condition being represented by the co-ordinates of the corresponding point on the curve AB. In general, the temperature corresponding to any point will vary from point to point, so that in order to effect the transformation indicated by the curve AB heat must be supplied to, or taken from, the body, as it passes from point to point of the curve, in a manner which becomes completely determined when the nature of the curve is known. It may of course happen that the temperature of the substance remains constant throughout the transformation, and in this case the curve AB is termed an *isothermal* line, and a transformation may also be such that heat is neither added to, nor taken from, the substance at any stage of the process, and in this case the transformation is said to be *adiabatic*, and the curve is called an adiabatic line.

67. Graphic Representation of Work.—When a substance passes from the condition A (Fig. 4) to the condition B its volume has increased by an amount $A'B'$, and, as it has been under pressure (varying according to a definite law) throughout the transformation, it follows that work has been done by the body in expanding against this external pressure. This is termed the external work, and it is easy to show that it is represented by the area $ABB'A'$, included between the curve AB, the axis OX, and the ordinates AA' and BB'. For this purpose let us take the case of a substance, say a gas, enclosed within a cylinder which is closed by a piston of area A. Let p be the pressure (per unit area), and let us suppose this remains constant while the piston is drawn out a distance x (which we can suppose as small as we like). The whole pressure on the piston is pA and the work done is therefore pAx, but Ax is the change of volume, so that if we denote it by dv, the work done by the substance in expanding by an amount dv will be pdv. Referring again to Fig. 4, we see that if the substance passes from M to an adjacent point N, the volume changes by an amount $M'N' = dv$, and that the external work pdv is consequently represented by the narrow strip of area $MNN'M'$. Hence the whole work done in passing from A to B is represented by the area $ABB'A'$—that is,

$$W = \text{area } ABB'A' = \int pdv.$$

If the equation of the curve be given, p can be expressed as a function of v, and the integral expressing the area $ABB'A'$ may be evaluated.

The external work done while a substance passes from any state A to any other state B depends, therefore, not only on the positions of

these points, but also on the nature of the curve AB, along which the
transformation takes place.　　Hence, if a substance be caused to pass
from A to B along the path AMB (Fig. 5), an amount of work
represented by AMBB′A′ will be done by the substance while it
Closed cycle. expands, and if it be caused to return from B to A along a different
path BNA, an amount of work represented by the area BNAA′B′ will
be done on it by compression, so that throughout the whole operation,
while the substance passes round the complete cycle AMBNA, a

Fig. 5.

quantity of work represented by
the area of the cycle is done by
the substance.　If, on the other
hand, the substance had passed
round the cycle in the opposite
direction ANBMA, the work represented by the area of the cycle
would have been done on the
substance, for in this case the expansion takes place along ANB
at the lower pressures and the compression is effected at the higher.

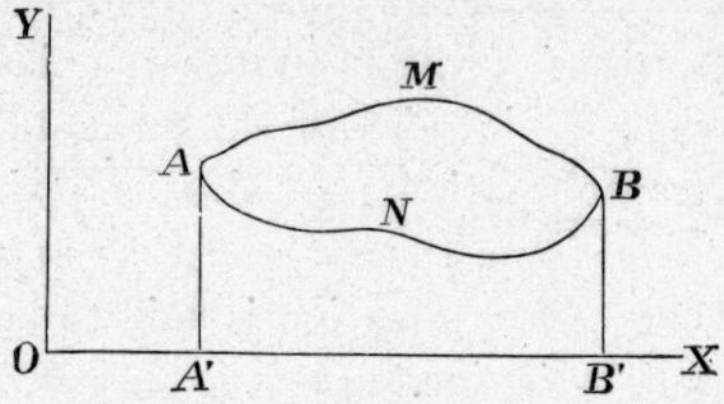

We have thus the general result that if a substance be made to
pass through any complete cycle of operations, returning to its initial
condition, so that the indicator diagram is a closed curve, the external
work done is represented by the area of the cycle, and is done by, or
on, the body according to the direction in which the cycle is described.
If the direction of motion opposite to that of the hands of a watch be
taken as positive, while the opposite is considered negative, then when
a cycle is described in the positive direction a positive quantity of work,
represented by the area of the cycle, is done on the substance ; but if
it be described in the negative direction a negative quantity of work,
represented by the same area, will have been done on the substance,
negative work done on the substance being merely work done by it.

The first law of thermodynamics informs us now that when a
substance passes through any closed cycle of transformations, and
returns again to its initial state, the area of the cycle is the mechanical
equivalent of the heat evolved or absorbed by the substance during
the process.　It is very important to notice, however, that when the
cycle is not closed, so that the body has not returned to its initial
condition A, but is in some other state B, then the heat supplied to
the body is not the equivalent of the external work done, but is used
up partly in doing this work and partly in altering the thermal
condition of the substance.　When the cycle is completed the body has
returned to its initial condition, and for this reason the external work
is, in this case, the equivalent of the heat supplied during the cycle.

Examples

1. Show that the isothermal lines for a perfect gas are a system of rectangular hyperbolas.

(The equation of any isothermal will be $pv =$ constant, and this is the equation of a rectangular hyperbola having the axes of reference for asymptotes.)

2. In the case of a gas prove that the isothermal elasticity is equal to the pressure.

(The elasticity of a substance is the reciprocal of its compressibility, and the latter is the change of volume, per unit volume, for unit increase of pressure. Hence, if a volume v changes by an amount dv for increase of pressure dp per unit area, the change per unit volume for unit increase of pressure will be $-\dfrac{1}{v}\dfrac{dv}{dp}$, so that the elasticity will be

$$- v\frac{dp}{dv}.$$

This quantity, and therefore the elasticity of a substance in a given state, is indefinite, unless we specify the particular transformation which it is supposed to be undergoing. Now for the isothermal changes of a gas $pv =$ constant, therefore $p + v\dfrac{dp}{dv} = 0$, or $-v\dfrac{dp}{dv} = p$.)

3. If a tangent drawn to an indicator curve at any point P (Fig. 6) meets the axis of pressure at L, and if M be the foot of the perpendicular from P on the same axis, show that the elasticity of the substance at the point P of the transformation is represented by LM.

(We have $LM = MP \tan LPM = v \tan LPM = -v\dfrac{dp}{dv}$, ∴, etc.

Since the intercept made by the asymptotes on any tangent to a hyperbola is bisected at the point of contact, it follows that $LM = MO$ in the case of a gas during an isothermal transformation; or the isothermal elasticity of a gas is equal to the pressure.)

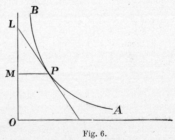

Fig. 6.

4. Prove that the adiabatic lines of a substance, in which compression causes increase of temperature, are steeper than the isothermal lines.

(For a given value of dv the increase of pressure dp will be greater for the adiabatic transformation than for the isothermal, on account of the increase of temperature, and therefore LM will be greater.)

5. Assuming the adiabatic equation of a gas to be

$$pv^\gamma = \text{constant},$$

prove that the adiabatic elasticity is γp, and hence that γ is the ratio of the adiabatic to the isothermal elasticity.

68. Mean Kinetic Energy of a System of Material Particles in Stationary Motion.—When the velocity of a point fluctuates between certain limits while the point oscillates about a mean position, the motion is said to be stationary. All periodic motions, such as the vibrations of an elastic solid, are of this kind, and such also is supposed to be the molecular motion of a body which constitutes its heat.

In Art. 55 we considered the behaviour of a system of molecules so thinly scattered that their mutual influence might be neglected ; we shall now consider the case in which the molecules are close to each other, and within the sphere of each other's attraction.

Let the co-ordinates of any molecule [1] be x, y, z, and let the component forces on it parallel to these axes be X, Y, Z. Then $m\dfrac{d^2x}{dt^2}=X$.

But by differentiation we find

$$\frac{d^2}{dt^2}\Big(x^2\Big)=2\frac{d}{dt}\Big(x\frac{dx}{dt}\Big)=2\Big(\frac{dx}{dt}\Big)^2+2x\frac{d^2x}{dt^2}.$$

Hence

$$\tfrac{1}{2}m\Big(\frac{dx}{dt}\Big)^2=\tfrac{1}{4}m\frac{d^2(x^2)}{dt^2}-\tfrac{1}{2}xX.$$

The mean value of the left-hand member during any time t will be

$$\frac{m}{2t}\int_0^t\Big(\frac{dx}{dt}\Big)^2dt=\frac{m}{4t}\Big[\frac{d(x^2)}{dt}-\Big(\frac{d(x^2)}{dt}\Big)_0\Big]-\frac{1}{2t}\int_0^t xX dt.$$

The two terms involving the sign of integration in this equation are the mean values of the quantities under this sign, during the time t. For periodic motions t may be taken the periodic time, and in this case the first term of the right-hand member of the equation will vanish, for $\dfrac{d(x^2)}{dt}$ will have the same value at the beginning and end of a complete period. We shall then have

$$\text{mean value of }\tfrac{1}{2}m\Big(\frac{dx}{dt}\Big)^2=-\text{ mean value of }\tfrac{1}{2}xX.$$

For irregular motions such as those which occur in gases and liquids, we need only suppose t large compared with the time that a molecule moves steadily in the same direction. The term within the square bracket will vary within certain limits; and as it is divided by t, it follows that when t is large this term becomes negligible. The same reasoning applies to the motions parallel to the axes of y and z, so that we have

$$\text{mean of }\tfrac{1}{2}\Sigma m\Big[\Big(\frac{dx}{dt}\Big)^2+\Big(\frac{dy}{dt}\Big)^2+\Big(\frac{dz}{dt}\Big)^2\Big]=-\text{ mean of }\tfrac{1}{2}\Sigma(xX+yY+zZ),$$

or

$$\text{mean of }\tfrac{1}{2}\Sigma(mV^2)=-\text{ mean of }\tfrac{1}{2}\Sigma(xX+yY+zZ).$$

This mean value has been termed by Clausius the *virial* of the system, and this theorem may therefore be stated in the form "the mean kinetic energy of the system is equal to its virial."

Cor. 1. If the force between two particles be $\phi(r)$ a function of the distance r between them, then if x, y, z and x', y', z' be the co-ordinates of the particles, we have for one

$$X=\phi(r)\frac{x-x'}{r},\quad Y=\phi(r)\frac{y-y'}{r},\quad Z=\phi(r)\frac{z-z'}{r},$$

with equal and opposite values of X, Y, and Z for the other, therefore

$$Xx+X'x'=X(x-x')=\phi(r)\frac{(x-x')^2}{r},$$

with corresponding expressions for the other two co-ordinates, so that

$$\tfrac{1}{2}\Sigma(xX+yY+zZ)=\tfrac{1}{2}\Sigma r\phi(r).$$

[1] Clausius, *Phil. Mag.*, August 1870.

Cor. 2. In the case of a gas enclosed in a vessel a uniform normal external pressure p exists all over the surface of the mass, and the virial of this will be

$$\tfrac{1}{2}p\!\int\!xdydz + \tfrac{1}{2}p\!\int\!ydzdx + \tfrac{1}{2}p\!\int\!zdxdy = \tfrac{3}{2}pv,$$

where v is the volume of the gas.

Hence in this case we have

$$\tfrac{1}{2}\Sigma m\mathrm{V}^2 = \tfrac{3}{2}pv + \tfrac{1}{2}\Sigma r\phi(r),$$

or

$$pv = \tfrac{1}{3}\Sigma m\mathrm{V}^2 - \tfrac{1}{3}\Sigma r\phi(r).$$

Consequently, if the molecules are out of the sphere of each other's attraction, that is, if $\phi(r) = 0$, the product of the pressure and volume will be equal to two-thirds of the mean kinetic energy of the molecules; but if the molecules are within the sphere of each other's attraction, the effect is to diminish the product pv by an amount equal to two-thirds of the virial of the intermolecular forces. Hence, when a gas is compressed it is anticipated that the product pv will vary and not remain constant at constant temperature. The experimental investigations on this point will be considered later on (see Art. 248).

CHAPTER II

THERMOMETRY

SECTION I

LIQUID THERMOMETERS

69. Discontinuous Thermoscopes.—A thermoscope is an instrument for indicating relative temperatures, and its indications may be either continuous or discontinuous according to the property of matter employed. In continuous thermoscopes a property of matter which varies continuously is made use of, such as change of volume with heat, and the indications of discontinuous thermoscopes depend on the employment of some abrupt change of state, such as fusion. Any substance acts as a thermoscope, solids for a single temperature and liquids for two temperatures. Thus a piece of paraffin wax immersed in a bath will indicate whether the temperature of the bath is above or below the temperature of fusion of the wax, and by this means we could separate a series of given temperatures into two sets, those higher than the melting point of the wax and those lower. In the same way a piece of butter will tell us whether the temperature of a room is higher or lower than the melting point of butter. A liquid gives us more information; it tells us whether a temperature is higher or lower than either the boiling point or the freezing point of the liquid. The water in a basin not only tells us that the temperature of the room is higher than the freezing point of water, but also that it is lower than the temperature of boiling. It thus places the temperature of the room between two others, which are definite and recoverable.

If an instrument merely indicates whether the temperature of a body to which it is applied is higher or lower than a single definite temperature, it is called a single intrinsic thermoscope, because its indication depends upon some intrinsic quality of the instrument.

94

The paraffin wax referred to is a single intrinsic thermoscope, the single temperature being its melting point, and the intrinsic quality the property of melting always at this definite temperature.

A multiple discontinuous intrinsic thermoscope shows several definite temperatures, or indicates whether the temperature of any body to which it is applied lies between any pair of these temperatures. Such an instrument may be constructed by preparing a system of metallic alloys or other substances arranged and numbered in the order of their melting points, and a multiple intrinsic thermoscope has been constructed on this plan in a form convenient for use by Mr. J. J. Coleman.[1] It consists of a set of paraffins which melt at definite temperatures between 40° and 100° F., and mixtures of glycerine [2] and water which freeze at temperatures from 30° to − 35° F. By multiplying the number of substances in such an instrument the consecutive definite temperatures which it indicates may be made to approach each other closer and closer. Ideally the system may be made nearly continuous by making a system of alloys with fine enough gradation of composition, but the method is essentially discontinuous.

70. Continuous Thermoscopes and Thermometers.—A thermoscope becomes continuous in its indications when the property of matter employed varies continuously with temperature. When such an instrument is properly graduated according to some arranged scale, it not only indicates whether the temperature of a body to which it is applied is higher or lower than some definite temperature, but it also informs us how much it is higher or lower, according to the chosen

---

[1] J. J. Coleman, *Proc. Phil. Soc. Glasgow*, 1884, vol. xv. p. 94.

[2] Glycerine when pure crystallises a little below 0° C., but when mixed with a little water its freezing point is about 40° C. below zero, and the solidification here is not of a crystalline but of a buttery nature. By varying the quantity of water the freezing point may be varied at pleasure.

A discontinuous intrinsic thermoscope for the measurement of high temperatures was proposed by Prinsep (*Phil. Trans.*, 1828, p. 79). He formed a series of definite percentage alloys of silver and gold, and of platinum and gold. These alloys gave a series of fixed temperatures between the melting points of silver and gold and of gold and platinum. An observation is taken by exposing in a small cupel a set of small flattened specimens of the alloys, not necessarily larger than pin-heads, and noticing which of them are fused. The temperatures of fusion of these alloys have been determined by Erhard and Shertel by a porcelain-air-thermometer (*Jahrb. für das Berg- und Hüttenwesen in Sachsen*, 1879). An objection has been raised to Prinsep's alloys on the ground of silver taking up oxygen at high temperatures and ejecting it again on cooling, which renders it inadvisable to use the same specimen twice.

A similar method has been employed by Carnelley and Carleton Williams (*Chem. Soc. Journal*, 1876, 1877, 1878), in which metallic salts with high fusing points were used instead of alloys. The fusing points were initially determined by the calorimetric method.

scale.   In this case the instrument becomes not merely an indicator, but also a measurer of temperatures, and is termed a thermometer. In selecting a system of thermometry, any physical property of matter which varies continuously with heating might be chosen.   We have already described how temperature may be defined and measured by the apparent volume of mercury enclosed in a glass vessel (p. 15).   If this be taken as our standard instrument, then all other thermometers must be graduated by comparison with it, so that when placed in the same uniformly heated bath they may all agree in their indications. We shall thus have a uniform system of measurement, and experiments conducted at any place may be repeated at any other.

Standard-
ising.

The main object to be secured in thermometry is that all thermo-meters shall be strictly comparable, and since liquid thermometers are easily portable the simplest means of obtaining this object is by com-paring all thermometers, directly or indirectly, with some standard instrument.   All thermometers would then be copies of the same original, and would agree perfectly in their indications.   This being arranged, thermometers may be constructed of other liquids than mercury, or by measuring, not the increase of volume, but the increase in length of a bar, or the increase in pressure of a gas kept at constant volume, or the change in electrical resistance of a wire, or change in pressure of the saturated vapour of a liquid, or change in shape of a spiral composed of strips of different metals, or change in the shape of a single elastic solid subject to stated stress.

The condition implied in all cases is that the thermometers shall all be graduated according to the same standard, and that the property of matter made use of shall always give the same indication when the temperature is brought again and again to the same value.   It is upon this last property that the accuracy of a thermometer depends.   The constitution of the material of which the instrument is constructed must be permanent, so that the property made use of in measuring temperatures is always the same at the same temperature.

Sensibility.

The sensibility or delicacy of the instrument depends only upon the recognisability of changes in the indicating property with very small changes of temperature.   A thermometer may be delicate in two ways—(1) when it detects very small changes of temperature, and (2) when it rapidly assumes the temperature of any body with which it is placed in contact.   The delicacy of a thermometer is consequently to some extent similar to that of a balance, one of the circumstances determining it working in opposition to the other.   Thus, in order to secure the first condition the bulb should be large and the bore narrow ; but in order to secure the second the bulb should be small, have a large surface, and be filled with a liquid which will rapidly take up the temperature of the medium in which it is immersed, that is, of high conductivity. If the bulb is large the weight of the contained liquid produces strain effects which may seriously affect the accuracy ; and if the initial temperature of the thermometer differs from that of the body with which it is placed in contact, the final indication of the instrument will not be the initial temperature of the body, but will be intermediate between that of the body and the initial temperature of the thermometer, for the body will become cooled in warming the thermometer. This final reading will differ from the original temperature of the body more and more the greater the heat capacity of the thermometer, the less that of the body, and the greater their initial difference of temperature. In the construction of a thermometer, then, the nature of the work for which it is intended must be taken into account. A thermometer which is best adapted for one class of work may be quite unsuited for another.

71. Construction of a Liquid-in-glass Thermometer.—We shall now briefly describe the construction of a liquid-in-glass thermometer, such as the ordinary mercury thermometer. Such a description, besides being important in itself, affords an excellent example of the method by which the scientific investigation of such a phenomenon as temperature must be proceeded with. In making a thermometer a glass tube possessing a uniform capillary bore is selected, and a bulb of suitable size is blown (or fused) on one end, the other end being left open. It is important that the bore of the tube should be as uniform as possible, and this should be ascertained beforehand by sliding a short thread of mercury through the tube, and observing its length in different parts. If this length is approximately the same at all parts of the tube the bore is fairly uniform, and the tube may be employed. Slight want of uniformity can be corrected for afterwards, as will be explained subsequently. The tube and bulb should now be well cleaned, and all organic matter removed from its inside surface by means of boiling nitric acid.

Some of the best thermometer tubes are furnished with a pear-shaped reservoir or funnel at the open end, to facilitate the process of filling. If such a reservoir be not already attached, the end of the tube may be simply bent round, so that it may be dipped with facility under the surface of some mercury or other liquid with which it is desired to fill the instrument.

In order to introduce the liquid, the empty bulb is heated over a lamp, and the air within expands and is partly expelled. The open end of the stem is immediately dipped under the surface of the liquid,

H

and kept there while the bulb and the enclosed air cool. During this process the pressure of the air within diminishes, and some of the liquid is forced through the stem into the bulb by the pressure of the atmosphere outside. By this means the bulb is partially filled. To complete the process, the liquid thus introduced is boiled till all the air is expelled, and the instrument contains only the liquid and its vapour. If the open end be dipped into a cup of the liquid while the boiling is still in operation, and if the instrument be allowed to cool, the vapour will condense, so that the bulb and stem will become completely filled with the liquid.

The process of filling a thermometer is a matter of some difficulty to a beginner, as it is by no means easy to ensure that all the air has been expelled. Minute bubbles are nearly always found remaining, which adhere with the greatest pertinacity to the sides of the glass and resist expulsion. Caution must also be exercised in the process of boiling the liquid, especially in the case of mercury, which has a high boiling point, and if heated over a lamp the bulb may fuse and lead to disaster. To avoid this a special heating apparatus may be used, by means of which the bulb and stem may be gradually heated throughout its entire length to the boiling point of the liquid.

When the bulb and stem are filled the instrument is raised to the highest temperature that it is intended to measure, and in this state the end of the tube is hermetically sealed. In order to avoid bursting when the thermometer is inadvertently subjected to temperatures higher than the highest that it is intended to register, the upper end of the bore is, in the best instruments, widened out into a small reservoir into which the mercury may expand. This reservoir is important, as it not only prevents the danger of bursting, but can be used to contain some of the mercury separated from the bulb in the process of calibrating, as well as in the separation of minute air bubbles, if any exist in the bulb. Besides, by placing some of the mercury in it the same part of the scale can be used, if desired, at a high and also at a low temperature.

If now the size of the bulb and the length of the stem have been properly adjusted, the bulb and a small part of the stem will be filled with liquid at the lowest temperature which the instrument is intended to register. In this case the fixed points may be determined and the process of graduation proceeded with.

72. **Determination of the Fixed Points.**—In order to furnish a thermometer with a scale, two points are first marked on the stem which correspond to two definite temperatures. The temperatures generally chosen for this purpose are those originally suggested by

Hooke,[1] and adopted by Newton, namely, the melting point of ice and the boiling point of water. The temperature of boiling water is not now employed, but rather the temperature of the vapour of water boiling under the pressure of one standard atmosphere. This pressure is that exerted at the freezing point by a column of mercury 760 mm. high in the latitude of Paris, which is equivalent to a column of 29·905 inches in the latitude of London. The temperature of the steam is chosen, because it is found that the temperature of boiling water depends to some extent on the presence of impurities and the nature of the vessel in which it is boiled, whereas the temperature of the steam depends only on the pressure, the former point having been established by Gay-Lussac and the latter by Rudberg.

The Freezing Point.—The freezing point, as the lower fixed point is called, is determined by placing the thermometer in a vessel containing broken ice, from which water is dripping, so that the bulb and stem, so far as it is filled with mercury, are surrounded with ice, and the top of the mercurial column is just visible. The vessel (Fig. 7) is usually shown with a perforated bottom, so that as the ice melts the water drips away, and the thermometer is surrounded with ice at the melting point. After standing for some time the level of the mercury becomes stationary, and a mark is carefully traced on the glass at this point.

Fig. 7.

The advantage gained by allowing the water to drain away as the ice melts is not obvious. As long as there is plenty of ice present the temperature of the water will remain stationary, and the pressure on the bulb of the thermometer will be more uniform than when the water is allowed to drain off. In the latter case angular fragments of ice will be sometimes pressed with their sharp edges against the bulb, and this may cause distortion and consequent displacements of the zero point.

Another question which presents itself is—does the temperature of melting ice depend on whether the ice has been formed from ordinary or distilled water? Both these points have been examined by Mr. F. D. Brown,[2] and his conclusions, after a series of observations on different kinds of ice, and mixtures of ice and water, were that a constant temperature is more rapidly and certainly obtained with a

---

[1] Hooke, 1681 ; see Birch's *History of the Royal Society*, vol. iv.
[2] F. D. Brown, *Phil. Mag.* vol. xiv. 1882.

mixture of ice and water than with ice alone, that the temperature
thus obtained is really that of melting [1] ice, and that it is preferable to
wash and mix the ice with distilled water, as ordinary water lowered

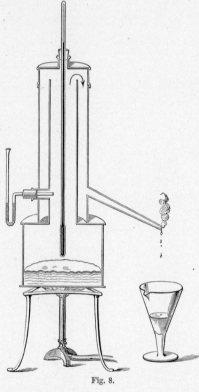

Fig. 8.

the temperature to a slight
extent. The quantity of water
mixed with the ice should be
just sufficient to fill up the
spaces between the fragments.

Boiling Point.—The boiling
point is determined, as already
stated, by placing the thermometer in the steam [2] of boiling
water, the pressure being one
standard atmosphere. The
thermometer is so far plunged
into the steam that the surface
of the mercury is just visible,
as shown in Fig. 8. When the
level of the mercury becomes
stationary, a mark is made
on the stem at its surface,
and this is the boiling point.
The pressure corresponding to
a standard atmosphere is in this
country taken to be that of the
atmosphere when the barometer
stands at 29·905 inches at the
sea-level in the latitude of Lon-
don, the temperature being that of the freezing point. In order to
know the pressure of the steam in which the thermometer is placed

[1] This, however, will depend on what is meant by the *temperature of melting ice.*
[2] In the apparatus used for determining the boiling point the vapour inside is
usually and erroneously represented by clouds, and this perhaps fosters the idea commonly prevalent among beginners that steam is visible like a cloud. This mistake
probably arises from the application of the word in ordinary language. Thus Robison, in his *Mechanical Philosophy*, vol. ii. p. 1, defines steam as " the visible moist
vapour which arises from all bodies which contain juice easily expelled by heat. . . .
It is distinguished from smoke by its not having been produced by combustion, by
not containing any soot, and by its being condensible by cold into water, oil, in-
flammable spirits, or liquids composed of these. . . . The visibility of the matter
which constitutes the steam is an accidental or extraneous circumstance, and requires
the admixture with air, yet this quality again leaves it when united with air by
solution." What we now term steam or vapour is an invisible substance, but
when this condenses into small globules it becomes visible and is then called cloud,
or mist.

during the determination of the boiling point, a gauge is attached. This consists simply of a bent glass tube, open to the atmosphere at one end, and containing a little water. The difference of level of the water in the two arms gives the difference of pressure between the steam inside and the atmosphere outside the apparatus. If the escape orifice is large enough this difference will be scarcely sensible.

When the boiling point is marked the barometer will probably not be at the standard height, so that the mark made on the stem must not be regarded as the standard boiling point, and a corresponding correction must be made in graduating it. This correction will be found from tables of vapour tensions.

73. Graduation of the Thermometer.—The freezing and the boiling points having been marked, the interval between them may be divided into any desired number of equal parts. Each of these parts is called a degree, and hence we speak of a temperature being so many degrees above or below the freezing point. Three systems of division have been proposed, which are at present in general use. The centigrade scale was introduced by Celsius,[1] and is generally used in France and in all scientific work. In this scale the freezing point is marked 0°, and is called zero, and the boiling point is marked 100°, the interval between being divided into 100 equal parts.

The scale generally used by English-speaking people is that introduced by Fahrenheit,[2] of Dantzig, about 1714. In this scale the boiling point is marked 212° and the freezing point is marked 32°, the graduation extending above and below the fixed points. A point 32° below the freezing point is marked 0°, and is called zero. This point corresponded to the lowest known temperature in the time of

---

[1] Professor of Astronomy in the University of Upsala.

[2] The view advanced in explanation of the mode of division of the Fahrenheit scale is that the interval between the freezing point and the boiling point was divided into 180 points like a semicircle. If this view has no foundation, it is certainly a strange coincidence that there should be on this scale exactly 180° between what are now taken as the two fixed points.

Professor A. Gamgee (*Proc. Camb. Phil. Soc.*, 1890, vol. vii. pt. iii. p. 95) states that this view is nevertheless incorrect,—that Fahrenheit had settled the basis of his scale and constructed a large number of thermometers many years before the discovery by Amantons that water boils at a constant temperature under constant pressure. The thermometers first constructed by Fahrenheit were sealed alcohol-in-glass thermometers provided with a scale. The lower fixed point of the scale was determined by a mixture of snow and salt, and the upper by placing the thermometer under the armpit, or inside the mouth, of a healthy man. In the early thermometers the interval between these two fixed points was divided into 24 equal parts, and later on into $4 \times 24 = 96$. It was subsequently found that the 32nd degree corresponded to the melting point of ice, and the 212th to the boiling point of water. The basis of Fahrenheit's scale was then simply duodecimal division.

Fahrenheit, namely, that of a mixture of snow and salt. The only arguments in favour of this scale are its early introduction and the fact that it is actually used by so many of our countrymen. A remarkable fact, however, is that mercury expands almost exactly $\frac{1}{10000}$ of its volume at 142° F. for every degree Fahrenheit, so that Young[1] defined the degree Fahrenheit as corresponding to an expansion of mercury equal to $\frac{1}{10000}$ part of its bulk.

The third thermometric scale is that of Réaumur. In this scale the freezing point is marked 0° and the boiling point 80°, the interval being divided into 80 equal parts. This scale is very generally used in Germany for domestic purposes, but possesses no special advantages.

The relation between the readings of thermometers graduated according to these three methods is easily found, for 100 divisions of the centigrade scale are equal to $212 - 32 = 180$ divisions of the Fahrenheit and also equal to 80 of the Réaumur scale. Hence if C, F, R denote the readings of the three thermometers for the same temperature, we have

$$\frac{C}{100} = \frac{F - 32}{180} = \frac{R}{80},$$

or

$$C = \tfrac{5}{9}(F - 32) = \tfrac{5}{4}R.$$

From these equations, when the temperature is given by one scale, the corresponding number expressing the temperature on either of the others can be easily found.[2]

In the best modern thermometers the scale is marked on the glass stem of the instrument itself, but in most ordinary thermometers the graduations are made on a piece of wood, or ivory, or porcelain, to which the thermometer is securely attached. Some of the best ordinary thermometers (German bath thermometers) have the scale marked on a slip of paper which is enclosed in a glass tube hermetically sealed round the stem of the thermometer, and in this form the graduation is clearer and more easily read than in any other. The paper scale is completely protected from damp and damage by the sealed glass tube which encloses it. The lightness of the paper renders its attachment to the stem, by gum or otherwise, secure and trustworthy, and if the thermometer be never exposed to a temperature high enough to brown or injure the paper, it is cheaper and better than any other form of scale. The graduation on the glass of the stem itself is, however, superior to all others, except in respect to the ease of reading the divisions.

[1] Young, Lectures on Nat. Phil. p. 485.

[2] The scale called after Réaumur was proposed by De Luc (Recherches sur l'atmosphère, tom. ii. pp. 244-283). The true scale proposed by Réaumur marked 80 at the boiling point of alcohol, and consequently the boiling point of water on it differed little from 100°. It thus differed little from the centigrade scale.

Lens front tubes are used for delicate thermometers of fine bore. The stem itself thus plays the part of a magnifying glass, and enlarges the bore about fifteen times.

74. On the Choice of a Thermometric Substance.—In respect to general convenience for a large variety of purposes, liquid-in-glass thermometers are with good reason preferred to all others, but the reason for the general preference for mercury or spirits of wine as the thermometric substance is not so obvious.   The indications of a liquid thermometer depend both on the expansion of the liquid and on that of the glass envelope which contains it.   If the glass and the liquid expand equally with rise of temperature, the apparent volume of the liquid in glass will remain constant.   Since the indications of the instrument depend only on the difference of the expansions of the liquid and the glass, the greater the expansion of the liquid the more sensitive the thermometer, and for a given liquid the length of a degree on the stem will be greater the larger the bulb and the smaller the bore of the tube.   The high specific gravity of mercury limits the size of the bulb, for besides increasing the liability to break, the weight of the mercury strains the bulb and tends to give distorted readings, especially at high temperatures.   Further irregularity is also introduced by the variations in the shape of the meniscus in the capillary tube.   Besides the large value of the surface tension of mercury, the angle of contact varies from about 45° when the mercury is rising to 90° when it is falling.   For this reason the internal pressure on the bulb is greater when the temperature is rising than when the temperature is falling, and a consequent variation in the volume of the bulb occurs which produces an irregularity in the indications of the instrument.   On this account the mercury rises by jerks and not continuously when the temperature is increasing, and falls in the same discontinuous manner when the temperature is falling.   This jerky motion of the mercury is very noticeable in delicate thermometers, and in some instruments is more so than in others.   This Joule believed to be due largely to the slight oxidation of the mercury before sealing.

Surface tension.

Liquids which wet the glass have a great superiority over mercury in their much smaller surface tension and in their practically constant angle of contact (180°).   The variations of internal pressure are thus much less when the liquid is rising or falling and the motion in the tube is continuous.   The large expansion of such liquids as alcohol, ether, chloroform, etc., gives the instrument in addition a great sensibility, and they possess a further advantage over mercury in their much smaller specific gravity, so that larger bulbs may be used with consequent greater sensibility, and less liability to break or produce disturbed readings through distortion of the bulb by the weight of the liquid.

One objection to alcohol and other volatile liquids is their liability to distil into the head reservoir of the stem if this part of the instrument is colder than the bulb. On this account the stem of a spirit thermometer should be at least as warm as the space in which the bulb is situated.

A serious objection to liquids of high expansibility is the difficulty of allowing for the expansion of the liquid in the stem if it be not at the same temperature as that in the bulb. The error arising from this cause will, under the same conditions, be proportional to the expansibility of the liquid, but in every case in which the bulb and stem can be kept at the same temperature, a thermometer constructed with a highly expansive and light liquid, such as alcohol or ether, or other organic liquid of permanent chemical constitution, should be more accurate and sensitive than one filled with mercury. The low boiling points of these liquids render them unfit for the construction of thermometers which are to be used at high temperatures, but for low temperatures they make very valuable instruments. A sulphuric ether thermometer was employed by Lord Kelvin in his experiments on the lowering of the freezing point of water by pressure, and thermometers filled with ether or chloroform (which expands 4 per cent more than ether) were used by Joule and Thomson in their experiments on the change of temperature of bodies moving in air. In one of these thermometers there were as many as 330 scale divisions to 1° C.

Another objection frequently urged against spirit thermometers, is that when the temperature is rapidly falling a thin film of the liquid lags behind adhering to the sides of the tube, so that before the stationary temperature can be correctly read it is necessary to wait some time to allow the liquid to trickle down and join the main column. Adaptability to the measurement of rapidly-varying temperatures would thus seem to be wanting. With mobile liquids, such as alcohol and ether, there will, however, be practically no time lost on this account, and when proper care is exercised by the observer no inaccuracy will be incurred.[1] When the temperature has been rapidly falling, and has nearly reached its lowest point, a false balance must be guarded against, which arises from the descent of the liquid surface due to fall of temperature being counterbalanced by the rise caused by the liquid trickling down from the sides of the tube. This may

[1] Sir Wm. Thomson, *Math. and Phys. Papers*, vol. iii. p. 142.

give a false steadiness when the free surface has nearly reached the true position for the final temperature.[1]

The great convenience of the mercury thermometer is its freedom from distillation and the smallness of the error arising from any difference between the temperature of the bulb and that of the stem. It is further well suited to the measurement of ordinary temperatures, the boiling point of mercury being 350° C., and its freezing point 40° C. below the freezing point of water.

Ordinary mercury thermometers cannot be used above about 250° C. owing to the boiling of the mercury, but when filled up with nitrogen under pressure they can be used up to about 420° C.

A liquid-in-glass thermometer, which can be used down to the temperature of liquid air, has been constructed by L. Holborn,[2] in which the liquid used is obtained by distilling petroleum ether, boiling at 33°, and retaining a more volatile portion, boiling at about 20° C. Or pentane may be substituted for the petroleum ether, as suggested by Rothe.[3] Either of these substances remains liquid down to − 190° C., but becomes somewhat viscid at that temperature. Pentane has the advantage of being a definite chemical compound, whereas the petroleum ether is a mixture.

75. Overflowing Thermometers.—In ordinary liquid-in-glass thermometers the expansion is noted by the rise of the liquid in a tube divided into parts of equal or known capacities. The same result may be also attained by allowing the liquid to overflow, and determining the volume of the overflow by weighing. This is the method practised in what is known as the *weight thermometer*, and the difficulties attending the calibration and change of zero of the ordinary thermometer are thus avoided. This instrument consists of a glass bulb capable of containing about 200 grammes of mercury, which is furnished with a short capillary tube, and filled at zero in the ordinary way and weighed. Let W_0 be the weight of mercury which fills the instrument at the freezing point, w the weight which overflows at any temperature θ. Then w is the apparent expansion of a weight $W - w$ of mercury in rising from 0° to $\theta°$; consequently if a denotes the apparent expansion of mercury in glass, we have

Fig. 9.

$$(W - w)a\theta = w,$$

or

$$\theta = \frac{w}{(W - w)a}.$$

[1] For the graduation of spirit thermometers see a note by M. A. Angot, *Journal de Physique*, Sept. 1891.

[2] *Ann. der Physik*, Oct. 1901.

[3] *Zeitschr. f. Instrumentenk.*, p. 47, 1904.

To determine a it is only necessary to make an experiment at 100° C., which gives

$$a = \frac{w_{100}}{100(W - w_{100})}.$$

This coefficient varies with the nature of the glass, and it is therefore necessary to determine it directly for each instrument (see also p. 184).

76. Maximum and Minimum Thermometers.—Thermometers for registering the highest or lowest temperature attained during any interval may be devised in several ways. Thus the weight thermometer may be arranged as a maximum thermometer, for if the mercury as it overflows is allowed to drop into a cup, the quantity expelled in any time gives the highest temperature reached by the instrument during that period. This, in fact, is the principle of Walferdin's maximum thermometer.

The ordinary mercury thermometer will, however, serve as a maximum thermometer if a small iron index is placed in the tube so as to move before the surface of the mercury. As the mercury expands

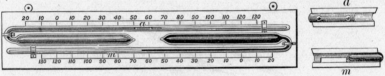

Fig. 10.—Rutherford's.

the index is pushed before it in the stem, and when the temperature falls the index is left behind. The position of the index at any time thus gives the highest temperature that has been attained since the instrument was last set. This is the principle used in Rutherford's maximum and minimum thermometers (Fig. 10). The two thermometers are attached to a frame with their stems directed horizontally. One of these thermometers registers the maximum temperature, and the other the minimum. The former is an ordinary mercury thermometer furnished with a light steel index which is movable in the stem, and can be brought to the surface of the mercury by means of a magnet when it is desired to set the instrument. The reading of that end of the index which is next the surface of the mercury at any other time gives the maximum temperature attained since the instrument was last set. The minimum temperature is registered by the other thermometer. This is a spirit thermometer, and is furnished with a light dumb-bell-shaped enamel or glass index, which is generally coloured. When the spirit expands it flows past the index without displacing it, but when the temperature falls, and the surface of the spirit reaches the index, the latter is retained by the capillary action of the surface and is carried back in its grasp. As the surface recedes, the end of the index, which is directed away from the bulb, marks the temperature, and at any other time this end of the index marks the lowest temperature attained. The index is brought back by inclining the thermometer. Thus in each thermometer that end of the index which is directed towards the surface of the liquid marks the highest or lowest temperature attained.

Six's self-registering thermometer is one of the oldest of this class of instruments, and acts both as a maximum and minimum thermometer. It is shown in Fig. 11, and consists of one continuous tube, the two ends of which contain alcohol[1] (or creosote), and the intermediate space is filled with mercury. The large cylindrical bulb A is also filled with alcohol. The part BC contains mercury, and above C there is some more alcohol, which also partly fills the bulb D, some space being left for expansion. Thus both extremities of the mercurial column are in contact with alcohol, and situated in the alcohol above the mercury, in each arm, is a light steel index which is held in its place by a delicate spring, just strong enough to prevent slipping down the tube. When the alcohol expands in the bulb A the mercury rises in the left arm, and pushes the index before it, leaving the index in the right arm behind in the alcohol; and when the temperature falls the liquid contracts, and the mercury rises in the right arm, pushing the index in this arm before it and leaving the other behind. Thus the index in the left arm gives the maximum, and that in the right gives the minimum, temperature.

Fig. 11.—Six's.

Negretti and Zambra.

In the maximum thermometer of Negretti and Zambra there is an obstruction in the tube close to the bulb, so that the bore is nearly choked at this point. As a consequence, the mercury expanding in the bulb forces its way past the obstruction into the stem above; but, on the other hand, when the temperature falls, the thread of

[1] Alcohol after some time evolves small bubbles of gas which give trouble. Sulphuric acid would probably serve better. Herr von Lupin of Munich recommends dilute sulphuric acid and a solution of 10 or 15 per cent of anhydrous calcium chloride in spirit as liquids free from distillation errors and possessing regular expansion (*Nature*, 1893, p. 206, 29th June).

mercury beyond the obstruction in the stem fails to make its way back again into the bulb. This isolated thread furnishes the means of determining the highest temperature reached by the instrument since it was last set, for when one end of the thread is placed against the obstruction, the other end gives the maximum temperature—a correction being applied for the expansion of the thread if extreme accuracy be desired. In setting this thermometer, the thread of mercury in the stem is shaken past the obstruction till it joins the main mass in the bulb, and the instrument is now ready for another observation.

Clinical.   The same principle is adopted in the clinical thermometers now generally used. These instruments (Fig. 12), being employed to register only a very limited range of temperature, are furnished with

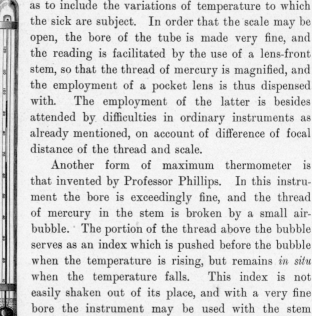

a very open scale graduated from 95° to 113° F., so as to include the variations of temperature to which the sick are subject. In order that the scale may be open, the bore of the tube is made very fine, and the reading is facilitated by the use of a lens-front stem, so that the thread of mercury is magnified, and the employment of a pocket lens is thus dispensed with. The employment of the latter is besides attended by difficulties in ordinary instruments as already mentioned, on account of difference of focal distance of the thread and scale.

Phillips.   Another form of maximum thermometer is that invented by Professor Phillips. In this instrument the bore is exceedingly fine, and the thread of mercury in the stem is broken by a small air-bubble. The portion of the thread above the bubble serves as an index which is pushed before the bubble when the temperature is rising, but remains *in situ* when the temperature falls. This index is not easily shaken out of its place, and with a very fine bore the instrument may be used with the stem vertical, as in Fig. 13, which represents a Phillip's

Fig. 12.   Fig. 13.   thermometer enclosed in a strong glass tube as

Deep wells. designed by Lord Kelvin for the observation of temperatures in deep wells. The enclosing tube is hermetically sealed and protects the thermometer from outside pressure, to which it would otherwise be subject. In the lower part of the case a small quantity of spirit surrounds the bulb, which places it in better thermal communication with the outside medium.

77. Strain Thermometers.—Temperature may also be indicated by the strain, or change of shape of a heterogeneous substance through inequalities of expansion of its constituents. On this principle depend several forms of pocket thermometers and self-registering thermometers. Bréguet's metallic thermometer (Fig. 14) is a good example. In this Bréguet's. instrument three thin strips of platinum, gold, and silver are fastened together (by being passed through a rolling mill) so as to form a thin ribbon, the core of which is gold and the surface layers platinum and silver respectively. This ribbon is then coiled into a spiral, one end of which is held fixed while the other carries a pointer moving round a graduated scale. The silver, which is most expansible, forms the inner face of the spiral; and the platinum, which is least expansible, the outer face. When the temperature rises the silver expands more than the gold or platinum, and the spiral unwinds itself, moving the pointer round the scale, the contrary effect being produced when the temperature falls. The instrument may be made a meter by graduating it by direct comparison with a standard thermometer, and if a light index be placed on the scale so as to move before the pointer, it will give the maximum temperature during any period. A second index placed on the other side will give the minimum temperature. This thermometer is sensitive to very small changes of temperature.

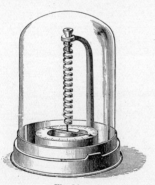

Fig. 14.

Fig. 15.

Another class of strain thermometer depends upon the change of shape of a thin flexible metal tube filled with a highly expansive liquid such as alcohol, chloroform, or a mixture of both (Fig. 15). The tube thus filled is sealed at a low temperature and bent into a circular arc. If now the temperature rises the volume of the contained liquid increases, and the tube straightens itself so as to increase its internal Bourdon's. capacity. Hence if one end is fixed the other end will move with every variation of temperature, and if a pointer be attached to it the motion may be used to register temperatures. This method was due to

Bourdon, and it has since been adopted as a meteorological recording instrument, and also as a convenient form of pocket thermometer, which, when furnished with a maximum index, may be used as a clinical thermometer.

78. Joule's Air-Temperature Thermometer.—A thermometer indicates its own temperature, and for this reason it is difficult to determine the exact temperature of the air at any place, for the indications of a thermometer placed there will be influenced by the radiation of neighbouring bodies. To avoid this disturbing influence Joule[1] invented an apparatus depending on the motion (caused by an air current) of a spiral of fine wire suspended by a filament of silk, and carrying a small mirror which reflects a beam of light to a distant scale. The spiral wire is contained in a copper tube (Fig. 16) surrounded by another co-axial cylinder, and the space between the two is filled with water, the temperature of which is noted by means of a thermometer. The lower end of the tube containing the spiral is furnished with a lid which can slide backwards

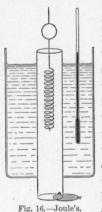

or forwards, so as to open or shut the aperture at pleasure. When the tube is closed the air within it comes to the temperature of the water, and if the lid be now removed, an upward current will set through the tube if the air within is warmer than that outside, and a downward current will set in if the reverse is the case. In case of equality there will be no current and no deflection of the mirror, or spot of light on the scale. Joule found that a difference of 1° F. produced an entire twist of the filament, and that the temperature of the water when equilibrium was secured was generally higher than that indicated by a thermometer exposed in the air outside.

Fig. 16.—Joule's.

(For radiometers and sensitive thermometers see Chap. VI. sec. iv.)

79. Standard Thermometer.—Before we can measure temperatures with precision, and compare our results with those of other observers, it is necessary to fix on a standard scale of temperature, by means of which all thermometers may be compared and standardised. Such a scale must be perfectly definite, readily reproducible, and capable of indicating very small differences of temperature. Liquid-in-glass thermometers are not suitable for this purpose, for though they are capable of considerable delicacy, yet, owing to the variation

[1] Joule, *Proc. Manchester Lit. and Phil. Soc.* vol. vii. p. 35.

in the properties of the glass envelope with temperature, it is difficult
to avoid indefiniteness. Besides, such a scale would not be readily
reproduced with certainty, since glass is not a definite chemical substance, and it is by no means easy to manufacture glass of given
composition and properties, as would be necessary in order to make
all thermometers give the same indications. These objections do not
apply in the same degree to the use of a gas as thermometric substance,
since the expansibility of a gas is so much greater than that of its
solid envelope, that variations in the properties of the latter are of
much less consequence than in liquid thermometers. The gas thermometer is also capable of greater delicacy than the liquid thermometer and has a far greater range of temperature. The scale which
is now universally recognised as the best scale to adopt as a standard
is Lord Kelvin's absolute scale of temperature,[1] which is founded on
theoretical principles and does not depend on the properties of any
particular substance. This scale cannot, however, be directly realised
in practice. For a very large number of observations at moderate
temperatures mercury-in-glass thermometers are the most convenient
to use. Such thermometers can be standardised by comparison with
a thermometer which has itself been compared with a specially
constructed gas thermometer, the readings of which can be corrected,
if required, for its deviations (generally very small) from the ideal
absolute scale (see Art. 365).

Standard thermometers are verified and supplied by the Bureau
International des Poids et Mesures at Sèvres. Thermometers of all
kinds, whether for ordinary purposes or for the most accurate scientific
work, can be sent for testing and tabulation of corrections to the
National Physical Laboratory at Bushy House, Teddington. In
Germany the testing of thermometers is carried out at the Physikalisch-
Technische Reichsanstalt at Charlottenburg.

Comparison of thermometers.

Accurate Mercurial Thermometry [2]

80. Correction of Errors.—Although several objections to the
use of mercury have been mentioned in Art. 74, yet, as the errors to
which mercurial thermometers are liable have been very carefully
investigated, the corrections to be applied are better known, and
consequently the temperatures indicated less uncertain, than when
other liquids are used. The advantages which mercury possesses
are its range of liquidity; its regularity of expansion (judged by

Advantages of mercury.

[1] This is discussed in Chap. VIII. sec. viii.
[2] C. E. Guillaume, *Traité pratique de la thermométrie de précision.* C. Chree,
Phil. Mag., March and April 1898.

comparison with the gas thermometer); the ease with which it can be obtained pure; its property of not wetting glass; its low vapour pressure; and its low specific heat and high conductivity, which enable it to take up readily the temperature of its surroundings.   For these reasons mercury is much more used than other liquids.

The first essential condition which must be fulfilled by a good thermometer is that it must always give the same reading when submitted again and again to the same temperature.   Thus when placed in melting ice the reading should always be the same, no matter what variations of temperature the instrument has suffered, or how long the interval, between two such comparisons.   For this purpose not only should the volume of the mercury be always the same at the same temperature, but glass should also satisfy this condition, or at least the apparent volume of mercury in glass should be always the same at the same temperature.   This, however, is not

Secular rise of zero.

the case.   Glass when heated and allowed to cool does not immediately return to its original volume.   It is in some degree plastic, and after it has been highly heated or strained a process of gradual recovery goes on for a long time afterwards.   For this reason the reading of a thermometer depends not only on its actual temperature but also to some extent on the previous history of the glass.   After a thermometer has been filled and sealed the capacity of the bulb gradually diminishes to a slight extent and its zero rises, rather rapidly at first, and then very slowly for years afterwards.[1]   By properly annealing the tubes and storing them for several years before dividing them, this defect may be very largely if not entirely got rid of; and it can in any but a very new thermometer be easily allowed for in reducing observations.   This change of zero, be it noticed, is believed to occur, however uniform be the temperature at which the thermometer is kept.[2] A delicate thermometer possessed by Dr. Joule[3] was examined at intervals extending over a period of nearly forty years, and showed this gradual rise of the zero.   The change, however, was exceedingly slow in the later years.   Thirteen scale divisions corresponded to 1° F., and the reading of the zero point was found as follows, in scale divisions :—

[1] This gradual change of the zero point was first noticed by Flaugergues, *Ann. de Chimie et de Physique*, vol. xxi. p. 333, 1822.

[2] According to M. L. Marchis, small oscillations in temperature are to a large extent responsible for the gradual approach of thermometer readings to a fixed value (*Journ. de Physique*, tom. vii., 1898).

[3] Joule, *Scientific Papers*, p. 558 ; *Phil. Soc. Manchester*, 22nd February 1870.

Date.	Zero Reading.	Date.	Zero Reading.
April 1844	0	March 1867	11·8
February 1846	5·5	January 1877	12·71
April 1856	9·5	December 1882	13·26

When we expose a thermometer to changes of temperature, a Depression further defect presents itself, which for thermometry of the highest of zero. accuracy is much more troublesome. Within certain limits the increase of volume in glass accompanying rise of temperature from, say, t to t' does not wholly disappear at once when the temperature is rapidly reduced to t. A thermometer taken through such a cycle reads lower on the second exposure to the lower temperature. This phenomenon is conspicuous when we compare ice-readings taken immediately before and after exposure to temperatures between 50° C. and 100° C. ; the *depression of zero*, as it is called, is greater the higher the previous temperature. Exposure for only a minute or two to a high temperature is only partially effective ; but twenty or twenty-five minutes' exposure usually produces practically the full effect. On the other hand, the depression takes a considerable time to disappear ; it is a question of days or even weeks if the high temperature has approached 100° C.

Both the rise and depression of zero just noticed are evidently due to the same cause, a hysteresis in the glass or lag in completely recovering from the expansion produced by heating. In the case of the secular change of zero, the thermometer is gradually recovering from the effect of heating during manufacture. In Dr. Guillaume's work on thermometry, already referred to, this property of glass is called *residual expansion*.[1]

In the more infusible kinds of glass the residual expansion is least and the recovery most rapid. Hitherto at the Bureau International attention has been mainly directed to a standard glass, French *verre dur*, at temperatures between − 30° C. and 100° C. At the Reichsanstalt certain Jena glasses, notably 16^{III} and 59^{III}, have been examined in similar detail. The conclusion reached for these glasses, throughout "Movable at least this range, is that the difficulty can be met by treating a read- zero" ing z_t in ice immediately *after* the measurement of any temperature t reading. as the zero of the thermometer for the preceding observation. This is equivalent to the conclusion that the residual expansion, whose existence is made manifest by the depression of zero, remains practically

---

[1] "*Résidus de dilatation.*" See note, p. 111, for reference to Dr. Guillaume's work.

I

unchanged during the brief interval required to observe both t and z_t. If t has been preceded by a higher temperature the residual effect is in reality larger, but it depresses equally the readings t and z_t. The method of a *movable zero* requires that in determining the fundamental interval the boiling point 100° C. be first determined, and that the ice-reading z_{100} be taken immediately after.

" Fixed zero " method.

The ordinary practice in this country proceeds on the hypothesis of a *fixed zero*. In determining the fundamental interval the observation of the ice point precedes that of the boiling point ; and in ordinary use the observed departure from 0° C. in a preliminary observation in ice is applied as a constant correction at all points of the scale. The relative merits of the movable zero and fixed zero methods will be discussed later on.

81. Lag of Thermometer.—Another source of error is the fact that thermometers require a sensible time to follow a change of temperature. This lag in a mercury thermometer increases with the mass of the mercury and the thickness of the glass. It also depends on the nature of the surrounding medium. A clinical thermometer, for instance, initially at 15° C., will rise to the temperature of the body faster in a moist than in a dry mouth, and much faster in a well-stirred bucket of water than in either. In still air, where temperature is altering rapidly, two adjacent thermometers of different sluggishness may differ by degrees.

Determination of lag.

If the medium in which the thermometer is immersed preserves a uniform temperature, the thermometer will soon attain that temperature, and no correction is necessary. Let the time be measured along a straight line AB (Fig. 17), and let the ordinates represent differences of temperature between the thermometer and the medium. Then if the instrument is plunged in a fluid warmer than itself whose temperature is kept constant, its rise of temperature will be represented by a curve PQ. At Q the difference of temperature has become too small to observe. When the reading of the thermometer ceases to vary, the temperature indicated will be that of the medium.

The most frequent case which occurs in the laboratory is that of a medium whose temperature varies in some continuous manner. In such a case we may apply a correction as follows. Suppose that the temperature is gradually rising. Let the curve DE (Fig. 18) represent the rise of temperature as indicated by the thermometer. Then, owing to lag, the actual temperature of the medium will be somewhat greater

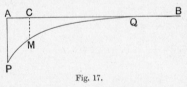

Fig. 17.

at every point.   Let another experiment be made, in which the thermometer is immersed in a similar medium preserved at a constant temperature by some thermostat arrangement, and let the curve PQ (Fig. 17) be plotted for this experiment.   If we assume that the lag of the thermometer depends, not on the absolute temperature of the surrounding fluid, but only on the rate at which that temperature is changing, we may obtain the actual temperature by finding a point M on PQ, where the slope of the curve is the same as that of the curve DE at any point N (Fig. 18).   Since the slope of the curve measures the rate of change of temperature and therefore the amount of lag,

the lag at N is the same as at M, and thus by adding an amount NF = MC to the ordinate at N, we find a point F giving the actual temperature of the medium. Continuing this process for a succession of points, we get a curve representing the corrected temperatures.

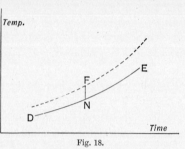

Fig. 18.

If T denote time, t the thermometer reading, and τ the temperature of its surroundings, the formula usually advanced to represent the phenomena is—

$$\frac{dt}{d\mathrm{T}} + \lambda \, (t - \tau) = 0,$$

where λ is a constant.   The solution of this differential equation

$$t = \tau + (t_o - \tau) \, e^{-\lambda \mathrm{T}},$$

where t_o is the value of t when T = 0.   The value of λ is determined by observing the lag when the temperature of the surroundings is kept constant, as just described.   The mean of a number of determinations should be taken.

82. Pressure Coefficients.—The application of increased pressure to the outside of a thermometer, whether through rise of barometric pressure or immersion in a liquid, compresses the glass and reduces its internal volume.   This makes the mercury rise in the stem, and, supposing the increase in pressure uniform over the outer glass surface, the rise bears to the increase in pressure a constant ratio, known as the *external pressure coefficient*.   The unit of pressure usually employed is that of a millimetre column of mercury at 0° C., the rise in the stem being measured in degrees.   Knowing the external pressure coefficient, one can calculate the correction necessary to reduce the readings taken with the thermometer under any known external pressure to what they would have been under the standard pressure.

External pressure coefficient

Again, when the horizontal position is adopted as the standard
one, as is done at the Bureau International and the Reichsanstalt, a
correction is necessary when the thermometer is read in the vertical
position, to allow for the influence of increased internal pressure. This
pressure expands the bulb and compresses its contents, both effects
contributing to lower the reading. If we treat the internal pressure
as uniformly distributed and proportional to the length of the mercury
column measured from the centre of the bulb, we can, by observing
the difference in the readings of a thermometer when vertical and
when horizontal at any one temperature, calculate an *internal pressure
coefficient*. This may conveniently be the ratio of the observed rise of
reading in degrees—when the thermometer is transferred from the
vertical to the horizontal position—to the length of the mercury column
measured in millimetres. Knowing the internal pressure coefficient,
we can calculate a table giving the correction for internal pressure to
be applied to any reading taken with the thermometer vertical.

Applying the mathematical theory of elasticity, Guillaume has
deduced a very simple relation between the external and internal
pressure coefficients, measured of course in the same units. Calling
these coefficients β_e and β_i respectively, this relation may be written

$$\beta_i - \beta_e = c,$$

where c is proportional to the difference between the compressibility of
mercury and that of the particular glass of which the thermometer is
made. Thus in all thermometers of the same glass $\beta_i - \beta_e$ should be
constant. Taking the units recommended above, viz. rise of 1° C. in
reading and 1 mm. of mercury pressure, the results deduced at the
Bureau International [1] and the Reichsanstalt [2] are as follows :—

Glass.	$\beta_i - \beta_e$.
Verre dur	·0000154
Jena glass 16[III]	·0000143
,, ,, 59[III]	·0000138

The proof of the foregoing relation as given by Guillaume is not
quite satisfactory. A rigid mathematical demonstration has, however,
been given by C. Chree,[3] who shows that the relation is exact
under two restrictions—absolute homogeneity in the glass, and uniformity in the distribution of the external and internal pressures over
their respective surfaces, inclusive of bulb, stem, and any auxiliary
chambers. These conditions are sufficiently nearly realised in practice.

In determining β_e the thermometer, immersed in a liquid, is
exposed to various air pressures, from an atmosphere downwards.

[1] *Thermométrie*, pp. 102, 103.
[2] *Wiss. Abhandl.* vol. i. p. 70, 1894.
[3] *Phil. Mag.*, Oct. 1894.

The fact that the changes of pressure tend to affect the temperature of the liquid is pointed out in the publication of the Reichsanstalt,[1] and it is apparently recommended that water—preferably near 4° C.—should be used rather than glycerine or mercury.[2]

Observations of the thermometer alternately in the vertical and horizontal positions, at any convenient temperature, supply the means of calculating β_i. There is some uncertainty, however, due to capillarity and the unsymmetrical shape of the meniscus in the horizontal position. On this account Guillaume recommends that it be deduced from the observed value of β_e by means of the theoretical relation between the two coefficients.

By adopting the vertical as the standard position, the practice followed at the National Physical Laboratory, the necessity for an internal pressure correction can usually be avoided, at least for accuracy of the order 0°·01 C. When the stem is vertical the reduction of the reading, like its two contributory causes, expansion of the bulb and compression of the mercury, is proportional, at least as a first approximation, to the length of the mercury column measured from the middle of the bulb; but in an ordinary thermometer increment of stem-length is sufficiently nearly proportional to increment of reading. Hence at any temperature t the depression due to internal pressure is, in stem divisions, $q + \dfrac{t}{p}$, where p and q are constants for the thermometer.

Thus to make a Bureau International thermometer register correctly in the vertical position, we need only lower the freezing point mark q divisions below the point answering to a horizontal reading, and shorten each degree division by $\dfrac{1}{p}$ of itself. This obviously comes to the same thing as marking the freezing and boiling points with the thermometer vertical and subdividing the fundamental interval in the usual way.

Under ordinary conditions the external pressure correction is of trifling importance compared with the internal pressure correction. But if the thermometer is immersed in a heavy liquid such as mercury, or in a gas under pressure differing appreciably from that of the atmosphere, the correction may be of the order 0°·01 C.

83. Error due to Capillarity.—The attraction of the mercury particles for each other, which gives rise to the phenomenon of surface tension, and which manifests itself by the curved meniscus at the free

---

[1] *Wiss. Abhandl.* vol. ii., 1895, pp. 7, 8.

[2] See Lord Kelvin's *Math. and Phys. Papers*, vol. iii. pp. 236-239. Also Joule, *Phil. Trans.*, 1859, pp. 133-136. The temperature of water at 4° C. is not altered by a moderate change of pressure.

end of the column, serves a useful purpose in ensuring the return of the liquid into the bulb when the temperature is falling. The surface tension of mercury undergoes a slight regular diminution with rise of temperature. If the pressure due to surface tension varied with the same regularity, no correction would be required on account of it, as the same conditions exist when the fixed points of the thermometer are being determined. Several causes, however, contribute in producing irregular changes in the internal pressure, and thus lead, in the indications of delicate thermometers, to variations of which it is very difficult to take account, and which, more perhaps than any other phenomenon, assign the limit of precision which it is possible to attain with the mercury thermometer.

Effect of change in bore. Differences in the diameter of the tube at different points are an important cause of variation in the interior pressure. In calibrating a thermometer measurements are made of the bore at successive parts of the stem, but as these only give the mean value of the bore over a short length of tube, they are not much affected by considerable irregularities extending over very short portions only.

Attraction of mercury and glass. Further, owing to the capillary attraction which exists between mercury and glass, the angle of contact between the liquid and the sides of the tube depends on whether the temperature is rising or falling. If, for instance, the temperature is falling, the free surface is flatter than if it were rising, and if a feeble rise of temperature should take place, the first effect would be an increased curvature of the meniscus, and the resulting increase of internal pressure might expand the bulb sufficiently to allow for the expansion of the mercury without any rise in the stem. A rising column will always read somewhat lower than a falling one at the same temperature.

The angle of contact is also somewhat affected by slight changes in the nature of the interior surface of the glass, such as would be caused by the stem having been strongly heated at any point.

To correct for errors due to such variations in the bore as are detected during calibration, Guillaume employs the formula

$$p = \frac{c}{r},$$

where p is the capillary pressure, r the radius of the tube, and c a constant whose value he finds to be 32·4 in milligrammes per millimetre.

As the rise of the mercury in the stem is less disturbed by the capillary attraction of the glass than its fall, the best practice is to arrange, if possible, to make all readings with a rising column.

84. Emergent Column.—Elementary theory assumes all the glass and mercury of a thermometer to be at one temperature. Even in well-stirred baths in physical laboratories this is rather an ideal state of matters. In ordinary use there is often an appreciable, sometimes a long, mercury column exposed to a temperature differing from that of the bulb. This is especially true of thermometers employed to measure the temperature of a liquid which is largely in excess of that of the surrounding air. In such a case, if a long mercury column be emergent, the thermometer, if correct, will read considerably below the true temperature of the liquid. An approximate correction may be obtained by supposing the immersed part of the thermometer to be unaffected by the existence of the emergent part, and assuming the whole emergent part, glass and mercury, to be at one temperature.

Let the liquid reach to the division t_1 on the stem (Fig. 19), let t be the temperature read, t' the temperature assigned to the emergent column, x the required correction, v_o the volume at $0°$ C. of one stem-division, and m and g the coefficients of expansion[1] of mercury and glass.

The volume of the emergent mercury is

$$v_0(t - t_1)(1 + gt')$$

and its temperature is t'. If its temperature were raised to t, its volume would become

$$v_0(t - t_1)(1 + gt') \cdot \frac{1 + mt}{1 + mt'},$$

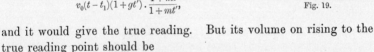

Fig. 19.

and it would give the true reading. But its volume on rising to the true reading point should be

$$v_0(t + x - t_1)(1 + gt),$$

therefore

$$v_0(t - t_1)(1 + gt')\frac{1 + mt}{1 + mt'} = v_0(t + x - t_1)(1 + gt)$$

whence

$$x = e(t - t_1)(t - t'),$$

where

$$e = \frac{m - g}{(1 + gt)(1 + mt')}$$

$$= m - g \quad \text{approximately};$$

so that e is approximately the reciprocal of the number of degree

[1] See next chapter, secs. i. and ii.

volumes included in the bulb up to the zero mark. It is a constant for any particular kind of glass, and in all ordinary kinds of glass it is a little less than 1/6000. Knowing the glass, we should at once know the correction, provided we knew t'.

In reality, of course, the emergent column varies in temperature from base to summit, so that t' must be regarded as its mean temperature. To determine t' directly, the Reichsanstalt employs a *Faden-thermometer* (see Fig. 19), placed apparently with its very elongated bulb closely adjacent to the emergent column. Taking the reading of this auxiliary thermometer for t', and replacing e by 1/6100, they claim to obtain with thermometers of Jena glass 59^{III} corrected temperature-readings which are consistent to 0°·1 C. even up to 500° C. This practice of the Reichsanstalt seems a development of an idea which originated with Regnault.

Dr. Chree has obtained good results by employing the formula

$$x = \mathrm{C}(t - t_1)(t - t')$$

of the same type as the last, but where t' denotes the temperature of the room. For experiments conducted under similar conditions C is a constant for any particular thermometer, but varies from one instrument to another. It is determined experimentally for each instrument.

85. Calibration of the Tube.—If it is agreed to measure equal increments of temperature by equal increments of the volume of some chosen substance contained in a glass envelope, it will be necessary to divide the stem of the thermometer into parts of equal capacity. Thermometer tubes are drawn and not bored, so that inequalities generally exist in the diameter of the capillary bore, and equal lengths will not have equal capacities from part to part of the tube. To test this a thread of about 20 or 30 mm. of mercury is placed in the tube and moved from part to part of its length. This may be conveniently effected by gently blowing into a piece of india-rubber tubing fastened to one end of the tube. In each position there will be slight variations found in the length of the thread as it is moved from place to place, but if any considerable variation is detected the tube should be rejected and one of more uniform bore sought. In order to measure equal rises of temperature by equal increments of volume, it is necessary to know the capacity, or volume per unit length, of the stem, in terms of its capacity at some selected part. The process of effecting this is termed *calibration*.

In the French and German standard thermometers the stem is divided into equal lengths, not equal volumes. English standard thermometers, on the other hand, are calibrated before they are subdivided, and the calibration results are used to guide one in dividing the stem into equal volumes, not equal lengths.[1]

86. Determination of Fixed Points.—In the determination of the freezing point Dr. Guillaume finds good lake ice or freshly-fallen snow moistened with distilled water best. The temperature in the centre of large blocks of artificial ice is apt to be somewhat below 0° C. The determination should be made rapidly, especially in the case of thermometers intended for high temperatures, so as not to aggravate the secular rise of zero. This remark does not, however, apply to English thermometers used according to the fixed zero method.

Variations in external pressure alter the melting point of ice, but the changes are very small, an increase of one atmosphere lowering the melting point by about 0°·0075 C. The effect of external pressure in altering the volume of the glass is more considerable. Care is required that no external pressure effect is produced by too tight packing of the ice, or by allowing the bulb to rest unsupported on large ice crystals.

In determining the boiling point it is highly important that the atmospheric pressure should be determined with the greatest possible accuracy. On account of the lag of a barometer, and possibly the lag of steam in adjusting its temperature as the pressure changes, it is important that determinations of boiling points should be made at times of steady barometric pressure.

For reasons already pointed out in Art. 80, the boiling point is determined before the freezing point on the Continent. In English thermometers the freezing point is first found. *Order of determination.*

87. Comparison of Thermometric Methods.[2]—It remains for us to consider briefly the relative defects and advantages of the ordinary British methods of thermometry and the more refined methods of the Bureau International. In favour of the latter is the strong argument that when a *verre dur* thermometer verified at the Bureau International is used in a carefully prescribed way, one can deduce the corresponding temperature on the scale of the hydrogen thermometer (at least throughout the range – 20° C. to 100° C.) to a very high degree of accuracy. In a physical laboratory the probable error may be as small as ± 0°·002 C. or even ± 0°·001 C.

On the other hand, it must be conceded that the existence of lengthy tables is an evil, however necessary, both on account of the

---

[1] An account of methods of calibration of thermometer tubes will be found in the first edition of this book. It is, however, unnecessary to consider them, as the correct graduation of a liquid-in-glass thermometer depends ultimately on comparison with a standard hydrogen thermometer, either directly or through the intermediary of another thermometer.

[2] C. Chree, *Phil. Mag.*, April 1898.

very appreciable labour their application entails, and on account of the large increase their calculation makes to the prime cost of the instrument.   The fact that for high accuracy an ice-reading is desirable after every temperature observation is also a drawback.   Very considerable skill is required when the preceding temperature is high, the risk of breaking the thermometer being appreciable; and the frequent preparation of ice is both troublesome and expensive.   The conditions under which it is safe to dispense with an ice observation and use the Bureau's table of depressed freezing points for *verre dur* are somewhat uncertain.

In favour of the customary methods of using English glass thermometers there are certain advantages.   The necessity for an internal pressure correction, as we have seen, is avoided by adopting the vertical as the standard position.   The actual readings of a correctly divided thermometer, after allowance is made for any secular change of zero, are likely to give at ordinary atmospheric temperatures—where nearly all very exact absolute measurements are made—results agreeing with those of the hydrogen thermometer to within $0°\cdot1$ C.   To those physicists and chemists who are accustomed to record temperatures to $0°\cdot001$ C., or even $0°\cdot0001$ C., this may seem a paltry claim; but it does not seem so to many scientific men, whose interests extend beyond the temperature of the thermometer to that of its surroundings.

On the other hand, there unquestionably exist physical and chemical investigations, tending to increase in number, in which the absolute determination of temperatures with the highest possible precision is of fundamental importance.   For these, in the meantime, English glass thermometers and ordinary British methods are not suitable.   However good the workmanship, and however accurate the calibration, there exist the following defects :—

1. Ice-readings corresponding to infinitely prolonged exposure to $0°$ C. are not practically obtainable; and ordinary ice-readings, being affected to some extent by the previous temperature, are not strictly comparable.

2. So long as changes of $3\frac{1}{2}$ inches of mercury in barometric pressure are possible, and occasions arise for the immersion of thermometers in heavy liquids, corrections for external pressure cannot always be avoided.

3. Unless frequently subjected to temperature-cycles of considerable range, an ordinary English glass thermometer is apt to be influenced for days, it may be weeks, by exposure to any temperature much over $120°$ F.

4. For accuracy of a higher order than $0°\cdot1$ F., it is certainly

unsafe to assume the natural scale of an English glass thermometer identical with that of the hydrogen or nitrogen thermometer, even for the restricted range 22° F. to 212° F.

5. Whether through variety in the constitution of the glass, or differences in its treatment, the natural scales of ordinary English glass thermometers do not appear sufficiently accordant to render practicable the use of any general table of reductions to a standard scale of temperature.

Most of these sources of error would be greatly reduced if it were found possible to construct thermometers of fused quartz instead of glass, since this material, besides being a perfectly definite chemical compound, has a very small coefficient of expansion and experiences very small zero changes, and can be safely exposed to sudden changes of temperature. The difficulties of manufacture have not yet been overcome.

SECTION II

GAS AND VAPOUR-PRESSURE THERMOMETERS

88. Gas Thermometers.—The indications of mercury thermometers are complicated by the effects due to changes in the volume of the glass envelope, which depend not only on the temperature, but also on the previous history of the glass. The influence of the nature of the glass on the indications of the instrument will become less and less the greater the coefficient of expansion of the contained liquid. In this respect thermometers filled with highly expansive organic liquids will be superior to those filled with mercury, and air or permanent gas thermometers will be superior to the most accurate liquid thermometers. The permanent gases expand about twenty times as much as mercury for the same change of temperature, and as a consequence the errors arising from inequalities in the expansion of glass produce much less effect. Gases also possess a very low specific gravity, and can be obtained of the same purity in any part of the world. Their properties are in addition permanent, and they expand nearly equally under the same conditions, so that thermometers filled with different permanent gases all agree very closely amongst themselves.

No two solids or liquids, on the other hand, can be found which will agree throughout the scale, and in absence of any other reason for choosing a permanent gas as the standard thermometric substance, the close agreement of so many different substances throughout such a wide range of temperature attaches great practical importance to the scale of temperature furnished by their expansion. The permanent gases besides, when not subjected to too great pressure, maintain their state and behave in the same manner (at least very approximately) at very high as well as very low temperatures. They consequently furnish a scale of measurement which is continuous and embraces a very wide range of temperature.

The uniformity of composition of the atmosphere all over the world has led to the employment of air, as a permanent gas, for

124

thermometric purposes. Precautions of the strictest character are, however, taken to remove all moisture and other variable impurities, such as carbonic acid, from any sample used in a thermometer. This is effected by passing the air through a system of tubes containing calcium chloride, pumice-stone moistened with sulphuric acid, caustic soda, and phosphoric anhydride, to absorb the aqueous vapour and to take up any carbonic acid gas which may be present. The removal of moisture is of prime importance, as a small quantity of aqueous vapour, although of small influence at low temperatures, might have a very serious effect on the indications of the instrument when the temperature becomes high. On this account the bulb is filled (and emptied) several times with perfectly dry air, and at the same time heated to a high temperature to expel all moisture which may be condensed on the interior surface or lurking in the minute crevices or pores of the glass. When every precaution has been taken to thoroughly dry the interior of the bulb, it is finally filled at 0° C. with pure dry air, or other gas as desired.[1]

The instrument may now be used to measure temperature in two ways—(1) by change of volume while the pressure is kept constant; (2) by change of pressure while the volume is kept constant. Regnault used both methods, but found that in practice he could only arrange the apparatus to give good results with the second method, and on it he founded what he called the "normal air thermometer." For the sake of perfect definiteness he chose as the density of the air in his normal thermometer the density of air at the melting point of ice and under a pressure of one standard atmosphere, and he marked the freezing and boiling points 0° and 100° in accordance with the centigrade scale. We shall now prove that the second method agrees with the first in the case of a substance which obeys Boyle's law.

Constant pressure or constant volume.

89. Characteristic Equation of a Thermometric Substance obeying Boyle's Law—The Perfect Gas Law.—Boyle's law states that the product of the pressure and volume of a given mass of gas is constant when the temperature is constant. The characteristic

---

[1] A gas should be chosen which does not attack the other materials used in the construction of the instrument. Pure oxygen is objectionable on this account, as it attacks the mercury employed to measure the pressure of the gas. A film of oxide is formed on the surface of the mercury, and this is not only detrimental to the free motion of the mercury in the tube, but the whole quantity of oxygen in the bulb becomes diminished, and the readings of the instrument are influenced accordingly. For this reason hydrogen and nitrogen are preferable to air. Regnault, however, does not appear to have experienced any ill effect in this direction from the use of air in his normal air thermometer, but he found great irregularities with pure oxygen (*Expériences*, tom. i. p. 77).

equation of a substance which obeys Boyle's law exactly is therefore

$$pv = f(\Theta),$$

where p is the pressure, v the volume of unit mass, and Θ the temperature measured on any scale. If now, using the substance in question in a thermometer, we define temperature by the equation

$$\frac{\Theta}{\Theta_0} = \frac{pv}{p_0 v_0} \qquad \cdot \qquad \cdot \qquad \cdot \qquad \cdot \qquad \cdot \qquad (1)$$

where p_0 is standard pressure, Θ_0 the temperature of melting ice, and v_0 the corresponding volume of unit mass, then the temperature indicated by such an instrument will be the same, whether we use it as a constant pressure thermometer, keeping the pressure always at p_0, or whether we use it as a constant volume thermometer, keeping the volume always equal to v_0. For in the former case we shall have

$$\frac{\Theta}{\Theta_0} = \frac{v}{v_0},$$

and in the latter we shall have

$$\frac{\Theta}{\Theta_0} = \frac{p}{p_0}.$$

We may assign any positive value we please to Θ_0, but the most convenient course to adopt will be to make the interval between the boiling point of water and the melting point of ice exactly 100 degrees. Representing the boiling point by Θ_{100} and putting

$$\Theta_{100} - \Theta_0 = 100$$

we have, from (1),

$$\frac{\Theta_{100}}{\Theta_0} = \frac{p_{100} v_{100}}{p_0 v_0},$$

so that

$$\frac{100}{\Theta_0} = \frac{p_{100} v_{100} - p_0 v_0}{p_0 v_0}.$$

The value to be assigned to Θ_0 is therefore no longer arbitrary, but is to be determined by experiment from the last equation.

Boyle's law is not exactly obeyed by any actual gas, but all the more permanent gases—air, hydrogen, nitrogen, etc.—exhibit only very small deviations from the law over a wide range of temperature, provided that the pressures applied are not very great. The scales of temperature determined (in the manner just described) by thermometers filled with such gases are closely accordant, and lead to values of Θ_0 which are all very nearly $273°$ (Arts. 121, 122, 247).

Perfect
gas law.

If we put $R = p_0 v_0 / \Theta_0$ in (1), we get

$$pv = R\Theta,$$

where R is a constant, and this is therefore the characteristic equation of a substance which obeys Boyle's law and which is itself employed as the standard thermometric substance.   This formula is usually referred to as the "perfect gas law."   A perfect gas is an ideal substance which obeys this law and possesses certain other properties as well.   In particlar, we shall see later that if, in addition, the ratio of the specific heats (at constant pressure and constant volume respectively) is a constant, then the temperature scale of the perfect gas thermometer is identical with the absolute scale referred to in Art. 79 (see Chap. VIII. sec. viii.).   It will be noticed that if the pressure is kept constant the volume of the gas vanishes at the zero of the scale, thus suggesting that there exists an absolute zero of temperature at about $-273°$ C. below which the temperature of a body cannot fall.   All experimental work at very low temperatures accords with this view, the lowest temperature yet obtained—by the evaporation of liquid helium at a very low pressure—being slightly below $-272°$ C.

90. Constant Volume and Constant Pressure Air Thermometers. —The great objection to a constant pressure air thermometer lies in the temperature correction which must be applied to that part of the air which occupies the stem of the instrument.   This correction will always be necessary, unless the bulb and all that part of the stem occupied by air are immersed in the same bath, and its influence will manifestly be more and more important as the temperature rises, and as more and more air is expelled from the bulb into the stem, so that the mass of air contained in the stem becomes comparable with that enclosed by the bulb.   For this reason it is almost impossible to work with a constant pressure air thermometer, and after repeated trial Regnault found that he could only obtain consistent results with gas thermometers when they were arranged so that the gas was kept at constant volume, and the temperature was measured by the variation of the pressure.

The form of apparatus adopted by Regnault is shown side and front view in Fig. 20.   The bulb A, which has a capacity of from 600 to 800 c.c., is filled with pure dry air (or other permanent gas), and is connected to a manometric tube FGHIJ.   When the temperature varies mercury is poured into the branch IJ, or allowed to escape through the tap K, so that the level [1] of the mercury in the branch FG is kept always at a fixed mark a.   If the glass were non-expansive

[1] The pouring of mercury into the tube IJ may be conveniently avoided by forming a reservoir at K, and furnishing it with a screw plunger.   By screwing the plunger forwards or backwards the level of the mercury may be adjusted as desired.

the volume of the air would thus be kept always the same, but on account of the expansion of the glass a corresponding correction becomes necessary. The difference of level between the surfaces α and β in the two arms may be measured by means of a cathetometer, and the corresponding pressure of the air in the bulb deduced.

If it is desired to work under constant pressure the difference of level between the surfaces α and β must be kept constant ; conse-

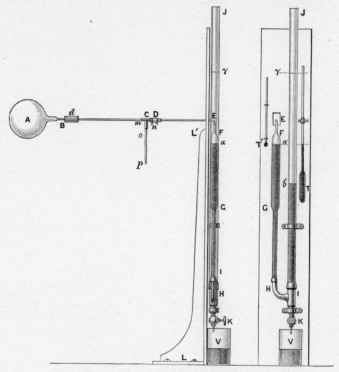

Fig. 20.—Regnault's Constant Volume Air Thermometer.

quently when the temperature rises the air expands into the tube FG and the volume and temperature of this expelled portion must be accurately determined. For this purpose the arm FG is accurately calibrated and immersed in a bath, as shown in Fig. 21, so that its temperature may be maintained uniform.

A convenient form of constant volume air thermometer has been devised by Professor Jolly,[1] and is represented in Fig. 22. The capillary stem is bent twice at right angles, and united at B to a tube of larger bore, on which a fixed mark is placed near the junction of

[1] Jolly, *Pogg. Jubelband*, p. 82, 1874.

the capillary.   In all measurements the level of the mercury contained
in BD is brought to this fixed mark, so that the volume of the air
in the bulb and stem is constant if we neglect changes of volume
of the glass envelope.   CE is a glass tube, preferably of the same
diameter as B, to avoid difference of capillary pressure influencing the
results.   If, however, the diameters of the tubes be fairly large this
effect will be negligible, and the tube CE may be replaced by a

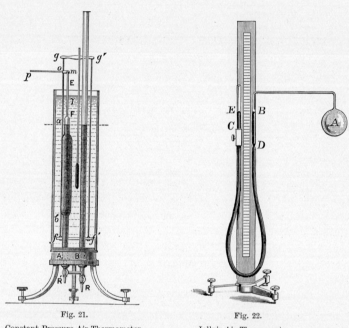

Fig. 21.

Constant Pressure Air Thermometer.

Fig. 22.

Jolly's Air Thermometer.

spherical bulb.   The tubes B and C are joined by an india-rubber
tube, which is strong and flexible, and allows CE to be raised or
lowered so as to keep the level of the mercury at B.   The difference
of level of the mercury at E and B, added to the barometric height,
gives the pressure of the air in the thermometer.   This difference of
level may be obtained by means of a cathetometer, but for ordinary
work a scale attached to the frame on which the instrument is
mounted suffices.   The scale is engraved on the back of a strip of
plane mirror before it is silvered, and the divisions are carried
sufficiently far across the scale for the reflections of the two surfaces
of mercury to be seen behind the scale.   Parallax is thus avoided,
and the use of the cathetometer dispensed with.

Assuming the internal volume of the thermometer to remain

K

constant, and that the temperature of the air throughout is the same, we have for any two temperatures Θ_0 and Θ_1

$$p_0 v = R\Theta_0, \qquad \text{and } p_1 v = R\Theta_1.$$

Therefore

$$\frac{p_1}{p_0} = \frac{\Theta_1}{\Theta_0}.$$

If such an instrument be graduated so that the boiling point is denoted by $100°$, and the freezing point by $0°$, then

$$100 = \Theta_{100} - \Theta_0 = \frac{v}{R}(p_{100} - p_0).$$

According to the most accurate observations of Regnault

$$p_{100} = 1 \cdot 3665 p_0,$$

and therefore

$$\frac{v}{R} = \frac{100}{0 \cdot 3665 p_0} = \frac{272 \cdot 85}{p_0}.$$

Consequently, any temperature θ on this scale will be given by the formula

$$\theta = \Theta - \Theta_0 = \frac{v}{R}(p - p_0) = 272 \cdot 85 \left(\frac{p}{p_0} - 1 \right).$$

In general, however, the volume of the glass envelope will vary, and the temperature of the air in the stem will differ from that in the bulb, and corrections will be necessary in both respects. These corrections will be considered more fully in connection with the general problem of dilatation. The source of greatest uncertainty in gas thermometers lies in the allowance for the expansion of the glass. This requires the careful examination of the volume of the bulb and tube throughout the whole range of temperature for which the instrument is to be employed. The volume of any such apparatus is most accurately determined by observing the weight of mercury which it contains at different temperatures, and when the variation of the density of mercury with temperature is known the volume can be immediately determined. This, in fact, was the process adopted by Regnault.

Jolly's constant volume air thermometer is a convenient form, and fairly accurate for moderate temperatures. At high temperatures, however, a correction becomes necessary on account of the air expelled from the bulb into the capillary tube. If the temperature of the bulb were always the same as that of the tube, the mass of gas contained in the tube would be constant; but as the tube is colder than the bulb, at high temperatures the pressure will be largely increased, and a corresponding increase will take place in the mass of gas contained in the tube.

The pyrometer of Deville and Troost[1] is a modified form of air

---

[1] Deville and Troost, *Ann. de Chimie et de Physique*, 3e série, tom. lviii. p. 257, 1860.

thermometer furnished with a porcelain bulb.   A glass bulb cannot
be used for high temperatures on account of the fusion of the glass,
and platinum bulbs were found by Deville and Troost to be perme-
able to gases at high temperatures.   The porcelain bulb is filled with
dry air and placed in the furnace, and when equilibrium of temperature is attained the stem is sealed by an oxyhydrogen flame.   The
apparatus is then allowed to cool and the end of the stem is nipped
off under mercury, so that the mercury rises into the bulb.   The bulb
is then depressed until the mercury stands at the same level within
and without.   The stem is now closed with wax, and the apparatus
removed and weighed, with the mercury it contains.   It is afterwards
completely filled with mercury and weighed again.   By this means
the fraction of the gas which escapes by expansion while in the furnace
is determined, and consequently the whole expansion under constant
pressure is known, and the temperature of the furnace determined.

The pressure of the residual air instead of its volume may be
determined when it has cooled.   For this purpose the bulb is provided with a long fine neck and a tap, which communicates with a
manometer.   This tap is left open while the bulb is in the furnace,
and is closed when the final temperature is reached.   The bulb is then
allowed to cool, and the residual pressure determined by connecting
it with the manometer.

To complete the accuracy of this instrument, it is necessary to
know the coefficient of expansion of porcelain, and any uncertainty in
the value of this coefficient will limit the accuracy of the indications
of the instrument.   All uncertainty from this cause disappears in a
vapour-pressure thermometer, in which it is the pressure alone that is
to be measured, and not the volume or the pressure under any given
volume.

An objection to all forms of constant volume thermometers exists
in the pressure of the gas on the internal surface of the bulb, and this
becomes more serious at high temperatures.

91. Callendar's compensated Air Thermometer. — The great
practical difficulties attending the use of the constant pressure air
thermometer have been overcome in the form of apparatus devised
by Professor Callendar.[1]   In this instrument the pressure of the
air enclosed in the thermometer bulb T (Fig. 23), instead of being
adjusted to equality with the pressure of the atmosphere, is maintained
constantly at the same standard pressure as that of the air in another
bulb S kept at a constant temperature in melting ice, the equality of
the pressures in T and S being indicated by a sulphuric acid gauge

[1] H. L. Callendar, *Proc. Roy. Soc.* vol. l. p. 247, 1891.

G. By this means the trouble of reading the barometer is completely avoided, and by a most ingenious device the errors arising from the uncertainty of the temperature of the connecting tubes are compensated for and entirely eliminated. When the temperature of the thermometer bulb T rises, the air expands and passes through the narrow connecting tube into the mercury reservoir M. The quantity of mercury in M is adjusted, so that the pressure in T is equal to that in S, any difference of pressure being indicated by the sulphuric acid gauge G, which connects S and T. The bulb S being kept in ice the pressure of the air within it remains constant, and when the

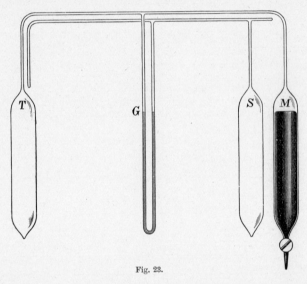

Fig. 23.

gauge shows that equality of pressure exists between T and S, it is certain that the pressure in T is always adjusted to the same value.

The correction for the capacity of the tube joining T and M is eliminated by attaching to S an exactly similar tube (as shown in figure), which has the same form and capacity, and which is placed close to it, so that the two have the same mean temperature throughout. By this means the compensation is rendered automatic, and will be perfect if (1) the two sets of connecting tubes have the same capacity, and are at the same mean temperature; (2) if the mass of air in the standard pressure bulb S is equal to that in the thermometer bulb T and the mercury bulb M combined; (3) if the pressures in T and S are adjusted to equality.

Thus if m be the total mass of air in T and M and the connecting tube and p its pressure, and if Θ be the temperature of T on the scale of the air thermometer and v its volume, while Θ_1 and v_1, Θ_2 and v_2 are the corresponding quantities for the connecting tube and the air space in the bulb M respectively, we have by the law of Charles

$$p\left(\frac{v}{\Theta}+\frac{v_1}{\Theta_1}+\frac{v_2}{\Theta_2}\right)=m\mathrm{R},$$

where R is a constant. In the same manner, if v' denotes the volume of S and v_1' the volume of the tubes attached, m' the total mass of air contained, p' the pressure, and Θ' and Θ_1' the corresponding temperatures, we have for this system

$$p'\left(\frac{v'}{\Theta'}+\frac{v_1'}{\Theta_1'}\right)=m'\mathrm{R},$$

so that if $m = m'$, and $p = p'$, and if the temperatures Θ_1 and Θ_1' and the volumes v_1 and v_1' of the two sets of connecting tubes are the same, we have

$$\frac{v}{\Theta}+\frac{v_2}{\Theta_2}=\frac{v'}{\Theta'}.$$

If M and S are both kept in melting ice, we have further $\Theta_2 = \Theta' = \Theta_0$, and hence

$$\Theta=\Theta_0\frac{v}{(v'-v_2)},$$

or writing T, S, M, for the volumes of the air in these bulbs the formula becomes $\Theta = \Theta_0 T/(S - M)$, so that the influence of the connecting tubes is completely eliminated.

The volume of the standard pressure bulb S may also be adjusted at pleasure by means of mercury, and in this manner the pressure may be varied and the behaviour of the gas investigated at high temperatures, and the indications of the instrument reduced to the absolute scale of temperature (Chap. VIII. sec. ii.).

If the volume of the connecting tube is small compared with that of the bulb T, a small difference of pressure will not lead to any serious error, and on account of the compensating tube the connecting tube may be made long and flexible, and the bulb T may be placed at a convenient distance from the indicating apparatus, which is a matter of great convenience in many operations.

For moderate ranges of temperature the auxiliary bulb M may be dispensed with, and the sulphuric acid gauge G may be graduated so as to indicate the difference of temperature between T and S directly. In ordinary use it would be inconvenient to keep the bulb S always at a fixed temperature, and this may be avoided by adjusting the volume of sulphuric acid in the pressure gauge, so that its expansion may compensate for the dilatation of the air in the standard pressure bulb, a compensation which can be effected with sufficient accuracy for

moderate ranges of temperature. Such thermometers, Prof. Callendar
states, are "exceedingly convenient and satisfactory for rough work at
temperatures beyond the range of mercury thermometers. They can
be made to read easily to the tenth of a degree at 450° C., and if
properly compensated their indications are very reliable. Such a
degree of accuracy is amply sufficient for most purposes, and the
absence of all necessity for calculation or correction of the readings
is a very great advantage."

The actual instrument is shown in Fig. 24. C is the compensating
lead and the other letters correspond to those of Fig. 23. In setting
up the instrument, after the bulbs and connecting tubes have been

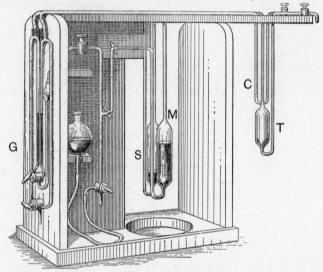

Fig. 24.

calibrated, the masses of gas on the two sides are adjusted as nearly
as possible to equality, which is done with all the bulbs in melting
ice. The bulb T is then heated in steam to determine the fundamental interval. A weight w of mercury is removed from the overflow bulb M to equalise pressures again. Let W be the weight of
mercury required to fill the bulb T at 0° C., and W + δW the weight
of mercury at 0° C., which would fill a volume equal to that of the
bulb in steam. Referring to the last equation on the previous page,
we see that when $\Theta = \Theta_0$, then $v' - v_2 = v$. Now if v becomes $v + \delta v$
in steam (due to the expansion of the glass) and v_2 becomes $v_2 + \Delta v_2$
owing to the removal of mercury, we get

$$\frac{\Theta}{\Theta_0} = \frac{v + \delta v}{v - \Delta v_2} = \frac{W + \delta W}{W - w},$$

so that we have the following equation for determining the coefficient of expansion a or the fundamental zero Θ_0—

$$a\theta = \frac{\theta}{\Theta_0} = \frac{\Theta - \Theta_0}{\Theta_0} = \frac{w + \delta W}{W - w}, \qquad (\theta = 100).$$

Similarly, if θ is any other temperature, and w the corresponding overflow, we get a precisely similar equation to determine θ in terms of Θ_0. The oil-gauge is observed with a cathetometer microscope; no observation of the barometer or any mercury column is required, the only measurement necessary being a weighing which can be made at leisure.[1]

The constant pressure gas thermometer has not hitherto been much used in research. Eumorfopoulos [2] made a determination by its means of the normal boiling point of sulphur, using a thermometer of Jena glass 16^{III}. His result, corrected for the absolute expansion of mercury derived from the experiments of Callendar and Moss, was $444^{\circ}\cdot55$ C.

92. Standard Hydrogen and Nitrogen Thermometers.— The temperature scale adopted as the standard by the International Bureau is defined as the centigrade scale of the constant volume hydrogen thermometer, having as fixed points the temperature of melting ice ($0°$), and that of the vapour of distilled water in ebullition under the normal atmospheric pressure ($100°$); the hydrogen being under a pressure of one metre of mercury when the temperature is $0°$. The improved form of manometer used is represented in Fig. 25. The bulb of the thermometer consists of a cylindrical vessel of iridio-platinum, somewhat over a metre in length and 36 mm. in diameter. It is connected to the manometer by a tube c 1 metre in length and 0·7 mm. in internal diameter.

The pressure to which the gas is subjected consists of the atmospheric pressure, given by the barometer; and an additional pressure due to an open mercury manometer. In general, this would entail four readings of mercury level, but by combining the barometer and manometer, the readings are reduced to two. The manometer is composed of two tubes m, m'. The stem of the barometer B dips into m. The tube m' is made up of two portions which are not in direct communication, but are connected to m above and below respectively. The two parts of m' are separated by a piece of steel P. It will be noticed that the three surfaces of the mercury are all in one vertical line. Their readings are taken by means of three telescopes all sliding on the pillar of a cathetometer (not represented in the figure). In order to find the pressure of the gas the levels

---

[1] *Ency. Brit.* article "Thermometry."
[2] N. Eumorfopoulos, *Proc. Roy. Soc.* lxxxi. p. 339, 1908.

of only the upper and lower surfaces need be read. Four auxiliary thermometers serve to determine the temperature of the apparatus.

Calculation of temperature.

Let V_0 = volume at 0° of the gas in the bulb.

δ = mean coefficient of expansion of the material of the bulb between 0° and T°.

a_p = mean pressure coefficient of the gas between 0° and 100° (Art. 124).

v = volume of the "dead space," *i.e.* connecting tube, etc.

t = temperature of the gas in the dead space.

H_0 = initial pressure of the gas at 0°.

$H_0 + h$ = pressure of the gas at T°, the temperature to be measured.

β_i = coefficient of internal pressure of reservoir.

The mass of the gas in the apparatus when at 0° is (taking the density under standard conditions as unity)

$$\left(V_0 + \frac{v}{1 + a_p t}\right)\frac{H_0}{760},$$

and the same mass, when at T°, is represented by the expression

$$\left\{\frac{V_0(1 + \delta T) + \beta_i h}{1 + a_p T} + \frac{v}{1 + a_p t}\right\}\frac{H_0 + h}{760}.$$

Equating these two, we get

$$V_0 H_0 = \frac{\{V_0(1 + \delta T) + \beta_i h\}(H_0 + h)}{1 + a_p T} + \frac{vh}{1 + a_p t},$$

whence

$$a_p T = \frac{H_0 + h}{H_0}\frac{V_0(1 + \delta T) + \beta_i h}{V_0} + \frac{hv}{H_0 V_0}\frac{1 + a_p T}{1 + a_p t} - 1.$$

By means of this formula we may determine the value of a_p between two known temperatures, 0° and 100° for example, using the method of successive approximations. Having found a_p and substituted its value in the equation,[1] we may use the formula to determine any temperature T.

Corrections have to be made on account of the variations in the volume and temperature of the dead space which occur when the temperature of the bulb is changed. For a complete account of the observations and corrections required, the student is referred to Guillaume's *Thermométrie de précision*.

Instead of using iridio-platinum, the bulb of the thermometer may be made of hard Jena glass or of glazed porcelain.

Nitrogen thermometer for high temperatures.

Up to about 500° C. the hydrogen thermometer is perfectly satisfactory. If, however, the temperature is much above this, hydrogen passes freely through the platinum. The difficulty is not got over by substituting glass or porcelain in the material of the bulb. Glass is not sufficiently refractory to be used at high temperatures. Porcelain is not gas-tight unless glazed, and the glaze begins to melt at 1100° C. At high temperatures both glass and porcelain are acted

[1] Values of a_p for hydrogen and other gases are given in Art. 124.

on to some extent by hydrogen. For these reasons, the nitrogen thermometer is substituted for high temperatures.[1] A porcelain bulb may be used, but a better material is iridio-platinum, both on account of the higher range and because its expansion follows a more regular law than that of porcelain.

According to the experiments of M. Chappuis made with a gas thermometer whose bulb was of Berlin porcelain, the coefficient of expansion of nitrogen diminishes more and more slowly as the temperature rises, approaching a limit at about 75° C., the limiting value being

$$a_{lim} = 0\cdot 00367380.$$

Above 75° C. nitrogen appears to behave as a perfect gas, the coefficient of expansion remaining constant at the above value. Assuming this to be the case, M.

[1] Chappuis, *Phil. Mag.*, Oct. 1900 ; Feb. 1902. Holborn and Day, *Amer. Journ. Science*, Sept. 1899.

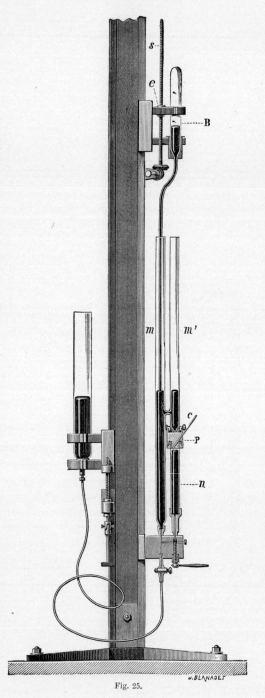

Fig. 25.

Chappuis shows that a nitrogen thermometer whose pressure at 0° C. is 1 metre of mercury is equivalent to one whose pressure at 0° C. is 1·000086 metre, and which behaves as a perfect gas from 0° C. upward, having the foregoing coefficient of expansion. He gives the following corrections to be applied to the readings of the nitrogen thermometer in order to reduce them to the normal hydrogen scale :—

Temp.	H-scale – N-scale Initial press. = 1 metre.
100°	0°·000
200°	0°·023
300°	0°·047
400°	0°·070

These differences are so small that they are of less account than those due to other sources of uncertainty.

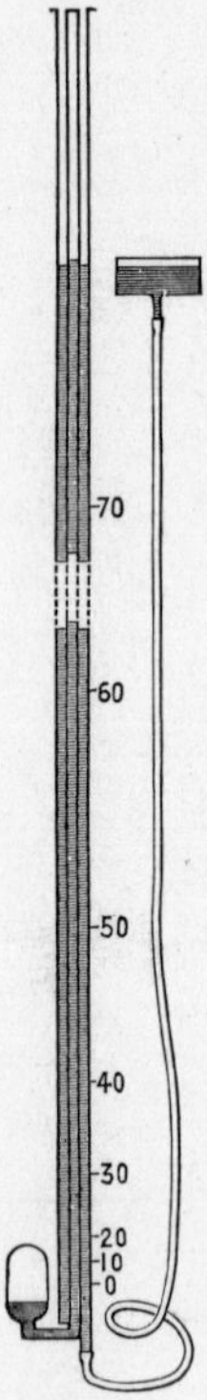

Fig. 26.
Vapour-
pressure
Thermometer.

Holborn and Day used a nitrogen thermometer with a bulb of iridio-platinum (20 per cent iridium, 80 per cent platinum). This could be used up to 1300° C. Nitrogen does not pass through the platinum walls at high temperatures. The bulb was heated by an electric current flowing in a nickel wire coiled round a thin porcelain tube which surrounded the bulb.

Day and Clement,[1] and later Day and Sosman,[2] carried out a series of determinations of melting points with the nitrogen thermometer at high temperatures. In order to obtain accurate results they found it necessary to enclose the furnace in an air-tight iron chamber filled with nitrogen at the same pressure as the gas in the thermometer, thus avoiding strains in the bulb ; they also reduced the volume of the "dead space," and adopted special precautions to ensure as uniform a temperature as possible at all parts of the bulb. Day and Clement used a bulb of iridio-platinum (10 per cent iridium). An objection to this alloy is that iridium is somewhat volatile at high temperatures and contaminates the thermo-elements which are used to compare the temperatures at different parts of the bulb. Day and Sosman substituted a bulb of rhodio-platinum (20 per cent rhodium), which is better, since rhodium is much less volatile than iridium. The observations of the latter experimenters extended up to 1550° C.

93. Vapour-pressure Thermometers.—A system of thermometry in which all delicate measurements of change of volume

---

[1] Day and Clement, *Amer. Journ. Science*, xxvi. p. 405, 1908.
[2] Day and Sosman, *Amer. Journ. Science*, xxix. p. 93, 1910.

are avoided may be founded on the observation of the pressure of a
saturated vapour.   The pressure of a vapour in contact with its own
liquid depends only on the temperature, and is independent of the
relative proportions of liquid and vapour.   If, therefore, the pressure
is observed by some means, and if the data are known which connect
the pressure with the temperature, we are furnished with a thermometric method of great range and delicacy.   A simple form of vapour-
pressure thermometer is shown in Fig. 26.   The bulb is partly filled
with a liquid free from air, and the remainder of the bulb is occupied
by its saturated vapour.   The liquid also partly fills the tube and acts
as a manometer, the pressure of the vapour in the bulb being greater
than the pressure at the upper surface by the weight of the column
of liquid, whose height is equal to the difference of level of the liquid
in the bulb and tube respectively.   If the stem is closed, and
contains only vapour of the liquid above the upper surface, the
pressure will be determined by the temperature of this part of the
apparatus.   For this reason the stem must be jacketed with a bath
kept at some known temperature, say that of melting ice.   The
vapour-pressure in the stem is by this means kept constant, and the
temperature and density of the liquid in the stem are also kept
uniform, as well as the surface tension of the liquid.

The stem may, however, be open at the top, and the pressure
determined by a reading of the barometer, or it may be closed and
contain a gas whose compression registers the pressure, or it may be
connected to any form of pressure gauge.

For high temperatures mercury may be employed as the thermometric substance, and for low temperatures sulphurous acid, but
in all cases the bulb must be made of a material which is not attacked
by the vapour or liquid.   For example, water vapour attacks glass at
elevated temperatures.

The importance of this system of thermometry has been insisted
on by Lord Kelvin,[1] who considered it destined to be of great service,
both in the strictest scientific thermometry as well as in a great
variety of useful applications.   The consideration of the data necessary to the estimation of temperature by this method will be entered
into later on (see Chap. VIII.).

A simple form of vapour-pressure thermometer has been designed
by A. Stock,[2] who claims that it is superior in accuracy to any other
practical type of thermometer, whether mercury, thermo-electric, or
platinum resistance.   It is simple in use, but not readily portable.

---

[1] Art. " Heat," *Ency. Brit.*
[2] A. Stock, *Zeitschr. für Elektrochemie*, vol. 29, p. 354, 1923.

The essential features of the instrument are shown in Fig 27, some constructional details being omitted. The tube on the left is filled with pure mercury and serves as a manometer. The rest of the glass vessel is filled with a pure gas or vapour of volatile liquid. Special precautions must be taken in filling the apparatus with gas, in order

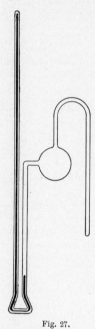

Fig. 27.

to ensure perfect purity, and also to obtain the requisite pressure. By using a series of such thermometers, filled with different gases, any temperature within the range − 200° C. to 25° C. may be measured. The substances employed are carbon bisulphide (25° to − 10°), sulphur dioxide (− 10° to − 40°), ammonia (− 30° to − 77°), carbon dioxide (− 75° to − 100°), hydrochloric acid (− 85° to − 111°), ethylene (− 100° to − 150°), methane (− 150° to − 185°), and oxygen (− 180° to − 200°). At ordinary temperatures the thermometer (except the first of the above) has the long manometer limb completely filled with mercury as in the figure. The limb on the right is dipped into the vessel wherein the temperature is to be determined. When liquefaction of the gas takes place in this limb the mercury sinks in the manometer and the pressure is read off. The temperature corresponding to that pressure is found from a set of tables (given in the paper cited) prepared by comparison of the thermometers with a standard hydrogen thermometer. The constriction in the lower part of the manometer tube is intended to prevent sudden movements of the mercury.

94. Comparison of Thermometers.—Mercury thermometers are compared with the hydrogen thermometer by immersing them in the bath in which the bulb of the latter is heated. A mercury thermometer which agrees with the hydrogen scale at 0° and 100° will not agree with it at intermediate temperatures. With all ordinary kinds of glass the greatest divergence is exhibited at about 40° C. In the case of a thermometer of *verre dur* the maximum difference is rather more than one-tenth of 1° C. For accurate work with a mercury thermometer, if standard temperatures are required, the instrument must be directly compared with the standard hydrogen thermometer and a table of corrections drawn up.

Exercises

1. If the thermometric substance obeys Boyle's law, and if changes of tempera-

ture be taken proportional to changes of pressure at constant volume, show that the characteristic equation of the substance is $pv = \mathrm{R}\Theta$.

{As in Art. 89 we have $\theta - \theta_0 = (p - p_0)\phi(v)$, or

$$\Theta = p\phi(v),$$

the zero of temperature being that at which the pressure is zero, and the right-hand member of the equation is the function of p and v which remains constant at constant temperature, namely pv, therefore $\phi(v)$ is proportional to v, etc.}

2. Find the characteristic equation of a substance which, when used as a thermometric substance, will give the same scale of temperature, whether it is designed to measure equal changes of temperature by equal changes of volume under constant pressure, or by equal changes of pressure at constant volume.

{In the former case we have, as before, the temperature proportional to the volume, or

$$\Theta = vf(p) \; ;$$

and in the second method we have

$$\Theta = p\phi(v).$$

Hence if Θ is to be the same in both cases we must have

$$vf(p) = p\phi(v),$$

or
$$\frac{f(p)}{\phi(v)} = \frac{p}{v}.$$

That is, $f(p)$ is proportional to p and $\phi(v)$ to v, and therefore the substance obeys Boyle's law. The characteristic equation then becomes

$$pv = \mathrm{R}\Theta.\}$$

3. If ρ_1 and ρ_2 be the densities of two gases under the same pressure and at the same temperature, show that

$$\rho_1 \mathrm{R}_1 = \rho_2 \mathrm{R}_2.$$

{Let v be the volume of unit mass of a gas of density ρ, then $\rho v = 1$, so that the equation $pv = \mathrm{R}\Theta$ becomes

$$\frac{p}{\rho} = \mathrm{R}\Theta, \quad \text{or} \quad \rho \mathrm{R} = \frac{p}{\Theta}.$$

Hence if different gases are at the same temperature and pressure, we have

$$\rho_1 \mathrm{R}_1 = \rho_2 \mathrm{R}_2 = \text{etc.} = \frac{p}{\Theta}.$$

For air $\rho = 0{\cdot}001293$ when $p = 760$ mm. of mercury $= 1033{\cdot}3$ grammes per square centimetre $= 1033{\cdot}3 \times 981$ in dynes per sq. cm. Therefore

$$\mathrm{R} = \frac{1033{\cdot}3 \times 981}{0{\cdot}001293 \times 273} = 2871 \times 10^3.$$

For any other gas the value of R will be found by means of the relation established above, that is by dividing the value of R for air by the relative density of the gas. The density of nitrogen relative to air is $0{\cdot}97137$, and the value of R is 2956×10^3. For oxygen the relative density is $1{\cdot}10563$, and the value of R is 2597×10^3. For hydrogen the relative density is $0{\cdot}06926$, and the value of R is 4146×10^4.}

4. If a gas departs from Boyle's law, show how to calculate the temperatures of a constant volume air thermometer from observations on a constant pressure instrument.

SECTION III

95. Standardisation of Thermometers.—At the Fifth Conference of Weights and Measures, held at Paris in 1913, it was agreed that the absolute scale should be substituted for the normal hydrogen scale (Art. 92) as the fundamental scale of temperature, as soon as the tables of reduction from one scale to the other had attained a sufficient measure of stability. This is Lord Kelvin's scale already referred to in Art. 79, in which the degree is defined as the one-hundredth part of the difference between the temperatures of the normal melting point of ice and the normal boiling point of water. The chief uncertainty in the reduction is in the change of zero. The exact position of the absolute zero (relative to the centigrade zero) cannot be observed directly, but is derived by calculations based on elaborate experiments on the properties of gases (see Art. 365). The best determinations place it at $-273°\cdot1$ C. or $-273°\cdot2$ C., and though the uncertainty is small, still it is sufficient to make it inconvenient to reckon temperatures from the absolute zero, at least in recording such moderate temperatures as can be fixed with great precision on the centigrade scale. But this objection to the absolute scale does not apply in regard to temperatures above 500° C., since the observation of high temperatures is subject to an experimental error which is greater the higher the temperature and which exceeds the uncertainty in the zero of the scale. High temperatures, such as the melting points of refractory metals, are, in fact, frequently recorded in Kelvin's scale, which is indicated by the letter K ; thus 1273° K. would be equivalent to 1000° C.

There are two kinds of thermometer whose readings, subject to certain corrections, give the thermodynamic scale of temperature, and which can therefore be used to standardise other types of thermometer ; these are the gas thermometer and the radiation thermometer. The helium gas thermometer can be used down to the lowest attainable temperatures, and the hydrogen thermometer also at very low temperatures. Either of these gases is satisfactory up to about 500° C., but for higher temperatures nitrogen is substituted (see Art. 92). The upper limit at which gas thermometers may be used is at present about 1600° C., though it is quite possible that the range may be extended in the future, if the experimental difficulties can be overcome. The principles on which radiation thermometers are constructed and calibrated are explained in Chap. VI. secs. iv. v. vi. It is sufficient to notice here that they are suitable for measuring temperatures above those at which the gas thermometer is available. Gas thermometers are very troublesome to work with, owing to their bulk, their slowness in adjusting themselves to the temperature of their surroundings, the precautions to be observed, and the corrections which have to be made. Accordingly, they find their chief application in the standardisation of thermometers of simpler construction, some of which will be described in the following pages. The comparison of any thermometer with a standard gas thermometer may be made either directly, by exposing the two thermometers to the same temperature, or by comparing the thermometer which it is desired to calibrate with another which has already been standardised, or again, by noting the readings of the thermometer at certain fixed temperatures which have been already referred to the standard scale by means of the gas thermometer.

96. Siemens's Pyrometer.—The electric resistance of a metallic wire is found to increase gradually with the temperature, and conse-

Fig. 28.

quently on this property a system of thermometry may be established. The pyrometer invented by Siemens[1] depends on the change of the electric resistance of a platinum wire when heated. The wire (Fig. 28) was doubled and wound on a cylinder of refractory fireclay. When thus coiled its ends were fastened to stout platinum wires of such a length that their further ends are never very warm, and these in turn were connected by copper wires to the binding screws on the outside of the case of the pyrometer. The copper wires were enclosed in a stout wrought-iron tube of about 3·5 cm. diameter and 120 cm. in length which projected from the furnace or other space whose

[1] C. Wm. Siemens, *Phil. Mag.* vol. xlii. p. 150, 1871; see also *Brit. Assoc. Report,* 1874. A pyrometer is an instrument designed for the measurement of high temperatures.

temperature was to be measured, and formed a handle of support for the whole instrument.   The platinum coil was enclosed in a sheath, of platinum or wrought iron, fastened to one end of the iron tube, and the coil was packed in this sheath with asbestos to prevent shifting.

The most important point to determine is the constancy of the resistance of the coil at a given temperature, or if it will always be the same at the same temperature.   A thermometer should be free from secular changes of its zero, and it should therefore be determined how much, if any, permanent alteration occurs in the resistance of the platinum wire after prolonged or repeated exposure to high temperatures.   These points were examined by a committee of the British Association.[1]   Denoting the resistance of the coil at $10°$ C. by R_{10}, and its resistance at $\theta°$ by R_θ, the formula employed was [2]

$$R_\theta = R_{10}[1 + a(\theta - 10)],$$

where a is a constant depending on the nature of the wire.

[1] See *Brit. Assoc. Report* for 1874.

[2] The earliest formula for the purpose of expressing the relation between the resistance and temperature of a metallic wire was given by Clausius (*Pogg. Ann.* vol. civ., 1858) on the results of experiments made by Arndtsen.   Clausius found that according to these experiments the resistance of the ordinary metals, with the exception of iron, could be represented by the formula

$$R = R_0(1 + \cdot 00366\theta),$$

where R is the resistance at $\theta°$ C., and R_0 that at $0°$ C.   If this formula were true for all ranges of temperature, the resistance would vanish at the absolute zero, the metal becoming a perfect conductor.

Later experiments, however, showed that the above formula does not represent the facts accurately even at ordinary temperatures.

The problem of the variation of electrical resistance with temperature was also attacked by Sir Wm. Siemens.   He proved that the formula given by Matthiessen,

$$R_0 = R(1 + a\theta + \beta\theta^2),$$

was quite inapplicable except between the limits $0°$ and $100°$ C.   His own experiments led him to suggest the formula

$$R = a\Theta^{\frac{1}{2}} + \beta\Theta + \gamma,$$

but the more recent experiments of Callendar have proved that this formula does not represent the results of observation so well as a simple formula of the ordinary type,

$$R = R_0(1 + a\theta + \beta\theta^2).$$

The formula in the text is a particular case of this in which $10°$ C. is taken instead of the zero.

Siemens's experiments were published in the *Transactions of the Society of Telegraph Engineers*, 1875.   They were of a very rough character, and were undertaken merely with the object of graduating a commercial pyrometer.

Siemens applied the variation of the resistance of platinum to the measurement of deep-sea temperatures.   Two coils of platinum wire of equal resistance were employed.   One of these was let down to the sea bottom, and the other was placed in a bath, the temperature of which was varied till equality of resistance was restored between the coils.   The temperature of the sea bottom was then the same as that of the bath.

In the case of coils surrounded by a platinum sheath exposure to high temperatures caused no serious permanent change in the resistance, but a considerable permanent increase of resistance was caused in those coils which were enclosed in iron sheaths. These alterations were due to prolonged exposure to high temperatures rather than to alterations from high to low, and, as Professor Williamson pointed out, arose from a permanent alteration of the platinum coil caused by the combined action of the atmosphere inside the iron case, and the silica of the fireclay cylinder on which the coil is wound. Such permanent alterations of the resistance of the spiral of course destroy the accuracy of the instrument, and it is obvious that the fireclay cylinder should be replaced by something less objectionable, or dispensed with altogether. With this view the thorough examination of the properties of the instrument, and of its qualifications as a reliable standard of reference, was undertaken by Prof. Callendar [1] with such favourable results, that he considers the platinum resistance thermometer not only a trustworthy instrument in pyrometry, but also that it possesses those permanent qualities which recommended it specially as a standard of reference in thermometry.

97. Platinum Resistance Thermometers.—After a careful investigation of the variations of the resistance of platinum wire with temperature, Prof. Callendar concluded that pure platinum wire, free from alloy with silicon, carbon, tin, or other impurities, when not subjected to strain or rough usage, possessed always the same resistance at the same temperature. Different lengths of the pure wire were found to behave similarly, and their resistances were not found to be subject to any permanent change from heating and cooling, provided they were not strained or chemically altered. It therefore possesses in a high degree the qualifications necessary to a scientific standard. Thus while the gas thermometer possesses several advantages as an ultimate standard it is practically impossible to use it in ordinary work, while the platinum thermometer, on the other hand, when once standardised by comparison with the gas thermometer, can be readily used, and may be subsequently employed as a standard of comparison for other thermometers, and thus the elaborate precautions and special apparatus otherwise necessary for this purpose are avoided. The practical difficulty in the comparison of thermometers is the maintaining of an enclosure at a constant temperature, but in the standardising of the platinum thermometer this difficulty is avoided by enclosing the spiral in the bulb of the air thermometer.

Assuming the simple formula $R = R_0(1 + a\theta_p)$, it follows that the

---

[1] H. L. Callendar, *Phil. Trans.*, 1887, p. 161.

temperature θ_p, registered by the platinum thermometer when its resistance is R, will be

$$\theta_p = 100\frac{R - R_0}{R_{100} - R_0}.$$

This will differ somewhat from the temperature θ registered by the gas thermometer, because the assumed formula for R is not applicable through any extended range, but Callendar found that the difference of the indications of the two instruments may be represented through a very wide range with great accuracy by the parabolic formula

$$\theta - \theta_p = \delta\left\{\left(\frac{\theta}{100}\right)^2 - \frac{\theta}{100}\right\},$$

where δ is a constant to be determined for the particular specimen of wire employed, and may be obtained from a single observation of the boiling point of sulphur[1] or mercury, or some other substance, whose boiling point θ is accurately known. The first work of Callendar was soon afterwards confirmed by Griffiths,[2] who found that the above formula possessed even greater accuracy than Callendar supposed.

In the form adopted by Griffiths the platinum wire was wound on a roll of asbestos paper, its ends being soldered to thick copper leads (communicating with binding screws) which for the sake of insulation were enclosed in narrow glass tubes.

The great superiority of the platinum resistance thermometer over liquid-in-glass thermometers lies not only in its far wider range, but also in its comparative freedom from changes of zero. The wire when pure and well annealed has always sensibly the same resistance at the same temperature. Thus while it is difficult to attain an accuracy of $\frac{1}{10}$th of a degree at temperatures as low as 200° C. with a mercury thermometer, with a properly constructed platinum thermometer the zero does not vary by $\frac{1}{100}$th of a degree at any temperature up to 500° C., and in some of Callendar's thermometers it was found not to change more than $\frac{1}{10}$th of a degree up to 1300° C. For temperatures below 700° C. the coil and leads may be enclosed in a tube of dimensions similar to those of an ordinary thermometer, and the leads may be of copper or silver and the tube of hard glass. For accurate work at high temperatures platinum leads must be used, and the whole must be enclosed in a tube of glazed porcelain. For insulating the coil and leads nothing answers so well as mica.[3] Most varieties of clay are apt to attack the wire at high temperatures, and the large mass of a clay cylinder reduces the delicacy of the instrument. The wire is preferably doubled on itself like an ordinary resistance coil and

[1] See Callendar and Griffiths, *Phil. Trans.*, A, p. 161, 1887.
[2] E. H. Griffiths, *Proc. Roy. Soc.*, December 1890.
[3] H. L. Callendar, *Phil. Mag.*, July 1891, p. 104.

then wound on a thin plate of mica (Fig. 29), the leads being insulated
by being made to pass through a series of mica wads cut to fit the
tube containing the instrument.   This gives very perfect insulation,
and prevents convection currents of air up and down the tube.

In order to eliminate the effect due to variation in the resistance of
the leads, a pair of *compensating leads*, consisting of a loop
of wire of the same material and dimensions as the leads,
are included in the instrument, and their terminals connected up so as to form part of the adjacent arm of
the Wheatstone's resistance bridge.   Thus an increase in
resistance of the leads is balanced by an equal increase
in the resistance of the compensating leads.   By this
means leads of any convenient length and flexibility may
be employed, and the observations will be independent of
the length of stem immersed.[1]

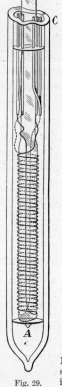

With a mercury thermometer, on the other hand, some
portion of the stem must be exposed to the air, and the
correction arising in this respect is so uncertain that it is
now often avoided by using a series of thermometers of
"limited scale."   Each of these must have at least two
points of its scale specially determined.   This has been
hitherto done by means of substances of known boiling
points and freezing points, but, as Griffiths has shown,[2] the
graduation may be more easily and accurately effected by
comparison with a single platinum thermometer.   Thus a
single platinum thermometer may be used to do the work of
a whole series of liquid-in-glass thermometers with far
greater accuracy and without the necessity of applying any
troublesome and uncertain corrections.[3]

The method recommended by Callendar and Griffiths
for standardising the platinum thermometer is by the
observation of the boiling point of sulphur, on the supposition that the temperature of the vapour of sulphur boiling under
760 mm. pressure is $444°\cdot53$ C. on the air thermometer, allowing
$0°\cdot082$ C. for each mm. of pressure different from this.[4]   This temperature of boiling sulphur was obtained previously from a series of
very careful experiments.

Fig. 29.

Method of
standard-
ising.

---

[1] For a full description of the instrument and the arrangement of the Wheatstone's bridge, see an article by E. H. Griffiths in *Nature*, Nov. 1895, p. 39.

[2] E. H. Griffiths, *Brit. Assoc. Report*, 1890.

[3] Callendar and Griffiths, *Phil. Trans.*, 1891, A, pp. 119-157.

[4] The boiling point of sulphur given by Mueller and Burgess (*Am. Chem. Soc.
Journ.* vol. 41, p. 745, 1919) is $t = 444\cdot60 + 0\cdot0910 \ (p - 760) - 0\cdot000049 \ (p - 760)^2$.

Thus when R_0 and R_{100} have been determined as well as R for some third known temperature (the boiling point of sulphur), then θ_p for this temperature becomes completely determined, and by substituting in the formula for $\theta - \theta_p$ the value of δ is deduced. The determination of the resistance in boiling sulphur is attended with difficulties, and requires a special apparatus, but it has been recently shown by Griffiths and Clark that this determination may be avoided by assuming, in accordance with the observations of Dewar and Fleming, that the resistance of certain pure metals (including platinum) diminishes at low temperatures in such a way as to lead to the conclusion that at absolute zero it vanishes.[1] This gives $R = 0$ when $\theta = -273$, and consequently when a high order of accuracy is not a *sine qua non*, and when the spiral is known to be tolerably pure, this value may be used with R_0 and R_{100} to determine δ, and the instrument can be graduated by direct observations of R in steam and melting ice alone. For accurate work it is essential that the thermometer should be standardised by observation at the three temperatures mentioned above, and also that the resistance wire should be of a high degree of purity. If the platinum is not pure, two different instruments may not agree at intermediate points. Further, the resistance coils of the bridge should be made of a material whose resistance has a very small temperature coefficient, and should be kept at a nearly uniform temperature. Manganin wire is commonly used for the bridge coils. In special cases it may be necessary to place them in a thermostat. A good test of the purity of the platinum is furnished by the values of the constant δ and the mean temperature coefficient of resistance a. If the platinum is pure, $a \left(= (R_{100} - R_0)/100R_0 \right)$ will not be less than $0 \cdot 00386$ and δ will not be greater than $1 \cdot 51$. A platinum thermometer so calibrated will record temperatures (calculated by Callendar's formula) which agree within the limits of experimental error with those given by the standard gas thermometer between $-40°$ C. and $450°$ C. The investigations of Heycock and Neville[2] and of Waidner and Burgess[3] show further that the formula can be extrapolated up to $1083°$ C. (the melting point of copper) without appreciable error, the variation from the gas thermometer reading at that temperature amounting to little more than $1°$, which is comparable with the experimental error of the gas thermometer.

Platinum resistance thermometers can also be employed for

[1] E. H. Griffiths and G. M. Clark, *Phil. Mag.* vol. xxxiv. p. 515, Dec. 1892. See, however, Art. 104.

[2] Heycock and Neville, *Journ. Chem. Soc.* vol. lvii. p. 376, 1890.

[3] Waidner and Burgess, *Phys. Rev.* vol. xxviii. p. 467, 1909.

the measurement of low temperatures, and are undoubtedly very convenient to use. According to the experiments of Dewar and Fleming,[1] the resistance of all pure metals diminishes in such a way as to indicate that it would vanish, or nearly vanish, at absolute zero (see Fig. 30). The resistance of an alloy, however, diminishes far less rapidly, and may even increase. At very low temperatures the slightest impurity in a wire of a single metal has an enormous effect in increasing the resistance, and hence, by taking the resistance of a

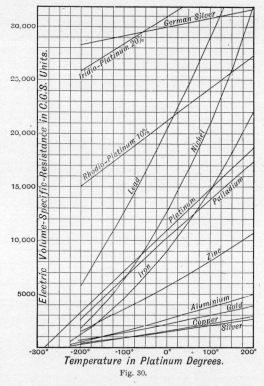

Fig. 30.

metal when immersed in liquid air, a very delicate test of its purity is afforded, so much so that Professor Fleming considers that, as an analytical method, it ranks almost with the spectroscope. This effect is very marked in the case of bismuth.[2]

[1] *Phil. Mag.*, Sept. 1893.

[2] Dewar and Fleming (*Proc. Roy. Soc.* lx. p. 425, 1896–97) also found that the resistance of a bismuth wire at ordinary temperatures was rather more than doubled by the application of a powerful transverse magnetic field (21,800 C.G.S. units); but, when immersed in liquid air, the resistance was increased to 150 times its normal amount at that temperature by the application of the same magnetic field.

Kamerlingh Onnes has shown that the electrical resistance of pure metals is

Dewar[1] also compared the readings of resistance thermometers of various metals at the temperature of liquid hydrogen. Using the formulæ given above, he found that the readings of all the thermometers were too high. The best results were given by the gold and platinum thermometers, the former registering $-249°·4$ and the latter $-243°·6$, the correct value being $-252°·7$. This result is confirmed by the experiments of Kamerlingh Onnes and Clay[2] on gold wire at low temperatures.

The behaviour of platinum resistance thermometers at low temperatures has been studied also by Travers and Gwyer, by Onnes, Braak and Clay, by E. H. and E. Griffiths, and others. Henning and Heuse,[3] at the Reichsanstalt, found that the resistance of a platinum thermometer between $0°$ and $-193°$ C. could be represented by the formula

$$R = R_0(1 + a\theta + b\theta^2 + c\theta^4),$$

where R_0 is, as usual, the resistance at $0°$ C. The other constants, a, b, c, can be determined by measuring the resistance at the freezing point of mercury $(-38°·87)$, the normal sublimation point of carbon dioxide $(-78°·51)$, and the normal boiling point of oxygen $(-183°·00)$. If the purity of the platinum is assured, and Callendar's coefficients a and δ known, then the value of R at the freezing point of mercury can be calculated from Callendar's formulæ, also the coefficient c in the above equation may be put equal to $-5·08065 \times 10^{-12}$. One observation at the oxygen boiling point will then be sufficient to complete the calibration. A table or curve of corresponding values of R and θ can then be constructed.

98. Thermo-electric Thermometers.—When a circuit is formed of wires of two different metals, and the junctions of the two metals are kept at different temperatures, an electric current will, in general, be produced in the circuit, its magnitude and direction depending on the nature of the metals and the temperatures of the junctions. If one junction is kept at a steady temperature, e.g. by immersion in

---

extremely small at very low temperatures, and at the liquefying point of helium $(-268°·6$ C.) there is a sudden further diminution of resistance, so that in a circuit of pure mercury, for instance, a current will circulate for hours without any sustaining electromotive force. The supra-conductive state, as it is called by Onnes, disappears in a strong magnetic field. For an account of theories of electronic conduction, with reference to Onnes' papers, see O. W. Richardson's *Electron Theory of Matter*, chap. xvii. (1916).

[1] *Proc. Roy. Soc.* lxviii. p. 360, 1901.

[2] *Comm. Phys. Lab. Leiden*, 95c, p. 165, 1906.

[3] *Zeits. für Phys.* vol. xxiii. p. 95, 1924.

melting ice, the temperature of the other may be estimated by observing the deflection of a galvanometer included in the circuit.

This method was first used by Becquerel in 1826, and afterwards more carefully studied by Tait, Barus, H. Le Chatelier, and others.[1] The dependence of the electromotive force on the temperatures of the junctions was investigated by Tait, who found that for many metals the thermo-electric power is a linear function of the temperature.[2] The couple proposed by Tait for pyrometric purposes consisted of platinum and an alloy of platinum with 10 per cent of iridium. Barus used the same couple as Tait, and found that the electromotive force could be represented closely as the sum of two exponential functions of the temperature. Le Chatelier used a similar alloy, substituting rhodium for iridium. This alloy is superior to that used by Barus and Tait, as iridium volatilises sufficiently at high temperatures to contaminate the platinum wire. The rhodium alloy, in conjunction with pure platinum, is now preferred to any other for accurate work above 0° C. It has been used up to the temperature at which the platinum melts, i.e. 1755° C., but when in continuous use it will deteriorate at temperatures above 1500° C. For pyrometric work each wire is enclosed in a capillary tube of fireclay, porcelain, or fused silica, and the two tubes surrounded by a protecting sheath of similar material or of metal. The leads may be of copper, and the cold junction immersed in a vacuum vessel containing ice. At temperatures below 500° C. hard glass capillary tubes and sheaths may be employed, and varnished cotton or silk insulation at lower temperatures.

Two methods of measurement may be employed. The electromotive force developed in the circuit may be balanced against a known electromotive force in a potentiometer, or the current may be measured by the deflection of a galvanometer. If the greatest precision is required, the former method is preferable, as it is independent of variations in the resistance of the circuit; but the galvanometer method is simpler and can be used to give a continuous record. If a sensitive galvanometer or voltmeter of high resistance is employed, the deflection will be very nearly proportional to the electromotive force, as the resistance of the thermometer and leads will be only a small part of the total resistance.

[1] E. Becquerel, *Ann. de Chimie et de Physique*, tom. lxviii. p. 49, 3e, 1863. Rosetti, *Ann. de Chimie et de Physique*, 5e, tom. xvii. p. 177, 1879. Tait, *Edin. Phil. Trans.* vol. xxvii. H. Le Chatelier, *Journ. de Phys.*, 2e, tom. vi. p. 23, 1887. C. Barus, *Amer. Journ. Sci.* vol. xlviii. p. 332, 1894.

[2] More recent investigations show that the relation is not nearly so simple, and cannot even be represented by a quadratic function, except over limited ranges.

Fig. 31 shows a simple form of instrument with a galvanometer.

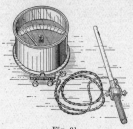

The couple is protected by a porcelain tube which can easily be removed. Inside are two small reels of platinum and iridio-platinum wire, so that if the couple should be destroyed at any time, it is only neces-sary to unscrew the reels, pull out a little wire, fuse the ends together again, and the couple is ready for use. In this simple type no special provision is made for keeping the cold junction at a uniform temperature. Each division on the scale represents 10° C.

Fig. 31.

Thermo-electric thermometers are usually standardised by measur-ing the electromotive force at three known fixed temperatures. The temperature corresponding to any other reading is then calculated from a formula involving three constants. For a platinum platinum-rhodium couple the formula

$$E = A\theta + B(1 - e^{c\theta})$$

represents the connection between electromotive force and tempera-ture satisfactorily between 0° and 400°. Between 300° and 1200° the quadratic formula

$$E = -A + B\theta + C\theta^2$$

is employed, and a similar formula, with different constants, between 1100° and 1750°. Thus, in order to standardise a thermocouple which is to be used within the range 300°—1200°, for instance, the constants A, B, C must be calculated from three observations at known temperatures within that range. Thermocouples are liable to secular change, particularly when in use at high temperatures; they should therefore be standardised at intervals.

Thermo-electric thermometers have also been used in work at low temperatures, down to about − 250° C., various metals and alloys being recommended as thermocouples by different experimenters. But they are insensitive at very low temperatures, and resistance thermometers are generally preferred.

We shall now consider some of the various methods which have been proposed for the estimation of high temperatures.

99. The Method of Cooling. — One of the earliest attempts at pyrometry was that of Newton,[1] in the estimation of the temperature of red-hot iron. The method employed consisted in observing the time required by the heated mass to cool under given conditions. Assuming

[1] Newton, "Scala Graduum Caloris," *Phil. Trans.* vol. xxii. p. 824, 1701.

a certain law of cooling to hold at all temperatures, then by observing the rate of cooling at known temperatures, the data necessary to estimate the initial temperature may be obtained from the time of cooling to some other known temperature. The law assumed by Newton Newton's was that the rate of cooling of a body under given conditions is law of cooling. proportional to the temperature difference between the body and its surroundings, and this law has since passed under the name of Newton's law of cooling.

If such a law were found to hold accurately at all temperatures within the range of our standard thermometer, then such an agreement might warrant the use of the law and methods founded on it to extend the scale of temperatures beyond the limits of the standard thermometer. No such agreement has, however, been found, and it is only for very moderate differences of temperature that the law appears to be even approximately verified. In this case, then, the application of the method to the measurement of temperatures beyond the range of standard instruments would be illegitimate and unreasonable.

100. Pyrometry by Vapour Densities.—The direct observation of the density of mercury vapour was suggested by Regnault [1] as a method of estimating high temperatures. Some mercury is placed in a wrought-iron flask and exposed to the temperature to be measured. As the mercury boils away the air is expelled, and the flask is finally left filled with the vapour of mercury at the temperature of the furnace. When temperature equilibrium is attained the mouth of the flask is covered with a lid, so that the neck is closed and the flask is allowed to cool. The vapour condenses, and the liquid mercury is collected and weighed. Assuming the vapour to obey the laws of a perfect gas, the temperature may be easily calculated from the known density of mercury vapour and the volume of the flask corrected for expansion. A porcelain flask furnished with a ball stopper may be used instead of one of wrought iron.

The vapour of iodine has been used by Deville and Troost for the same purpose. The iodine was enclosed in a porcelain flask of about 300 c.c. capacity, furnished with a fine stem, which just protruded from the furnace chamber. The nozzle was closed by a loosely fitting stopper, past which the vapour could escape. When the iodine was completely vaporised and equilibrium of temperature established, the stopper was fused into the nozzle by an oxyhydrogen blowpipe. The weight of the iodine still remaining in the flask was determined as soon as it cooled, and the volume of the flask and the density of iodine vapour being known, the temperature of the furnace was

---

[1] Regnault, *Ann. de Chimie et de Physique*, 3e, tom. lxiii. p. 39, 1861.

estimated.   The correction for the expansion of the flask was made by noting the elongation of a rod of porcelain for temperatures up to 1500° C.[1]

101. Calorimetric Method.—The determination of the melting points of refractory metals by calorimetry has been studied by M. Violle.[2]   This method is convenient, and often employed to determine the temperatures of furnaces.   For this purpose the law of variation with temperature of the specific heat of some metal, such as copper, platinum, or wrought iron, must be determined in advance.   A portion of the chosen metal is then heated in the furnace, and when it has attained the temperature of the latter it is removed and placed in a calorimeter.   The quantity of heat it gives out in cooling in this instrument is measured, as explained in Chapter IV., and from this experiment the temperature of the mass of metal when placed in the calorimeter can be computed.   This method is subject to a serious error in the loss of heat which inevitably accompanies the transference of the metal from the furnace to the calorimeter, besides suffering from all the errors which attend such a difficult experiment as the determination of a quantity of heat by means of a calorimeter.

102. Expansion Method—Joly's Meldometer.—The measurement of high temperatures by the elongation of a bar of metal has been frequently employed.   The first pyrometer of this kind is attributed to Muschenbroeck, and others were devised in the early part of last century by Des Aguliers, Ellicot, Graham, Smeaton, Ferguson, Brongniart, Laplace and Lavoisier, and later by Pouillet.[3]   This method can be employed with accuracy only if the expansion is referred to a scale kept at a fixed temperature, as explained in Art. 108, and in this respect Pouillet's pyrometer is superior to those previously employed. In Daniell's pyrometer the relative expansion of a metal bar in an earthenware socket was used, and more recently Steinle and Harting[4] employed the expansion of graphite.   Weinhold,[5] however, after investigating this class of instruments, states that it is not possible to obtain trustworthy results by the relative expansion of solids.   Wedgwood's pyrometer[6] depended on the contraction of a short cylinder of fine fireclay when exposed to a high temperature and then allowed to

---

[1] The use of the vapour of iodine in this method is objectionable, as its expansion does not follow the law for a perfect gas, owing to the dissociation of the iodine molecule into simpler molecules at high temperatures.

[2] *Comptes rendus*, tom. lxxxix. p. 702, 1879.

[3] See art. "Pyrometry," *Ency. Brit.*

[4] Beckert, *Zeitschr. f. anal. Chem.*, A, vol. xxi. p. 284, 1882.

[5] Weinhold, *Pogg. Ann.* vol. cxlix. p. 186, etc., 1873.

[6] Described in *Phil. Trans.*, 1782, pp. 84, 86.

cool. Such an instrument, of course, could only give a very rough idea of the temperature of a furnace.

A form of high temperature thermometer, depending on the expansion of platinum, and capable of considerable accuracy, has been designed by Prof. J. Joly.[1] It is not intended for general thermometric work, its use being restricted to the determination of melting points and the observation of substances when exposed to a high temperature. For these purposes it is more convenient than any other form of instrument, on account of the ease and rapidity with which it can be manipulated, and the very small quantity of material required. As it is principally used to determine melting points it is called by the inventor a *meldometer*.

The instrument consists of a rectangular piece of slate cut as shown, Fig. 32, on which are affixed two forceps, one of which is rigid, and the other free to rotate about a vertical axis, the lower end of which axis dips into a trough of mercury, to ensure good electrical contact. Between the two forceps a platinum ribbon AA is kept stretched by a weak spiral spring attached to the axis of the movable forceps. Two binding screws at the back of the slate are in connec-

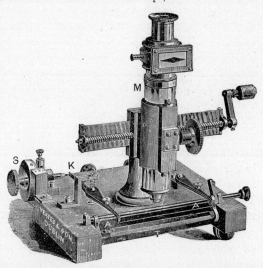

Fig. 32.

tion with the two forceps, so that the ribbon can be raised to any desired temperature—short of the melting point of platinum—by putting it in circuit with a battery and variable resistance. The temperature is estimated by the expansion of the platinum ribbon. To measure this, a flat steel spring K is fixed to the far end of the movable forceps. When the micrometer screw S is moved forward, its platinum point makes contact with a small gold plate attached to the further end of K, and completes an auxiliary electric circuit through a galvanometer which is contained in the eye-piece of the microscope M. This affords

[1] *Proc. Roy. Irish Acad.* vol. ii. p. 38, 1891.

a very delicate means of determining the exact point at which contact first occurs, and the deflection of the galvanometer needle can be seen without removing the eye from the microscope. As the arm K is flexible, the ribbon is not broken by accidentally screwing S too far. The forceps are bent over at the ends to allow of the trough T being raised so as to surround the ribbon and exclude draughts. The cooling action of the forceps on the ends of the ribbon is compensated by tapering the ends and thus increasing the heating effect of the current. The substance whose melting point is to be determined is finely powdered, and a small portion of the powder placed on the ribbon. The temperature is then gradually raised till the particles, viewed through the microscope, are seen to flow. The instrument is calibrated by observing the expansion for a number of substances whose melting points are known.

103. Other Methods.—An optical pyrometer, based on the variation of the refractivity of a gas with temperature, has been proposed by D. Berthelot.[1] If μ is the index of refraction of a gas, then $\mu - 1$ is proportional to the density (Gladstone and Dale's law. See *Theory of Light*, Art. 84). This law has been verified by Chappuis and Rivière for pressure changes, and by Benoît as well as by Chappuis and Rivière for temperature changes. If now a beam of white light is split up into two, which are allowed to pass through two tubes, and then caused to produce interference fringes, the central interference band will be displaced if one tube is heated. By altering the pressure in the other tube the band can be restored. The alteration of pressure in the cold tube gives a measure of the temperature of the hot tube. This method could be applied to the measurement of very high temperatures. The chief objection to it is that the ends of the tube would be cooler than the middle portion. Berthelot proposes to eliminate the end effect by making experiments with tubes of different lengths, and finding the displacement due to the middle portion alone by difference. It might, however, not always be possible to apply this correction.

Refractivity of a gas.

The viscosity of a gas increases with temperature, the volume also increases with temperature if the pressure is constant. If, then, gas under pressure be allowed to escape through a capillary tube, the rate of efflux will decrease rapidly with temperature. The relation, however, does not appear to be a very simple one.

Viscosity of a gas.

Pyrometers founded on this principle have been suggested by Barus[2] and later by Callendar. A simple form of apparatus designed

[1] *Comptes rendus*, April 1895. The variation of refractivity of gases with temperature has been studied by G. W. Walker (*Phil. Trans.*, A, vol. cci., 1903).
[2] *Geological Survey of U.S.*, 1889.

by A. Job[1] is the following. Gas is liberated by electrolysis in a
closed vessel, the only exit being by a capillary tube. The gas being
disengaged at a uniform rate, the pressure, which can be measured by
a manometer, rises until the efflux is equal to the rate of production
of the gas. When a steady state is attained, the pressure gives a
measure of the temperature of the capillary tube. This instrument
was graduated by comparison with the thermo-electric pyrometer of
Le Chatelier.

A very interesting form of apparatus is Prof. Callendar's *Transpira-* Callendar's
tion Balance.[2] The idea of measuring the resistance offered to the flow Transpiration
of a gas through a small aperture by an arrangement similar to the Balance.
Wheatstone's bridge in electrical measurements was first suggested
by W. N. Shaw. The complete analogy to the platinum resistance
thermometer was carried out by Prof. Callendar. The fine wire
resistances are replaced by a graduated series of fine tubes, which can
be short-circuited by taps of relatively large bore corresponding to
plugs of negligible resistance. The galvanometer is replaced by a gas-
current-indicator or rheostat, consisting of a delicately suspended vane
which would be deflected by a current of gas. The pyrometer consists
of a fine platinum tube. A steady flow of gas being kept up through
the apparatus, if the platinum tube is heated, an increased resistance
is offered to the passage of the gas, owing to its increased volume and
viscosity. This causes a deflection of the vane, which can be balanced
by shutting off some of the short-circuiting taps in the adjacent arm of
the bridge. The resistance due to heating is thus measured, and the
temperature deduced. As in the case of the platinum thermometer,
the pyrometer is provided with " compensating leads."

In pottery works Prinsep's alloys have commonly been used to
determine the temperature of the furnace (see p. 95), or Seger's
" normal pyrometric cones." [3] These latter are cones of fusible clays
of graduated melting points, like Prinsep's alloys. These rough
methods are being superseded by the use of platinum thermometers.

The superior limit of temperature at which the pyrometers here
described can be used is about 1500° C. or 1600° C., often much less.
For higher temperatures recourse must be had to methods in which
the intensity of radiation from a heated body is measured. The discussion of these methods will be found in the chapter on Radiation
(see Chap. VI.).

**104. Temperature Ranges of different Thermometers—Fixed
Points.**—In selecting a thermometer for any particular purpose,

---

[1] *Comptes rendus*, Jan. 1902.   [2] See *Nature*, March 1899.
[3] *Thoninindustrie-Zeitung*, pp. 135, 145, 168, 1886.

regard must be had to the part of the scale in which the temperatures to be measured are likely to lie.[1] For research work at very low temperatures, the hydrogen or helium gas thermometer is indispensable. Since gases deviate farthest from Boyle's law when near liquefaction, it might be supposed that a gas thermometer would become untrustworthy at a temperature approaching the liquefying point of the contained gas. The experiments of Olszewski,[2] Dewar,[3] and Kamerlingh Onnes show that this is not the case, and that in fact such a thermometer can be used to measure temperatures below the normal liquefying point of the gas, since the gas in the bulb can be kept at a sufficiently reduced pressure to prevent liquefaction.

Except at very low temperatures, gas thermometers are seldom used, other than as standards of reference. Platinum resistance thermometers are convenient and reliable in use and have a wide range of application, $-190°$ C. to $1550°$ C. Thermocouples are less suitable than resistance thermometers for the measurement of very low temperatures, but the convenience of a thermometer which only occupies a very small space is, for many purposes, so great that thermocouples are often used for low temperature work, even down to $-200°$ C. or lower. Constantan against steel has been recommended by Onnes[4] as a suitable couple for very low temperatures. If very carefully standardised, thermo-elements of iron-constantan or copper-constantan will afford measurements correct to $0°·1$ down to about $-190°$ C. Between $-190°$ C. and $0°$ C. the pentane thermometer (Art. 74) or Stock's vapour-pressure thermometers (Art. 93) could be used. The latter will read to $0°·01$. Toluol or alcohol liquid thermometers may be used down to about $-78°$ C. Mercury thermometers can be used from $-38°$ C. to $250°$ C. or, if filled with gas under pressure, up to about $500°$ C. Copper-constantan couples can also be used in the same interval. Thermocouples of platinum with platinum-rhodium are not very sensitive below $300°$ C., but above this temperature are very useful, and are perhaps the best thermometers to use in the range between the melting points of palladium and platinum ($1550°—1775°$). Both resistance thermometers and thermocouples have been adapted to give continuous records of temperature. From $500°$ C. upward radiation and optical thermometers are available for use, and these

---

[1] A full description of methods of standardising, comparing, and using thermometers will be found in *Methods of Measuring Temperature*, by E. Griffiths.

[2] *Wied. Ann.* vol. xxxi. p. 58, 1887.

[3] *Phil. Mag.*, Sept. 1893.

[4] Onnes and Crommelin, *Proc. Roy. Acad.*, Amsterdam, No. 95a, 1906.

are the only instruments which can be used above the temperatures which limit the use of the thermocouple.

The appended table gives a list of temperatures of fixed points referred to the thermodynamic centigrade scale. The boiling points are those corresponding to a normal pressure of 760 mm. of mercury. Those temperatures which lie between the boiling point of oxygen and the melting point of palladium are suitable for use in standardising resistance thermometers and thermocouples.

FIXED TEMPERATURES IN DEGREES CENTIGRADE

(*Thermodynamic Scale*)

Absolute zero	− 273·2	Sulphur boils	444·6
Helium melts (26 atmos. press.)	− 272	Antimony melts	630
Helium boils	− 268·6	Silver melts	961
Hydrogen melts	− 258	Gold melts	1064
Hydrogen boils	− 252·8	Copper melts	1083
Oxygen boils	− 188·0	Palladium melts	1449·5
Carbon dioxide sublimes	− 78·5	Nickel melts	1452
Mercury melts	− 38·87	Platinum melts	1775
Benzophenone boils	305·9	Tungsten melts	3400
Cadmium melts	320·9	Crater of electric arc (carbon)	3430
Zinc melts	419·5	Effective temperature of sun	5800

CHAPTER III

DILATATION

SECTION I

DILATATION OF SOLIDS

105. Cubical Expansion.—In approaching the subject of expansion by heat it is necessary to bear distinctly in mind the exact meaning, and mode of measurement, of temperature. It being agreed to measure changes of temperature by changes of the volume of some substance, under given conditions of pressure (hydrogen for example under constant pressure), we have then by definition a distinct relation between the volume and temperature of this substance, of the form

$$V = V_0(1 + a\theta).$$

In this formula V_0 is the volume at the chosen zero of temperature, and equal changes of temperature are measured by equal changes of volume of this substance. The change of volume for one degree of temperature is aV_0, and a is a constant throughout the whole scale.

For other substances we might still retain a formula of the same shape in which a must be replaced by a function of the temperature, and the general expression for the volume at any temperature θ will be of the form

$$V = V_0(1 + a\theta + b\theta^2 + c\theta^3 + \ . \ . \ .) = V_0(1 + a\theta),$$

where

$$a = a + b\theta + c\theta^2 + \text{etc.}$$

For most substances the coefficients b, c, etc., diminish very rapidly and the equation $V = V_0(1 + a\theta)$ holds very approximately when a is regarded as a constant for each particular substance.

In the foregoing equations it is tacitly assumed that the volume of any substance under constant pressure is always the same at the same temperature, that is, that the volume, under given conditions of pressure, is a function of the temperature. This assumption will be legitimate if the volume depends only on the temperature and pressure, and this appears to be the case. Apparent exceptions occur in such substances as glass, in which the previous treatment becomes a factor of importance and modifies the characteristics of the substance. The volume in such cases is not always the same at the same temperature, but it is to be observed that here we are not sure that the conditions of pressure are the same throughout the mass. In fact the well-known case of Rupert's drops indicates that glass which has been suddenly cooled is subject to intense internal stress, and the recovery from such stress is a very slow process. The process of "annealing" has been specially devised to obviate such abnormal conditions in solids. In the case of fluids there is, however, apparently no reason why the volume should not always be the same at the same temperature and under the same external pressure.

The mean coefficient of expansion between any two temperatures has already been defined as the mean increase in bulk of a unit volume per degree of temperature or

$$\frac{V' - V}{V(\theta' - \theta)}.$$

If the difference of temperature $\theta' - \theta$ be taken very small, the change of volume $V' - V$ will also be very small, and denoting these by $d\theta$ and dV respectively, the coefficient becomes

$$\frac{1}{V}\frac{dV}{d\theta} \ . \ . \ . \ \text{(true coefficient)}.$$

This expression may be termed the *true* coefficient of expansion at the temperature θ.

Another coefficient is sometimes used which may be termed the *zero* coefficient of expansion. In this the zero volume V_0 replaces V as indicated by the expression

$$\frac{1}{V_0}\frac{dV}{d\theta} \ . \ . \ . \ \text{(zero coefficient)}.$$

In the case of the standard thermometric substance, it is this zero coefficient of expansion that appears in the equation

$$V = V_0(1 + a\theta),$$

and in this case a is absolutely constant, whereas the true coefficient will be aV_0/V, and this varies inversely as V.

In the equation given above, viz.—

$$a = a + b\theta + c\theta^2 + \text{etc.},$$

a is the *mean* coefficient of expansion between $0°$ and $\theta°$. This is the

M

coefficient used in correcting for the expansion of the bulb of the gas thermometer. The *zero* coefficient of expansion would of course be

$$a + 2b\theta + 3c\theta^2 + \text{etc.}$$

Cor. If the true coefficient of expansion be a constant a, the relation between volume and temperature is

$$\frac{d\mathrm{V}}{\mathrm{V}} = a d\theta,$$

or

$$\mathrm{V} = \mathrm{V}_0 e^{a\theta}.$$

106. Apparent Expansion.—In the case of fluids contained in a solid envelope which acts as a measuring flask, we have another coefficient termed the coefficient of *apparent* expansion. In this case the rise or fall of the surface of the fluid in the neck of the flask indicates the apparent change of volume of the fluid.

Let V_a be the apparent volume of the fluid at the temperature θ, and let V_0 be its real volume at zero. Thus the flask may be standardised and graduated at zero so that the volume indicated at this temperature is the real volume of the fluid. In this case the coefficient of apparent expansion is defined by the equation

$$\mathrm{V}_a = \mathrm{V}_0(1 + a\theta). \qquad . \qquad . \qquad . \qquad . \qquad (1)$$

The relation between the coefficient a and the real expansion of the fluid may be easily determined. For the real volume of the fluid is

$$\mathrm{V} = \mathrm{V}_0(1 + a\theta). \qquad . \qquad . \qquad . \qquad . \qquad (2)$$

and if g denotes the coefficient of cubical dilatation of glass (or the material of the flask) we have also

$$\mathrm{V} = \mathrm{V}_a(1 + g\theta). \qquad . \qquad . \qquad . \qquad . \qquad (3)$$

since V_a is the internal capacity of this portion of the flask at zero. Hence equating (2) and (3) we have

$$\mathrm{V}_0(1 + a\theta) = \mathrm{V}_a(1 + g\theta).$$

And using (1) we obtain

$$1 + a\theta = (1 + a\theta)(1 + g\theta),$$

or approximately, since all the coefficients are small,

$$a = a + g.$$

107. Linear and Superficial Expansion.—In the case of bars the elongation of linear expansion also comes into consideration. In this case the coefficient of linear expansion is defined as before, as the elongation per unit length for one degree change of temperature. If l denotes the length of the bar at temperature θ, and l_0 its length at zero, the true coefficient of linear expansion at θ will be

$$\frac{1}{l}\frac{dl}{d\theta},$$

and the zero coefficient will be

$$\frac{1}{l_0}\frac{dl}{d\theta}.$$

Denoting the latter by λ we have the general equation

$$l = l_0(1 + \lambda\theta),$$

since λ may be regarded as approximately constant. The relation connecting the linear and cubical dilatations is easily found. For the volume at temperature θ of a cube whose side is l_0 at zero is $l_0^3(1 + \lambda\theta)^3$ and the volume of the same cube is $V_0(1 + \alpha\theta)$. But $l_0^3 = V_0$, therefore

$$1 + \alpha\theta = (1 + \lambda\theta)^3,$$

or approximately

$$\alpha = 3\lambda.$$

The coefficient of superficial expansion is defined in the same manner and may be shown to be twice the coefficient of linear expansion.

108. Determination of the Linear Expansion of Bars—Method of Comparator.—The usual mode of determining the coefficient of linear expansion of a substance is by the direct observation of the change of length of a bar of the material, the measurement of the length and change of length being referred to a scale kept at a fixed temperature. This method is applicable when bars of suitable length can be procured and was adopted by Ramsden to estimate the linear expansion of the bars used by General Roy [1] in his measurement of a base-line on Hounslow Heath.

The form of apparatus used by Ramsden is shown in outline in Fig. 33, and consists essentially of three troughs fixed parallel to each other. The middle trough contains the bar to be experimented on, and can be heated by lamps placed underneath. The first and third troughs contain each an iron bar packed in broken ice so that they are kept constantly at a fixed temperature, and furnish a fixed length with which the length of the bar in the middle trough may be compared. In order to carry out this comparison the ends of the bars are furnished with adjustable uprights carrying lenses, eye-pieces, and cross-wires. The first bar carries an eye-piece at each end supplied with a cross wire, and the middle bar is supplied at each end with a lens, so that each of these lenses acts as an object-glass to the corresponding eye-piece on the first bar. The lenses on the middle bar and the eye-pieces on

[1] Roy, *Phil. Trans.*, 1785, p. 461.

the first thus constitute two telescopes, and these are adjusted so as to
view two cross-wires supported on the ends of the third bar and
illuminated by mirrors situated behind.   Since the first and third bars
are kept in melting ice the eye-pieces and cross-wires attached to them
remain fixed, but when the temperature of the bar in the middle
trough changes, the object-glasses attached to it will be displaced.   In
making an experiment the three troughs are filled with ice and the
apparatus adjusted so that the images of the cross-wires on the third
bar are in exact coincidence with the cross-wires of the eye-pieces, and
matters are so arranged that the middle bar is fixed at one end and
free to move at the other so that when the temperature rises the lens
at this end alone will move.   If the other end should move during the

(3) Cross
wire.

(2) Object-
glass.

(1) Eye-
piece.

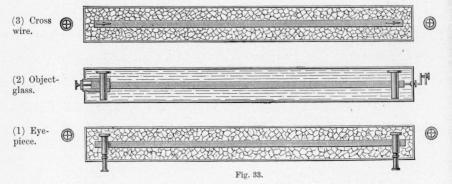

Fig. 33.

experiment it can be easily detected and allowed for.   Hot water is
now placed in the middle trough and the temperature kept as
stationary as possible by means of the lamps underneath.   The bar in
this trough expands and the object-glass on the free end is displaced by
an amount $l - l_0$, where l is the length of the bar at the temperature θ
of the bath and l_0 its length at zero.   This displacement is measured
by a very fine micrometer screw.   By means of this screw the lens
may be moved back into its original position so that the image of the
distant cross wire is again superposed on the cross-wire in the eye-piece.
The length $l - l_0$ being thus determined, the mean coefficient of expansion of the bar between $0°$ and $\theta°$ is

$$\lambda = \frac{l - l_0}{l_0 \theta}.$$

In Ramsden's apparatus the micrometer was not attached to the
object-glass on the end of the middle bar, but to the eye-piece at the
end of the first bar.   Coincidence of the cross-wires was then restored
by moving the eye-piece.   This displacement of the eye-piece was not
the expansion $l - l_0$, but greater than this in the ratio of the distance

between the first and third bars to the distance between the second and third. By attaching the micrometer to the object-glass on the middle bar the necessity for determining these distances is avoided.

The parallelism of the three bars is desirable, but excessive precaution in this respect is not absolutely necessary.

In the measurement of lengths by means of graduated rules it is important to know accurately the coefficient of linear expansion of the material. Also, as has been pointed out in the preceding chapter, in accurate work with the gas thermometer, a knowledge of the cubical coefficient of expansion of the material of the reservoir is necessary. It is usual to retain two terms in the expressions for these coefficients. Thus, putting

$$l = l_0(1 + a\theta + b\theta^2)$$

we get

$$V = V_0(1 + a\theta + b\theta^2)^3$$
$$= V_0\{1 + 3a\theta + 3(a^2 + b)\theta^2\},$$

neglecting θ^3 and higher powers. The mean coefficients of linear and cubical expansion are therefore $a + b\theta$ and $3a + 3(a^2 + b)\theta$ respectively.

Ramsden's method has been much improved and elaborated. In the determination of the expansion of the iridio-platinum standards of length adopted by the Bureau International, the comparator method was used. In the apparatus employed, the bar of material experimented on rests freely on rollers and is entirely enclosed in a double-walled box provided with glass windows through which the ends of the bar and the enclosed thermometers can be observed. A steady flow of water is kept up through the space between the walls of the box, the temperature being regulated by a thermostat arrangement. The expansion is measured by observing the displacement of a mark near each end of the bar by means of micrometer telescopes mounted on massive stone pillars. The box containing the bar is mounted on rails, and can be run aside and another exactly similar one substituted. This latter is kept at a constant temperature throughout the experiments, and thus any slight variation in the distance between the micrometer telescopes eliminated from the observations.[1]

The method here adopted of observing marks on the expanding bar, removes an objectionable feature in Ramsden's apparatus. The object-glasses (Fig. 33) have to be raised some distance above the bar to which they are fixed, and hence any slight bending of the bar due

---

[1] A full description of this apparatus, with diagrams, is given in Guillaume's *Thermométrie de précision.*

to unequal heating, or unequal strain in the material, may cause them to converge or diverge appreciably.

The apparatus just described is intended for use within moderate ranges of temperature only. For this purpose it is neither so convenient nor so delicate as Fizeau's method, as described in the section dealing with the expansion of crystals. It is important, however, that estimations of the values of coefficients of expansion at high temperatures should be directly made, particularly in the case of materials used in high temperature gas thermometry. Fizeau's apparatus would not easily lend itself to such a modification, but the method of the comparator has been adapted to this purpose by Bedford,[1] Holborn and Day, and others.

The method employed by Holborn and Day [2] for determining the expansion of Berlin porcelain between 0° C. and 1000° C. was as follows. A rod of unglazed porcelain about half a metre long was enclosed in a porcelain tube, and this again in a second tube. The inner tube was heated by a coil of nickel wire which could be raised to incandescence by an electric current. Two marks, scratched on the rod near the ends, were viewed through holes in the surrounding tubes. The temperature was measured by a thermocouple. The expansion of several metals and alloys was similarly determined. In the same way Holborn and Grüneisen [3] measured the expansion of Jena glass 59[III] as well as of Berlin porcelain. An important result of these experiments was to show that the expansion of porcelain is irregular and cannot be represented accurately over any long interval by a two-term function. This shows the danger of extrapolating the results of experiments conducted at lower temperatures.

In Day and Sosman's experiments [4] with the nitrogen gas thermometer, the bulb of the thermometer was made of an alloy of platinum and iridium in one series of experiments, and of an alloy of platinum and rhodium in another series. In order to find the coefficient of expansion of the material of the bulb, observations were made of the linear coefficient of expansion of a bar of the same alloy over the range of temperature 0°—1400° C. The bar was 50 cm. long and 6 mm. thick. Flats were filed on the ends of the bar, and a short length at each end was graduated by engraving fine lines on the flat. The bar was heated in an electric tube furnace, and a uniform temperature maintained along its whole length by means of a sub-

[1] *Phil. Mag.*, Jan. 1900.

[2] *Ann. der Physik*, Bd. iv. p. 505, 1900. *Preuss. Akad. der Wiss., Berlin*, Bd. xliv. p. 1009, 1900.

[3] *Ann. der Physik*, Bd. iv. p. 136, 1901.

[4] Day and Sosman, *Amer. Journ. Science*, vol. xxix. p. 93, 1910.

sidiary coil at each end, the current in which was regulated so as to counteract the natural tendency of the ends of the furnace to be cooler than the middle. The temperature was measured by a pair of thermocouples fastened together which could be moved back and forth along the whole length of the bar. The graduations on the bar were observed by means of telescopes through holes in the walls of the furnace, these holes being directed downwards, so as to prevent the access of cold air to the interior, and the graduations were illuminated by the rays of an incandescent glow-lamp through the same holes. A right-angled prism placed below each hole enabled the telescope to be used in a horizontal position. The two telescopes were attached rigidly together by a pair of invar[1] bars, and their distance apart was kept unaltered throughout the whole series of observations. In order to prevent the measuring apparatus from being affected by the heat of the furnace, the latter was enclosed in a jacket filled with water. The exact distance between the telescopes was determined by observations on a carefully standardised brass bar placed in the furnace and maintained at 20° C. The following results were obtained :—

$$10^6\lambda = 8\cdot79 + 0\cdot00161\theta \quad (80\% \text{ Pt}, 20\% \text{ Rh}),$$
$$10^6\lambda = 8\cdot84 + 0\cdot00131\theta \quad (90\% \text{ Pt}, 10\% \text{ Ir}).$$

109. Method of Laplace and Lavoisier.—In the method devised by MM. Laplace and Lavoisier, the expansion $l - l_0$ is not directly

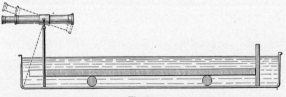

Fig. 34.

measured, but is amplified into a much greater length by means of a lever arrangement. The bar (Fig. 34) whose expansion is to be measured, is fixed at one end, but free to move at the other, which presses against the stiff arm of a lever. The other end of this arm carries a telescope directed towards a distant vertical scale. When the bar expands it pushes the arm before it, and turns the telescope round a horizontal axis, as shown (exaggerated) in figure.

If a be the length of the arm, and b the distance of the axis of rotation of the telescope from the fixed scale, and δ the observed displacement on this scale, we have at once

---

[1] Invar is a nickel steel having a very small coefficient of expansion.

$$\frac{l - l_0}{a} = \frac{\delta}{b}.$$

Hence the mean coefficient of linear expansion is given by the equation

$$\lambda = \frac{a\delta}{b l_0 \theta}.$$

In this method, although the distance δ may be very much larger than $l - l_0$, yet there are many sources of error attending the accurate estimation of the quantity a, and any error in this gives rise to a proportional error in the value of λ.

110. Relative Expansion—Differential Method.—A differential method of observing the expansion of a bar, by comparison with another of known coefficient of expansion, was suggested by De Luc,[1] and adopted by Borda,[2] to determine the expansion of the bars used in the measurement of the French meridian degree.

Two bars, AB and A'B' (Fig. 35), are fastened together at one end, AA', and are free to slide on each other, during expansion, through-

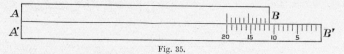

Fig. 35.

out their entire length, to their other ends. At their free ends, BB', they are graduated so that the two scales constitute a vernier which measures the relative expansion of the bars. The longer bar is made of platinum, and the shorter may be of any other metal which it is desired to compare with platinum.

A pair of bars arranged in this manner indicates its own temperature, for if the reading of the vernier be noted when the system is at 0° and 100°, or any other two known temperatures, the temperature of the apparatus may be deduced at any other time by means of the reading of the vernier alone.

When the coefficient of absolute expansion of the platinum bar is known, that of the other can be inferred, and, in this manner, Dulong and Petit determined the expansion of several solids.

Different specimens of the same metal vary considerably in their physical properties, on account of impurities, or different mechanical actions to which they may have been subjected. For this reason, the coefficient of expansion obtained for any metal will depend on the specimen employed, and considerable discrepancies exist between the results obtained by different observers. Hence, if the expansion of

[1] De Luc, *Journal de Physique de Delamétherie*, tom. xviii. p. 363, 1781.

[2] See Biot's *Traité de physique*, tom. i. p. 164.

any particular bar is required accurately, it must be determined by direct observation, for it cannot be assumed to be the same as that of any other specimen of the same material.

This differential method was employed by K. Scheel[1] in finding the linear coefficient of expansion of metals and of various Jena glasses. A tube of quartz glass (or of Jena glass 1565^{III}), closed at the lower end, was set up vertically in a bath maintained at a constant temperature. Placed upright within it was a rod of the material to be investigated, which rested on a flattened point fused into the bottom of the tube. Another rod, of the same material as the tube and having a flattened projection at its lower end, rested on the top of the first rod. The upper part of this latter rod and of this tube was cut away to the diametral plane and furnished with graduations. The relative movement of the two sets of graduations was observed. The expansion of quartz glass (or of the Jena glass) had been previously determined by Fizeau's method (Art. 129). The experiments extended over the range of temperature $-78°$ C. (in a bath of carbon dioxide snow) to $500°$ C. (in a bath of fused nitrates).

[1] K. Scheel, *Zeitschr. f. Physik*, vol. v. p. 167, 1921.

SECTION II

DILATATION OF LIQUIDS

111. Comparison of Densities.—In the case of fluids we have to deal with the cubical expansion only, and, as in the case of solids, the approximate formula,

$$V = V_0(1 + a\theta),$$

may be employed, when a is regarded as a constant, namely, the coefficient of absolute expansion at zero.

In general, liquids are more highly expansive than solids, and it is for this reason that the level of the mercury rises in the stem of a thermometer when the instrument becomes warmer. Such an instrument is, therefore, well suited to the measurement of the relative or apparent expansion of a liquid, and, if the absolute expansion of the glass of the instrument be known, the absolute expansion of the liquid can be deduced by means of the formula of Art. 106. The linear expansion of glass may be found by the methods of the foregoing section, and from this the cubical expansion is deduced by means of the formula $a = 3\lambda$. Having determined the cubical expansion of glass in this manner, Lavoisier [1] and Laplace deduced the coefficient of absolute expansion of mercury by the comparison of the mercury thermometer with a standard air thermometer between 0° and 100° C.

The weight thermometer (Art. 75) also gives the apparent expansion of the liquid with which it is filled, and, when the dilatation of the glass is known, the absolute expansion of the liquid is obtained. In this manner, Regnault deduced the absolute expansion of mercury by comparing the indications of an air and a weight thermometer immersed in the same bath. The bulb of the air thermometer was a long cylinder of glass, and its linear expansion was measured by direct observation.

The inference of the cubical expansion of one piece of glass from the linear expansion of another is a procedure which is scarcely

[1] *Mémoires de Lavoisier*, tom. i. p. 308.

allowable in very accurate scientific work, owing to the difference in
the properties of different specimens of the same substance, arising
from impurities and previous treatment. We have seen that all
solids are more or less, and glass especially, subject to this malady.
It is desirable, therefore, that some method should be devised for
measuring the expansion of liquids, which does not involve the expansion of the enclosing envelope.[1]

Such a method is afforded by the comparison of the densities of
the liquid at different temperatures. Thus, if V_0 and ρ_0 denote the
volume and density of a given mass of the liquid at $0°$, and V and ρ
the volume and density of the same mass at any other temperature θ,
we have

$$V_0\rho_0 = V\rho.$$

But since

$$V = V_0(1 + \alpha\theta),$$

it follows that

$$1 + \alpha\theta = \frac{\rho_0}{\rho}.$$

Here, then, we have the means of determining the coefficient of
absolute expansion of any liquid by simply comparing its densities at
two different temperatures. There are two general methods of comparing the densities of liquids. The first depends on weighing equal
volumes of the liquids, or on weighing a solid in the liquids and
observing the loss of weight. In this method the expansion of the
solid would again appear and complicate the operation.

The ratio of the densities of two liquids can, however, be determined directly by balancing a column of one against a column of
the other in a U-tube ; their densities are then in the inverse ratio of
the heights of the corresponding columns above their common inter-
face. This method may, therefore, be applied to compare the densities
of two columns of the same liquid at different temperatures. It is
founded on the principle stated by Boyle, that if the pressures of two
columns of the same liquid at different temperatures are equal, their
heights are inversely as their densities. By this means, then, the
complications introduced by the expansion of the vessel in which it
is necessary to enclose the liquid, are entirely got rid of.

**112. Method of Equilibrating Columns—Experiments of Dulong
and Petit.**—The principle of the method of equilibrating columns, as

---

[1] The method was used by Chappuis to find the absolute expansion of mercury
(*Trav. et Mém. du Bureau Int. des Poids et Mesures*, tom. xiii. C, 1907). The linear
expansion of the long cylindrical glass bulb was determined, and the cubical
expansion deduced. The same method was also used by Thiesen, Scheel, and
Sell (*Wiss. Abhand. der Physikalisch-Technischen Reichsanstalt*, Bd. ii. p. 73,
1895). Chappuis' experiments were made in 1890 (see Art. 114).

adopted by Dulong and Petit,[1] in their experiments on the absolute expansion of mercury, is illustrated in Fig. 36.   The mercury to be experimented on is contained in a two-arm tube, AA′ BB′, one arm of which, AA′, is kept in a chamber filled with broken ice, and the other, BB′, is surrounded by a bath which can be heated to any temperature desired.   The cross-tube, A′B′, is much smaller in bore than the upper arms, and is arranged so that its axis is accurately horizontal. This being secured, the heights of the surfaces at A and B above the axis of the cross-tube, when equilibrium is attained, will be inversely

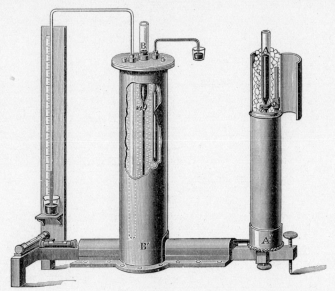

Fig. 36.

as the densities of the mercury in the corresponding arms.   Hence, if AA′ be at 0°, and BB′ at θ° C., we have

$$1 + a\theta = \frac{\rho_0}{\rho} = \frac{h}{h_0},$$

where h is the height of the surface B above the axis of the horizontal tube, and h_0 that of A above the same level.   Hence the mean coefficient of absolute expansion of mercury between the temperatures 0° and θ° C. is given by the equation

$$a = \frac{h - h_0}{h_0 \theta}.$$

The determination of a is thus reduced to the measurement of the heights h and h_0.

[1] Dulong and Petit, *Ann. de Chimie et de Physique*, 2e, tom. vii. p. 113, 1817.

Strictly speaking, equilibrium is never secured in this experiment, for, on account of the difference of density, there will always be two feeble currents in the cross-tube—an upper current from the hot arm into the cold arm, and a lower current in the reverse direction. At the level of the axis of the tube, equilibrium may, however, be regarded as existing, and it is for this reason that the heights h and h_0 are measured from the axis of this tube. In order to reduce this flow the bore of the horizontal tube is made narrow, but still wide enough to allow of equilibrium being freely established. The vertical branches, on the other hand, are about 2 cm. wide in their upper parts, so that no error may be caused in the difference of height $h - h_0$ by capillary depression. If these tubes were narrow, and yet of the same bore, such an error would be introduced into $h - h_0$ by the difference of temperature of the arms, for the capillary depression (or elevation) of a liquid in a tube depends on the temperature, being less at high than at low temperatures.

At the beginning of the experiment the arm AA' was jacketed with ice, and the arm BB' was encased in a copper cylinder containing oil, and heated by a furnace. Mercury was poured into the tubes till the free surface in the hot tube rose approximately into view above the bath chamber. When the temperature of the bath became stationary, a few drops of mercury at zero were added to the cold arm so as to bring the surface of the mercury in the warm arm into view over the top of the bath cylinder. A door in the ice jacket was then opened, and some of the ice removed, so that the surface of the mercury in the cold arm could be seen, and the heights h and h_0 determined. The temperature of the bath was registered by means of an air thermometer with a long cylindrical bulb, and also by a weight thermometer. The bulbs of these thermometers being long, they were supposed to indicate the mean temperature of the bath, and this was taken to be the average temperature of the mercury in the arm BB'.

The heights h and h_0 were determined by means of a specially constructed cathetometer, which read directly to $\frac{1}{20}$th mm., and by estimation to $\frac{1}{50}$th mm. The surface of the hot column was first observed, and then the surface of the cold column. This gave the difference of level $h - h_0$. The height h_0 was determined by measuring the distance between the surface of the mercury and a fixed reference mark near the top of the mercury column. This reference mark was carried by an iron rod which passed down through the ice jacket, and its distance from the axis of the cross-tube was determined accurately once for all.

At high temperatures the air and weight thermometers [1] gave discordant results, so that the indications of the former were used exclusively by Dulong and Petit. The following table contains the results of their experiments. It gives the mean coefficient of expansion between 0° and 100°, 0° and 200°, 0° and 300°, on the air thermometer with the corresponding indications of the weight thermometer. Between 0° and 100° the coefficient is nearly constant, but it increases as the temperature becomes more elevated.

Air Thermometer.	Weight Thermometer.	Mean Coefficient a.		
		max.	min.	mean.
0°	0°			
100°	100°	$\frac{1}{5547}$	$\frac{1}{5552}$	$\frac{1}{5550}$
200°	204°·61	$\frac{1}{5419}$	$\frac{1}{5431}$	$\frac{1}{5425}$
300°	314°·15	$\frac{1}{5289}$	$\frac{1}{5309}$	$\frac{1}{5300}$

In this form of the experiment it is not easy to secure that the mean temperature of the bath surrounding the thermometer bulb shall be the same as that surrounding the tube which contains the mercury, and from the method of heating the bath it is difficult to maintain its temperature stationary while the observations are being made, so that very great expedition is required in making the readings. Furthermore, it is essential that the air in the thermometer shall be perfectly dry, for if it contains any water vapour a considerable correction will become necessary at high temperatures. Finally, the value of the coefficient of dilatation of air ('00375), used by Dulong and Petit, was that deduced by Gay-Lussac, and was not sufficiently accurate.

For these reasons the determination of the coefficient of absolute expansion of mercury was undertaken by Regnault, on the same principle, but with improved apparatus, in which the errors of his predecessors were completely avoided. The close accordance of his results with those of Dulong and Petit shows, however, how excellently their experiments were conducted.

113. Regnault's Experiments.—In the form of apparatus employed by Dulong and Petit the chief source of uncertainty was the temperature of the bath, arising from the fact that being always filled to the top it could not be properly stirred to ensure uniformity of temperature throughout. A column of liquid heated from below may

---

[1] In such an investigation as this it is of course illegitimate to employ a weight thermometer or any liquid-in-glass thermometer, unless it has been standardised by comparison with an air or gas thermometer.

present great differences of temperature in different parts if not kept constantly stirred, and the difficulty is not entirely overcome by making the thermometer bulb the whole length of the bath, for even then the temperature registered by the thermometer may not represent the mean temperature of the column of mercury situated in another part of the bath. Besides this source of error others occur in the direct observation of the summit of the warm column, which necessitates a little of the mercury being outside the bath, and it is also objectionable to have the surfaces of the two columns at different temperatures, as the surface tension will not be the same in both. The latter error is lessened, but not completely got rid of, by making the upper parts of the tubes wide. Besides this the columns were only

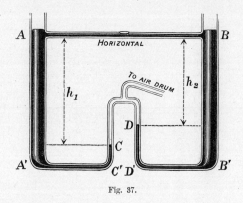

Fig. 37.

about 50 or 60 cm. long, and the temperature of the column $h - h_0$ was not known with certainty.

For these reasons Regnault modified the apparatus in such a way that the bath could be constantly stirred, and its temperature kept uniform. Further, the surfaces of the mercurial columns which were to be observed were enclosed in the same bath, and kept at a constant temperature.

The principle of the disposition of Regnault's apparatus is shown in Fig. 37. The vertical tubes AA′ and BB′ are made of iron, and are joined at their tops, A and B, by a horizontal cross-tube AB. The horizontal cross-tube joining the lower ends of AA′ and BB′ in the experiments of Dulong and Petit is here interrupted in its middle part at C′ and D′, where two vertical glass tubes, CC′ and DD′, are screwed in and connected with each other, and with a reservoir of air, which can be modified in pressure by means of an air-pump. In these glass tubes the mercury stands at C and D, and at these surfaces the pressure is the same, viz. the pressure of the air in the reservoir. The long vertical tubes AA′ and BB′ are kept in baths at known temperatures, and the mercury in them is at a common level, viz. that of the horizontal communicating cross-tube AB.   Hence if the temperatures

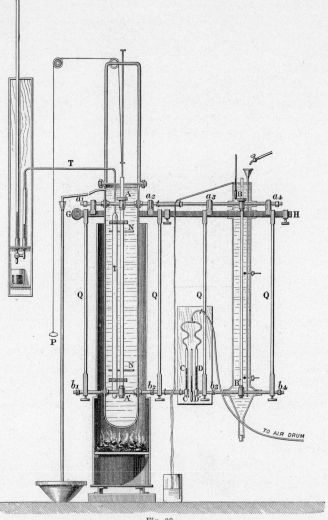

Fig. 38.

be θ_1 and θ_2, while the difference of level AC is h_1, and the height of B above D is h_2, we have [1]

$$\frac{h_1}{1 + a\theta_1} = \frac{h_2}{1 + a\theta_2};$$

---

[1] We have here assumed, for simplicity, that the whole of AC is at temperature θ_1 and BD at temperature θ_2.

so that

$$a = \frac{h_1 - h_2}{h_2\theta_1 - h_1\theta_2}.$$

The details of the apparatus are shown in Fig. 38.

The vertical tubes AA' and BB' were made of iron, and were much longer than those used by Dulong and Petit, their length being about 150 cm., and their diameter 1 cm. Their upper ends above the connecting cross-tube were open, so that the mercury could be introduced at will. One of them, BB', was kept cold by a bath, through which a constant current of cold water circulated, and the horizontal arms were cooled both above and below by a stream of the same water. The other vertical tube AA' was heated in a bath of oil, whose temperature was rendered uniform by means of agitators, NN, worked by a cord P passing over a pulley.

The temperature was registered by means of an air thermometer, whose bulb extended throughout the whole length of the tube AA'. To support the apparatus and secure the horizontality of the cross-tube AB, Regnault attached it to a strong horizontal bar GH, movable round one extremity G, and supported on two screws, one at its middle and the other at its extremity H. The cross-tube AB rested on it, and carried four brass rings, a_1, a_2, a_3, a_4, on which cross marks were traced to mark the axis of the tube, and these were arranged horizontally by observation of a cathetometer, and by adjustment of the controlling screws of the supporting bar GH. From this bar ran also four metal rods, Q, Q, Q, Q, descending vertically, and supporting the lower parts of the apparatus, the points of attachment there being controlled by screws by which the lower cross-tubes could be made horizontal by means of marks, as in the case of the upper tube. In order to measure the heights h_1 and h_2 a small hole was drilled in the cross-tube AB, and the pressure in the air reservoir was increased till the mercury rising in the tubes just began to overflow at this aperture.

As soon as this was secured the temperatures of the baths were noted as well as the heights of the mercury in the middle vertical tubes of glass, CC' and DD'. Let H and H' be the heights [1] in the long vertical tubes, and h and h' the heights in the short vertical tubes, and let θ be the temperature in AA', and θ' the temperature in all the other tubes. Then we have the pressure of the air in the reservoir exceeding the pressure of the atmosphere by that due to AA' minus

---

[1] H is the vertical height of the horizontal tube a_1, a_4 above b_1, b_2, and H' the height of the same tube above b_3, b_4, while h and h' are the heights of surfaces at C and D above b_1, b_2, and b_3, b_4 respectively. If H = H' for one temperature of the bath, then these heights will differ slightly for every other temperature, on account of the expansion of the tube AA'.

that due to CC', and this must be also equal to that due to BB' minus
that due to DD'; hence, denoting the coefficient of absolute expansion
of mercury by m, we have—

$$\frac{H}{1+m\theta} - \frac{h}{1+m\theta'} = \frac{H'}{1+m\theta'} - \frac{h'}{1+m\theta''}$$

or

$$\frac{H}{1+m\theta} = \frac{H'+h-h'}{1+m\theta'}.$$

Hence

$$m = \frac{H'-H+h-h'}{\theta'H - \theta(H'+h-h')}.$$

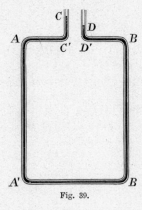

Fig. 39.

Second Form of the Apparatus.—M. Regnault also worked with another form of
apparatus in which the lower cross-tube
(Fig. 39) was uninterrupted, as in the
apparatus of Dulong and Petit. The upper
cross-tube was, however, interrupted by two
vertical glass tubes CC' and DD', in which
the mercury columns stood at levels C and
D. The mercury columns are thus in
direct equilibrium. The axes of the tubes
AC' and BD' are horizontal, and at the
same level, but the lower tube A'B' is more
or less inclined on account of the unequal
dilatations of AA' and BB'. On equating the pressures at the lowest
part of the apparatus we have

$$\frac{H}{1+m\theta} + \frac{h}{1+m\theta'} + \frac{\epsilon}{1+m\theta'} = \frac{H'}{1+m\theta'} + \frac{h'}{1+m\theta'},$$

where ϵ is the small difference of level of the ends of A'B'. If the
lower tube be horizontal $\epsilon = 0$, and we have

$$\frac{H}{1+m\theta} = \frac{H'+h'-h}{1+m\theta'}.$$

Therefore

$$m = \frac{H'-H+h'-h}{\theta'H - \theta(H'+h'-h)}.$$

Regnault executed four series of experiments, which comprised in
all about 130 observations, at temperatures varying between 25° C.
and 350° C. The results of these experiments were then plotted
graphically, and a curve traced which exhibited the relation between
the temperature and the whole dilatation at any temperature. If m
denotes the mean coefficient of expansion between 0° and θ, the whole
dilatation per unit volume between these temperatures will be

$$\Delta_\theta = m\theta,$$

and if m be constant, the curve obtained by plotting the temperatures along the axis of x and the dilatation Δ along the axis of y will be a right line $y = mx$ inclined to the axis of x at an angle, whose tangent is m. The curve obtained by Regnault was, however, not a right line, but was convex towards the axis of x, indicating that m increased with the temperature. Taking m to be of the form

$$m = a + b\theta,$$

the dilatation will be

$$\Delta_\theta = a\theta + b\theta^2,$$

and the curve will be parabolic.

Assuming the above formula to hold, the true coefficient of dilatation at any temperature will be

$$m_\theta = \frac{1}{V}\frac{dV}{d\theta},$$

where V is the bulk at $\theta°$ of the mass which has unit volume at zero $= 1 + \Delta = 1 + a\theta + b\theta^2$. Therefore

$$m_\theta = \frac{a + 2b\theta}{1 + a\theta + b\theta^2}.$$

The coefficient of expansion referred to the zero volume, or what we have termed the zero coefficient of expansion, is

$$m_0 = \frac{1}{V_0}\frac{dV}{d\theta} = a + 2b\theta.$$

The results of Regnault's experiments gave

$$a = 0\cdot0001791, \quad b = 0\cdot000000025,$$

so that the mean coefficient of expansion of mercury was found to be

$$m = 0\cdot0001791 + 0\cdot000000025\theta,$$

and the zero coefficient of expansion was found to be

$$m_0 = 0\cdot0001791 + 0\cdot00000005\theta.$$

Between $0°$ and $100°$ the coefficient m is sensibly constant, its value at $50°$ C. being $\frac{1}{5547}$. The corresponding value found by Dulong and Petit was $\frac{1}{5550}$.

The absolute method of measuring the expansion of mercury was also employed by Callendar and Moss[1] and by Chappuis.[2] An ingenious device was used by Callendar and Moss to avoid the use of very long columns of mercury, while at the same time obtaining an equivalent difference of level between the hot and cold columns. The principle of the method is illustrated by Fig. 40. HH and CC are vertical columns of mercury, of which those marked H are kept hot and those marked C cold. The

[1] Callendar and Moss, *Phil. Trans.* vol. ccxi. p. 1, 1911.

[2] Chappuis, *Trav. et Mém. du Bureau Int. des Poids et Mesures*, tom. xvi. p. 7, 1917.

whole tube being filled with mercury, it is clear that the difference
in level between the ends at A and B will be the same as that
due to a single pair of columns whose lengths are equal to the
sums of the lengths of HH and CC respectively.   In the actual
apparatus the arrangement was modified as follows : the tube,
instead of being bent up and down as in the figure, was in the
form of a rectangular coil, thus bringing all the hot limbs close
together, and similarly all the cold limbs.   There were six turns

Fig. 40.

in the coil, so that there were six hot and six
cold columns, each 2 metres long and 3·5 mm. in
bore.   The tubes were made of steel, the horizontal
portions above and below being only 1 mm. in
bore.   The lower connecting tubes were kept
rigidly horizontal, and there was an arrangement
by which a certain portion DE of each of the
upper connecting tubes could be made horizontal
after the temperature of the columns had been
adjusted, the narrow steel tubes being sufficiently
flexible for the purpose.   It is evident that if the
cold column C on the left is at a uniform temperature up to D, while the hot column H on the right
is likewise at a uniform temperature up to E, then the middle of the
bore in the horizontal portion DE may be taken as the top of the cold
column on the left and of the hot column on the right.   The temperature was measured by platinum resistance thermometers extending the
whole length of the columns.   The results obtained differed somewhat
from those obtained by Chappuis by means of the weight thermometer method (Art. 114).   On this account Chappuis carried out
a new series of experiments, using the same method as Callendar
and Moss with slight modifications, chiefly in the dimensions of the
apparatus.   His results thus obtained by the absolute method agreed
closely with those which he had previously got by the weight
thermometer method, and they also agree well with those of Thiesen,
Scheel, and Sell, who used the weight thermometer.   The mean
coefficient of expansion given by Chappuis is

$$m = 0\cdot18162884 \times 10^{-3} + 8\cdot5962282 \times 10^{-9}\theta.$$

114. Application of the Weight Thermometer.—If the linear
coefficient of expansion of the bulb of the weight thermometer is
directly observed, the cubical expansion may be inferred, and thus
(Art. 106) the absolute expansion of the liquid in the thermometer
deduced from an observation of the apparent expansion.   This

method was used by Chappuis[1] for mercury, and also by Thiesen, Scheel, and Sell.[2] Again, once the coefficient of absolute expansion of mercury is known, the weight thermometer may be applied with facility to the determination of the coefficients of absolute expansion of other liquids. For when the instrument is filled with mercury, a single observation gives us the apparent expansion of the mercury in the glass of the thermometer. Thus if w be the weight that flows over at θ degrees and W_0 the weight that fills it at zero, we have

$$a = \frac{w}{\theta(W_0 - w)},$$

consequently the coefficient of expansion of the glass g can be found from the equation (Art. 106)

$$1 + m = (1 + a)(1 + g),$$

where m is used to denote the coefficient of absolute expansion of mercury.

The coefficient g being known, the instrument can be filled with any other liquid, and its apparent coefficient a' determined in a similar manner. The real coefficient a of the liquid will then be found from Liquids. the formula

$$1 + a = (1 + a')(1 + g).$$

Repeating the observations at various temperatures, the variation of a with temperature may be found, and the coefficients in the formula

$$a = a + b\theta + c\theta^2$$

determined.

In a similar manner the weight thermometer may be employed to

Fig. 41.

determine the cubical dilatation of solids. Thus, when the coefficient of absolute expansion of any liquid is known, a single observation gives the cubical dilatation of the material of which the bulb of the thermometer is constructed. It was in this manner that Dulong and Petit[3] first attempted to measure the coefficient of expansion of iron, knowing the absolute expansion of mercury, and using a weight ther- Solids. mometer with an iron bulb. They soon, however, abandoned this process for the more simple and general method of enclosing a bar of the solid under investigation inside the bulb of an ordinary weight thermometer made of glass, as shown in Fig. 41. In the case of solids

[1] *Trav. et Mém. du Bureau Int. des Poids et Mesures*, tom. xiii. C, 1907.
[2] *Wiss. Abhand. d. Phys.-Tech. Reichsanstalt*, Bd. ii. p. 73, 1895.
[3] Dulong and Petit, *Ann. de Chimie et de Physique*, 2e, tom. ii. p. 261, 1816.

which are not attacked by mercury no precautions are necessary, further than the attachment of bearings to the ends of the bar to keep it steady, and avoid fracture of the bulb. In the case of solids which are attacked by mercury, another liquid may be used, or their surfaces may be varnished or oxidised.

In all cases it is necessary to know the weight W'_0 and the density ρ'_0 of the solid at zero. Its volume at zero is then W'_0/ρ'_0, and its volume at θ is

$$\frac{W'_0}{\rho'_0}(1+x\theta),$$

where x is its coefficient of expansion. The remainder of the bulb and stem is filled with mercury. If W_0 and ρ_0 be the weight and density of this at zero, and if a quantity w flows over at θ, then the weight left in the bulb is $W_0 - w$, and its volume is

$$\frac{W_0-w}{\rho_0}(1+m\theta).$$

Now the volume of the bulb at zero is

$$\frac{W_0}{\rho_0} + \frac{W'_0}{\rho'_0}.$$

Therefore its volume at θ is

$$\left(\frac{W_0}{\rho_0} + \frac{W'_0}{\rho'_0}\right)(1+g\theta).$$

Hence we have the equation

$$\left(\frac{W_0}{\rho_0} + \frac{W'_0}{\rho'_0}\right)(1+g\theta) = \frac{W'_0}{\rho'_0}(1+x\theta) + \frac{W_0-w}{\rho_0}(1+m\theta),$$

or finally

$$\left(\frac{W_0}{\rho_0} + \frac{W'_0}{\rho'_0}\right)g\theta = \frac{W'_0}{\rho'_0}x\theta + \frac{W_0}{\rho_0}m\theta - \frac{w}{\rho_0}(1+m\theta).$$

The quantities W_0/ρ_0, W'_0/ρ'_0, and w/ρ_0 are obviously the zero volume of the mercury contained in the instrument, the volume of the solid at zero, and the zero volume of the mercury which overflows.

It is to be remarked that the sensibility of the weight thermometer increases with the density of the liquid employed, and also with its coefficient of expansion. For this reason the great density of mercury, and its tolerably large coefficient of expansion, recommend it especially for use in the weight thermometer. In addition, mercury does not evaporate sensibly, and in this respect possesses a great advantage over volatile liquids. When such liquids are employed, every precaution must be taken to prevent loss by evaporation. In such cases, however, it is better to dispense with the overflowing method, and adopt the following.

Weight thermometer.

115. The Dilatometer—Application of the Ordinary Thermometer.—In the case of volatile liquids of small specific gravity, the

accuracy obtained by reducing the observation to a weighing is more
than counterbalanced in the weight thermometer by the errors introduced by evaporation.   For this reason, the employment in these cases
of an apparatus similar to the ordinary thermometer, as suggested by
De Luc,[1] is preferable.   The instrument (Fig. 42) is simply a
large-bulbed thermometer, with an accurately graduated stem,
the volume of the bulb and of each division of the stem being
known.   An experiment with mercury gives the coefficient of
expansion of the instrument ; and, when it contains any other
liquid, two observations of the apparent volumes of the liquid
at any two temperatures give the mean coefficient of apparent
expansion between these temperatures.

This method is at once exceedingly simple and precise,
and was employed by Kopp,[2] and also by M. Is. Pierre,[3] in
their classical researches on the expansion of liquids.

116. Maximum Density of Water.—In the case of water a
notable anomaly in the expansion is exhibited in the neighbourhood of 4° C.   At, or very near, this point the liquid possesses
a greater density than at any other temperature, and expands
whether its temperature be raised or lowered.   Thus water
becomes specifically lighter in passing from 4° either up or
down the scale, and the volume of any given mass is least Fig. 42.
at this temperature.

Hope's[4] well-known experiment places the whole process clearly   Hope's ex-
in view.   A tall glass beaker containing water is furnished with two   periment.
thermometers, and an annular trough, as shown in Fig. 43.   A freezing

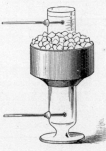

mixture of snow and salt is placed in the
trough, and the middle of the water column
is gradually cooled.   While this cooling is in
progress the indications of the thermometers
are most interesting.   Before the application
of the freezing mixture the temperature
registered by the upper thermometer slightly
exceeds that of the lower, for the warmer and
lighter portions of the water float to the top.
The first effect of the freezing mixture is to
reduce the lower thermometer to 4° C. without

Fig. 43.

seriously affecting the upper.   The lower thermometer now remains

---

[1] De Luc, *Recherches sur les modifications de l'atmosphère*, tom. ii. p. 124, etc.

[2] Kopp, *Pogg. Ann.* Band lxxii., 1847.

[3] I. Pierre, *Ann. de Chimie et de Physique*, 3e, toms. xv. xix. xx. xxi.
xxxi. xxxiii.

[4] Thos. Chas. Hope, *Ann. de Chimie*, 1re, tom. liii. p. 272, 1805.

stationary, and the upper begins to fall rapidly till its temperature is reduced to zero, and ice begins to form on the top. The explanation is that water is heaviest at 4° C., and that it sinks as it cools, the layers which first reach 4° collecting at the bottom. After a certain stage certain layers become cooled below 4°, and the coldest parts rise above those which are less cold till ice forms on the top.

This property of water may also be well illustrated to a class by means of a float which rises to the surface in water near 4° C., and sinks when the temperature is a little above or below this point. The float may be constructed of a piece of glass tubing closed and so weighted that it will float in water at 4°, and sink in water at zero. A beaker of ice-cold water may be placed on the lecture table, with the float immersed, and lying at the bottom, the water not being dense enough to float it at zero. In the warm room, however, the temperature of the water begins to rise, the 4° layers sink to the bottom, and the float begins to creep towards the surface. Here it remains till the temperature passes 4°. The warmer layers now rise to the surface, and the float begins to sink gradually to the bottom.

It is on account of this property that a small pool of water on the surface of a glacier gradually eats its way into the ice, growing deeper and deeper with every return of the sun. Thus, if the whole mass of water in the pool is at zero, then, in the sunshine, the surface layer grows warm, and sinks to the bottom, where it melts another film of ice, and this process proceeds as long as the surface heat is supplied.

The anomalous expansion of water in the neighbourhood of 4° C. is a warning against the choice of any liquid at random as a standard thermometric substance. A thermometer filled with water would give the same indication, whether it grew warmer or colder from 4° C. In fact, the temperature at which the apparent volume of water in glass is least (or about what we call 5° C.) would be the lowest possible temperature attainable if water were the standard thermometric substance. Such an illustration shows us how utterly unintelligible and chaotic any system of thermometry founded on the expansion of a liquid might be.

117. Study of the Dilatation of Water.—The study of the dilatation of water has attracted much attention, not merely because of its anomalous behaviour at 4° C., but also because of the fact that water is the standard of density to which all other substances are referred. The unit of weight being defined as the weight of unit volume of water at some definite temperature and pressure, the variations of the density of water with temperature and pressure become a study of prime importance. It was in this connection that the first precise experiments on the expansion of water were undertaken by Lefèvre-Gineau.[1] The method employed was by observing the loss of weight of a metallic cylinder when weighed in water at various temperatures. This method was also adopted by Hälström, who used a sphere of glass, and afterwards by Hagen and Matthiessen.

In the experiments of Hälström,[2] the coefficient of linear expansion of a rod of glass was directly determined by the method of Ramsden, observations of the elongation being made at different temperatures between $0°$ and $30°$.   Any two of these observations are sufficient to determine the coefficients a and b in the formula

$$l = l_0(1 + a\theta + b\theta^2),$$

and when these are known the volume V at any temperature $\theta°$ is given by the equation

$$V = V_0(1 + a\theta + b\theta^2)^3.$$

For the glass rod Hälström found the values

$$a = 0.000001960, \quad b = 0.000000105,$$

and he assumed that the same values would apply to the expansion of the glass sphere used in the weighing experiments.

This supposition is not strictly allowable, and the expansion of the glass sphere should be determined directly by means of the weight thermometer, or otherwise, as was done by Matthiessen.

When the glass sphere, suspended by a fine platinum wire from a pan of a balance, and counterpoised, is immersed in water, the weight required to be added to the pan to restore equilibrium is the weight of the volume V of water displaced by the sphere.   Denoting this by W, we have W some function of the temperature depending both on the expansion of the glass and on that of the water.   Thus we may write

$$W = W_0(1 + a\theta + \beta\theta^2 + \gamma\theta^3 + \ldots).$$

By means of experiments at different temperatures Hälström found

$$a = +0.000058815, \quad \beta = -0.0000062168, \quad \gamma = +0.00000001443.$$

Now the density ρ of water at any temperature θ is given by the formula

$$\rho = \frac{W}{V} = \frac{W_0}{V_0} \frac{1 + a\theta + \beta\theta^2 + \gamma\theta^3}{(1 + a\theta + b\theta^2)^3} = \rho_0(1 + l\theta + m\theta^2 + n\theta^3),$$

where the coefficients l, m, n are known in terms of a, β, γ, and a, b.

The density will be a maximum when

$$\frac{d\rho}{d\theta} = 0,$$

---

[1] Lefèvre-Gineau, *Expériences faites pour déterminer la valeur du gramme.*   See report in the *Journal de Physique de Delamétherie*, tom. xlix. p. 161.

[2] Hälström, *Ann. de Chimie et de Phys.*, 2e, tom. xxviii. p. 56, 1825.

which gives the equation

$$3n\theta^2 + 2m\theta + l = 0.$$

This equation gives two values of θ, one of which lies outside the limits of temperature, to which the above formulæ apply, and the other being equal to $4°\cdot108$ C. The coefficients l, m, and n were

$$l = 0\cdot000052939, \quad m = -0\cdot0000065322, \quad n = 0\cdot00000001445.$$

The following table gives the volume at various temperatures up to $30°$ of a mass of water possessing unit volume at zero, according to Hälström :—

Temperature.	Volume.	Temperature.	Volume.
0°	1·0000000	8°	0·9999872
1°	0·9999536	9°	1·0000421
2°	0·9999202	15°	1·0006273
3°	0·9998996	20°	1·0014406
4°	0·9998818	25°	1·0025398
4°·1	0·99988177	30°	1·003916
5°	0·9998968	...	...

According to this table the maximum density would appear to be somewhat above $4°$ C. ; but as the variation is small in the neighbourhood of a maximum it is difficult to fix the temperature of maximum density with absolute precision.

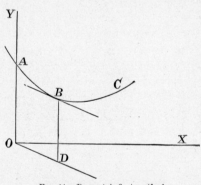

FIG. 44.—Despretz's first method.

Most of the other experimenters in this subject have proceeded by the dilatometer or ordinary thermometer method (Art. 115). By this method Despretz[1] plotted a curve, the ordinates of which represented the apparent volume in glass, and the corresponding abscissæ the temperature. This curve is approximately parabolic, as shown in Fig. 44, the vertex of the parabola corresponding to the temperature of about $5°$ C. This then is the temperature of least apparent volume. The real volume of the water at any temperature may be found by adding to the corresponding ordinate of this curve the dilatation of the glass. For this purpose it is only necessary to construct a curve below

[1] Despretz, *Ann. de Chimie et de Physique*, 2e, tom. lxx. p. 5 ; tom. lxxiii. p. 296, 1840.

OX representing the dilatation of the glass.   If the glass be supposed
to expand uniformly through the range of temperature employed, this
curve will be a right line OD, such that, if v be the volume at $\theta°$, and
v_0 the volume at $0°$, the dilatation of the glass will be $v - v_0 = v_0 g\theta$,
and therefore [1] the tangent of the angle DOX will be $v_0 g$, where g is
the mean coefficient of expansion of the glass, and is determined by a
previous experiment by the method already indicated in Art. 114.
The vertical ordinate intercepted between the curve ABC and the line
OD will therefore represent the real volume of the water at the corresponding temperature.   Hence, to obtain the temperature of least
volume it is only necessary to find the least ordinate between ABC
and OD.   This is done by drawing a line parallel to OD so as to touch

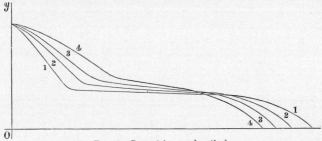

FIG. 45.—Despretz's second method.

the curve ABC, and the corresponding ordinate BD cuts the axis OX
at a point which corresponds to the temperature of maximum density.

In these experiments when the water was pure and free from air,
it did not solidify at zero; but remained liquid to $-20°$ C.   The
curve ABC could accordingly be continued far below zero, and it
showed that at these low temperatures the water continued to increase
in volume up to the point of solidification.   The sudden change of
volume of water in solidifying at zero is thus merely a leap replacing
the gradual change which is here shown to occur.

A form of experiment very similar to Hope's was also conducted
by Despretz.   A beaker of water furnished with four thermometers,
as in Hope's experiment, was allowed to cool in a cold atmosphere, and
the indications of the thermometers were carefully noted.   A curve
was constructed for each thermometer (Fig. 45), showing its variations
of temperature, the time being measured along the axis of x and the
corresponding temperatures parallel to the axis of y.   The lowest
thermometer (1) fell most rapidly in temperature at first, and the
highest (4) most slowly.   The lowest then remained stationary at $4°$,

[1] v_0 is the apparent volume of the water.

while the others gradually fell, the highest falling most rapidly till its temperature became zero. The curve appertaining to the lowest thermometer was thus at first below the others, and was cut by them at 4°, and this thermometer was the last to attain to zero. The mean result obtained by Despretz by the first method was 4°·007, and by the second 3°·997. Numbers agreeing very closely with these were obtained by other experimenters. Thus Hälström found 4°·108, H. Kopp 4°·08, and Is. Pierre 3°·92. From these numbers we may conclude that 4° C. represents very approximately the temperature of the maximum density of water. A general table of the results of various observers will be found in Rosetti's [1] memoirs on the dilatation of distilled water.

The most accurate method of finding the temperature of maximum density of water is that of Joule and Playfair.[2] The apparatus is

Fig. 46.

represented in Fig. 46. Two upright vessels of tinned iron, aa, each 4½ feet high and ·6 inches in diameter, were connected at the bottom by a brass pipe b, 6 inches long and furnished with a wide stopcock affording a clear passage 1 inch in bore. A rectangular trough c, 1 inch square in section, formed a communication between the tops of the vessels. In the middle of this trough there was a slide by which the motion of a current could be stopped when requisite. Wooden brackets dd supported the vessels, which were covered with hay-bands to insulate them from the surrounding air. Each of the vessels was provided with a stirrer and with a very accurate thermometer. A glass ball, whose weight was adjusted so that it just floated, was placed in the trough c. The vessels were filled with distilled water as free as possible from dissolved air.

The method of experimenting was as follows: The vessels having been filled with water at about 37° F., the temperature of one of them was increased to about 41°·5 by the addition of a small quantity of hot water. The thermometers, suitably supported, were then placed so as to dip about 6 inches in the vessels. The stopcock was closed and the slide adjusted so as to close the trough. The water in each vessel was then thoroughly stirred and the temperatures noted. The stopcock was then opened and the slide carefully

[1] Rosetti, *Ann. de Chimie et de Phys.*, 4ᵉ, tom. x. p. 461; tom. xvii. p. 370, 1867–69.

[2] *Joule's Scientific Papers*, vol. ii. p. 173.

removed from the trough.   After waiting three minutes the glass
ball was placed in the trough and its motion watched for two or
three minutes with the help of a graduated rule placed at the top of
the trough.   The stopcock was then closed, the slide replaced, and
the temperatures again noted.   The mean of the temperatures thus
observed before and after each trial of the velocity of the current was
taken as the temperature of the observation.

It is clear that it is possible in this way to find two temperatures,
one slightly above and the other slightly below the point of maximum
density, such that the densities of the two columns are equal.   On
opening the communications the glass ball would then remain
stationary, and the temperature of maximum density would then be
very accurately given by the mean of the observed temperatures of
the two columns.   In practice, the velocity of the glass ball was
measured, a curve was drawn from the results of a series of observations, and thus in calculating the temperature of maximum density
allowance was made for the small residual difference of density in
the two columns.   As an example, the results of the first series of
experiments is appended—

Temperature of Water in Warmer Vessel.	Temperature of Water in Colder Vessel.	Mean.	Velocity of Current in Inches per Hour.
41°·183	37°·348	39°·265	280 from warmer
41°·129	37°·368	39°·248	240 ,, ,,
40°·959	37°·363	39°·161	20 ,, ,,
40°·905	37°·368	39°·136	8 ,, ,,
40°·711	37°·317	39°·014	40 from colder

The temperature of the laboratory during the above series of
experiments was about 38° F.   The temperature of maximum density
calculated from the observations was 39°·102 F.   In the last series
of experiments the difference of temperature between the two columns
was only about 1°·5.   The mean result for all four series of experiments was 39°·101 F., which is equal to about 3°·95 C.

The variation of the density of water with temperature has been
determined by Chappuis[1] by the dilatometer method.   The water
was enclosed in an iridio-platinum vessel similar to the bulb of the
standard hydrogen thermometer.   In connection with this vessel was
a small U-tube containing mercury, and as the water expanded it expelled mercury, and the volume expelled was determined by weighing.
The U tube was kept at a constant temperature at which the density

[1] *Ann. der Physik*, Bd. lxiii. p. 202, 1897.

of mercury was accurately known.   The expansion cannot, according to M. Chappuis, be well represented by a formula, even if four powers of the temperature were retained.

The foregoing results apply to the case of water under the pressure of one atmosphere.   When the pressure is increased the temperature of maximum density recedes towards zero, and in a series of experiments, M. Amagat [1] finds the mean rate of retrogression to be about $0°\cdot025$ C. per atmosphere increase of pressure.   Thus under the pressures $41\cdot6$, $93\cdot3$, $144\cdot8$ atmos. the temperatures of greatest density were found to be $3°\cdot3$, $2°\cdot0$, and $0°\cdot6$ respectively.

118. Maximum Density of Saline Solutions.—It was established by Despretz [2] that other liquids, especially saline solutions, exhibit temperatures of maximum density under a given pressure.   The solutions were observed in the dilatometer, and in this they could be reduced in the liquid state to temperatures considerably below their normal freezing points, and their variations of volume could be noted as in the case of water.   The effect of salts dissolved in water is usually to notably lower the temperature of maximum density as well as the normal freezing point.

An elaborate series of experiments was carried out by P. G. Tait on the properties of fresh and salt water.[3]   The following are some of the results obtained :—

The temperature of maximum density of fresh water is lowered about $3°$ C. for each ton per square inch pressure (150 atmos.).   This agrees fairly well with Amagat's result given in Art. 117.

The lowering of the freezing point of fresh water under pressure, as determined by experiment, accords well with the theoretical value given by J. Thomson (see Art. 178), i.e. it is about $1°\cdot13$ C. per ton pressure on the square inch.   Hence under a pressure of $2\cdot14$ tons per square inch the maximum density point would coincide with the freezing point, at $-2°\cdot4$ C.   The compressibility of fresh water diminishes as the temperature rises from $0°$ C. under atmospheric pressure.   At about $60°$ C. it attains a minimum value, increasing again at higher temperatures.   Increase of pressure lowers the temperature of minimum compressibility.

The behaviour of salt water agrees in its general character with that of fresh.   The expansibility of water, salt or fresh, increases considerably with pressure.

---

[1] Amagat, *Comptes rendus*, 1st May 1893, tom. cxvi. p. 946.   The diagrams illustrating the results of these experiments are exceedingly interesting.

[2] Despretz, *Ann. de Chimie et de Phys.*, 2ᵉ, tom. lxx. p. 49, 1839.

[3] Tait, *Scientific Papers*, vol. ii. p. 1.

An interesting question discussed by Tait is the equilibrium of a column of water. He points out that in a very tall column of water (salt or fresh) at the same temperature throughout, the equilibrium might be rendered unstable in consequence of the heat developed by a sudden large increase of pressure. For, as the expansibility of water is notably increased by pressure, the lower parts of the column will become hotter and less compressible than the upper. This effect is not produced in a tall column of air, for the expansibility is practically unaltered by pressure.

It may be gathered from these experiments of Tait's that vertical currents might occur in ocean depths. The stability is not such as it would be if the water at the bottom were at its maximum density. In fact, as we have seen, the maximum-density point would overtake the freezing point in fresh water at $-2°\cdot4$ C. under a pressure corresponding to a depth of about 1800 fathoms. The depth at which this would occur in salt water would probably not be very different, and the freezing of the water would prevent the condition above mentioned being attained. The results of the *Challenger* expedition show that the temperature of the ocean-floor is remarkably uniform, and (except in cold latitudes) above the normal freezing point. In general, after the surface layers are passed, the temperature falls steadily at first but more slowly as the depth increases. From about 1500 fathoms down to the bottom it is nearly constant. At the bottom, which in some soundings was found at depths of over 3000 or even 4000 fathoms, the temperature in the Atlantic Ocean was about 36° or 37° F. ($2°\cdot5$ C.), and in the Pacific Ocean about 35° F.

119. Dilatation of Liquids at Temperatures above the Normal Boiling Point.—The normal boiling point of a liquid is the temperature at which it boils under the pressure of one standard atmosphere. Under this pressure the substance remains in the liquid state, only up to the boiling point, and is then vaporised with a sudden and large change of volume. By increasing the pressure, however, ebullition may be prevented indefinitely, and the substance may be maintained in the liquid state up to a certain temperature (called the critical temperature), at which it *appears* to be completely and suddenly vaporised.[1]

For the present it is sufficient to know that a liquid may be maintained at temperatures far above its normal boiling point, and that consequently its expansion may be investigated at high temperatures. In general, the coefficient of expansion of a liquid increases with the temperature, and at temperatures which are high for a

---

[1] This transformation is considered in Chapter V. section vi.

liquid—that is, temperatures near the critical temperature of that liquid—the coefficient of expansion may equal or exceed that of the permanent gases. Thus Thilorier[1] found that liquid carbonic acid expanded between zero and 30° by half its volume at zero, which shows an expansion four times greater than that of air, and Drion[2] obtained similar results for ether, sulphurous acid, and nitrous acid.

A series of experiments was executed by Hirn[3] on the same subject, with a modified form of the weight thermometer, consisting of a huge bulb containing the liquid, and a long stem containing mercury which overflowed at a point 11·25 m. above the bulb, so that the liquid expanded under a constant pressure of nearly 15 atmospheres.

He expressed the dilatation Δ by means of formulæ of the type

$$\Delta = a\theta + b\theta^2 + c\theta^3 + d\theta^4,$$

and found that the coefficient of expansion of water at 180° C. was about half that of air, while that of alcohol at 160° was 0·017843, or about five times greater than that of air.

[1] Thilorier, *Ann. de Chimie et de Phys.*, 2ᵉ, tom. lx. p. 427, 1835.
[2] Drion, *Ann. de Chimie et de Phys.*, 3ᵉ, tom. lvi. p. 5, 1859.
[3] Hirn, *Ann. de Chimie et de Phys.*, 4ᵉ, tom. x. p. 32, 1867.

SECTION III

DILATATION OF GASES

120. Dilatation of the Thermometric Substance.—Having agreed
to measure equal increments of temperature by equal absolute increments of volume of some chosen substance under constant pressure,
we have already seen that for this substance the equation

$$V = V_0(1 + a\theta)$$

always holds true, where a is a constant, namely, the coefficient of
expansion of the substance at the chosen zero of temperature, or the
mean coefficient of expansion between zero and θ. In order to determine a for the thermometric substance it is necessary to observe the
volume V_0 at zero and the absolute increase of volume $V - V_0$ corresponding to any temperature θ, or if the volume v of a degree
measure be known we have simply $a = v/V_0$. The practical determination of a consequently requires an accurate knowledge of the expansion
of the envelope, and this may be found by the methods already
described.

These remarks apply to the thermometric substance whatever it
may be. For this substance the relation between any two temperatures and the corresponding volumes will always be, under the given
conditions of pressure,

$$\theta - \theta' = A(v - v'),$$

which merely expresses that the change of temperature is proportional
to the change of volume. The factor A is a constant under given
conditions of pressure, and is therefore a function of the pressure only,
which can be determined when the laws of compressibility of the substance are known. If the thermometric substance happened to be a
liquid at all temperatures obtainable, and if it reached a least volume
v_0 at some temperature (like water at $4°$), then this would correspond
to the lowest temperature which it would be possible to register with
this substance. Taking this as our zero, the temperature measured
from this zero might be called the absolute temperature for this

substance, and, denoting this by θ, we should have

$$\Theta = A\,(v - v_0).$$

For many reasons, already mentioned, it has been decided to take some permanent gas as the standard thermometric substance. The ideal limit to which such a substance approximates is exact obedience to Boyle's law. If this law is obeyed, it follows that the product of the pressure and volume is proportional to the temperature measured from the absolute zero of an ideal thermometer filled with a substance, always obeying Boyle's law, so that the volume v_0 is zero, and the constant A is proportional to the pressure. Hence for all such substances when temperature is measured in this manner, we have the equation

$$pv = R\Theta.$$

If $\theta°$ be the corresponding temperature on the centigrade scale, and Θ_0 the absolute temperature corresponding to the melting point of ice, then

$$\Theta = \Theta_0 + \theta.$$

Let us now seek the mean coefficient of expansion of such a substance. In working with solids and liquids it was not necessary to consider small variations of pressure. A small change of pressure does not sensibly affect the volume of a solid or liquid. In the case of gases, however, variations of pressure notably affect the volume, and in all practical investigations such changes must be determined and allowed for.

In the first place, let us suppose that the pressure is maintained constant, and that the temperature and volume vary. At any temperature $\theta°$ C. we have the equation

$$pv = R\Theta,$$

and at $0°$ C. we have

$$pv_0 = R\Theta_0,$$

consequently

$$\frac{v - v_0}{v_0} = \frac{\Theta - \Theta_0}{\Theta_0} = \frac{\theta}{\Theta_0},$$

and therefore

$$a = \frac{v - v_0}{v_0\theta} = \frac{1}{\Theta_0}.$$

Hence the relation between the absolute temperature Θ and the centigrade temperature θ is

$$\Theta = \Theta_0 + \theta = \frac{1}{a} + \theta.$$

It thus appears that the mean coefficient of expansion between $0°$ and $\theta°$ C. of any thermometric substance obeying Boyle's law is the reciprocal of the absolute temperature of the freezing point. This coefficient is independent of R, that is, of the other properties of the substance, and it therefore follows that if all the gases obey Boyle's law, and if they all give the same absolute zero when used as a thermometric substance, they will all possess the same coefficient of expansion, and *vice versa*. The whole question about gases, then, reduces to the examination of how closely they obey Boyle's law. This point will be considered in Art. 247. At present we shall consider the methods by which the mean coefficient a has been obtained in the case of ordinary gases. There are in general two methods of attack,—either by keeping the pressure constant and observing the change of volume between $0°$ and $100°$ C. (or any other temperature $\theta°$ C.), or by keeping the volume constant and noting the corresponding change of pressure. The former gives the mean coefficient of increase of volume, or the dilatation in the proper sense of the term, while the latter gives the coefficient of increase of pressure. If Boyle's law is obeyed these two coefficients are equal, for the former is

$$\frac{v - v_0}{\theta v_0} = \frac{1}{\Theta_0},$$

and the volume being constant the latter is

$$\frac{p - p_0}{\theta p_0} = \frac{1}{\Theta_0}.$$

In general, when the pressure is kept constant, we have

$$\frac{1}{v}\frac{dv}{d\theta} = \frac{1}{\Theta}, \quad \frac{1}{v_0}\frac{dv}{d\theta} = \frac{1}{\Theta_0}.$$

Similarly when the volume is kept constant,

$$\frac{1}{p}\frac{dp}{d\theta} = \frac{1}{\Theta}, \quad \frac{1}{p_0}\frac{dp}{d\theta} = \frac{1}{\Theta_0}.$$

The extent to which the coefficient of increase of pressure is found by experiment to agree with the coefficient of increase of volume will consequently furnish a test as to how nearly the gas under examination obeys Boyle's law.

121. Dilatation under Constant Pressure.—The coefficient of expansion of the thermometric substance must be determined by directly observing its volume under constant pressure at two fixed temperatures, unless some law connecting the pressure and volume at constant temperatures has been previously established. If such a law be known other methods in which the pressure is variable and volume constant, or in which both pressure and volume vary, may be devised. If Boyle's law had not been known all experiments on the expansion of gases would have been made by observing the volume under constant pressure. As a matter of fact, this method was adopted in the earlier investigations, but it was ultimately superseded by other methods depending on the application of Boyle's law. The practical difficulties attending the observation of the volume under constant pressure, and the errors attending the experiment, are much greater than those attending the observation of the pressure under constant volume. Nevertheless, it is of prime importance that the coefficient of expansion under constant pressure should be measured by direct experiment, and the comparison of this coefficient with that obtained by any other method founded on some previously determined pressure - volume -

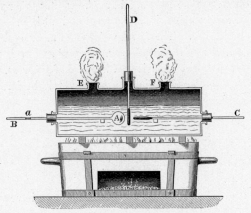

Fig. 47.—Gay-Lussac's Apparatus.

relation at constant temperature, will furnish a test of the truth and range of applicability of this relation.

The early experimenters on this subject were not aware of the great importance of procuring the air, or other gas, quite pure and perfectly free from aqueous vapour. Gay-Lussac [1] seems to have been the first to pay some attention to this important point. The apparatus (Fig. 47) employed by this philosopher was simply a glass bulb, A, furnished with a straight stem, AB, which was carefully calibrated. The air which filled the bulb was freed from moisture by being passed through desiccating tubes before entering the bulb. The bulb was first filled with mercury and then turned upside down, so that the mercury escaped and air entered through the drying tubes to take its place. A short index a of mercury was left in the stem to mark the volume of the air enclosed. The stem was maintained horizontal, so that the pressure of the enclosed air was that of the atmosphere. By

[1] Gay-Lussac, *Ann. de Chimie et de Physique*, 1re, tom. xliii. p. 137, An Xe.

reading the barometer it can be ascertained if this remains constant during the experiment; if not, corresponding corrections must be applied for the variation of volume arising from change of pressure.   The bulb and part of the stem were immersed in melting ice and afterwards in boiling water, the temperature of which was noted by mercury Gay-thermometers.   The volume was noted in both cases, and the mean Lussac. coefficient of expansion deduced was 0·00375.   Correction, of course, must be made in such an experiment for the expansion of the glass. The volume of the bulb and of each division of the stem at some definite temperature is ascertained by weighing the quantity of mercury it contains at this temperature, and from the known expansion of the glass the volume at any other temperature can be calculated.

The same value for this coefficient was independently arrived at by Dalton,[1] and afterwards these experiments were repeated and confirmed by Dulong and Petit,[2] and consequently this value of the coefficient was universally accepted as correct until Rudberg, a Swedish Rudberg. physicist, published a memoir giving the lower value 0·003646. Rudberg here pointed out the great importance of thoroughly desiccating not only the air admitted to the bulb, but also the bulb itself.   For this purpose the bulb was repeatedly filled with dry air and exhausted, while at the same time it was highly heated so as to expel all moisture from its walls.   The experiments of Rudberg were, however, conducted at constant volume, so that Magnus[3] undertook the re-determination Magnus. of the coefficient of expansion under constant pressure by the method of Gay-Lussac.   The mean of thirty-two experiments gave a value differing little from that of Gay-Lussac, the extreme values being 0·0038769 and 0·00355.   The great divergence exhibited here led Magnus to abandon the method of Gay-Lussac altogether.   This method suffers

---

[1] Dalton found that 1000 measures of air at 55° F. became 1325 at 212° F. (*Memoirs of the Manchester Phil. Soc.* vol. v. pt. iii. p. 599), and in his *Chemical Philosophy* he states that 1000 measures at 32° F. become 1376 at 212°, according to his own and Gay-Lussac's experiments.   Regnault appears to have mistaken Dalton's meaning and fancied that an error had crept in here, for he says (*Mémoires de l'Académie*) : "Rudberg termine son Second Mémoire par une remarque importante, qui avait été déjà faite en 1813 par Gilbert (*Annales de Gilbert*, tom. xiv. p. 267), mais qui depuis était tombée tout à fait dans l'oubli ; savoir, que les expériences de MM. Dalton et Gay-Lussac, que l'on avait regardées comme ayant donné des résultats presque identiques, diffèrent, au contraire, beaucoup."

This statement arose from the supposition that Dalton took the initial volume to be 1000 at 32° F. instead of 55° F.   He, however, expressly states that when the volume was 1000 at 55° F. it was 1325 at 212°, and he mentions in addition that he had not the means of obtaining the volume at 32° F.   The coefficient is thus 0·00373, which is sensibly the same as the mean of Gay-Lussac's experiments.

[2] Dulong and Petit, *Ann. de Chimie et de Physique*, 2e, tom. ii. p. 240, 1816.

[3] Magnus, *Pogg. Ann.* vol. lv., 1842 ; *Ann. de Chim. et de Phys.*, 3e, tom. vi. p. 330.

from defects which render the results obtained by it open to doubt, even though the air enclosed by Gay-Lussac had been perfectly dry. These defects lie in the method of measuring the volume of the air by means of a moving index of mercury. In the first place, it may be objected that the index does not properly close the tube so as to prevent all communication between the air inside and outside.[1] Magnus, in fact, found that when the apparatus was brought to zero the air enclosed scarcely ever exhibited the same volume. Besides this a mercury index always sticks somewhat to the walls of the tube, so that the pressure inside and outside may differ slightly without moving the index. The errors arising from these sources are consequently sufficient to condemn the method.

122. Regnault's Experiments.—After executing several series of experiments by other methods depending on the application of Boyle's law to gases, Regnault next attacked the problem of directly determining the expansion under constant pressure. For this purpose he employed the apparatus shown in Figs. 20 and 21, which may be termed a constant-pressure air thermometer. The bulb was well dried and filled with dry air at the pressure of the atmosphere, the mercury being adjusted so as to stand at a fixed mark a on the arm FG, and at the same level on the other arm, IJ, of the manometer. The tube op (Fig. 20) was then sealed up while the bulb was surrounded with melting ice. The bulb at this stage contained air at zero, and at the pressure H of the atmosphere, which was determined by reading the barometer at the time of sealing the tube op. The ice was then removed, and the bulb was placed in a steam bath, the mercury being allowed to escape from the manometer till equality of level, or a small difference of level h', which was measured by means of a cathetometer, was secured. During this process the air expanded

---

[1] Regnault (*Ann. de Chim. et de Phys.*, 3ᵉ, tom. iv. p. 43, 1842) also made some experiments on the expansion of air by the method of Gay-Lussac, and obtained the numbers

$$0.003641, \ 0.003626, \ 0.003635, \ 0.003647, \ 0.003552.$$

All these numbers are less than those obtained by other methods, and this Regnault considers remarkable. This might arise from the imperfect closing of the stem by the mercury index. Thus if the index does not slide air-tight in the stem, then when the gas is expanding the internal pressure is greater than the external, and some air will escape from the bulb, and the final volume will appear too small. So again when the air is contracting the external pressure exceeds the internal, and air enters the bulb. In the first process warm air escapes, and in the second cold denser air enters, so that when the apparatus again returns to zero the volume of the air enclosed would be greater than before. In an experiment the index at zero stood at the division 152·7, and at 100 the reading was 534·5, and after returning to zero the reading was 154·5, the barometer not having sensibly changed.

and occupied part of the graduated arm FG.   Let V_0 be the volume of the bulb at zero, v_1 the volume of the stem up to the fixed mark a, and v_2 the volume of the graduated tube from a to the surface of the mercury.   Then if the whole mass of gas were at the same temperature its volume at zero would be $V_0 + v_1$ and its volume at θ would be $(V_0 + v_1 + v_2)(1 + g\theta)$, and if the pressure were exactly the same in the second case as in the first the coefficient of expansion would be given at once by the equation

$$(V_0 + v_1)(1 + a\theta) = (V_0 + v_1 + v_2)(1 + g\theta),$$

the temperature θ being approximately $100°$ C., the difference arising on account of the atmospheric pressure being not necessarily exactly 760 mm.

In the experiment, however, the gas occupying the stem and tube was not at the same temperature as that in the bulb, and the final pressure was not exactly the same as the initial.   If the volume v_1 is at the temperature θ_1, and v_2 at θ_2, while the bulb is at θ and the initial and final pressures are $H + h$ and $H' + h'$, then the full equation for a will be

$$\left[\frac{V_0(1 + g\theta)}{1 + a\theta} + \frac{v_1(1 + g\theta_1)}{1 + a\theta_1} + \frac{v_2(1 + g\theta_2)}{1 + a\theta_2}\right](H' + h') = \left[V_0 + \frac{v_1(1 + g\theta_1)}{1 + a\theta_1}\right](H + h).$$

This equation follows from the application of the equation $\Sigma pv/(1 + a\theta)$ = constant for the whole mass of gas.   From this we have Regnault's formula [1]

$$1 + a\theta = \frac{(H' + h')(1 + g\theta)}{H + h + \dfrac{v}{V_0}\dfrac{H + h}{1 + a\theta_1} - \dfrac{v}{V_0}\dfrac{H' + h'}{1 + a\theta_1} - \dfrac{v'}{V_0}\dfrac{H' + h'}{1 + a\theta_2}},$$

where v is written for $v_1(1 + g\theta_1)$ and v' replaces the corresponding terms in θ_2 and v_2.   The terms in the denominator which embrace v and v' also include a, the quantity sought, but on account of the small values of v and v' compared with V_0, an approximate value of a

---

[1] In this equation θ_1 and θ_2 are practically constant, while θ and v_2 vary.   Hence differentiating with respect to θ we have

$$\frac{V_0 g}{1 + a\theta} - \frac{V_0 a(1 + g\theta)}{(1 + a\theta)^2} + \left(\frac{1 + g\theta_2}{1 + a\theta_2}\right)\frac{dv_2}{d\theta} = 0.$$

Hence

$$\frac{dv_2}{d\theta} = \frac{(1 + a\theta_2)(a - g)V_0}{(1 + g\theta_2)(1 + a\theta)^2} \text{ which varies as } \frac{1}{\Theta^2}.$$

That is, the increase dv_2 of volume corresponding to a definite rise of temperature $d\theta$ varies inversely as the square of the absolute temperature.   Hence the sensibility of the instrument decreases as the temperature rises, and this circumstance led Regnault to reject the constant-pressure air thermometer.   In the case of the constant volume thermometer, on the other hand, the sensibility is as good at high temperatures as at low.

may be used in these terms, and the resulting value of α deduced from the equation. In this experiment the accurate determination of the volumes V_0, v_1, and v_2 is of prime importance, as well as certain knowledge of the temperature θ_2 of the bath enclosing the manometer. The volumes are determined by weighing the mercury which fills the corresponding spaces at some definite temperature, and the temperature of the bath is kept uniform by constant agitation. Another point of importance is the thorough desiccation of the manometer tube FG as well as the bulb.

The value of α obtained in this manner slightly exceeds that obtained by the other methods, but the excess is not so notable as to lead to the conclusion that within the limits of the experiments Boyle's law is sensibly deviated from. The first series of experiments gave the same coefficient for air and hydrogen, but in the later experiments the coefficient for hydrogen was somewhat less than that of air. A similar result was obtained by Magnus.[1] The difference, however, was within the limits of experimental error, and consequently nothing definite could be inferred from it (cf. Art. 248).

By varying the initial pressure the expansion under different pressures may be examined in the same way. The results obtained by Regnault were as follows :—

EXPERIMENTS UNDER ATMOSPHERIC PRESSURE

Air . . . . . 0·0036706	Carbon Monoxide . . 0·0036688
Hydrogen . . . . 0·0036613	Nitrous Oxide . . . 0·0037195
Carbonic Acid . . . 0·0037099	Cyanogen . . . . 0·0038767
Sulphurous Acid . . 0·0039028	

When the pressure was between 250 and 260 centimetres of mercury the coefficients found for air, hydrogen, and carbonic acid were 0·0036944, 0·0036616, and 0·0038455 respectively.

In the case of sulphurous acid great difficulty was always experienced in thoroughly drying the gas, and it consequently had to be allowed to enter the bulb very slowly, and so remain a long time in the drying tubes.[2] The coefficient of this gas (or of any other), near its condensing point, increases with the pressure. Thus at 760 mm. the coefficient of SO_2 was 0·003902, and at 980 mm. it was 0·003980.

Within certain limits, however, all gases may be regarded as expanding equally, that is, all gases sufficiently far removed from their condensing points approximately obey the law of Charles.

---

[1] Magnus, *Ann. de Chimie et de Physique*, 3e, tom. iv. p. 334, 1842.

[2] With any such gas all air should be carefully swept out of the drying tubes before filling the bulb.

The values of the coefficient of expansion of air have been determined by Witkowski[1] for a very wide range of pressure and temperature. His method consisted in filling two similar bulbs with air at the same pressure, but at different temperatures. The quantities of air in the two bulbs were then compared by discharging them into eudiometers at atmospheric temperature and pressure. From these data he deduced the mean coefficient of expansion for the given pressure and temperature as follows.

Let m_1, v_1, and θ be the mass, volume, and temperature of the air in one bulb, and m_2, v_2, and t the corresponding quantities for the other bulb, both being at the same pressure p. Then if the air in the first bulb be cooled to zero without altering its pressure, its volume will become

$$\frac{v_1}{1 + a_{p\theta}\theta},$$

where $a_{p\theta}$ is the mean coefficient of expansion between $0°$ C. and $\theta°$; and if it be now heated to $t°$, its new volume will be

$$\frac{v_1(1 + a_{pt}t)}{1 + a_{p\theta}\theta},$$

where a_{pt} has a similar signification. The density of the air will now be

$$\frac{m_1(1 + a_{p\theta}\theta)}{v_1(1 + a_{pt}t)},$$

and this will be equal to the density of the air in the second bulb, therefore

$$\frac{m_1(1 + a_{p\theta}\theta)}{v_1(1 + a_{pt}t)} = \frac{m_2}{v_2},$$

from which we obtain

$$a_{p\theta} = \frac{1}{\theta}\left\{\frac{m_2 v_1}{m_1 v_2}(1 + a_{pt}t) - 1\right\}.$$

In most of the experiments t was $16°$ C. The values of a_{pt} were found by experiments in which θ was equal to t, and the temperature of the second bulb was zero.

The pressure was deduced from the observed expansion of the air in the bulb at $16°$ C. when measured in the eudiometer at the same temperature, making use of Amagat's determinations of the compressibility of air at $16°$ (see Art. 248). Witkowski compared this method of measuring pressures with that of the ordinary nitrogen manometer. He found that the pressures indicated by his method were slightly less than those registered by the nitrogen manometer. This may be

[1] *Phil. Mag.*, April 1896.

due, as Prof. Callendar remarks, to surface condensation in the capillary tube of the gas-manometer.

Fig. 48 exhibits the results of Witkowski's experiments. It will be noticed that the curves for the various temperatures all converge at low pressures. This is in accordance with the known fact that the mean coefficient of dilatation of air at atmospheric pressure is practically independent of the temperature.

A table of the values of $a_{p\theta}$ is given in the paper.

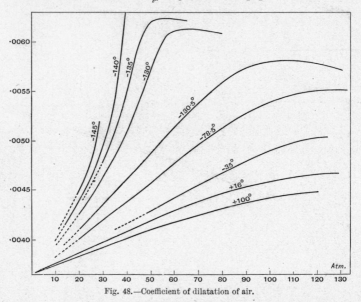

Fig. 48.—Coefficient of dilatation of air.

123. The Pressure Coefficient.—The so-called dilatation of a gas at constant volume, or, more properly speaking, its coefficient of increase of pressure, has been studied by Rudberg, Magnus, and Regnault. The apparatus employed by all was almost exactly the same, the original apparatus adopted by Rudberg being slightly improved and perfected by the others. In its ordinary form it constitutes a constant-volume air thermometer (Fig. 20). The bulb is dried and filled with dry gas as already described, and the mercury is adjusted so that its surface stands at a fixed mark a on the manometer arm. This mark was placed by Regnault on the wide part of the tube, and not on the capillary arm. He states that he could never obtain consistent results when the fixed mark was on the capillary connecting-tube.

Let us suppose that the bulb is placed in ice and filled with air when the pressure of the atmosphere is H, and the difference of level

in the arms of the manometer h.   When it is immersed in steam let
the difference of level in the two arms of the manometer be h', and
the barometric height H$'$.   The pressure of the gas in the bulb is now
H$' + h'$ C., and its temperature is $\theta°$ C., which is approximately $100°$ C.,
the difference being determined by the deviation of H$'$ from the
standard height 760 mm.   As before, if V_0 denotes the zero volume
of the bulb, and v_1 the volume of the stem up to the fixed mark, the
equation for a will be

$$\left(V_0 + \frac{v_1}{1 + a\theta_1} \right)(H + h) = \left[\frac{V_0(1 + g\theta)}{1 + a\theta} + \frac{v_1}{1 + a\theta_1} \right](H' + h').$$

Hence we have Regnault's formula

$$1 + a\theta = \frac{(1 + g\theta)(H' + h')}{H + h - \dfrac{v_1(H' + h' - H - h)}{V_0(1 + a\theta_1)}}.$$

The second term in the denominator being small, an approximate
value of a may be employed in it, and the calculation proceeded with
by the method of successive approximations.   The mean of three
series of experiments by this method gave

$$a = 0\cdot0036679.$$

By varying the initial pressure, that is the height h, the effect of
pressure may be examined.   The following table is taken from Reg
nault's second memoir : [1]—

PRESSURE COEFFICIENT FOR AIR

Pressure at Zero.	Pressure at 100°.	a.
109·72 mm.	149·31 mm.	0·0036482
174·36	237·17	0·0036513
266·06	395·07	0·0036542
374·67	510·35	0·0036587
375·23	510·97	0·0036572
760·00	...	0·0036650
1678·40	2286·09	0·0036760
1692·53	2306·23	0·0036800
2144·18	2924·04	0·0036894
3655·56	4992·09	0·0037091

From this table it appears that a increases gradually for air as
the pressure becomes greater.   This indicates that there is a small
deviation from Boyle's law, which becomes more and more marked as

---

[1] Regnault, *Ann. de Chimie et de Physique*, 3e, tom. v. p. 66, 1842.

the pressure becomes more elevated.   In the case of carbonic acid this deviation is much more distinct, as shown by the following table :—

CARBONIC ACID

Pressure at Zero.	Pressure at 100°.	a.
758·47 mm.	1034·54 mm.	0·0036856
901·09	1230·37	0·0036943
1742·73	2387·72	0·0037523
3589·07	4759·03	0·0038598

124. Later Experiments.—Careful determinations of the values of the pressure coefficients of hydrogen, nitrogen, and carbon dioxide have been made by Chappuis[1] by means of the constant volume thermometer described in Art. 92.   In that article the pressure coefficient β (or a_p) is treated as a known quantity.   Using the formula there given, β may be determined if the temperature is known.   Taking the pressure at 0° C. to be equal to that of a column of 1 metre of mercury under standard conditions, and observing the pressure at 100° C., Chappuis found for hydrogen

$$\beta = 0·00366254.$$

This is, of course, a constant on the scale of the hydrogen thermometer. In the case of nitrogen he enclosed the gas in a constant volume thermometer with a porcelain bulb and measured the temperature with a hydrogen thermometer.   The values of β obtained between 0° C. and 100° C. were the following :—

Temperature.	β.	Temperature.	β.
0°	0·00367698	70°	0·00367384
20	560	80	378
40	461	90	381
50	427	100	393
60	400		

According to this table the pressure coefficient for nitrogen diminishes up to about 80° C. and then increases again.   This increase, which is of the same order of magnitude as the probable errors, is not in accordance with our knowledge of the variations of the coefficients of

---

[1] *Travaux et Mémoires du Bureau international des Poids et Mesures,* tom. vi., 1888.   *Phil. Mag.,* Oct. 1900, Feb. 1902.

gases.   Hence Chappuis considered it more probable that the coefficient approaches a definite limiting value for each initial pressure which in this case seems to be attained at about 75° C.   If so, nitrogen would, at all higher temperatures, behave like hydrogen, its compressibility being less than is required by Boyle's law.

This assumption being made, it is easy to calculate the correction to be applied to the readings of the nitrogen thermometer to reduce them to the standard scale.   *Correction for nitrogen thermometer.*

Let the curve P_0IA (Fig. 49) represent the relation between the temperature and pressure of nitrogen when the volume is constant, according to Chappuis' experiments.   The ordinates are pressures and the abscissæ temperatures.   Putting

$$P = P_0(1 + \beta\theta) \quad . \quad . \quad . \quad . \quad . \quad . \quad (1)$$

where P_0 is the pressure at 0° C. and P the pressure at $\theta°$, we have (if we regard β as constant in differentiating)

$$\beta = \frac{1}{P_0} \cdot \frac{dP}{d\theta},$$

so that β is proportional to $dP/d\theta$, that is, to the tangent of the angle of slope.   The curve will have a point of inflexion at I corresponding to a temperature of about 75° if the values given above for β are correct.   Chappuis, however, assumes that at about 75° β attains a limiting value

$$\beta_{lim.} = \cdot 00367380,$$

so that beyond I the curve becomes straight.   As the pressure at 100° is more accurately known than that at 75°, it is better to represent the relation above 100° by a straight line AB′ through A and parallel to the tangent at I, rather than by the tangent at I.   If we continue this line backwards to cut the pressure axis at P'_0, then P'_0 is the fictitious pressure which the gas would have at 0° if its pressure coefficient remained constant down to 0° C.

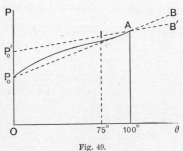

Fig. 49.

We have evidently

$$P'_0 = P_{100} - 100P_0\beta_{lim.}$$
$$= 1 \cdot 000086$$

where $P_0 = 1$, and $P_{100} = 1 \cdot 367466$ in metres of mercury.   Putting then, to represent the line P'_0B',

$$P = P'_0(1 + \beta'\theta),$$

we have

$$\beta' = \frac{1}{P'_0} \cdot \frac{dP}{d\theta}$$

$$= \frac{P_0}{P} \beta_{lim}.$$

$$= 0.00367348.$$

In the formula ordinarily used, *i.e.* equation (1) above, β is taken as the *mean* coefficient between 0° and 100°, and the line $P_0 B$ represents the relation. To calculate the error for any temperature-reading θ, find the corresponding ordinate to AB and then find the temperature which gives an equal ordinate to AB′; this will be the corrected reading (see Art. 92).

The following table contains the mean values of the expansion and pressure coefficients for hydrogen, nitrogen, air, and carbon dioxide according to Chappuis, and for krypton, argon, and helium according to Ramsay and Travers.[1]

Gas.	Const. Press. 76 cm.	Const. Vol. $P_0 = 100$ cm.
Hydrogen	.00365985	.00366254
Nitrogen	.0036708	.00367466
Air	.0036709	.00367425
Carbon dioxide	...	.00372477
Krypton	.0036812	.0036761
Argon	.0036717	.0036710
Helium	.0036628	.0036640

We have seen (Art. 120) that the mean coefficient of expansion of a perfect gas between 0° and 100° C (or between 0° and any other temperature) and the mean pressure coefficient between the same temperatures are the same, each being equal to the reciprocal of the number of degrees between 0° and absolute zero. Also, as has been stated in Art. 89, the temperature scale indicated by a gas will coincide with the thermodynamic absolute scale, if the gas obeys Boyle's law, and if the ratio of the specific heats is a constant. Now the kinetic theory of gases and the results of numerous experiments teach us that a gas will obey Boyle's law more and more closely as the pressure tends to zero ; and Witkowski's experiments (Art. 122) show that each of the specific heats tends to a constant value (independent of the temperature) as the pressure tends to zero. We infer, then, that the mean expansion coefficient and mean pressure coefficient of ordinary gases between 0° and 100° both tend to the same limiting value as the pressure is diminished, and that this value

[1] *Phil. Trans.*, A, 1901.

is the same for all gases, being the reciprocal of the temperature
of the ice-point on the absolute scale. This limiting value, calculated
from Chappuis' experiments, was given by D. Berthelot[1] as
36618×10^{-7}. Kamerlingh Onnes and Braak[2] obtained the value
36617×10^{-7}. The researches of Henning and Heuse[3] on the
mean expansion and pressure coefficients of helium, hydrogen, and
nitrogen, led to the values 36606×10^{-7} for helium, 36607×10^{-7} for
hydrogen, and 36606×10^{-7} for nitrogen. Taking the mean of
these, viz. 36604×10^{-7}, as the true values, Henning and Heuse
give the following expressions for the mean coefficient of expansion
(a) between $0°$ and $100°$ and the mean pressure coefficient between
$0°$ and $100°$:—

	$10^7 a$.	$10^7 \beta$.
Helium	$36604 - 19 p_0$	$36604 - 4 p_0$
Hydrogen	$36604 - 12 p_0$	$36604 + 17 p_0$
Nitrogen	$36604 + 127 p_0$	$36604 + 134 p_0$

It will be noticed that the temperature of the absolute zero on
the centigrade thermodynamic scale is $- 273·09$, $- 273·10$, and
$- 273·20$, according to Berthelot, Onnes and Braak, and Henning
and Heuse respectively.

125. Method of Variable Pressure and Volume.—A method in
which neither the volume nor the pressure remained constant throughout the experiment was also employed by Regnault. This method is
based on the assumption that the gas obeys Boyle's law, and was
devised by Dulong and Petit for their experiments on the comparison
of the air and mercury thermometers. It was also employed by
Rudberg to determine the expansion of air. The bulbs used by Rudberg were spherical and small, containing only 150 to 200 grammes
of mercury. Regnault employed much larger bulbs, which contained
800 to 1000 grammes of mercury, and were cylindrical, so as to avoid
errors due to refraction in observing the level of the mercury surface
through the glass. The first operation was to fill the flask with dry
air at the boiling point. For this purpose it was immersed in the
steam of boiling water, and connected with drying tubes and an air
pump, as shown in Fig. 50, so that it could be exhausted and dry air
admitted several times. The bulb, having been thoroughly desiccated
and filled with dry air, was allowed to remain in the steam for about
half an hour. The drying tubes were then removed and the tip of
the stem sealed up, the height H of the barometer being noted at the

[1] D. Berthelot, *Trav. et Mém. du Bureau int. des Poids et Mesures*, tom. xiii.
12-14, 1907.

[2] *Proc. R. Academy of Amsterdam*, vol. x. p. 589.

[3] Henning and Heuse, *Zeitschr. f. Physik*, vol. v. p. 285, 1921.

same time.   The flask now contains air at a pressure H and temperature θ° which is approximately 100° C.

The second operation consists in placing the flask as shown in Fig.
51, with its stem dipping under the surface of a basin of mercury and
its bulb surrounded by melting ice.   In this position the tip of the
stem is broken with iron pincers, and the mercury rises in the tube
and partly fills the bulb.   While the mercury is rising, the bulb may
be gently tapped to facilitate the passage through the stem and prevent a false equilibrium occurring through the sticking of the mercury
to the walls of the tube.   After standing thus for an hour or more

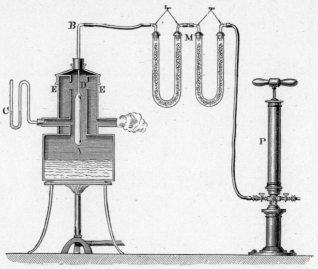

Fig. 50.

with the bulb surrounded by broken ice, the height h of the level of
the mercury in the bulb, over that in the cistern, is measured by
means of a cathetometer.   If H′ be the height of the barometer the
pressure of the air in the bulb is now H′ – h, and its mass is the same
as before.   It now remains to determine its volume.   For this purpose
a small metal cap containing soft wax is slipped over the tip of the
stem so as to close it, that the bulb and the mercury it contains may
be weighed.   When this weighing is effected, the instrument is completely filled with mercury at zero and weighed again.   The difference
of weight gives the volume previously occupied in the bulb by the
air at zero.   For if V_0 be this volume and V the volume of the whole
bulb and stem at 0°, and if W_0 be the weight of mercury that fills
the bulb at zero, and w the weight of the mercury that ascended into
it from the bath, we have

$$\frac{V}{V_0} = \frac{W_0}{W_0 - w}.$$

The volume of the whole instrument at $\theta°$ is $V(1 + g\theta)$, owing to the expansion of the glass; therefore, making use as before of the combination of Boyle's and Charles's laws, we have

$$\frac{V(1 + g\theta)H}{1 + a\theta} = V_0(H' - h),$$

or, from the previous equation,

$$W_0(1 + g\theta)H = (W_0 - w)(1 + a\theta)(H' - h),$$

or

$$1 + a\theta = \frac{W_0(1 + g\theta)H}{(W_0 - w)(H' - h)}.$$

The coefficient deduced by Regnault as the mean result of his experiments by this method was 0·0036623, the extreme numbers being 0·0036689 and 0·0036549. His mean result is thus somewhat greater than that deduced by Rudberg; and Regnault attributes this to a source of error arising in this form of experiment and not noticed by Rudberg. This occurs in the drawing in of small bubbles of air with the mercury as the latter rises into the bulb in the second part of the experiment, and the errors arising from this source will be more marked the smaller the bulb. This aspiration, in Regnault's opinion, arises from the fact that the mercury does not wet the glass stem, and a film of air enclosed between the mercury and glass is drawn in with the mercury as it rushes up the stem after the tip is broken off.

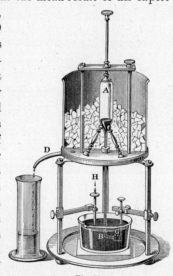

Fig. 51.

In order to avoid this, Regnault encircled the stem with small brass rings which amalgamated and made perfect contact with the mercury. He also covered the surface of the mercury with a layer of sulphuric acid, which was removed before the measurement of the height h.

Regnault conducted a further series of experiments with a modified form of apparatus. In these investigations the stem of the air-flask was made long, so that when it was opened under mercury the mercury rose to a considerable height in the stem, but did not enter the bulb. In this case h is large, and the pressure $H' - h$ of the gas

P

enclosed is small, but its volume is nearly the same throughout the whole investigation, so that the apparatus is practically a form of constant volume air thermometer. The coefficient found by this method was sensibly equal to that obtained by the foregoing, being 0·0036633.

The general conclusions at which Regnault arrived after his elaborate investigations were—

(1) That Gay-Lussac's coefficient, 0·00375, was too high, and that Rudberg's, 0·003645, was too low, and should be replaced by the number 0·003665.

(2) That all gases do not possess exactly the same coefficient of expansion, and that for the same gas the coefficient at constant volume differs somewhat from that under constant pressure.

(3) That the coefficient of expansion of all the gases examined (except hydrogen) increased with the density or initial pressure of the gas.

(4) That the coefficients of the several gases approach equality as the pressure of the gas decreases—that is, when the gas is taken in a highly rarefied condition.

These conclusions imply that all gases do not obey the perfect gas law with the same degree of accuracy, but that when they are taken at low pressures and high temperatures, or in a highly rarefied state, their obedience to the law becomes more and more exact.[1]

---

[1] The mean coefficient found by Balfour Stewart (*Phil. Trans.*, 1863, p. 425) was 0·0036728. The method employed was similar to that adopted by Rudberg and used by Regnault, but abandoned for the form of apparatus in Fig. 20. The manometer tubes dipped into a closed reservoir of mercury furnished with a screw plunger, by means of which the mercury could be forced into the tubes and the level kept at the fixed mark.

The following numerical coefficients were obtained by Regnault for his various gas thermometers :—

Air thermometer normal	$272·85 = (·003665)^{-1}$
440 mm. pressure ,,	$272·98 = (·0036632)^{-1}$
1490 mm. pressure ,,	$272·70 = (·003667)^{-1}$
CO_2 at 464 mm.	$271·59 = (·003682)^{-1}$
,, ,, 741 mm.	$270·64 = (·003695)^{-1}$
SO_2 at 588 mm.	$263·6 = (·003794)^{-1}$
,, ,, 751 mm.	$261·4 = (·003825)^{-1}$

In the case of hydrogen, Regnault states that the coefficient used was $(·003652)^{-1}$ $= 273·82$. This, as Lord Kelvin points out, must be a mistake, as the coefficient of dilatation of hydrogen was found to be ·0036678 at constant volume, and ·0036613 at constant pressure (*Relation des exp.* tom. i. pp. 78, 80, 91, 115, 116), and he nowhere finds any smaller value than ·003661.

SECTION IV

DILATATION OF CRYSTALS

126. Three Principal Dilatations.—In the case of isotropic substances, the dilatation, like the other physical properties, is the same in all directions, but in crystals the expansion in any direction depends on the relation of that direction to three mutually rectangular axes, called the principal axes of dilatation, which are not necessarily the same as the axes of symmetry or crystallographic axes. Thus, in general, crystals expand differently in different directions; and some, while expanding with rise of temperature in one direction, contract in the perpendicular direction. For this reason a portion of a crystalline substance which is spherical at one temperature will not be spherical at any other, and a cubical portion at one temperature will not remain cubical when the temperature changes.

If small bars be cut from a crystal parallel to the dilatation axes, their coefficients of linear expansion will differ. The linear coefficient of expansion of a bar cut parallel to one axis will be λ_1, that cut parallel to another λ_2, and that parallel to the third λ_3. It follows, therefore, that if a cube of side l_0 at zero be cut from a crystal with its edges parallel to the dilatation axes of the crystal, its edges at any other temperature $\theta°$ will be

$$l_0(1+\lambda_1\theta), \quad l_0(1+\lambda_2\theta), \quad l_0(1+\lambda_3\theta).$$

Hence its volume will be

$$V = l_0{}^3(1+\lambda_1\theta)(1+\lambda_2\theta)(1+\lambda_3\theta),$$

or

$$V = V_0(1+\lambda_1\theta)(1+\lambda_2\theta)(1+\lambda_3\theta).$$

The coefficient of cubical dilatation is therefore

$$a = \frac{V - V_0}{V_0\theta} = \lambda_1 + \lambda_2 + \lambda_3,$$

neglecting the products $\lambda_1\lambda_2$, etc.

In the case of amorphous solids and crystals of the cubic system

211

$\lambda_1 = \lambda_2 = \lambda_3$, and the cubical dilatation is three times the linear expansion.

In uniaxal crystals there is an axis of crystalline symmetry, perpendicular to which the physical properties are alike in all directions. If λ_1 be linear expansion parallel to this axis, then the other two principal elongations are equal, or $\lambda_3 = \lambda_2$; therefore for such crystals there are only two principal dilatations, and the cubical dilatation is

$$a = \lambda_1 + 2\lambda_2.$$

127. Change of the Dihedral Angles of Crystals.—One of the most noticeable effects of crystalline expansion is the change of the dihedral angles, that is the angles between the plane faces of the crystal, with change of temperature. Thus if ABCD (Fig. 52 (a)) be

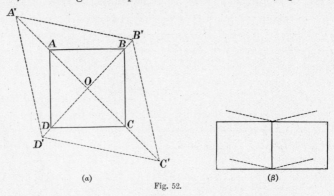

(a)

Fig. 52.

(β)

the cross-section of a square prism of a crystalline substance, cut so that the diagonals AC and BD of the section are parallel to two of the principal axes; then, when the temperature rises, AC and BD become elongated by different amounts, and the cross-section of the prism remains no longer square, but changes into a rhombus A′B′C′D′. The angles at A and C become acute, while those at B and D become obtuse. If two such prisms be cemented together with two edges in contact, whose angles become more obtuse by heating, then if when cool the two upper faces form one continuous plane, they will, when heated, be inclined as shown in Fig. 52 (β). Exceedingly small inequalities of expansion in different directions may be detected in this manner by observing through a telescope the image of a distant object formed by reflection at the polished surfaces of the combined prisms.

Mitscherlich seems to have been the first to notice that crystals expanded differently in different directions, and his method of observation [1] consisted in determining the variations of the dihedral angles of crystals with change of temperature. The angles between the plane faces of a crystal may be measured with great accuracy by optical instruments, such as the reflecting goniometer, and such measurements are in general more exact for these investigations than any direct measurement of length. The method, however, does not give the absolute dilatation, but only the difference of the coefficients of linear expansion in the direction of the diagonals of the prism. Denoting these by λ_1 and λ_2 we have

$$\tan OB'A' = \frac{1 + \lambda_1 \theta}{1 + \lambda_2 \theta} = 1 + (\lambda_1 - \lambda_2)\theta, \text{ approx.},$$

and $OB'A'$ is half the measured angle of the rhombus.

Another relation between the principal elongations is obtained by measuring the cubical dilatation. This gives the sum $\lambda_1 + \lambda_2 + \lambda_3$, and may be determined by means of the weight thermometer. If the crystal is uniaxal we have $\lambda_2 = \lambda_3$, and these two measurements determine the elongations λ_1 and λ_2. Mitscherlich [2] and Dulong determined the cubical dilatation of a number of crystals by the method of the weight thermometer. Any two other observations combined with this determine the three quantities $\lambda_1, \lambda_2, \lambda_3$. A series of experiments on this subject was executed by Pfaff,[3] who found that Iceland spar and beryl contract transversely with rise of temperature.

128. Linear Dilatation in any Direction.—So far we have only considered the linear dilatations parallel to the principal axes of dilatation. The linear dilatation in any other direction may be simply expressed in terms of the quantities $\lambda_1, \lambda_2, \lambda_3$, and the angles α, β, γ, which the direction makes with the axes of reference.

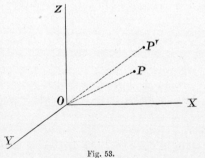

Fig. 53.

Let the axes of reference OX, OY, OZ (Fig. 53) be taken parallel to the three principal axes of dilatation, and let the co-ordinates of any point P be x, y, z, at the temperature zero. The distance of P from the origin is given by the equation

$$r^2 = x^2 + y^2 + z^2.$$

[1] Mitscherlich, *Ann. de Chimie et de Physique*, 2e, tom. xxv. p. 108, 1824 ; tom. xxxii. p. 111, 1826.   [2] Mitscherlich, *Pogg. Ann.* vol. xli.

[3] Pfaff, *Pogg. Ann.* vols. civ. cvii., 1859.

At any other temperature θ, P will occupy a position P′, the co-ordinates of which are

$$(1+\lambda_1\theta)x, \quad (1+\lambda_2\theta)y, \quad (1+\lambda_3\theta)z,$$

and the distance r' of P′ from the origin will be

$$r'^2 = (1+\lambda_1\theta)^2x^2 + (1+\lambda_2\theta)^2y^2 + (1+\lambda_3\theta)^2z^2,$$

or approximately

$$r'^2 = r^2 + 2\theta(\lambda_1 x^2 + \lambda_2 y^2 + \lambda_3 z^2).$$

Now, by the expansion, the line OP becomes the line OP′, and there-fore the linear dilatation in the direction OP, that is of a bar cut parallel to OP, is

$$\lambda = \frac{r'-r}{r\theta}.$$

But since $r + r'$ is very nearly equal to $2r$, we have

$$\lambda = \frac{r'-r}{r\theta} = \frac{r'^2 - r^2}{2r^2\theta} = \frac{\lambda_1 x^2 + \lambda_2 y^2 + \lambda_3 z^2}{r^2},$$

or

$$\lambda = \lambda_1 \cos^2\alpha + \lambda_2\cos^2\beta + \lambda_3\cos^2\gamma,$$

where α, β, γ are the angles which OP makes with the axes of reference. Thus by three measurements of λ made in any three known directions, the quantities λ_1, λ_2, λ_3 can be calculated.

COR. 1. The linear dilatations, λ', λ'', λ''', in any three mutually rectangular directions are such that their sum, $\lambda' + \lambda'' + \lambda'''$, is constant, and equal to the cubical dilatation.

COR. 2. In a direction equally inclined to the axes we have

$$\cos^2\alpha = \cos^2\beta = \cos^2\gamma = \tfrac{1}{3},$$

and a single measurement of λ in this direction gives the cubical dilatation $a = 3\lambda$.

COR. 3. There are an infinite number of directions parallel to the generators of the cone (when real)

$$\lambda_1 x^2 + \lambda_2 y^2 + \lambda_3 z^2 = 0,$$

along which there is neither contraction nor expansion.

This property is possessed by certain classes of marble. Brewster suggested the use of a rod of marble cut in this direction as a pen-dulum of invariable length.

129. Fizeau's Optical Method.—An optical method depending on the colours of thin plates was designed by M. Fizeau [1] for the measure-ment of the dilatations of crystals and other substances, which can

---

[1] Fizeau, *Ann. de Chimie et de Physique*, 4^e, tom. ii., 1864 ; and tom. viii. p. 335, 1866.

only be obtained in small fragments. The substance to be examined
was cut into a plate with parallel faces, and from 1 to 10 mm. thick.
This plate, P (Fig. 54), rested on a plane metal disc, AB, which was
supported on three adjustable screws passing through it near the
circumference. On the upper extremities of these screws rested a
glass plate, CD, which could be brought very close to the crystalline
plate by adjusting the supporting screws.
A beam of light fell perpendicularly on the
glass plate, and passing through was partially
reflected at the upper surface of the crystal.
When the air film between the glass plate
and the crystal is sufficiently thin, coloured
fringes are produced, which vary with the
thickness of the film.[1] When the tem-

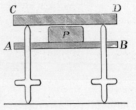

Fig. 54.

perature rises the thickness of the crystalline plate changes, as
well as the lengths of the screws supporting the glass plate.
Hence the thickness of the air film between the glass plate and
the crystal will change by an amount equal to the difference of
the expansion of the crystal, and the expansion of the length of
screw between the metal and glass plate. But when the thickness
of the air film changes the fringes are displaced, and from observation
of this displacement the change of thickness can be calculated, and
hence the expansion of the crystal deduced.

By this means exceedingly small changes of thickness can be
observed. Thus in order to displace Newton's rings through the
width of a bright or dark band, a change of thickness of the air film
of one-fourth of a wave-length of light is sufficient. For yellow light
the wave-length is about 0·00059 mm., and a displacement of one-
fifth of a band width can be easily observed, so that a change of
thickness of the air film of less than $\frac{1}{30000}$ of a millimetre can be
detected. Thus a plate of rock crystal 5 mm. thick dilates by about
$\frac{1}{370}$ of a millimetre, when the temperature changes from 10° to 50°
C., and this would give a displacement through nine entire fringes.

In order to observe the displacement of the fringes, lines were
ruled on the glass, and the position of the fringes with respect to
them could be observed. The light thus acts the part of a most
delicate micrometer, the only condition necessary being an exact
knowledge of the wave-length of the light employed.

---

[1] If the surfaces were accurately plane and parallel, a beam of parallel light
falling on the apparatus would not produce fringes, but only a certain colour over
the film ; in practice, however, perfectly plane surfaces are never realised, and
fringes of some sort are always presented.

The whole apparatus could be placed in an oven, and maintained at any desired temperature. The expansion of the screws was determined by making observations without the plate of crystal between. The earlier forms of the apparatus were made of steel, but in the later an alloy of platinum with $\frac{1}{10}$ of iridium was used, on account of its greater stability in all respects. If the crystalline plate is transparent its lower face should be blackened to prevent reflection at that face, and thus secure greater distinctness of the fringes.

Fizeau worked with three equidistant temperatures—10°, 40°, 70° C. Writing λ and a in the forms

$$\lambda = a + b(\theta - 40°),$$
$$a = c + d(\theta - 40°),$$

he obtained for emerald, which belongs to the hexagonal system,

$$\lambda_1 = -0\cdot00000106 + 0\cdot0000000114(\theta - 40°),$$
$$\lambda_2 = +0\cdot00000137 + 0\cdot0000000133(\theta - 40°) ;$$

hence

$$a = \lambda_1 + 2\lambda_2 = 0\cdot00000168 + 0\cdot0000000380(\theta - 40°).$$

Thus within the range observed λ_1 is negative, and emerald contracts along this axis as the temperature increases. It also appears that the cubical dilatation a is positive above the temperature $-4°\cdot2$ C. and negative below it, and consequently at this temperature emerald appears to present a maximum density as in the case of water at 4° C. For diamond, which belongs to the cubic system,

$$a = 3\lambda = 0\cdot00000354 + 0\cdot0000000432(\theta - 40°),$$

and a maximum density is presented at the temperature $-42°$ C.

In the case of oxide of copper (cubic system)

$$a = 3\lambda = 0\cdot00000279 + 0\cdot000000063(\theta - 40°),$$

so that a maximum density is presented at the temperature $-4°\cdot3$.

Iodide of silver exhibited a negative coefficient of dilatation throughout the whole range of temperature employed, $-10°$ to $+70°$. Within these limits it contracts when the temperature rises, and expands again on cooling. The formula for a, however, points to a minimum density at the temperature $-60°$ C.

An improved form of Fizeau's apparatus has been used by A. E. Tutton [1] in determining the expansion of crystals and also of porcelain. The light was produced by a Geissler tube, the C and F lines of hydrogen and the green line of mercury being found most useful. The cover-glass CD (Fig. 54) was slightly wedge-shaped, so as to throw the light reflected from the first surface out of the field of

[1] *Phil. Trans.* vol. cxci. p. 313, 1898.

view of the observing telescope, as this light would interfere with the production of fringes.   The wedge-shaped cover-glass was corrected by a similar wedge-shaped glass arranged above it, but turned the opposite way.   The temperature could be raised to 120° C.   It was found that, in order to measure the temperature accurately, the thermometer should be in actual contact with the tripod and not merely hung in the enclosure.   The instrument could be arranged to give approximately the absolute linear expansion of the substance, by eliminating the effect of the expansion of the screws by means of an *aluminium compensator*.   This is a plate of aluminium of such thickness that its expansion is very nearly the same as that of the projecting parts of the iridio-platinum screws.   As the expansion of aluminium is more than double that of iridio-platinum, when the compensator is laid on the table AB plenty of room is left above it for the crystal to be experimented on.   If the crystal does not reflect well, the compensator may be laid on it, and the reflecting surface of the aluminium used instead.   The compensator does not, however, add anything to the accuracy of the instrument.   The reflecting surfaces being nearly true planes, the fringes produced were nearly straight and travelled across the field of view as the substance was heated. A correction was made for the change in refractive index of air on heating.

Fizeau's method was used by K. Scheel[1] as well as the differential method (Art. 110).   A ring of quartz glass about 1 cm. high took the place of the tripod (Fig. 54).   The expansion of this ring was measured directly, and the expansion of other substances by comparison.   The same apparatus was used afterwards by J. Disch,[2] and the expansion of a number of metals determined.   The coefficient of linear expansion of quartz glass between 0° and 500° C is given, according to Scheel, by the formula

$$\lambda = 0\cdot395 \times 10^{-6} + 0\cdot1282 \times 10^{-8}\theta - 0\cdot1698 \times 10^{-11}\theta^2.$$

[1] *Zeitschr. f. Physik*, vol. v. p. 167, 1921.   [2] *Ibid.* p. 173.

CHAPTER IV

CALORIMETRY

SECTION I

INTRODUCTORY

130. The General Methods of Calorimetry.—The measurement of quantities of heat by any method has been styled calorimetry, and there is perhaps no department of scientific research in which experimental skill is more constantly and severely tested. In such measurements we require no knowledge of the ultimate nature of heat, whether it be a fluid or an action, either at a distance or propagated through a medium; the estimation is simply based on the measurement of some effect attributed to heat. For this reason the term "quantity of heat," although introduced at a time when heat was supposed to be a fluid, may still be retained with a certain definiteness of meaning, independent of any theory, just as quantities of light and quantities of electricity are referred to with a certain amount of intelligibility without necessarily implying a complete knowledge of the ultimate nature of either.

The general methods adopted for the measurement of quantities of heat may be placed under two heads, depending on

(1) Change of State, or Latent Heat Calorimetry.

(2) Change of Temperature, or Thermometric Calorimetry.

The first group embraces those methods which are founded on the fusion of solids, or the condensation of vapours, or on the reverse operations, and includes the ice and steam calorimeters. This method, since it depends on the latent heat of fusion or evaporation, requires the use of fixed temperatures only, and does not necessitate the employment of a thermometer. The second group, on the other hand, embraces those methods in which the temperature is variable, and the measurement essentially depends on changes of temperature. In this system the estimation is reduced to the observation of temperatures, and the thermometer becomes the instrument of prime importance. For this reason it has been termed thermometric calorimetry. It embraces the celebrated method of mixtures so extensively employed by Regnault, and the method of cooling which was perfected by Dulong and Petit.

131. Units and Quantities of Heat.—The employment of these two general methods in calorimetry has led to the adoption of two different units of heat. In the method of latent heat the substance usually employed was ice, and quantities of heat were measured by the quantities of ice which they melted. The unit of heat in this system was naturally the quantity of heat required to convert unit weight of ice (at the melting point) into ice-cold water. In the second system, quantities of heat were measured by the quantities of water which they raised through some definite range of temperature, and the unit chosen in this system was that which is now generally adopted, namely the quantity of heat required to raise unit weight of pure water one degree in temperature. When the unit of weight is taken as one gramme, and the degree centigrade as the interval of temperature, the unit of heat may be termed a *calorie*, and it is in terms of this unit that quantities of heat are now chiefly expressed. The first unit is about eighty times as large as this, or the quantity of heat required to liquefy any mass of ice without raising its temperature would raise the temperature of a mass of water eighty times as great through one degree centigrade. It is in this sense that the latent heat of ice is said to be 80.

A third method of obtaining equal quantities of heat, or any multiple of a quantity, is by means of a steady flame, or any body maintained in a state of steady incandescence, or by a wire kept at a steady temperature by means of an electric current. Thus a certain quantity of heat will be developed by the combustion [1] of a gramme

[1] If equal quantities of heat be given to equal masses of two substances their specific heats will be inversely as the corresponding changes of temperature. The electric method was employed by Joule, and the combustion method was used by Black, but soon abandoned on account of its many sources of inaccuracy. It was, however, more recently used by Thomsen (*Journal de Physique*, tom. i. p. 35) with greater success. (Hirn's method is mentioned below, p. 321.) Thomsen operated with about a litre of liquid placed in a calorimeter, which was heated centrally by the combustion of a certain mass of hydrogen, which was the same in all experiments. He commenced each experiment with the temperature of the calorimeter as much below that of the air as its final temperature was above it. Marignac employed a large-bulbed thermometer filled with water as heater (Hirn's method), and eliminated the radiation correction by varying the mass of liquid in the calorimeter, so that the final temperature was the same in all experiments, and the same as that attained by a known quantity of water in another experiment. The quantity of heat supplied being the same in all cases, it followed that the specific heats of the various sub-

of hydrogen in oxygen, and n times as much will be produced by the combustion of n grammes under the same conditions. This method, however, suffers from many imperfections, and is difficult to work with, besides requiring for accuracy many precautions and auxiliary experiments.

The convenience of the calorie arises partly from the comparative facility with which pure water can be procured, and from the fact that sensibly the same quantity of heat is required to raise the temperature of a given mass of water one degree at any temperature between the freezing and boiling points. This property of water must be tested by mixing equal masses, or known masses, of water at different temperatures, and observing the resulting temperature of the mixture. If equal masses at temperatures θ and θ' be mixed, and if the same quantity of heat is required to raise the temperature of each one degree at all parts of the scale, then the temperature of the mixture will be the arithmetic mean of θ and θ', that is $\frac{1}{2}(\theta + \theta')$. If the temperature of the mixture differs from this when all corrections are allowed for, it is to be concluded that the quantity of heat required to raise the temperature of the mass one degree is not the same at all temperatures, or, in other words, the thermal capacity (Art. 23) of the mass varies with the temperature.

Specific heat of water.

If the unit of heat is definitely chosen as the quantity of heat which will raise the temperature of one gramme of water from $19°·5$ to $20°·5$ C., then a quantity Q of heat is that which will raise the temperature of Q grammes of water through the same interval, and not the quantity which will raise the temperature of one gramme of water $Q°$ C. The latter quantity will be the same as the former only if water happens to possess the same thermal capacity at all temperatures. The most recent investigations on this subject show that the thermal capacity of water is not exactly constant, but diminishes slightly from zero to about $40°$ C., and then gradually increases again. It thus exhibits a minimum value at about $40°$ C. The variation is, however, very small, and consequently we shall hereafter speak generally of water as if its thermal capacity remained constant at all ordinary

___

stances were inversely as the masses. For if Q be the quantity of heat supplied in each case by the heater, R the quantity lost by radiation, and θ the change of temperature, we have for masses m and m'—

$$Q - R = ms\theta = m's'\theta,$$

or

$$\frac{s}{s'} = \frac{m'}{m}.$$

The results obtained by Thomsen and Marignac by these methods agree remarkably well.

temperatures, and with this license we can say that the quantity of heat required to raise the temperature of m grammes of water from θ to θ' is

$$Q = m(\theta' - \theta),$$

and this assumes that the specific heat of water is unity between the temperatures θ and θ'.

In most cases in which quantities of heat are measured it is assumed that in the interchange of heat between two bodies the quantity of heat which one loses is the same as the quantity which the other gains. No third body is supposed to take part in the opera- tion, and heat is supposed not to be developed or destroyed by chemical or other actions between the bodies. Thus if two bodies A and B at different temperatures are simultaneously immersed in a known weight of water, they raise its temperature by a certain amount, and it is found that the final temperature of the water is the same if A and B are first brought into contact, so as to come to the same temperature before immersion. In the first case the heat is directly transferred from A and B to the water; in the second case some of the heat passes from A (supposed the warmer) to B before immersion, and is afterwards transferred to the water; finally, however, the whole quantity received by the water is the same in the two cases.

The final admission is, that if a body absorbs a quantity Q of heat in changing its temperature from θ to θ' under given conditions, then during the reverse process, during the passage of the body back again from θ' to θ under exactly the same conditions, the same quantity Q of heat will be evolved by the same body. If this were not so, a body, when alternately heated and cooled under the same conditions, would act perpetually as a source or sink of heat, and the principle of the conservation of energy would be violated. To the calorists, who regarded heat as an indestructible fluid, this equality appeared self- evident, and was accordingly tacitly assumed. From the point of view of the dynamical theory, however, heat may be called into existence by mechanical actions, and it is not the quantity of heat, but the quantity of energy in a system that is conserved. Hence it does not necessarily follow that a body will absorb the same quantity of heat in passing from one state A to another B as it will evolve in returning from B to A. If, however, it passes back again from B to A in the reverse order, through exactly the same series of states and under exactly the same conditions as during its passage from A to B, the quantity absorbed will be equal to that evolved. The consideration of such transformations will be more fully entered into in Chap. VIII.

132. Specific Heat.—The specific heat of a substance has been already defined (Art. 23) as its thermal capacity per unit mass, or, in other words, the ratio of the quantity of heat required to raise the temperature of a given weight of it by a given amount to the quantity necessary to raise the temperature of an equal weight of water by the same amount. Now, since the unit of heat is taken to be the quantity which raises the temperature of one gramme of water $1°$ C., it follows that the quantity which will raise the temperature of a gramme from θ to θ' will be simply $\theta' - \theta$; and consequently if a quantity Q raises the temperature of one gramme of any substance from θ to θ', the specific heat of the substance will be, by definition,

$$s = \frac{Q}{\theta' - \theta}.$$

In this case s is the *mean* specific heat of the substance between θ and θ'; and if we wish to speak of the specific heat of a substance at any temperature θ, we must take θ' infinitely near θ. Denoting the infinitesimal difference $\theta' - \theta$ by $d\theta$, and the corresponding quantity of heat by dQ, we have

$$s = \frac{dQ}{d\theta}.$$

That is, the specific heat of any substance at the temperature θ is the ratio of the quantity of heat dQ required to change the temperature of unit mass by an amount $d\theta$ to the change of temperature $d\theta$.

Case of gases.

In general, when the specific heat of any substance is spoken of, the conditions under which the change of temperature occurs should be distinctly specified, for the temperature of a body may be varied by mechanical actions alone. Thus, the temperature of a gas may be raised by compression, so that here we have dQ equal to zero, while $d\theta$ does not vanish, and the specific heat would appear to be zero. On the other hand, a finite quantity of heat may be given to a gas, while at the same time it is allowed to expand so as to remain at a fixed temperature. In this case $d\theta$ vanishes and dQ does not, so that the specific heat is infinite. The expansion of the gas might also be permitted to proceed so far that, although heat is actually given to it, yet its temperature will be lowered, that is, $d\theta$ will be negative, and the specific heat may thus have any negative value. It thus appears that the specific heat of a gas may have any value between $+ \infty$ and $- \infty$, according to the conditions under which the heat is communicated. To speak with definiteness, therefore, of the specific heat of a gas, it is necessary to assign the conditions under which the temperature changes. For example, we may speak of the specific heat under constant pressure, or at constant volume.

In the case of liquids and solids, the compressibility is so small that under the conditions of all ordinary experiments changes of volume need not be taken into account, and we are not complicated with a multiplicity of specific heats, as in the case of a gas.   Each liquid and solid may therefore be said to have a definite specific heat at each temperature ; but the specific heat of each substance is not the same at all temperatures.   As a general rule it may be said that the specific heat of a solid or liquid increases with the temperature.

Liquids and solids.

Setting out with a solid, say at zero, the relation between the quantity of heat supplied to it, and the corresponding elevation of temperature, is roughly shown by Fig. 55.   Measuring temperature parallel to the axis of OX, and quantities of heat parallel to OY, the ordinate of any point on the curve OA represents the quantity of heat given to the solid in raising its temperature from zero to that repre-

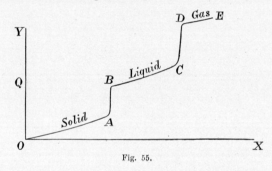

Fig. 55.

sented by the corresponding abscissa.   If the specific heat were constant, OA would be a right line, and the tangent of the angle which it makes with OX would represent the specific heat.   If, however, the specific heat increases with the temperature, OA will be convex towards the axis of x, and the trigonometrical tangent of the angle which the tangent to OA at any point makes with OX will be the specific heat $dQ/d\theta$ at the temperature corresponding to that point.

At the point A, fusion is supposed to begin, and a certain quantity of heat (the latent heat of fusion), represented by the vertical line AB, is communicated to the body without any change of temperature. At B liquefaction is complete, and the curve BC applies to the liquid in the same manner as OA does to the solid.   Similarly, CD represents the latent heat of vaporisation, and DE applies to the vapour under some definite conditions of pressure and volume.

In the foregoing, the comparison has been made between equal masses of different substances, and this may therefore be referred to as the *mass* specific heat.   If the comparison had been made between

Mass and volume.

equal volumes, that is, if the specific heat had been taken to be the quantity of heat required to raise the temperature of unit volume of the substance 1° C., this might be termed the *volume* specific heat. The relation between the two is very simple. For if a quantity Q of heat raises the temperature of a mass m through $\theta°$, then

$$Q = ms\theta,$$

and if the same quantity raises a volume v through $\theta°$, we have

$$Q = vs'\theta,$$

where s' is the volume specific heat and v is the volume of the mass m. Hence

$$s' = s\frac{m}{v} = s\rho,$$

where ρ is the density of the substance referred to water.

SECTION II

THE METHOD OF MELTING ICE

133. Black's Ice Calorimeter.—The earliest form of ice calorimeter was that devised by Black. It consisted merely of a block of pure ice, free from bubbles, in which a cavity (Fig. 56) was hollowed out. The mouth of this cavity was covered over by another slab of ice, so that a chamber was obtained, which was enclosed on all sides by ice at the melting point.

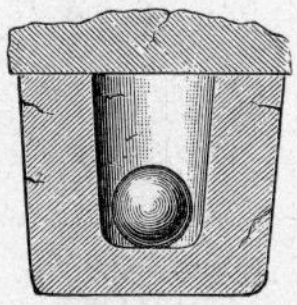

In making an experiment, a known weight of the substance under examination was heated to some definite temperature, say the boiling point of water. The ice chamber was then carefully dried with a

Fig. 56.

sponge or blotting-paper, so that no water was left adhering to its walls. The heated body was then quickly placed within, and the upper slab laid over the mouth of the chamber. The body quickly fell to the temperature of melting ice, and a certain quantity of ice was liquefied. This quantity was estimated by wiping dry the whole interior of the cavity, as well as the surface of the body, with a cold sponge (or blotting-paper), which had been previously weighed. The increase of weight gave the quantity of water absorbed—that is, the mass of ice melted.

If the unit of heat be taken as that which melts unit mass of ice at zero, then the quantity of heat given out by the body in this experiment will be numerically the same as the mass of ice melted, that is w, suppose. But if the initial temperature of the body be θ', its final temperature $0°$, its mass m, and its specific heat s, the quantity of heat given out will be $ms\theta$. Consequently we have the equation

$$ms\theta = w,$$

where m and w are expressed in the same units. Expressed in ordinary units of heat (calories) the equation would be

$$ms\theta = Lw,$$

where L is the latent heat of ice, or the quantity, expressed in calories,

225   Q

which will melt a gramme of ice ($= 79\cdot 25$). If the value of L, which may
be called the constant of the calorimeter, be not known, an experiment
will be necessary in order to determine it.   This may be effected by
introducing into the ice-chamber a weighed quantity of water at a known
temperature, and finding as before the quantity of ice melted.

The chief objection to this apparatus is the difficulty of procuring
large pieces of ice of sufficient purity.

134. Lavoisier and Laplace's Ice Calorimeter.—A modified form
of Black's calorimeter was devised by MM. Lavoisier and Laplace,[1] in
which the necessity for large blocks of pure ice is avoided.   It consists
essentially of three chambers (Fig. 57) contained one within the other.

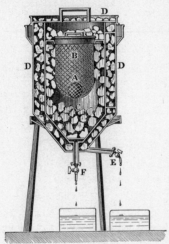

Fig. 57.
Lavoisier and Laplace's Ice Calorimeter.

The inner chamber AB contains the
hot body whose specific heat is
desired.   This chamber is surrounded
by another, and the space C between
them is packed with broken ice at
zero.   A tube F leads from this
chamber and drains off the water
resulting from the melting of the ice.
This water is weighed and the
specific heat of the substance is
estimated as before.   In order to
avoid heating from outside, a jacket
of ice DDD surrounds the second
chamber.   For this purpose, the
space between the second chamber
and the outside walls of the instrument is filled with broken ice, and
as the ice is melted in this chamber
by radiation from outside, the water drips away by the tap E.
When the apparatus is in proper condition for an experiment, there
should be no flow from the tap F, but a constant drip from the tap E.
If now a hot body is placed in the chamber A, its heat will be given
out to melt the ice in C, causing a corresponding flow of water
from F.

This apparatus requires a large quantity of ice, and large masses
of the substance under examination, and consequently a long time for
the execution of an experiment, and the trifling advantage it possesses
over Black's simple apparatus in not requiring the use of large blocks
of pure ice is more than counterbalanced by difficulties of the gravest
nature in estimating the quantity of ice melted.   This arises from the

[1] *Mémoires de l'Académie*, 1780 ; *Œuvres de Lavoisier*, tom. ii. p. 283.

water adhering to the ice, and remaining in the interstices between the fragments.   At the beginning of the experiment, the ice is mixed with a certain quantity of adhering water, which in all probability will be considerably different at the end of the experiment, for during the experiment the size and arrangement of some of the ice fragments will alter.   Hence the quantity of water which drains off through the tap F during the experiment does not accurately represent the quantity of ice melted, nor have we any means of estimating the probable error thus introduced.

In the hands of Lavoisier and Laplace this instrument yielded fair results, but with less scientific and careful experimenters the adhesion of the water to the ice might easily lead to great inaccuracies. In order to avoid this difficulty, Sir John Herschel suggested that the water should not be drained off, but that it and the ice should be kept together, and the whole bulk measured before and after melting. The diminution of bulk would thus give the quantity of ice melted during the experiment.   An ingenious method of measuring this change of volume has been devised by Bunsen [1] in his ice calorimeter, an instrument possessing many novel features of remarkable beauty and interest.   It is particularly valuable for measuring small quantities of heat, and by means of it Professor Bunsen has determined the specific heats of rare metals, such as indium, which can only be obtained in small quantities.   It is,

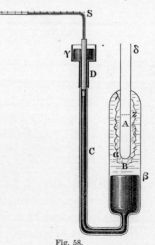

Fig. 58.

however, by no means easy to work with, and the theoretical conditions which are supposed to be fulfilled are difficult to realise in practice.

135. Bunsen's Ice Calorimeter.— As already stated, this apparatus is designed especially for the measurement of the change of volume which occurs during the liquefaction of ice. For this purpose a cylindrical test-tube A is fused into a larger cylindrical glass bulb B, as shown in Fig. 58. The bulb B is furnished with a glass stem CD, which terminates in an iron collar D.   This stem is filled with pure boiled mercury, which also occupies the bulb to the level β.   The remainder of the bulb above β is filled with pure boiled water.   A

---

[1] *Pogg. Ann.* vol. cxli. ; *Ann. de Chimie et de Phys.*, 3e, tom. xxiii. p. 50 ; *Phil. Mag.*, 1871, vol. xli. p. 161.

calibrated narrow glass tube S, furnished with a millimetre scale, is
fitted into a cork with fine sealing-wax, and then passed through the
mercury in the collar D, and made fast in the mouth of the tube CD,
so that it becomes filled with mercury ; and by adjusting the cork in
the mouth of the tube CD, the extremity of the mercury column in the
scale-tube S can be placed at any convenient point.   To effect this
without risk to the fragile apparatus, the instrument is supported by
the iron collar D in a vice.

In conducting an experiment, the first operation is to freeze some
of the water in the bulb B.   For this purpose the ice-producing
apparatus shown in Fig. 59 was employed by Bunsen.   F and G
are two semi-cylindrical tin-plate
vessels, which are connected by
tubes with the test-tube A of the
calorimeter, as shown in figure.
The vessels F and G contain
alcohol, and are both placed in a
freezing mixture.   By suction the
cold alcohol can be passed to
and fro from F to G through the
calorimeter tube A, and by this
means the water in the bulb B
can be reduced to the freezing
point.

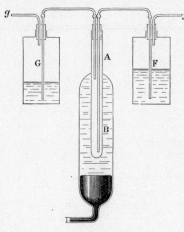

Fig. 59.

The temperature of the air-
freed water in B must be reduced
far below the normal freezing point
before solidification sets in, while
the outside of the bulb becomes covered with a coating of ice, deposited
from the moisture of the atmosphere.   At last, when the temperature
has been greatly reduced, the formation of ice suddenly begins, and
spreads in a few seconds from the bottom of the tube A to the top of
the bulb B.   Within these limits the bulb is filled with thin plates
and needles of ice, but from the bottom of A to the level of the
mercury below, the water is not frozen.   By continued cooling a
shell of solid ice may be gradually formed around A, from 6 to 10 mm.
in thickness.   On account of the low temperature of the alcohol, the
ice shell is much below zero, and if the instrument is now packed in
snow at zero a slow progressive freezing will take place in the water
for a long time.   Bunsen found that in this manner about 2 grammes
of water were frozen at the temperature of melting snow during the
first seven hours, and that this progressive freezing was sensible for

114 hours.   After this time the whole apparatus had come to zero, and the freezing ceased.

In making an experiment, the instrument is packed in pure snow, and some pure water is placed in the tube A.   The temperature of the whole apparatus is now zero, and it may be maintained in this condition for a week or more if some fresh snow is added from day to day.   It is very important that the snow should be quite pure, for if it contains even traces of impurities its melting point is lowered, and a slow progressive freezing of the water in the bulb takes place.[1]   It is also well to work in a room which is at a temperature not much above the freezing point, and before the instrument has assumed the constant temperature of the snow it is necessary to see that a thin layer of water is formed between the ice shell and the sides of the glass tube A, so as to avoid inequalities of pressure.

In order to interpret the indications of the instrument, a known mass of water m, at a definite temperature θ, may be introduced into the tube A.   In falling to zero this gives out a quantity of heat $m\theta$, and in consequence of the melting of the ice the mercury in the tube S recedes through n divisions of the scale.   This gives the relation between the quantity of heat supplied in any experiment in the tube A, and the corresponding recession of the mercury along the scale S, for if q is the quantity of heat corresponding to each division, we have

$$m\theta = nq.$$

In determining the specific heat of any substance, a fragment of it is heated in a steam-jacket, and the test-tube is partially filled with pure distilled water.   The heated fragment is quickly immersed in it, a plug of cotton-wool being placed at the bottom of A to prevent fracture.   The water in A is initially at zero, and its lower strata become warmed by the hot body ; but water being denser for some range above zero than at zero, the heated water remains at the bottom of the tube, and gives up its heat in melting the ice in the bulb B.   If the mercury recedes through n' divisions of the scale, the whole heat given up by the body in cooling to zero is $n'q$.   Hence, if m' be the mass of the body and θ' its original temperature, its specific

---

[1] Professor C. V. Boys found that this effect was largely reduced when the bulb was provided with a protecting glass cover (*Phil. Mag.* vol. xxiv. p. 214, 1887). It is still better to place the instrument in a Dewar vacuum vessel and surround the latter with snow or pounded ice.   This renders the effect of any slight difference of temperature between the ice in the instrument and that surrounding it negligible, as the passage of heat through a vacuum is extremely slow (see Glazebrook's *Dictionary of Applied Physics*, art. "Calorimetry ").

heat is given by the equation

$$m's\theta' = n'q.$$

Hence

$$s = \frac{mn'\theta}{m'n\theta'}.$$

In practice, the end of the mercury column does not remain stationary, but may vary in either direction by two or three divisions per hour. The error arising from this variation is approximately proportional to the time, and is corrected by observing the motion of the index for half an hour before and half an hour after the experiment. If a variation of n_1 scale divisions occurs in a time t_1 before the experiment is commenced, and n_2 in a time t_2 after it is completed, the mean rate of variation during the experiment may be taken equal to $\frac{1}{2}\left(\frac{n_1}{t_1} + \frac{n_2}{t_2}\right)$, and this multiplied by the time of the experiment gives the whole correction to be applied to the reading arising from this cause.

The accuracy of the instrument depends essentially on the care with which all the air has been expelled from the water enclosed by the bulb B. In order to secure this, the bulb is at first about half-filled with water, and placed mouth downwards over a lamp, so that the water can be boiled and the air expelled through the tube CD. During this process the mouth of the tube CD, which has not yet been fitted with the iron collar, dips into a vessel of boiling water. When the water in the bulb has been boiled away to about one-third of its original bulk the lamp is removed, and as the instrument cools the air-free water is siphoned over into it through the tube CD from the vessel into which it dips. The instrument is now placed upright, and the water for the most part siphoned out of the tube CD, which is then well dried by a current of dry air, and the iron collar is fastened on with the finest sealing-wax. The final filling-in of boiled mercury is done with a capillary glass tube, so as to avoid the remaining of any air bubbles on the sides of the tube.

By pressing the cork which carries the scale S a little deeper into the mouth of the tube CD, the end of the mercury thread may be placed at the same point of the scale at the beginning of each experiment, and the same part of the scale may be used throughout a series of investigations. Over a hundred experiments may be made with the same cylinder of ice, so that a single freezing will suffice for a week, if care be taken to renew the snow around the instrument every night and morning.

From the mode of standardising the instrument, it is clear that no error is introduced by an inaccurate knowledge of the latent heat of ice. Radiation errors are also entirely eliminated by the packing in snow, if the temperature of the latter experiences no variation.

The accuracy attainable in Bunsen's method of calorimetry is limited by the fact that a given specimen of water can freeze into ice of different densities. The error due to this cause would not, however, exceed about 1 in 1000.[1] This may be due, as Leduc has suggested, to the presence of variable small quantities of dissolved air remaining in the ice. The slight difference of temperature which is usually found to exist between the ice in the bulb and the ice in which the instrument is packed may also be due to differences in the amount of dissolved air.

By means of this apparatus the latent heat of fusion of ice may be estimated if the volume of each division of the scale tube be known, and if the expansion of water on solidifying at zero be also known. By this means Bunsen found the value 80·025, while the values found by Regnault, Person, and Hess, by other methods, were 79·4, 80·0, 80·3, respectively.

[1] J. H. Vincent, *Proc. Roy. Soc.* vol. lxix. p. 442, 1902.

SECTION III

THE METHOD OF MIXTURES

136. Preliminary Considerations.—The most prevalent method of calorimetry hitherto employed has been founded neither on the melting of ice, nor on the evaporation or condensation of a liquid, nor on any principle of latent heat, but on the measurement of heat by the change of the temperature of water. This method passes under the name of the method of mixtures,[1] and since the time of Regnault has been regarded as the method *par excellence* in the science of calorimetry.

Let us suppose that two bodies, A_1 and A_2, of masses m_1 and m_2, and specific heats s_1 and s_2, are at temperatures θ_1 and θ_2. If A_1 and A_2 are placed in contact, heat will pass from one to the other, and a common temperature θ intermediate between θ_1 and θ_2 will be attained. The quantity of heat lost by A_1 will be $m_1 s_1 (\theta_1 - \theta)$, and the quantity gained by A_2 will be $m_2 s_2 (\theta - \theta_2)$. Consequently, if the only interchange of heat is between A_1 and A_2, that is, if they neither obtain heat from nor lose heat to other bodies during the period of equalisation of temperature, the heat lost by A_1 will be equal to that gained by A_2, or

$$m_1 s_1 (\theta_1 - \theta) = m_2 s_2 (\theta - \theta_2).$$

If A_2 be a mass of water, s_2 will be equal to unity by definition, and the specific heat of A_1 will be given by the equation

$$s_1 = \frac{m_2 (\theta - \theta_2)}{m_1 (\theta_1 - \theta)}.$$

In this equation s_1 represents the mean specific heat of A_1 between the temperatures θ and θ_1.

It has been supposed so far that thermal equilibrium takes place between A_1 and A_2 without loss or gain of heat, that they neither give heat to nor receive heat from other bodies during the period of equal-

---

[1] This method was employed by Black.

232

isation of temperature. In practice it is impossible to secure this condition accurately, and in general there will be interchange of heat with other bodies. For this reason corrections must be applied, and special apparatus adopted, to eliminate or minimise such errors. The whole science of calorimetry consists in the invention of such apparatus and the adoption of such precautions as will lead to an accurate estimate of these corrections.

137. The Water Calorimeter.—The principal piece of apparatus necessary for the determination of specific heats by the method of mixtures is the water calorimeter. This consists of a cylindrical vessel (Fig. 60) made of very thin brass or copper or silver, and sustained within a somewhat larger and stronger vessel by non-conducting supports. The inner vessel contains a known quantity of water in which the body under investigation is placed at a known temperature, and the change of temperature of the water is noted by means of a delicate thermometer immersed in it, which may be observed at a distance through a telescope. In order to diminish the loss of heat by radiation and conduction during this observation the outside of the inner vessel and the inside of the outer are both carefully polished.

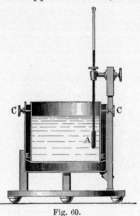

Fig. 60.

By this means the emissive power of one and the absorbing power of the other are greatly reduced. The inner vessel is supported by feebly-conducting threads EE stretched horizontally across the outer, and it is maintained in its place by wooden pegs CC which pass through the walls of the outer vessel near its mouth, and press against it so as to keep it steady.

The method of lagging the calorimeter with cotton-wool or other non-conductors, which is often recommended, diminishes the loss of heat considerably, but renders it very uncertain and variable, and should never be used in work of precision. The bad conductors take so long to reach a steady state that the rate of loss of heat at any moment depends on the past history more than on the temperature of the calorimeter at the moment. A more serious objection to the use of lagging of this kind is the danger of its absorbing moisture. The least trace of damp in the lagging, or of moisture condensed on the surface of the calorimeter, may produce serious loss of heat by evaporation.[1]

[1] *Ency. Brit.* art. "Calorimetry."

In every investigation it is supposed that the inner vessel and its accessories, such as the stirring-rod and the thermometer, have all the same temperature at the beginning and also at the end of an experiment. Let us suppose that a body of mass m, at a temperature θ, and of specific heat s, is immersed in the water, and let the temperature of the water rise in consequence from θ_1 to θ_2. During this process not only the water, but also the metal of the inner vessel and the material of the thermometer and stirring-rod, have been raised from θ_1 to θ_2, and their thermal capacities must therefore be taken into account. In the case of a body of mass m_1 and specific heat s_1 the quantity of heat necessary to raise its temperature $1°$ C. is $m_1 s_1$, and this is numerically the same as the mass of water which the same quantity of heat would raise $1°$ C. in temperature. For this reason $m_1 s_1$ is termed the *water equivalent* of the body, for it is numerically equal to the mass of water which possesses the same thermal capacity. Hence if W be the water equivalent of the calorimeter and its accessories, as well as of the water w contained, we have

$$W = w + m_1 s_1 + m_2 s_2 + m_3 s_3,$$

where m_1, m_2, m_3 refer to the metal of the vessel, the mercury of the thermometer, and the glass of the stirring-rod and thermometer respectively.[1] When the temperature of the apparatus rises from θ_1 to θ_2, the heat received will be $W(\theta_2 - \theta_1)$, and consequently the equation for the specific heat of the body immersed is

$$ms(\theta - \theta_2) = W(\theta_2 - \theta_1) + R,$$

where R is the correction arising from loss of heat by radiation and conduction during the period of equalisation of temperature.

In general, the terms in W arising from the vessel and its accessories are small compared with the terms representing the water enclosed, so that an imperfect knowledge of s_1, s_2, s_3 will have little influence on the accuracy of the results. These quantities may, however, be determined by three preliminary experiments, in which the substance m is taken to be glass, mercury, and brass (substance of vessel A) respectively. We shall then have three equations, involving

[1] To estimate the heat capacity of the glass and mercury of a thermometer, advantage may be taken of the fact that the *volume* specific heats of glass and mercury are practically the same ($0·46$ per c.c.). It will usually be sufficient to measure the volume of the immersed portion. The simplest way to do this is to weigh a beaker of water, and then find the increase in weight when the thermometer is hung from an extraneous support so as to be immersed to the same depth as in the calorimeter. The increase of weight in grammes gives the submerged volume in c.c. (Ostwald, *Physico-Chemical Measurements*, Eng. trans. by J. Walker, p. 121).

the three unknowns, s_1, s_2, s_3, from which they may be determined, and a complete knowledge of W obtained.

It should be noticed that the temperature of the hot body immersed in the water will always exceed that of the water, and if the substance happens to be a bad conductor of heat, the average temperature throughout its mass may considerably exceed that of the water, when the latter reaches its maximum temperature θ_2. For this reason feebly-conducting substances should be broken into small fragments when their specific heats are being determined.

Bad conductors.

138. The Radiation Correction.[1]—The equation of the preceding article was derived on the supposition that a hot body at a temperature θ was placed in a mass of water at a temperature θ_1, and that a common temperature θ_2 was attained. What actually happens, however, is somewhat different. The temperature of the water rises gradually to a *maximum* θ_2. During this process the water loses heat by radiation and conduction, and gains heat from the body immersed. When the maximum temperature θ_2 is first attained the immersed body is still warmer than the water, and heat is being lost by the water just as fast as it is being received. The temperature remains stationary as long as exact compensation takes place in this manner, and it then begins to fall. Furthermore, the thermometer will always be somewhat behind the water in its indications; during the period of rising temperature its readings will be slightly too low, and when the temperature is falling they will be too high, so that the highest temperature of the water will never be exactly attained by the thermometer. The maximum temperature registered will therefore be slightly below that actually attained by the calorimeter, but the discrepancy will be smaller the quicker the action of the thermometer. For this reason a resistance thermometer (Art. 97), though more troublesome to use, gives more accurate results, besides which it is more sensitive, and better adapted to give the mean temperature of a considerable depth of liquid.

The correction for heat losses cannot be made with any certainty unless the conditions of experiment are made as precise as possible. The outer vessel (Fig. 60) should be double-walled, and maintained at a steady temperature by a flow of cold water between the walls. The calorimeter should have a close-fitting lid to prevent loss by evaporation,[2] holes being provided for the thermometer and stirrer. A good

---

[1] The term *radiation correction* is somewhat objectionable, since a large part of the correction will usually be due to gains or losses of heat by conduction. Loss by evaporation will also be included.

[2] Loss by evaporation may be greatly diminished by introducing a trace of non-

form of stirrer is a small screw attached to a vertical shaft. The screw is caused to revolve in a vertical copper tube which is open at both ends and fixed in the calorimeter so that it is wholly immersed. A steady circulation of the water in the calorimeter is produced by the rotation of the screw.

The radiation correction is determined by observing the rate at which the calorimeter cools throughout the range of temperature of the experiment. If the range of temperature be small the radiation may be taken proportional to the difference of temperature between the calorimeter and the surrounding air, and the whole loss by radiation (and conduction) will be approximately equal to that which would occur if the calorimeter had been at its mean temperature $\frac{1}{2}(\theta_1 + \theta_2)$ throughout the whole time of the experiment, that is, the time of rising from θ_1 to θ_2. If the rate of cooling at this mean temperature be observed, then, from the known water equivalent W, the quantity of heat lost per second at this temperature will be known, and this multiplied by the time of the experiment will give the correction R.

Otherwise the interval between the immersion of the hot body and the attainment of the maximum temperature θ_2 may be divided into a series of epochs, t_1, t_2, t_3, etc., at the end of each of which the temperature of the calorimeter is noted and found to be θ', θ'', θ''', etc. During the first epoch t_1, the mean temperature is $\frac{1}{2}(\theta_1 + \theta')$, and during the second epoch t_2, the mean temperature is $\frac{1}{2}(\theta' + \theta'')$, etc. Hence the heat lost during these epochs will be, taking θ_0 to be the temperature of the air,

$$\mathrm{A}t_1\left(\frac{\theta_1 + \theta'}{2} - \theta_0\right), \quad \mathrm{A}t_2\left(\frac{\theta' + \theta''}{2} - \theta_0\right), \text{ etc.,}$$

where A is a constant to be determined by observation of the rate of cooling of the calorimeter. This loss of heat by radiation causes a diminution of the maximum temperature θ_2, which can thus be calculated, so that if we write $\mathrm{R} = \mathrm{W}\Delta\theta$, the maximum temperature which would have been attained by the water would have been $\theta_2 + \Delta\theta$, and the equation for s becomes

$$ms(\theta - \theta_2) = \mathrm{W}(\theta_2 + \Delta\theta - \theta_1).$$

The radiation correction increases with the difference of temperature $\theta_2 - \theta_1$, and it is therefore well to arrange that the mass of water placed in the calorimeter shall be so great that the elevation of temperature shall not be very considerable. This, however, diminishes

---

volatile paraffin oil into the calorimeter, which forms a film over the surface of the water.

the sensitiveness of the operation, and to counterbalance its effect a very delicate thermometer must be used.

The correction may be more readily made by a graphic method. If the surroundings of the calorimeter are kept at a constant temperature, then we may proceed as follows. Let the temperature indicated by the thermometer be taken at short intervals, say of 20 seconds, starting before the hot body is introduced, and continuing for a few minutes after the temperature has begun to fall, and let the temperatures be plotted against the time, as in Fig. 61 a. The changes of

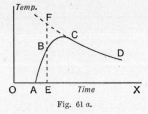

Fig. 61 a.

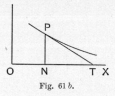

Fig. 61 b.

temperature are represented by the curve OABCD, in which the ordinates are proportional to the excess of temperature of the thermometer above its surroundings. The portion OA corresponds to the preliminary period when the calorimeter is at the temperature of its surroundings. On the introduction of the hot body the temperature rises rapidly and then falls slowly, as shown by the curve ABCD. If C is the point at which thermal equilibrium is established between the calorimeter and its contents, then the part CD is the ordinary curve of cooling. Now let us compare this curve with that which would be shown by an ideal calorimeter, in which thermal equilibrium is instantaneously established. In the latter case the temperature would rise immediately to the equilibrium value on the introduction of the hot body at A, and would at once begin to fall slowly according to the law of cooling. As soon as the temperature fell to C, the remainder of the curve would be the same as CD, but the whole curve of cooling would be shifted a little to the left, because the ideal calorimeter would begin to lose heat at the maximum rate the moment the hot body was put in, and the state represented by C would be attained sooner. Let OEFCD represent the curve of temperature of the ideal calorimeter when the hot body is introduced at time E sufficiently later than A to make the two curves identical along CD. Assuming Newton's law of cooling (Art. 99) we may write

$$W d\theta = dQ - dq \quad . \quad (1) \qquad\qquad -\frac{dq}{dt} = k\theta \quad . \quad (2)$$

where W is the water equivalent of the calorimeter and its contents (excluding the hot body), θ is the temperature excess of the calorimeter above its surroundings, dQ is the gain of heat from the hot body and dq the loss by radiation corresponding to a change of temperature $d\theta$, and k is a constant. Substituting in (1) from (2) and integrating

$$W\theta = Q + k \int_o^t \theta dt,$$

where Q is now the total heat communicated by the hot body to the calorimeter in any time t. Taking t to correspond to the point C, $W\theta$ is the same for both the actual and ideal cases, and so is Q, since the hot body gives up heat to the calorimeter only. It follows that $\int_o^t \theta dt$ is the same in both cases, and as this integral represents the area between the axis OX and the curve, the areas must be equal. Thus we arrive at the following construction : Continue the curve CD backwards towards F, and draw an ordinate EF at such a point that it will make the areas ABE and BFC equal; the height of the ordinate EF will then give the true excess of temperature corrected for losses. In producing the curve CD backwards, it will be useful to remember that (assuming Newton's law of cooling) the subtangent NT (Fig. 61 b) is constant all along the curve. For if we draw the tangent PT to the curve of cooling, the rate of cooling at P is the gradient of the curve, *i.e.* it is PN / NT. But by Newton's law the rate of cooling is proportional to the excess temperature PN, therefore NT must be constant.[1]

Rumford's method.

The radiation correction may be practically eliminated by a method of procedure suggested by Rumford. Thus, if the highest temperature θ_2 of the calorimeter be approximately known by a preliminary experiment, then if the experiment be commenced by having the initial temperature θ_1 of the calorimeter as much below that of the air of the chamber as θ_2 is above it, heat will be received by the calorimeter during the first part of the experiment, and will be given out during the second ; the whole experiment is thus divided into two parts, during one of which its temperature is lower than that of the air, and during the other higher. A complete compensation is not, however, effected by this process. During the first stage the calorimeter receives heat rapidly from the body immersed, and during the second much more slowly. For this reason the first period is much shorter than the second, and the quantity of heat received from the chamber during the first period will be less than that given out during the second.

---

[1] For other graphic methods, see Glazebrook's *Dictionary of Applied Physics*, vol. i. art. " Calorimetry."

To secure complete compensation by this method it would be necessary to begin the experiment with the calorimeter at some calculated temperature below that of the chamber, and such that the initial difference of temperature between the chamber and the calorimeter is greater than the final. It may also happen that when the calorimeter is cooled 5° or 6° below the temperature of the air, dew may be deposited on its surface, which will evaporate during the experiment as the temperature rises, and thus lead to a diminution of the final temperature and consequent error in the determination. For these reasons, greater accuracy is attained by calculating and allowing for the radiation error than by attempting to eliminate it in this way. The method is chiefly useful in rough experiments, where it is intended to neglect the radiation correction.

Another method of avoiding the radiation correction has been recommended by M. N. Hesehus,[1] as practised in the university of St. Petersburg. The principle of the method consists in maintaining the temperature of the calorimeter stationary, and the same as that of the room in which the experiment is made. This is effected by adding cold water gradually to the calorimeter, so as just to counterbalance the heating effect of the body immersed. A mixture of ice and water affords a convenient supply of cold water at a known temperature. From the quantity of cold water added the specific heat of the body immersed may be easily calculated. For let θ be the initial temperature of the body immersed, and θ_1 that of the calorimeter. Then, since the calorimeter is kept at θ_1 throughout, it follows that the heat given out by the body immersed is $ms(\theta - \theta_1)$, and if M be the mass of cold water added, and θ_0 its temperature, the heat gained by this water is $M(\theta_1 - \theta_0)$, so that

$$ms(\theta - \theta_1) = M(\theta_1 - \theta_0).$$

It may be observed that in this method the water equivalent of the calorimeter is eliminated as well as the radiation error. The only quantity which it is necessary to observe is the mass M of cold water added to keep the temperature stationary, the temperatures θ, θ_0, θ_1 and the mass m of the body immersed being supposed known.

To effect this in practice an air calorimeter was used. This consisted of a large-bulbed air thermometer, having a brass tube protruding into its bulb somewhat in the manner of the test-tube in Bunsen's ice calorimeter. The hot body was placed in this tube, and cold water was poured in so as to maintain the indication of the manometer constant. In order to avoid errors arising from variations

Method of stationary temperature.

---

[1] Hesehus, *Journal de la Société Physico-chimique Russe*, Nov. 1887 ; *Journal de Physique*, tom. vii. p. 489, 1888.

of the temperature of the surrounding air, the air reservoir of the thermometer was placed in a vessel of water at the temperature of the room.   Before placing the hot body in the brass tube a weighed quantity of water was placed in it, and the body was then immersed in this water, as in Bunsen's ice calorimeter [1] (Art. 135).

139. Regnault's Apparatus.—The apparatus devised by Regnault [2]

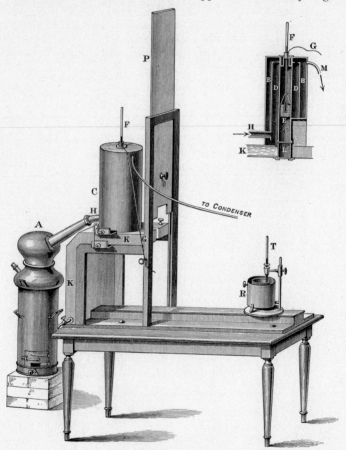

Fig. 62.—Regnault's Apparatus.

for the measurement of specific heats by the method of mixtures is shown in Fig. 62.   It consists of a heater, C, and a calorimeter, R. The heater is that part of the apparatus in which the substance under experiment is warmed to some known temperature before immersion

---

[1] For an improved form of Hesehus's calorimeter, see an article by F. A. Waterman, *Phil. Mag.*, Nov. 1895.

[2] Regnault, *Ann. de Chimie et de Physique*, 2e, tom. lxxiii. p. 5, 1840.

in the calorimeter. It is simply a form of steam-jacket, comprising
three coaxial cylindrical compartments, B, C, D, as shown in section.
The body to be heated is placed in a small wire gauze basket, E, and
suspended in the inner compartment. This basket possesses two coaxial compartments, the inner of which contains the bulb of a thermometer, and the outer carries the substance to be heated. The
inner compartment of the heater in which the basket hangs can be
opened at each end. The upper end is closed by a cork through
which passes the stem, F, of the thermometer, and also the thread
which supports the basket. The lower end, L, of this compartment
is closed by a double sliding shutter, which, when open, permits of the
basket and the substance which it contains being lowered into the
calorimeter by means of the suspending thread G.

The second and third compartments of the heater are traversed by
a current of steam supplied by a boiler, A. The steam enters the
second compartment, DD, through H, and after passing through the
outer compartment, BB, escapes by the tube M into a condenser.
The presence of the steam in the outer jacket prevents cooling and
condensation in the second compartment, and the temperature of
the inner is kept constant, being surrounded by a current of dry
vapour.

A considerable time is required before the substance in the basket
attains its final temperature. It generally attains a maximum of about
98° C., and should be allowed to remain in the heater for half an hour
after its temperature has become stationary. When this has been
effected the calorimeter R is run along rails (provided for the purpose)
into position under the shutter which closes the lower end of the
inner compartment of the heater. The shutter is then withdrawn,
and the basket quickly lowered into the calorimeter. The time occupied in the transference of the basket is so small that no very sensible
error can arise through radiation during the passage from the heater
to the calorimeter.

In order to prevent radiation to the calorimeter from the heater
and boiler during the experiment, the support, KK, on which the
heater stands is made hollow, and contains water at the temperature
of the air. A thick plate of cork is placed under the heater, so that
the water in the supporting stand does not become warm by conduction. A vertical cylindrical aperture is constructed in the stand, so
as to permit of the basket being lowered into the calorimeter. While
the substance is being heated the calorimeter is withdrawn to a
distance along the rails, as shown in the figure, and a thick cork screen,
P, cuts off all radiation from the heating apparatus. This screen is

R

movable, and can be raised when it is desired to run the calorimeter under the heater.

The quantity of water placed in the calorimeter is gauged in a measuring flask of known volume at all temperatures. After the immersion of the heated substance a continual stirring is kept up by agitating the basket by means of the thread employed to suspend it.

With the form of heater described in this apparatus a continuous variation of the initial temperature θ of the substance under examination cannot be obtained unless the vapour is produced in a manner which permits of the pressure being varied continuously. Different fixed temperatures may be obtained by using other liquids than water to furnish the vapour. A continuous variation of the initial tempera-

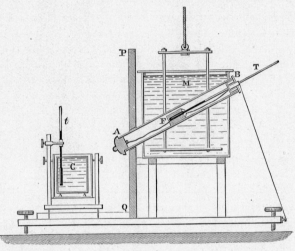

Fig. 63.

ture may be conveniently obtained by means of a later form of heater employed by Regnault,[1] and shown in Fig. 63. The wire basket containing the substance under examination is placed in a tube AB, running in a sloping direction through an oil bath which can be heated to any desired temperature. When the temperature of the substance has become stationary it is let down into the calorimeter by means of the thread to which it is attached. The oil bath may be replaced by a freezing mixture, and the specific heat may thus be determined over a wide range of temperature, and its variations investigated.

140. Specific Heats of Liquids.—The specific heats of liquids and

---

[1] Regnault, *Ann. de Chimie et de Physique*, 3e, tom. xlvi. p. 270, 1856.

powders and substances soluble in water may be examined by the method of mixtures by sealing them up in thin glass or metal tubes. In the case of bad conductors of heat, however, considerable error may arise from the slowness with which the sealed-up mass yields its heat to the calorimeter, so that not only is the radiation correction enlarged, but it is impossible to determine how far the average temperature of the sealed-up mass differs from the indications of the thermometer both before immersion and at the time of maximum temperature of the calorimeter. In the case of solids, which are poor conductors and soluble in water, another liquid of known specific heat

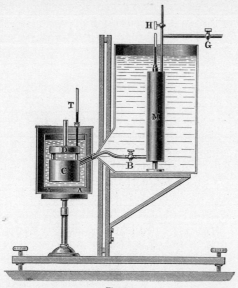

Fig. 64.

in which they are insoluble may be used in the calorimeter, and the sealing up in a tube can be thus avoided. In the case of liquids, Regnault used the apparatus shown in Fig. 64. The liquid was first heated (or cooled) in a reservoir, M, immersed in a bath (or freezing mixture). A tube furnished with a tap, B, led from this reservoir to the calorimeter, where it entered another reservoir, CD, which was completely immersed in the water of the calorimeter. The liquid having attained a definite temperature in the reservoir M, the tap B was opened, and the liquid forced by air pressure, communicated through the tube GH, into the calorimetric reservoir CD. The change of temperature of the calorimeter was noted, and the necessary corrections applied as before. The thermal capacity of the reservoir CD must, of course, be reckoned as part of that of the calorimeter.

141. Favre and Silbermann's Calorimeter.—A special form of calorimeter was devised by MM. Favre and Silbermann,[1] for the purpose of studying thermal phenomena which require some time for completion, such, for example, as the measurement of the quantity of heat evolved during the chemical combination of two or more substances. The principle of the instrument is somewhat the same as that of Bunsen's ice calorimeter, the bulb being, however, filled entirely with mercury, and the heat communicated being measured by the expansion of the mercury in the stem. It is thus a kind of large-bulbed thermometer, the stem of which is bent round at a right angle, so that the part in which the end of the mercury column travels is horizontal, as in the ice calorimeter of Bunsen (Fig. 58). The bulb, which is generally an iron sphere, is fitted with two tubes of glass or platinum, which protrude into the interior of the mercury, and into which the hot body, or the substance under examination, is placed. The bulb is also fitted with a steel plunger, which may be screwed forward into the mercury (or backwards), and by this means the end of the mercurial column can be brought to any part of the stem desired at the beginning of an experiment. The instrument is standardised by introducing a known weight of hot water into one of the tubes and noting the displacement of the index as well as the fall of temperature of the water. If the end of the mercurial column advances n divisions when a mass m of water cools from θ_1 to θ_0, then the heat equivalent of each division of the stem is $m(\theta_1 - \theta_0)/n$. This being known, the heat yielded to the calorimeter during any other experiment may be inferred from the displacement of the end of the mercurial column in the stem. During an experiment the bulb of the instrument is encased in cotton-wool or some other non-conducting stuff, so as to secure uniformity of conditions during all experiments, and to prevent as far as possible loss of heat by radiation and conduction.

The apparatus of Favre and Silbermann has been somewhat modified by M. Jamin,[2] the reservoir of the new instrument being of the form of a glass beaker closed at the top. The stem rises vertically from the top of the reservoir, and the receiving tubes pass down vertically through the top into the interior of the mercury.

142. Experiments of Nernst, Koref, and Lindemann.[3]—It is of course impossible to use water in finding specific heats of substances

[1] Favre, *Ann. de Chimie et de Physique*, 3e, tom. xxxvi. p. 5 ; tom. xxxvii. p. 416 ; tom. xl. p. 293 ; 4e, toms. xxvi. xxvii. xxix. ; 5e, tom. i.

[2] Jamin, *Cours de physique*, tom. ii., 2e, fasc., p. 17.

[3] *Sitz. der K. Preuss. Akad.* (Berlin), 1910, p. 247.

at temperatures 0° C.   Nernst, Koref, and Lindemann employed a
calorimeter in which a copper block of about 400 grammes took the
place of the water in the ordinary calorimeter, and this instrument
was used for determinations both above and below the freezing point.
The apparatus is shown in Fig. 65.   K is the copper block which had
a central cavity bored in it to receive the body whose
specific heat was being sought.   This block was turned
to fit the inside of a vacuum vessel, and the fit was
made more perfect by the use of Wood's fusible alloy.
Owing to the good conductivity of copper, equilibrium
of temperature was soon attained.   This device gets rid
of the troublesome stirring which is necessary in a water
calorimeter, and the low specific heat of copper is a
further advantage, since the temperature rise is greater
for the same access of heat than in a water calorimeter
of equal weight.   The rise of temperature was measured
by constantan-iron thermo-elements T, T, whose junctions
were sunk in holes bored in the copper block, and were
insulated from the copper by enclosing them in thin
glass tubes.   To improve the thermal contact, Wood's
alloy was used to fill all vacant spaces both inside and
outside the glass tubes.   The other junctions of the
thermo-elements were fixed in another copper block C
which was maintained at the temperature of the bath

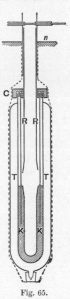

Fig. 65.

in which the apparatus was sunk.   A glass tube R passed through
this latter block to allow of the introduction of the body experimented on.   The whole was enclosed in a water-tight sheath of
thin sheet copper.   The surface of liquid in the bath is seen
at n.   The body was enclosed in a thin silver vessel, and had a
narrow hole bored down its centre to receive a thermo-element.   It
was so arranged that, on opening a shutter (seen in the upper part of
the figure), the silver vessel could be let down by a thread into the
calorimeter.   A wad of cotton-wool placed on the top of the silver
vessel served to close the calorimeter and prevent the escape of warm
air.   The rise of temperature, when the cooled body was let down
into the calorimeter, was usually 2° or 3°.   To calibrate the instrument,
water was used for ordinary temperatures and lead for low temperatures.   The specific heat of copper between 21°·6 and 2°·4 was found
to be 0·09155, that of lead between − 3°·0 and − 76°·8 was 0·03003,
and that of pure ice 0·4329 between − 2°·9 and − 76°·9, and
0·2658 between − 81°·7 and − 189°.   Many other substances were
also examined.

SECTION IV

THE METHOD OF COOLING

143. Principle of the Method.—The method of cooling in calorimetry is founded on the supposition that when a body cools in a given enclosure the quantity of heat, dQ, emitted by it in a time dt depends only on the excess θ of the temperature of the body above that of the enclosure, and on the nature and extent of the surface of the body. On this supposition we may write down the equation

$$dQ = Af(\theta)dt,$$

where A depends on the surface of the body, that is, on its area and radiating power, and $f(\theta)$ is an unknown function of the difference of temperature which will be the same for all bodies. Thus, if Newton's law of cooling be true, this function is simply the difference of temperature θ.

Now, if the body cools through an interval of temperature $d\theta$ in the time dt, we have

$$dQ = msd\theta,$$

where m is the mass and s the specific heat of the body, hence

$$msd\theta = Af(\theta)dt,$$

and therefore the time of cooling from a difference of temperature θ_1 to a difference θ_2 will be

$$t = \frac{ms}{A} \int_{\theta_2}^{\theta_1} \frac{d\theta}{f(\theta)} = \frac{ms}{A} \left[F(\theta_1) - F(\theta_2) \right],$$

where $F(\theta)$ is the function obtained by performing the integration. In the same manner, if another body of mass m' and specific heat s' requires a time t' to cool through the same range in the same enclosure, we have

$$t' = \frac{m's'}{A'} \left[F(\theta_1) - F(\theta_2) \right];$$

246

and therefore

$$\frac{t}{t'} = \frac{ms}{m's'} \cdot \frac{A'}{A};$$

and if circumstances can be so arranged that the surfaces of the two bodies shall be the same, so that $A = A'$, we shall have

$$\frac{ms}{m's'} = \frac{t}{t'}.$$

That is, the thermal capacities of the two masses will be in the ratio of the times required to cool through the same range of temperature under the same conditions. We shall now see how far these conditions have been realised in practice.

144. Apparatus of Dulong and Petit.—The first accurate researches by the method of cooling were made by Dulong and Petit. The substance under examination was placed in a small silver vessel and suspended in an enclosure, the walls of which were lamp-blacked and kept at zero by melting ice. The apparatus is shown in Fig. 66. The silver vessel D consisted of two concentric cylinders, the inner of which was just wide enough to contain the bulb of a small delicate thermometer, and the substance was placed in the annular space between the two cylinders. In the case of solids they were finely powdered and tightly packed into this space, so as to be in close contact with its walls. The outside of the silver was brightly polished, so that it might always possess the same radiating power and prolong as much as possible the time of cooling, which is the subject of observation. This time is also extended by exhausting[1] the chamber in which the radiation occurs.

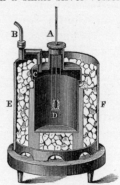

Fig. 66.

In Fig. 66 the silver thimble containing the substance under examination is shown suspended at the centre of an air-tight vessel, the stem of the thermometer, which indicates its temperature, projecting through the top. In making an experiment this vessel is heated, thoroughly desiccated and exhausted, and then surrounded by ice, as shown in figure. The time of falling through some definite range of temperature is then observed—for example, the times of falling from 15° to 10°, and from 10° to 5° C.

The simple equation of the foregoing article becomes somewhat modified when the thermal capacities of the silver vessel and the

---

[1] The time of cooling was nearly twice as long in vacuum as in air in some of Regnault's experiments.

thermometer are taken into account. Denoting the sum of their thermal capacities by k, the equation becomes

$$\frac{ms+k}{m's'+k}=\frac{t}{t'},$$

where k is the same in all experiments, and may be determined by finding t and t' for two substances of known specific heats. It may also be determined by estimating the masses of silver, glass, and mercury respectively, and using their previously determined specific heats. Both methods were employed by Regnault, but the results were not very concordant. The observation of t and t' for two different masses of water would also lead to a value of k.

145. Regnault's Experiments.—A series of experiments was executed by Regnault [1] with the object of ascertaining how far the method of cooling could be relied on in the estimation of specific heats. In the case of solids the mode of procedure was the same as that of Dulong and Petit, already described. With liquids the experiments were conducted in the same manner, and also with a modified form of apparatus. In the second form of apparatus the silver thimble was dispensed with, and the liquid was enclosed in a small cylindrical bulb of glass, the neck of which was just wide enough to allow a small thermometer to pass down into the liquid within the bulb. The cooling of the liquid was then observed as before.

Method unsuitable for solids.

After an extensive series of experiments on substances whose specific heats had been already determined by the method of mixtures, Regnault was convinced that in the case of solids the method of cooling could not be accepted as a method of sufficient accuracy in calorimetry ; and he was forced to this conclusion, not only by the differences between the results obtained by this method and those obtained by other methods for the same substances, but also by the discrepancies existing between the various determinations by this method of the specific heat of the same substance.

With solids the conditions assumed in the deduction of the fundamental equation are never even approximately satisfied. Thus, although the external surface of the silver thimble may always have the same radiating power, yet the contact of the powdered solid with the inside surface will depend on how tightly the powder is pressed into the vessel, and this will not only vary with different substances, but also in different experiments with the same substance. Thus, although we may have $A = A'$ for the external surface of the silver,

[1] Regnault, *Ann. de Chimie et de Physique*, 3e, tom. ix. p. 327 ; and 2e, tom. lxxiii. p. 5.

the communication of heat from the interior outwards will depend
both on the conductivity of the powdered solid, and on its contact
with the walls of the vessel.   For this reason, nothing like equality
of temperature can exist throughout the mass, and the temperature
registered by the thermometer being that of the interior may be
considerably higher than that of the external silver surface, which is
that which should appear in our equations.

In the case of liquids the conditions assumed are much more
nearly satisfied. Here the contact with the silver vessel will be
much the same in all experiments, and equality of temperature will
be fairly established throughout the mass by convection currents, so
that the question of conductivity scarcely comes into account.   This
method is therefore exceedingly convenient in the case of liquids,
especially in the case of liquids which cannot be obtained in considerable quantities.

The advantage of this method is that there is no transference or
mixture ; the defect is that the whole measurement depends on the
assumption that the rate of loss of heat is the same in the two
experiments, and that any variation in the conditions, or uncertainty
in the rate of loss, produces its full effect in the result, whereas in the
method of mixtures it would only affect a small correction.   Other
sources of uncertainty are, that the rate of loss of heat generally
depends to some extent on the rate of fall of temperature, and that
it is difficult to take accurate observations on a rapidly falling
thermometer.   Instead of using a small polished silver calorimeter,
it would be better to use a fairly large one, the surface of which, as
well as that of the enclosure, should be permanently blackened, so
as to increase the loss of heat by radiation as much as possible compared with the losses by convection and conduction, which are less
regular.   For accurate work it is essential that the liquid in the
calorimeter should be continuously stirred, and that the lid as well as
the sides of the enclosure should be surrounded with water also kept
stirred, and preserved at a constant temperature.[1]

[1] H. L. Callendar, *Ency. Brit.* art. "Calorimetry."

146. Joly's Steam Calorimeter.—The method of condensation does not appear to have been used in calorimetry, at least with success, until near the end of the last century. This probably arose from the mechanical difficulties and the many sources of error which apparently attend this method. In 1886, however, Professor Joly [1] proved that the steam calorimeter was not only an accurate scientific instrument, but that, besides being of more general application, it was probably susceptible of greater accuracy than any other method till then employed. He has since proved that in the hands of a skilled experimenter the steam calorimeter gives not only exceedingly consistent and reliable results for solids and liquids, but that by means of it the experimental determination of the specific heats of gases at constant volume, previously regarded as impossible, can be readily effected.

The simplest form of Prof. Joly's apparatus consists essentially of a thin metal enclosure, which we shall call the steam-chamber, in which hangs from the arm of a balance a small platinum pan (Fig. 67), carrying the body to be experimented on. Steam is admitted into this chamber at the upper end, through a tube (as shown by the arrows), and escapes through a tube leading from the lower extremity. The steam can be admitted rapidly and shut off at pleasure, or allowed to flow gently through the apparatus.

At the beginning of an experiment a known weight of any substance is placed on the pan, and after remaining some time, so as to take up the temperature of the chamber, its temperature θ_1 is noted by means of a thermometer inserted in a tubulure passing through the side of the steam-chamber. Steam in the meantime is got up in the boiler, and is suddenly admitted, so that the whole chamber becomes at once filled with saturated vapour. Condensation at once begins on the substance, and the resulting water is caught in

[1] J. Joly, *Proc. Roy. Soc.* vol. xli. p. 352, 1886.

the pan—weights being added to the other pan of the balance so as to restore equilibrium. During this process the steam is admitted very slowly (by opening an escape tube leading from the boiler) into the calorimeter, so that there is no sensible steam draught on the pan, and the weighing is not interfered with. After four or five minutes the substance has attained the temperature of the steam, and the condensation is completed. The pan then ceases to increase sensibly in weight, and the equilibrium of the balance is maintained permanent. A very slow increase of three or four milligrammes per hour (due to radiation) is, however, noticed. Equilibrium having been

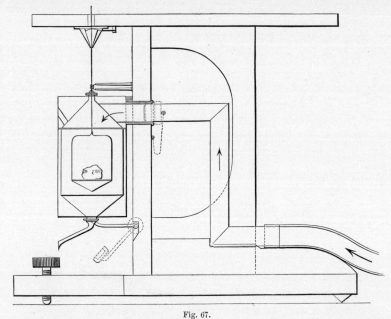

Fig. 67.

obtained, the total increase of weight w is noted, and the experiment is over. Let θ_2 be the temperature of the steam, and L its latent heat. The quantity of heat given out by the condensation is wL, and this is expended in raising the substance and pan from θ_1 to θ_2. If W be the weight of the substance and s its specific heat, the heat acquired by the substance will be $Ws(\theta_2 - \theta_1)$, and that acquired by the supporting pan will be $k(\theta_2 - \theta_1)$, where k is the thermal capacity of the pan, that is, the quantity of heat necessary to raise its temperature $1°$ C. Hence we have

$$Ws(\theta_2 - \theta_1) + k(\theta_2 - \theta_1) = w\text{L}.$$

The quantity k is determined by a previous observation, and the temperature θ_2 is found either directly, by a thermometer inserted in the steam chamber, or by means of Regnault's tables and a reading of the barometer.

For extreme accuracy a small correction is still necessary. The weight W of the substance is found in air at θ_1, and the weight w is found when the substance and pan are in steam at θ_2. The weight of steam per cubic centimetre at 100° is little more than half that of air at ordinary temperatures, and for this reason the weight w is greater than the weight of vapour condensed by the excess in weight of a volume v of air at θ_1 over the same volume of steam at θ_2, where v is the volume of the substance and pan together. The difference in weight of a cubic centimetre of air at 15° C. and a c.c. of steam at 100° is ·000636 gramme, according to Regnault; hence the correction to be applied to w is ·000636v. This correction being applied gives the weight of water condensed, but it must be remembered that it is weighed in steam; and if extreme accuracy be desired, it is still necessary to multiply by the factor 1·000589, in order to reduce the weighing to vacuum. The actual weight in a vacuum of the water condensed will therefore be

$$1\cdot000589(w - 0\cdot000636v),$$

so that s is determined from the equation

$$(Ws + k)(\theta_2 - \theta_1) = 1\cdot000589(w - 0\cdot000636v)L.$$

Where according to Regnault

$$L = 606\cdot5 - 0\cdot695\theta_2 - 0\cdot00002\theta_2{}^2 - 0\cdot0000003\theta_2{}^3,$$

or very approximately $L = 536\cdot5 + 0\cdot7(100 - \theta_2)$.

In order to avoid the condensation of steam on the suspending wire, where it leaves the steam-chamber, it passes, not through a small hole in the metal, but through a small hole pierced in a plug of plaster of Paris. Without the plaster the steam condenses on the metal and forms a drop at the aperture through which the suspending wire passes, and destroys the freedom of motion of the wire and prevents accurate weighing. With the plaster of Paris plug no such drop collects, and the weighing can be performed with accuracy. In his later experiments, Prof. Joly placed a small spiral of platinum wire around the suspending wire just outside the aperture, and by passing an electric current through the spiral, sufficient heat is produced to prevent all condensation on the suspending wire in the neighbourhood of the aperture. Besides accuracy in weighing, a point of prime importance is the rapid introduction of the steam at the beginning of the experiment. When the steam first enters the calorimeter, partial condensation occurs by radiation to the cold air and the walls of the chamber. Some of the condensed globules may fall upon the substance and lead to an error in the value of s. If the steam enters slowly this error may be large, and it is therefore important to fill the chamber at once with steam. This necessitates a good supply of steam and a large delivery tube, but when the chamber is well filled with steam a very gentle after-flow suffices. If the steam supply be cut off, the weight of condensed vapour slowly diminishes. This arises from distillation over to the colder walls of the chamber, and if the steam be again turned on the weight increases.

The error arising from the deposition of condensed globules on the pan during the initial stages of the experiment is somewhat counterbalanced by radiation from the steam to the substance. This latter is analogous to the transference error in the other methods of calorimetry.

One advantage of the steam calorimeter is that it applies equally to solids, liquids, and gases, and may be used for large or small masses, so as to enable us to find by this means the specific heats of rare substances which are not easily procurable in large quantities. Liquids, powders, and solids acted on by steam may be sealed up in a glass envelope, the thermal capacity of which can be determined. The method therefore appears not only exceedingly accurate, but also universal in its application.

The method of evaporation, on the other hand, is important in estimating quantities of heat in many scientific investigations. It is particularly useful in evaluating the quantity of heat developed by the combustion of coal or other kinds of fuel, and in measuring the economy of various kinds of furnaces.

Method of evaporation.

147. The Differential Steam Calorimeter—Specific Heats of Gases at Constant Volume.—In a more recent form[1] of the steam calorimeter, the correction for the weight of the steam displaced by the pan is avoided. This form is named the differential steam calorimeter, and has been applied by Prof. Joly to determine the specific heats of gases at constant volume. In this form (shown in front and side view in Fig. 68) two similar pans hang in the steam-chamber, one suspended from each arm of the balance, so as to counterpoise each other. The thermal capacities of the pans can be made equal, so that k will vanish from the equation, and the radiation error will also disappear, as it will cause equal condensation on the two pans.

The chief use of the differential form is, however, its application to the calorimetry of gases. For this purpose the pans are

[1] J. Joly, *Proc. Roy. Soc.* vol. xlvii. p. 218, 1889.

replaced by two equal spherical shells of copper, one containing the gas at a known pressure and temperature, and the other empty. The spheres are furnished with small pans, or "catch-waters," to collect the water resulting from condensation. Greater condensation occurs on the sphere which contains the gas, and the excess gives the quantity of

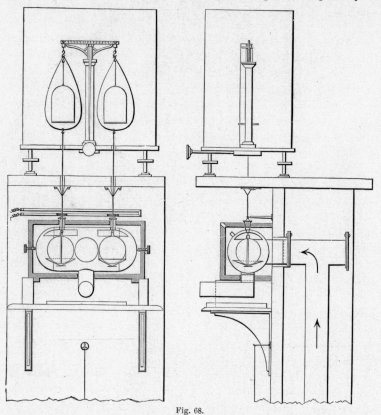

Fig. 68.

heat required to heat the contained mass of gas from θ_1 to θ_2. This determines the specific heat of the gas at constant volume.

The great advantage of the differential calorimeter is, that any source of error common to the two spheres is eliminated, and the gas or other substance enclosed in one of them merely bears its own share of error, and not also that of the containing sphere. Thus an error in the observation of the temperature disappears with regard to the sphere, and the effect is practically the same as if the gas were contained in a vessel of zero thermal capacity in the single steam calorimeter form.

In making an experiment, the sphere used to hold the gas is repeatedly washed out with the dry pure gas, the sphere being both heated and exhausted before each admission of the gas. It is then filled and hung in the steam-chamber and counterpoised against the empty sphere, the difference of weight being noted. This gives the weight of gas enclosed. The stationary temperature θ_1 being noted, the steam is admitted, and in about five minutes the condensation will be complete. The upper temperature θ_2 is then noted. The lower temperature θ_1 is registered by a delicate standardised low-range thermometer, and θ_2 is registered by a similar high-range thermometer. The spheres are now removed from the calorimeter and carefully dried, their high temperature being sufficient to completely evaporate all moisture from their surfaces. When cool, they are again placed in the calorimeter, and equilibrium tested. This is in order to detect if any leakage has occurred during the experiment.[1] Some of the gas may now be let out, and another experiment made with what remains.

The spheres employed by Prof. Joly were of copper, and about 6·7 cm. in diameter, the one containing the gas being made to stand a safe working pressure of about 35 or 40 atmospheres. If at the beginning of the experiment this space is filled with air at about 22 atmospheres at θ_1 the pressure will be about 30 at θ_2. In an experiment the weight of air contained was 4·2854 grammes. The condensation due to the sphere was 1·5 gramme, and that due to the air 0·11629, or about $\frac{1}{13}$ that of the sphere, the range of temperature $\theta_2 - \theta_1$ being 84°·52 C. In a series of six experiments the mean precipitation per degree centigrade was 0·018004.

The corrections necessary for extreme accuracy are—

(1.) Correction for the thermal expansion of the vessel, and the consequent work done by the gas in expanding to this increased volume.

(2.) Correction for the dilatation of the sphere under the increased pressure of the gas as the temperature rises.

(3.) Correction for the thermal effect of stretching of the material of the sphere. Wires are generally cooled by sudden extension, but the cooling of the copper in this case is too small to merit consideration.

(4.) Correction for displacement, or buoyancy, arising from the increased volume of the sphere, both in the air at θ_1 and in the steam at θ_2.

[1] In the later experiments all leakage was completely stopped.

(5.) Correction for unequal thermal capacities of the spheres.

(6.) Reduction of the weight of the precipitation to vacuum.

Prof. Joly's experiments show that in the case of air and carbonic acid the specific heat increases with the density, but with hydrogen the opposite seems to be the case.

For air the specific heat at constant volume at a mean pressure of 19·51 atmospheres, and a mean density of 0·0205, was found to be 0·1721. For carbon dioxide, the change with pressure is shown by the following table :—

Pressure in Atmospheres.	Density.	C_v.
7·20	0·011530	0·16841
12·20	0·019950	0·17054
16·87	0·028498	0·17141
20·90	0·036529	0·17305
21·66	0·037802	0·17386

The mean result of the experiments on hydrogen gives a specific heat 2·402.

148. Dewar's Liquid Air and Liquid Hydrogen Calorimeters.— Instead of measuring the amount of vapour which will, by its condensation, bring the temperature of a cold body up to the temperature of the vapour, we might measure the amount of a liquid at its boiling point which would be evaporated by a hot body in being cooled to the temperature of the liquid. Suppose, for instance, that we had a vessel containing water and steam at 100° C., with a narrow horizontal side tube containing a thread of mercury, the whole being steam-jacketed. If now by some means we rapidly introduced a body heated to 200° C. into the water, we could deduce the mean specific heat of the body between 100° and 200° from the volume of steam generated, as indicated by the displacement of the mercury thread. This method was used by Professor Dewar [1] for finding the specific heats of various substances for low ranges of temperature, the liquid evaporated being liquid air or hydrogen. The apparatus in which liquid air was used is shown in Fig. 69. The calorimeter C is a vacuum bulb containing liquid air and provided with a wide stem, to the upper end of which a tube T, closed at one end, is attached by a short length of bent rubber tube. This latter tube T contains the substance whose specific heat is to be determined. When possible, spherical bullets of the substance were used. The tube T was immersed in a vessel containing solid carbon dioxide, or otherwise maintained at a known temperature. By tilting the tube T the

[1] *Proc. Roy. Soc.* vol. lxxvi. (A) p. 325, 1913 ; vol. lxxxix. (A) p. 158, 1913.

bullets were caused to fall into the calorimeter one at a time, and the air evaporated was collected over water and its volume measured. To prevent access of heat from outside, the calorimeter bulb was immersed in a large Dewar vacuum flask D, filled with liquid air. Old liquid air, from which most of the nitrogen had evaporated, was

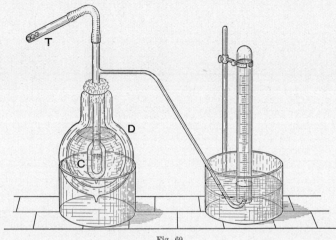

Fig. 69.

used both in the outer and inner vessels. As used by Dewar, the method was a comparative one, the specific heat of lead being taken as known, and an experiment made with a leaden bullet immediately before or after the experiment with the body under investigation. The volumes of gas liberated are proportional to the thermal capacities of the bodies over the range of temperature. A small error is introduced by the loss of heat of the body while falling into the calorimeter. The apparatus in which liquid hydrogen was used was the same in principle. Dewar gives the following results, as well as a long list of atomic heats of metals.

SPECIFIC HEAT OF SOLID

Substance.	18° to −78°	−78° to −188°	−188° to −252°·5
Lead . . .	0·0295	0·0290	0·0280
Diamond . . .	0·0794	0·0190	0·0043
Graphite . . .	0·1341	0·0599	0·0133
Ice * . . .	0·463	0·285	0·146

* The first range of temperature for ice was from −18° C. to −78° C.

Dewar also used his apparatus to determine the latent heats of evaporation of oxygen, nitrogen, and hydrogen.

S

SECTION VI

THE METHOD OF ELECTRICAL HEATING

149. Conversion of Units.—Since heat is a form of energy, and a given amount of mechanical or other form of energy is always convertible into the same amount of heat energy (Art. 35), it is not necessary that the calorie should be taken as the unit of heat. There would be some advantage in using the absolute dynamical unit of energy, the erg or joule. As long, however, as the calorie is adopted as the unit of heat, the method of mixtures must be regarded as the most direct process for determining the specific heat of a body. If we use an electric current in a wire to heat a weighed quantity of any substance and measure the rise of temperature, we cannot deduce the specific heat of the substance unless we are able to measure the amount of electrical energy supplied, and also know what amount of electrical energy, in terms of our electrical units, is equivalent to one calorie. The measurement of electric current, resistance, and potential in terms of the absolute electric units is a very difficult mattter, but when once carried out, the reproduction of the standards is comparatively easy. For example, the electromotive force of any electric battery can easily be compared with that of a standard Clark or Weston cell, and the electromotive forces of these cells are, under proper conditions, always the same, and have been measured with extreme accuracy. The determination of the relation between the dynamical or electrical [1] unit of energy and the calorie, that is, of the dynamical equivalent of heat, forms the subject of sec. ix. It was because of these initial difficulties that the electric method was not used earlier in calorimetry (see Art. 174). It appears to have been first employed in determining the dynamical equivalent of heat, but it possesses just the same advantages in general calorimetry.

In the method of electrical heating the amount of heat supplied is

---

[1] Since the electric units are defined in terms of the standards of mass, length, and time, the electric unit of energy is the same as the dynamical.

under perfect control, and can be measured with great precision. The whole of the heat, except a very small fraction, is given to the body under investigation, and is generated exactly where desired, usually in the interior of the body whose specific heat is being sought. It is especially suitable for finding specific heats at low temperatures and over small ranges of temperature, and thus affords much more exact information regarding the law of variation of specific heat with temperature than methods in which only the mean specific heat over a wide range is determined. A further convenience, which is often taken advantage of, is that the same wire may be used to supply heat and (as a resistance thermometer) to measure the temperature.

150. Experiments of Nernst and of E. H. and E. Griffiths.— A series of experiments was made by Nernst,[1] using a method of electrical heating due to Eucken, in which the specific heat of a number of substances was determined over a wide range of temperature.

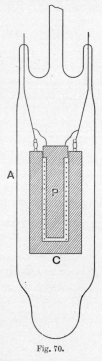

In experiments on metals, the piece of metal C (Fig. 70), in the form of a cylindrical block, acted as its own calorimeter. A wide hole was bored concentrically in the block and was filled by a cylindrical plug P which fitted closely at the top but left a narrow annular space for most of its length. This space contained an insulated coil of platinum wire, by means of which the block was heated through a small range of temperature (a few degrees or less). The energy communicated to the metal was measured electrically and the platinum wire served also as a resistance thermometer to measure the rise in temperature. In the case of poor conductors (diamond, sulphur, etc.), the substance was hermetically sealed up in a silver vessel in the middle of which was a wide silver tube round which the platinum wire was wound. The cylindrical block of metal or silver vessel was suspended in a glass vessel A by the two ends of the wire, this vessel being in communication with another contain-

Fig. 70.

ing cocoa-nut charcoal. The charcoal being heated to redness, the glass vessel was evacuated by means of a Gaede pump and the charcoal subsequently cooled in liquid air. By this means a very high vacuum was obtained, ensuring very perfect heat-insulation. At the lowest

[1] *Ann. der Phys.* vol. xxxvi. p. 395, 1911 ; *Sitz. der K. Preuss. Akad.* (Berlin), p. 262, 1910.

temperature, that of liquid hydrogen, the specific heat of diamond was too small to be measured, its conductivity being at the same time remarkably high. For lead, Nernst gives a formula for the atomic heat which, reduced to specific heat, is

$$Cp = 0 \cdot 0305 + 0 \cdot 00001\theta,$$

where Cp is the specific heat at constant pressure.

The method of electrical heating was used later by E. H. and E. Griffiths [1] in two elaborate series of experiments on the specific heats of metals. Special features of these researches were the care used in standardising all measuring instruments (thermometers, resistance coils, etc.), the attention paid to the purity of the metals, and the large masses used for experiment (1 to 4 kilos). Also, to eliminate possible sources of error, variations were introduced such as altering the rate of heat supply, using different thermometers, etc. In addition, the estimation of the radiation correction (which was very small) was made as exact as possible by fitting the block of metal into a thin silver case, so that the radiating surface was always the same ; and by making separate measurements (by means of a Bunsen ice calorimeter) of all substances, such as glass, petrol, etc., whose specific heats entered into the correction.

In the first series of experiments, at ordinary temperatures, all parts of the apparatus were duplicated, the two calorimeters being immersed in the same bath, the block of metal in one being electrically heated, while the other was not. The difference of temperature between the blocks was measured by a differential platinum thermometer. The bath was electrically maintained with great constancy at any required temperature, and vigorously stirred. In order to obtain specific heats at definite temperatures the rise of temperature was made small (less than $1° \cdot 4$). The space between the silver vessel and the calorimeter in which it was suspended was not vacuous but filled with air. It was so arranged that this space formed the bulb of a constant volume air thermometer, so that the heat absorbed by the air could be accurately calculated. The results for copper and lead may be selected for comparison with those of other experimenters. These were—

$$Cp = 0 \cdot 09088 \ (1 + 0 \cdot 0005341\theta - 0 \cdot 00000048\theta^2) \quad \text{(Copper)}.$$
$$Cp = 0 \cdot 030196 \ (1 + 0 \cdot 0004000\theta - 0 \cdot 00000036\theta^2) \quad \text{(Lead)}.$$

In the second series of experiments the apparatus was constructed to measure specific heats at low temperatures. The block of metal G under investigation (Fig. 71) was suspended by a glass tube H in the middle of a thick copper enclosure E. Round this enclosure

[1] *Phil. Trans.* vol. ccxiii. (A) p. 119, 1914 ; vol. ccxiv. (A) p. 319, 1914.

was wound an insulated copper wire F, which served as a resistance thermometer to measure the temperature of the enclosure. A wide leaden tube D was also coiled round the enclosure, which could be cooled to any desired temperature by passing a current of cold air through the tube D. The cooling of the air in D was produced by the same means as are used in the production of liquid air (see Art. 240). The air entering the pipe A at high pressure passed through the interchanger coils BB and was cooled by expansion on escaping through the valve C. It then passed through the tube D and passed back over the interchanger coils, the amount of cooling being regulated by the valve C. The heating coil O was of manganin wire and was fastened in the taper plug K of the same material as the block G. This plug closed a cavity in the centre of the block G which contained petrol, into which the heating coil dipped. Another hole bored in G received the platinum thermometer T, which was insulated by a packing of asbestos thread. The copper enclosure E was packed in slag wool, and could be withdrawn through a cardboard tube N, which

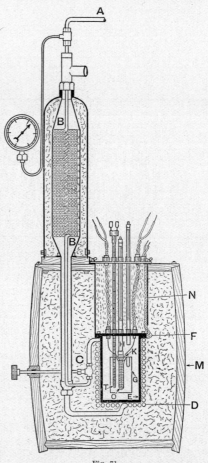

Fig. 71.

latter was packed with felt matting. The whole was contained in the wooden vessel M. In making an experiment, the enclosure was cooled till the block was at the desired temperature and the current of air in D was then stopped. The temperature of the enclosure would slowly rise, and when it was about 3° higher than that of the block, the air current was re-started and adjusted so as to keep the temperature of the enclosure constant. The gradual rise of temperature of the block, due to radiation, etc., was observed (at equal intervals of temperature $0°.04$) for a time, then the heating current was switched on, and the observation of the rise of temperature (at equal intervals of $0°.2$) continued. When the block was $2°$ or $3°$ above the temperature of the enclosure, the heating current was stopped, and the observations resumed. In this way complete data for calculating the radiation correction were obtained. The results were very concordant, and agreed well with Nernst's mean values for the same metal. Tables of specific heats for a number of metals are given in the paper for intervals of $10°$ down to about $-150°$ C.

151. Specific Heat of Bulky Materials.—A method of measuring the specific heats of light bulky materials such as cork or charcoal was devised by E. Griffiths[1] and modified by Strand. The calorimeter was a closed cylinder which was kept rotating or rocking about its axis to promote the equalisation of temperature in the substance, which was finely powdered. There was a fixed heating coil inside the cylinder. This was a flat zig-zag of platinum wire and was also used as a resistance thermometer. To eliminate the heat loss, an insulated flat nichrome tape was wound round the case through which a current was passed to maintain equality of temperature inside and outside the case, as indicated by differential thermocouples.

[1] *Phys. Soc. Proc.* vol. xxxiii. p. 355, 1921.

SECTION VII

ON THE SPECIFIC HEATS OF GASES

152. The Two Specific Heats of a Gas.—It has been already pointed out (Art. 132) that the specific heat of a substance can be spoken of with definiteness only when the conditions under which the heating takes place are stated. If a body be allowed to expand when heated, work will be done against the external pressure and an equivalent quantity of heat will be required, and if the specific heat be merely defined as the quantity of heat necessary to raise the temperature of unit mass of a substance 1° C., its value will depend on the amount of external work done during the change of temperature, as well as on the nature of the substance. Thus, in general, the specific heat of a substance may have any value whatever if the conditions under which the change of temperature takes place are not defined.

In the case of solids and liquids the change of volume, and therefore the external work done, during change of temperature is small, so that although the specific heats so far determined are those under constant pressure, yet it has not been necessary to allude to the fact. In the case of gases, however, under constant pressure, the change of volume with rise of temperature is considerable, and the thermal equivalent of the external work done during expansion is a large part of the whole heat supplied during the change of temperature. For this reason the conditions under which the heating of a gas takes place must be stated when referring to the specific heat; and it has become customary to speak of two specific heats in connection with any gas, namely, the specific heat at *constant volume*, and the specific heat under *constant pressure*. The former is the quantity of heat required to raise the temperature of unit mass of the gas 1° C. when its volume is kept constant, and the latter the quantity of heat required to raise the temperature of unit mass 1° C. when the pressure is kept constant. In the former, the pressure increases while the volume is kept constant and no external work is done. In the

263

latter, the volume increases under constant pressure, and an amount of external work is done which is measured by the product of the mean pressure by the change of volume.

The experimental determination of the specific heats of gases at constant volume has been already considered under the method of condensation, and we shall now proceed to the experimental determination of the specific heat under constant pressure.[1] This investigation is attended by great difficulties, arising chiefly from the small specific gravities of gases, so that a large volume must be passed through the calorimeter in order to produce any appreciable change of temperature. This requires a considerable time, and during the interval all the causes of error which accompany calorimetric determinations are in operation. The relations connecting the two specific heats, and the methods by which they may be determined indirectly, will be considered afterwards.

153. Specific Heat under Constant Pressure—Regnault's Apparatus.—The apparatus adopted by Regnault to determine the specific heats of gases under constant pressure was a modified form of that used by Delaroche and Bérard. The gas to be operated on was stored dry and pure in a large reservoir, V (Fig. 72), which was immersed in a bath kept at a constant temperature. The pressure of the gas in this reservoir was measured by an open manometer attached to the delivery tube. When the stop-cock R was opened the gas flowed from the reservoir through the spiral tube, immersed in a hot oil bath EC, which could be maintained at any chosen temperature. This spiral was so long that the gas in passing through it attained the temperature of the surrounding bath. After passing through this spiral the gas entered the calorimeter. Here it passed through a brass reservoir consisting of a series of chambers, and gave up its heat to the calorimeter, emerging finally at the temperature of the calorimeter by the tube D.

The first point of prime importance was to secure a uniform flow of the gas, so that it should pass through the calorimeter uniformly

---

[1] The first researches on the specific heats of gases were made by Crawford, who applied the method of mixtures and found that the specific heat of air was nearly twice that of water! Afterwards Lavoisier and Laplace (*Œuvres de Lavoisier*, tom. ii.) found by means of their ice calorimeter a more correct value ·33, and subsequently Gay-Lussac (*Ann. de Chimie et de Physique*, tom. lxxxi. p. 98) attacked the subject; but by far the best determinations previous to Regnault's work are those of Delaroche and Bérard (*Ann. de Chimie et de Physique*, 1re série, tom. lxxxv. p. 72), crowned by the Academy of Sciences. They caused a uniform current of gas, heated to 100° C. (by passing through a tube contained in a vapour jacket), to pass through a spiral tube contained in the calorimeter. Joule also made an accurate determination of the specific heat of air (*Phil. Trans.* pt. i. p. 65, 1852).

and under constant pressure. As the gas escapes the pressure in the
reservoir V diminishes, while the pressure outside (the atmosphere)
remains constant, consequently the velocity of efflux will gradually
diminish.   To avoid this Regnault placed a manometer, M, in
connection with the conducting tube at N, which registered the
pressure at that point.   Between this manometer and the reservoir
V a screw R was placed (shown enlarged in Fig. 72, *b*B), which
obstructed the flow of the gas, but which could be gradually with-

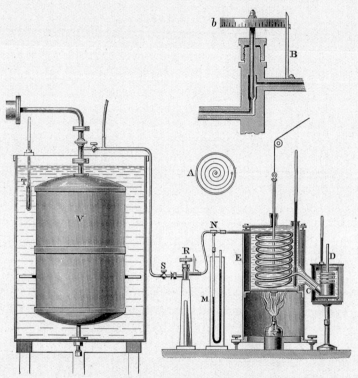

Fig. 72.—Regnault's Apparatus.

drawn so as to leave a wider passage and keep the pressure registered
by M constant.   This secured a constant pressure, and hence a
uniform flow.   Just beyond the manometer the tube was very
narrow.   In order to make certain that the gas actually acquired the
temperature of the bath in passing through the long serpentine
EC, Regnault made some preliminary experiments in which a thermometer was placed in the tube, so as to take the temperature of the
gas just before leaving the bath.   By this means he found that there was
no sensible difference of temperature.   Hence, in subsequent investiga-

tions the temperature of the gas entering the calorimeter was taken to be that of the bath. Particular precautions were taken to avoid loss of heat by the gas in passing from the bath to the calorimeter, and also to prevent, as far as possible, conduction of heat from the bath to the calorimeter through the connecting tube. For this purpose the connecting parts at C were made of non-conducting material, and the calorimeter was enclosed in a wooden case. In order to ascertain if the pressure of the gas was the same at entering as at leaving the calorimeter, water manometers were placed at the entrance C and the exit D. These showed no more than 1 mm. difference.[1] A thermometer placed at D also showed that the temperature of the escaping gas was the same as that of the calorimeter.

It now remained to calculate the weight of gas which passed through the calorimeter during the experiment. In the first place, the total weight of gas in the reservoir is, by Boyle's law, proportional to the pressure if the volume of the reservoir remains constant. This volume was influenced by both temperature and pressure, and to correct the former the reservoir was placed in a bath, and to minimise the latter the reservoir was made strong. For any pressure p Regnault assumed that the weight of gas W in the reservoir was given by the formula

$$(1 + a\theta)W = Ap + Bp^2 + Cp^3,$$

in which A, B, C were determined by experiment. Thus the weight W′ at any other pressure p' was, at the same temperature,

$$(1 + a\theta)W' = Ap' + Bp'^2 + Cp'^3,$$

and consequently their difference w was

$$(1 + a\theta)w = A(p - p') + B(p^2 - p'^2) + C(p^3 - p'^3).$$

By making three such experiments, three values of w and three equations to determine A, B, C were obtained. These being once determined could be used in all further experiments.

In carrying out an experiment the gas was compressed pure and dry in the reservoir V under a sufficient pressure. The oil bath was heated to a stationary temperature, and a known weight of water was placed in the calorimeter. The whole observation was then divided into three parts.

---

[1] In the earlier editions of this work it was stated that if this is not the case the gas will have expanded in the calorimeter, doing work and absorbing heat, thus causing error. This is a mistake, as has been pointed out by G. F. C. Searle (*Proc. Camb. Phil. Soc.* vol. xiii. p. 245, 1906). The gas is necessarily expanding, since it is being heated at constant pressure. Even if an appreciable fall of pressure existed, it would produce only a very minute effect on the temperature, as in the porous plug experiment (see Art. 364).

(I.) The calorimeter was observed for ten minutes in order to determine the heat received per minute through (a) conductivity from the oil bath ; (β) radiation from the screens ; (γ) radiation to or from the surrounding air.   The effects (a) and (β) are practically constant, for the temperature of the bath is always much higher than that of the calorimeter ; but (γ) may be either positive or negative, and must be found by observation of the temperatures of the air and calorimeter from minute to minute.   If k represents the change of temperature per minute arising from (a) and (β) together, and if θ_0 be the mean temperature of the air and θ that of the calorimeter during any particular minute, the corresponding change of temperature $\delta\theta$ of the calorimeter arising from the perturbations a, β, γ will be

$$\delta\theta = A(\theta - \theta_0) + k \quad . \quad . \quad . \quad . \quad . \quad (1)$$

(II.) After the lapse of ten minutes, spent in the observation of the perturbations due to radiation and conduction, the gas was turned on, and during this phase of the experiment the temperature of the calorimeter was changed by the passage of the gas through it, and also, but to a much smaller extent, by the perturbation mentioned in (I.).   If the flow is continued for n minutes the total change of temperature arising from the latter causes is

$$\Sigma\delta\theta = A\Sigma(\theta - \theta_0) + nk.$$

If $\Sigma\delta\theta$ be positive it must be subtracted from the final temperature of the calorimeter in order to obtain the temperature which would have been attained if no perturbations existed.   Denoting the initial temperature of the calorimeter by θ_1 and its observed final temperature by θ_2, the true final temperature will be $\theta_2 - \Sigma\delta\theta$, and if W denotes the water equivalent of the calorimeter the heat gained by it from the gas will be $W[(\theta_2 - \Sigma\delta\theta) - \theta_1]$, and if w be the weight of gas transmitted, and s its specific heat, the whole mass of gas may be considered as having fallen from the temperature θ of the bath to the mean temperature $\frac{1}{2}(\theta_1 + \theta_2)$ of the calorimeter ; consequently the heat lost by the gas will be $ws[\theta - \frac{1}{2}(\theta_1 + \theta_2)]$, and the equation which determines s is

$$ws[\theta - \tfrac{1}{2}(\theta_1 + \theta_2)] = W[(\theta_2 - \Sigma\delta\theta) \quad \theta_1]. \quad . \quad . \quad . \quad (2)$$

(III.) The third part of the experiment consisted in observing the variation of the temperature of the calorimeter for ten minutes after the flow of gas was stopped.   It was now only subject to the perturbations, and the change of temperature was due to these causes alone.   Denoting the change of temperature per minute of the calorimeter by $\delta\theta'$, and the mean temperature of the air during this minute by θ'_0, while that of the calorimeter is θ', we have

$$\delta\theta' = A(\theta' - \theta'_0) + k \quad . \quad . \quad . \quad . \quad . \quad (3)$$

This equation, combined with (1), enables us to determine A and k, and hence the quantity $\Sigma\delta\theta$, which, when substituted in (2), gives the specific heat.

In the case of gases which attack copper the spiral tubes were made of platinum, and when pressures higher than the atmosphere were required, the narrowing of the tube just beyond N was dispensed with, and the mouth D of the tube where the gas escaped was made very narrow. The water manometer M was also replaced by a mercurial manometer. The following results were obtained by Regnault :—

Specific Heats of Gases under Constant Pressure.
Simple Gases

Air .	. . .	0·23741	Nitrogen [1] .	. . .	0·24380
Oxygen .	. .	0·21751	Chlorine	. . .	0·12099
Hydrogen	. .	3·4090	Bromine	. . .	0·05552

154. Method of Stationary Temperature.—In the process just described the temperature of the calorimeter varies from θ_1 to θ_2, and it may therefore be called the method of variable temperature. Delaroche and Bérard employed in addition the method of stationary temperature. In this method the hot gas is passed through the calorimeter till the temperature of the latter becomes stationary. At this stage the heat gained per second by the calorimeter is equal to that lost by radiation to the surroundings. Denoting the weight of gas which passes through the calorimeter per unit time by w and its specific heat by s, the total heat gained by the calorimeter per unit time will be $ws(\theta - \theta') + k$, where θ' is the stationary temperature of the calorimeter, θ that of the bath, and k the gain of heat by conduction through the connections. But if θ_0 be the temperature of the air, the loss by radiation will be $A(\theta' - \theta_0)$, and consequently

$$ws(\theta - \theta') + k = A(\theta' - \theta_0).$$

The coefficients A and k may be found as before by two observations on the rate of change of temperature of the calorimeter. In determining θ' Delaroche and Bérard warmed the calorimeter initially to a temperature a little inferior to the stationary temperature, and then allowed the gas to pass through, observing the maximum indication of the thermometer placed in the calorimeter, that is, the temperature indicated when it ceased to change by more than $\frac{1}{10}$ of a degree in ten minutes. They then heated the calorimeter a little

---

[1] The specific heat of nitrogen was deduced from that of air combined with that of oxygen.

above the stationary temperature, and allowed the gas to pass. This time the calorimeter cooled to a stationary temperature. The mean of the two temperatures thus observed they took as the true stationary temperature θ'.

155. Later Experiments.—Regnault's experiments on the specific heat of air have been criticised by Swann and also by Scheel and Heuse. Swann points out that the conduction of heat along the connecting tube between heater and calorimeter is greater when no current of air is passing, leading to an over-estimate of the loss of heat due to this cause. This is because the temperature of the connecting tube is more uniform when the current of air is passing. Scheel and Heuse state that Regnault assumed that the specific heat derived from experiments in which the gas-flow was rapid was correct, although he was aware that the result varied somewhat with the rate of flow; that his experiments show that the unwarmed gas was slightly cooled, but he thought that this effect was too small to be taken into account; and further, that he assumed the specific heat of water to be constant. They find that if the necessary corrections were applied, the result of Regnault's experiments would give 0·2404 as the specific heat of air at constant pressure and 20° C. temperature.

The electrical method of heating was applied by Holborn and Henning [1] to the measurement of the specific heats of nitrogen, carbon dioxide, and steam, the principle of the process being the same as in Regnault's experiments. The temperature of the heater varied in different experiments between 800° and 1400° C., while the calorimeter was maintained at 110° C. The gas passed through a preliminary heater and thence to the top of the heater proper, which consisted of a double-walled platinum tube which was raised to a high temperature by passing an electric current down the inner and up the outer tube. The annular space between the tubes contained rings of magnesia for insulation. Thus the inner tube was protected from loss of heat by radiation. A wider platinum tube, welded to the outer tube, made connection with the calorimeter below. To minimise conduction of heat from the connecting tube, rings of asbestos packing and rubber were interposed between it and the calorimeter, and to prevent radiation from the heater to the calorimeter, platinum screens were placed within the connecting tube and a magnesia ring outside. The temperature in the heater was measured by a platinum rhodio-platinum thermocouple. The calorimeter was a cylindrical vessel of sheet silver, and contained three silver tubes filled with silver clippings

[1] *Ann. der Phys.* vol. xxiii. p. 809, 1907.

and connected in series so that the gas passed through them successively. The space between the silver tubes and the calorimeter
walls was filled with a non-volatile paraffin oil and kept at a constant temperature by means of an outer vessel containing rape-seed
oil. The calorimeter and the outer vessel each had a stirrer electrically
driven. The calorimeter also contained a platinum thermometer
(naked in the oil), and a resistance of constantan wire by means of
which its thermal capacity was measured. The radiation correction was calculated in the usual manner from observations preliminary and subsequent to the passing of the gas. One calorie was
taken to be equivalent to 4·188 joules. The following results were
deduced :—

Nitrogen : $C_p = 0·2350 + 0·0000019\theta$.
Carbon dioxide : $C_p = 0·2010 + 0·0000742\theta - 0·0000000018\theta^2$.

Measurements of the specific heats of air and carbon dioxide at
moderate temperatures were made by Swann,[1] using the electrical
method of heat estimation. GF is a wide double-walled tube of
metal (Fig. 73). A current of water or steam at a steady temperature
was introduced into the space between the walls by the inlet i, and
after passing between the walls of
another double-walled tube FE,
issued at o. The tube GF was
packed with discs of copper gauze
and served as the preliminary
heater. The gas whose specific heat was to be measured
entered the tube GF at m and, after passing down through
the space J, entered the calorimeter AB at n, passing up
and issuing by the side tube near the top. It is evident
from the figure that, if no further heating had taken place,
the gas, after having attained in GF the temperature of
the jacket, would have remained at a uniform temperature
for the remainder of its course through the apparatus. A
further quantity of heat, measured electrically, was communicated to it by the platinum heating coil P. The rise

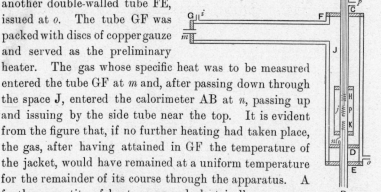

Fig. 73.

in temperature was measured by the platinum thermometers K and H,
used differentially. The tube AB was of glass, and was closed at the
ends by rubber corks, through which passed the leads of the heating
coil and the platinum thermometers. There were four leads to the
heating coil, as both the current and electromotive force had to be
measured. The part of the tube AB where the heating coil and
thermometers were situated was surrounded by another tube j, closed

[1] *Phil. Trans.* vol. ccx. (A) p. 199, 1911.

at each end.   There were several discs of copper gauze between the
coil P and the thermometer H to mix the heated gas.   The discs
C, D, E closing the tube FE were of rubber.   The disc D was
necessary to prevent cooling of the current of gas by impinging on
the disc E.   The radiation correction could be estimated by varying
the flow of gas and the heating current.   For the method of measuring
the flow of gas the original paper must be consulted.   Swann gives
the following results :—

> Air : $C_p = 0\cdot24173$ at $20°$; $C_p = 0\cdot24301$ at 100 .
> Carbon dioxide : $C_p = 0\cdot20202$ at $20°$; $C_p = 0\cdot22141$ at $100°$.

Brinkworth,[1] using a method similar to Swann's, found the specific
heat of steam at constant pressure at $104°\cdot5$ to be $0\cdot4856$.

A method identical in principle with Swann's, but differing in
constructional details, was used by Scheel and Heuse [2] to determine
the specific heats at constant pressure of air, helium, hydrogen,
nitrogen, oxygen, and carbon monoxide ; and Heuse [3] also measured
the specific heats of argon and carbon dioxide.   The heating coil was
of constantan, and the part of the calorimeter where the heating took
place and the rise of temperature was measured was surrounded by
a Dewar vacuum vessel silvered inside, the whole being immersed in
a constant temperature bath.   The following values were obtained :—

SPECIFIC HEATS AT CONSTANT PRESSURE

Air.		Helium.		Hydrogen.	
Temp.	Sp. Heat.	Temp.	Sp. Heat.	Temp.	Sp. Heat.
$20°$	$0\cdot2408$	$18°$	$2\cdot260$	$16°$	$3\cdot403$
$-78°$	$0\cdot2432$	...	...	$-76°$	$3\cdot157$
$-183°$	$0\cdot2525$	$-180°$	$2\cdot245$	$-181°$	$2\cdot644$

Nitrogen.		Oxygen.		Carbon Dioxide.	
Temp.	Sp. Heat.	Temp.	Sp. Heat.	Temp.	Sp. Heat.
$20°$	$0\cdot2492$	$20°$	$0\cdot218$	$20°$	$0\cdot202$
...	...	$-76°$	$0\cdot214$	$-75°$	$0\cdot183$
$-181°$	$0\cdot2556$	$-181°$	$0\cdot228$	...	...

156. Influence of Pressure and Temperature.—Delaroche and
Bérard were of opinion that the specific heat of a gas depended on the
pressure ; but Regnault, who investigated this point carefully, came to

[1] *Phil. Trans.* vol. ccxv. (A) p. 400, 1915.
[2] *Ann. der Physik*, vol. xxxvii. p. 79, 1912 ; vol. xl. p. 473, 1913.
[3] *Ibid.* vol. lix. p. 86, 1919.

the conclusion that the specific heat of a gas under constant pressure was sensibly independent of the pressure. This would be expected in the case of a substance rigorously obeying Boyle's law; but in the case of gases like carbonic acid, which deviate considerably from this law, it would not be anticipated. In fact, we have already seen from Dr. Joly's experiments on the specific heat at constant volume that a notable increase of specific heat with density occurs not only in carbonic acid, but also, though to a less degree, in the case of the more perfect gases,[1] while hydrogen behaves in the opposite manner.

The influence of temperature was also studied by Regnault, and for this purpose the bath surrounding the spiral was kept at different constant temperatures, sometimes being replaced by a freezing mixture. He obtained the following results :—

Air.		Carbonic Acid.	
Temperature.	Specific Heat.	Temperature.	Specific Heat.
From $-31°$ to $+10°$	0·23771	From $-30°$ to $+10°$	0·18427
$0°$ to $+100°$	0·23741	$+10°$ to $+100°$	0·20246
$0°$ to $+200°$	0·23751	$+10°$ to $+210°$	0·21692

According to this table the specific heat of air remains sensibly constant, while that of carbon dioxide rises considerably with the temperature, and it is probable that all gases which deviate from Boyle's law follow the general law of solids and liquids, and show an increase of specific heat with temperature. On the other hand, a perfect gas, when used as a thermometric substance, shows equal rises of temperature for equal increments of heat.

Experiments were made at low temperatures by A. Witkowski [2] using a modified form of the method of Regnault and E. Wiedemann. The quantity of air used in an experiment was measured directly by the balance. Pure dry air was compressed to 80 or 100 atmospheres in steel or copper flasks, and a known quantity (13 to 60 grammes) was passed through a refrigerator and then through the calorimeter. The temperature of the refrigerator was given by a hydrogen thermometer, and the difference of temperature between the refrigerator and the air just at the entrance to the calorimeter by a thermocouple of copper and nickel. Witkowski found that the specific heat of air at constant atmospheric pressure is sensibly independent of the temperature, its value being 0·2372 in

[1] Such an increase, or decrease, becomes quite intelligible when the existence of groups of molecules is recognised as pointed out in Art. 52.

[2] *Bull. de l'Acad. des Sciences de Cracovie*, p. 290, Oct. 1895.

calories. A small departure at the lowest temperature was attributed to a change in pressure.

The variation of the specific heat with pressure was not measured directly, but calculated from the determinations of the dilatation of air referred to in Art. 122. Writing the result of Ex. 24, Art. 345, in heat units, we have

$$C_p = C_1 - \frac{\tau}{J} \int_1^p \frac{d^2v}{d\tau^2} dp \quad . \quad . \quad . \quad . \quad (1)$$

when C_1 is the specific heat at constant atmospheric pressure and has

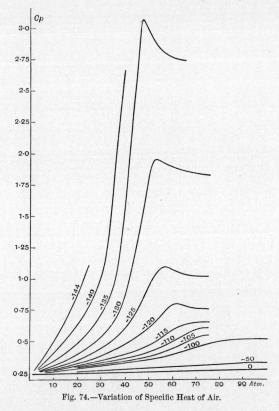

Fig. 74.—Variation of Specific Heat of Air.

the value 0.2372 for all temperatures, and τ is the absolute temperature. Now with the notation of Art. 248

$$\eta = \frac{\epsilon(1+at)}{1+a_{pt}t}(1+a_p\theta\theta)$$
$$= \eta_0(1+a_p\theta\theta),$$

where η_0 is independent of θ; therefore

$$v = \frac{\eta p_0 v_0}{p} = \frac{\eta_0 p_0 v_0}{p}(1+a_p\theta\theta) \ ;$$

therefore, writing a for $a_{,\theta}$ to avoid cumbrousness,

$$\left(\frac{d^2v}{d\theta^2}\right)_p = \frac{n_0 p_0 v_0}{p}\left\{\theta\left(\frac{d^2a}{d\theta^2}\right)_p + 2\left(\frac{da}{d\theta}\right)_p\right\},$$

and this formula furnishes a means of calculating $(d^2v/d\theta^2)_p$, since the terms on the right-hand side can be obtained graphically from the curves of Fig. 48, Art. 122. As Witkowski used the hydrogen scale in measuring θ, we may put $d^2v/d\tau^2 = d^2v/d\theta^2$, and therefore obtain the value of C_p for various pressures and temperatures from equation (1). Fig. 74 shows Witkowski's curves for the variation of C_p with pressure at various temperatures.

157. Specific Heat at Constant Volume.—Besides Joly's experiments (Art. 147), very few direct determinations of the specific heats of gases at constant volume have been made. Eucken[1] measured the specific heat of hydrogen at constant volume at temperatures ranging from $0°$ C. to $-238°$ C., using the same method as Nernst (Art. 150). The hydrogen was compressed into a thin-walled steel vessel and was heated by a resistance coil of constantan. The temperature was measured by a platinum thermometer. As the resistance of constantan is nearly independent of the temperature, this separation of the heating and thermometer elements made the apparatus easier to handle. He found that the molecular heat of hydrogen varies from $2·98$ at $35°$ K. to $4·84$ at $273°·1$ K. $(0°$ C.). This makes the specific heat at constant volume and 1 atm. pressure equal to $2·408$.

Determinations of the specific heats of hydrogen and carbon dioxide were also made by Trautz and Grosskinsky.[2] The gas was contained in a large glass vessel, and was momentarily heated by an electric current flowing in a thin platinum ribbon. The rise of pressure was measured by balancing it against a known pressure of gas in a similar vessel which could be connected to the first through a differential oil manometer; thus the rise of temperature was deduced. Since the heat was generated in the middle of the vessel, the authors consider that there was no time for the heat to be lost. They found that for hydrogen $C_v = 2·396$ at $20°$ C., and for carbon dioxide $C_v = 0·1575$ at the same temperature, the pressure being 1 atm. in each case.

158. Difference of the Two Specific Heats.—A perfect gas is usually considered as an ideal substance whose molecules are outside the sphere of each other's attraction. When such a substance expands no work will be spent in separating the molecules further apart, for by

---

[1] *Sitz. der K. Preuss. Akad.* (Berlin), 1912, p. 141.

[2] *Ann. der Physik*, vol. lxvii. p. 462, 1922.

supposition they do not attract each other. The whole work done during a change of volume will consequently be external. Thus, if the volume changes from v_1 to v_2 under a constant pressure p, the external work is $p(v_2 - v_1)$. Now the specific heat at constant volume C_v is the quantity of heat required to raise the temperature of unit mass 1° C. when the volume is kept constant, and the specific heat under constant pressure C_p will exceed this merely by the thermal equivalent of the work done under constant pressure, while the temperature changes by 1° C. We have therefore

$$J(C_p - C_v) = p(v_2 - v_1) = R(\Theta_2 - \Theta_1),$$

or, since the difference of temperature is one degree, it follows that

$$J(C_p - C_v) = R,$$

J being Joule's equivalent. This equation, combined with a knowledge of either specific heat, determines the other, or combined with their ratio, or any other relation connecting them, determines both.

The experimental examination of the assumption made here, namely, that no internal work is done when a gas expands, or rather that in the case of ordinary gases the internal work is very small, was first undertaken by Joule.

To calculate the value of $C_p - C_v$ we may make use of the value already given for R (Ex. 3, Art. 94) in the case of hydrogen,

$$R_h = 4146 \times 10^4,$$

so that if μ is the molecular weight of any gas, putting $J = 41·8 \times 10^6$, we get

$$C_p - C_v = \frac{R}{J} = \frac{2R_h}{J\mu} = \frac{1·984}{\mu} \text{ approx.}$$

This formula assumes the equation for a perfect gas. Witkowski has calculated the values of C_v for different pressures and temperatures by means of the more general relation given in Ex. 1, Art. 345, viz.—

$$J(C_p - C_v) = -\frac{\tau \left(\dfrac{dp}{d\tau}\right)_v^2}{\left(\dfrac{dp}{dv}\right)_\tau} \quad . \quad . \quad . \quad . \quad . \quad (1)$$

Putting, as in the preceding article, $pv = \eta p_0 v_0$, we get

$$v + p\left(\frac{dv}{dp}\right)_\tau = p_0 v_0 \frac{d\eta}{dp},$$

whence

$$\left(\frac{dp}{dv}\right)_\tau = \frac{p}{p_0 v_0 \dfrac{d\eta}{dp} - v},$$

and substituting in equation (1), we have

$$C_v = C_p - \frac{\tau}{Jp}\left(\frac{dp}{d\tau}\right)_v^2 \left(p_0 v_0 \frac{d\eta}{dp} - v\right).$$

The values of $dp/d\tau$ and $d\eta/dp$ were obtained by Witkowski from the results of his experiments on the pressure coefficient and compressibility of air (see Art. 122). He found that C_v increased with the pressure when the temperature was constant, and this increase was much more rapid at low temperatures. The value of γ, or the ratio of the two specific heats thus obtained, increased with pressure. At constant pressure γ increased rapidly as the temperature diminished, attaining a maximum in the neighbourhood of $-120°$ C. This is about the critical temperature of oxygen. At the critical point γ must be infinite.

159. Joule's Experiment.—In determining the heat developed by compressing air in a vessel, Joule was struck by the accuracy with which it represented the equivalent of the work spent in effecting the compression, and similarly, the quantity of heat lost during expansion appeared to be accurately the equivalent of the work done against the external pressure. He consequently determined to investigate if the temperature of a gas changed when the volume merely increased without doing external work. For this purpose two receivers, A and B (Fig. 75), which were connected together by means of a tube furnished with a stop-cock, were immersed in a bath of water, which acted the

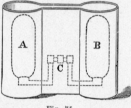

Fig. 75.

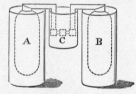

Fig. 76.

part of a calorimeter. One of the receivers, A, was filled with dry air at about 22 atmospheres, and the other was exhausted. The water was thoroughly stirred, and its temperature noted by means of a very sensitive thermometer reading to $\frac{1}{200}$ of a degree F. The stop-cock was then opened by means of a key, and the air allowed to pass from A to B till equilibrium was established. The water was again stirred, and the temperature was found not to have changed by any appreciable amount. His conclusion was that "no change of temperature occurs when air is allowed to expand in such a manner as not to develop mechanical power."

Joule's law, or Mayer's hypothesis. In order to analyse this experiment, Joule inverted the receivers as shown in Fig. 76, each, as well as the connecting pipe, being immersed in a separate bath. When the air compressed in A was allowed as before to expand into the exhausted vessel B, the temperature of the bath containing A fell, while that containing B rose, as well as that containing the connecting pipe C, the heat lost by A being exactly compensated by that gained by B and C, a small error arising only from those parts of the pipe which were not immersed in water.

From these experiments [1] it follows that no internal work is done by a gas during expansion, or, in other words, the molecules are so far removed from each other as to be practically out of the sphere of each other's attraction. This is not rigorously the case with ordinary gases, which do not accurately obey Boyle's law, but only holds for the ideal perfect gas, to which the more permanent gases approximate. The deviations of ordinary gases from the ideal state have been investigated by Joule and Thomson by another method, which will be described later (Chap. VIII.).

160. Fundamental Equation for a Perfect Gas.—We are now in a position to write down the fundamental equations connecting the heat supplied dQ, the change of temperature $d\theta$, and the external work done pdv, during any elementary transformation of a perfect gas. Since there is no internal work, the heat supplied must be all spent in changing the temperature of the gas and in doing external work. The quantity required per unit mass for the former purpose is $C_v d\theta$, where C_v is the specific heat at constant volume. If the volume changes by an amount dv under pressure p, the external work will be pdv, and the thermal equivalent of this is $\dfrac{pdv}{J}$. Hence the whole heat necessary for the transformation is

$$dQ = C_v d\theta + \frac{pdv}{J}.$$

If dQ and C_v be measured in mechanical units (ergs), or if pdv be expressed in thermal units, the symbol J disappears, and for convenience we shall always suppose that the former system is adopted, and write the equation in the form

$$dQ = C_v d\theta + pdv.$$

This equation, combined with the equation $pv = R\theta$, must furnish the solution of all problems concerning the variations of the properties of a perfect gas under any stated conditions.

161. Adiabatic Transformations.—When the volume and pressure of a substance change while no heat is allowed to escape from it or enter it from outside, the transformations are said to be adiabatic. We are now in a position to determine the relation connecting the

---

[1] An analogous experiment had been previously made by Gay-Lussac (*Mémoires d'Arcueil*, 1807). This method, however, is not susceptible of any extreme delicacy, as the thermal capacity of the mass of gas employed must necessarily be small compared with that of the calorimeters.

volume and pressure of a perfect gas under such conditions. In this case, since heat neither enters nor leaves the substance, we have $dQ = 0$, and therefore

$$C_v d\theta + pdv = 0 . \qquad . \qquad . \qquad . \qquad . \qquad (1)$$

The problem before us now is to find the relation between p and v, that is, to eliminate θ by means of the equation $pv = R\Theta$. From this equation we have

$$pdv + vdp = Rd\theta \qquad . \qquad . \qquad . \qquad . \qquad (2)$$

since $d\Theta = d\theta$. Substituting for $d\theta$ in (1), and replacing R by its value $C_p - C_v$ (measured in ergs), we obtain

$$C_p pdv + C_v vdp = 0.$$

Or, if γ denotes the ratio of C_p to C_v,

$$\gamma \frac{dv}{v} + \frac{dp}{p} = 0,$$

which, by integration, gives at once

$$\gamma \log v + \log p = \text{const.}$$

That is,

$$pv^\gamma = \text{const.} \qquad . \qquad . \qquad . \qquad . \qquad . \qquad (3)$$

which is the required relation between p and v.

Combining equation (3) with the characteristic equation of the gas $pv = R\Theta$, we obtain the adiabatic relations between the pressure and temperature, and between the volume and temperature. Thus

$$\Theta p^{\frac{1-\gamma}{\gamma}} = \text{const.} \qquad . \qquad . \qquad . \qquad . \qquad (4)$$

and

$$\Theta v^{\gamma-1} = \text{const.} \qquad . \qquad . \qquad . \qquad . \qquad (5)$$

162. Ratio of the Two Specific Heats of a Gas.—Until the perfection of steam calorimetry by Dr. Joly, no successful measurement of the specific heat of a gas at constant volume was effected. The specific heat under constant pressure was determined by the methods already described, and from this the specific heat at constant volume was evaluated by means of further considerations of the properties of gases; such, for example, as the formula of Art. 158 for the difference of the specific heats. Another method follows from the theoretic formula for the velocity of sound in air. Laplace showed that the velocity of sound in a gas is determined by the formula

$$V = \sqrt{\gamma \frac{P}{D}},$$

where P is the pressure, D the density, and γ the ratio of the two specific heats. Hence a knowledge of v, P, and D gives a determination of γ, which leads at once to the value of C_v when C_p is known. By this method the value $\gamma = 1\cdot408$ has been found for air.

This method has been applied by Witkowski [1] to check the results obtained from calculations of the specific heats (Art. 158). The velocity of sound in air was determined by Kundt's method at two different temperatures ($0°$ and $-78°\cdot5$ C.) and at pressures ranging from 1 to 120 atmospheres. As the above formula of Laplace assumes air to be a perfect gas, Witkowski used the general formula

$$V = \sqrt{\frac{\text{elasticity}}{\text{density}}} = \sqrt{-v^2\left(\frac{dp}{dv}\right)_\phi}$$

$$= \sqrt{-\gamma v^2\left(\frac{dp}{dv}\right)_\theta} \qquad . \qquad \text{(Ex. 2, Art. 345),}$$

an assumption being made here that the sound is propagated adiabatically, *i.e.* without any conduction of heat from the compressed to the rarefied portions of gas. For notes of high frequency this is very nearly exact. A correction was applied for the effects of viscosity and conduction. The results obtained followed the same trend as those got by the specific heats, but the values of γ obtained by the present method were uniformly a little larger. Owing to the uncertainty of the correction just mentioned, Witkowski considers the values calculated from the specific heats more reliable.

This method was also used by Hebb,[2] not using a Kundt's tube, but measuring the wave-length in air directly. Two sound-reflecting paraboloids were arranged with their axes in line, facing each other. A telephone transmitter was placed in the focus of one, and another telephone transmitter near the focus of the other paraboloid. At the focus of the latter a whistle was blown. An induction coil with two primaries had one primary and its battery in series with each telephone transmitter. The secondary was in series with a telephone receiver. When the distance between the paraboloids was altered, the intensity of sound in the receiver passed through maximum and minimum values due to interference, and thus the wave-lengths could be counted. The whistle could be kept in unison with a tuning-fork of known pitch. Four forks were used, of frequencies 1280, 1536, 2048, and 3072. The experiments were performed in a basement hall, so that the air was still, and as a paraboloid could be moved

[1] *Bull. de l'Acad. des Sciences de Cracovie*, March 1899.
[2] *Physical Review*, vol. xiv. p. 44, 1919.

80 to 100 feet, the wave-length was found correct to 0·1 per cent. The velocity of sound is got by multiplying the wave-length by the frequency of the fork. Corrections were made for the deviation of air from the perfect gas law, and for the presence of moisture in the atmosphere. In two series of experiments (in 1904 and in 1919) Hebb found that for dry air at 0° C. $\gamma = 1\cdot4026$ and $\gamma = 1\cdot4031$ respectively.

Rücker [1] found for hydrogen $\gamma = 1\cdot4046$ at 15° C., by comparing the wave-length of sound in hydrogen with that in dry air by means of a Kundt's tube. Corrections were made for the diameter of the tube and the deviation from the perfect gas law.

The velocity of sound in gases at high temperatures was investigated by Dixon, Campbell, and Parker.[2] They found that for nitrogen γ varies from 1·408 at 0° C. to 1·374 at 1000° C., and for carbon dioxide from 1·296 at 0° C. to 1·230 at 600° C.

The kinetic theory furnishes a method of calculating the value of γ when the ratio of the internal energy of a molecule of gas to its energy of translation is known. Let the temperature of the gas be raised 1° C. at constant volume. The heat required is C_v. We may put

$$C_v = Q + Q'$$

when Q is the increase in energy in calories due to increased molecular velocity, and Q' is that due to increased internal energy of the molecules. If the velocity of a molecule changes from V_1 to V_2, we have

$$JQ = \tfrac{1}{2}(\overline{V_2^2} - \overline{V_1^2}) = \frac{3}{2\rho}(p_2 - p_1) = \tfrac{3}{2}R$$

(see Art. 55), so that

$$Q = \frac{3}{2}\frac{R}{J} = \frac{2\cdot976}{\mu}$$

by Art. 158 ; and if we know the ratio $Q'/Q = \beta$, we get

$$C_v = \frac{3}{2}\frac{R}{J}(1 + \beta) = \frac{2\cdot976}{\mu}(1 + \beta),$$

$$C_p = \frac{3}{2}\frac{R}{J}(\tfrac{5}{3} + \beta) = \frac{2\cdot976}{\mu}(\tfrac{5}{3} + \beta),$$

$$\therefore \ \gamma = \frac{C_p}{C_v} = \frac{\tfrac{5}{3} + \beta}{1 + \beta}.$$

In the case of a gas whose molecules have no internal energy $\beta = 0$, and $\gamma = \tfrac{5}{3}$. Kundt and Warburg, by measuring the velocity of

---

[1] *Ann. der Physik*, vol. lxv. p. 393, 1921.
[2] *Proc. R. Soc.* vol. c. p. 1, 1921.

sound in mercury vapour, obtained the value 1·67 for γ, and Ramsay found for argon 1·659, and for helium 1·652. These gases are monatomic.

163. Method of Clément and Desormes.—The adiabatic equation $pv^\gamma = \text{const.}$ leads to an experimental determination of γ first devised by MM. Clément and Desormes.[1]   A large flask (Fig. 77) is furnished with a very wide stop-cock B, which communicates with the exterior air, and also with a sensitive water[2] manometer aa'.   Initially the flask A is partially exhausted, so that the liquid stands at a level a in the manometric tube.   The cock B is then suddenly opened for a short interval, and again closed.   During this interval the air rushes into[3]

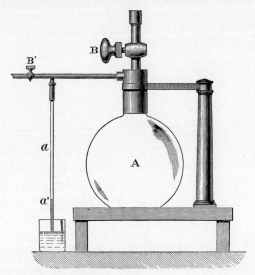

Fig. 77.

the flask, and the pressure within becomes equal to that outside ; the temperature, however, is elevated inside in consequence of the inrush of air.   The tap B being closed, the air in the flask cools, and, as a consequence, the internal pressure diminishes, and the liquid, which, at the closing of the tap B, stood at the bottom of the tube, now rises to a height a'.

---

[1] *Journal de Phys. de Delamétherie*, tom. lxxxix. p. 333, 1819.   See also Laplace, *Mécanique céleste*, tom. v. p. 148, etc.   From the measurements of Clément and Desormes, Laplace deduced the value $\gamma = 1·354$.

[2] Sulphuric acid would be less objectionable.

[3] The converse method in which the pressure within the flask was initially greater than that of the atmosphere, so that an outrush occurred when the tap was opened, was first used by Gay-Lussac and Welter.   See Ostwald's *Outlines of General Chemistry*, p. 75.

Let the pressure of the atmosphere be p_0, that of the air in the flask p_1 before opening B, and p_2 finally after the air has cooled to its original temperature.

Then, since the first process occurs so rapidly that it may be regarded as adiabatic, we have for the air in the flask

$$p_1 v_1{}^\gamma = p_0 v_0{}^\gamma,$$

v_1 and v_0 being the volumes of unit mass of air before and after opening B. Hence,

$$\gamma(\log v_1 - \log v_0) = \log p_0 - \log p_1.$$

But since the initial and final temperatures are the same,

$$p_1 v_1 = p_2 v_0 ;$$

since the manometer tube is narrow, the volume of the unit mass of the gas will not be appreciably altered by the small rise of the liquid in the tube.   Hence $v_1/v_0 = p_2/p_1$, and

$$\gamma = \frac{\log p_0 - \log p_1}{\log p_2 - \log p_1},$$

the quantities p_0, p_1, p_2 being noted, the value of γ is obtained.

This method is open to serious objections, for it is difficult to arrange the experiment so that the pressure within the flask shall be exactly equal to the external pressure at the instant the cock is closed, while at the same time the operation must be conducted so quickly that no sensible quantity of heat has been communicated by the air within to the sides of the flask.   When the stop-cock is opened there is an over-rush[1] of air, and an oscillation is set up, that is, more air rushes in at first than would fill the flask at the external pressure.   A back-rush then sets in and an oscillation to and fro of air takes place through the orifice.   Consequently, when the tap is closed the pressure within the flask may be either greater or less than the external pressure, unless sufficient time has been allowed for the oscillatory motion to subside.   When the stop-cock B is wide this inconvenience is to a great extent avoided.   By this means M. Röntgen[2] found the value $\gamma = 1\cdot 4053$.

A further objection is pointed out by Poynting and Thomson,[3] viz. that we cannot assume that when the stop-cock closes, the air which rushes in will have the same temperature the moment after introduction as the air already in the flask.   It would be much

[1] Cazin, *Ann. de Chimie*, 3e sér., tom. lxvi. p. 206.
[2] Röntgen, *Pogg. Ann.* vol. cxlviii. p. 580, 1873.
[3] *Heat*, p. 292.

more reasonable to suppose its temperature to be atmospheric. If we make this assumption, then, when all the contents of the flask have acquired the original temperature, the pressure is the sum of the partial pressures due to the original gas and the air which has been admitted. But the original gas at atmospheric temperature causes a pressure p_1; and the air admitted, causing a pressure p_0 when in volume $v_1 - v_0$, would cause a pressure $p_0(v_1 - v_0)/v_1$ when in volume v_1; thus the resultant pressure p_2 is the sum of these, or $p_1 + p_0(v_1 - v_0)/v_1$. This equation may be written in the form

$$\frac{v_1 - v_0}{v_1} = \frac{p_2 - p_1}{p_0},$$

or

$$\frac{v_1}{v_0} = \frac{p_0}{p_0 + p_1 - p_2},$$

and thus

$$\gamma = \frac{\log p_0 - \log p_1}{\log v_1 - \log v_0} = \frac{\log p_0 - \log p_1}{\log p_0 - \log (p_0 + p_1 - p_2)}.$$

In order to secure good results, dry air should be used as well as a dry flask, for the aqueous vapour ordinarily in the atmosphere leads to error.

Another variation of Clément and Desormes' method was adopted by Messrs. Lummer and Pringsheim.[1] The globe A was of copper and immersed in a vessel of water. The temperature of the water was kept constant, and a continual circulation was kept up by means of electrically driven screws. A sensitive thermometer immersed in the water gave the temperature of the gas in A, and the sudden change of temperature on opening the stop-cock B was measured by a specially constructed bolometer. Only two pressures were measured, the original pressure p_1 and the atmospheric pressure p_0.

Equation (4) of Art. 161 gives, if Θ_1 and Θ_0 are the temperatures before and after opening B,

$$\Theta_1{}^\gamma p_1{}^{1-\gamma} = \Theta_0{}^\gamma p_0{}^{1-\gamma},$$

from which, by taking logarithms, and solving for γ,

$$\gamma = \frac{\log \dfrac{p_1}{p_0}}{\log \dfrac{p_1}{p_0} - \log \dfrac{\Theta_1}{\Theta_0}}.$$

Lummer and Pringsheim obtained the values 1·4025 for air, 1·3977 for oxygen, 1·2995 for carbon dioxide, and 1·4084 for hydrogen, all at temperatures lying between 4° and 16° C.

[1] *Ann. der Physik*, Bd. lxiv. p. 555, 1898.

Further investigations were made by Partington and Howe,[1] and also by Brinkworth,[2] using Lummer and Pringsheim's method. Various refinements were introduced to increase the accuracy of the determinations. Brinkworth gives the following values for γ :—

Temp.	Air.	Hydrogen.	Nitrogen.
10° C.	...	...	1·4054
17°	1·4032	1·4070	...
−78°	1·4077	1·4427	1·4103
−118°	1·4154	1·4800	...
−183°	...	1·6054	1·4454

164. Method of Jamin and Richard.—The ratio γ of the specific heats has been determined by MM. Jamin and Richard,[3] by means of the method of comparison already noticed (footnote, p. 219), the gas being heated under constant pressure, and also under constant volume, by means of a platinum spiral carrying an electric current. By running the current for a definite time a certain quantity of heat Q may be given to the gas under either circumstance.

Let w be the weight of the gas, and $\theta - \theta_0$ the change of temperature, when the pressure is kept constant. Then

$$Q = wC_p(\theta - \theta_0),$$

and if with the same quantity Q the elevation of temperature be $\theta' - \theta_0$ under constant volume, we have

$$Q = wC_v(\theta' - \theta_0).$$

Hence,

$$\frac{C_p}{C_v} = \frac{\theta' - \theta_0}{\theta - \theta_0} = \frac{(p' - p_0)v_0}{(v - v_0)p_0};$$

the ratio of the two specific heats is therefore obtained by observing the change of pressure and the change of volume produced in the two cases, the initial volume v_0 and pressure p_0 being supposed known. These changes are measured by means of a manometer attached to the flask which contains the gas. By this means Jamin and Richard obtained—for air, 1·41 ; carbonic acid, 1·29 ; hydrogen, 1·41.

Examples

1. Calculate C_v from the equation $J(C_p - C_v) = R$ for the gases mentioned in Ex. 3, p. 141, assuming the value 427 for J and Regnault's value of C_p (p. 268).

---

[1] *Proc. R. Soc.* vol. cv. p. 286, 1925.
[2] *Ibid.* vol. cvii. p. 510, 1925 ; vol. cxi. p. 124, 1926.
[3] *Comptes rendus*, tom. lxxi. p. 336, 1870.

2. Assuming the value $\gamma = 1·41$, calculate the value of J by means of the equation of Ex. 1, and Regnault's value of C_p for air.

3. Assuming the values of J and R, calculate both C_p and C_v from the equation of Ex. 1, and the value 1·41 of γ.

4. A certain quantity of a gas at the freezing point is compressed adiabatically, so that its volume is reduced successively to $\frac{1}{2}$, $\frac{1}{4}$, and $\frac{1}{10}$ of the original bulk. Find the corresponding changes of temperature.

{*Ans.* 90° C., 209° C., 429° C., respectively.}

5. If E be the whole molecular energy of the molecules of a gas, and if E_t be the energy of translation, show that

$$\frac{E_t}{E} = \frac{3}{2}\frac{C_p - C_v}{C_v} \qquad . \qquad . \qquad . \qquad . \qquad \text{(Clausius).}$$

{Assuming the energy of a gas to be all heat energy,

$$JC_v\Theta = E,$$

also $$pv = \frac{2}{3}E_t \qquad . \qquad . \qquad . \qquad . \qquad . \qquad \text{(Art. 55),}$$

but $$pv = R\Theta = J(C_p - C_v)\Theta,$$

whence the above expression follows.}

ON ATOMIC AND MOLECULAR THERMAL CAPACITIES, AND THE
VARIATIONS OF SPECIFIC HEAT WITH TEMPERATURE

165. Atomic Thermal Capacities—Dulong and Petit's Law.—In
considering the subject of specific heats it is natural to inquire if the
specific heats of various substances, simple and compound, are in any
way related or connected by any general law. The first attempt in
this direction was made by Dulong and Petit[1] in 1819. From the
consideration of the specific heats of a series of simple substances, such
as iron, lead, gold, silver, etc., these philosophers concluded that the
atoms of all the simple substances have the same thermal capacity,
or, in other words, "the product of the specific heat by the atomic
weight is the same for all the elementary substances."

The range of application of this law was investigated by Regnault
in numerous researches carried on between 1840 and 1862, with the
result that he found it held approximately for most of the elements
which ordinarily occur in the solid state, if the specific heats employed
be taken at temperatures sufficiently below the melting point. For
thirty-two of these substances the mean product was 6·38, with
extremes 6·76 and 5·7, taking the atomic weight of hydrogen as
unity.

That variations from constancy in this product should occur is
certainly to be expected, if it be remembered that the specific heat
of a substance depends on the temperature at which the determination is made, and also on the physical state, whether it is solid,
liquid, or gaseous; and, in the case of solids, to some extent on the
treatment and mechanical actions to which it has been subjected.
These variations will be considered immediately.

An approximate value for Dulong and Petit's constant has been
calculated by F. Richarz[2] by a method based on the kinetic theory.

---

[1] Dulong and Petit, *Ann. de Chimie et de Phys.*, 2ᵉ sér., tom. x. p. 395, 1819.

[2] *Ann. der Physik*, Bd. lxvii. p. 702, 1899. See also H. Staigmüller, *Ann. der
Physik*, Bd. lxv. p. 670, 1898.

In the case of an element which in the solid state obeys Dulong and Petit's law, and which in the state of gas is monatomic like mercury vapour, the total energy of the molecules of the solid element is half kinetic and half potential. In the state of vapour the energy is all kinetic. But the mean kinetic energy is independent of the state of aggregation of the molecules, being merely proportional to the absolute temperature. Therefore the atomic heat, and also the specific heat at constant volume, is half as great in the vapour as in the solid. This has been shown to be the case with mercury.[1] If C_v is the specific heat at constant volume for the vapour, and c_v for the solid, then $c_v = 2C_v$, and using the value given for C_v in Art. 162, we get, since $\beta = 0$ for a monatomic gas,[2]

$$c_v = \frac{3\,R}{J}\,; \quad c_v\mu = 5\cdot952.$$

According to Richarz, the ratio c_p/c_v for many metals lies between $1\cdot01$ and $1\cdot04$ in the solid state, so that

$$c_p\mu = 6\cdot01 \text{ to } 6\cdot19.$$

166. Extensions of Dulong and Petit's Law—Molecular Thermal Capacities.—An extension of the law of Dulong and Petit, by which the specific heat of a compound might be inferred from those of its constituents, was suggested by Woestyn,[3] on the supposition that the atoms, when in combination, preserve their original thermal capacities, and consequently that the thermal capacity of a molecule of any compound is equal to the sum of the thermal capacities of its constituents. Thus, if there be n_1, n_2, n_3, etc., atoms of atomic weights w_1, w_2, w_3, etc., in the molecule, then the molecular weight is

$$W = n_1 w_1 + n_2 w_2 + n_3 w_3 + \text{etc.},$$

and if the specific heats of the constituents be s_1, s_2, s_3, etc., while that of the compound is s, we have under the supposed condition

$$Ws = n_1 w_1 s_1 + n_2 w_2 s_2 + n_3 w_3 s_3 + \text{etc.} \quad . \quad . \quad . \quad . \quad (1)$$

In this equation $w_1 s_1$, $w_2 s_2$, etc., are the thermal capacities of the corresponding atoms, and if these are each equal to the mean value $6\cdot38$ given by Dulong and Petit's law, we have

$$Ws = (n_1 + n_2 + n_3 \ldots)6\cdot38 = 6\cdot38N,$$

a formula which has been verified by Regnault[4] in the case of metallic alloys, the constituents of which were taken in proportions

[1] Lothar Meyer, *Moderne Theorien*, p. 109, 1884.
[2] Using a more recent value for R, the equation becomes $c_v\mu = 5\cdot958$.
[3] Woestyn, *Ann. de Chimie et de Phys.*, 3e sér., tom. xxiii. p. 295, 1848.
[4] Regnault, *Ann. de Chimie et de Phys.*, 3e sér., tom. i. p. 129, 1841.

which were multiples of their atomic weights. The constant 6·38 was, however, not maintained, but increased considerably when the temperature approached the fusing point of the alloy.

The general equation (1), being supposed established, may be employed to determine the specific heat of any element in combination with others of known specific heats. Thus, if all the quantities which occur in the equation be known except s, then the value of s becomes determined. By this means H. Kopp[1] has shown that, as previously announced by Garnier,[2] the specific heat of water in combination in the various hydrates is the same as that of ice, that is, water substance in the solid state.

Neumann's law.

While investigating the specific heats of compounds of the same general formula Neumann[3] found that the product of the molecular weight and specific heat remained constant for all compounds belonging to the same general formula and similarly constituted, but that the product varied from one series to another. This is known as Neumann's law.

167. Variation of Specific Heats with Temperature.—The considerations brought forward in Art. 52 lead us to suspect that the specific heat of any substance may change (either increase or decrease) as the temperature varies. The idea that the specific heat of a substance is not the same at all temperatures seems to have been suggested by Dalton. He supposed that a certain quantity of heat was employed in producing the dilatation which accompanies changes of temperature in bodies, and that therefore as the dilatation for 1° change of temperature varies, the quantity of heat necessary to effect the change of temperature must vary also. He concluded, consequently, that the thermal capacity of a given mass of a substance varied with the temperature, but that the thermal capacity of a definite volume remained constant. This idea, however, was not founded on any experimental investigation of the variations of specific heat with temperature, and it can therefore only be regarded as a conjecture. The first comprehensive series of experiments on the subject were made by Dulong and Petit,[4] who found that the specific heats of all the substances examined by them increased gradually with the temperature, and the general truth of their conclusions has been confirmed by the results of the experiments made by all subsequent investigators.

[1] Liebig, *Ann.*, Supplement, vol. iii. pp. 1 and 289.

[2] Garnier, *Comptes rendus*, tom. xxxv. p. 278, 1852.

[3] F. E. Neumann, *Pogg. Ann.* vol. xxiii. p. 1, 1831.

[4] Dulong and Petit, *Ann. de Chimie et de Physique*, 2e sér., tom. vii. p. 147 ; tom. x. p. 395.

The majority of solids exhibit only a small increase of specific heat as the temperature rises, until the melting point is approached. Near the melting point, however, the specific heat may change rapidly, especially in the case of amorphous substances which pass gradually into the liquid state, as already noticed in Art. 132. A few substances, however, show large variations of specific heat with temperature, and the most noted of these is carbon, which exists in several varieties. Numerous experiments have been conducted from time to time on the specific heats of the several varieties of carbon, chiefly on account of the wide deviation of this element from the law of Dulong and Petit. The experiments of Regnault, of De la Rive and Marcet, of Kopp, and of Wüllner and Bettendorf, show that at temperatures lying between $0°$ and $100°$ the specific heat of wood charcoal is a little over $0\cdot2$, that of native graphite and furnace graphite is rather less, while that of diamond is about $0\cdot14$. F. Weber [1] points out that the discrepancies between the results of different observers are quite too large to be accounted for by experimental errors or impurities, and he considered that they must depend upon some source of variation of specific heat, such as change of temperature.

To test this point Weber executed a careful series of experiments at different temperatures with Bunsen's ice calorimeter, and, for the specific heat of diamond between $0°$ and $200°$ C., deduced the formula

$$s = 0\cdot0947 + 0\cdot0009994\theta - 0\cdot000000036\theta^2.$$

Thus, at $200°$ C. the specific heat of diamond is more than three times its value at zero.

For temperatures above $200°$ C. the water calorimeter was used, but the experiments were not so reliable. Similar variations were found in the case of silicon and boron, so that, although these elements seemed at first to overthrow the generality of Dulong and Petit's law, the large variations of specific heat with temperature show us that the applicability of the law to any element depends on the temperature at which the specific heat is determined.

The experiments of Nernst (see Art. 150) show that the specific heat of diamond diminishes very rapidly at low temperatures, and for graphite, Magnus,[2] using a copper block calorimeter, obtained the formula

$$C_p = 1\cdot824 + 9\cdot3324 + 10^{-3}\theta - 10\cdot278 \times 10^{-6}\theta^2 \times 7\cdot065 + 10^{-9}\theta^3 - 2\cdot631 \times 10^{-12}\theta^4.$$

Great light was thrown on the laws of variation with temperature

[1] F. Weber, *Pogg. Ann.* vol. cliv. pp. 367, 553 ; *Phil. Mag.* vol. xliv. p. 251, 1872.

[2] *Ann. der Physik*, vol. lxx. p. 303, 1923.

of the specific heats of pure elements by the experiments of Nernst and his pupils (Art. 150). These experiments gave the specific heat at constant pressure C_p. The relation between the two specific heats is

$$C_p - C_v = \frac{9\lambda^2\Theta}{JK\rho},$$

where λ is the coefficient of linear expansion, K the compressibility, and ρ the density (see Art. 345, Ex. 25).

At high temperatures the atomic heat (product of the atomic weight into the specific heat at constant volume) of solid elements was found to approximate closely to the theoretical value 5·96. At low temperatures the value of the atomic heat diminished, tending to zero at the absolute zero of temperature. When curves were drawn representing the connection between the atomic heat and the absolute temperature, it was found that the curves corresponding to different elements differed only in such a way that they could all be represented by a single curve, provided that the scale of temperature on the diagram was different for different elements. The shape of the curve is shown in Fig. 79.

168. Debye's Theory of Specific Heats.—If N is the number of molecules in unit mass of a monatomic gas, v its volume, and m the mass of a molecule, then by Art. 375 we have

$$\frac{1}{3}\overline{c^2} = NR_0\Theta ;$$

so that the mean kinetic energy of a molecule is given by

$$\frac{1}{2}m\overline{c^2} = \frac{3}{2}R_0\Theta,$$

since $Nm = 1$. Now consider the case of a solid element in which there are N atoms per unit mass, m being the mass of an atom; and suppose that each atom possesses three degrees of freedom and vibrates about its mean position (see footnote, p. 64). Then if we employ the doctrine of equipartition of energy, the mean energy of an atom is half kinetic and half potential, and the mean kinetic energy is the same as that of a monatomic gas, since the atom in each has the same number of degrees of freedom. The total mean energy of an atom of the solid is therefore $3R_0\Theta$. Putting a = atomic weight, m_h = mass of hydrogen atom, E = energy of unit mass of solid, we get

$$a\mathrm{E} = 3\frac{m}{m_h}NR_0\Theta = \frac{3R_0\Theta}{m_h},$$

whence

$$a\mathrm{C}_v = \frac{a}{J}\frac{d\mathrm{E}}{d\Theta} = \frac{3R_0}{m_h J}.$$

This result is the same as that of Art. 165 giving $aC_v = \text{const.} = 5\cdot96$. The variation of the atomic heat with temperature has been accounted for by Debye by making use of Planck's quantum theory, according to which the energy is not divided equally among the various degrees of freedom but according to the law given by Planck. Since unit mass of the solid contains N atoms each of three degrees of freedom, the whole unit mass possesses 3N degrees of freedom, that is, it is capable of vibrating in 3N different ways, and these must be classified according to their frequency before we can apply Planck's law. This can be done as follows : [1]—

Let the unit mass of solid under consideration be in the form of a rectangular parallelepiped whose linear dimensions are p, q, and r. The vibrations will consist of trains of waves which will be reflected at the surface, so that the angle of reflection is equal to the angle of incidence. If a, β, γ are the direction cosines of any wave-front, then the wave after any reflection will travel in some one of the eight directions whose direction cosines are $\pm a$, $\pm \beta$, $\pm \gamma$. In order that no energy may be gained

Fig. 78.

or lost at the surface, a wave starting from any point A on the surface (Fig. 78) must be in the same phase when it comes back to A—that is, the distance travelled between two successive reflections at A must be some multiple of λ, when λ is the wave-length. Or, what is the same thing, if AB is a line drawn perpendicular to the face to cut the opposite face at B, then the distance travelled by the wave in passing from A to B must be some multiple of $\frac{1}{2}\lambda$. Let AP be the direction of propagation of the wave, and let $AB = p$, so that $\cos BAP = a$. Draw a plane through B perpendicular to AP, cutting it in P. Then, since BP is a line in the wave-front, a wave starting from A will reach B when the distance travelled by the wave-front is AP, which is equal to ap, so that ap must be a multiple of $\frac{1}{2}\lambda$. We must therefore have

$$2ap = \lambda x, \quad 2\beta q = \lambda y, \quad 2\gamma r = \lambda z,$$

where x, y, z are integers. From the relation

$$a^2 + \beta^2 + \gamma^2 = 1$$

we deduce the equation

$$\frac{x^2}{p^2} + \frac{y^2}{q^2} + \frac{z^2}{r^2} = \frac{4}{\lambda^2} = \frac{4v^2}{V^2},$$

[1] The method of calculating the number of vibrations corresponding to a given frequency is due to Jeans, with a simplification by Lorentz (*Theory of Electrons*, p. 93).

where ν is the frequency of the vibration and V the velocity of wave-propagation, so that $V = \nu\lambda$.

Now, if we change ν into $\nu + \delta\nu$ we get a similar, slightly larger ellipsoid. The number of modes of vibration of frequency lying between ν and $\nu + \delta\nu$ is equal to the number of points whose co-ordinates are positive integers, which lie within the ellipsoidal shell bounded by the two ellipsoids (*i.e.* one-eighth the number of points whose co-ordinates are integers, positive or negative). Since these points occur at the rate of one per unit volume, their number is equal numerically to one-eighth the volume of the shell. The volume of the first ellipsoid is $\frac{4}{3}\pi.8pqr\nu^3/V^3$, therefore, since $pqr = v$ (the volume of unit mass), the number of modes of vibration which we are seeking is $4\pi v\nu^2\delta\nu/V^3$. In an elastic solid two kinds of wave are possible, compressional and distortional, and since any distortional wave of given frequency and direction may be resolved into two independent rectangular components, we must multiply the number by two in calculating the number of distortional waves. If V_1 and V_2 are the velocities of propagation of compressional and distortional waves respectively, the total number of possible modes of vibration whose frequencies lie between ν and $\nu + \delta\nu$ is

$$4\pi v\nu^2\delta\nu\left(\frac{1}{V_1{}^3}+\frac{2}{V_2{}^3}\right).$$

If ν could take all values from 0 to ∞, then the total number of modes of vibration of all frequencies, that is, the total number of degrees of freedom of the solid, would be infinite. This number is, however, 3N. Obviously there must be some limit to the magnitude of ν (or the smallness of λ), since the matter is not infinitely fine-grained. The special assumption which Debye makes is that the frequency may have any value between zero and some finite value ν_m. Thus we have for the total number of degrees of freedom

$$3N = 4\pi v\left(\frac{1}{V_1{}^3}+\frac{2}{V_2{}^3}\right)\int_0^{\nu_m}\nu^2 d\nu$$

$$= \frac{4}{3}\pi v\left(\frac{1}{V_1{}^3}+\frac{2}{V_2{}^3}\right)\nu_m{}^3. \qquad (1)$$

According to the quantum theory (Art. 285), the average energy corresponding to each degree of freedom is not $R_0\Theta$ but

$$\frac{h\nu}{e^{\frac{h\nu}{R_0\Theta}}-1}.$$

The total energy E is therefore given by the equation

$$E = 4\pi v \left(\frac{1}{V_1^3} + \frac{2}{V_2^3} \right) \int_0^{\nu_m} \frac{h\nu}{e^{\frac{h\nu}{R_0\Theta}} - 1} \nu^2 d\nu$$

$$= \frac{9Nh}{\nu_m^3} \int_0^{\nu_m} \frac{\nu^3 d\nu}{e^{\frac{h\nu}{R_0\Theta}} - 1}$$

by relation (1). And since the exponent of e must be a pure number, $h\nu/R_0$ must be of the dimensions of a temperature. Putting $h\nu/R_0 = \Theta'$, $h\nu_m/R_0 = \Theta_m$, the integral transforms to

$$E = \frac{9NR_0}{\Theta_m^3} \int_0^{\Theta_m} \frac{\Theta'^3 d\Theta'}{e^{\frac{\Theta'}{\Theta}} - 1}.$$

If Θ is large compared with Θ_m, $e^{\frac{\Theta'}{\Theta}} - 1 = \Theta'/\Theta$ approximately, and the value of E reduces to $3NR_0\Theta$ as in the last article. The integral cannot be evaluated in finite terms, but its form shows that we may write

$$\frac{dE}{d\Theta} = 3NR_0 f\left(\frac{\Theta_m}{\Theta} \right),$$

where $f(\Theta_m/\Theta)$ is a function [1] whose value is zero for $\Theta = 0$ and tends to unity for large values of Θ. Thus we get for the specific heat

$$Cv = \frac{1}{J} \frac{dE}{d\Theta} = \frac{3NR_0}{J} f\left(\frac{\Theta_m}{\Theta} \right),$$

and

$$aCv = 5 \cdot 96 \times f\left(\frac{\Theta_m}{\Theta} \right).$$

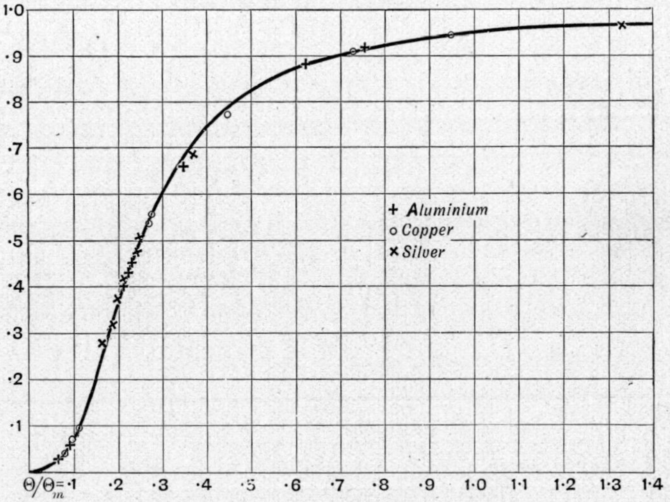

Fig. 79.—Variation of Specific Heat with Temperature.

[1] The values of $f(\Theta_m/\Theta)$ computed by Debye are given in his paper, also in Jeans's *Dynamical Theory of Gases*, 4th ed., p. 398.

The value of Θ_m is different for different elements. In Fig. 79 the abscissæ represent values of Θ/Θ_m and the ordinates the corresponding values of $f(\Theta_m/\Theta)$, the values given to Θ_m being those which accord best with the observations on specific heat (indicated by marks), and are given in the first column of the following table. The values of Θ_m can, however, be calculated independently from the elastic constants of the elements, and these are the values given in the second column of the table.

Debye's results are confirmed by the experiments of Keesom and Onnes [1] on the specific heats of lead and copper at low temperatures. The method of Nernst (copper block calorimeter) was used, the temperature being measured by a gold resistance thermometer. The specific heat of lead was investigated between 14° K. and 80° K., and that of copper between 15° K. and 22° K. The results gave good concordance with Debye over the whole range.

Element.	Θ_m (observed).	Θ_m (calculated).
Aluminium . . .	396	399
Copper . . .	309	329
Silver	215	212
Lead	95	72

169. Influence of Change of Density and State.—Besides the large changes of specific heat which occur when a body passes from the solid into the liquid or gaseous conditions, it is found that other small variations accompany such alterations as the changes of density of solids caused by hammering. As a general rule, the specific heat of a metal is diminished when the density is increased by hammering, but in many cases the changes are negligible. Thus in the case of steel, lead, and tin, hammering does not sensibly affect the specific heat, but in the case of annealed copper the specific heat is reduced from 0·09501 to 0·0936 by hammering.

A more marked difference occurs in the specific heats of the allotropic varieties of some substances. Thus for carbonate of calcium in the state of aragonite or spar it is 0·2085, and for chalk it is 0·2148, and for marble 0·2158.

The specific heat of a substance is generally very different in the three states of matter—solid, liquid, and gaseous. In general, the specific heat in the solid state is much less than in the liquid, but

[1] *Proc. Amst. Acad.* vol. xvii. (2) p. 894, 1914.

sometimes the specific heat of the gas is very nearly the same as that of the solid. For example, the specific heat of water is nearly twice that of ice or of water vapour.

For the metals the change of specific heat arising from fusion is small, being of the same order as the change of specific gravity.

SECTION IX

ON THE DYNAMICAL EQUIVALENT OF HEAT

170. Joule's Experiments.—The development of the dynamical theory of heat has been briefly sketched in Arts. 30-42 from the time of Rumford and Davy (who first placed it upon an experimental basis) up to the middle of the present century, when Joule completed his celebrated experiments on the dynamical equivalent, and forced the conclusions of Rumford and Davy upon the attention of the scientific

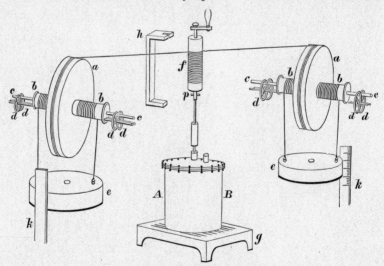

Fig. 80.—Joule's Apparatus.

world. These experiments have been already described in outline (Art. 35), but on account of the great importance of the dynamical equivalent as a physical constant, as well as the fundamental bearing of the principle of equivalence in the theory of heat, we shall now enter into a more detailed description of the investigations made in this department—investigations which would well merit a special attention if only as examples of the highest class of experimental research.

Of the various methods employed by Joule for estimating the value of the dynamical equivalent, that which he was finally led to prefer to all others was the direct method of simply stirring a quantity of water by means of a paddle-wheel—the work spent in turning the paddle, and the heat generated in the fluid by friction, being both accurately measured.

The apparatus employed in these experiments is shown in Fig. 80. The water was contained in a copper vessel AB, which we shall refer to as the calorimeter. The lid of this vessel fitted water-tight, and was furnished with two tubulures—one to receive the axis of the revolving paddle, and the other for the insertion of a thermometer, which registered the temperature of the apparatus. The paddle was made of brass, and consisted of eight sets of revolving arms, which worked between four sets of stationary vanes fixed to the frame of the vessel.   Fig. 81 represents a vertical section, and Fig. 82 a horizontal section of the calorimeter and paddle, the revolving arms being marked a and the stationary vanes b. The axis of the paddle worked freely (but without shaking) on its bearings, and was interrupted at d by a cylinder of boxwood, which prevented conduction of heat to or from the calorimeter.

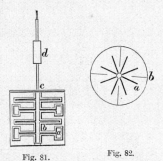

Fig. 81.   Fig. 82.

The paddle was set in motion by leaden weights e, e, suspended by string from the rollers bb, bb, of the wooden pulleys a, a. These pulleys were supported by their steel axles c, c, on brass friction wheels dd, dd, dd, dd. The weights which set the apparatus in motion were suspended over the pulleys by fine twine, which was wound doubled on the central roller f, so that the parts passing over the pulleys left the roller at the same level, and produced a couple round its vertical axis, thus avoiding the horizontal thrust which would otherwise be brought into play. The roller could be detached from the paddle at pleasure by withdrawing the pin p, so that the weights could be wound up without turning the paddle in the calorimeter. The wooden stool g, on which the calorimeter stood, was perforated by a number of transverse slits cut out in such a manner that the metal came in contact with the wood at only a few points, while the air had free access to almost every part of it. In this way loss of heat by conduction was avoided, and radiation from the person of the experimenter was cut off by a large wooden screen.

In making an experiment the temperature of the calorimeter was ascertained, the weights were wound up by placing the roller f in the stand h, and the roller was then pinned to the axis of the paddle. The height of the weights above the ground (about $5\frac{1}{4}$ feet) having been exactly determined by means of the graduated slips of wood kk, the roller was set at liberty, and allowed to revolve till the weights reached the floor. The roller was then unpinned and placed in the stand h, while the weights were wound up again, and the friction of the water was renewed. After this operation had been repeated twenty times, the experiment was concluded with another observation of the temperature of the apparatus. The mean temperature of the laboratory was determined by observations made at the commence-ment, middle, and termination of each experiment; and previous to, or immediately after, each experiment a test was made as to the effect of radiation and conduction of heat to or from the atmosphere in raising or depressing the temperature of the apparatus.

The following account [1] will sufficiently indicate the mode of procedure. The leaden weights, together with the string attached, weighed 203066 grains and 203086 grains respectively. Their velocity on reaching the floor was 2·42 inches per second, and the time occupied by each experiment (twenty falls) was thirty-five minutes. The total fall of the weights during an experiment was therefore the sum of the heights passed over in twenty falls.

From the results of this series of experiments it was inferred that the heating or cooling effect of the atmosphere upon the apparatus was 0°·04654 for each degree of difference between the mean temperature of the apparatus and that of the air. The excess of temperature of the air over that of the apparatus was 0°·32295 in the mean of the radiation experiments, but only 0°·305075 in the mean of the friction experi-ments. Hence 0°·000832 was added to the difference between 0°·57525 and 0°·012975, and the result, viz. 0°·563017, represented approximately the heating effect of the friction. To this quantity a small correction was applied on account of the mean of the temperatures of the apparatus at the beginning and end of each friction experi-ment having been taken for the true mean temperature, which was not strictly the case, owing to the somewhat less rapid increase of temperature towards the termina-tion of the experiment when the water had become warmer. The mean temperature of the apparatus in the friction experiments was therefore estimated 0°·002184 higher, which diminished the heating effect of the atmosphere by 0°·00102, and this added to 0°·563107 gave 0°·563209 as the correct mean increase of temperature due to the friction of water. This increase is a mixed quantity depending partly on the friction of the water, and partly on the friction of the vertical axis on its pivot and bearings. The latter, however, was only about $\frac{1}{80}$ of the former.

The total thermal capacity of the apparatus with the water contained was equivalent to that of 97480·2 grains of water, so that the total quantity of heat generated by friction was 0°·563209 in this weight of water, or 1° F. in 7·842299 lbs. of water. Now the weights amounted to 406152 grains, and from this a certain deduction must be made on account of the friction arising from the pulleys and the rigidity of the string. This was found by connecting the two pulleys with twine passing round a roller of equal diameter to that employed

---

[1] Joule, *Phil. Trans. Roy. Soc.*, 1850, pt. i.

in the experiments. Under these circumstances the weight required to be added to one of the leaden weights in order to maintain them in equable motion was found to be 2975 grains.[1] The same result, in the opposite directions, was obtained by adding 3035 grains to the other leaden weight. Deducting 168 grains (the friction of the roller on its pivots) from 3005, the mean of the foregoing numbers, we have 2837 grains as the portion of the weight expended in friction of the pulleys and string. This subtracted from the leaden weights leaves 403315 grains as the weight available for the generation of heat in the apparatus.

Cause of Change of Temperature.	Mean Total Fall of Weights in Inches.	Difference between Mean Temp. during Experiment and Mean Temp. of Air.	Gain or Loss of Heat during Experiment.
Mean Friction	1260·248	− 0·305075	0·575250 gain
Mean Radiation	0	− 0·322950	0·012975 gain

A correction has still to be applied on account of the velocity possessed by the weights when they reached the floor. This velocity was 2·42 inches per second, and is equivalent to a fall through an altitude of 0·0076 inch. This multiplied by 20 (the number of falls in each experiment) gives 0·152 inch, which, when subtracted from the mean total fall, 1260·248, leaves 1260·096 inches as the corrected height. This fall of the above weights is equivalent to 6050·186 lbs. falling through a height of 1 foot, and to this is added $0·8464 \times 20 = 16·928$ foot-pounds as a correction for the elasticity of the strings, which comes into play after the weights have reached the ground.

The mean corrected result was therefore 6067·114 foot-pounds as the work spent in raising the temperature of 7·842299 lbs. of water 1° F., and this gives 773·64 as the dynamical equivalent of heat in the latitude of Manchester.

In Joule's second and third series of experiments the fluid employed was mercury, the apparatus being constructed of iron, and somewhat modified in other respects, to suit the purpose. In the fourth and fifth series the heat was developed, not by fluid friction, but by means of a bevelled cast-iron ring rubbing against another bevelled iron ring in mercury. The following table contains the final results of these series of experiments, the fourth column giving the values when the weighings are made in a vacuum :—

No. of Series.	Material employed.	Equivalent in Air.	In Vacuum.	Mean.
1	Water	773·640	772·692	772·692
2	Mercury	773·762	772·814	} 774·083
3	,,	776·303	775·352	
4	Cast Iron	776·997	776·045	} 774·987
5	,,	774·880	773·930	

---

[1] The number 2955 given in Joule's Memoir is probably a misprint.

Of these results, that derived from the friction of water was considered by Joule as the most reliable, both on account of the number of experiments performed, and the great thermal capacity of the apparatus. And since, even in the friction of fluids, it was impossible to entirely avoid vibration and the consequent expenditure of energy in sound, Joule thought it probable that the number 772·692 was slightly too large, and therefore adopted the round number 772. It must be remembered, however, that the unit of temperature

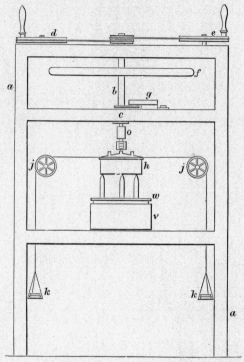

Fig. 83.—Joule's Later Apparatus.

employed here is the degree on the mercury thermometer [1] employed by Joule, and that the specific heat of water is taken as unity at the temperature of each experiment.

At the request of the British Association Joule [2] executed a new series of experiments, which he completed in 1878. In this investigation the arrangement of the apparatus and the principle of the method employed for measuring the work differed from that

[1] An error of 1 per cent may arise from want of comparison of the mercury thermometer with the air thermometer.

[2] Joule, *Phil. Trans. Roy. Soc.*, 1878, pt. ii.

adopted in the earlier experiments.   The calorimeter, h (Fig. 83), instead of resting on a fixed stool, was suspended by a bearing on the vertical axis of the paddle, so as to be capable of rotating freely about it.   With this arrangement, when the paddle was set in motion, the friction between the moving fluid and the walls of the calorimeter, as well as that which occurred at the bearing, produced a couple tending to turn the calorimeter round the vertical axis.   The rotation of the calorimeter was prevented by an equal and opposite couple produced by the action of a fine silk cord, which passed round an accurately turned groove in the surface of the calorimeter.   The ends of this cord were thrown over two light wooden pulleys, j, j, and were attached to scale-pans, k, k, which contained weights sufficient to keep the calorimeter in equilibrium.[1]

The whole apparatus was contained in a massive wooden case, aa, which was divided into three compartments, and permanently boxed in on three sides.   The fourth side or front was closed by shutters furnished with windows, which could be removed at pleasure.   The paddle was kept in motion by means of doubling hand-wheels, de, and the vertical shaft, b, which carried a fly-wheel, f (weighing about 1 cwt.), was supported by a conical collar turned on it at c.   The hydraulic supporter, v, w, was not employed in the initial stages of the investigation ; but as irregularities were found to arise from time to time from the variations in the friction of the bearing which supported the calorimeter, the supporter, v, w, was designed, so that the pressure on the bearing and the metallic friction were almost reduced to zero.   This supporter consisted of two concentric vessels, v and w. The lid of the inner vessel was surmounted by three uprights, and when water was poured into the space between the vessels the inner floated up, so that the uprights pressed against the bottom of the calorimeter, and the pressure on the bearing was thus relieved.

The calorimeter is shown in section in Fig. 84, and in plan in Fig. 85.   There were four stationary vanes and two sets of rotating vanes, each of five arms, the upper set (dotted lines, Fig. 85) being fixed to the axis $9°$ behind the lower set, so that no two of the rotating vanes passed the fixed ones at the same moment, and as the momentary alteration of resistance at crossing took place forty times during each revolution, the resistance was practically uniform.   The axle of the paddle worked easily in the collar m, and was screwed into the boxwood piece n.   The boxwood piece o (Fig. 83) was introduced

---

[1] The principle of this method, which is a kind of friction balance, was designed by Hirn (*Théorie mécanique de la chaleur*, 3rd ed., p. 92), and was subsequently used by Rowland and others.

in order to prevent conduction of heat along the axis; but this precaution was found to be unnecessary.

In making an experiment the calorimeter was filled with a known weight of distilled water, and screwed on to the axis. Its temperature was noted, and the silk cord adjusted. The thermometer was then removed, and a caoutchouc stopper placed in the tubulure. The axle was then rapidly brought up to a speed sufficient to raise the weights about 1 foot from the floor, and they could be kept very steadily in this position during the whole time of an experiment (35 minutes). The wheel was then rapidly brought to rest, and the temperature of the calorimeter again noted.

The work spent is determined by knowing the number of revolutions and the moment of the couple required to keep the calorimeter in equilibrium. Thus, if w denotes the sum of the suspended weights,

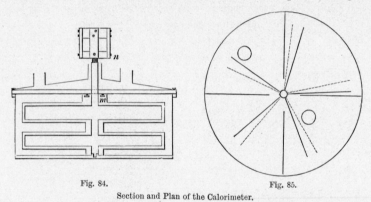

Fig. 84.   Fig. 85.
Section and Plan of the Calorimeter.

and r the radius of the calorimeter, the moment of the couple tending to turn the vessel is wr, so that in turning through an angle θ the work done is $wr\theta$, or if n be the number of revolutions the work is

$$W = 2\pi nwr.$$

In calculating n, the number of revolutions of the axis when the weights were off the ground was added to half the number employed in the acts of starting and stopping the apparatus. The revolutions of the axis were registered by a counter at g (Fig. 83).

The results of five sets of experiments by this method are collected in the table on p. 303. In the first two sets the hydraulic supporter was not employed, and the metallic friction at the bearing of the calorimeter was a considerable fraction of the whole.

The mean value deduced for J at the temperature of 60° F. was 773·369 foot-pounds at Manchester. This reduced to Greenwich and

Series.	Number of Experiments.	Proportion of Metallic to Total Friction.	Mean Rise of Temperature.	Temperature of the Calorimeter.	Equivalent.
1	17	$\frac{1}{7\cdot7}$	45·907	58·46	777·72
2	15	$\frac{1}{8\cdot3}$	48·803	54·76	774·57
3	21	$\frac{1}{106}$	44·777	59·98	773·136
4	6	$\frac{1}{43}$	14·355	58·14	766·97
5	7	$\frac{1}{108}$	67·620	63·14	773·99

the sea-level becomes 773·492, or when the weighings are made in a vacuum the value of J at 60° F. is 772·55. Joule's results, corrected by comparison of his thermometers with one of Rowland's, and for other errors (see Arts. 35 and 171), gave the value (at 12°·7 C.)

$$J = 778\cdot5.$$

171. Rowland's Experiments.—In 1879 Professor Rowland,[1] feeling that Joule's work required to be extended in some directions and completed, undertook a careful and elaborate series of experiments on the value of the dynamical equivalent of heat. In Joule's work the experiments were made only at the ordinary temperatures of the atmosphere, and the mercury thermometers employed were not standardised by comparison with the air thermometer. Errors of 1 or 2 per cent may arise from this cause in calorimetric work, for even between 0° and 100° a difference of several tenths of a degree may exist between the mercury and the air thermometer.

The principal defect of Joule's plan of experiment, however, is the small rate of rise of temperature, and Professor Rowland, in designing his apparatus, aimed at procuring a large change of temperature in a short time. This involved the expenditure of a considerable power, and necessitated the use of a steam-engine, combined with an accurate method of measuring the power supplied.

The apparatus finally adopted is shown in Fig. 86. In principle it resembles Hirn's friction balance and the apparatus employed by Joule in his final experiments. The calorimeter was attached to a vertical shaft *ab*, and the whole was suspended by a torsion wire. The axis of the paddle left the calorimeter through the bottom and was attached to the shaft *ef*, which was kept in uniform motion by the wheel *g* driven by a steam-engine. To the axis *ab* an accurately turned wheel *kl* was attached, and the couple tending to turn the

[1] H. A. Rowland, *Proc. American Academy of Arts and Sciences*, New Series, vol. vii., 1879–80.

calorimeter was measured by weights *o* and *p*, attached to silk tapes passing around the circumference of this wheel, in combination with the torsion of the suspending wire.   To this axis also a long arm was attached, having two sliding weights *q* and *r*, by means of which the

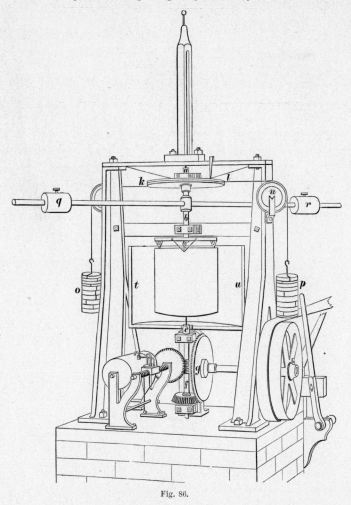

Fig. 86.

moment of inertia could be varied or determined.   The number of revolutions of the paddle was determined by means of a chronograph set in motion by a screw on the shaft *ef*.   On this chronograph was recorded the transit of the mercury over the divisions of the thermometer.   A water-jacket *tu*, made in halves, was placed round the calorimeter, so that the radiation could be estimated, and a wooden box surrounded the whole and screened the calorimeter from the observer.

When the paddles were in motion, the couple tending to turn the calorimeter was balanced by the weights o, p, and the equilibrium was rendered stable by the torsion of the suspending wire. The amount of torsion was read off on a scale on the edge of the wheel kl, and this gave the correction to be applied to the weights o, p. One observer constantly read the circle kl, and another recorded the transits of the mercury over the scale divisions of the thermometer. In this manner a series of observations, extending over the space of half an hour to an hour, embraced a rise of temperature of from 15° to 25°, in which a record was made for perhaps each tenth of a degree, and contained several hundred observations from any two of which the dynamical equivalent of heat could be obtained.

The correction for radiation is inversely proportional to the ratio of the rate at which the work is done to the rate at which the heat is lost, and this for equal ranges of temperature is only $\frac{1}{50}$ as great in these experiments as in Joule's, for Joule's rate of increase was only 0°·62 C. per hour, and in these experiments was about 35° C., and could be increased to over 45° C. per hour.

The calorimeter and paddle arrangement was more complicated than Joule's. The number of paddles was increased so that there should be no jerk in the motion, and that the resistance should be great. Their shape was also such as to cause the whole of the water to run in a constant stream past the thermometer, and to cause constant exchange between the water at the top and bottom. A section of the calorimeter with paddle is shown in Fig. 87, and the paddle is shown separately in Fig. 88.

To a steel axis a stout copper cylinder was attached by means of stout wires. To this cylinder four rings were attached which supported the paddles. Each ring had eight paddles, and was displaced through a small angle with reference to the one below it, so that no one paddle came over another. By this means the resistance was rendered continuous rather than jerky. The lower rows of paddles were turned backwards, so that they threw the water outwards and kept up the circulation. Around these movable paddles were the stationary vanes, consisting of five rows of ten each. These were attached to the movable paddles by bearings at the extremities of the shaft, and were removed with the latter when it was taken out of the calorimeter. These outer paddles were fixed to the calorimeter by four screws so as to be stationary.

Two apertures were made in the cover of the calorimeter—one to

X

receive a thermometer, and the other for filling the vessel with water.
A copper tube, perforated with large holes, descended from the thermometer aperture, almost to the centre of the calorimeter.   The thermometer was contained within this sieve-like tube, with its bulb at a
short distance from the centre of the calorimeter, with the revolving
paddles outside it and the stream of water circulating around it.

If D denotes the diameter of the torsion wheel, then (p. 302) the
work done during n revolutions of the paddle is

$$W = \pi w n D.$$

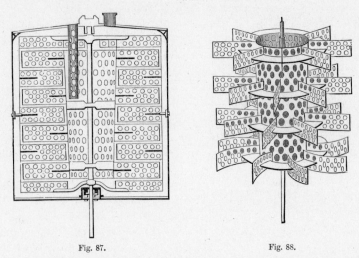

Fig. 87.   Fig. 88.

Hence, if the temperature rises by an amount $\Delta\theta$ (corrected for radiation) in the time occupied by n revolutions, the value of the dynamical
equivalent will be given by the equation

$$J = \frac{\pi w n D}{C \Delta\theta},$$

where C is the thermal capacity of the calorimeter and the water contained.   To reduce this to absolute measure, we must multiply by
$g = 9\cdot78009 + 0\cdot0508 \sin^2\lambda$ where λ is the latitude of the place.   At
Baltimore the value is $g = 9\cdot8005$ in metres per sec. per sec.

The corrections to be applied are—(1) For weighing in air, which must be applied
to w and C ; if ρ denotes the density of air under the given conditions, this correction amounted to $- 0\cdot835\rho$.   (2) For the weight of the tape by which the torsion
weights were suspended ; this amounted to $0\cdot0006/w$.   (3) For the expansion of the
torsion wheel ; if D$'$ be its known diameter at 20°, then its diameter at any other
temperature θ was $D' + 0\cdot000018 D'(\theta - 20)$.   The corrected formula was then

$$J = \frac{\pi n w D' g}{C \Delta\theta} \left\{ 1 + 0\cdot000018(\theta - 20) + \frac{0\cdot0006}{w} - 0\cdot835\rho \right\}.$$

Owing to the rapid rise of temperature (generally about $0°·6$ per minute) the correction for radiation was proportionately small. This correction was $0·0014\theta°$ per minute, where θ is the difference of temperature between the calorimeter and its jacket. This amounts to 1 per cent for $10°·7$, and to 4 per cent for $14°·2$. Generally the calorimeter was cooler than the jacket at the outset, and so an elevation of $20°$ could be obtained in the temperature of the calorimeter without a rate of correction of more than 4 per cent at any point, and an average correction of less than 2 per cent. An error of 10 per cent was therefore required in the estimation of the radiation to produce an average error of 1 in 500, or an error of 1 in 250 at a single point. The radiation correction was estimated by allowing the calorimeter to cool while the paddles were slowly turned, the work done being allowed for. The losses of heat placed under this head include conduction and convection as well as radiation proper, and were made up as follows :—

Conduction along shaft	·00011
,, ,, suspending wires .	·00006
True radiation	·00017
Convection	·00106
Total	·00140

Among the corrections to be applied to the temperature as read off from the thermometer that arising from the unequal temperature of the stem was the greatest and most difficult to estimate. The other corrections arise in pressure on the bulb, conduction along the stem, and the fact that the thermometer is always behind the calorimeter as the temperature of the latter changes.

The following table gives Professor Rowland's results in grammetres at Baltimore :—

Air Thermometer.	Equivalent.	Air Thermometer.	Equivalent.	Air Thermometer.	Equivalent.
°		°		°	
5	429·8	16	427·2	27	425·6
6	429·5	17	427·0	28	425·6
7	429·3	18	426·8	29	425·5
8	429·0	19	426·6	30	425·6
9	428·8	20	426·4	31	425·6
10	428·5	21	426·2	32	425·6
11	428·3	22	426·1	33	425·7
12	428·1	23	426·0	34	425·7
13	427·9	24	425·9	35	425·8
14	427·7	25	425·8	36	425·8
15	427·4	26	425·7	...	...

To reduce to latitude of Manchester and Berlin $0·5$ must be subtracted, and for Paris $0·4$.

In 1897 a series of comparisons was undertaken at the Johns Hopkins University between Rowland's thermometers, three Tonnelot mercury thermometers standardised at the Bureau International, and a Callendar-Griffiths platinum thermometer. The result has been a recalculation of Rowland's figures. In the following table the values of the mechanical equivalent are given in ergs as calculated by Dr.

W. S. Day.[1] Rowland's old values are also given in ergs for the sake
of comparison.

Temperature.	Equivalent in Ergs (Rowland).	Equivalent in Ergs (Day).	Temperature.	Equivalent in Ergs (Rowland).	Equivalent in Ergs (Day).
°			°		
5	$4\cdot212 \times 10^7$	...	13	$4\cdot194 \times 10^7$	$4\cdot191 \times 10^7$
6	$4\cdot209$,,	$4\cdot203 \times 10^7$	14	$4\cdot192$,,	$4\cdot189$,,
7	$4\cdot207$,,	$4\cdot201$,,	15	$4\cdot189$,,	$4\cdot188$,,
8	$4\cdot204$,,	$4\cdot199$,,	16	$4\cdot187$,,	$4\cdot186$,,
9	$4\cdot202$,,	$4\cdot198$,,	17	$4\cdot185$,,	$4\cdot185$,,
10	$4\cdot200$,,	$4\cdot196$,,	18	$4\cdot183$,,	$4\cdot184$,,
11	$4\cdot198$,,	$4\cdot194$,,	19	$4\cdot181$,,	$4\cdot182$,,
12	$4\cdot196$,,	$4\cdot192$,,	20	$4\cdot179$,,	$4\cdot181$,,

For the sake of comparison with his own determinations, Professor
Rowland also reduced Joule's results to the air thermometer and the
latitude of Baltimore,[2] deducing the value 426·75 at 14°·6 C. from
Joule's experiments, and 427·52 from his own.

172. Miculescu's Experiments.—M. Miculescu [3] also adopted the
friction balance method of determining the dynamical equivalent
of heat. In the investigations of Joule and Professor Rowland the
axis of the rotating paddle was vertical, passing through the lid of the
calorimeter in Joule's apparatus, and through the bottom in Professor
Rowland's. In the apparatus adopted by M. Miculescu, on the other
hand, the axis of the paddle was horizontal. The work was supplied
by a motor supported on a wooden frame, which was suspended from
a horizontal axis, round which it could swing freely ; and this axis
coincided geometrically with the rotating axis of the paddle. With
this arrangement the suspended frame, when the apparatus was in
motion, tended to incline itself to the vertical in a direction opposite
to that of the rotation. It was brought back into its position of
equilibrium by a couple of known moment, and the motor thus played
the part of its own dynamometer, the work being measured as before
(p. 302).

The heat generated was measured by the method of *stationary
temperature*. Around the calorimeter (which was fixed independently
of the oscillating frame), and through the water in which the paddles
turn, a current of cold water circulated in such a way that the temperature of the calorimeter remained fixed. The heat developed in any

---

[1] *Phil. Mag.*, July 1898. Rowland's figures were also recalculated by Waidner
and Mallory, *Phys. Rev.* vol. viii., 1899.

[2] *Proc. American Acad. of Arts and Sciences*, vol. viii. (New Series) pt. i. p. 44,
1880–81.

[3] M. C. Miculescu, *Ann. de Chimie et de Physique*, 6e sér., tom. xxvii. p. 202,
October 1892.

time was consequently determined by the weight of water which passed through the apparatus in the same time.

Taking the specific heat of water to be unity between 10° and 13° C., the mean result of these experiments gave the number 426·7; or when temperatures were referred to the hydrogen thermometer, the result was

$$J = 426 \cdot 84.$$

173. Reynolds and Moorby's Experiments. — Reynolds and Moorby[1] determined the mechanical equivalent of the mean thermal unit between 0° and 100° C. on a very large scale, with a Froude-Reynolds's hydraulic brake and a steam-engine of 100 horse-power. This brake is practically a Joule calorimeter, ingeniously designed to churn the water in such a manner as to develop the greatest possible resistance. The admission of water at 0° C. to the brake was controlled by hand in such a manner as to keep the outflow nearly at the boiling point, the quantity of water in the brake required to produce a constant torque being regulated automatically, as the speed varied, by a valve worked by the lifting of the weighted lever attached to the brake. With 300 lbs. on a four-foot lever at 300 revolutions per minute, the rate of generation of heat was about 12 kilo-calories per second. In spite of the large range of temperature, the correction for external loss of heat amounted to only 5 per cent with the brake uncovered, and was reduced to less than 2 per cent by lagging. This is the special advantage of working on so large a scale with so rapid a generation of heat. But, for the same reason, the method necessarily presents peculiar difficulties, which were not overcome without great pains and ingenuity. The principal troubles arose from damp in the lagging, which necessitated the rejection of several trials, and from dissolved air in the water, causing loss of heat by the formation of steam. Next to the radiation loss, the most uncertain correction was that for conduction of heat along the 4-inch shaft. These losses were as far as possible eliminated by combining the trials in pairs, with different loads on the brake, assuming that the heat-loss would be the same in the heavy and light trials, provided that the external temperature and the gradient in the shaft, as estimated from the temperature of the bearings, were the same. The values deduced in this manner for the equivalent agreed as closely as could be expected, considering the impossibility of regulating the external condition of temperature and moisture with any certainty in an engine-room. The extreme variation of results in any one series was only from 776·63 to 779·46 foot-pounds, or less than ½ per cent. Great pains were taken to

Sources of error.

[1] *Phil. Trans.* p. 381, A, 1897.

discuss and eliminate all the sources of constant error which could be foreseen. There can be no doubt that the final result is the most accurate direct determination of the value of the mean calorie in mechanical units. As it was only necessary to determine temperatures in the neighbourhood of 0° and 100° C. the results are almost independent of the *nature* of the temperature scale, as all temperature scales must be in agreement at the two standardising points, while the range was so great that an error in measurement at either end of it would have but a small effect.

Mean calorie. The value of the mean calorie between 0° and 100° C. as determined by Reynolds and Moorby is $4\cdot1833 \times 10^7$ ergs.

The experiments of Reynolds and Moorby do not furnish us with the value in dynamical units of the standard calorie at 15° C. or any other chosen temperature. Nevertheless, they are of great value as a test of the accuracy of the indirect determinations of the mechanical equivalent by the electrical method, which we shall now describe.

174. Later Electrical Methods. — The electrical method of determining the mechanical equivalent consists in heating a given mass of water through a known range of temperature by immersing in it a wire heated by an electric current, and measuring the heat-energy communicated to the water in terms of electric units. This method was tried by Joule, but was regarded by him as less trustworthy than the direct process. The reliability of the results obtained by it depends not only on the care with which the actual determination is carried out, but also upon the accuracy with which the electric units employed have been measured. The equations (omitting all corrections) expressing the heat-energy required to raise m grammes of water through $\theta°$ in electrical units are

Three methods.
$$J m\theta = ECt = C^2Rt = \frac{E^2}{R}t,$$

where C is the current, R the resistance of the wire, E the E.M.F. between its terminals, and t the time in seconds. If these are measured in amperes, ohms, and volts, J will be the number of *joules* (1 joule = 10^7 ergs) required to raise a gramme of water 1° C. We see here that it is only necessary to measure *two* of the quantities E, C, R, in order to obtain an equation for J. A choice of three methods is thus at our disposal.

Griffiths's experiments. In the experiments carried out by E. H. Griffiths[1] E and R were measured. The obvious difficulty lies in the measurement of R ; because, unless measured actually during the progress of the heating experiment, it is necessary to know the temperature of the wire and

[1] *Phil. Trans.* p. 361, A, 1893.

the temperature-coefficient of its resistance ; and its temperature is *no*
that of the surrounding water.   To obviate this difficulty Griffiths
made a series of subsidiary experiments which were designed to give
the difference in temperature between the water and the wire when the
former was at a known temperature and an E.M.F. of known strength
was applied to the latter.   The resistance of the wire was then
measured at a known temperature and its temperature-coefficient was
also measured ; therefore, when in the course of a heating experiment
the temperature of the water was read, the resistance of the wire
could be calculated.

Griffiths's apparatus consisted of a platinum wire (diam. 0·010 cm.,
length 33 cm., resistance about 9 ohms) coiled inside a cylindrical

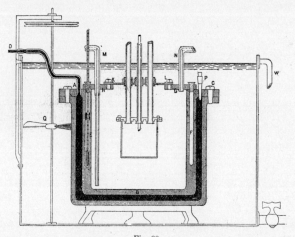

Fig. 89.

calorimeter, 8 cm. in height and 8 cm. diameter, whose water equivalent
was 85.   This wire was heated by a current from storage cells.   The
terminals of the wire were maintained at a constant difference of
potential by balancing against sets of Clark cells ; and, while the
temperature of the water in the calorimeter was raised from 14° to
25° C., the time varying from forty to eighty minutes, observations of
the temperature and time were made every degree.   The E.M.F. used
varied from that of three to six Clark cells.   Experiments were made
using different quantities of water ; and by taking *differences* in the
energy and the heat produced in the different sets, many errors were
eliminated, and the water-equivalent of the calorimeter disappeared
from the equation.

Fig. 89 shows a section of the constant temperature chamber in
which the calorimeter was suspended by glass tubes.   ABC is a large

steel vessel with double walls, the annular space (printed black in figure) being filled with mercury which is connected with a gas-regulator by the tube D. The steel vessel stood in a large tank filled with water, which was rapidly stirred by the paddle Q. A small stream of water flowed continuously into the tank, the excess passing away at W. The temperature of the incoming water was controlled by the regulator which was governed by the mass of mercury (exceeding 70 lbs.) within the walls ABC. A very constant temperature could thus be maintained within the steel vessel. The space between the calorimeter and the steel walls was thoroughly dried and the pressure reduced to less than 1 mm.

Griffiths found that most rapid and thorough stirring of the water was necessary in order to secure consistent or satisfactory results. He designed a most efficient stirrer which made about 2000 revolutions per minute, the rise in temperature produced by the stirrer alone being in some cases equivalent to 10 per cent of the whole work spent in raising the temperature. The necessary correction, owing to this, was ascertained by a series of preliminary experiments.

The thermometer used by Griffiths was a Hicks mercury thermometer which had been compared with a Callendar-Griffiths platinum thermometer and with a Tonnelot thermometer standardised at the Bureau International.

Schuster and Gannon.

Not long afterwards Professor Schuster and Mr. Gannon [1] made a determination of the value of J in the neighbourhood of 19° C., measuring the work done in terms of E, C, and t. The wire heated by the current was insulated from the water by shellac varnish; it was made of platinoid and was 760 cm. long and of about 31 ohms resistance. The stirring was so slow that its heating effect could be neglected. Radiation errors were minimised by making the experiments of short duration (10 mins.) and using a small rise of temperature (about 2°·2 C.). The mean current was measured by the amount of silver deposited in a silver voltameter, and the rise in temperature by a Baudin mercury thermometer which was directly compared with a Tonnelot thermometer standardised at the Bureau International. The result obtained was 4·191 joules per calorie at 19° C.

Callendar and Barnes.

The method depending on the measurement of E and C was also used in a series of experiments carried out by Professor Callendar and Dr. Barnes,[2] but the mode of procedure was essentially different. Fig. 90 shows the form of the calorimeter. A steady current of liquid flowing through a fine glass tube, 1 or 2 mm. in diameter, is heated

[1] *Phil. Trans.* p. 415, A, 1895.

[2] *Ibid.* vol. cxcix. A, 1902.

by a steady electric current during its passage through the tube, and the difference of temperature $\delta\theta$ between the inflowing and the out-flowing liquid is measured by a single reading with a delicate pair of differential platinum thermometers. The difference of potential E on the central conductor is measured in terms of a Clark cell by means of a very accurately calibrated potentiometer, which serves also to measure the current C by the observation of the difference of potential

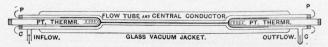

Fig. 90.—Diagram of Callendar and Barnes's steady-flow Electric Calorimeter.

on a standard resistance R included in the circuit. Neglecting small corrections, the general equation of the method may be stated in the form

$$ECt = JM\delta\theta + H,$$

M being the total mass of water which has flowed through in the item t and H the heat-loss due to radiation, etc.

The advantage of this method is that all the conditions are steady, so that the observations can be pushed to the limit of accuracy and sensitiveness of the apparatus. The water-equivalent of the calorimeter is immaterial, since there is no appreciable change of temperature. The heat-loss can be reduced to a minimum by enclosing the flow-tube in a hermetically sealed glass vacuum jacket. No stirring is required if the tube is sufficiently fine and the velocity of flow adequate. The conditions can be easily varied through a wide range. The heat-loss H, which is very small and regular, is determined and eliminated by varying the flow of liquid and the electric current simultaneously, in such a manner as to secure approximately the same rise of temperature for two or more widely different values of the flow of liquid.

The range of temperature $\delta\theta$ was generally from $8°$ to $10°$, in the series of experiments on the variation of J, but other ranges were tried for the purpose of testing the theory of the method and the application of small corrections. The thermometers were read to the ten-thousandth part of a degree, and the difference was probably in all cases accurate to $0°{\cdot}001$ C. This order of accuracy could not possibly have been attained with mercury thermometers under the conditions of the experiment. Another advantage was that there was no question of lag of the thermometers.

The chief source of uncertainty in the results of all these experiments lies in the value assumed for the E.M.F. of a Clark cell. The accepted value, $1{\cdot}4342$ volts at $15°$ C., was derived from the work of

Uncertainty in electric unit of E.M.F.

Glazebrook and Skinner. Later experiments tend to show that this value is too high. The following table,[1] calculated on the old value for the E.M.F., is given for the sake of comparison :—

CAPACITY FOR HEAT OF WATER IN JOULES PER 1° C.
(NITROGEN THERMOMETER)

Name.	Method.	Standards.	Results.	
			At 15° C.	At 20° C.
Joule	Mechanical	...	4·171	...
Rowland	,,	...	4·186	4·180
Griffiths	E, R	Clark cell = 1·4342	4·198	4·192
{ Schuster and { Gannon	E, C	{ Clark cell = 1·4340 { Ag. = 0·001118	...	4·190*
{ Callendar { and Barnes	E, C	Clark cell = 1·4342	4·190	4·184

* Strictly, 4·1905 joules at 19°·1 C.

It will be seen here that the results of the electrical methods are all a little higher than Rowland's result. The ampere was re-determined at the National Physical Laboratory in 1905–7, and the E.M.F. of the Clark cell was found to be only 1·4323 at 15° C. Griffiths has re-calculated [2] the above results, applying also certain corrections to Rowland's value (which of course is not dependent on electrical units), and arrives at the following figures for the mechanical equivalent of the calorie at 20° C. in joules :—

Rowland.	Schuster and Gannon.	Griffiths.	Callendar and Barnes.
4·182	4·182	4·184	4·181

The mean of these is 4·182 joules, which is equivalent to 426·6 grammetres. On account of the doubt as to the true value of the E.M.F. of the Clark cell, Professor Callendar estimated the value of the mechanical equivalent as follows.[3] The experiments carried out by Barnes between 0° and 100° C. (see Art. 177) show that (whatever the absolute value of J may be) the mean thermal capacity of water between 0° and 100° is 1·0016 times its thermal capacity at 20° C. Taking therefore the value 4·1833 of Reynolds and Moorby for the mean thermal capacity between 0° and 100°, we obtain 4·179 as the value at 20°. Again, Rowland's value at

Choice of most valuable probe of J.

---

[1] This table is taken (with slight alteration) from Griffiths's *Thermal Measurement of Energy*, 1901.

[2] Glazebrook's *Dictionary of Applied Physics*, vol. i. p. 493.

[3] *Ency. Brit.*, tenth edition, art. "Calorimetry."

20°, corrected to the hydrogen scale by W. S. Day (see Art. 171), is 4·181. Taking the mean of these two values as the most probable, we get

$$1 \text{ calorie} = 4\cdot180 \text{ joules at } 20° \text{ C.}$$

The value at any other temperature may now be determined from the curve of variation given by Barnes; thus

$$1 \text{ calorie} = 4\cdot184 \text{ joules at } 15° \text{ C.}$$

A careful series of experiments on the specific heat of water between 0° and 50° C. was made by Jaeger and Steinwehr.[1] A very large calorimeter was used, holding 50 litres of water, and the energy was measured electrically, taking the E.M.F. of the Weston cell to be 1·0183 volt at 20° C. They found the specific heat to be a minimum at 33°·5, and the calorie at 15° C. to be 4·1842 joules.

175. Experiments of Laby and Hercus.—An ingenious mode of measuring J was suggested by MM. Baille and Féry.[2] A uniformly rotating magnetic field is produced by means of polyphase alternating electric currents. Within the field is placed a copper cylinder balanced on a vertical axis, and surrounded by water. The cylinder tends to turn with the magnetic field, but is held stationary by a couple which is accurately measured. The product of this couple into the number of revolutions of the magnetic field represents the work done in producing eddy currents in the copper cylinder. This work is spent in heating the copper, and the heat produced is measured by observing the rise in temperature of the water. As the temperature rises the couple diminishes owing to increase in resistance of the copper, but this difficulty could be got over by employing the steady-flow method, which, moreover, could be arranged so as to ensure proper mixing. The point in favour of this method is that, while it possesses the advantages of the electrical method, yet the work done is measured in mechanical units, thus avoiding the uncertainties in the electric measurements.

This method has been successfully employed by Laby and Hercus.[3] The rotating magnetic field was not produced by alternating currents, owing to the difficulty of making its axis coincide with that of the copper calorimeter in which the currents are generated. A rotating field magnet excited by a direct current was used instead, the current being introduced by slip-rings on the axis of rotation. The rotating magnet was driven by an electric motor, and special precautions were taken to keep the exciting current and the rate of rotation constant.

[1] *Ann. der Physik*, vol. lxiv. p. 305, 1921.
[2] *Comptes rendus*, tom. cxxvi. p. 1494, 1898.
[3] *Phil. Trans.* vol. ccxxvii. (A) p. 63, 1927.

Fig. 91 shows the construction of the calorimeter. The upper diagram shows a horizontal section through the line AB, and the lower a section through CD. The calorimeter was enclosed in a vacuum flask G. The continuous-flow method was used, the difference of temperature of the water before entering and after leaving the calorimeter being measured by two platinum thermometers, each enclosed in a double-walled vacuum tube. The current of distilled water was conducted by a rubber tube to the upper part of the tube H, and flowed past the thermometer in that tube; thence it passed by the tube seen in the figure to an annular channel in the armature, from which it flowed through fourteen copper tubes T to another annular channel in the lower part of the armature, passing up by the pipe seen in the figure and past the second thermometer in the tube J. The whole of this stator, as it is called, was mounted on ball bearings and also supported by a torsion wire. The armature was made of stalloy stampings, so that most of the heat was generated in the copper tubes. The position of the stator having been accurately determined when no couple was acting, it was kept in this position and prevented from turning when the rotating field magnet was excited, by a couple applied in the same way as in Joule's and Rowland's experiments (see Fig. 83). The measurement of the couple was rendered more accurate by mounting the pulleys (j, j, Fig. 83), not on axles but on agate knife-edges, like those of the beam of a balance. When the axis of rotation of the field magnet coincides with the axis of the stator and of the couple which holds the latter steady, all the work done by the rotating magnet is converted into heat, which is directly measured in mechanical units. To prevent loss of heat through the mouth of the calorimeter, it was arranged that the temperature at the upper end of the calorimeter should be that of the room. The thermocouple K was used for this purpose, and another thermocouple, E, was used to estimate loss of heat through the vacuum vessel G; this loss was very small. The apparatus was run for about an hour before the observations were begun, then the current of water was switched into a weighed flask and collected for fifteen minutes. In this time about 4 kilos of water flowed through,

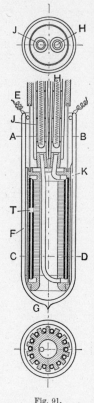

Fig. 91.

the change of temperature being somewhat over 5°. The mean temperature of 23 experiments was 16°·7, and the corresponding value obtained for J was 4·1841 joules.

Using Callendar's values for the temperature variation of the specific heat of water, the authors calculate that the calorie at 15° C. is 4·1860 joules, and the calorie at 20° C. is 4·1809 joules.

176. Various Methods of Determining the Dynamical Equivalent. —Of the various methods of determining the value of the dynamical equivalent of heat, the method of fluid friction and the electrical method are up to the present the only ones which can lay claim to a high degree of precision. In addition, however, to these accurate investigations many others have been carried out by methods of considerable interest though of less precision.

An indirect method depending on the theory of gases has been already noticed (p. 285) ; but this method is at best very imperfect, for a small error in the determination of the ratio of the specific heats will produce a considerable change in the value of J. Another method, depending on the assumption that all the work employed in compressing a gas is spent in raising its temperature, has also been adopted. In applying this method Joule [1] forced air into a strong receiver kept under water in a calorimeter, so that the heat developed during the compression could be measured by the change of temperature of the calorimeter. The work spent during the compression was easily calculated on the assumption that air obeys Boyle's law throughout the range of the experiment (Ex. 3, Art. 323), and the materials for the determination of J are thus at hand. Instead of compressing the gas and measuring the heat developed, the reverse process may be employed. The gas may be first compressed into a receiver, from which it can be subsequently allowed to escape into the atmosphere, and the cooling produced by the expansion against the external pressure may be measured. Both methods were employed by Joule, who obtained 823 and 795 foot-pounds by the compression process, and 820, 814, 760 by expansion.

Before any inference can be made as to the equivalence of the work done and the heat developed in such a process, it must be ascertained that the whole work is spent in generating heat, and that no part of it is employed in altering the state of the substance, or, in other words, in doing internal work. For this reason Joule felt compelled to execute those experiments (Art. 159) by which he proved that no appreciable internal work is done during the compression or expansion of a gas. The only reliable mode of procedure, therefore, is

[1] Joule, *Phil. Mag.*, 3rd Series, vol. xxiii., 1845 ; *Scientific Papers*, p. 172.

to adopt a method in which the state of the substance is the same at the end of the operation as at the beginning.   This holds good in all fluid friction methods, which are consequently much superior to all methods depending on compression, or expansion, or percussion.

An interesting determination of J by estimating the heat developed by percussion in a mass of lead was made by Hirn.[1]   Lead was chosen because it is highly inelastic.   It is for this reason that when a leaden bullet strikes a target (or is struck), nearly all the energy of motion is converted into heat.   In addition, lead when struck yields but little sound, and its state is not appreciably altered by hammering.   Elastic bodies, on the other hand, when they collide, rebound and regain a large proportion of their original energy, so that but little heat is generated by the impact.   The apparatus devised by Hirn is shown in Fig. 92.

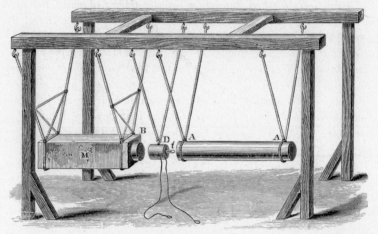

Fig. 92.—Hirn's Percussion Apparatus.

A cylinder of iron AA weighing 350 kilos was suspended, with its axis horizontal, by two pairs of cords which compelled it to move in a vertical plane with its axis always horizontal.   This cylinder was used as the hammer or instrument of percussion.   The anvil MB was a large prismatic mass of stone weighing 941 kilos, and suspended in the same way as the hammer.   The mass of lead D to be operated on was suspended between the two, and the face B of the anvil adjacent to the lead was cased with iron to receive the blow.

In making an experiment the hammer was drawn back by a tackle, and the height to which it was raised was accurately measured.   It was then let fall upon the lead, and the recoil of the anvil was registered by a sliding indicator which was pushed back and then

[1] Hirn, *Théorie mécanique de la chaleur*, tom. i. p. 96, 3rd ed.

remained *in situ*. An observer also noted the advance or recoil of the
hammer after the blow, and from these data the work spent in percussion could be easily calculated. Before the blow was delivered the
temperature of the lead was taken by inserting a thermometer t into a
cylindrical cavity made in the mass, and immediately after the blow
the mass of lead was removed and hung up by two strings provided
for the purpose, so that the axis of the cavity was vertical. This
cavity was immediately filled with ice-cold water, which was stirred
and the rise of temperature noted. The value 425 grammetres was
obtained by Hirn in this manner, which is remarkably good considering the nature of the experiment.

An indirect method depending on the theory of saturated vapours
(Art. 346) has also been employed, but on account of the difficulty
of experimentally determining the densities or specific volumes of
saturated vapours, this method is better suited for the calculation of
vapour densities from the knowledge of the value of J than for the
calculation of the latter quantity.

The heat developed in a copper disc when rotated in a magnetic
field also furnishes a method of evaluating J, but the heat lost while
the disc is rotating and while it is being transferred to the calorimeter
must lead to uncertain corrections. This method was used by M. Violle
in 1870.

Other methods, such as the steam-engine experiments of Hirn
(p. 46), and those of Edlund on the expansion and contraction of
metals, are excellent as illustrations of the dynamical theory, but they
cannot be regarded as possessing any accuracy. The chemical action
which takes place in a voltaic battery or in a voltameter also furnishes
a method of evaluating J.

The dynamical equivalent of heat has also been determined
experimentally by the change of temperature produced when a liquid
escapes under pressure from an orifice, or when a liquid is forced
through capillary tubes. By the escape of water under pressure Hirn
found the value 433 grammetres, and by forcing water through a
piston perforated with small holes Joule obtained the number 770
foot-pounds. The table at the end of this chapter contains the results
obtained by the various methods.

177. Specific Heat of Water.—One of the most important researches in calorimetry is the accurate investigation of the variations
of the specific heat of water, especially between 0° and 100° C.
If the unit of heat be defined as the quantity necessary to raise
the temperature of unit mass of water from 19°·5 to 20°·5 C.,
then if the thermal capacity of unit mass be not the same at all

temperatures, and if the variations with temperature be not known, it would be necessary in any experiment to start always with as much water in the calorimeter at 19°·5 C. as would just attain the final temperature of 20°·5 C. The quantity of water employed (together with the equivalent of the calorimeter, etc.) would then represent the quantity of heat given out by the immersed body in cooling from its initial temperature to 20°·5 C.

The direct mode of investigating the variations of the specific heat of water is that adopted by the earliest experimenters on this subject (De Luc and Flaugergues), namely, by mixing known weights of water at different temperatures and observing the temperature of the mixture. By this method Flaugergues [1] found that the specific heat of cold water was slightly greater than that of warm water. It does not appear certain, however, that due precautions were taken to guard against errors arising from radiation and evaporation, or to correct for the thermal capacity of the calorimeter.

The first experiments of any accuracy were those of F. E. Neumann,[2] who found in 1831 that the specific heat of water at the boiling point was about 1·0127 times that at 28° C.   The next experiments were those of Regnault [3] in 1840, from which he deduced that the mean specific heat between 15° C. and 100° C., compared with that between 10° and 15°, was from 1·00709 to 1·0089.   He further extended his researches to temperatures above the boiling point, and found that the results of his experiments at temperatures up to 230° C. were represented by the formula

$$s = 1 + 0{\cdot}000004\theta + 0{\cdot}0000009\theta^2.$$

This formula indicates a gradual increase of specific heat as the temperature rises.

Somewhat later Pfaundler and Platter [4] supposed that they had discovered important variations in the specific heat of water in the neighbourhood of the temperature of maximum density. They estimated that it fell from unity at zero to 0·9512754 at 1°, and then increased gradually to 1·1933497 at 6°·5, and afterwards fell to 1·0728772 at 10° C. The method of mixtures was employed, but almost immediately afterwards it was shown by the investigations of Hirn, as well as those of MM. Jamin and Amaury, that no such

[1] Quoted by Rowland, *Proc. American Academy of Arts and Sciences*, vol. vii. p. 120, 1879–80.

[2] Neumann, *Pogg. Ann.* vol. xxiii. p. 40, 1831.

[3] Regnault, *Relation des expériences*, tom. i. p. 729 ; or *Mémoires de l'Académie des Sciences*, tom. xxi.

[4] Pfaundler and Platter, *Pogg. Ann.* vol. cxl. p. 575 ; vol. cxli. p. 537, 1870.

variations occur.   The method adopted by Hirn [1] was excellent and ingenious in design, but difficult to carry into execution with accuracy. It consisted essentially in supplying equal quantities of heat to a given mass of water when at different temperatures, and observing the change of temperature.   The method by which the equal quantities of heat were supplied was by heating a large water thermometer, with a metal bulb of about 200 c.c. capacity, and then immersing it in the calorimeter till the column in its stem fell through a certain interval, when it was at once withdrawn.   The change of temperature of the calorimeter by this communication of heat was only about 1° or 1°·5 C., and the chief difficulty was to estimate this change with accuracy.   In the method [2] adopted by Jamin and Amaury [3] the water was heated by the passage of an electric current through a spiral of wire immersed in it, and if proper precautions were taken in the observations, and due allowance made for the variation of the resistance of the spiral with temperature, the method should be capable of giving excellent results.   The formula deduced as representing the results of their experiment was

$$s = 1 + 0\cdot0011\theta + 0\cdot0000012\theta^2.$$

This formula indicates a gradual increase of specific heat as the temperature rises, but the amount of variation indicated is exceedingly high.

The first experiments of sufficient accuracy to discover the true nature of the variations of the specific heat of water were those made by Rowland in his exhaustive determination of the dynamical equivalent of heat.   If it be assumed that the value of the dynamical equivalent, determined by means of the friction of a liquid of assumed constant specific heat, must be the same whatever the initial temperature of the liquid, then if variations in its value are observed when the liquid is used at different temperatures, these variations must be attributed to changes of the specific heat of the liquid.   In operating through a wide range of temperature Rowland found that the values of J obtained at different temperatures indicated that the specific heat of water fell to a minimum at about 30° C.   That is, that the specific heat of water did not gradually increase from zero, but that a gradual diminution occurred up to about 30° C., and then a gradual increase

Minimum for water.

---

[1] Hirn, *Comptes rendus*, tom. lxx. pp. 592, 831, 1870.

[2] The method of generating equal quantities of heat in two calorimeters by means of an electric current, and thus comparing the specific heats of two liquids, was first suggested by Joule as an accurate method in calorimetry.—Joule, *Mem. Manchester Phil. Soc.* vol. vii. p. 559, 1845.

[3] Jamin and Amaury, *Comptes rendus*, tom. lxx. p. 661, 1870.

set in. This point was further tested and placed beyond doubt by actual calorimetric observations of the most careful nature, the apparatus employed for this purpose being similar to that designed by Regnault (Fig. 64) for the determination of the specific heats of liquids. The results obtained by the dynamical equivalent apparatus are, in Rowland's opinion, of surpassing accuracy (see Art. 171).

The work of Rowland was confirmed by Bartoli and Stracciati,[1] who found a minimum value of the specific heat at 20° C.

The researches of Dr. Barnes with the apparatus described in Art. 174 afford perhaps the most reliable results as to the variation of the specific heat of water. According to his determinations the specific heat attains a minimum value at a temperature of 37°·5 C. The accompanying curve shows the character of the variation.

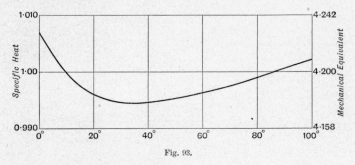

Fig. 93.

Appended below is a table containing the values of the specific heat at different temperatures in terms of that at 20° as unit. This table was given by Prof. Callendar.[2]

Temp. C.	Joules.	Sp. Heat.	Temp. C.	Joules.	Sp. Heat.	Temp. C.	Joules.	Sp. Heat.
0	4·208	1·0094	35	4·173	0·9983	100	4·211	1·0074
5	4·202	1·0054	40	4·173	0·9982	120	4·231	1·0121
10	4·191	1·0027	50	4·175	0·9987	140	4·254	1·0176
15	4·184	1·0011	60	4·180	1·0000	160	4·280	1·0238
20	4·180	1·0000	70	4·187	1·0016	180	4·309	1·0308
25	4·177	0·9992	80	4·194	1·0033	200	4·341	1·0384
30	4·175	0·9987	90	4·202	1·0053	220	4·376	1·0467

[1] A. Bartoli and E. Stracciati, *Boll. mens. dell' Acc. Gioenia*, 18, 26th April 1891. *Beiblätter zu den Annalen der Physik und Chemie*, Band xv. p. 761, 1891.

[2] *Ency. Brit.* art. "Calorimetry."   Dr. Barnes also gives a table (*Phil. Trans.* vol. cxcix., 1902) but adopts a different standard, and does not reduce to the hydrogen thermometer.

The same method was applied by Barnes[1] to determine the variation of the specific heat of mercury with temperature, using the mercury itself to convey the current. He gives the formula

$$s_\theta = \cdot 033458 - (1 \cdot 074\theta - \cdot 00385\theta^2)10^{-5}.$$

A very careful series of observations on the variation of the specific heat of water between 0° and 100° C. was carried out by Lüdin[2] under the direction of Prof. Pernet, using the method of mixtures. Great attention was paid to the thermometry, thermometers of the Paris type being employed, with the usual precautions. The experiments were arranged to give a rise of temperature of 11° to 18° and the results were closely concordant. The values obtained indicate a minimum at 25° and a maximum at 87°. It is not at all certain, however, that the method is free from constant errors. Prof. Callendar thinks that the rapid rise in value of the specific heat from 25° to 75° may possibly be due to radiation error from the hot-water supply, and the fall between 90° and 100° to loss of heat by evaporation of the nearly boiling water on its way to the calorimeter. These sources of error could not occur in the Callendar-Barnes method, and besides the range in the latter was only 8° to 10°, so that the results would be less affected by the variation between the limits of temperature in any one experiment. It should be noticed, however, that Lüdin's results agree very well with those of Barnes except at the higher temperatures.

(margin note: Lüdin's experiments.*)*

The variation of the specific heat of water was also investigated by W. R. and W. E. Bousfield.[3] The water was heated by an electric current flowing through a mercury resistance, as it was held that the resistance of a solid wire depends not only on its temperature, but also on the current flowing in it. The mean value of J over the range 13°—54°·5 was first determined, using tap water. Comparisons were then made with distilled water, and the experiments extended up to 80°. The value 4·179 joules was found for the calorie at 15° C., and the curve of variation of specific heat resembled that of Lüdin, with a minimum at 25°.

178. Choice of Thermal Unit.—The question of the choice of a thermal unit is a somewhat vexed one. Since the specific heat of water varies, the *calorie* will not be fully defined unless we specify the particular degree of temperature through which the unit mass of water is to be heated. In Art. 21 we have adopted the range 19°·5 to 20°·5, which amounts to taking the specific heat of water at 20° C.

[1] *Brit. Assoc. Rep.* p. 530, 1902.
[2] *Jubelband der Naturforschenden Gesellschaft*, Zürich, 1896.
[3] *Phil. Trans.* vol. ccxi. (A) p. 199, 1911.

as the unit of specific heat. The temperature 4° to 5° was commonly adopted some years ago, but there is no advantage in selecting the temperature of maximum density of water; indeed, the temperature of minimum specific heat would be a more natural one to choose, as the value is here practically constant over a considerable range. But the paramount consideration is to choose a temperature at which the value of the dynamical equivalent is known with the greatest certainty, and the best determinations are those which have been carried out at ordinary temperatures. Many physicists are in favour of choosing 15° C. as the standard, and it possesses the simplification of being a temperature to which several other physical measurements are referred, and it is usually adopted on the Continent. Prof. Callendar adopts 20° C. and suggests that the calorie be defined, not as the heat required to raise 1 gramme of water from 19°·5 to 20°·5, but as the *mean* value between 15° and 25° of the quantity of heat required to raise 1 gramme of water 1°. This is because all calorimetric measurements practically involve a range of several degrees, and the mean calorie between 15° and 25° is not very different from the mean between 0° and 100° which is sometimes convenient. The unit proposed by a committee of the British Association in 1896, namely, the value of the calorie at such a temperature as would make it equal to 4·200 joules, is, as Prof. Callendar remarks, merely an absolute unit in disguise, and leaves the actual temperature uncertain.

The specific heat of a saturated vapour is discussed in Chap. VIII. sec. v., and the case of a non-saturated or superheated vapour is noticed in Art. 205.

[TABLE

DYNAMICAL EQUIVALENT OF HEAT
(Grammetres)

DIRECT METHODS

Date.	Observer.	Method.	Result.
1843	Joule (1)	Friction of water in tubes . . .	424·6
,,	,,	Electromagnetic currents . . .	460
,,	,,	Decrease of heat produced by a pile when the current does work . .	442·2
1845	,,	Compression of air	443·8
,,	,,	Expansion of air	437·8
1847	,, (2)	Friction of water in a calorimeter .	428·9
1850	,,	,, ,, ,, .	423·9
,,	,,	Friction of mercury in a calorimeter .	424·7
,,	,, (3)	Friction of iron plates in a calorimeter	425·2
1857	Favre (4)	Decrease of heat produced by a pile doing work	426-464
,,	Hirn (5)	Friction of metals	371·6
1858	,,	,, ,, ...	400-450
,,	Favre (6)	Friction of metals in mercury calorimeter	413·2
,,	Hirn (5)	Boring of metals	425
1860–61	,,	Water in friction balance . . .	432
,,	,,	Escape of liquids under high pressure .	432, 433
,,	,,	Hammering lead	425
,,	,,	Friction of water in two cylinders .	432
,,	,,	Expansion of air	440
,,	,,	Steam-engines	420-432
1865	Edlund (7)	Expansion and contraction of metals .	428·3-443·6
1870	Violle (8)	Heating of a disc between the poles of a magnet	435
1875	Puluj (9)	Friction of metals	425·2-426·6
1878	Joule (10)	,, water . . .	423·9
1879	Rowland (11)	,, water between 5° and 36° .	429·8-425·8
1891	D'Arsonval (12)	Heating of a cylinder in a magnetic field	421-427
1892	Miculescu (13)	Friction of water	426·84
1897 }	Reynolds and { Moorby (14) {	,, ,, mean between 0° and 100°	} 426·27
1926	Laby and Hercus (15)	Heating of water by current (energy measured mechanically) . . .	430·4

INDIRECT METHODS

Date.	Observer.	Method.	Result.
1842	Mayer (16)	By the relation $J = \dfrac{p_0 v_0 a}{C_p - C_v}$ for gases .	365
1857 }	Quintus Icilius { (17) {	Heat developed in a wire of known resistance	} 399·7
,,	Weber (18)	Heat due to electric currents . .	432·1
,, ,,	Favre { Silberman {	Heat developed by zinc on sulphate of copper	} 432·1
,,	Bosscha (19)	Measure of E.M.F. of a Daniell's cell after the absolute measure 10257×10^7	432·1
1859	Joule (20)	Heat developed in a Daniell's cell .	419·5
,,	Bosscha	E.M.F. of Daniell's cell . . .	419·5

INDIRECT METHODS—*continued*

Date.	Observer.	Method.	Result.
1859	Lenz-Weber	Heat developed in wire of known resistance	396·4-478·2
1867	Joule (21)	Heat developed in wire of known resistance	429·5
1878	Weber	Heat developed in wire of known resistance	428·15
1888	Perot (22)	By the relation $L = \tau \, (v_2 - v_1)\dfrac{dp}{dt}$ . .	424·63
1889	Dieterici (23)	Heat of electric currents . .	432·5
1893	Griffiths (24)	,, ,, . .	427·45
1894 }	Schuster and Gannon (25) }	Electric current, E and C being known }	427·19
1899 }	Callendar and Barnes (26) }	,, ,, ,, }	426·52
1910 }	Bousfield and Bousfield (27) }	,, ,, ,, }	425·9
1912 }	Jaeger and Steinwehr (28) }	,, ,, ,, }	426·4

References to Foregoing Table

(1) Joule, *Phil. Mag.*, 3rd Series, vols. xxiii. and xxvi.

(2) *Ibid.* xxvii.

(3) Joule, *Phil. Trans.* p. 61, 1850.

(4) Favre, *Comptes rendus*, tom. xlv. p. 56.

(5) Hirn, *Théorie mécanique de la chaleur*.

(6) Favre, *Comptes rendus*, tom. xlvii. p. 337.

(7) Edlund, *Pogg. Ann.* vol. cxiv.

(8) Violle, *Ann. de Chimie et de Physique*, tom. xxi.

(9) Puluj, *Sitzungsberichte der k. Akad. der Wissenschaften in Wien*, 1875 ; March, p. 667 ; June, p. 53.

(10) Joule, *Phil. Trans.* p. 365, 1878.

(11) Rowland, *Proc. American Acad.* p. 75, 1879–80.

(12) D'Arsonval, *Lumière électrique*, March 1891.

(13) Miculescu, *Ann. de Chimie*, 6ᵉ série, tom. xxvii. p. 202, 1892.

(14) Reynolds and Moorby, *Phil. Trans.* A, 1897.

(15) Laby and Hercus, *Phil. Trans.* vol. ccxxvii. A, 1927.

(16) Mayer, *Liebig's Annalen*, vol. xlii.

(17) Quintus Icilius, *Pogg. Ann.* vol. ci. p. 69.

(18) Weber, *Phil. Mag.*, 4th Series, vol. xxx.

(19) Bosscha, *Pogg. Ann.* vol. cxviii. p. 162.

(20) Joule, *Brit. Assoc. Rep.*, 1873, p. 175.

(21) Joule, *Phil. Trans.*, 1850, p. 61.

(22) Perot, *Journal de Physique*, 2ᵉ série, tom. vii. p. 129.

(23) Dieterici, *Annalen der Physik*, vol. xxxiii. p. 417.

(24) Griffiths, *Proc. Roy. Soc.* vol. liii. p. 6, 1893.

(25) Schuster and Gannon, *Phil. Trans.* vol. clxxxvi. A, 1895.

(26) Callendar and Barnes, *ibid.* vol. cxcix. A, 1902.

(27) Bousfield and Bousfield, *ibid.* vol. ccxi. A, 1911.

(28) Jaeger and Steinwehr, *Ann. der Physik*, vol. lxiv., 1921.

In order strictly to compare the above results of various observers, it would be necessary to reduce all the observations to the same temperature and the same value of the constant of gravitation.

CHAPTER V

CHANGE OF STATE

SECTION I

FUSION

179. Normal Fusing Point.—When the temperature of a solid is gradually raised, a stage is reached at which the substance passes into the liquid state. For each crystalline substance there is, generally speaking, a definite temperature at which, under given conditions, it passes from the solid to the liquid state, or *vice versa*. That is, when the temperature is above this point the substance exists in the liquid state, and below it in the solid state. This temperature is called the fusing point (or the melting point) of the substance under the given conditions, and is such that when the temperature of the solid is rising liquefaction occurs here, and when the temperature of the liquid is falling solidification sets in at the same point. Thus at 0° C. ice melts and water solidifies under the pressure of one atmosphere, and 0° C. is said to be the normal fusing point of ice. We say the *normal* fusing point, for circumstances may occur, as we shall see later on, under which water may not solidify even though its temperature is considerably below 0° C. Similar abnormal results are presented by other substances, the liquid state often persisting at a temperature considerably below that at which the substance ordinarily solidifies.

In the case of ice the melting point is distinct and sharply marked. There is no perceptible difference of temperature between the melting solid and the liquid into which it passes. At 0° C. water substance can exist in three very distinct forms, either as a hard solid, a mobile liquid, or an attenuated vapour. It is very different, however, with many other substances. In the case of fats, wax, glass, iron, and other amorphous substances, there is no definite point, sharply marked, Amorphous at which it can be said the substance melts. As the temperature of solids.

the solid rises the substance becomes more and more plastic. It gradually attains a semi-solid viscous condition, in which it possesses neither the properties of a solid nor of a liquid distinctly. The process of fusion is gradual, and the body passes by no sudden transition from the solid to the liquid state.

Crystals.   This gradual passage from the solid to the liquid state is characteristic of amorphous bodies, whereas those which crystallise on solidification have in general a definite fusing point at which the substance may exist simultaneously in the two states. It is only solids having a crystalline structure that have a definite melting point, and at other temperatures only one of the states is stable. At this temperature the molecules arrange themselves in the regular order which determines the crystalline structure

In amorphous bodies, on the other hand, there is no definite arrangement of the molecules at any temperature, the amorphous condition of the solid forms a continuation of the liquid state as far as want of regular molecular arrangement is concerned, and such substances have no definite melting point.

180. Laws of Fusion.—The general laws which govern the phenomena of fusion and solidification may be summarised as follows :—

(1) For a given pressure the temperature of fusion is fixed, and is the same as that of solidification, and consequently, while fusion (or solidification) is taking place the temperature of the whole mass remains constant.

(2) During fusion heat is absorbed by the substance (latent heat), and an equal quantity of heat is disengaged during solidification.

181. Surfusion — Unstable Condition. — A liquid which has a definite freezing point—that is, one which crystallises on solidifying, may, if carefully and slowly cooled, be reduced to a temperature much below the normal freezing point without solidification setting in. This anomalous condition is, however, unstable, for if the over-cooled liquid be disturbed, or if a small piece of the crystalline solid be placed in contact with it, solidification at once sets in and continues until the temperature rises to the normal freezing point.

This phenomenon of surfusion, as it is termed, was noticed as early as 1724 by Fahrenheit.[1] He found that a glass bulb filled with water and hermetically sealed remained at a temperature considerably below the freezing point without solidification setting in, but that on breaking off the stem solidification set in with rapidity. Gay-Lussac[2] also observed that water placed in a vessel and covered with a layer of oil

---

[1] Fahrenheit, *Phil. Trans.* vol. xxxviii. p. 78, 1724.
[2] Gay-Lussac, *Ann. de Chimie*, 2e série, tom. lxiii. p. 363, 1836.

remained liquid at $-12°$ C., but a slight shake was sufficient to start solidification. Despretz [1] observed the same effect in capillary tubes filled with water; and it is perhaps for this reason that at low temperatures the sap often remains unfrozen in the capillary vessels of plants.

This property is not peculiar to water. It may be observed in many other substances when the cooling is conducted cautiously. In the case of melted phosphorus cautiously cooled below the freezing point, a fragment of amorphous phosphorus is found to be inactive in producing solidification, while a fragment of ordinary phosphorus at once starts congelation. The introduction of a fragment of the solid is not in general necessary to set up solidification in the over-cooled liquid. Mechanical actions, such as the vibration caused by the friction of a glass rod against the bottom of the containing vessel, suffices in general to initiate solidification.

As soon as solidification sets in there is an evolution of heat, and the freezing continues till the heat evolved is sufficient to bring the whole mass to the normal fusing point. Further solidification will now cease, unless the substance continues to lose heat by radiation or otherwise.

This property has been utilised by M. Gernez [2] and others to determine the normal temperature of fusion. The liquid under examination is cautiously cooled to a temperature below the normal fusing point. Solidification is then excited, and part of the substance separates in the solid form, the temperature at the same time rising to that of normal fusion. This is noticed by means of a thermometer placed in the substance.

M. Dufour [3] contrived to cool small spherules of water to $-20°$ C. without solidification. The method adopted was similar to that employed by M. Plateau in the study of the equilibrium of liquids relieved from the action of gravity. Small droplets of the liquid were suspended in another liquid of equal density and lower freezing point. The suspended drops were thus freed from the action of gravity, and floated freely in the bath as spherical globules. In this manner M. Dufour succeeded in reducing to $-20°$ C. the temperature of water droplets suspended in a mixture of chloroform and oil of sweet almonds. The temperature of similar drops was also raised as high as $178°$ C. without boiling, while drops of liquid sulphur were reduced below $0°$ C. in a solution of chloride of zinc, and in a water bath drops of naphthalene were cooled to $40°$ C.

---

[1] Despretz, *Comptes rendus*, tom. v. p. 19, 1837.

[2] *Journal de Physique*, tom. v. p. 212.

[3] Dufour, *Ann. de Chimie*, 3ᵉ série, tom. lxviii. p. 370, 1863.

In these experiments the over-cooling of the drops is more easily and securely obtained the smaller their diameters, and the over-cooled drops at once solidify when touched with a fragment of the solid. They also solidify when touched with a solid of different material; in this case, however, the solidification does not appear to be so certain, and the action probably arises from local agitation of the drop.

Similar over-cooling of small water drops may occur in the atmosphere, and if this happens the experiments of Dufour throw light upon the formation of hail, hoar-frost, etc., whether in the atmosphere itself or in contact with the surfaces of other bodies.

182. Fusion of Alloys.—Alloys formed of two or more metals, although they obey the general laws of fusion, possess the peculiar property of fusing at a temperature generally lower than the melting point of any of the constituent metals. Thus an alloy of 5 parts of tin and 1 part of lead fuses at 194° C., and Rose's fusible metal, which consists of 4 parts of bismuth, 1 of lead, and 1 of tin, melts at 94° C.

Similar results occur in the case of mixed salts. Thus a mixture of the chlorides of sodium and potassium fuses at a lower temperature than either constituent, and a mixture of equivalent quantities of the carbonates of sodium and potassium melts at a temperature below the fusing point of either, and is used in the decomposition of certain minerals in chemical analysis.

In most cases, however, alloys melt like amorphous bodies. There is at first a general softening of the whole mass. As the temperature is raised the most fusible constituent melts first, and if it is plentiful in the alloy it liquefies the whole mass, but if it is present only in a small proportion its liquefaction only brings the mass to the pasty condition of an amalgam; so that complete liquefaction is only attained when the melting point of the less fusible constituent is reached. If the liquid substance be now gradually cooled, the temperature is found to fall till the melting point of the less fusible constituent is reached. Here it remains stationary till the solidification of this part is completed, the latent heat of liquefaction being at the same time evolved. This completed, the temperature of the now more or less pasty mass gradually falls to the melting point of the more fusible part of the alloy. Here the temperature again remains stationary till complete solidification is effected.

Rudberg,[1] to whom these observations are due, found that in the case of a mixture of lead and tin the lower fixed point remained stationary at 187°, whatever the proportions of lead and tin. The

[1] Rudberg, *Pogg. Ann.* vol. xviii. p. 240, vol. xix. p. 125; and *Ann. de Chimie*, 2ᵉ série, tom. xlviii. p. 353, 1831.

higher fixed point, on the other hand, depended on the proportion of the constituents. It approached the lower fixed point, and finally coincided with it as the composition of the alloy approached the formula $PbSn_3$, in which case there is only a single fixed point, and the fusion takes place as for a simple body. On increasing the proportion of either lead or tin the variable point of fusion reappears and attains a maximum at the fusing point of lead or tin, according as one or other is in excessive preponderance.[1]

183. Change of Volume during Fusion.—The majority of substances occupy a larger volume in the liquid than in the solid state. In general, expansion occurs during liquefaction. Several substances, however, contract on melting, a notable example being ice. In the former case the solid will sink in the liquid, and in the latter it will float.

The change of volume which accompanies the change of state from solid to liquid may be estimated by the weight thermometer (Art. 75). A known weight w_1 of the solid substance is placed in the bulb of the thermometer, and the instrument is then filled up with a weight w_2 of some liquid which has no action on the solid. By noticing the weight of liquid expelled between two chosen temperatures below the melting point, the coefficient of expansion of the solid may be obtained in the ordinary way ; and similarly, by observations above the melting point, the coefficient of expansion of the same substance in the liquid state may be obtained. A curve may then be plotted, showing the relation between volume and temperature under constant pressure, both in the solid and liquid states as well as in the passage from the one state to the other. To determine the latter we require the weight w of the liquid expelled from the thermometer during fusion.

The observations of the change of volume may be made in a continuous manner by enclosing the substance in a large thermometer bulb, furnished with a graduated stem. The variation of level of the liquid in the stem indicates the manner in which the volume changes in the neighbourhood of the fusing point. This relation has been examined by G. A. Erman[2] and H. Kopp.[3]

The force attending the expansion during change of state, especially in the solidification of water, seems to have very early attracted the attention of experimental philosophers. Boyle[4] found that water confined in a strong brass tube while it froze lifted a weight of 74 lbs.

---

[1] A mixture of two substances in such proportions that the whole fuses or solidifies together like a simple body is called a *eutectic* mixture.

[2] G. A. Erman, *Pogg. Ann.* vol. ix. p. 557, 1827 ; *Ann. de Chimie et de Physique*, 2e série, tom. xl. p. 167.

[3] H. Kopp, Liebig's *Annalen*, vol. xciii.   [4] Boyle, *History of Cold.*

placed on the stopper, and Huygens [1] succeeded in bursting a cannon by freezing water confined in it. The Florentine academicians in the same manner burst a small brass shell, and in 1784–85 Major Williams [2] burst strong iron shells.

The expansion of water during freezing is attended by many beneficial and many destructive results in nature. Those commonly observed are the bursting of water-pipes, the raising of pavements, the bursting of plant cells, and the splitting of trees and rocks, while the general fertility of the soil is increased by the disintegration of its parts.

The expansion of water commences while it is yet a little warmer (4° C.) than the freezing point. This seems to have been first noticed by Beaumé, and is mentioned in his account of his hydrometer. De Luc and Rumford [3] also examined this point more attentively, and the latter pointed out some important consequences of this singularity in the great operations of nature.

The expansion of some substances in solidifying is taken advantage of in the manufacturing arts. Thus iron, bismuth, and antimony expand during solidification, and when cast in any mould they expand into every chink and take up its impression exactly. The contraction of phosphorus, on the other hand, prevents it adhering to the mould in which it is cast, and it is for the same reason that basaltic columns are found in nature.

184. Influence of Pressure on the Melting Point.—So far we have considered fusion and solidification under a constant pressure, and it remains now to be determined whether the melting point of a substance depends in any way upon the pressure, or if melting takes place at the same temperature whatever be the pressure to which the substance is subjected. Attention was first directed to this matter by Professor James Thomson [4] in 1849, who showed that it followed from the principles of the mechanical theory of heat that the melting point of a substance like ice, which contracts on liquefaction, should be lowered by increase of pressure, and by analogous reasoning it followed that the melting point will be raised by increase of pressure if the substance expands during liquefaction. Such a result might be surmised without either theoretic or experimental demonstration ; for if the substance expands on fusing, then increased pressure is

[1] Du Hamel, *Hist. de l'Acad. Roy.* tom. i. p. 1 § 2, chap. i.
[2] *Edin. Phil. Trans.* vol. ii.
[3] Count Rumford, *Essays*, vol. vii. p. 281, etc.
[4] J. Thomson, *Edin. Phil. Trans.*, Jan. 2, 1849. See also Sir Wm. Thomson's *Mathematical and Physical Papers*, vol. i. p. 156.

unfavourable to liquefaction, whereas the contrary holds if the substance contracts in passing from the solid to the liquid state. A proof of Thomson's conclusion will be given in Chap. VIII.

Having deduced that an increase of pressure lowers the freezing point of any substance which expands on solidification, Thomson proceeded to calculate its amount from the known data for ice. He found that for this substance the theoretical lowering of the freezing point ought to be about ·0075 of a degree centigrade per atmospheric increase of pressure. From this it appears that to liquefy ice at $-1°$ C. a pressure of nearly 150 atmos. would be required.

The conclusions to which Professor James Thomson was led by theory were soon put to the test of experiment by his brother Lord Kelvin,[1] the result being a remarkably close confirmation. A strong glass cylinder (Fig. 94) similar to Œrsted's apparatus for the compression of water, was filled with pieces of clean ice and pure water. A glass tube about a foot long and $\frac{1}{10}$ of an inch in diameter was enclosed in the water with its open end downwards to indicate the pressure by the compression of the air which it contained. A leaden ring BB was inserted about the middle of the apparatus, so as to keep free from ice that part of the thermometer-tube where the readings were expected, and more ice was then added above the ring, the clear space being about 2 inches deep. The thermometer was enclosed in a strong glass case to protect it from the straining influence of the high pressure to which it would

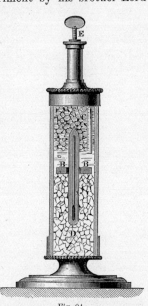

Fig. 94.

otherwise be exposed. The liquid used in this thermometer was sulphuric ether. This substance was chosen because its dilatation for heat is eight or nine times greater than that of mercury, and as its density is only about $\frac{1}{20}$ that of mercury, the thermometer-tube could be made large without suffering much from strain due to the weight of the liquid. For these reasons the instrument was very delicate, each division of the stem corresponding to about $\frac{1}{70}$ of a degree Fahrenheit.

[1] Sir William Thomson, *Proc. Roy. Soc. Edin.*, 1850 ; *Phil. Mag.* vol. xxxvii., 1850.

At the beginning of the experiment the thermometer column stood at the division 67 on the stem, and when a pressure of from 12 to 15 atmos. was applied by screwing down the piston, the reading of the thermometer rapidly descended to 61. The pressure was then suddenly removed, and the column rose again rapidly in the thermometer. The results of two experiments are given in the following table, and compared with theory on the supposition that the pressure was truly indicated by the air gauge :—

Pressure observed.	Fall of Temp. observed.	Fall of Temp. calculated.	Difference.
8·1 atmos.	0°·106 F.	0°·109 F.	− 0°·003 F.
16·8 atmos.	0°·232 F.	0°·227 F.	+ 0°·005 F.

More recent experiments by Professor Dewar[1] give a mean reduction of the melting point of 0°·0072 C. per atmo. increase of pressure up to 700 atmos.

Fig. 95.

It has thus been proved that if melting is accompanied by contraction the effect of increase of pressure is to lower the fusing point. The effect on substances which expand on melting was studied by Bunsen,[2] with the simple apparatus shown in Fig. 95. The shorter arm CD contains the substance under examination, and the longer arm AB contains air which by its compression registers the pressure. The intermediate space is filled with mercury. When the temperature rises the mass of mercury expands, and the substance in the arm CD is strongly compressed. By this means Bunsen found that paraffin wax, which melted at 46°·3 C. under atmospheric pressure, melted at 49°·9 C. when the pressure was raised to 100 atmos. Similarly spermaceti, which fused at 47°·7 C. under 1 atmo., had its melting point raised to 50°·9 C. by a pressure of 156 atmos. Hopkins made similar experiments on wax and stéarin, and Mousson[3] by enormous pressure lowered the freezing point of water to − 20° C. ; M. Amagat[4] also found that C_2Cl_4 (then unknown in the solid state) congeals under a pressure of 150 atmos. Other liquids were subjected to pressures ranging up to 3000 atmos., but without success.

[1] Dewar, *Proc. Roy. Soc.* vol. xxx. p. 533, 1880.
[2] Bunsen, *Pogg. Ann.* vol. lxxxi. p. 562, 1850.
[3] Mousson, *Pogg. Ann.* vol. cv. p. 161, 1858.
[4] See *Phil. Mag.* vol. xxiv. p. 446, 1887.

185. Properties of Ice, Glacier Motion, and Regelation.—The lowering of the freezing point of water by pressure, or, as it may be put, the melting of ice under pressure, explains many phenomena which would otherwise be very puzzling. This melting of ice under pressure, and re-solidification when the pressure is removed, presents itself in many ordinary occurrences. The wheel-track in snow of a heavy cart is generally sheeted with a plate of clear ice. The snow, if not too cold, melts, or partially melts, under the pressure of the wheel, and solidifies again into transparent ice as soon as the pressure is removed. The same process comes into operation in the making of a snowball. If the snow is near the melting point, the pressure of the hand is sufficient to squeeze it into a compact partially-solidified mass. When the snow is squeezed between the hands, melting occurs at the points of greatest pressure, and solidification follows as soon as the resulting liquid is relieved of the pressure. If the snow be much below the freezing point, however, the pressure of the hand will not be sufficiently great, and the ball will not "make." Placed in a press, however, the snow may be squeezed into water, which, when the pressure is removed, becomes a transparent mass of ice. If snow be packed in a cylinder in which it can be strongly compressed by screwing forward a piston, thin rods of transparent ice will be forced through a small aperture made in the bottom of the cylinder. The snow is actually liquefied by the pressure, and solidification occurs as it escapes from the aperture. In the same way fragments of broken ice placed in a mould may be squeezed into a homogeneous mass, and ice-lenses of any shape, or masses of any shape or pattern, may be turned out like butter-prints by simply squeezing snow or ice in a mould of the required design.

Fusion under pressure.

A beautiful experiment showing the melting of ice under pressure, with solidification on relief, has been suggested by Dr. Bottomley.[1] A stout bar of ice is supported by two wooden props, one placed at each end. A wire is then looped round its middle and attached to a heavy weight, which thus hangs supported by the bar of ice. The weight causes the wire to press tightly against the ice, and, as a consequence, melting occurs under the wire. The water thus formed under the wire escapes from underneath and solidifies behind it, and, as this process continues, the wire gradually cuts its way through the ice until the weight falls upon the ground. The wire thus passes completely through the bar, but the bar is not cut in two. Reunion occurs by freezing behind the wire as fast as separation takes place by melting in front. The plane of section can be distinctly seen by

[1] See Tyndall's *Heat a Mode of Motion*, p. 151.

means of the air bubbles which form in it, but so firmly are the two portions frozen together that breaking will take place elsewhere quite as readily as along this surface of regelation. An interesting and important process which persists throughout the whole operation is

Flow of
heat.

the constant flow of heat from the upper to the lower parts of any cross-section of the wire. Thus the water behind the wire is solidifying at zero, and the ice underneath the wire is melting at a lower temperature, so that the upper surface of the wire is warmer than the lower. Now we have solidification and evolution of heat above, while below there is liquefaction accompanied by absorption, and both processes are maintained in action at the same time by the flow of heat downwards from the warmer to the colder parts of the wire. For this reason it is clear that the better the conductivity of the wire the more rapid will be the flow of heat and the more quickly will the wire cut its way through the ice.

The *slipperiness* of ice, as has been pointed out by Professor J. Joly,[1] is due to its melting under pressure. Thus, in skating, the pressure of the skate liquefies a small portion of the ice, and this acts as a lubricant. Very cold ice is not slippery.

From what has been already said the gradual motion of glaciers down mountain slopes will be easily understood; but in order to make the matter quite clear, let us consider the condition of things in a very tall vertical column of snow, the temperature of the whole mass being somewhat below the freezing point. At the top we have snow pure and simple, but at the bottom the pressure will be great, and if the column be tall enough, the pressure at the base will be

Glacier
motion.

sufficient to melt the snow. The water thus formed will escape from beneath, and being below zero will solidify as soon as free. If snow be continually added on at the top there will be continual liquefaction and after-freezing going on at the base, and a continual transformation of snow into transparent ice. Let us now consider the case of a tall block of ice. If the temperature is not too low, or if the height of the block is sufficiently great, melting will occur at the base; and if the block is situated on a hillside, the water escaping from beneath will flow downwards, solidifying as it escapes. This is what happens on the slopes of snow-laden mountains. The snow accumulates to immense depths above the snow-line. The bottom layer liquefies under the pressure of the superincumbent mass, and a gradual slipping-away of the base occurs. The lower strata are being continually squeezed out (and on a slope this means downwards) by the pressure of the upper ones. Below the snow-line we have a stream of trans-

[1] J. Joly, *Proc. Roy. Dublin Soc.* vol. v. p. 453, 1886.

parent ice gradually oozing out from underneath the snow. As the mass descends it enters warmer regions where melting occurs under a less pressure. At the points of greatest pressure melting occurs, and the stress is relieved, and the forward motion of the whole mass is effected by a continual process of alternate melting and freezing.

The, at first sight, peculiar property of ice known as *regelation* was first noticed by Faraday. It will now be easily understood that if two pieces of melting ice be squeezed together the pressure at the points of contact will cause melting, and the water flowing away from these points will solidify around them when free from pressure. The two pieces of ice thus become welded together. This union or regelation takes place when two pieces of ice are placed in contact under water, even under warm water, and arises from the fact that when the ice is melting its temperature is at $0°$ C., and a very slight pressure at any point will cause liquefaction there, with subsequent freezing around it. It is also found that the plane faces of two blocks of ice firmly unite when placed together with their plane faces vertical, so that there is apparently no pressure between the faces. In this case, however, the blocks are really squeezed together to some extent; for on account of the capillary action of the film of water between the plane faces the internal pressure is less than the external, and if the blocks be free to move—for example, if they be afloat in water—they will be squeezed together, and melting with subsequent regelation will occur at the points of contact; but if they are not free to move the pressure inside the film will be less than the atmospheric pressure, and solidification may occur if the temperature of the film does not sensibly exceed zero.

The causes of the motion of glaciers have from time to time been very eagerly discussed, and a perfect unity of opinion on the subject does not appear to exist even yet. This perhaps arises from the variety of phenomena attending the motion, and to different minds different phenomena may present themselves as those which most conspicuously require explanation. Thus regarded as a whole the glacier appears to move as a viscous solid,[1] the top moving faster than the bottom, and the middle faster than the sides, so that the upper layers must be continually shearing over the lower, and the middle parts over the lateral. This motion occurs in arctic as well as

Regelation.

[1] That a bar of ordinary ice yields continuously to pressure or tension, like a plastic solid, was proved by M'Connel and Kidd in 1879, and from M'Connel's later experiments (*Proc. Roy. Soc.* vol. xlix. p. 323) it appears that a bar of ice cut from a single crystal will bend freely when the optic axis of the crystal is in the plane of bending and at right angles to the length of the bar; but when the optic axis is perpendicular to the plane of bending, the bar refuses to yield.

in temperate regions, and proceeds by night as well as by day. According to a theory propounded by Canon Mosley,[1] a glacier moves downhill like any solid body simply by alternations of temperature (Art. 15). When the mass suffers a rise of temperature it expands, the motion taking place, of course, in the direction of least resistance, namely, down the bed. When the temperature falls contraction will ensue, and, the backward motion being opposed by gravity, a complete return to the original position will not be effected, and a gradual creeping down the bed will occur. During the contraction cracks may be formed, and these may become filled with snow, which on the next rise of temperature will promote the further forward motion of the lower end. A sheet of lead placed on a roof creeps downwards in the same manner. This theory explains longitudinal as well as transverse crevasses; and since the surface will experience greater changes of temperature than the lower strata, it will move more rapidly.[2]

From the observations of Koch and Klocke[3] it appears that the motion of a glacier is by no means a continuous sliding down towards the valley. The motion was found to be very irregular in the morning hours, but during the afternoon a slow downward motion took place. During the night there was on the whole a backward motion.

The controversies on this subject seem to have arisen from the desire to explain all the phenomena of glacier motion by attributing them all to a single cause. It is, however, clear that several actions are in operation, and each plays a part in the motion. Thus, while the downward motion of the mass may be explained by liquefaction arising from pressure, yet there can be no doubt that ice, like every other body in nature, is to some extent viscous, and the motion therefore becomes influenced by shearing. So also variations of temperature influence the motion, and probably cause a downward creeping as well as longitudinal and lateral fissures. To attempt to explain all the phenomena by attributing them to any single action is certainly not reasonable.

LATENT HEAT OF FUSION

186. Experimental Determination of the Latent Heat of Fusion.—The latent heat of fusion of any substance is defined as the quantity of heat required to convert unit mass of the solid at the melting point into liquid at the same temperature. Its experimental

---

[1] *Phil. Mag.*, 1869 and 1870.

[2] W. R. Browne, *Proc. Roy. Soc.* vol. xxxiv. p. 208, 1882.

[3] *Wied. Ann.* vol. viii. p. 661, 1879 ; *Phil. Mag.*, 5th Series, vol. ix. p. 274, 1880.

estimation may be made in several manners founded on the general methods of calorimetry. There are, however, two general methods of procedure applicable, according as the substance is liquid or solid at the ordinary temperature of the air. In the first case a weighed quantity of the liquid is placed in a freezing mixture and solidified. The solid, while at some known temperature below the freezing point, is then placed in the calorimeter, and the amount of heat absorbed by it in liquefying and rising to some known temperature above the melting point is noted. In the second case a known weight of the solid is fused, and, while it is at some known temperature above the point of fusion, is placed in the calorimeter, and the heat evolved while cooling to some temperature below the melting point is observed. The reverse operation might of course be applied in either case.

Let θ_0 be the temperature of the solid when placed in the calorimeter, θ the temperature of fusion, and θ_1 the initial and θ_2 the final temperature of the calorimeter. Then if the mass of the substance be m, and L its latent heat of fusion, s the specific heat of the solid, and s' that of the liquid, the total heat gained by the substance in rising from θ_0 to θ in the solid state, fusing at θ and then rising from θ to θ_2 in the liquid state, is obviously

$$ms(\theta - \theta_0) + mL + ms'(\theta_2 - \theta) ;$$

and if W denotes the water equivalent of the calorimeter, the heat lost by it will be

$$W(\theta_1 - \theta_2) + R,$$

where R is the radiation correction, and may be positive or negative according to the conditions of the experiment. Consequently the equation which determines L is

$$ms(\theta - \theta_0) + mL + ms'(\theta_2 - \theta) = W(\theta_1 - \theta_2) + R.$$

In order to determine L from this equation the values of s and s' are required. If these are not known by previous experiments, their values may be determined simultaneously with that of L from a single experiment by noting the changes of temperature of the calorimeter while the temperature of the solid rises through a given range between θ_0 and θ, and also while the liquid rises through some interval between θ and θ_2. Or three experiments may be made, starting with different values of θ_0 and θ_1, and thus obtaining three equations similar to the above, involving the unknown quantities s, s', and L.

If the substance, on the other hand, be solid at ordinary temperatures, a known quantity of it at a temperature θ_0 above the fusing point θ is placed in the calorimeter, and the final temperature θ_2 of the calorimeter will be higher than its initial temperature θ_1. The equation then becomes

$$ms'(\theta_0 - \theta) + mL + ms(\theta - \theta_2) = W(\theta_2 - \theta^1) + R.$$

187. Latent Heat of Fusion of Ice.—The accurate determination of the latent heat of fusion of ice has been the subject of much skilled investigation. The method sketched above was employed by Person.[1] His calorimeter was of the ordinary form, but closed so as to prevent loss of heat by evaporation, and the stirrer was kept in constant motion by means of clockwork. The water under investigation was enclosed in a thin copper flask furnished with a thermometer which indicated its temperature. Before immersion in the calorimeter its temperature was reduced to about $-20°$ C. by means of a freezing mixture. The flask therefore, when placed in the calorimeter, contained a known weight of ice at a temperature considerably below the freezing point.

The whole observation was now divided into two parts—(1) the observation of the change of temperature of the calorimeter while the temperature of ice rose through a certain range, and (2) the observation of the final temperature of the calorimeter. The first observation gave the specific heat of ice; and this being known, the second gave its latent heat when the necessary corrections were made. In this manner Person found for ice

$$s = 0·504, \quad L = 80·02,$$

the specific heat of water at $10°·5$ C. being unity.

MM. De la Provostaye and Desains[2] proceeded in a somewhat different manner. Their calorimeter was of the ordinary form, and the correction for evaporation was determined by weighing and estimating the rate of evaporation within the range of temperature employed during the experiment. A fragment of ice at zero was then carefully dried and quickly immersed in the calorimeter, and the fall of temperature observed. The quantity of ice thus introduced was estimated by weighing the calorimeter before and after its introduction. The ice being at zero, its specific heat does not appear in the equation for L; and since the temperature of fusion is zero, as well as the initial temperature of the solid, we have, if θ_1 and θ_2 be the initial and final temperatures of the calorimeter,

$$mL + m\theta_2 = W(\theta_1 - \theta_2) + R.$$

Hence

$$L = -\theta_2 + \frac{W}{m}(\theta_1 - \theta_2) + \frac{R}{m}.$$

---

[1] C. C. Person, *Ann. de Chimie*, 3e série, tom. xxx. p. 73, 1850.

[2] F. de la Provostaye and P. Desains, *Ann. de Chimie*, 3e série, tom. viii. p. 5, 1843.

The correction R will be small, but W will be much larger than m, and it thus appears that an error in the observation of $\theta_1 - \theta_2$ will be increased in the ratio W/m. Thus, if $W = 10m$ an error of $\frac{1}{10}$ of a degree in the value of $\theta_1 - \theta_2$ will introduce an error of a whole unit of heat in the value of L. For this reason MM. Provostaye and Desains employed a thermometer which could be depended on to $\frac{1}{100}$th of a degree. Their final result was

$$L = 79 \cdot 25.$$

More recently Bunsen[1] applied his ice calorimeter (Art. 135) to the determination of the same constant. The specific gravity of ice was first measured by a species of weight thermometer, containing mercury and a known weight of water which could be frozen. The end of the stem of the thermometer dipped into a cup of mercury, so that when the ice melted, mercury entered the instrument, and from the increase of weight the contraction during fusion was estimated. Bunsen thus found the density of ice to be $0 \cdot 91674$. This being known, a definite quantity of heat Q was imparted to the ice calorimeter and the contraction estimated. The quantity of heat Q will liquefy Q/L grammes of ice, and the known contraction v will furnish the equation for L,

$$\frac{Q}{L}\left(\frac{1}{\rho_1} - \frac{1}{\rho_0}\right) = v,$$

where ρ_1 is the density of ice and ρ_0 the density of ice-cold water. By this means Bunsen found

$$L = 80 \cdot 03,$$

the mean specific heat of water between $0°$ and $100°$ C. being taken as unity.[2]

A. W. Smith[3] determined the latent heat of fusion of ice by the electrical method. Pure ice, cut into small cubes, was cooled below $0°$ C. and immersed in refined paraffin, also cooled. The calorimeter, containing the ice, paraffin, and heating coil, with thermometer and stima, was surrounded by another vessel containing broken ice. The temperature was slowly raised till the calorimeter was at about $-1°$ C. The amount of heat energy, measured electrically, which was required to raise the temperature to about $0° \cdot 5$ C. was determined, and allowance made for the small amount of heat used in the preliminary and subsequent heating and for the radiation correction. The result obtained was $334 \cdot 25$ joules, equivalent to $79 \cdot 77$ calories, taking the

[1] Bunsen, *Pogg. Ann.* vol. cxli. ; and *Ann. de Chimie et de Physique*, 4ᵉ série, tom. xxiii. p. 66, 1871.

[2] If we take the unit of heat to be the calorie at $20°$ C. and the mean calorie between $0°$ and $100°$ to be $1 \cdot 0016$ times this unit, as in Art. 174, the above figure becomes $80 \cdot 16$.

[3] *Phys. Review*, vol. xvi. p. 383, 1903.

calorie at 15° C. as equal to 4·184 joules. In this investigation the
E.M.F. of the Clark cell was taken as 1·433 volts at 15° C.

188. Latent Heat of Fusion of Metals.—Experiments on the
latent heat of fusion of a number of metals were made by Awbery and
E. Griffiths,[1] using the method of mixtures. A quantity of the metal,
together with the crucible in which it was melted, was introduced
into a sheet-metal vessel immersed in water. There was an arrangement by which this vessel could be completely closed and then
submerged. The heat lost in transfer from the furnace, where the
initial temperature was measured by a thermocouple, was allowed for
by making another experiment with the empty crucible; this also
gave the amount of heat yielded up by the crucible in cooling. The
method adopted was to make a series of experiments with each metal,
with different initial temperatures. Thus, for aluminium, the initial
temperatures were respectively 443°, 516°, 591°, 597°, 615°, 640°,
650°, 664°, 686°, 706°, and 763°, the final temperature being about
20° in each case. From the measurements of the heat given up in
cooling a curve like that in Fig. 55 could be plotted, consisting of two
straight or nearly straight portions OA, BC, from which the length
of the vertical portion AB was deduced. The following results were
obtained :—

Metal	Al	Sb	Bi	Pb	Mg	Sn	Zn
Melting Point	657	630	269	327	644	232	420
Latent Heat	92·4	24·3	13·0	6·26	46·5	14·6	26·6

189. Fusion of Amorphous Solids.—In the case of amorphous
substances, such as glass and iron, the passage from the solid to the
liquid state is gradual and not sudden as in the case of ice and other
crystalline bodies which have a distinct melting point.

During this interval of transition through the viscous stages, from the
hard solid to the mobile liquid, there is a continuous absorption of heat,
but no sudden absorption without change of temperature. For this reason
we cannot speak definitely of the latent heat of fusion of such a substance. The passage from the liquid to the solid state is continuous. One
state might be regarded as differing from the other merely in the degree
of viscosity. Thus solids [2] often show traces of the liquid properties,

---

[1] *Proc. Phys. Soc.* vol. xxxviii. p. 378, 1926.
[2] Unless we classify as solids only those substances which do not suffer plastic
yielding under stress until some definite limit is reached. A fluid would then be
any substance (hard or otherwise) which yields plastically in time under any stress,
however small.

for example, in the gradual flow of pitch and the sagging of long glass
rods supported horizontally.   Even in the case of crystalline substances
the change from the solid to the liquid state may be continuous in the
same manner, but exceedingly rapid.   Thus, if quantities of heat be
measured along the axis OY, and temperatures along OX (Fig. 55),
when the substance is in the solid state, the line OA will represent
the relation between the increase of temperature and the increase of
heat.   If the substance melts suddenly a certain quantity of heat will
be absorbed without change of temperature, and this is represented by
the right line AB parallel to OY.   At B the fusion is completed, and
the absorption of heat will again be accompanied by rise of temperature.   This is represented by the line BC.   If, however, the substance

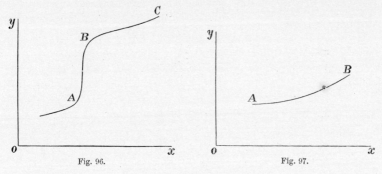

Fig. 96.   Fig. 97.

softens gradually, the line AB representing the change of state will not
be straight, but the whole curve ABC will be continuous, as shown in
Fig. 96.   The part AB will represent the stage at which there is a
large absorption of heat, that is, the period of high, but not infinite,
specific heat.   There is here no sudden discontinuity.   The change of
state is merely characterised by a rapid increase in the slope and
inflexion of the curve.   It may even happen that a marked increase of
slope does not characterise the period of change of state, but that
during softening, the curve, as in Fig. 97, shows no evidence of change
of state.   Thus the discontinuity observed in the case of water and
other substances which solidify suddenly may be regarded as merely
extreme cases of that exhibited in Fig. 96.   In these bodies, too, the
change from one state to the other may be continuous but rapid.

SECTION II

EVAPORATION AND EBULLITION

190. Molecular Motion in Liquids.—The general distinctions be tween solids, liquids, and gases, from the point of view of the molecular theory, have been already sketched in Art. 53. In a solid each molecule may vibrate about a position of equilibrium, but cannot move from one part to another of the mass. In a gas, on the other hand, each molecule is not only free to move throughout the mass (except in so far as it is jostled by the others), but between any two consecutive collisions its path is supposed to be straight, and the molecule is free from the action of its neighbours.

Liquids form a connecting link between the solid and gaseous states of matter. The molecules of a liquid are continually wandering through the mass, but each spends nearly all its time within the sphere of influence of the others. In a gas the ratio of the time spent by any molecule in collision to that occupied in free motion is supposed to be small, but in liquids nearly all the time is spent in collisions, there is practically no free path, and each molecule is constantly under the attractive influence of those which surround it. In the interior of the liquid this influence will probably have little directive action on the motion of a molecule. Each molecule will be attracted pretty much the same in all directions, and the path travelled over by any one will depend upon its fortuitous collisions with the others.

At the surface of the liquid, however, the state of things will be very different. A molecule in this region is not equally surrounded on all sides by other molecules; so that although in the interior of the liquid a molecule may be attracted equally in all directions, and there may be no resultant molecular attraction on it, yet at the surface there will be on each molecule a resultant attraction directed towards the interior of the liquid, and along the normal to the surface. Through-out a thin surface-layer there will thus be a force on each molecule directed towards the interior. This film consequently exerts a pressure

344

on the liquid within, and acts like a tense elastic membrane stretched over the surface; hence the expression surface-tension.

Let us now consider a molecule in motion towards the surface. As soon as it enters the surface-layer alluded to above, a force directed towards the interior begins to act on it, so that, leaving accidental collisions out of account for the present, the motion of the molecule may be arrested and even reversed. If, however, the normal component of the velocity of the molecule be great enough, it will be able to pass completely through the surface-film, and continue its motion into the space outside the liquid. The kinetic energy of the molecule will, however, be considerably reduced by its passage through the surface-layer on account of the opposing attractive force, so that although a molecule may be in rapid motion on approaching the surface from the interior, its velocity after escape may be very small. Thus, on the whole, while some molecules escape, others are brought to rest and return into the liquid, so that the surface-film is being constantly renewed, the molecules which constitute it at any instant passing into the interior and giving place to others. Those molecules which effect an escape are free to move about in the outside space, and constitute what is termed the *vapour* of the liquid, and this process of molecular escape is termed *evaporation*.

191. Evaporation in a Closed Space.—When a liquid is placed in a closed chamber (which is otherwise empty and at a uniform temperature) evaporation will take place more or less rapidly at first. After some time, however, the space outside the liquid will become partially filled with stray molecules which have escaped through the surface-film. These, after escape, move about indiscriminately in the chamber, and are reflected from its walls and from each other. In this manner some, after a fitful career, will return to the liquid, and once they fall upon its surface they may be attracted into the interior. It will thus happen that a certain stage will be ultimately attained at which as many molecules will return to the liquid per second as leave it, and an equilibrium will be established. At this stage evaporation may be said to have ceased. There is no further loss to the liquid or gain to the vapour outside it; there is, however, a continual exchange going on—new molecules are being continually projected from the surface, and others are falling into it in equal number. In this case the chamber is said to be filled with saturated vapour, or the vapour is simply said to be *saturated*; while in any state before this final stage is arrived at the vapour is said to be non-saturated. A saturated vapour is thus one which is in equilibrium with its own liquid.

192. Evaporation in an Unlimited Space.—When the space into which evaporation takes place is unlimited, it is clear that when a molecule escapes from the surface it may wander about in the atmosphere and never return to the liquid. There will thus be a continual flow of molecules from the surface into the space outside, and evaporation will continue in this manner at a steady rate as long as the temperature is kept constant. The liquid will thus gradually all pass into the condition of vapour. The rate at which vapour is formed depends upon the temperature. For a given temperature it is not, however, proportional to the area of the surface of the liquid, as ordinarily supposed, but to the linear dimensions of the surface; and in an open vessel evaporation takes place more rapidly near the boundaries of the surface than at the centre. The rate of evaporation is thus not the same at all parts of the surface. This question has been examined theoretically by M. Stefan,[1] and he finds that for a circular vessel the quantity of vapour formed per second is proportional to the diameter, and, further, that the lines of flow of the vapour from the surface are hyperbolas, of which the foci are on the bounding edge of the circular surface. The surfaces of equal pressure are the orthogonal system of ellipsoids. These are nearer each other at the edge of the surface than over the centre, consequently near the edge of the vessel the vapour-pressure decreases most rapidly, and it is here therefore that the flow is greatest.

The rate of evaporation at the various parts of a free surface has been studied experimentally by A. Winkelmann,[2] and although he was unable to verify Stefan's theory very closely, he attributes the discrepancies rather to the mode of experiment than to any defect in the theory.

The rate of evaporation at a given temperature and pressure varies very much with different liquids. This would of course be expected, for the escape of a molecule depends on its normal velocity and the nature of the surface-layer, both of which will depend upon the nature of the substance. Thus a drop of ether let fall through the air disappears almost at once, a drop of alcohol less rapidly, and a drop of water much less rapidly still.

From a series of experiments on the rate of evaporation of liquids contained in narrow tubes, Stefan [3] was led to the law that the velocity

---

[1] Stefan, *Journal de Phys.*, 2e série, tom. i. p. 202, 1882.

[2] *Wied. Ann.* vols. xxxiii. xxxv., 1888.

[3] The differential equations of the motion of vapours are analogous to those of the potential of electric field. If a liquid evaporates in an indefinite atmosphere the mass of vapour which leaves any unit of the surface per second is proportional to

of evaporation varies inversely as the distance of the surface from the open end of the tube. The application of the theory of the diffusion of gases to this process led to the same law, and furnished a complete determination of the velocity of evaporation, which rendered it possible to calculate the coefficient of diffusion of vapours. These experiments have been extended by Winkelmann to several series of liquids, and have been used to determine the coefficients of diffusion of their vapours.

Similar experiments to those on evaporation may be made on the solution of solids in liquids, and the coefficient of diffusion determined.

193. Ebullition.—The rate of evaporation, depending as we have seen on the facility with which the molecules escape through the surface-layer, will be favoured by anything which increases the average velocities of the liquid molecules or diminishes the surface tension. Increase of temperature has both these effects, the latter being a consequence of the former; and for this reason evaporation from a given liquid under given conditions takes place more rapidly the higher the temperature.

The effect of evaporation is to carry off those molecules of the liquid which are in most rapid motion, and consequently to diminish the temperature of the liquid. Steady evaporation carries off a steady flow of heat, so that if the temperature of the liquid is maintained constant a steady supply of heat must be given to it. Equilibrium is therefore established when the rate of supply is equal to the rate at which heat is carried away by evaporation. If the supply is considerable and the free surface small, it may be impossible for this equilibrium to be established; and as the temperature rises a point is reached at which the surface is unable to afford the means of sufficiently rapid escape to the molecules, and bubbles of vapour are formed in the interior of the liquid. At this stage the vapour-pressure is sufficient to support a bubble inside the liquid, and the temperature

---

the electric density at this part of the surface when charged. The direction of the current of vapour is along the lines of force, and the surfaces of equal pressure are coincident with the equipotential surfaces. If a be the radius of a circular basin, k the coefficient of diffusion, P the atmospheric pressure, p' and p'' the pressure of the vapour at the surface and very far away from it respectively, the mass of vapour which escapes from the basin per unit time is

$$M = 4ka \, \log_e \frac{P - p''}{P - p'}.$$

Thus M is proportional to the radius of the basin and not to its surface, as commonly supposed (Stefan, *Trans. Vienna Acad.*, 1881, abstract in *Journal de Physique*, tom. i. p. 202, 1882).

ceases to rise. When a bubble is formed, evaporation takes place at its surface, so that the effect of the formation of such a bubble is to increase the surface through which evaporation takes place, and by this means equilibrium between loss and supply is established. Each bubble as it is formed rises to the surface, increasing in size during its ascent, and escapes into the space outside. If now the rate of supply of heat be augmented, it is found that the temperature of the liquid remains stationary. Bubbles merely form more rapidly, so that the rate of loss is still maintained equal to the rate of supply of heat. The temperature at which this occurs is termed the *boiling point*, and the process of vaporisation by bubble-formation is called boiling. The temperature of boiling depends upon the pressure. The higher the pressure, the greater the difficulty of forming bubbles, and the higher the temperature at which boiling occurs. Thus the temperature of water boiling under a pressure of 760 mm. of mercury is 100° C., while under a pressure of 92 mm. boiling will occur at a temperature of 50° C., and under a pressure of 1520 mm. the temperature of boiling is 121°·4 C.

No definite law has, however, yet been discovered connecting the boiling point with the pressure, but several have been proposed. These will be considered later on. The general law of ebullition is analogous to that of fusion, viz. that a given liquid under a given pressure always boils at a definite temperature, or, in other words, the boiling point depends only on the pressure. In the case of fusion the influence of pressure is small, but the effect on the boiling point is considerable. In general, when the boiling point is spoken of, the temperature of boiling under the standard atmosphere (760 mm. of mercury) is meant.

The boiling point under any pressure is often defined as the temperature at which the pressure of the saturated vapour of the liquid is equal to the external pressure to which the liquid is subject. It would, however, appear much more straightforward to define the boiling point as the temperature at which boiling occurs, that is, the temperature at which a liquid gives off bubbles of its own vapour. It might then be stated as a result of experiment that at this temperature the pressure of the saturated vapour of the liquid is equal to that under which the liquid boils.

The pressure of the vapour in a rising bubble must of course be somewhat greater than the pressure outside the liquid, and even at the surface of the liquid the vapour-pressure must be a little greater than that at some distance away, for the vapour is flowing away from the surface, and it of course flows from places of higher to places of lower pressure. The apparatus employed for fixing the boiling point on thermometers (Fig. 8) shows, however, that the pressure of the saturated vapour within the boiler is scarcely appreciably greater than that of the atmosphere outside if the escape tube be fairly wide.

194. Superheating—Variation of the Boiling Point under Constant Pressure—Circumstances which determine Ebullition.[1]—The temperature of a liquid boiling under constant pressure depends to some extent on the nature of the containing vessel. The discovery of this influence of the containing vessel is generally attributed to Gay-Lussac (1812), but as early as the middle of the 18th century it seems to have been generally known that the temperature of water boiling under a definite pressure was not always the same. It was found to vary within certain limits, which led to incongruities in the fixing of the boiling point on thermometers. For this reason a report on the subject was made by some of the most distinguished members of the Royal Society in 1777, in which it was recommended that the thermometer during the fixing of the boiling point should be immersed in the steam of the boiling water. From this it would appear that, even at that date, it was known that although the temperature of the liquid might depend on the nature of the vessel, or even vary with the same vessel at different times, yet the temperature of the steam was always the same under the same pressure.

As early as 1784 it was shown by Achard[2] that the boiling point of water, under constant pressure, varied much more in metallic than in glass vessels. He also noticed that if, when water was boiling steadily, some iron filings, or other finely-divided insoluble substance, were thrown in, the temperature of the boiling liquid was lowered 1° R. or more, and that this depression varied considerably according as the substance thrown in was powdered or in lump. The effect of soluble substances, on the other hand, was determined during the experiments of Dalton, Watt, Robison, Southern, and others on the pressure of saturated steam at various temperatures. These experiments will be considered in the next section.

The effect of dissolved air in the operation of boiling was studied by De Luc;[3] and in 1772 he propounded a theory which states in

---

[1] See a paper by Charles Tomlinson, *Proc. Roy. Soc.* vol. xvii., 1868–69, p. 240. An interesting history of the whole subject is also given by the same author, *Phil. Mag.* vol. xxxvii. p. 161, 1869.

[2] Achard, *Nouveaux Mémoires de l'Académie Royale de Berlin*, 1785, p. 2; *Ann. de Chimie*, tom. x. p. 49. Gay-Lussac's note on the subject will be found in tom. vii. *Ann. de Chimie et de Physique*, 1817.

[3] De Luc, *Recherches sur les modifications de l'atmosphère*, Geneva, 1772. *Introduction à la physique terrestre par les fluides expansibles*, Paris, 1803.

very precise terms that boiling is initiated and sustained by the bubbles of air which become disengaged from the liquid when heated. These bubbles may be seen collecting in large numbers on the sides of a glass beaker in which water is being heated. As the temperature rises evaporation takes place from the liquid into the bubble, which grows in size and rises to the surface. The part played by the air is to form a centre of evaporation, and give a start to the formation of a **Dissolved** vapour bubble. If the liquid is quite purged from dissolved air, then **air.** according to this theory there is nothing to start bubbles in the interior, and evaporation can take place only at the free surface. In confirmation of this view De Luc found that water from which the air had been carefully expelled by boiling could be heated in a tube to a temperature of $234°·5$ F. without boiling.

A similar experiment showing the same effect was made by Donny [1] in 1844. Water was placed in a glass tube previously well washed out with sulphuric acid and rinsed. The water was then boiled for some time in order to expel all the dissolved air, as well as the air in the upper part of the tube. When this was effected the tube was hermetically sealed. The extremity of the tube containing the water was then placed in a bath of glycerine, the temperature of which was raised to $137°$ C. without ebullition of the water. At this point, however, a sudden rupture of the liquid occurred with explosive violence, projecting part of the mass to the further end of the tube. This is known as boiling by bumping. It occurs in most cases when liquids are subjected to prolonged boiling, and has been suggested as a possible cause of boiler explosions.

The influence of copper turnings, powdered charcoal, pounded glass, etc., in reducing the boiling point was also investigated by Gay-Lussac.[2] He considered that the boiling point depended on the nature of the surface of the containing vessel as regards its polish and conductivity for heat. Marcet,[3] on the other hand, maintained that metal turnings depressed the boiling point, because their molecular attraction for water is less than that of glass, so that the water adheres more tenaciously to the sides of the glass vessel than to those of a metallic one or to metal filings. This adhesion to the sides of the glass vessel will be influenced by dirt and impurities on the sides of the vessel, and consequently variations would be expected in the temperature of a liquid boiling in different glass vessels, or even in the same vessel at different

[1] Donny, *Ann. de Chimie et de Physique*, 3e série, tom. xvi., 1844.

[2] Gay-Lussac, *Ann. de Chimie*, tom. lxxxii. p. 171 ; and *Ann. de Chimie et de Physique*, tom. vii. p. 307.

[3] Marcet, *Ann. de Chimie et de Physique*, 3e série, tom. v. p. 449.

times.   When a glass flask is thoroughly washed out with sulphuric acid and rinsed with pure water, the boiling point of pure water was found by Marcet to be 106° C.   These variations were referred to molecular changes in the surface of the glass.

M. Gernez [1] describes an experiment in which copious ebullition ensued in a liquid at the boiling point, from the surface of a small bubble of air placed in its interior ; and Mr. Tomlinson [2] found that a wire gauze cage containing air might be lowered into the interior of the liquid without exciting ebullition, provided the cage and air be what he terms chemically clean.   From this experiment it appeared Suspended that clean air did not cause ebullition.   The specks of dust which it dust. usually contains are the active agents.

Mr. Tomlinson's experiments on this subject are full of interest.   A test tube, one third or one half full of the liquid to be examined, was placed in a warm bath and maintained at or near its boiling point, but not actually boiling.   While the liquid in the tube was thus silently evaporating, its surface was touched with the end of a brass wire, and violent ebullition set in immediately.   As soon as the wire was removed the boiling ceased, but it commenced again when the surface was touched with a slip of paper, or the end of an iron wire, or a glass rod.   In the case of a glass rod the whole surface was active at first as the rod was passed down into the liquid.   Bubbles, however, soon ceased to be given off, except at two small points.   Tomlinson's explanation is that the surface became clean, and therefore inactive in separating vapour. The two specks from which vapour continued to be given off were impurities in the glass, probably iron or carbon, which were porous, or not so easily cleaned as the glass.   In a tube containing ether, bubbles were rapidly discharged from two specks in the glass.   Specks of this kind are often very active in separating gas from saturated solutions, such as soda-water, etc., and in setting up crystallisation in super-saturated solutions of salts.

With respect to the action of surface rugosities, the action of a rat's-tail file was examined.   The surface of the hot liquid was touched with the file, and furious boiling ensued.   The file was then held in the flame of a spirit-lamp, and while hot, was held in the upper part of the tube to cool in the vapour of the liquid, being thus sheltered from the air. The file was now found to be inactive, even though passed slowly down to the bottom of the liquid.   However, when taken out and waved in the air it again became active; but when left in the liquid it soon ceased to be active, or, according to the theory, became clean.

[1] *Ann. de Chimie et de Phys.*, 5e série, tom. iv. p. 335, 1875.
[2] *Loc. cit.*

A small pellet of writing-paper thrown into ether caused rapid ebullition for some time, the paper being tossed violently about till it suddenly sank dead and ceased to be active. A brass wire passed down to the bottom of the tube evolved bubbles from all parts of its surface, but after some time it became clean and ceased to promote ebullition, except at one point at its end, from which bubbles continued to stream off. The wire was taken out and filed, but on being inserted into the liquid again bubbles continued to stream off from two points. In the same manner a piece of flint, when dropped into methylated spirit at its boiling point, gave off bubbles in abundance all over its surface. On being taken out and broken in two it was found that when replaced in the liquid the newly fractured surfaces were inactive, while bubbles were freely liberated at the old surfaces as before.

The behaviour of nuclei is the same in the case of supersaturated saline or gaseous solutions, and, in the opinion of the author of these experiments, any surface will be active or inactive in promoting evolution of gas or separation of crystals, according as it is chemically unclean or clean. A liquid at the boiling point is regarded throughout as a saturated solution of its own vapour.

While non-porous substances become inactive after some time in promoting separation of vapour, it is found that porous substances do not become inactive. Such substances, therefore, as charcoal, coke, etc., are the proper nuclei for promoting the liberation of vapour in the operations of boiling and distilling, and for preventing bumping.

Super-heating.

The possibility of superheating a liquid, as well as that of over-cooling it, will depend on any circumstance which reduces the chance of the molecules at any place coming into the condition in which vaporisation or solidification may start at that place. For this reason it would be expected that very mobile liquids would be more difficult to superheat or overcool than those which are viscous. For the same reason superheating and overcooling will be more difficult the larger the quantity of liquid employed ; for since it is sufficient that the required arrangement of molecules should occur at any single place for ebullition or crystallisation to set in, the probability of this happening at some place will increase with the quantity of liquid employed. Thus Dufour [1] found that drops of water suspended in a mixture of oil of cloves and linseed oil could be heated much above the boiling point. Drops 10 mm. in diameter were heated to 120° C., and those which were only 1 to 3 mm. in diameter remained liquid up to a temperature of 178° C. These drops burst into vapour with a hissing noise when touched with a glass rod, or when they floated against the

[1] Dufour, *Ann. de Chimie et de Phys.*, 3e série, tom. lxviii. p. 370, 1863.

thermometer or the sides of the vessel. The effect of surface tension may, however, have a considerable influence in this as well as in all other cases of superheating.[1]

When a volatile liquid is placed in a tube and cautiously heated in a bath to a temperature above its boiling point without boiling, very rapid evaporation takes place at the surface, and the cooling thus produced may be sufficient to keep the liquid at a temperature considerably below that of the bath. Thus M. Gernez[2] found that in a tube 14 mm. in diameter, containing carbon bisulphide and placed in a bath at 80° C., the temperature of the liquid in the tube did not exceed 72° C.

195. The Spheroidal State. — An apparently singular pheno-menon connected with vaporisation is that known as the spheroidal state. When a drop of water is let fall on a hot metal plate the drop ordinarily boils away violently with a hissing noise. If, however, the temperature of the metal is sufficiently high, the drop does not enter into ebullition, neither does it spread over the surface and wet it as at lower temperatures, but it rolls about on the surface like a globule of mercury. The phenomenon may be easily studied by raising a metal capsule to a white heat over a Bunsen flame, and dropping a globule of water carefully into the dish from a pipette. While the temperature of the dish is maintained the drop remains as if on a greased sur-face, while evaporation proceeds rapidly but silently from its under surface. If the lamp be removed and the dish allowed to cool, a point will be reached at which the drop comes into contact with the surface, and violent ebullition sets in, with the formation of a cloud of vapour.

During the spheroidal condition it may be easily verified that the drop is out of contact with the hot metal. It is supported on a cushion of its own vapour or of air. The eye placed on a level with the surface can easily observe through the interval between the drop (especially if it is coloured dark) and the surface any bright object, such as a flame, placed on the other side. Professor Poggendorf proved this want of contact in another manner. The two terminals

---

[1] The pressure of saturated vapour in contact with a curved surface of its own liquid depends on the curvature of the surface. It is greater when the surface of the liquid is convex and less when the surface is concave than when it is flat. On this account, a very small bubble forming in a liquid would tend to condense again, even if the temperature were several degrees above the boiling point. But if the bubble were large enough for the vapour within it to be below saturation-pressure it would grow rapidly. This explains boiling by bumping and the effect of nuclei of air, dust, etc., in facilitating boiling (see Art. 216).

[2] Gernez, *Ann. de Chimie et de Phys.*, 5e série, tom. iv., 1875.

of an electric battery were placed in contact, one with the drop and
the other with the hot metal.   While the spheroidal condition lasted
no current passed, but as soon as the temperature of the metal fell to
the point at which boiling occurred, the galvanometer was deflected,
showing that contact had been established.

M. Boutigny,[1] by placing a small thermometer in the drop, found
that the temperature of the drop when in the spheroidal state was
always below its boiling point ; and Berger [2] afterwards found that in
a large globule the temperature registered by a thermometer placed
in its interior marked from 96° to 98° near the bottom, and about
90° at the upper surface.

In the case of liquid sulphurous acid the temperature of the
globule is low enough to freeze a drop of water placed in it.   This
was first shown by Boutigny, and hence the apparently extraordinary
statement that water may be frozen in a red-hot crucible.   The red-
hot crucible has nothing to do with the freezing.   It follows merely
from the fact that a liquid in the spheroidal state is below its boiling
point, and the boiling point of sulphurous acid is below the freezing
point of water.   Faraday in the same way succeeded in solidifying
mercury by using solid carbonic acid instead of the sulphurous acid
employed in Boutigny's experiment.

If the surface of the heated metal be flattish, so that lateral
escape of the vapour is impeded, it will burst up through the
centre of the drop ; and it sometimes happens that when the
vapour can escape laterally it issues in regular pulses, which throw
the surface of the drop into beautiful undulations.   As the temperature of the metal falls the vibration of the drop subsides till it becomes
motionless ; it then suddenly spreads over the metallic surface with a
hissing noise.   Contact is now established, and the spheroidal condition has terminated.

The mode of experiment may be reversed.   The heated capsule
may be placed afloat on the surface of a basin of hot water.   While
the capsule is hot it floats silently on the surface of the water supported on a cushion of vapour.

The first observation of the spheroidal state is attributed to
Leidenfrost, but in some of its forms it must have been known from
very early times.   The laundress's mode of testing the temperature
of a smoothing iron by means of a drop of water is an example.   A
white-hot iron may be licked with the tongue without injury, contact

[1] Boutigny, *Ann. de Chimie et de Phys.*, 3e série, tom. ix. p. 250 ; tom. xi. p. 16 ;
tom. xxvii. p. 54 ; tom. xxviii. p. 178.
[2] Berger, *Pogg. Ann.* tom. cxix. p. 594, 1863.

with the metal being prevented by the vapour developed. Similarly the hand if wet may be passed through a stream of molten metal, and solid carbonic acid may be placed in the mouth without injury. Many escapes from fiery ordeals are perhaps attributable to the same protective influence. After the hand has been moistened with ether it can be plunged into melted lead without experiencing any extreme sensation of heat.

The use of a heated metallic surface is not essential to the production of the spheroidal state. The only necessary condition is a sufficiently elevated temperature. Liquid drops may assume the spheroidal state on the surface of another liquid which is sufficiently hot ; and solids such as carbonic acid snow, which vaporise without liquefaction, assume an analogous state when placed on a surface whose temperature is sufficiently high to vaporise them with the necessary rapidity.

That a liquid drop in the spheroidal state is supported on a cushion of its own vapour is confirmed by the experiment of Budde, who found that in the exhausted receiver of an air-pump water assumes the spheroidal state at temperatures as low as 80° or 90° C. In this case the vapour pressure under the drop is only that necessary to the support of the drop, whereas in air the vapour pressure under the drop must support the drop and the atmospheric pressure as well.[1]

It has been shown by K. S. Kristensen [2] that the heat radiated by the dish to a drop in the spheroidal state is not sufficient to account for the phenomenon, but that the heat conducted through the vapour must also be taken into account. The investigation shows that the heat conveyed in the latter manner preponderates.

196. Evaporation from Solids : Sublimation. — Of the three states of matter the liquid forms a connecting link between the solid and the gaseous. Solids when heated generally pass into the liquid, and then into the gaseous condition. Solids may, however, pass directly into the state of vapour without apparently passing through

---

[1] The explanation formerly given, *i.e.* that vapour is generated so rapidly under a drop in the spheroidal condition as to keep up a pressure sufficient to support the drop, is inadequate to account for the facts. Mr. R. J. Moss (*Proc. Roy. Dublin Soc.*, 1877–78, p. 87) found that drops of cold ether would float on warm ether, and drops of melted paraffin on a hot silver plate. The first experiment shows that a difference of temperature is an essential feature of the phenomenon, and the second that the production of vapour is not essential, since the paraffin was found not to have lost weight after the experiment. The excess of pressure in the vapour or air under the drop appears to be due to molecular action somewhat similar to that which occurs during the thermal transpiration of gases (see Art. 384).

[2] *Tidsskrift for Physik og Chimie* (2), vol. ix. p. 161 ; *Beiblätter der Physik*, vol. xiii. p. 155.

the intermediate stage—that is, solids evaporate.   Ice and snow, as is well known, gradually evaporate; and in the Arctic regions this is the manner in which evaporation must mainly occur.   Carbonic acid snow when exposed in the air rapidly passes off into gas, and can only with difficulty be liquefied in an open tube.

In these cases vaporisation occurs at the surface of the solid, and the process is termed sublimation.   A liquid boils or passes into vapour at a temperature at which the pressure of its saturated vapour is equal to that which the liquid supports.   If now the pressure of the vapour of any substance at the fusing point is equal to or greater than one atmosphere, then this substance will not exist under atmospheric pressure in the liquid state, for as soon as the solid melts the liquid will pass off into vapour.   Boiling will thus, as it were, occur at the surface of the solid.   This will always occur at a given temperature if the pressure is less than that of the saturated vapour of the substance at this temperature; but if the pressure be greater than this value the liquid form will be possible, and melting will occur if the given temperature is above the fusing point.   Thus arsenic volatilises without melting under the atmospheric pressure, but if the pressure is increased, fusion may be effected; and Carnelley[1] showed that mercuric chloride and camphor do not melt below a certain pressure peculiar to each substance, and which he proposed to call the critical pressure.

This subject has been investigated experimentally by Professors Ramsay and Young,[2] their object being to determine if solids have definite volatilising points under different pressures just as liquids have definite boiling points.   By the term volatilising is here implied a condition of the solid analogous to that of a liquid when it is said to be boiling, and not the mere passing off into vapour analogous to evaporation in liquids.   The volatilising point of a solid under a given pressure is the maximum temperature at which it will remain in the solid state under that pressure.   The experiments with camphor were characteristic of the whole series. Some camphor was congealed round the bulb of a thermometer which registered its temperature.   The thermometer with the solid camphor thus surrounding its bulb was inserted into an air reservoir in which the pressure could be varied by means of an air-pump.   A tube led from the reservoir to a condenser placed in a freezing mixture.   At low pressures the camphor vapour passed over into the condenser, but at somewhat higher pressures it deposited in the connecting tube, showing that at these pressures the vapour was much nearer its condensing

---

[1] See *Nature* for 1881 and 1882.

[2] W. Ramsay and S. Young, *Phil. Trans.*, 1884, part i. p. 37.

point. When the pressure was increased to 370 mm. the camphor melted, and a liquid drop hung from the end of the solid camphor coating the thermometer; but when the pressure was again reduced to 358 mm. this drop solidified.

Young has shown that if a piece of ice is formed about the end of a glass rod and suspended in the middle of a flask containing only water vapour, then the ice cannot be melted by applying heat to the flask, provided the pressure of the water vapour is kept below that of 4 mm. of mercury. The ice will evaporate, but remains quite dry.

197. Cold produced by Evaporation—Freezing Machines.— Evaporation is always accompanied by the disappearance of heat, and for this reason a liquid cannot continue to evaporate and at the same time maintain its temperature unless it is supplied with heat from some source. A liquid evaporating in an open vessel placed in a room at uniform temperature must therefore be at a somewhat lower temperature than the room. There is a gradual flow of heat from the room into the liquid to supply the place of that which disappears or becomes latent in evaporation. If the supply of heat be cut off while the evaporation is caused to continue, the heat necessary for the evaporation will be drawn from the liquid itself, and its temperature will fall accordingly. It is clear, therefore, that if rapid evaporation be forced by any means while the liquid at the same time is, as far as possible, prevented from receiving heat, the temperature of the liquid may be reduced to its freezing point, and solidification may be brought about as a result of the evaporation.

Fig. 98.

This was first effected in the case of water by Leslie.[1] The apparatus is shown in Fig. 98. A small capsule B containing some water is supported over a dish A filled with sulphuric acid, and the whole is placed under the receiver of an air-pump. On exhausting the receiver the pressure is diminished, and as a consequence the water evaporates rapidly, and begins to boil when the pressure is sufficiently reduced. The evaporation is greatly facilitated by the presence of the sulphuric acid, which absorbs the vapour almost as rapidly as it is formed. The temperature of the water is thus quickly reduced, and it ultimately solidifies, pre-

[1] Leslie, *Ann. de Chimie*, 1re sér., tom. lxxiii. p. 177.

senting the curious spectacle of a liquid freezing in the act of
ebullition.

A freezing machine has been constructed by M. Carré on this
principle, by which considerable quantities of water may be frozen in a
short time.   The water to be frozen is contained in a flask (Fig. 99),
which is attached by means of a tube to a cylindrical reservoir, made

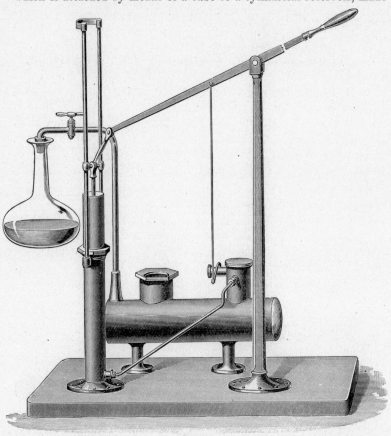

Fig. 99.

of an alloy of lead and antimony, and containing strong sulphuric acid.
From the further end of the sulphuric acid chamber, a tube leads to
the vertical cylinder of an air-pump.   A rod attached to the handle of
the pump works a stirrer which keeps the acid in agitation, and, by
thus presenting fresh acid to the vapour, hastens the evaporation.
The pump is worked till freezing begins, and the acid being in
constant agitation, the vapour is rapidly absorbed by it.   Once freezing
has commenced, the pump is worked at intervals to stir the acid.

The rate of freezing depends on the strength of the acid, and when this becomes diluted it must be renewed.

Another instrument for showing the solidification of water by evaporation is Wollaston's *cryophorus* (Fig. 100), which consists of a bent glass tube furnished with a bulb at each end. Some water is at first introduced and boiled, so as to expel all the air, and the apparatus is then hermetically sealed, so that it contains only water and water vapour, that is water under a small pressure at ordinary temperatures. When it is desired to solidify the water it is all placed in one of the bulbs, B, and the other bulb, A, is immersed in a freezing mixture. The vapour rapidly condenses in A, and is as rapidly formed in B. The cooling produced in B by this rapid evaporation is sufficient to cause solidification of the water.

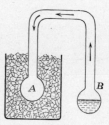

Fig. 100.

By using liquids more volatile than water, a temperature much lower than the freezing point of water may be obtained. Thus by the evaporation of sulphurous acid, which boils at − 10° C., or with chloride of methyl, a temperature low enough to freeze mercury may be easily obtained. By directing a jet of liquid carbonic acid on the bulb of an alcohol thermometer the reading of the instrument was reduced by Thilorier to − 100° C.

Another form of freezing machine, also manufactured by M. Carré,[1]

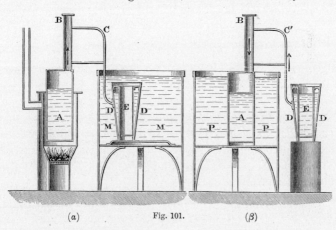

(α)   Fig. 101.   (β)

depends upon the distillation and subsequent evaporation of ammonia. The apparatus consists of a boiler A (Fig. 101) which contains a

[1] Carré, *Comptes rendus*, December 24, 1860.

strong solution of ammonia.   This boiler is connected by a tube C to
a slightly conical vessel DD called the *freezer*, and a brace binds the
two firmly together.   These vessels are made of strong galvanised iron
plate, and can bear a pressure of 7 atms.   A tubulure inserted in the
upper part of the boiler is filled with oil and contains a thermometer.
The freezer DD consists of two concentric chambers, and it is only the
space between these that the tube C communicates with.   The inner
chamber E receives a metal vessel containing the water to be frozen.

The process of freezing necessitates two distinct operations.   (a)
The boiler is first heated to about 130° over a furnace, while the freezer
is placed in a bath of cold water.   The ammonia gas is thus expelled
from the solution in the boiler, and condenses under its own pressure in
the jacket of the freezer together with about one-tenth of its weight of
water.   When sufficient gas has been thus condensed, the second part
(β) of the process is commenced.   This consists in placing the boiler
in a cold water bath, and the freezer outside covered with flannel or
other non-conducting stuff, so that it cannot receive much heat from
surrounding objects.   The cylinder E containing the water to be
frozen is then placed in the interior chamber of the freezer.   As the
boiler cools, the ammonia gas dissolves again in the water, and the
liquid ammonia in the jacket of the freezer rapidly evaporates.
During this distillation, the temperature of the freezer falls, and the
water in its interior chamber is solidified.   In order to secure better
contact between the water cylinder and the sides of the freezer, alcohol
is poured in between them.   In about $1\frac{1}{4}$ hour a compact cylinder of
ice is obtained.   The apparatus represented in Fig. 101 gives about
4 lbs. of ice per hour.   Large continuously-working forms of
apparatus which produce 800 lbs. of ice per hour have, however,
been built.

Latent Heat of Vaporisation

198. Early Determinations.—The latent heat of vaporisation of
a liquid ordinarily means the quantity of heat necessary to convert
one gramme of the liquid at the boiling point into saturated vapour at
the same temperature and pressure.

The experimental investigation of latent heats commenced with
Black and culminated in the work of Regnault.   The method first
employed by Black [1] was both primitive and interesting.   A tin vessel
containing water was set on a red-hot iron plate placed over a fire and
kept at a steady temperature.   The rate at which the temperature of

---

[1] Black, *Lectures on Chemistry*, vol. i. p. 156.

the water rose was carefully noted, and the quantity of water in the vessel being known, this gave the quantity of heat gained by it per minute. The time was then noted from the instant the water commenced to boil till it all boiled away. This gave the quantity of heat received during complete vaporisation. The result obtained by this rough method was 450—that is, the quantity of heat necessary to convert a pound of water at the boiling point under the pressure of the atmosphere into saturated vapour at the same temperature and pressure would raise the temperature of 450 pounds of water 1° C.

Some time afterwards Irvine,[1] at the invitation of Black, employed the method of condensation in a calorimeter, and found the number 430. Afterwards Watt, also at the request of Black, investigated the matter much more carefully, and found the number 533 for the latent heat of steam. This number is tolerably close to the best recent results, those of Regnault giving 536·5. The apparatus generally employed before the time of Regnault was similar to that shown in Fig. 102, and was not designed to give the accuracy attained by recent experimental research. The liquid was boiled in a retort C furnished with a thermometer which registered the temperature. The vapour distilled over and condensed in a spiral tube immersed in the water of a calorimeter. Two modes of procedure are now open for adoption. The spiral may open into a vessel situated outside the calorimeter into which the water drips as it is condensed, or the spiral may terminate in a closed reservoir R situated inside the calorimeter where the water collects and is drawn off at the termination of the experiment.

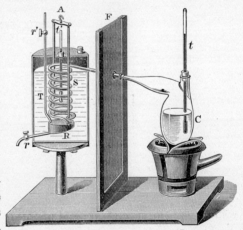

Fig. 102.

Let w be the weight of liquid arising from condensation, s its specific, and L its latent heat. Let θ be the temperature of the vapour at its condensing point, θ_1 the initial, and θ_2 the final temperature of the calorimeter. The heat given out by the condensation of the weight

---

[1] See Robison's *Mechanical Philosophy*, vol. ii., where other early determinations are cited.

w of the liquid will be $w\text{L}$, and if the liquid thus condensed be allowed
to drip away from the extremity of the condensing tube into a vessel
situated outside the calorimeter, the liquid first condensed will fall to
θ_1, if the spiral be long enough, and that condensed at the end of the
experiment will fall to θ_2, so that the whole liquid condensed may be
taken to have fallen to the mean temperature $\frac{1}{2}(\theta_1 + \theta_2)$ of the calorimeter during the experiment.   The heat given out by this cooling of
the liquid will be $ws[\theta - \frac{1}{2}(\theta_1 + \theta_2)]$.   Also if W be the complete water
equivalent of the calorimeter and water contained, the heat gained by
the calorimeter will be $\text{W}(\theta_2 - \theta_1)$, so that if R be the radiation correction

$$w\text{L} + ws\{\theta - \tfrac{1}{2}(\theta_1 + \theta_2)\} = \text{W}(\theta_2 - \theta_1) + \text{R}.$$

If s be known, this equation gives L directly, but if s be not known,
another experiment in which θ_1 and θ_2 are different will give us
another equation containing L and s, and by means of these two
equations both L and s may be determined.

It is better to collect the liquid in a reservoir attached to the condensing spiral, and situated inside the calorimeter.   In this case all the
liquid condensed attains ultimately the final temperature of the calorimeter, so that the equation becomes

$$w\text{L} + ws(\theta - \theta_2) = \text{W}(\theta_2 - \theta_1) + \text{R}.$$

An experiment conducted with this form of apparatus is subject
to many sources of error, for the vapour in passing through the neck
of the retort leading into the calorimeter may become partially condensed and arrive in the calorimeter deprived of part of its latent heat.
This will lead to too small a value in the determination of L, and
may be partially avoided by sloping the neck of the retort upwards,
so that any liquid condensed in the neck of the retort may run
back again into the boiler.   Heat also passes over to the calorimeter
by conduction through the connecting tube, and this increases the value
of L; but there is no reason why the diminution arising from the
former error should be exactly counterbalanced by the latter.

Evidently the vapour tube should be so arranged that any vapour
which condenses outside the calorimeter should remain outside, and all
that condenses inside should remain inside.   Want of precaution in
the former respect leads to too low a value of L, and in the latter too
high.   It is probably for this reason that Rumford obtained such a
high figure as 571 for water vapour.   Despretz[1] subsequently found
540, and Brix,[2] who closely discusses the sources of error, obtained the
same number.

[1] *Ann. de Chimie*, tom. xxiv. p. 323, 1823.
[2] *Pogg. Ann.* vol. lv. p. 341.

Up to the time of Regnault's work on the latent heat of water vapour it was generally admitted that the *total* [1] heat of water vapour was independent of the pressure.   Watt considered it established by Watt's law. his experiments that the quantity of heat required to convert a given mass of water at zero into saturated vapour was the same whatever the pressure of the vapour might be, and this supposed property was known as Watt's law.   Later experiments by Clément and Desormes [2] in 1819 appeared to confirm it, so that the law became generally admitted on insufficient evidence, perhaps because it was very convenient in many calculations concerning the steam-engine.   Several attempts were also made to deduce it theoretically.

Another law, namely, that the latent heat of vaporisation was constant, was proposed by Creighton and Southern [3] in 1803.   This was known as Southern's law.

That both laws are incorrect was shown subsequently by Regnault, as will appear from the account of his experiments given in Art. 201.

199. Berthelot's Apparatus.—M. Berthelot [4] has shown that many of the errors attending the early method of experimenting may be avoided by means of the apparatus shown in Fig. 103, by means of which the latent heat of a vapour may be rapidly and accurately determined without having recourse to the elaborate apparatus and precautions employed by M. Regnault.   In M. Berthelot's apparatus the flask containing the liquid under examination is heated by a circular gas-burner l, burning under a metallic disc m.   The centre of the flask is traversed by a wide tube TT, through which the vapour descends into the calorimeter, [5] where it condenses in the spiral SS and collects in the reservoir R.   The calorimeter is placed inside a water-jacket, and is protected from the radiation of the burner by a slab of wood covered by a sheet of wire gauze.   By means of this arrangement partial condensation is avoided before the vapour enters the calorimeter, and the error arising from conductivity is corrected by observation of the motion of the thermometer placed in the calorimeter before the distillation commences and after it is completed.   The weight of liquid condensed is about 20 to 30 gr. at most,

---

[1] The expression "total heat" is an abbreviation for the quantity of heat required to convert unit weight of the liquid at the freezing point into saturated vapour at any other temperature.

[2] Thenard, *Traité de chimie*, tom. i. p. 78.

[3] Robison, *Mechanical Philosophy*, vol. ii. p. 160.

[4] *Comptes rendus*, tom. lxxxv. p. 647 ; and *Journal de Physique*, tom. vi. p. 337.

[5] It would seem advisable to introduce a sleeve of insulating material between the glass tube TT and the burner in this apparatus, to prevent a possible superheating of the vapour.

and the time occupied is only from 2 to 4 minutes. By this means
M. Berthelot found for the latent heat of water the value 536·2,
whereas the elaborate investigation of Regnault gave 536·5. The close
agreement here shows the value of the apparatus in combining speed
with accuracy, and it consequently may be used to determine with
sufficient precision the latent heats of rare organic liquids.

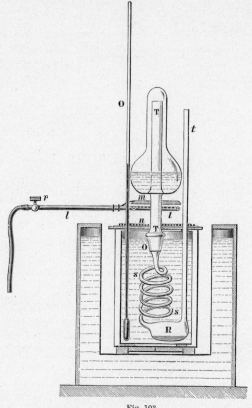

Fig. 103.

200. Method of Superheating.—The greater part of the exact
investigations have been made by heating the vapour above its condensing point before it passes into the calorimeter, and in this case the
specific heat of the vapour, as well as that of the liquid, appears in the
equation which determines the specific heat. Let, as before, the temperature of condensation of the vapour be θ, while the initial and
final temperatures of the calorimeter are θ_1 and θ_2. Let the vapour
entering the calorimeter be superheated at the temperature θ', and
let the specific heat of the vapour be σ. The quantity of heat given

out by the vapour in cooling from θ' to its point of condensation θ is $w\sigma\ (\theta' - \theta)$, so that the equation for L becomes

$$w\sigma(\theta' - \theta) + wL + ws(\theta - \theta_2) = W(\theta_2 - \theta_1) + R,$$

supposing that the condensed liquid is all retained in the calorimeter and attains the final temperature θ_2. Three experiments in which the temperatures are varied give us three equations to determine L, σ, and s. It is here supposed that σ is constant. This is not the case with non-saturated vapours, and for the range here employed σ represents the mean specific heat of the vapour.

201. Regnault's Determination of the Latent Heat of Water Vapour.—The problem which Regnault proposed to himself was the determination of the *total heat* of saturated water vapour at divers pressures—that is, the estimation of the quantity of heat necessary to convert unit weight of water at 0° C. into saturated vapour at any pressure.

The apparatus by means of which this investigation was conducted is shown in profile in Fig. 104, and front view in Fig. 105. The vapour was generated in a strongly made boiler (Fig. 104) of 300 litres capacity, which contained about 150 litres of pure distilled water. The vapour accumulated in the upper part of the boiler, and there entered a serpentine tube, enclosed within the boiler, the open end of which projected above the surface of the water. This tube carried the vapour from the boiler to the calorimeter K, and in the interval between the two the tube was furnished with a steam-jacket T, the outside of which was well wrapped in non-conducting woollen stuff. By this means the vapour entered the calorimeter saturated, but quite dry, that is, free from mist. The temperature of ebullition was indicated by thermometers passing down into the boiler. At high pressures the reading of the thermometer would be incorrect owing to the influence of the pressure on the bulb, and for this reason iron tubulures closed at the lower end were let into the boiler. These descended into the interior, and contained mercury in which the thermometers were placed free from all perturbations arising from the pressure of the steam.

Having arrived at the distributing piece R, the vapour could be let into either of two exactly similar calorimeters K and K′ (Fig. 105) or it could pass on into the condenser E. Immersed in each calorimeter was a condensing system consisting of two copper spheres and a spiral copper tube, as shown in Fig. 105. The vapour condensed here (when allowed to pass in), and the water resulting was drawn off in a flask and weighed.

The amount of vapour condensed during an experiment could be thus determined, and as some of the liquid adhered to the walls of the spiral and copper spheres, it was assumed that this adhesion remained constant, and therefore the water drawn off in any experiment represented the amount of condensation.

In order that the temperature of ebullition might be varied at

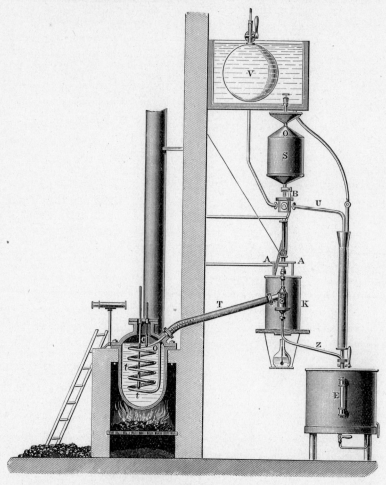

Fig. 104.

pleasure, a large air-drum V, immersed in a bath which kept its temperature constant, was connected to B, and thence with every part of the apparatus. By pumping air into (or out of) this drum the pressure in the boiler could be varied at pleasure. This pressure was measured by an open-air manometer M.

In making an experiment the boiler was heated, and the steam was allowed to pass through the connecting tubes into the condenser for nearly an hour, so that the whole apparatus took up a stationary temperature, and the air was completely chased from the boiler. A preliminary experiment was made by noting for five minutes the rate of

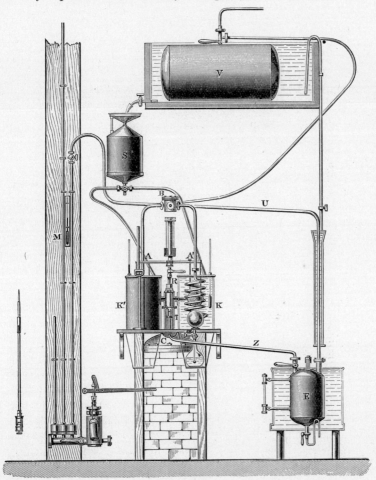

Fig. 105.

change of temperature of each of the calorimeters. The water when first placed in the calorimeter was below the temperature of the air, so that during an experiment it received heat by radiation, and also by conduction through the connecting tubes. An observation made in the same way before the boiler was heated gave the radiation correction, and this, combined with that now made after heating, gives the

correction for conduction.   In correcting for radiation it was found
sufficiently accurate to employ Newton's law of cooling, viz. that the
rate of change of temperature due to radiation is equal to the difference of temperature between the calorimeter and the air multiplied by
a constant ; the value of the constant was found in this case to lie
between the limits 0·001 and 0·002.

The two calorimeters were now filled with water at $\theta_1^{\,\circ}$, and the
vapour was allowed to pass into one of them till its temperature
became $\theta_2^{\,\circ}$.   If w be the weight of water condensed in this operation,
and W the water equivalent of the calorimeter, then the approximate
equation for L is

$$wL + ws(\theta - \theta_2) = W(\theta_2 - \theta_1),$$

where θ is the temperature of condensation of the vapour—that is, the
temperature of the vapour in the boiler, and s the mean specific
heat of water between θ and θ_2.   It is to be noted that θ_2 is not the
temperature of the calorimeter at the instant the steam is shut off.
During the process of condensation the temperature of the water in
the condensing apparatus is above that of the calorimeter, so that after
the steam is shut off the temperature of the calorimeter continues to
rise for a short time to a maximum temperature $\theta_2^{\,\circ}$.   If no loss or gain
of heat took place through radiation and conduction the maximum
temperature would be $\theta_2 + \Sigma\delta\theta$, where $\Sigma\delta\theta$ is the sum of the corrections
to be applied for all perturbating influences, and the equation for L
becomes

$$wL + ws(\theta - \theta_2) = W(\theta_2 + \Sigma\delta\theta - \theta_1).$$

A similar experiment was then made with the other calorimeter.
Thus when the steam was shut off from one it was turned into the
other, so that while one was subject to the heating arising from the
condensation of the vapour, as well as to the perturbations of radiation
and conduction, the other was subject to the latter influences alone.
Hence, if the two calorimeters are identical in all respects, the observations made on the variations of temperature of one can be used to
determine the corrections to be applied to the other.   Perfect identity
could not, however, be realised, so that it became necessary to consider
the corrections to be applied to each separately.

During an experiment each calorimeter was subject to two sources
of error,—one due to conduction through the connecting tubes, which
may be taken proportional to the difference between the temperatures
of the vapour and the calorimeter, the other due to radiation and
proportional to the difference of temperature of the atmosphere
and the calorimeter.   Denoting these differences by Δ_1 and Δ_2, the

change of temperature per minute of the calorimeter due to these
causes will be

$$\delta\theta = A_1\Delta_1 + A_2\Delta_2 \quad . \quad . \quad . \quad . \quad . \quad (1)$$

The coefficients A_1 and A_2 were determined by first allowing the vapour
to pass through the distributing piece R into the condenser, so that
the calorimeters were heated by conduction and radiation only. Observations on the rate of change of temperature gave $\delta\theta$, Δ_1 and Δ_2
in equation (1).   Another equation was formed between A_1 and A_2,
with different coefficients, by allowing the vapour to pass into either
calorimeter for some time, so that its temperature became elevated,
and Δ_1 and Δ_2 became $\Delta_1{}'$ and $\Delta_2{}'$.   The steam was then shut out from
the calorimeter and allowed to pass, as before, into the condenser, and
observations were made on the rate of cooling or heating of the calorimeter.   This gave

$$\delta\theta' = A_1\Delta_1' + A_2\Delta_2' \quad . \quad . \quad . \quad . \quad . \quad (2)$$

Equations (1) and (2) determine A_1 and A_2, and these being known
for each calorimeter, the total correction $\Sigma\delta\theta$ to the temperature of
either calorimeter during an experiment can be easily found.

By this means Regnault determined the quantity of heat

$$L + s(\theta - \theta_2)$$

necessary to convert a gramme of water at $\theta_2{}^\circ$ into saturated
vapour at θ°, where s is the mean specific heat of water between θ°
and $\theta_2{}^\circ$.   The experiments were conducted under pressures varying
from 0.22 to 13.625 atmospheres, and between these limits Regnault
found that the *total heat* of steam, or the heat necessary to convert
1 gramme of water at 0° into steam at any temperature θ, was
represented by the formula

$$Q = 606.5 + 0.305\theta.$$

In 38 experiments made under the ordinary atmospheric pressure Total heat
the mean value of the total heat was found to be 637.67, the extreme of steam.
values in the series being 635.6 and 638.4.

Taking the specific heat of water to be unity, the formula for the
latent heat at any temperature θ will be, according to Regnault,

$$L = Q - \theta = 606.5 - 0.695\theta.$$

These results overthrew the laws of Watt and Southern, and
settled all controversy on the subject.

When the variation of the specific heat of water is taken into
account the latent heat of steam falls from 606.5 at 0° C. to 536.5
at 100° C. and to 464.3 at 200° C., and if the formula for L is quite

2 B

general, it follows that the latent heat of water vapour will become
zero at the temperature

$$\theta = \frac{606 \cdot 5}{0 \cdot 695} = 872 \text{ (approx.)},$$

and this consideration stands in close relation to what is known as the
continuous passage from the liquid to the gaseous state in the celebrated experiments of Cagniard de la Tour and Andrews (Art. 238).
The critical point for water, however, appears to be 365° C.

202. Griffiths' Experiments.—The value of the latent heat of
evaporation of water at the temperatures 30° and 40° C. was
determined by Griffiths,[1] using the calorimeter described in Art.
174 (Fig. 89). A known weight of water was put in a glass bulb
with a narrow jet; this was placed in a small silver flask, to which was
attached a coil of silver tube 18 feet long. Between the flask and
the coil of tube was the spiral of platinum-silver wire which, heated
by an electric current, supplied the heat necessary to vaporise the
water. The flask, tube, and wire were all enclosed in the calorimeter,
which was filled with aniline in the earlier experiments, but later
with a special petroleum oil which was non-volatile and a good
insulator. The calorimeter, being surrounded by a vacuum and
thermostat, was kept at a constant temperature, never varying as
much as 0°·01 C. The end of the silver tube passed outside the
apparatus and was connected with an air-pump. On working the
pump the water was made to issue drop by drop from the bulb, so
that the rate of evaporation could be kept quite regular. Thus the
vapour formed in the flask had to pass up the whole length of the
silver spiral tube and issued at the temperature of the calorimeter and
free from water mechanically carried over. As in the experiments
for determining the mechanical equivalent of heat, the liquid in the
calorimeter was vigorously stirred. The equation for determining
the latent heat of evaporation may be put in the following form :—

$$ML = Q_e t_e + Q_s t_s + \Sigma q,$$

M being the mass of water evaporated, Q_e the heat per second
supplied by the electric current, Q_s the heat generated by the stirrer,
t_e and t_s the times during which heat was supplied by these two
sources respectively (t_e and t_s being practically equal), and Σq the total
heat received owing to other causes such as radiation and conduction.
Although Q_e was necessarily measured in electric units, it was reduced
to thermal units by employing the value of J determined by means of
the same calorimeter and the same method of electric measurement.
Thus any error due to uncertainty in the values of the electric units

[1] *Phil. Trans.* p. 261, A, 1895.

was eliminated.   The greatest uncertainty was in the estimation of Q_s, but this constituted only about 1 per cent of the rate of heat supply.   The following are the values of L obtained :—

Temp. by Nitrogen Thermometer.	Latent Heat (15° C. unit).	Latent Heat (20° C. unit).
40°·15 C.	572·60	573·15
30°·00 C.	578·70	579·25

The figures in the last column are calculated from the value of the ratio of the two units given in Art. 174.

The advantages of Griffiths' method over most of the others that have been made use of are that it is practically independent of errors in thermometry and is not affected by changes in the specific heat of water.   The temperature being stationary, the heat capacity of the calorimeter or of its contents does not enter into consideration, and the radiation correction is very small and determinate.

Of previous measurements of the latent heat of evaporation of water, one of the most reliable is that which was carried out by Dieterici [1] at 0° C.   His method resembles Griffiths' in the use of a constant temperature and in being largely independent of thermometry.   He used a Bunsen calorimeter, and estimated the heat required to evaporate a known mass of water at 0° by the quantity of mercury expelled from the calorimeter during the formation of ice.   He gave his results in mean calories, assuming that the mean calorie corresponded to the expulsion of 15·44 mg. of mercury, taking the average value deduced from the experiments of Bunsen, Schuller and Wartha, and Velten.   The value given by Dieterici for the latent heat is 596·73 calories at 0° C. *Dieterici's experiments.*

Although Griffiths' experiments were not sufficiently extended to justify the calculation from them of a formula for the relation of latent heat to temperature, yet if a linear relation between these quantities be assumed,[2] the result shows a very striking agreement with the values obtained by Regnault at 100° and by Dieterici at 0°. The linear formula suggested by Griffiths is *Variation with temperature.*

$$L = 596 \cdot 73 - 0 \cdot 6010\theta,$$

using the calorie at 15° C. as the unit.   This unit is very nearly equal to the mean calorie (see Art. 174), so that the results are

[1] *Wied. Ann.* vol. xxxvii., 1889.

[2] The latent heat of vaporisation of benzene appears to be a linear function of the temperature (see next Article).   Probably, however, latent heats diminish more rapidly as the critical temperature is approached.

directly comparable.   At the higher temperatures Griffiths' formula
accords better with Regnault's results than Regnault's own formula,
while the experiments at low temperatures carried out by Regnault
appear to be less trustworthy—objections having been pointed out by
Winkelmann, the chief of which is that Regnault in this series of
experiments measured the temperature of the evaporating water by
the vapour pressure in the condenser.

   203. Latent Heats of Vaporisation by Comparison.—As the
accurate measurements of latent heats of vaporisation is tedious and
difficult, it is more convenient to determine the latent heats of liquids
other than water by comparison with water or other standard liquid.
The following simple method has been employed by Professor Ramsay
and Miss Marshall for comparing the latent heats of two liquids at
their boiling points under atmospheric pressure.[1]   Two glass vessels,
somewhat resembling incandescent electric lamps, were filled with the
liquids to be compared.   Each vessel was provided with a platinum
or platinum-silver wire spiral in its interior with thick platinum
terminals, and was enclosed within another vessel, so that the liquid
could be surrounded by a jacket of its own vapour.   When each vessel,
containing a known weight of liquid, had been heated just to the
boiling point, a known electric current was passed through the two
wires in series.   If the resistances are equal, the latent heats will be
inversely proportional to the amounts evaporated in a given time,
that is, to the respective losses in weight of the two vessels.   In
general, the latent heat is proportional to the resistance divided by
the amount vaporised in a given time.

   Water was found to be an inconvenient liquid to use for purposes
of comparison.   Its latent heat of vaporisation is very large, and its
insulating properties are insufficient when bare wires are used.   Consequently, a careful determination of the latent heat for benzene
was made by Griffiths and Miss Marshall,[2] using the same method and
instrument as had been employed by Griffiths for water, as described
in the preceding article.   The following values were obtained :—

Latent heat of evaporation of benzene.

Temp. (Nitrogen Scale).	Latent Heat of Benzene (Unit=calorie at 15° C.).
°	
50	99·14
40	100·71
30	102·30
20	103·82

[1] *Phil. Mag.*, Jan. 1896 ; Jan. 1897 (see also footnote, p. 321).
[2] *Phil. Mag.*, Jan. 1896 ; Jan. 1897.

These figures correspond closely with the linear formula—

$$L_\theta = 107 \cdot 05 - 0 \cdot 158\theta.$$

Assuming this formula to hold up to $80° \cdot 2$, the boiling point of benzene at atmospheric pressure, we get as the latent heat of vaporisation of benzene at its boiling point

$$L = 94 \cdot 34,$$

expressed in thermal units at $15°$ C. This does not differ very much from the direct determinations of R. Schiff [1] ($93 \cdot 4$) and K. Wirtz [2] ($92 \cdot 9$).

Andrews [3] investigated latent heats for the purpose of ascertaining whether any relation existed between the latent heats and the physical properties of vapours, but he failed to deduce any fixed law. In this inquiry he was preceded by Ure, Despretz, Brix, and Favre and Silbermann. It has since been suggested that for different liquids [4] the latent heat multiplied by the molecular weight is approximately proportional to the absolute temperature. In other words, the molecular latent heat is proportional to the absolute temperature. Thus for water at $100°$ C., $L = 536 \cdot 6$, the molecular weight $\mu = 18$, and $T = 373$.

$$\frac{\mu L}{T} = 25 \cdot 9.$$

Trouton's law.

204. Later Experiments on the Latent Heat of Evaporation of Liquids.—Since the experiments described in the preceding articles were performed, a considerable number of further investigations into the latent heats of evaporation of liquids have been made; only a brief account of these can be given. Two methods deserve particular mention. The first of these is the method of Joly's steam calorimeter ; this is the more direct method, if the latent heat is to be expressed in calories. A determination of the latent heat of steam was made by Joly himself with his steam calorimeter, the result being $539 \cdot 3$ calories. The same instrument was used by Carlton-Sutton.[5] A cylindrical glass bulb of 8 to 10 c.c. capacity was nearly filled with water, cooled to $0°$ C., immersed in steam at $100°$ C., and the increase of weight noted. Every gramme of water in the bulb required of course 100 mean calories to raise its temperature from $0°$ to $100°$, and thus the heat given up by a known quantity of steam in condensing was determined. The thermal capacity of the bulb was eliminated by

[1] *Liebig's Annalen*, vol. ccxxxiv. p. 338, 1886.

[2] *Wied. Ann.* vol. xl. p. 438, 1890.

[3] Andrews, *Quarterly Journal Chem. Soc. of London*, vol. i. p. 27.

[4] F. T. Trouton, *Phil. Mag.* vol. xviii. p. 54, 1884.

[5] *Proc. R. Soc.* vol. xciii. (A) p. 155, 1917.

making a second experiment with the bulb nearly empty. The value obtained was 538·88 mean calories.

Another method, which has been frequently employed, is to surround a vessel containing the liquid with a jacket filled with the vapour of the liquid used, then to evaporate a quantity of the liquid (determined by weighing) by means of a coil of wire heated by an electric current, and to measure the energy supplied in joules. This is much the same as the method of Griffiths (Art. 202). The use of a jacket of the vapour of the liquid in question seems to have been first adopted in direct determinations (see Art. 203) by Brown [1] and A. C. Smith,[2] who also evaporated the liquid by an electric current. The same device was used later by Mathews,[3] who suspended the vessel containing the liquid by a wire from the span of a balance, and introduced the heating current by wires dipping into mercury cups. He obtained 94·35 calories as the latent heat of evaporation of benzene, which is very close to the value given by Griffiths and Miss Marshall.

A possible source of error in this method is that the vapour of the boiling liquid may carry away some of the liquid in the form of spray. To avoid this A. W. Smith [4] adopted a different arrangement. A quantity of water contained in a vacuum vessel was maintained at a temperature of about 98° C. by a resistance wire electrically heated, while at the same time a steady current of dry air was passed over the surface of the water. When the temperature had become quite steady, the issuing air current was switched into a condenser, where most of the water vapour was condensed, the remainder being extracted by passing the air over sulphuric acid. The total quantity of water collected was weighed. To eliminate the radiation correction, experiments were made at the same temperature but with different rates of evaporation. Taking the mean calorie as 4·1826 joules, the value obtained for the latent heat of vaporisation of water at 100° C. was 536·7 calories.

The variation of the latent heat of steam with temperature was studied by Henning.[5] The water was boiled in a copper vessel communicating by a tube with a vessel in which the steam was condensed. The heat was communicated and measured electrically. By regulating the pressure, the temperature at which evaporation occurred was varied between 30° C. and 180° C. The vessel con-

[1] *J. Chem. Soc.* vol. lxxxiii. p. 987, 1903.

[2] *Proc. R. Soc. Edin.* vol. xxiv. p. 450, 1903.

[3] *J. Amer. Chem. Soc.* vol. xlviii. p. 562, 1926.

[4] *Phys. Review*, vol. xxxiii. p. 173, 1911.

[5] *Ann. der Physik*, vol. xxi. p. 849, 1906 ; vol. xxix. p. 441, 1909.

taining the boiling water was surrounded by another vessel which was
maintained at the same temperature by electric heating.   The residual
small radiation correction was eliminated by difference, using different
rates of evaporation at the same temperature.   He obtained results
which are fairly represented by the formula

$$L = 538\cdot86 + 0\cdot5994(100 - \theta) \; ;$$

or better, by the quadratic formula

$$L = 538\cdot46 - 0\cdot6422(\theta - 100) - 0\cdot000833(\theta - 100)^2.$$

Henning gives $538\cdot7$ as the latent heat at $100°$.

Thiesen,[1] starting from the consideration that the latent heat
must vanish at the critical temperature, showed that the latent heat
could be well represented by the formula

$$L = A(\theta_c - \theta)^n,$$

where θ_c is the critical temperature and $n = \frac{1}{3}$.   Henning, taking the
critical temperature of water to be $365°$ C., compared his results with
this formula, and found that they were very well represented by the
formula if $A = 94\cdot210$, $\theta_c = 365$, $n = 0\cdot31249$.   On the other hand, if
the critical temperature were deduced from the observations, the best
formula was

$$L = 93\cdot706(366\cdot25 - \theta)^{0\cdot31312}.$$

The quadratic formula given above agreed somewhat better with the
experiments when the whole range was taken into account, but it has
no theoretical justification, and would make the critical temperature
$606°$ C.

Thiesen's formula was tested by Marc de Hemptinne,[2] taking his
data from published tables.   He found that it agreed remarkably well
with the observations, but the limits of temperature were narrow and
far from the critical point.   The value of n did not vary much for
different liquids, and was about $0\cdot38$ or $0\cdot39$ for most.   The lowest
value noted was $0\cdot313$ for water, and the highest $0\cdot404$ for ethyl
acetate.

The latent heat of evaporation of a number of liquids of high
boiling points was measured by Awbery and E. Griffiths,[3] using the
method of mixtures and also the electric method.   Fogler and
Rodebush[4] found the latent heat of evaporation of mercury at $142°$ C.
to be 14490 calories, and that of cadmium at $321°$ C. to be 25350
calories.

[1] *Verhand. d. Physikal. Gesell. zu Berlin*, vol. xvi. p. 80, 1897.
[2] *Bull. of the R. Acad. of Belgium*, vol. xii. p. 296, 1926.
[3] *Proc. Phys. Soc.* vol. xxxvi. p. 303, 1924.
[4] *J. Amer. Chem. Soc.* vol. xlv. p. 2080, 1923.

Dewar found the latent heats of vaporisation of oxygen, nitrogen, and hydrogen at their respective boiling points at atmospheric pressure to be in calories (see Art. 148)—

Oxygen, 51·15 ; nitrogen, 50·4 ; hydrogen, 123·1.

For *internal* and *external* latent heats, see Chap. VIII. sec. v.

205. Specific Heats of Non-Saturated Vapours.—If the vapour be superheated before entering the calorimeter, then, as we have already seen, the equation for L embraces the specific heats of the substance in both the liquid and gaseous states; so that by three experiments both these quantities as well as L may be determined. In this manner Regnault[1] found that the specific heat of superheated water vapour under constant pressure was constant within the limits of temperature employed in his experiments. The results of four series of experiments gave for steam 0·46881, 0·48111, 0·48080, 0·47963.

Regnault[2] extended his researches to several other liquids. The vapour was superheated by passing through a spiral contained in an oil bath at a temperature higher than the temperature of boiling. The heat necessary to raise the liquid to its boiling point was accurately determined, and these experiments gave both the latent heat and the specific heat of the vapour. The latter is very small compared with the former, so that the specific heat of a vapour deter-

---

[1] Regnault employed another method for determining the latent heat of vapours at low temperatures. A known weight of the liquid was placed in a reservoir contained in the calorimeter at a temperature $\theta_1°$, and boiling was caused by reducing the pressure in the reservoir by means of an air-pump. The vapour condensed in a retort immersed in a freezing mixture of ice and sea salt. The pressure of the vapour coming from the liquid is always somewhat greater than that of the artificial atmosphere registered by the manometer. The liquid all boiled away, and the temperature of the calorimeter fell to $\theta_2°$. If $\Sigma\delta\theta$ denotes the correction of θ_2 for losses of heat during the experiment, then the heat lost by the calorimeter during the vaporisation of the liquid is

$$W(\theta_1 - \theta_2 + \Sigma\delta\theta).$$

If, on the other hand, the temperature of ebullition of the liquid be θ, the heat gained by the liquid is

$$Lw + w\sigma\left(\frac{\theta_1 + \theta_2}{2} - \theta\right) - sw(\theta_1 - \theta),$$

and we have the equation

$$Lw + w\sigma[\tfrac{1}{2}(\theta_1 + \theta_2) - \theta] = sw(\theta_1 - \theta) + W(\theta_1 - \theta_2 + \Sigma\delta\theta).$$

An uncertainty occurs in the value of θ arising from the reading of the pressure of the manometer.

By the above method experiments were made at pressures varying between 13·6 mm. and 3·9 mm.

[2] *Recherches*, etc., tom. ii. p. 163.

mined in this manner is subject to all the errors of a complicated experiment.

The specific heat of carbon dioxide is known to vary considerably near the condensing point, and it is highly probable that all other vapours vary in a similar manner in this respect.

Eilhard Wiedemann proposed a method for determining the specific heats of vapours under constant pressure, which applies to liquids that boil between 0° and 100°. Boiling is caused at a low temperature by partial exhaustion—that is, reduction of pressure by an air-pump. The vapour is then heated in a bath and allowed to pass through a calorimeter at a temperature of from 20° to 30° C., which is above the condensing point of the vapour. All the heat yielded to the calorimeter is due to the cooling of the vapour. An experiment lasts five or six minutes, and the results obtained agree with those of Regnault. They indicate that the specific heats of vapours increase notably as the temperature rises.

SECTION III

ON THE PRESSURE OF SATURATED VAPOURS

206. Vapour Pressure.—When a bubble of air is allowed to pass into the vacuum of a barometer tube a depression of the mercurial column is produced, which increases with the quantity of air introduced. A similar depression is produced by the vapour of a liquid, and it was in this manner that Dalton [1] first studied the pressures of saturated vapours. Small quantities of any volatile liquid may be conveniently introduced into a barometer by means of a curved pipette. If a very small globule of a liquid is allowed to ascend to the top of the mercurial column it will pass into vapour very rapidly, filling the space above the mercury, and producing a corresponding depression of the column. Another small globule will also evaporate and produce a further depression, and so on. A point is reached, however, at which further evaporation ceases, and the introduction of more liquid is not attended by an increase of vapour pressure in the space above the mercury, the temperature being supposed constant. If more liquid is introduced it merely floats on the top of the mercury (Fig. 106). Further evaporation ceases. Thus at a given temperature a definite quantity of a liquid will evaporate in a given space, and the pressure it exerts in this space is a function of the temperature only. If the space be increased, more liquid, if present, will evaporate, and if the space be reduced some of the vapour will condense. In this case the vapour (or space) is said to be saturated, and the corresponding pressure is the maximum vapour pressure for this temperature.

The behaviour of a vapour may be studied by depressing or raising the barometer tube in the cistern (Fig. 107). When the vapour is saturated the depression of the tube in the cistern merely reduces the space above the mercurial column. Some of the vapour condenses, and the height of the mercurial column remains fixed. The vapour pressure remains constant, and the glass tube slides over the column

[1] Dalton, *Memoir of the Manchester Soc.* vol. xv. p. 409.

of mercury as if it were a solid bar of metal.   If, however, the vapour is not saturated it behaves very nearly as a gas.   Elevation of the tube increases the height of the column—that is, decreases the pressure of the vapour, and depression of the tube in the cistern increases the vapour pressure and decreases the height of the mercurial column.   A non-saturated vapour nearly obeys Boyle's law.

The pressure of a saturated vapour depends on the temperature, and also on the nature of the liquid.   Thus at 20° C. the depression of

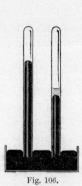

Fig. 106.

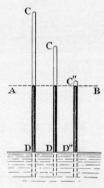

Fig. 107.

a barometer column by saturated water vapour is about 17 mm., by alcohol 60 mm., and by ether 460 mm.

If the temperature is kept constant a slight increase of pressure will produce complete condensation of a saturated vapour.   If the temperature is lowered condensation occurs also, and continues till the vapour pressure reaches the maximum value corresponding to the new temperature.   It is not necessary, however, to cool the whole space occupied by a saturated vapour in order to produce condensation.   The cooling of any part of it will suffice. Thus, if one bulb A of a bent tube AB (Fig. 108) contains a liquid, the remainder of the tube will be filled with saturated vapour.   If now B is cooled by being placed

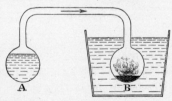

Fig. 108.

in a cold bath, or otherwise, the vapour in B will condense.   The vapour pressure in B will be less than that in A, and as a consequence a current of vapour will flow from A to B.   This state of things will continue as long as B is colder than A.   The liquid will gradually distil into the colder part of the apparatus.   The flow of vapour is accompanied by a flow of heat tending to equalise the temperatures.

The evaporation in A is accompanied by absorption of heat, and evolution of the same takes place in B. The apparatus illustrates the action of a heat engine. The current of vapour flowing from A to B might be employed to do mechanical work (as a mill is turned by a current of water), while heat passes from a body A to another B at a lower temperature.

207. Determination of Maximum Vapour Pressures.—The first fairly accurate measurements of the pressure of saturated vapours (or

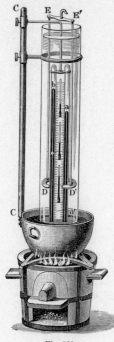

maximum vapour tensions, as it is generally termed) were made by Dalton.[1] Previously the matter had been investigated by Ziegler,[2] Watt,[3] Bétancourt,[4] Southern,[5] and Schmidt,[6] in a more or less unsatisfactory manner.

The apparatus employed by Dalton is shown in Fig. 109. Two similar barometer tubes a and b were attached to a scale which enabled the height of the mercury to be read off. Both stood in the same cistern of mercury, and were surrounded by a bath which could be heated from below, and the temperature was noted by means of three thermometers fixed along the scale, the mean of which was taken to represent the temperature of the bath. A little liquid was introduced into one of the tubes (a), and the depression of the mercurial column noted, together with the temperature of the bath. By varying the temperature the pressure of the saturated vapour was found for all temperatures within the range of the apparatus. As in this form of apparatus the temperature

Fig. 109.

of the mercury is different in different experiments, it is necessary to reduce the observed depression to that at which it would have been if the mercury were at zero—that is, the difference of height h must be divided by $(1 + m\theta)$, where m is the coefficient of expansion of mercury. With water vapour the pressure is equal to 1 atmo. at 100° C., and, consequently, this form of apparatus can be used only for temperatures below 100° C. At this temperature

[1] Dalton, *Memoir of the Manchester Soc.* vol. xv. 409.
[2] Ziegler, *Specimen physico-chimicum de digestore Papini*, p. 48, Basel, 1759.
[3] Watt, *Robison's System of Mech. Phil.* vol. ii. p. 29, Brewster's edition, 1814.
[4] Bétancourt, *Mémoire sur la force expansive de la vapeur*, Paris, 1792.
[5] Southern, *Robison's Mech. Phil.* vol. ii. p. 170.
[6] Schmidt, *Journal de Physique de Gren*, tom. iv. p. 151.

the mercury in the tube which contains the vapour will stand at the cistern level.

The chief objection to these early experiments was the want of precaution in securing uniformity of temperature in the bath. The use of several thermometers placed along the scale does not avoid this source of error. The vapour will be practically at the temperature of that part of the bath which surrounds it, and the mercury in a similar way will assume the temperature of that part of the bath around it. For accuracy the bath should be maintained throughout at the same temperature, or else some scheme should be devised by which the temperature of the vapour could be accurately known, and also that of the mercury. The pressure determined here is really the maximum pressure of the vapour in the coldest part of the tube.

The difference of height of the mercurial columns should also be measured for accuracy by means of a cathetometer; and for this purpose the use of a cylindrical glass vessel to contain the bath is objectionable, as errors due to refraction are introduced. A bath chamber with a plane glass front is much superior.

Accurate determinations in which these sources of error were avoided were first made by Kaemtz.[1] He merely exposed the tubes in the atmosphere, and noted the depressions through summer and winter, the temperature ranging between $-19°$ and $+26°$ C. These observations were made for meteorological purposes; but a much wider range is necessary in physical investigations. The gap thus left was filled up by Regnault.

A general law connecting the vapour pressures of different substances was announced by Dalton in 1801, to the effect that the pressures of the saturated vapours of all liquids were equal at temperatures equally removed from their boiling points. This law is, however, not near the truth. Water boils at $100°$ C., and ether under the same pressure at $35°$ C.; the pressure of water vapour at $80°$ C. (that is $20°$ below the boiling point) is 355 mm., while that of ether at $15°$ C. is 354 mm. These numbers agree excellently. In fact it was by the comparison of water and ether that Dalton deduced his rule. In the case of alcohol, however, the boiling point is $78°$ C., and the vapour pressure at $58°$ C. is only 330 mm. This is considerably too low according to Dalton's rule. Similar deviations occur with other substances.

Dühring's rule agrees much better with experiment. It is merely a modification of Dalton's law with a factor introduced depending on the nature of the substance. In it as we pass from temperatures of equal

---

[1] Kaemtz, *Traité de météorologie*, tom. i. p. 290.

vapour pressure for two substances to two other temperatures of equal pressure, the differences of temperature are not taken equal, but proportional, the constant of proportionality depending on the nature of the substance.

208. Vapour Pressures at Low Temperatures.—The determination of vapour pressures at temperatures below 0° C. was conducted

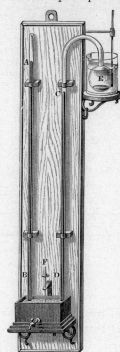

by Gay-Lussac[1] with a modified form of Dalton's apparatus. The vapour tube was an ordinary barometer tube CD having its upper end bent round (Fig. 110), and terminating in a pendent bulb E which could be conveniently immersed in a freezing mixture. This mixture should be fluid, so that it could be constantly stirred during an experiment. The liquid under examination was contained in the bulb, so that its temperature as well as that of its vapour was the same as that of the freezing mixture, if the temperature of the latter is kept steady for a sufficient time. Now, the vapour pressure in the whole apparatus is the maximum pressure corresponding to the temperature of the coldest part—that is, the temperature of the freezing mixture. Hence the depression of the mercurial column gives the maximum pressure of the vapour at the temperature of the freezing mixture.

Regnault, who also employed this method, took the precaution of using a freezing mixture of chloride of calcium and snow, which is a

Fig. 110.

liquid, and can be constantly stirred and kept at a uniform temperature throughout.

209. Vapour Pressures at High Temperatures.—The determination of the pressure of saturated water vapour at temperatures above 100° C. was undertaken by a commission of the Paris Academy of Sciences in 1829 under the direction of Dulong and Arago.[2] Their experiments ranged from 100° to 224° C.; corresponding to pressures varying from 1 to 24 atmospheres. The principle of the method consisted in heating a liquid in a closed boiler, and observing the temperature and corresponding pressure of the vapour. The liquid was first boiled for some time to expel all the air from the boiler,

[1] Gay-Lussac ; see Biot's *Traité de physique*, tom. i. p. 287.
[2] Dulong and Arago, *Mém. de l'Acad.* tom. x.

which was then closed and connected with a compressed air manometer. When the liquid was heated the pressure and the temperature rose together.   An observation was made by arresting the supply of heat and noting the maximum temperature attained, together with the corresponding pressure.   The temperature was registered by thermometers placed in iron tubulures protruding into the interior of the boiler.

These experiments were not sufficiently numerous to furnish reliable results, and the apparatus suffered from many defects.   The liquid never really entered into ebullition, so that the temperature could not be kept constant during an observation.   The necessity for new determinations was soon felt, and the task was undertaken by the committee of the Franklin Institute of Pennsylvania[1] in 1830. Their apparatus, however, was little better than that of Dulong and Arago, and their two series of observations agreed neither with each other nor with those of their predecessors.

The subject was consequently taken up nearly simultaneously by Magnus[2] and Regnault[3] in 1843.   The experiments of Magnus were free from the objections to which the earlier investigations were open, but they were not extended to temperatures above 115° C.   The liquid was enclosed in the shorter arm of a siphon barometer which was immersed in a bath, the temperature of which could be kept constant and was determined by means of an air thermometer.   The open branch of the barometer tube was connected with a free air manometer, and also with an air-pump, by means of which the pressure could be varied at pleasure.   The results of these experiments agree remarkably well with those of M. Regnault, whose researches were of a much more exhaustive character, extending from pressures of about 4 mm. to over 30 atmospheres.

Regnault's Experiments

210. Experiments between 0° and 50° C. — Nearly all the determinations of vapour pressures at low temperatures have been made by observation of the depression produced by the vapour in a barometer tube.   The chief source of uncertainty in the method is the difficulty of knowing the exact temperature of the vapour.   In Dalton's apparatus the bath extended over the whole length of the barometer tube, and in such a tall bath, heated from below, Regnault

---

[1] See *Ency. Brit.* vol. xx.

[2] Gustav Magnus, *Pogg. Ann.* vol. lxi. p. 225, 1844.

[3] Regnault, *Relation des expériences,* tom. i. p. 467.

found that the liquid rapidly settled into layers at different temperatures as soon as stirring was stopped.   Besides, in the apparatus
employed by Dalton it was impossible to stir the bath without causing
the mercury to oscillate in the tubes.   The method, in fact, would
only be fairly accurate for temperatures approximately the same as
that of the atmosphere.

For this reason Regnault adopted a modified form of Dalton's

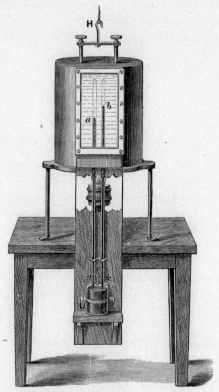

Fig. 111.

apparatus (Fig. 111) in his experiments at temperatures below 50° C.
The bath was considerably shortened, but of considerable capacity (45
litres), so that it could be constantly stirred (by H) and kept at a
uniform temperature throughout.   The bath-chamber was furnished
with a plane glass window through which the difference of level of the
mercury in the tubes *a* and *b* could be read by means of a cathetometer.   In order to ascertain if any error in the reading of this
difference of level was caused by refraction through the glass and
liquid, a fine mark was traced on the barometer tube near the level

of the mercury, and a centimetre scale was marked on the vapour tube. The difference of level between the mark on the barometer and each division of the centimetre scale on the vapour tube was then determined by means of a cathetometer—first in air, and then when the chamber was filled with water. An absolute deviation due to refraction was found, which sometimes amounted to half a millimetre; but the relative deviation—that is, the observed difference of level between any two points, one marked on each tube—was scarcely appreciable. In no case did it amount to so much as 0·1 mm.

An error in the difference of level of the mercurial columns, due to capillarity, had also to be taken into account. The surface tension in the barometer tube differs from that in the vapour tube, where the mercury is in contact with a liquid or the vapour of a liquid. To determine the amount of this error two barometer tubes A and A′ were connected by a three-way tap R (Fig. 112). Dry air was admitted several times and pumped out in order to thoroughly dry the spaces above the mercury. When this had been accomplished, the air was finally pumped out of both tubes, and the mercury stood at the same level in A and A′. Some liquid was then introduced into one of them (A′), and a difference of level immediately established itself, which, corrected for the

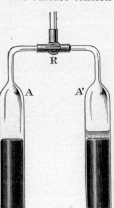

Fig. 112.

weight of the floating liquid, gave the capillary correction. For water there was an elevation of the column amounting to 0·12 mm.

At temperatures above that of the atmosphere the temperature of the bath was maintained by a spirit-lamp applied beneath. Observations were made at intervals of eight or ten minutes, and it could thus be ascertained if slight changes of temperature were accompanied by corresponding changes of pressure, and the accuracy of the method tested. One source of error may arise in the surface of the mercury not being at the same temperature as the bath. At temperatures above that of the atmosphere the mercury in the tube outside the bath will be colder than that inside, and by conduction the upper surface of the mercury may be somewhat colder than the bath. To avoid any error from this cause, Regnault always worked with the upper surface of the mercury well within the bath. When the bath is below the temperature of the air this source of error does not present itself, for the pressure of the vapour is that corresponding to

2 C

its coldest part—that is, in this case the temperature of the bath ; in
the former case it would be the temperature of the surface of the
mercury.

    In order to vary the mode of experiment and test the accuracy of
the results of one method by comparison with those derived from
another, Regnault modified the apparatus as follows :—The end of the

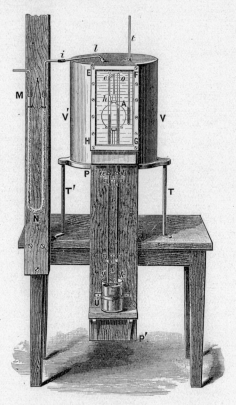

Fig. 113.

vapour tube was drawn out and attached by means of a three-way
joint to a glass globe A of about 500 c.c. capacity. Communication
was established with an air-pump, as shown in Fig. 113. The globe
and space above the mercury were carefully dried by admitting dry air
and exhausting several times. Finally the air was pumped out, the
exhaustion being carried to 1 or 2 mm.

    The liquid was previously sealed up in a small glass flask or piece
of glass tubing, and placed in the vapour globe A. The apparatus
being now ready, the temperature of the globe was raised till the

small flask containing the liquid burst. The space *h e* above the
mercury became filled with vapour, and the experiment was proceeded
with as before. The results of these experiments, in which vaporisation took place in the presence of a residual atmosphere of air, were
in close concord with those derived by the first method of procedure,
in which the vaporisation took place in a vacuum.

211. Temperatures below Zero.—In determining the pressure
of water vapour at temperatures below zero Regnault adopted the
method of Gay-Lussac. The second form of apparatus described in
the foregoing article was used. The globe containing the liquid was
first immersed in melting ice, and then in a freezing mixture of
crystallised chloride of calcium and snow, which was liquid and could
be kept in constant agitation. The temperature of the bath could be
maintained for a short time at its lowest point by adding small
quantities of snow. Observations were made at this point.

Exact determinations at low temperatures are exceedingly difficult,
for here the pressure is very low and rises slowly with temperature.
On the other hand, at a high temperature the pressure is high, and
changes considerably with a small change of temperature.

A more accurate method at low temperatures might be based on
the principle of the chemical hygrometer (Art. 235), namely, by
weighing the quantity of vapour contained in a large volume of
saturated air. This method might be easily adopted at low temperatures in high latitudes; but in those countries where the temperature
of the atmosphere is never very low, it would necessitate the adoption
of specially devised apparatus.

An accurate method of measuring very small vapour pressures,
such as the pressure of a vapour in equilibrium with its own solid,
was devised by Ramsay and Young,[1] and used to measure the
vapour pressures of ice, camphor, and acetic acid. The apparatus
(Fig. 114) consists of a wide vertical glass tube, A, closed below, to
which a side tube, B, is fused near the top. The side tube is connected with a bulb, C, which may be cooled by water or a freezing
mixture, and from the bulb passes a second tube, D, which is connected with an air-pump and gauge to measure the internal pressure.
A small tube, closed by an india-rubber tube and clip, E, serves to
admit air into the apparatus. The vertical tube is closed above by
an india-rubber stopper perforated with two holes, through one of
which passes a thermometer, F, and through the other a glass tube
provided with a stop-cock and reservoir, G, above. The bulb of the
thermometer is covered with cotton-wool, and the lower extremity of

[1] W. Ramsay and S. Young, *Phil. Trans.*, 1884, p. 461. S. Young, *Stoichiometry.*

the glass tube is drawn out and bent round so that the narrow end just touches the cotton-wool.

The liquid to be investigated is placed in the reservoir, and the apparatus is exhausted. A little liquid is then admitted so as to moisten the cotton-wool. The condensing bulb is then cooled, and the vertical tube is heated by means of a water or oil bath, which should always be kept at a temperature at least 20° higher than that registered by the thermometer.

The liquid on the cotton-wool evaporates rapidly and displaces the air in the lower part of the vertical tube, so that the remaining liquid is soon surrounded by vapour quite free from air. Under these conditions the liquid soon reaches its true boiling point, but it

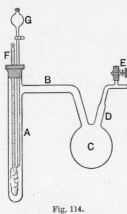

Fig. 114.

cannot become superheated, since evaporation takes place with perfect freedom, and, of course, ebullition is impossible. The temperature and pressure are read, and a small quantity of air is then admitted to raise the pressure, when the temperature rises at once, and soon becomes constant again at the boiling point under the higher pressure. Or, of course, the pressure may be reduced by pumping, when the temperature falls. Fresh quantities of liquid are added from time to time in small quantities from the reservoir. A large number of readings can thus be taken in an hour or two, and the reduction of pressure can be carried to any desired extent.

For pressures above about 500 mm. the boiling points are best determined in the ordinary way, the thermometer being placed in the vapour and not in the liquid.

With this apparatus Ramsay and Young showed that ice and water at the same temperature have different vapour pressures, as predicted by James Thomson. The essential feature of the method consisted in maintaining the ice and water at the same pressure and observing their temperatures as well as measuring their common pressure. By varying the pressure, the vapour pressure at different temperatures was found for each substance. Two tubes similar to A (Fig. 114) were employed, these being in communication with each other and with the same condenser C. The water in the cotton-wool surrounding the bulb of one of the thermometers was frozen, and the air thoroughly removed by a Sprengel pump. The condenser C was surrounded by a freezing mixture, and by varying the temperature of C the pressure in the apparatus could be varied at will. The water in the second tube froze at about $-5°$ C., but observations were made at temperatures lying between $-2°$ and $-5°$, which showed that the temperature of the ice was consistently higher than that of the water at the same pressure, so that at the same temperature the ice has a lower vapour pressure.[1] The pressure being varied from 3·80 to 3·20 mm. of mercury, the corresponding difference of temperature varied from 0·24° to 0·53°.

212. Experiments at High Temperatures.—When the pressure exceeds 300 mm. the apparatus (p. 386) becomes inconvenient. The length of the bath would have to be increased, and the difficulty

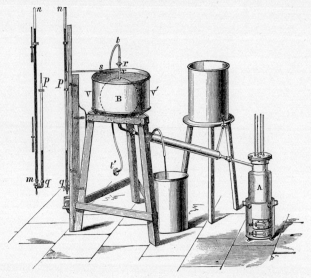

Fig. 115.

of maintaining its temperature uniform presents itself. For this reason M. Regnault designed a new form of apparatus suitable to the determination of vapour pressures at temperatures above 50° C. The special feature of the new apparatus was the design by which the temperature of the vapour could be accurately determined, and kept constant while an observation was being made.

The liquid was placed in an air-tight copper boiler A (Fig. 115), furnished with four thermometers to register the temperature. These thermometers, which read directly to the $\frac{1}{60}$ of a degree centigrade,

---

[1] The triple point, at which ice and water have the same vapour pressure, is very slightly above the normal freezing point (see Art. 349). The corresponding pressure is 4·6 mm.

were not exposed directly to the vapour, but were contained in iron tubulures (Fig. 116) which were closed at their lower extremities  and filled with mercury. The thermometers were thus enabled to take up the temperature of the boiler without being subject to the pressure of the vapour, which would lead to error at high temperatures. Two of the thermometer tubes protruded into the liquid, and the other two extended only into the vapour. Regnault carefully verified that the temperature registered by the thermometers was accurately that of the vapour. A tube surrounded by a water-jacket and overflow pipe led from the boiler to a large air-reservoir B (24 litres capacity), contained in a cylindrical vessel and surrounded with water to keep it at a constant temperature. This air-reservoir was connected to a manometer pq, which indicated the pressure, and also to an air-pump by means of the tube tt'. By working the pump the pressure in the reservoir could be regulated as desired, and the liquid in the boiler caused to boil under any chosen pressure. The temperature of the vapour was determined by means of the thermometers in the boiler, and the corresponding pressure of the saturated vapour of the boiling liquid was given by the manometer. The tube connecting the boiler to the air-reservoir was sloped upwards, and kept cool by the circulation of a stream of cold water. The vapour condensed in this tube, and the condensed liquid, flowed back again into the boiler. The air-reservoir was a large copper sphere surrounded by a water-bath contained in a zinc vessel, so that its changes of temperature were insignificant. For pressures below one atmosphere an exhaustion pump was employed, and for higher pressures a larger and much stronger apparatus of the same description was specially built.

Fig. 116.

The facility and precision of this method are extraordinary. When the pressure is brought to any desired value steady boiling soon sets in, and the temperature remains stationary for any length of time required.

The observations were carried up to 28 atmospheres, and Regnault projected carrying them to much higher pressures with a still stronger type of apparatus and a compressed air manometer.

213. Apparatus for Volatile Liquids.—In the case of volatile liquids the vapour pressure at ordinary temperatures is considerable, and the apparatus of Art. 210 becomes inadequate to meet the requirements of the investigation. The apparatus sketched in Fig. 117 is suitable for such liquids, and was used by both Regnault and Magnus.[1]

[1] *Pogg. Ann.* vol. lxi. p. 226 ; and *Ann. de Chimie,* 3e sér., tom. xii. p. 69, 1844.

The liquid is placed in the shorter arm a of a siphon barometer tube, the other arm of which communicates with an air-pump p and an open air manometer hk.

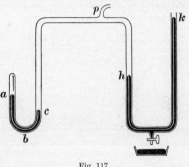

Fig. 117.

The arm ab is first filled completely with mercury, and some of the liquid is then introduced above it at c. This liquid is then boiled, so as to expel all air from the tube. While the liquid is still hot the tube is inclined, and some of the liquid free from air is allowed to ascend to the top of the arm a. The remainder of the liquid at c is then boiled off, and dry air is admitted, the pressure of which can be regulated at pleasure by means of the air-pump. This pressure is registered by means of the manometer hk. The apparatus now contains some liquid at a free from air, and is ready for experiment. The arm ac is now immersed in a bath, the temperature of which can be varied at pleasure, and the corresponding vapour pressure is furnished by the manometer. By sealing up the pump tube p, and pouring mercury into the open arm of the manometer, pressures above one atmosphere may be used.

214. Apparatus for Liquefiable Gases.—A somewhat similar apparatus was employed by Regnault for the determination of the vapour pressures of liquefiable gases, such as sulphurous acid and carbonic acid. The gas was forced into a chamber A (Fig. 118) by a compression pump connected with the aperture P, where it liquefied under the pressure. The other chamber B was in connection with a compressed air manometer by means of the tube M.

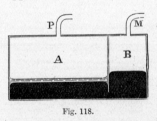

Fig. 118.

The chambers A and B were separated by a partition which descended nearly to the bottom of the vessel. The lower part of the vessel contained mercury, which could pass from A to B under the partition. The whole vessel could be placed in a bath, and kept at any desired temperature. The corresponding pressure of the vapour was determined by the manometer. In such experiments the pressures are so great that the difference of level of the mercury in A and B is negligible.

215. Vapour Pressure of a Liquid Mixture.—The pressure of the saturated vapour of a mixture of liquids was also investigated by Regnault.[1] The mixed vapours were found not to behave in general like a mixture of gases as regards pressure. Regnault distinguishes three cases—(1) When the liquids do not mix, as water and benzene. In this case the vapour pressure of the mixture is equal to the sum of the vapour pressures of the constituents. (2) When the liquids mix partially or dissolve each other to a limited extent, like water and ether. In this case the vapour pressure of the mixture is less than the sum of the pressures of the constituents, or even less than that of one of them. Thus Regnault found—

Temperature.	Water Vap. Press.	Ether.	Mixture.
15°·56 C.	13·16 mm.	361·4 mm.	362·95 mm.
33°·08	27·58 ,,	711·6 ,,	710·02 ,,

(3) The third case is that in which the liquids mix in all proportions. In this case the diminution of the vapour pressure of the mixture is still more marked.

According to the experiments of Wüllner,[2] the vapour pressure of any given mixture bears a constant ratio to the sum of the vapour pressures of the constituents—at least, when the liquids are mixed in nearly equal proportions. For other proportions the law is not quite exact.

216. Vapour Pressure at a Curved Surface.—The pressure of saturated vapour in equilibrium with its own liquid is not the same when the liquid surface is curved as when it is plane. The calculation of the vapour pressure at a curved surface was first given by Lord Kelvin.[3] Let a fine tube be placed in a liquid, and let the whole be placed in a vessel from which air is exhausted, so that the whole space above the liquid becomes filled with its vapour and nothing else.

Let the permanent level of the liquid be at A in the small tube and at B in the vessel, and let us suppose the temperature the same throughout the apparatus.

There is a state of equilibrium between the liquid and its vapour both at A and at B; otherwise evaporation or condensation would occur, and the permanent state would not exist.

Now the pressure of the vapour at B exceeds that at A by the

[1] Regnault, *Comptes rendus*, tom. xxxix., 1854; *Mémoires de l'Acad.* tom. xxvi.
[2] *Pogg. Ann.* Band cxxix. p. 353, 1866.
[3] *Proc. Roy. Soc. Edin.*, 7th February 1870. The above discussion is taken from Clerk Maxwell's *Theory of Heat*, chap. xx.

pressure due to a column of the vapour of the height AB.   It follows
that the vapour is in equilibrium with the liquid at a lower pressure
where the surface of the liquid is concave, as at A,
than where it is plane, as at B.

Let p_0 be the vapour pressure in contact with a
plane surface, *i.e.* the pressure at B, let p be the
vapour pressure just outside the liquid at A, and let
ϖ be the pressure just inside the liquid at A, then,
if σ is the density of the vapour (supposed uniform),
ρ the density of the liquid, and h the height AB,

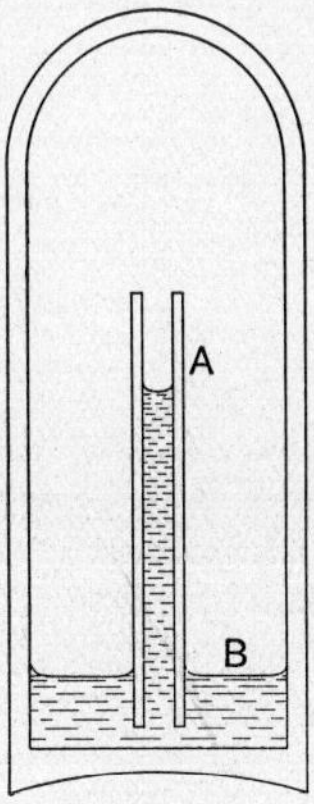

$$p_0 - p = g\sigma h,$$
$$p_0 - \varpi = g\rho h,$$

therefore

$$p_0 - \varpi = \frac{\rho}{\sigma}(p_0 - p).$$

But

$$p - \varpi = \frac{2T}{r},$$

Fig. 119.

where T is the surface tension, and r the radius of curvature of the
surface at A : therefore, subtracting and reducing, we get [1]

$$p = p_0 - \frac{\sigma}{\rho - \sigma} \cdot \frac{2T}{r} \qquad . \qquad . \qquad . \qquad . \qquad . \qquad (1)$$

In the case of a convex liquid surface, such as a spherical drop, the
formula becomes

Boiling by
bumping.

$$p = p_0 + \frac{\sigma}{\rho - \sigma} \cdot \frac{2T}{r} \qquad . \qquad . \qquad . \qquad . \qquad . \qquad (2)$$

This explains why liquids, in vessels to whose sides they adhere
closely, can be heated considerably above the boiling point without
ebullition taking place, if the vessel is perfectly clean.   For unless
there are nuclei present which the bubbles can form on, the small
bubbles which first form would condense—unless the temperature were
high enough for the vapour pressure to be able to support the internal
pressure due to surface tension in addition to the atmospheric pressure.
As soon as the temperature is high enough for bubbles to form, these
will grow with great rapidity, a large volume of vapour is emitted,
and the temperature falls nearly to the normal boiling point.   Thus
the boiling is intermittent and violent in character.

Similarly dust-free air may contain water vapour of a density

---

[1] If we take into account the variation in density of the vapour, we get the more
accurate formula

$$\rho R\theta \log \frac{p_0}{p} = p_0 - p + \frac{2T}{r},$$

which reduces to the above on expanding $\log (p_0/p)$, neglecting the higher powers of
$p_0 - p$, and putting $p_0 + p = 2p = \sigma R\theta$.

several times as great as that necessary for saturation. For if a very small drop were to form it would evaporate unless the vapour pressure were great enough to be in equilibrium with the curved surface. If drops of various sizes were present, the small ones would tend to evaporate and condense on the larger ones.

C. T. R. Wilson has shown [1] that if air containing water vapour be freed from dust and supersaturated by a sudden expansion, a cloud or fog will form if the air is *ionised* by the passage of Röntgen or similar rays, and this will take place with a much smaller expansion than is necessary to produce condensation if the rays are absent. In this case the charged ions appear to act as nuclei for the condensation of vapour.

217. Empirical Formulæ.—If the pressure of a saturated vapour depends only on the temperature, some general relation between the pressure and the temperature, such as

$$p = f(\theta),$$

must exist. The form of the function will probably depend on the nature of the substance; but no general law has yet been found. The first attempt in this direction was made by Dalton, who proposed the simple law that the vapour pressure increases in geometrical progression as the temperature increases in arithmetical. This assumes that the relation between the pressure and temperature is of the form

$$p = a a^\theta.$$

This formula, however, holds only for small limits of temperature near the point at which the constants are determined.

Young [2] proposed a more general formula including three constants, viz.—

$$p = (a + b\theta)^m,$$

where the constants a, b, m are to be determined by means of three experiments.

Regnault found that Young's formula might be used to represent the results of experiments within a limited range, but that beyond these limits it had to be abandoned.

In the course of a series of investigations founded on a particular hypothesis respecting the molecular constitution of matter, Rankine [3] arrived at the formula

$$\log p = \alpha - \frac{\beta}{\theta} - \frac{\gamma}{\theta^2},$$

---

[1] *Phil. Trans.* vol. clxxxix. p. 265, 1897.

[2] Young, *Nat. Phil.* vol. ii. p. 400. Young's formula was adopted by several physicists, notably Creighton, Southern, Tredgold, and Coriolis.

[3] Rankine, *Edinburgh New Phil. Journal*, July 1849.

where Θ is the absolute temperature. This formula, according to Rankine, represents the whole series of Regnault's experiments from $-30°$ C. to $+230°$ C.

Rankine also proposed the equation

$$pv^{\frac{17}{16}} = \text{constant}$$

for the steam-line of water substance, v being the specific volume of the saturated vapour.

In 1820 Young proposed the simple formula[1]

$$\log p = A + \frac{B}{\Theta} \qquad . \qquad . \qquad . \qquad . \qquad (1)$$

If we take Θ as representing absolute temperature here, then, if two different substances have the same vapour pressure p at the temperatures Θ' and Θ'' respectively, we get

$$\log p = A' + \frac{B'}{\Theta'} = A'' + \frac{B''}{\Theta''},$$

whence

$$\frac{\Theta'}{\Theta''} = \frac{1}{B''}\{B' + (A' - A'')\Theta'\},$$

so that the ratio Θ'/Θ'' of the temperatures at which the vapour pressures of the two substances are the same is a linear function of the temperature Θ' of one substance. This approximate formula has been applied by Ramsay and Young[2] to deduce the vapour pressure of any substance from those of a standard substance by means of two observations to determine the constants.

Kirchhoff[3] in 1858 and Rankine in 1866 independently suggested the formula

$$\log p = A + \frac{B}{\Theta} + C \log \Theta \quad . \qquad . \qquad . \qquad . \qquad (2)$$

which, as it has three constants to be determined by experiment instead of two, can be made to represent the facts more closely.

The formulæ (1) and (2) can be arrived at by theoretical considerations. If we write the characteristic equation of the vapour, after Callendar, in the form (see Art. 251)

$$v - a = \frac{R\Theta}{p} - \frac{c}{R\Theta^2}$$

and neglect the last term, since it is small for high temperatures, and if we put for v the specific volume v_2 of the saturated vapour, and for

[1] See the article "Vaporisation," by H. L. Callendar, *Ency. Brit.*, 10th ed., 1902.
[2] *Phil. Mag.*, 1887.
[3] *Pogg. Ann.* Bd. ciii. p. 185, 1858.

α the specific volume v_1 of the liquid (which is probably in most cases a fair approximation), we get

$$v_2 - v_1 = \frac{\mathrm{R}\Theta}{p}.$$

Combining this with the thermodynamic equation (5) of Art. 346, viz.

$$\frac{\mathrm{L}}{\Theta} = (v_2 - v_1)\left(\frac{dp}{d\Theta}\right),$$

we obtain

$$\frac{dp}{p} = \frac{\mathrm{L}}{\mathrm{R}}\frac{d\Theta}{\Theta^2} \quad . \quad . \quad . \quad . \quad . \quad . \quad (3)$$

Assuming L constant as a first approximation, this equation gives, on integration,

$$\log\frac{p}{p_0} = \frac{\mathrm{L}}{\mathrm{R}}\left(\frac{1}{\Theta_0} - \frac{1}{\Theta}\right),$$

which is Young's formula. A closer approximation is got by taking L to be a linear function of the temperature, as in Art. 201, and this leads to Kirchhoff's formula.[1]

---

[1] Nernst (*The New Heat Theorem*, p. 122) obtains equation (3) as applicable to a low temperature and small vapour pressure, and treating L as a quadratic function of the temperature, derives the formula

$$\log p = -\frac{\lambda}{\mathrm{R}\Theta} + \frac{\alpha}{\mathrm{R}}\log\Theta + \frac{\beta}{\mathrm{R}}\Theta + i,$$

where λ, α, and β are constants, and i is the constant of integration. It is an objectionable practice to write $\log p$ and $\log \Theta$ in a formula, as is done in the foregoing, and also in formulæ (1) and (2), for, strictly speaking, only the logarithms of pure numbers can occur in a physical formula. Nernst's formula should be written—

$$\log\frac{p}{p_0} = \frac{\lambda}{\mathrm{R}}\left(\frac{1}{\Theta_0} - \frac{1}{\Theta}\right) + \frac{\alpha}{\mathrm{R}}\log\frac{\Theta}{\Theta_0} + \frac{\beta}{\mathrm{R}}(\Theta - \Theta_0),$$

where p_0 and Θ_0 are some corresponding pressure and temperature.

SECTION IV

VAPOUR DENSITIES

218. Definition of Vapour Density.—The density of any substance generally means its mass per unit volume, taken at some standard pressure and temperature. The specific gravity of a substance, on the other hand, is expressed by the ratio of the weight of any volume of the substance to the weight, under given conditions, of an equal volume of some standard substance chosen for the sake of reference. The standard substance usually chosen is water, so that the specific gravity of a substance is the ratio of its density to that of water. Now, if the mass of unit volume of the standard substance (water at 4° C.) be taken as the unit of mass, then the density of this substance will be unity, and the density of any other substance will be expressed by the same number as its specific gravity. This plan is adopted in the C. G. S. system, in which the unit of mass (1 gramme) is taken as the mass of a cubic centimetre of water at 4° C.

What is generally spoken of as the density of a vapour is the weight of any volume under given conditions of temperature and pressure, compared with the weight of an equal volume of dry air (sometimes hydrogen) under the same conditions. This, then, is not the density of the vapour, in the correct sense of the word, but rather its specific gravity—air at the same pressure and temperature being taken as the standard of comparison.

Let w be the weight of a volume v of vapour at a pressure p and temperature Θ. Let w_0 be the weight of air per unit volume at 0° C. and a pressure of 760 mm. Then the weight of a volume v of air at temperature Θ and pressure p is

$$w' = w_0 v \frac{p}{760} \cdot \frac{273}{\Theta}.$$

Consequently by definition the vapour density is

397

$$\rho = \frac{w}{w'} = \frac{w}{w_0 v} \cdot \frac{760}{p} \cdot \frac{\Theta}{273} \quad . \quad . \quad . \quad (1)$$

where $w_0 = 0.001293$ gramme per cubic centimetre. Hence in order to measure ρ we require the volume, temperature, and pressure of a known weight of the vapour.

The result of a single experiment furnishes the vapour density at the temperature and pressure under which the experiment was made. If the vapour obeys the laws of Boyle and Charles (or rather obeys them to the same extent that air does), then the vapour density thus determined will always be the same whatever the pressure and temperature. For in this case we shall have $pv = R\Theta$ in the equation for ρ, and consequently

$$\rho = \frac{w}{w_0} \cdot \frac{760}{273R},$$

which is independent of pressure and temperature.

If, therefore, it were found by experiment that ρ remains constant as the pressure and temperature are varied, we should conclude that vapours up to their point of saturation obey the laws of perfect gases. It is found, however, that this is by no means the case. As a vapour approaches its point of condensation, its density, as defined above, increases. That is, for a given increase of pressure there is a greater diminution of volume, at constant temperature, than if Boyle's law were obeyed. In other words, the product pv is not constant at constant temperature, but diminishes as the pressure increases.

No perfectly general and accurate law connecting the pressure, volume, and temperature of a vapour, or gas, up to its condensing point has yet been discovered. Sufficient experimental work has not been executed in this department to lead to the deduction of any law possessing complete generality. Several formulæ have, however, been proposed which apply to the fluid state with more or less precision. These will be considered later on (section vii.). Up to the time of the experiments of Fairbairn and Tate (1860) no direct observations of vapour densities at the point of saturation had been made. The method previously employed consisted in making an observation of the density at some definite temperature and pressure, and deducing the density at all other temperatures and pressures (even that of saturation) on the supposition that the vapour obeyed Boyle's law. This method, though obviously inaccurate, is practised in most ordinary work up to the present day; we shall, therefore, describe some of the methods which have been employed in the investigation of vapour densities.

219. Gay-Lussac's Method.—The method employed by Gay-

Lussac [1] was exceedingly simple, and specially suitable for the measurement of the vapour densities of volatile liquids.   For liquids, however, which have a high boiling point the method fails.   The apparatus is shown in Fig. 120, and although it has been superseded by more accurate forms it sufficiently illustrates the principle of the method.   It consists of an iron dish containing mercury in which a tall graduated glass tube AB filled with mercury is inverted barometer-wise.   This tube is surrounded by a glass cylinder open at both ends, which is filled with water, and can be heated so as to keep the inner tube at a fairly fixed temperature.   The apparatus being ready for experiment, a weighed quantity of the liquid under investigation is sealed up in a small glass bulb, or placed in a small stoppered phial, which is slipped under the mouth of the inner tube.

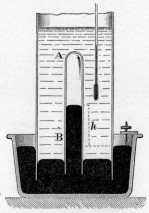

Fig. 120.

When let go it rises through the mercury to the top of the tube, where, under the diminished pressure and increased temperature, it bursts, and the liquid is all vaporised if the temperature is sufficiently high, or the space above the mercury sufficiently large. This being secured, the volume occupied by the vapour is read off by means of the graduations on the tube, and the pressure is determined by measuring the difference of level between the mercury in the tube and cistern.

The temperature is taken as that of the bath, which should be constantly stirred to secure uniformity.   Stirring, however, will cause oscillation of the mercurial columns, since the water rests on the mercury, and for that reason the apparatus is open to the same objection as that of Dalton for determining the pressures of saturated vapours.   The difference of level between the surfaces of the mercury in the tube and cistern is determined by means of a cathetometer and a vertical screw pointed at both ends.   The length of this screw is accurately determined, and the lower end is placed in contact with the surface of the mercury in the cistern.   The difference of level between the surface of the mercury in the tube and the upper end of the screw is determined by means of a cathetometer, and this, added to the length of the screw, gives the elevation of the mercury in the tube over that in the cistern.   This column corrected for temperature

[1] Gay-Lussac, *Ann. de Chimie*, 1re sér., tom. lxxx. p. 218, 1811.

and subtracted from the height of the barometer, also corrected for temperature, gives the pressure of the vapour.

The pressure, volume, and temperature of the vapour being thus known as well as its weight, the density is found by means of the formula of Art. 218—

$$\rho = \frac{760w\Theta}{0 \cdot 001293 \times 273pv}.$$

By varying the temperature of the bath or the quantity of liquid, the vapour density at different stages approaching the point of saturation may be determined, and a comparison of the results will indicate the extent and nature of the departure from Boyle's law. At high temperatures, however, the tension of the mercury vapour becomes considerable, and this method becomes inapplicable.

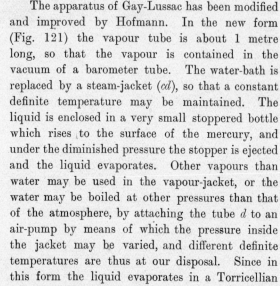

Fig. 121.

The apparatus of Gay-Lussac has been modified and improved by Hofmann. In the new form (Fig. 121) the vapour tube is about 1 metre long, so that the vapour is contained in the vacuum of a barometer tube. The water-bath is replaced by a steam-jacket (cd), so that a constant definite temperature may be maintained. The liquid is enclosed in a very small stoppered bottle which rises to the surface of the mercury, and under the diminished pressure the stopper is ejected and the liquid evaporates. Other vapours than water may be used in the vapour-jacket, or the water may be boiled at other pressures than that of the atmosphere, by attaching the tube d to an air-pump by means of which the pressure inside the jacket may be varied, and different definite temperatures are thus at our disposal. Since in this form the liquid evaporates in a Torricellian vacuum, the vapour is formed under a much lower pressure than in Gay-Lussac's apparatus, so that the vapour density of a liquid which boils in air, say at 150° C., may be determined by use of the steam-jacket. This is of great importance in the case of those substances which decompose at their boiling point under ordinary atmospheric pressure.

220. Regnault's Investigations.—The principle of the method employed by Regnault [1] in his study of vapour densities was the same

[1] Regnault, *Ann. de Chimie et de Physique*, 3e sér., tom. xv. p. 141, 1845.

as that of Gay-Lussac, but the apparatus was different in several respects, being similar to that used in his experiments on the pressure of saturated vapours (Fig. 111). A weighed quantity of the liquid was sealed up in a small bulb, and placed in the globe of the vapour chamber. The barometer tube was dispensed with, and the vapour tube was attached at its lower end to another vertical tube, open at its upper end, so that the two tubes thus joined formed the two branches of an open-air manometer. The surface of the mercury was always kept at a constant level in the vapour tube, so that the apparent volume of the vapour was always the same.

This volume being accurately known at one temperature, the volume at any other temperature is easily deduced from the known coefficient of expansion of glass. The weight of liquid was previously determined, so that it could be completely vaporised in this space at the temperatures employed. The pressure due to the residual air left in the apparatus was accurately determined before the vaporisation of the liquid, and this, corrected for change of temperature and subtracted from the pressure indicated by the apparatus, gave the pressure of the vapour. Being thus furnished with the pressure, volume, temperature, and weight of the vapour, its density may be determined as above.

The advantage of this form of apparatus over Gay-Lussac's lies in the structure of the bath, which could be constantly agitated and maintained at a uniform temperature throughout without disturbing the mercury.

Regnault's first series of experiments related to the density of water vapour at 100° C., and under pressures not greater than half an atmosphere. Within these limits he found that Boyle's law was very closely obeyed.

The second series of experiments investigated water vapour under feeble pressures and near the ordinary temperature of the air. From this series he concluded that Boyle's law might be applied up to a saturation fraction 0·8. The departure from the law after this point he thought might be due to anomalous condensation, arising probably from contact with the walls of the vapour chamber.

The third series dealt with the density of water vapour in air at its saturation point between 0° and 25° C., the conclusion being that Boyle's law was obeyed up to the point of condensation without very serious error.

221. Meyer's Method.—The method designed by Victor Meyer depends on an ingenious device for measuring the volume of the vapour. The apparatus is shown in Fig. 122. It consists of a

2 D

cylindrical bulb B furnished with a long narrow stem, from which a fine tube branches off near the top and dips under the surface of a basin of mercury.   Immediately over the end of this branch tube a graduated glass tube D filled with mercury is inverted barometer-wise in the basin of mercury.

In making an experiment, the bulb B is heated by immersion in a bath to the temperature at which it is desired to make the experi-

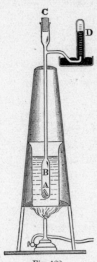

Fig. 122.

ment.   During this operation the air within the bulb expands, and may be allowed to escape into the air through the side branch, over the end of which the tube D has not yet been inverted. When B has attained its stationary temperature the graduated tube D is inverted over the end of the branch, and a small flask containing a known weight of the liquid under investigation is quickly introduced into B through the stoppered end C of the stem, which is immediately closed.

The temperature of the bulb being well above the boiling point of the liquid, the contents of the flask are vaporised at once, and the vapour thus quickly formed pushes the air before it through the side tube, whence it rises through the mercury into the graduated tube D.   When equilibrium is attained a certain mass of air has been expelled, which can be determined by observing its volume, temperature, and pressure in the tube D.   The result of the whole process is that the space previously occupied by this mass of air in the bulb is now occupied by a known mass of vapour at the same temperature and pressure.   The relative vapour density is conse-quently found by dividing the mass of the vapour by the mass of the air displaced.

In order to prevent fracture of the bulb when the small flask which contains the liquid is dropped in, some asbestos is placed at the bottom of the bulb.

222. Dumas's Method.—This method[1] is specially adapted for the study of the vapour densities of substances which possess a high boiling point, and for which an apparatus involving the use of mercury fails.

About 15 or 20 grammes of the substance are placed in a thin glass flask B (Fig. 123) of about half a litre capacity, and furnished with a narrow stem *p* drawn out to a point.   A glass flask may be used for

---

[1] Dumas, *Ann. de Chimie et de Physique*, 2ᵉ sér., tom. xxxiii. p. 337, 1826.

temperatures up to about 400° C., the point at which glass begins to soften.   For higher temperatures a porcelain vessel may be employed.

The flask is placed in a bath of oil, or some fusible metal, the temperature of which is well above the boiling point of the substance under examination.   Wood's fusible alloy is a very suitable substance for such a bath, as it fuses at 70° C., has a high boiling point, and gives off no fumes.

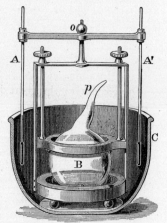

When boiling sets in, the air is gradually expelled from the flask, and after some time nothing remains inside but the boiling liquid and its vapour. The temperature of the bath being well above that of the boiling liquid, a strong jet of vapour issues from the nozzle of the flask as long as any liquid is left within.   When the liquid is completely vaporised the rapid escape of vapour suddenly ceases and the flask is left filled

Fig. 123.

with vapour, which soon takes up the temperature of the bath.   The nozzle is then hermetically sealed, and the flask is removed from the bath, allowed to cool, and its weight determined.

This weight W is the sum of the weights of the glass flask and its contained vapour minus the weight of the air displaced by the flask. Denote these by w_g, w, and w_a respectively, then

$$W = w + w_g - w_a.$$

Before the experiment the flask was weighed open, and its weight W′ represented the difference between the weights of the flask and of the air displaced by the glass constituting it.   Denoting these by w_g and w_a' we have

$$W' = w_g - w_a'.$$

Therefore

$$W - W' = w - (w_a - w_a').$$

The last term on the right-hand side of this equation is the weight of the quantity of air which will fill the flask at the temperature and pressure of the atmosphere when the weighing was conducted. Hence if v_0 is the internal capacity of the flask at zero, $\theta°$ C. and H the temperature and pressure of the air at the time of weighing, we have

$$w_a - w_a' = 0.001293 \frac{v_0(1 + g\theta)}{1 + a\theta} \cdot \frac{H}{760},$$

where g and a are the coefficients of expansion of glass and air respectively. Hence the weight of the vapour is

$$w = \mathrm{W} - \mathrm{W}' + 0.001293 \frac{v_0(1+g\theta)}{1+a\theta} \frac{\mathrm{H}}{760}.$$

Now, this weight of vapour filled the flask at the temperature of the bath and the pressure of the atmosphere at the time of sealing the flask. The volume, pressure, and temperature of a known weight of the vapour are therefore known, and its density is determined by the ordinary formula.

On account of the great length of time required to complete an experiment by this method, the weights W and W' are determined at times when the pressure and humidity of the air may differ considerably, and correction in this respect may be necessary. Further, in applying this method great care should be taken to procure the substance under investigation as pure as possible. If any impurity of a higher boiling point than the substance be present, then the substance whose vapour density is sought will vaporise first and the impurity will remain behind to the last, so that the vapour density determined will be that of the impurity or of an exaggerated mixture of the impurity and the substance.

If during ebullition the flask is connected with a partially exhausted chamber, the temperature of ebullition will be greatly reduced, and a modification similar to that applied by Hofmann to Gay-Lussac's apparatus will be introduced. This method of operation has been used by Habermann.

MM. Henri Sainte-Claire Deville and L. Troost,[1] by using a porcelain flask, the nozzle of which could be sealed by an oxyhydrogen blowpipe, have determined the vapour densities of some substances having very high boiling points. Stationary temperature baths were obtained by employing the vapour of such substances as mercury, which boils at $350°$ C., sulphur $440°$, cadmium $860°$, and zinc $1040°$. The flask was placed inside the vessel in which the vapour was generated, and was protected from radiation to the walls of it by being surrounded by a diaphragm of wire gauze.

223. Density of Saturated Vapour—Experiments of Fairbairn and Tate.—In order to determine the density of a vapour at the point of saturation with accuracy, it is not legitimate to find the density of the superheated vapour and then deduce that of the

---

[1] Deville and Troost, *Comptes rendus*, tom. xlv. p. 821 ; and *Ann. de Chimie et de Physique*, 3ᵉ sér., tom. lviii. p. 257, 1860. The boiling points of mercury, sulphur, etc., here given are the numbers assumed by Deville and Troost in their experiments.

saturated vapour, on the assumption that Boyle's law is obeyed up to the point of condensation.   The great difficulty to be overcome in the direct determination of the density of a saturated vapour lies in the accurate observation of the volume of a given weight of the vapour when saturated, or exactly at the condensing point.

The principle of the method employed by Fairbairn and Tate [1] for this purpose is illustrated by Fig. 124.   Let A and B be two equal globes connected, as shown in figure, by a tube containing mercury, and let A and B contain different quantities of a liquid.   For example, let A contain 20 grammes and B 30 grammes, and let the apparatus be placed in a bath the temperature of which can be gradually raised. As the temperature rises, more and more of the liquid in each bulb gradually passes into the state of vapour ; but as long as any liquid remains in each the pressure will be the same in both, namely, the saturated vapour pressure for the temperature of the bath.   A point will, however, be reached at which all the liquid in A will be vaporised and some liquid will still remain in B. Up to this point the level of the mercury in the arms of the connecting tube remains fixed. A small difference of level, arising from the difference of weight of liquid in the two arms,

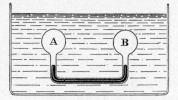

Fig. 124.

exists, and remains constant till all the liquid is vaporised in one of them.   Beyond this point the vapour in A will become superheated and obey the gaseous laws approximately, but the vapour in B will be saturated as long as any liquid still remains.   The pressure in B will now increase much more rapidly than that in A, so that the mercury will rise in the arm A.   This takes place because the press-ure of a saturated vapour increases more rapidly with temperature than that of a superheated vapour.

Hence, if the temperature be noted at which the mercury just begins to rise in A, then it is known that at this temperature the liquid in A is all vaporised and just beginning to be superheated. The volume of the bulb being known and the temperature noted, the pressure may be found from a table of saturated vapour pressures, or it may be found directly by any form of pressure gauge, so that the data for finding the density of the vapour at the saturation point are complete.

The experiments were conducted by means of the apparatus shown

[1] Fairbairn and Tate, *Phil. Trans.*, 1860, p. 185 ; and *Phil. Mag.* vol. xxi., 861, p. 230.

in Fig. 125.   A known weight of water was placed in a glass globe A, which was about 14 cm. in diameter ; this globe was furnished with a stem about 80 cm. long and 1 cm. wide ; the end of this stem dipped

Fig. 125.

under the surface of some mercury contained in a glass tube which surrounded the stem of A, and was firmly jointed to a metal reservoir B enclosing A.   This reservoir and the tube contained some water, so that the interior of B was saturated with water vapour at all the temperatures used in the experiments.   The pressure of this vapour was roughly measured by a pressure gauge G, and the temperature was registered by means of a thermometer exposed naked to the vapour, and corrected for the effect of pressure.   The temperature being known, the exact pressure can be found from Regnault's tables of vapour pressures.   A nozzle p allows of the steam being let off at pleasure.

The apparatus was heated by placing the end of the tube C in a sand-bath, and B was at the same time heated by a gas burner.   All the air was expelled from B by boiling for some time with the nozzle p open, and in order to ensure that A should contain no air it was filled with mercury, and inverted with the stem under mercury before the liquid was introduced.   As long as any liquid remains in A the vapour pressure will be the same in B and A, and the level of the mercury in the stem of A will remain fixed, but as soon as all the liquid in A is vaporised the mercury will rise in the stem. Before this point the mercury stands somewhat higher inside the stem than outside, on account of the weight of the column of liquid in the tube ob.   The volume of A being known up to any point in the stem, and the pressure and temperature at which the mercury just begins to rise in the stem being determined, the data necessary for the estimation of the density of the saturated vapour are at hand.   In order to determine the saturation point most accurately, the vapour in A was superheated 10° or 20° above the point of saturation, and the difference of level ab of the mercurial columns was noted with a cathetometer.   The temperature was then gradually reduced, and the determination of the saturation point was taken from the observations on the mercurial column when falling in the stem of A rather than when rising.

The results of these experiments show that the density of saturated vapour is invariably greater than that deduced from the laws of gases.

If v denotes the specific volume of the saturated vapour—that is, the volume per unit mass—then, according to the authors of these experiments, the relation between p and v may be written in the form

$$v = a + \frac{b}{p+c}.$$

The values of the constants deduced from the experiments were, if p is measured in millimetres in mercury,

$$v = 25 \cdot 62 + \frac{1257605}{p + 18 \cdot 29}.$$

Near the point of saturation the coefficient of expansion was almost five times that of air, but it gradually approached that of air with super-heating.

224. Later Experiments.—The determination of the densities of saturated vapours was undertaken more recently by M. Perot.[1] Two methods of experiment were adopted, both of which depended in principle on the isolation and weighing of a certain volume of the saturated vapour. In the first method a glass globe A, similar to that used in Dumas's method (Art. 222), was placed inside a closed vessel B, connected with an air-pump. Dry air was repeatedly admitted to and pumped out of B, so that both B and A were thus carefully dried. Finally, the vessel B was exhausted as closely as possible, the residual pressure being only $\frac{1}{2}$ mm. In this process the flask A became exhausted also. The liquid under investigation had been previously sealed up in a glass bulb and placed in B. The temperature was now raised till the bulb burst, and the vessel B, together with the flask A, became filled with saturated vapour. The temperature was now maintained constant for some time, and the nozzle of the flask A was then sealed up electrically. This being done, A was taken out and weighed. This gives the weight of the vapour contained, and hence its density may be found.

In the second method, two chambers A and B were connected by a tube furnished with a stop-cock. The vapour was generated in one, A, and when the tap was opened the other chamber, B, became filled with saturated vapour. The tap was then closed, and the vapour drawn off from B by means of an aspirator into drying tubes and weighed. The weight of the saturated vapour which filled the chamber B was thus determined, and its density calculated in the ordinary way.

M. Perot found that the two methods gave very concordant results. Thus the specific volume of ether vapour at 30° C. by the

[1] Perot, *Journal de Physique*, 2ᵉ sér., tom. vii. p. 129, 1888.

first method was 400 c.c., while by the second the specific volume at 30°·02 C. was 399·9 c.c. In the case of water, temperatures much above 100° C. could not be employed, on account of the solvent action of water vapour on glass at high temperatures. In the case of ether, the results of the experiments were represented by the formula

$$v = 400{\cdot}42 - 15{\cdot}7394\theta + 0{\cdot}539\theta^2.$$

SECTION V

MIXTURES OF GASES AND VAPOURS

225. Evaporation and Vapour Pressure in a Closed Space occupied by a Gas—Dalton's Experiment.—The first trustworthy experiments on the formation of vapours in spaces already occupied by air or other gases were executed by Dalton with an apparatus similar to that depicted in Fig. 126. An air-tight glass flask was fitted with a barometer AM and a delivery tube C, which communicated with an

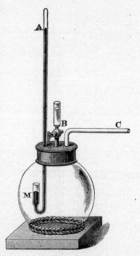

Fig. 126.

air-pump by means of which the flask could be exhausted or the pressure of the gas within it modified at pleasure. A funnel B, furnished with a tap, contained a quantity of the liquid under experiment, and by opening the tap a small quantity of the liquid could be passed into the flask in order that its vapour might be studied. If the flask is exhausted, the first drops of liquid are vaporised immediately after admission; but if the interior is occupied by air or any other gas the evaporation takes place much more slowly, and the greater the pressure of the gas the more slowly does the evaporation take place. In a vacuum the evaporation is rapid, and the vapour quickly attains its maximum pressure; but when air or any other gas is present, the vapour pressure gradually increases, and its progress may be observed by means of the barometer AM with which the flask is furnished. As the evaporation progresses the barometer rises, showing that the pressure within the flask is increasing; and as the volume of the flask and the quantity of gas within it remain fixed, this increase of pressure must be due solely to the formation of the vapour, and may be regarded as the vapour pressure. The total pressure within the flask, from this point of view, is regarded as the sum of the initial pressure of the gas and that of the vapour, and Dalton found that the increase of pressure ultimately produced by the evaporation of a liquid in such a closed space is the same whether the space be filled with a gas or empty, and that this increase is equal to the maximum vapour pressure of the liquid for the temperature at which the experiment is made. In other words, if a space of fixed volume be initially filled with a gas at pressure p, and if a quantity of liquid, whose maximum vapour pressure at the temperature of the experiment is F, be introduced into the space and allowed to evaporate so as to saturate the space, then the final pressure within the space will be

$$P = p + F.$$

Gay-Lussac.

The results arrived at by Dalton were subsequently confirmed by Gay-Lussac with the convenient form of apparatus shown in Fig. 127. One of the arms AB of an open-air manometer is furnished with a

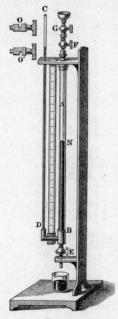

stop-cock F, over which a funnel, also furnished with a tap G, can be screwed on. The pin of the tap G is not pierced through with an aperture so as to permit of a continuous flow of liquid from the funnel above, but is merely furnished with a cavity O, which when turned upwards becomes filled with the liquid contained in the funnel, and when turned downwards discharges itself into the arm AB below. Thus each time this tap is turned the full of the cavity of liquid is introduced into the space below, and by this means a known quantity of liquid may be placed in the arm AB at any time.

In making an experiment the apparatus is first thoroughly dried by means of a current of dry air, and it is then filled with mercury. Some dry gas is then admitted into the arm AB by placing the tap F in connection with a reservoir of the gas, and permitting the mercury to escape through the tap E. These taps are finally closed, and the pressure and volume of the gas in the arm AB noted. Drops of liquid are then introduced by the tap G, and as they evaporate the mercury rises in the arm CD and falls in AB until the space A becomes saturated. The vapour has now reached its maximum pressure, and no increase of pressure is produced by the further introduction of liquid.

Fig. 127.

In this form of the experiment the conditions are not exactly the same as in the experiment of Dalton, for here the space occupied by the gas and vapour increases as the pressure rises, while in Dalton's experiment the space remained constant. Hence, if p and v be the initial pressure and volume of the gas, its pressure p', after the formation of the vapour in the experiment of Gay-Lussac, when the volume has increased to v', will be $p' = pv/v'$, the temperature being constant, and the final pressure will not be $p + F$ as before, but will be

$$P = p' + F = \frac{pv}{v'} + F.$$

By observing the pressures P and p and the volumes v and v' the vapour pressure F can be found. The results of the experiments of Gay-Lussac confirmed the conclusion of Dalton that the vapour exerted the same pressure whether in a vacuum or in presence of a gas or mixture of gases, the total pressure of a gaseous mixture being the sum of the pressures which the constituents would exert in the space if they occupied it separately. It was therefore concluded that, at least as far as the resultant pressure is concerned, the mixed gases are without influence on each other. Dalton's law.

These experiments were not sufficiently numerous or accurate to establish the general truth of Dalton's law on a sure basis. *A priori* the law does not appear probable, for if several liquids be admitted simultaneously into the flask in the experiment of Dalton, each should produce its maximum vapour pressure independently of the others, and by increasing the number of liquids the total pressure within the flask could be increased indefinitely.[1] The law can therefore be only approximately true within certain limits, and M. Regnault[2] was consequently induced to investigate the behaviour of mixed gases and vapours more closely and completely. The apparatus employed was the same as that used in the determination of the pressure of saturated vapours. Having determined the maximum vapour pressure in a vacuum between zero and 40° C., he repeated the same measurements when the apparatus contained air or nitrogen, and constructed a table of the maximum vapour pressures in presence of these gases :— Regnault.

---

[1] Jakob has pointed out that Dalton's law could not be strictly valid, unless Boyle's law were exact. For if two portions of the *same* gas are mixed, then Boyle's law may be deduced from Dalton's law. (*Zeitschr. für Physik*, vol. xli. p. 737, 1927.)

[2] Regnault, *Ann. de Chimie et de Physique*, 3ᵉ sér., tom. xv. p. 129, 1845.

[TABLE

Temperature.	Vapour Pressure.		Difference.
	In Air.	In a Vacuum.	
°	mm.	mm.	mm.
0	4·47	4·60	0·13
15·00	12·38	12·70	0·32
21·07	18·28	18·58	0·30
24·69	22·73	23·14	0·40
31·00	32·97	33·41	0·44
35·97	43·39	44·13	0·74
38·00	48·70	49·30	0·60
	In Nitrogen.		
0	4·31.	4·60	0·29
16·49	13·29	13·96	0·67
21·46	18·61	19·03	0·42
25·50	23·71	24·27	0·56
32·50	35·92	36·38	0·46
37·74	47·80	48·63	0·83
39·81	53·72	54·36	0·64

This table shows that the vapour pressures in the gas are very nearly equal to, but a little less than, the corresponding maximum pressure in a vacuum ; and as the measurements in both sets of experiments were made with the same apparatus, this difference cannot be attributed to the apparatus. Regnault feared that the oxygen of the air attacked the mercury, and for this reason he also employed nitrogen, but found the same difference, so that he was forced to the conclusion that the vapour pressure is a little less in a gas than in vacuo. Regnault thought this did not militate against the possible truth of Dalton's law, but considered that it might be explained by the condensation on the walls of the vapour chamber, and perhaps to some extent by the slowness of evaporation in a gas, which prevents the final stage being reached. This view appeared to be confirmed by the subsequent work of Herwig.[1] The effect was more marked the lower the temperature.

The foregoing experiments show, within the limits to which they were carried, that when a space already occupied by air or any other gas is saturated with a vapour, the pressure exerted by the vapour is practically equal to the maximum pressure which the vapour would exert in vacuo at the same temperature. It was for this reason

[1] Herwig, *Pogg. Ann.* Band cxxxvii. p. 592, 1869. Several foreign physicists, including Herwig, have stated that the pressure of a saturated vapour depends slightly on the relative volumes of liquid and vapour. Professors Ramsay and Young have found no such effect when great care was used to employ perfectly pure materials both in the vapour chamber and the bath used to keep its temperature constant. The presence of very small quantities of impurity were sufficient to produce the effect stated. See *Phil. Mag.*, February and December 1894.

assumed by Dalton and his followers that the vapour density in the Vapour density. gas—that is, the weight of vapour per unit volume—was the same as in vacuo. This, however, cannot be assumed as a consequence of the fact that the pressures are the same. The point remained to be tested by experiment. The question was finally settled in the affirmative by Regnault.[1] Air saturated with water vapour was drawn by means of an aspirator through a system of drying tubes as in the chemical hygrometer (Art. 235). The volume of air drawn through the tubes was measured by the quantity of water which escaped from the aspirator, and the weight of moisture contained was calculated by weighing the drying tubes before and after the experiment. The following table after Regnault shows how closely the observed and calculated weights agree :—

Temperature.	Weight of Vapour.		Difference.
	Calculated.	Observed.	
0	0·273	0·273	0·000
5·85	0·424	0·424	0·000
12·88	0·660	0·653	0·007
14·65	0·736	0·731	0·005
20·57	1·013	1·010	0·003
25·11	1·328	1·315	0·013

We conclude therefore that, at least within certain limits, in a space already occupied by a gas a liquid ultimately evaporates to the same extent as in a vacuum, the process being merely more slow.

226. Dalton's Law. — When several gases which have no chemical action on each other are contained in the same vessel, the pressure of the mixture may be determined by means of a simple rule known as Dalton's [2] law. According to this law the pressure of a gaseous mixture on the walls of the containing vessel is equal to the sum of the pressures which the constituents would exert if each occupied the vessel separately. According to Dalton's view, each gas in the mixture may be considered as diffused throughout the whole vessel, so that all occupy the same volume, namely, the whole chamber.

If the gases be taken as ideal substances obeying Boyle's law, and if the molecules in the mixture are outside the sphere of each other's attraction—that is, if they move about independently of each other,

---

[1] *Ann. de Chimie*, 3e sér., tom. xv. p. 129, 1845.

[2] Dalton, *Memoirs of Manchester Phil. Soc.* vol. v., 1802, p. 543.

except in so far as collisions may occur—then the bombardment on the walls of the containing vessel by the molecules of the mixture will be equal to the sum of the actions which would be exerted if each gas occupied the whole space separately. There will, however, obviously be a limit beyond which the law will cease to be true, and become more and more inaccurate. If the number or the quantities of the gases in a given space be greatly increased, or, what is the same thing, if the space occupied by a given mixture is largely reduced, so that the pressure of the mixture is great, then the molecules will not possess the freedom of motion necessary for the truth of the law. They will, under the great pressure, be brought into such close proximity that the motion of any molecule will be influenced by the others. The free path will be lost to some extent, and the molecular motion will begin to acquire the characteristics of that which occurs in a liquid. Boyle's law will be more and more departed from, and as a consequence Dalton's law will also cease to be true.

If, however, the gases are far removed from their condensing points, so that we may assume Boyle's law to hold for each constituent as well as for the mixture as a whole, then the sum of the products pv for the constituents will be equal to the product PV for the mixture, or

$$p_1v_1 + p_2v_2 + p_3v_3 + \ldots = PV.$$

If, now, each gas is diffused throughout the whole chamber, as Dalton supposed, then

$$v_1 = v_2 = v_3 = \text{etc.} = V,$$

so that the equation becomes

$$V(p_1 + p_2 + p_3 + \text{etc.}) = PV,$$

or

$$P = \Sigma p$$

—that is, the whole pressure is the sum of the partial pressures.

If, on the other hand, the gases are superimposed on each other in layers, they will have a common pressure P and

$$\Sigma v = V.$$

But in this case we have also

$$Pv_1 = p_1V, \quad Pv_2 = p_2V, \quad \text{etc.,}$$

so that

$$\Sigma p = P\frac{\Sigma v}{V} = P$$

—that is, the total pressure P is equal to the sum Σp of the pressures which the gases would exert if they each occupied the vessel separately.

In the case of vapours the law is approximately obeyed within certain limits and with certain restrictions. In 1815 Gay-Lussac [1] found that the vapours of alcohol and water mix like two gases which have no action on each other, the density and pressure of the mixed vapours agreeing closely with that deduced according to Dalton's law. In 1836 Magnus [2] proved that when two liquids which do not mix are introduced into the vacuum of a barometer tube, the pressure of the mixed vapours at any temperature is equal to the sum of the vapour pressures of the two liquids. But when the liquids possess the property of mixing with each other, the behaviour of the vapour is greatly modified. The pressure of the mixed vapour is no longer equal to the sum of the pressures of its constituents acting separately, but is always less than this sum, and often less than the vapour pressure of the most volatile constituent. This appears to contradict the observations of Gay-Lussac on the pressure of the mixed vapours of alcohol and water ; but, as Magnus has pointed out, the conditions under which Gay-Lussac's experiment was made differed from those by which these conclusions were established. In Gay-Lussac's experiment the mixture of water and alcohol was completely vaporised, whereas in those of Magnus an excess of the mixed liquids was always present in contact with the vapour.

Mixtures.

The matter was subsequently investigated by Regnault [3] in his work on the elastic force of vapours, and his experiments confirmed the conclusions of Magnus. Thus it was established that the pressure of the vapour of a mixture of two or more liquids which do not mutually dissolve each other was equal to the sum of the vapour pressures of the constituents considered separately, at the same temperature ; but volatile liquids which mutually dissolve each other gave a complex vapour pressure which was always less than the sum of the vapour pressures of its constituents. Thus when water is mixed with a substance, such as sulphuric acid, which is said to have a strong "affinity" for it, the vapour pressure of the mixture diminishes as the proportion of acid is increased. A weak solution has nearly the same vapour pressure as pure water, while the vapour pressure of a very strong solution is almost zero at ordinary temperatures. Regnault also extended his work to mixtures of gases and vapours, and concluded that in these cases Dalton's law is very closely obeyed, and that in all the cases examined it would probably have been verified rigorously but for the action of the walls of the enclosing vessel.

[1] Gay-Lussac, *Ann. de Chimie*, tom. xcv. p. 314, 1815.
[2] Magnus, *Pogg. Ann.* Band xxxviii. p. 488, 1836.
[3] Regnault, *Mém. de l'Académie*, tom. xxvi. p. 722.

These conclusions cannot, however, be pushed beyond certain limits. As already pointed out, if the pressure be increased, the vapours and gases cease to obey Boyle's law approximately, and Dalton's law ceases to be true under the same conditions. The pressures under which the foregoing experiments were conducted did not exceed two atmospheres, and for this reason Andrews[1] took up the question and examined the properties of a mixture of nitrogen and carbon dioxide under high pressures. The results of his investigation led him to conclude that under high pressures Dalton's law is largely deviated from, and that it is probably only strictly true for gases in the so-called perfect state.

It appears from the experiments of Andrews that when strongly compressed carbon dioxide and nitrogen are mixed a notable expansion occurs, varying from 9 % at 50 atmos. to as much as 39 % at 80 atmos. when 3 volumes of nitrogen were mixed with 4 volumes of carbon dioxide. On the other hand, no very marked difference was found between the total pressure and the sum of the partial pressures. A series of investigations with various gases has been made by F. Braun[2] which shows that when two gases, at the same pressure in different vessels connected by stop-cocks, are allowed to mix, a change of pressure occurs consequent on the mutual action of the two gases. This change may be either positive or negative. Thus there appears to be a decrease of pressure when SO_2 mixes with CO_2, hydrogen, nitrogen, or air, and an increase of a fraction of a millimetre when hydrogen mixes with CO_2, air, or nitrogen.

HYGROMETRY

227. Fraction of Saturation, or Humidity.—The atmosphere consists of a mixture of oxygen, nitrogen, and aqueous vapour, together with small quantities of other substances. The percentage of vapour is very variable, depending on the temperature and other modifying circumstances. We have already seen that at a given temperature a given space will contain a certain definite weight of vapour at its maximum pressure. This is the greatest weight of vapour which the space can accommodate,[3] and at this point the space is said to be saturated or filled with saturated vapour. It has been

---

[1] Andrews, *Phil. Trans.*, 1886–87.

[2] F. Braun, *Wied. Ann.* Band xxxiv. p. 943, 1887.

[3] This refers only to states of stable equilibrium. Supersaturation is possible, but the condition is unstable (Art. 216).

proved, moreover, by Regnault (Art. 225) that the presence of a gas, at least at ordinary pressures, does not affect the quantity of vapour which a given space can contain. It merely affects the rate of evaporation; but ultimately the quantity of vapour at the saturation point that can be contained in a given space is the same whether the space is vacuous or contains air or other gases. The quantity of vapour required to saturate a given space depends only on the temperature, and, when the temperature is known, the pressure of the saturated vapour can be found from the tables of saturated vapour pressures already compiled by Regnault and others.

If the space is not saturated, however, the vapour pressure will be less than the maximum value for the corresponding temperature. The ratio of the actual pressure of the vapour in a space to the maximum, or saturation pressure for the same temperature, is called *the fraction of saturation*. It is on this element that our opinions of the dryness or dampness of the atmosphere are chiefly formed. The air is ordinarily said to be damp when it is saturated or nearly saturated with vapour. It is not the absolute quantity of vapour in the air that determines its dampness, but merely the proximity to saturation. For example, an atmosphere saturated at 10° C. will be not nearly saturated at 20° C., although the quantity of vapour in it is exactly the same at the latter temperature as at the former. Heating an atmosphere lessens the fraction of saturation, and cooling increases it if the quantity of vapour in the atmosphere be kept constant. The fraction of saturation is often referred to as the *humidity*, or relative humidity, of the air, since our sensations of dryness and dampness depend rather upon this factor than upon the absolute quantity of vapour present. Thus in winter the humidity of the air is generally much greater than in summer, although the quantity of vapour present in the winter may be much less, on account of the lower temperature, than in summer.

The fraction of saturation may also be expressed as the ratio of the weight w of vapour contained in a given space to the weight W of the quantity which would saturate the same space at the same temperature. For if the vapour obeys Boyle's law up to the point of saturation (which is approximately the case), then the weight contained in a given volume is simply proportional to the pressure, and we have the equation

$$\frac{w}{W} = \frac{f}{F}.$$

It thus appears that two general methods are available for determining the fraction of saturation, or humidity, of the atmosphere. One by

2 E

ascertaining directly the weight w of vapour in a measured volume of air, and then ascertaining from Regnault's tables the weight W of vapour which would saturate the same volume at the same temperature.   This is the method practised in the chemical hygrometer. The other method consists in determining the actual pressure f of the vapour in the air, and then ascertaining the maximum pressure F at the same temperature, from the tables of vapour pressures.   This is the method practised in all dew-point instruments.

228. The Dew-Point.—If an atmosphere containing some aqueous vapour be gradually cooled, a temperature will be reached at which the vapour will begin to condense.   This temperature is called the dew-point.   It is obviously the temperature at which the quantity of vapour actually present would saturate the air, and it depends therefore only on the absolute quantity of vapour present per unit volume.

When the dew-point is known, the pressure f of the vapour in the air can be found at once.   For suppose we have a body A, the temperature of which can be gradually reduced.   As the temperature of A falls, a point will be reached at which dew will begin to be deposited on its surface.   Hence at this temperature the vapour around the body A is at its maximum pressure, for at this temperature and under this pressure (namely f, the vapour pressure sought) condensation is taking place.   The actual pressure of the vapour in the air is therefore equal to that which would bring it just to the condensing point at the temperature of the dew-point.   In other words, the actual pressure of the vapour is equal to its maximum pressure at the temperature of the dew-point.   If, therefore, the dew-point is known, the maximum pressure for this temperature can be found in the tables of vapour pressures, and this is the actual pressure f of the vapour in the air.   The fraction of saturation, then, will be the ratio of the maximum vapour pressure f at the dew-point to the maximum pressure F at the temperature of the air.

The above reasoning would not hold if the vapour pressure were appreciably altered by cooling the air to the dew-point.   When moist air is cooled under constant atmospheric pressure it contracts, and if the air and water vapour still support the same proportions of the total pressure as before, their coefficients of expansion must be equal. This is approximately the case.   See Dalton's law, Art. 226.

229. Dew-Point Hygrometers.—All dew-point hygrometers are merely instruments for determining the dew-point, and depend in construction on some method of cooling a body gradually in the air till dew begins to be deposited on it.   In the construction of such an instrument the two objects to be kept in view are : (1) an accurate means of determining the instant at which dew begins to be deposited, and (2) an exact knowledge of the temperature of the surface when the deposition of dew just begins.

A phenomenon commonly observed in dining-rooms is the deposition of moisture on the surface of a glass containing cold water. When water-carafes are filled with cold water and placed on the table of a warm dining-room, it often happens that their surfaces become covered with a deposit of dew, which sometimes accumulates to such an extent that drops of liquid trickle down the sides of the vessel. This happens because the temperature of the water is lower than the dew-point of the air in the room, and, as a consequence, the vapour condenses on the surface of the carafes or water-glasses, and continues to do so till the temperature of the water rises to the dew-point. If the temperature of the water were noted when it is just cold enough to produce condensation, we should then have the dew-point, and thence the fraction of saturation.

A similar condensation occurs on the surface of a tumbler containing water in which some ice is placed. If the ice[1] or ice-cold water were carefully added, the temperature could be gradually reduced to the dew-point and an observation made. The temperature of the water when the dew is first observed will be somewhat below the correct dew-point, for when the dew is observed it means that the condensation has started some time previously. A correction may, however, be applied by taking a second reading of the temperature when the water is allowed to stand till the dew disappears from the surface of the glass. During this period the temperature of the water rises by radiation from the warm chamber, and, as soon as it exceeds the dew-point, evaporation occurs at the surface of the glass and continues till all the previously deposited dew disappears. The temperature of the surface at which this occurs is somewhat above the dew-point.[2] The mean of the two is therefore taken as the dew-point.

A glass vessel is, however, not good for making such an experiment, because glass is not a good conductor of heat. For this reason, when the temperature of the water is falling, the outside surface of the glass will always be warmer than the water ; and when the water is rising in temperature, the outside surface of the glass will be again warmer than the water—if we suppose the heat to pass through the glass to the water, as always occurs in the dew-point instruments employed.

[1] This was the method first suggested by Le Roi in 1771 ; see also Daniell's *Meteorological Essays and Observations*, London, 1823.

[2] The temperature of the water within the glass may, however, be still below the dew-point.

The thicker the glass and the more badly it conducts, the greater will be the errors thus introduced. For this reason a thin metallic vessel will be much better suited for the purposes of the experiment. Silver is one of the very best conductors of heat, and its surface takes a beautiful polish, on which the slightest deposition of dew can be easily noticed, especially if a similar silver vessel, on which no dew is deposited, be placed beside it for the sake of comparison. This, in fact, is the principle of Regnault's dew-point hygrometer, which will be described immediately. Indeed, a single thin polished cup, the mouth of which is covered or closed by a cork, could be used for determining the dew-point with rapidity, and probably with greater accuracy than some of the more elaborate apparatus invented for the purpose. Ice-cold water could be siphoned as slowly as desired into the cup from another closed vessel, so that the air would not be affected by evaporation from any exposed liquid, and the temperature of the cup could be thus varied by small amounts at the dew-point, and its position could be repeatedly fixed.

230. Daniell's Hygrometer. — One of the oldest and most

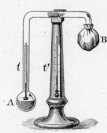

Fig. 128.

objectionable forms of direct dew-point hygrometers is that invented by Daniell.[1] This instrument (Fig. 128) consists of a bent glass tube furnished with a pendent bulb at each end. One of these, A, is naked and made of black glass. This bulb contains some ether, in which the bulb of a very sensitive thermometer dips. All air is expelled from the apparatus by boiling the ether previous to closing, so that it contains only the volatile liquid ether and its vapour. The other bulb, B, is made of ordinary glass and covered with a muslin or linen bag.

In making an experiment the ether is all passed into the naked bulb, and the bag covering the other is moistened with ether. The evaporation of this cools the covered bulb and causes condensation of the vapour within. This gives rise to evaporation of the liquid in the naked bulb and consequent cooling. The temperature of the naked bulb thus gradually falls, and by carefully watching its surface, the temperature at which dew first appears can be noted. This temperature is given by the thermometer within the bulb. The apparatus is now allowed to stand till evaporation ceases, and its temperature begins to rise again. The deposit of dew soon disappears, and the temperature at which this occurs is also noted. The mean of

[1] Daniell, *Meteorological Essays and Observations*, London, 1827.

these two temperatures is usually taken as that of the dew-point The temperature of the surrounding air is given by a thermometer attached to the stem of the instrument. The naked bulb is made of black glass in order to facilitate the observation of the deposition of dew, but, as already remarked, glass is a bad conductor, and consequently the temperature indicated by the thermometer within the bulb may differ considerably from that of the external surface of the bulb at the instant the dew appears or disappears. In both cases the temperature of the external surface is what is wanted, and in both cases this will be higher than that of the liquid within, for the liquid within is colder than the atmosphere, and throughout the whole experiment the flow of heat is from without inwards.

In this instrument the evaporation takes place at the surface of the liquid, and as the liquid mass is at rest, the surface layer will always be colder than the lower parts. Dew will consequently be deposited first at the level of this layer, and if the bulb of the thermometer be plunged below the surface, the temperature indicated by it will be too high. The presence of the observer close to the apparatus is objectionable, and in addition the rate of evaporation cannot be sufficiently controlled. The pollution of the air by the evaporation of ether from the covered bulb is also objectionable.

231. Dines's Hygrometer.—A more recent and less objectionable

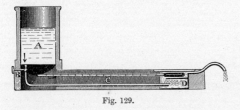

Fig. 129.

form of dew-point instrument is that invented by Dines (Fig. 129). This consists of a vessel A, fitted with a pipe through which cold water can flow into a double chamber D. This chamber contains the bulb of a delicate thermometer, and is closed above by a plate of black glass (or silver, which, for the reasons already mentioned, is better). Previous to the experiment, the chamber D is full of water at the temperature of the air, and some cold water or ice and water is placed in A. The tap B is then opened so as to allow the cold water to flow slowly into D. The temperature of this chamber is thus gradually reduced, and when sufficiently cooled, a deposit of dew appears on the surface of the glass plate. The thermometer is then read, and the flow of water stopped. The dew soon disappears and the temperature is again noted, the mean of the two temperatures being taken as before to represent the dew-point. The operation may be repeated again as often as desired, while any water remains in A at a temperature lower than the dew-point. The observation of the deposition of dew on the glass plate may be facilitated by viewing it by means of a beam of light reflected from its surface. As soon as any dew is deposited the surface becomes dulled, and the intensity of the reflected beam is greatly reduced. An adjacent plate on which dew is not deposited would facilitate the determination of the instant at which dew is deposited on the other plate by comparison, as in the case of Regnault's hygrometer, which we shall now describe.

232. Regnault's Hygrometer.—A more perfect form of dew-point instrument is that devised by Regnault,[1] and employed in his studies in hygrometry. The essential part of the apparatus is a glass tube D (Fig. 130) open at both ends, to the lower end of which a thin polished silver thimble is attached. This thimble contains ether or some other volatile liquid, such as alcohol. The upper end of the tube is closed air-tight by a cork, through which pass the stem of a thermometer T and an open piece of bent glass tubing A, the lower end of which penetrates nearly to the bottom of the liquid contained in the thimble. A tubulure in the side of this tube fits into a vertical brass tube which forms the support of the apparatus. The lower end of this brass tube is connected with an aspirator, by means of which a current of air can be drawn through the system, entering by the bent glass tube A and bubbling through the ether.

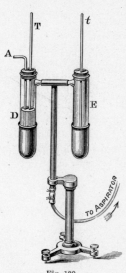

Fig. 130.

By this means evaporation of the liquid is produced, with consequent cooling, and dew is deposited on the surface of the polished silver. In order to facilitate the observation of this, a second tube E with a similar thimble is supported beside that just described. This tube is empty, and merely carries a thermometer t which gives the temperature of the air. Thus by comparison of the two silver thimbles the moment at which the dew appears or disappears can be ascertained with great delicacy. The aspirator is placed at a convenient distance, and the apparatus is viewed through a telescope, also situated at a distance. The air around the apparatus is thus undisturbed by the breath and

[1] Regnault, *Ann. de Chimie et de Physique*, 3e sér., tom. xv. p. 129, 1845.

presence of the observer, and the flow of liquid through the aspirator can be so nicely controlled that the temperature at which the dew appears will be almost exactly the same as that at which it disappears. If the aspirator is controlled with great delicacy, the dew may be even made to appear and disappear without any observable change in the reading of the thermometer. The process of cooling by the bubbling of air through the ether is a great advantage, for by this means the liquid is kept well stirred and at a uniform temperature throughout. This is the temperature registered by the thermometer, and it cannot differ very sensibly from that of the surface on which the dew is deposited, since the thimble is thin and a good conductor. The other obvious advantages of the method are the absence of the observer from the neighbourhood of the apparatus, and the delicacy with which the flow from the aspirator can be controlled.

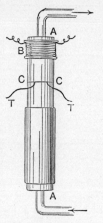

233. Holtzmann's Hygrometer.—In order to ensure that the temperature recorded by the thermometer is actually that of the surface on which dew is deposited, the dew-point instrument represented in Fig. 131 was constructed by M. Holtzmann.[1] AA is a thin tube of polished copper through which a steady current of cold water is made to flow in the direction shown by the arrows. B is a coil through which an electric current is passed, which warms one end of the tube AA. A fine line CC is traced round the tube, and the two wires TT of a thermocouple are soldered on at this line, so that the tube AA forms one junction of the thermocouple. The tube is cooled till dew deposits, and the electric current adjusted till the dew-line just reaches to CC. Both the water flow and the heating current are now reduced gradually, while preserving the adjustment, until the temperature gradient is very slight. The temperature is then given by the galvanometer. The instrument is calibrated by immersing the tube in water at a known temperature, and reading the galvanometer. The dew-point is given to within about $0°·03$.

Fig. 131.

234. Crova's Hygrometer.[2]—The dew-point instruments described in the preceding articles are not suited for use in the open air except in calm weather. When the air is still, the layer immediately in contact with the cooled metallic surface may no doubt be in thermal

---

[1] *Physikalische Zeitschr.* vol. 25, p. 443, 1924.
[2] *Mém. de l'Acad. des Sci. et Lettres de Montpellier*, tom. x. p. 411, 1883.

equilibrium with the latter, even though it is surrounded by layers of
warmer air, since air is a bad conductor ; but in a fresh breeze the
constant renewal of the air prevents its attaining the dew-point unless
the instrument is cooled to a considerably lower temperature.   On
this account these hygrometers, when used in the open air, give
results which do not agree with those of the chemical hygrometer and
are even very discordant amongst themselves.   The hygrometer
invented by M. Crova avoids this defect and affords very consistent
indications.

Fig. 132 gives a general view of the instrument, a section of which

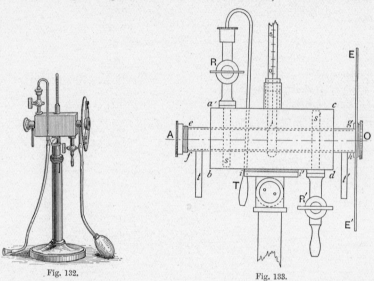

Fig. 132.

Fig. 133.

is shown in Fig. 133.   *efgh* is a tube of thin brass, nickel-plated
inside and carefully polished.   The end *ef* is closed by a disc of
ground glass which is illuminated by daylight or by a lamp, and
which is viewed through a lens *gh* (Fig. 134), which closes the other
end of the tube.   The image of the window *ef*, seen by reflection in

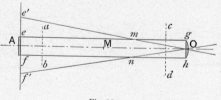

Fig. 134.

the polished sides of the
tube, appears as an annular
ring of light *ee'ff'* of three
times the diameter of *ef*.

Air can be slowly drawn
through the brass tube by
compressing and slowly releasing the india-rubber ball
(Fig. 132), and if the tube is cooled to the dew-point, the deposition

of dew is immediately indicated by the darkening of the reflected image of *ef*.

In order to regulate the temperature of the tube, the latter is surrounded by a brass box *abcd* containing bisulphide of carbon, through which air can be blown from the mouth by means of a rubber tube fitted to the tubulure T.   M. Crova prefers carbon bisulphide to ether, because it is more readily obtained pure, and also does not boil in hot weather.   Ordinary commercial ether contains water and

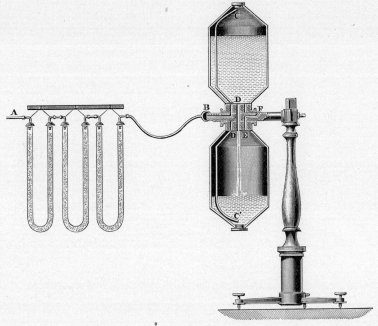

Fig. 135.

alcohol, which are left behind when the ether evaporates.   But it is possible to attain a lower temperature with ether than with carbon bisulphide.   A thermometer graduated in fifths of a degree dips into the liquid, and is in contact with the brass tube.   A blackened screen EE' protects the eye from external light.   *ii'* is a rubber disc insulating the brass box from its stand, through which heat might otherwise be conducted.

The advantage of this hygrometer is that the whole of an enclosed volume of air is cooled to the temperature of the dew-point, and that it is unaffected by draughts.   By attaching a long tube to the opening *t*, the air experimented on can be drawn from a point out of reach of the influence of the observer or of contamination by the vapour of

carbon bisulphide.   It can easily be regulated so that the appearance
and disappearance of dew are within $0°·1$ C. of each other.

235. The Chemical Hygrometer.—The fraction of saturation may
be obtained by the direct determination of the weight of vapour contained in a measured volume of the air.   This method seems to have
been first employed by Brunner,[1] and it leaves nothing to be desired
in point of accuracy.   The air is drawn by means of an aspirator
CDC′ (Fig. 135) through a series of drying tubes filled with fragments
of pumice-stone soaked in sulphuric acid, where all the moisture is
deposited and the dry air alone arrives in the aspirator.   The last
tube, viz. that next the aspirator, is intended to absorb any vapour
which may come from the aspirator.   The remaining tubes are
weighed before and after the experiment, the difference of weight
giving the weight of vapour deposited.   This is the weight of vapour
contained in a volume V of air as registered by the aspirator.   This
is not the volume which the same mass occupied in the atmosphere
before being drawn through the tubes.   In the aspirator it is
saturated with vapour at its maximum pressure F, corresponding to
the temperature θ of the aspirator.   This is given by a thermometer
inserted.   In the air this mass contained vapour at some unknown
pressure f and temperature θ'.   The problem then is to find the
volume V' at pressure $H - f$ and temperature θ' of a mass of air
whose volume is V at pressure $H - F$ and temperature θ.   This, by
the formula $vp = R(1 + a\theta)$, is

$$V' = V \frac{H - F}{H - f} \cdot \frac{1 + a\theta'}{1 + a\theta}.$$

This, then, is the volume of the vapour drawn in, and its mass is w.
Consequently we have

$$w = V'\rho = 0·001293 \times 0·622 \frac{V}{1 + a\theta'} \cdot \frac{f}{760}.$$

The equation for f, the actual pressure of the vapour in the air, is

$$w = 0·0008 \times \frac{H - F}{H - f} \frac{f}{760} \cdot \frac{V}{1 + a\theta'}$$

or

$$f = \frac{760wH(1 + a\theta)}{760w(1 + a\theta) + 0·0008V(H - F)}.$$

The humidity is w/W, where W is the weight of water vapour which
would saturate a volume V' at the temperature of the air.   W can be
found from Regnault's tables.   This method, although possessing the

[1] Brunner, *Ann. de Chimie et de Physique*, 3e sér. tom. iii. p. 305, 1841.

advantage of depending ultimately on a weighing, which is the most accurate process in physical investigation, is, nevertheless, exceedingly tedious in practice.   It is not suited, besides, to indicate rapid changes in the hygrometric state of the air, but rather measures the mean value of the humidity during the time of the experiment.   In this respect it is analogous to a voltameter, which measures the mean value of an electric current during a certain period, whereas a dew-point instrument by its rapidity of action will indicate fairly well the continuous changes of humidity.   These instruments, then, possess in a greater degree the property of being continuous registers of humidity as galvanometers are continuous registers of the strength of electric currents.   The continuity is not, however, complete; but we shall now consider a class of instruments which are continuous in their action.

236. Hygroscopes, or Empiric Hygrometers.—Any instrument which indicates changes in the humidity of the air is called a hygroscope.   Many substances possess the property of absorbing moisture from the air or surrounding bodies, and such substances are said to be hygroscopic.[1]   Most substances consisting of organic tissue are hygroscopic and change their length when they absorb or part with moisture.   Such substances, besides, do not change much with change of temperature; their changes of volume depend chiefly on moisture.   Thus it is well known that ropes and catgut strings grow shorter when moistened, and the same is true of twisted strings in general, as the twisted fibres swell when wet.   It is for this reason that fiddle-strings and tightly strung tennis-bats often fracture in damp weather.   A hair, on the other hand, increases its length when moistened, and this fact was first utilised by de Saussure[2] in the construction of a hygroscope.

A hair is ordinarily covered with a film of oil which protects it from the action of moisture.   In order to render it sensitive to changes of humidity, all the surface grease should be removed by boiling for about half an hour in a solution of carbonate of soda, in which it is

---

[1] The behaviour of various hygrometric substances has been investigated by H. Dufour (*Beiblätter der Physik*, No. VII., 1887 ; or *Phil. Mag.* vol. xxiv. p. 296, 1887).   Denoting the ratio of the weight of aqueous vapour absorbed to the weight of the dry substance by a, and the coefficient of hygrometric expansion by β—that is, the total expansion which a bar of unit length of the substance undergoes when it has absorbed the maximum amount of aqueous vapour—he finds

Substance.	a.	β.
Horn (10 mm. thick)	0·10	0·061
Gelatine	0·34	0·108
Goldbeater's skin	0·43	0·060

The last substance is that which he most strongly recommends.

[2] De Saussure (Horace Bénédict), *Essai sur l'Hygrométrie*, Neuchâtel, 1783.

then allowed to cool.   The hair is now ready to act as a hygroscope, and should not be handled or roughly used.   One end A (Fig. 136) of it is fixed, and the other extremity, after passing round a small pulley C, is attached to a light spring or a small weight p which keeps the hair stretched.   When the hair contracts or elongates, the wheel rotates, and a hand attached to it moves over a scale and indicates roughly the relative humidity of the air.   The scale may be graduated by direct comparison with a dew-point instrument.   De Saussure's

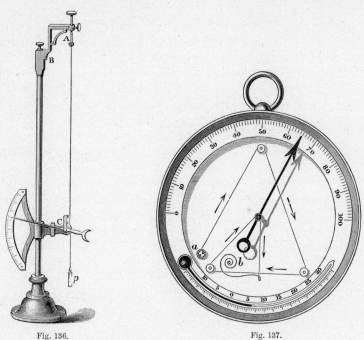

Fig. 136.   Fig. 137.

instrument has been modified by Monnier, so that the hair passes round four pulleys (Fig. 137) situated on a circular dial, and is kept stretched by being attached to a light spring.   The instrument in this form is portable.   The indications of hair hygrometers are, however, very variable, and their use has been abandoned in this country for all scientific purposes.   The work of Regnault [1] conclusively proved that no rule could be laid down for the graduation of such instruments, for not only do different instruments, graduated and prepared in the same way, differ in their indications, but each instrument is not self-consistent.

[1] Regnault, *Ann. de Chimie et de Physique*, 3ᵉ sér., tom. xv. p. 141, 1845.

237. The Wet and Dry Bulb Hygrometer.—This instrument is
that which is almost universally used for continuous records of
humidity, and depends in principle on the cooling produced by
evaporation. It seems to have been first proposed by Sir John
Leslie,[1] who converted his differential thermometer into a hygrometer,
by keeping one of the bulbs moist and the other dry, and noting the
difference of temperature.

The instrument as generally used consists of two exactly similar
delicate thermometers B and C (Fig. 138), the bulb of one being kept
moistened by means of a cotton wick or film of muslin surrounding
the bulb and dipping in a small covered vessel of water placed some
inches to the side. The other thermometer is placed on the same
stand and registers the temperature of the air.
Evaporation takes place more or less rapidly from
the damp cotton, and the bulb of the thermometer which it covers is cooled more or less
according to the humidity of the air. If the air
is saturated with vapour no evaporation will take
place, and the two thermometers indicate the
same temperature.

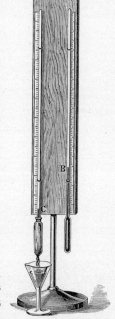

The power of the wick to keep up the supply
of moisture is much improved by boiling it in
a solution of carbonate of soda to remove all
grease, but in frosty weather the supply may be
completely cut off by the freezing of the water.
An objection to the instrument is the difficulty of
managing it in frost. In this case, when the
wick ceases to act, the bulb must be moistened
before making an observation, and some time
allowed for freezing and subsequent evaporation
from the ice.

In an instrument like this, whose indications
depend upon so many complex circumstances, it
seems impossible to deduce any theoretic formula
connecting the difference of temperature of the

Fig. 138.

two thermometers with the corresponding hygrometric state of the
air. The problem has been attacked with partial success by several

---

[1] It was subsequently introduced by Mason, and is often called Mason's hygrometer in this country, and August's psychrometer on the Continent. It was known
to Muschenbroek that a thermometer with a wet bulb always indicates a lower
temperature than one which is dry, and Hutton, the geologist, is reputed to have
used a wet bulb thermometer as a hygrometer.—Leslie (Nicholson's *Journal of
Nat. Phil.* vol. iii. p. 461).

scientists, and was proposed for consideration by the British Association on the occasion of its first meeting held at York. For this reason tables have been compiled by Glaisher [1] which give the dew-point corresponding to any difference of reading between the thermometers. These tables were constructed by comparing the reading of the wet and dry bulb hygrometer with simultaneous determinations of the dew-point taken by means of a Daniell's hygrometer for a long series of years at Greenwich Observatory, together with a corresponding series taken in India and at Toronto. According to these tables, the

Rule.

difference between the dew-point and the wet bulb reading bears a constant ratio to the difference of reading of the two thermometers when the temperature of the dry bulb thermometer remains constant. At 53° F. the reading of the wet bulb thermometer is the arithmetic mean between the dew-point and the temperature of the air, or dry bulb thermometer. At higher temperatures the reading of the wet bulb is lower than this mean, and at lower temperatures it is higher.

In the earlier editions of this book formulæ proposed by Apjohn, August, and Rizzo are given for determining the vapour pressure from the wet and dry bulb hygrometer without reference to tables. It is generally better and more convenient, however, to use tables.

[1] Glaisher, *Hygrometrical Tables,* adapted to the use of the Dry and Wet Bulb Thermometer. London : Taylor and Francis.

SECTION VI

ON THE CONTINUITY OF STATE

238. Critical Temperature — Experiment of Cagniard de la Tour.—When the temperature of a liquid contained in an open vessel reaches a certain point, depending on the pressure and the nature of the liquid, boiling sets in. This ceases to be the case, however, when a liquid is heated in a closed vessel. Here, at any given temperature, the space above the liquid becomes filled with saturated vapour, the pressure and absolute density of which depend on the temperature. As the temperature rises, the average kinetic energy of the molecules of the liquid increases, and they are projected in increasing numbers into the space above, so that the pressure of the vapour increases with the temperature ; the pressure supported by the liquid at any temperature is that of the saturated vapour at that temperature, and, as a consequence, the formation of bubbles in the interior of the liquid is impossible. Evaporation proceeds silently without ebullition as the temperature rises up to a certain point, and then a very striking transformation occurs. The meniscus separating the vapour and liquid grows indistinct and completely disappears ; the substance appears no longer to exist in two distinct states ; the whole mass has become apparently homogeneous and completely vaporised. The temperature at which this occurs for any substance is called the *critical temperature* for that substance, and the corresponding pressure and specific volume are similarly termed the *critical pressure* and *critical volume*.

This silent evaporation of a liquid in a sealed tube, and the apparently sudden vaporisation of the whole mass at a certain temperature, was first shown by Cagniard de la Tour.[1] The apparatus consisted simply of a bent tube, one end A of which contained air (Fig. 139) to indicate the pressure, the other end B containing the

---

[1] Cagniard de la Tour, *Annales de Chimie et de Physique*, 2e sér., tomes xxi. xxii. xxiii., 1822–23.

liquid to be experimented on. The space between A and B was filled with mercury. If, in addition, both arms are graduated, the critical pressure and volume may be determined simultaneously. At low temperatures the vapour pressure may be less than that caused by the air in A and the column of mercury, and there will be no vapour in B. As the temperature of B is raised the vapour pressure increases, a bubble of vapour forms in B, and the mercury is forced into the other arm, compressing the air in A. The surface of demarcation between the liquid and vapour gradually flattens as the temperature rises, and at a certain temperature it loses its curvature altogether and disappears. The whole space above the mercury in B now appears to be filled with vapour only, although the total volume may be only three or four times the initial volume of the liquid.

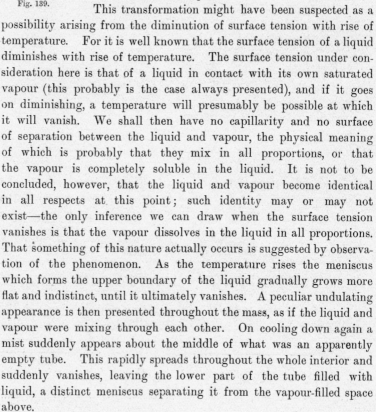

Fig. 139.

This transformation might have been suspected as a possibility arising from the diminution of surface tension with rise of temperature. For it is well known that the surface tension of a liquid diminishes with rise of temperature. The surface tension under consideration here is that of a liquid in contact with its own saturated vapour (this probably is the case always presented), and if it goes on diminishing, a temperature will presumably be possible at which it will vanish. We shall then have no capillarity and no surface of separation between the liquid and vapour, the physical meaning of which is probably that they mix in all proportions, or that the vapour is completely soluble in the liquid. It is not to be concluded, however, that the liquid and vapour become identical in all respects at this point; such identity may or may not exist—the only inference we can draw when the surface tension vanishes is that the vapour dissolves in the liquid in all proportions. That something of this nature actually occurs is suggested by observation of the phenomenon. As the temperature rises the meniscus which forms the upper boundary of the liquid gradually grows more flat and indistinct, until it ultimately vanishes. A peculiar undulating appearance is then presented throughout the mass, as if the liquid and vapour were mixing through each other. On cooling down again a mist suddenly appears about the middle of what was an apparently empty tube. This rapidly spreads throughout the whole interior and suddenly vanishes, leaving the lower part of the tube filled with liquid, a distinct meniscus separating it from the vapour-filled space above.

The matter may also be regarded from another point of view. Thus, as the temperature rises, the absolute vapour density increases, while that of the liquid diminishes, and therefore it is possible that a temperature may be attained at which the density of the liquid is equal to that of the vapour. This temperature, in fact, is the critical temperature, and from the equality of density of the vapour and liquid at this point Sir Wm. Ramsay [1] inferred that the phenomena presented in the experiment of Cagniard de la Tour found their explanation. Three years later M. Jamin [2] put forward the same theory. From this point of view it would appear that when two substances (or at least a liquid and its vapour) have the same density there should be no surface tension between them; or, in other words, they should mutually mix in all proportions. This, however, by no means follows as a consequence. Two substances may have the same density without possessing the property of mixing (otherwise Plateau's beautiful experiment could never have been made, see Art. 181). The property of mixing depends on the molecular attraction rather than on equality of density, and therefore the theory of Ramsay and Jamin fails to lead us any further than its first postulate—namely, the equality of density. If the molecular attraction as well as the density be the same throughout the liquid and vapour, there will be no distinctive difference between the two states at the critical temperature, and the whole mass may be regarded as simply vaporised, as Cagniard de la Tour supposed.

The critical temperature of a liquid is most easily determined by filling a strong glass tube with it and then boiling off about one-third the liquid and sealing up. The tube is now about two-thirds full of the liquid, and contains no air. On slowly heating, the meniscus gradually flattens and ultimately disappears. On cooling, the liquid reappears again, and the mean of the two observations may be taken as the critical temperature. [3] The critical pressure is much

---

[1] Sir Wm. Ramsay, *Proc. Roy. Soc.* vol. xxx. p. 326, 1880. Near the critical point small changes of pressure are attended by considerable changes of density. M. Gouy (*Comptes rendus*, tom. cxv. p. 720, 1892) has consequently directed attention to the important influence of the weight of superincumbent mass of fluid on the lower strata of a substance near its critical point. The effect of this pressure will be to place the lower strata under pressures higher than that appertaining to the critical point while the upper strata are still at lower pressures. The upper and lower strata may thus be at very different mean densities.

[2] Jamin, *Journal de Physique*, 2ᵉ sér., tom. ii. p. 389, 1883 ; *Annales de Chimie et de Physique*, 4ᵉ sér., tom. xxi. p. 208 ; *Phil. Mag.*, July 1883.

[3] Sir Wm. Ramsay (*Proc. Roy. Soc.* vol. xxx. p. 323, 1880) found that the temperature at which the meniscus disappeared varied with the quantity of liquid in the tube, being greater the greater the quantity of liquid originally taken. Thus with

more difficult to estimate. For this purpose the tube containing the liquid must be connected with a manometer, preferably filled with nitrogen, as the compressibility of this gas at high pressures has been very carefully investigated by M. Amagat (see Art. 248).

Impurity, or dissolved air or other gas, may lead to a considerable change in the critical temperature, so that discrepancies may arise in different experiments even by the same observer. The following table shows the rough results obtained by Cagniard de la Tour :—

Liquid.	Crit. Temp.	Pressure in Atmos.	Ratio of Volume of Vapour to Volume of Liquid.
	° C.		
Ether	175	38	$2\frac{6}{7}$
Alcohol	248	119	3
Carbon bisulphide .	254	71	$2\frac{1}{2}$
Water	362	Indeterminate [1]	4

Similar determinations were made by Drion [2] for sulphurous acid and ethyl chloride.

239. Andrews's Experiments.—In 1863 Dr. Andrews wrote as follows :—" On partially liquefying carbonic acid by pressure alone, and gradually raising at the same time the temperature to 88° F., the surface of demarcation between the liquid and gas became fainter, lost its curvature, and at last disappeared. The space was then occupied by a homogeneous fluid, which exhibited, when the pressure was suddenly diminished or the temperature slightly lowered, a peculiar appearance of moving or flickering striæ throughout its entire mass. At temperatures above 88° F. no apparent liquefaction of carbonic acid, or separation into two distinct forms of matter, could be effected, even when a pressure of 300 or 400 atmospheres was applied. Nitrous oxide gave analogous results." [3]

methyl formate, two-thirds filling the tube, the meniscus disappeared at 221°·5 C. ; with a greater quantity of liquid in a similar tube the meniscus vanished at 228° C. ; and with a less quantity at 215° C. It is possible, however, that these inconsistencies may be due to impurities, or to the difficulty of ascertaining the precise temperature inside a thick *glass* tube.

[1] Water vapour attacks glass at high temperatures and renders it opaque, so that the disappearance of the meniscus cannot be seen, and explosion soon occurs under the joint action of corrosion and pressure. In order to overcome these difficulties, La Tour added to the water some substance which prevented the attack on the glass, but the critical point of this mixture is not that of pure water.

[2] Ch. Drion, *Annales de Chimie et de Physique*, 3e sér., tom. lvi. p. 5, 1859.

[3] Miller's *Chemical Physics*, 3rd edit., p. 328.

The apparatus [1] employed in these investigations is represented in Figs. 140-142.   The gas to be compressed was introduced into a glass tube af (Fig. 140), having a capillary bore from a to b, and a diameter of about 2·5 mm. from b to c.   The diameter of the third part cf was about 1·25 mm.   The gas was first carefully dried and then passed for several hours through the tube, open at both ends, in order to expel all air.   Even after passing the current of gas through the tube for twenty-four hours, it was found that the residual air could not be reduced to less than $\frac{1}{500}$ to $\frac{1}{1000}$ of the entire volume of the carbon

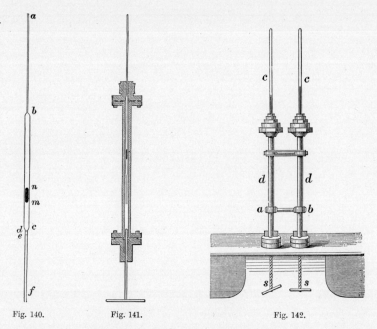

Fig. 140.   Fig. 141.   Fig. 142.

dioxide, and consequently in discussing the results of the experiment the presence of this small quantity of air must be taken into account.

The capillary end a of the tube was finally sealed, and the other end was temporarily closed and plunged below the surface of pure mercury.   The lower end while under the surface of the mercury was opened, and the tube was slightly heated so as to expel a little of the gas.   On cooling, contraction occurred, and a short column of mercury entered the tube.   The tube, with its lower end still under mercury, was then placed under the receiver of an air-pump, and a partial vacuum was formed till about one-fourth of the gas had escaped from the tube.   On restoring the pressure, a column of mercury entered and

[1] Andrews, *Phil. Trans.*, 1869, part ii. p. 575.

occupied the place of the expelled gas. By cautiously exhausting, this column of mercury could be rendered any length required. The tube was previously calibrated by means of a moving thread of mercury, and the volume of the gas at 0° C. and 760 mm. was calculated. The capillary tube was also calibrated with great care by weighing a column of mercury whose length in different parts of the tube was accurately measured.

Two massive brass flanges (Fig. 141) were firmly attached to the ends of a strong copper tube, and by means of these flanges two brass end-pieces were securely bolted to the ends of the copper tube, and the connections were made air-tight by leather washers soaked in lard heated in vacuo. The lower end-piece carried a steel screw 180 mm. long and 4 mm. in diameter, which easily held a pressure of more than 400 atmospheres. A similar end-piece attached to the upper flange carried the glass tube containing the gas.

The apparatus before being screwed up was filled with water, and the pressure was produced by screwing the steel plunger into the water. In order to register this pressure a similar tube containing air was placed beside the experimental tube which contained the gas (Fig. 142), and lateral communication between the two was established through a connecting tube ab, so that equality of pressure was maintained in both. The air-tube was also furnished with a steel screw, and either screw, or both, might be used in altering the pressure. The gas under examination could be kept at any required temperature by jacketing the tube with a bath or a freezing mixture if necessary.

The actual pressures were not deduced by Andrews, as he was not furnished with sufficient experimental data on the deviations of air from Boyle's law, and the pressures he speaks of are those calculated on the apparent compression of the air in the second tube ; but these are approximately correct, as the deviation from Boyle's law is small, as is also the change of internal volume of the tube under pressure. Andrews [1] found that no permanent enlargement of the glass tubes took place even when kept under high pressure for a long time, and that no oxidation of the mercury occurred in the air-tube during a period of two months' active work, and that after standing for five months all was found correct.

From the results of these experiments Andrews plotted the curves shown in Fig. 143.

At a temperature of 13°·1 C. liquefaction of the gas commenced at a pressure of 48·89 atmospheres, as measured by the compression

---

[1] Andrews, *Phil. Trans.* part ii. p. 421, 1876.

of the air in the tube. This point could not be determined by direct observation, inasmuch as the smallest visible quantity of liquid represented a column of gas at least 2 or 3 mm. in length. It was, however, determined indirectly by observing the volume of the gas at 0°·2 or 0°·3 above the point of liquefaction, and calculating the contraction the gas would sustain in cooling down to the temperature at which liquefaction began. A slight increase of pressure was required even in the early stages to carry on the process of liquefaction, the air-gauge indicating an increase of about ¼ atmo. during the condensation of the first and second thirds of the carbon dioxide. This rise of pressure during condensation may be explained by the presence of the trace of air $\left(\frac{1}{500}\right)$ already referred to, for during liquefaction increase of pressure is necessary in order to compress it. This small quantity of air disturbed the liquefaction in a marked manner when nearly the whole of the gas was liquefied, and when its volume relatively to that of the uncondensed carbon dioxide was considerable. It resisted for some time absorption by the liquid; but on raising

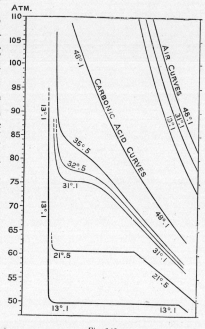

Fig. 143.

the pressure to 50·4 atmospheres, it was entirely absorbed. If the carbonic acid had been quite pure, the part of the curve for 13°·1, representing the fall from the gaseous to the liquid state, would doubtless have been straight throughout its entire course, and parallel to the lines of equal pressure.

The curve for the temperature 21°·5 agrees in general form with that for 13°·1. At 13°·1 the volume under a pressure of 49 atmos. is little more than ⅗ of that which a perfect gas would occupy under the same conditions. After liquefaction carbon dioxide yields to pressure much more than ordinary liquids, and the compressibility appears to diminish as the pressure increases; and the high rate of expansion by heat noticed by Thilorier (see p. 440) is fully confirmed by these experiments.

The next series of experiments was made at 31°·1, or 0°·2 above the temperature at which, by compression alone, carbon dioxide is capable of assuming visibly the liquid form.   This point was found after repeated trial to be 30°·92 C., or 87°·7 F.   For a few degrees above this temperature an increase of pressure produces a rapid change of volume, and when the gas is reduced to the volume at which it might be expected to liquefy no visible separation of the carbon dioxide into two distinct conditions of matter occurs.   By varying the pressure or temperature, but always keeping the latter above 30°·92, the great changes of density which occur about this point produce flickering movements, resembling in an exaggerated form the appearances exhibited during the mixture of liquids of different densities, or when columns of heated air ascend through colder strata.   The curve for 31°·1 shows that the volume diminishes regularly, but much faster than if the substance obeyed Boyle's law, till a pressure of about 73 atmos. is reached.   The diminution of volume then goes on very rapidly, a reduction of nearly one-half taking place, while the pressure is increased from 73 to 75 atmos.   The contraction is not, however, abrupt, as in the case of the formation of the liquid at lower temperatures, but a steady increase of pressure is necessary to effect it.   During this contraction there is no evidence of the presence of liquid in the tube, no heterogeneity can be detected in the whole mass.   Beyond 77 atmos. the substance yielded much less to pressure than before, its volume being now reduced to that which liquid carbon dioxide should occupy at this temperature.

The curve for 32°·5 closely resembles that for 31°·1.   The contraction, however, is less abrupt, and in the curve for 35°·5 it is still greatly diminished, and has nearly lost its abrupt character.   The range of pressure here extended from 57 to 107 atmos.   The contraction is most considerable from 76 to 87 atmos., where an increase of $\frac{1}{7}$ the total pressure produced a reduction to half the volume.   At 107 atmos. the volume is that which the liquid would occupy at this temperature, according to the expansion of the liquid by heat.

The curve for 48°·1 is very interesting.   The abrupt fall shown in the lower temperature curves has disappeared, and the curve approximates to that which would represent the change of volume of a perfect gas.   At the same time the compression is much greater than that indicated by Boyle's law.   Under 109 atmos. the substance is rapidly approaching the liquid volume.   Experiments above 48°·1 were not made ; but it is clear that as the temperature rises the curve will continue to approach that of a perfect gas.

Experiments were made at much higher pressures, and the substance was made to pass without break or interruption from what is universally regarded as the gaseous state to what is, in like manner, regarded as the liquid state. Take, for example, carbon dioxide at 50°, or at a higher temperature, and let the pressure be increased to 150 atmospheres. In this process its volume will steadily diminish as the pressure increases. When the full pressure has been attained, let the temperature be allowed to fall to the ordinary temperature of the atmosphere. During the whole of this process no breach of continuity occurs. The substance at the beginning is what is ordinarily regarded as a gas, and at the end it is liquid carbon dioxide, and nowhere during the process is there any abrupt change of volume or sudden evolution of heat. The closest observation fails anywhere to detect change of condition in the substance, nor is there any evidence that at any time one part of it is a gas and the other a liquid. The process of compression and cooling might also be conducted simultaneously, if care be taken to avoid having the pressure less than 76 atmos. when the temperature is 31°.

These properties are not peculiar to carbon dioxide. They are generally true of all substances which can be obtained as gases and liquids. Nitrous oxide, hydrochloric acid, ammonia, sulphur dioxide, etc., all exhibit critical points and rapid changes of volume with flickering movements when the pressure is changed in the neighbourhood of these points.

Below the critical temperature, when the pressure is increased to a certain value, the substance suddenly changes from the gaseous to the liquid state; but no such abrupt change occurs above this temperature, the substance being gradually reduced to the liquid volume. The change from the gaseous to the liquid state below the critical temperature is abrupt, like the change from the liquid to the solid state in crystalline substances, whereas above the critical temperature it is gradual, like the solidification of amorphous substances.

240. Liquefaction of Gases.—The experiments of Cagniard de la Tour and Drion show that at a certain temperature all visible distinction between a liquid and its vapour ceases. Above this temperature, then, it would appear to be impossible to liquefy the vapour by pressure alone. At least, compression will produce no visible condensation or formation of a liquid with a meniscus separating it from the vapour above, such as occurs when the temperature is lower than the critical temperature. For the visible condensation of a gas, then, the temperature must be reduced below the critical temperature, and then by applying sufficient pressure liquefaction may be produced.

Faraday [1] succeeded in liquefying by pressure, at the ordinary temperature of the air, many gases previously unknown in the liquid state. A few years later Thilorier [2] obtained solid carbon dioxide, and found that the coefficient of expansion of the liquid was greater than that of a gas. Faraday [3] published a second memoir on the effects of cold and pressure on gases, which greatly extended the knowledge of the subject. Subsequently Regnault and Pouillet carefully examined the change of volume of a few gases when subject to pressures up to 20 atmospheres, and Natterer [4] carried the inquiry up to the enormous pressure of nearly 3000 atmospheres. The results of the latter experiments were valuable at the time, but the method was not free from objection in point of accuracy.

The great problem of the time was the liquefaction of what were termed the permanent gases—oxygen, hydrogen, etc. It was in pursuit of this inquiry that Andrews was led to his classic investigations on the behaviour of carbon dioxide gas and other substances described in the last article.

The liquefaction of a gas is favoured both by increase of pressure and diminution of temperature. For every gas there exists a critical temperature, below which it must be cooled before it can be liquefied. Many gases can be liquefied by pressure alone at ordinary temperatures. The first instance of this was in the case Chlorine. of chlorine, which was liquefied by Northmore [5] in 1806. Faraday [6] subsequently liquefied a large number of gases, using a bent glass tube closed at both ends, one limb containing materials from which the gas was disengaged by heat, while the other limb—which in some cases was cooled by a freezing mixture—served to collect the liquid, which condensed under the pressure of its own vapour. Carbon In this way carbon dioxide and nitrous oxide were liquefied. dioxide. Oxygen, hydrogen, nitrogen, and a few compound gases resisted this treatment.

Oxygen. Oxygen was first liquefied by Cailletet [7] in 1877 by compressing it to about 300 atmospheres in a strong capillary glass tube cooled to − 29° C. and then suddenly relieving the pressure. The gas was cooled to the point of condensation by the resulting expansion,

[1] Faraday, *Phil. Trans.* pp. 160-189, 1823.

[2] Thilorier, *Ann. de Chimie*, 2e sér., tom. lx. p. 427, 1835.

[3] Faraday, *Phil. Trans.*, 1845, p. 155.

[4] Natterer, *Pogg. Ann.* vol. xciv. p. 436, 1855.

[5] *Nicholson's Journal*, vol. xii. p. 368.

[6] *Phil. Trans.*, 1823, p. 160.

[7] *Comptes rendus*, vol. lxxxv. p. 815, 1878.

and a thick mist was seen to form. Oxygen, nitrogen, and air were afterwards liquefied by Wroblewski, Olszewski, and Dewar in sufficient quantities to study their properties, the gas being compressed in a vessel cooled by liquid ethylene boiling under reduced pressure.

In 1884 Wroblewski obtained a mist of liquefied hydrogen by Cailletet's method, cooling the tube to the temperature of liquid oxygen before expansion. In 1895 Olszewski obtained sufficient liquid hydrogen in this way to make an estimation of its temperature. *Hydrogen.*

This method of sudden expansion does not admit of the continuous production of liquid. For this purpose the gas must be cooled below its critical temperature under a pressure sufficient for liquefaction. Hydrogen cannot, however, be liquefied in this way, as its critical temperature is − 234°·5 C., which is a lower temperature than can be produced by boiling oxygen under reduced pressure.

Lord Rayleigh and Kamerlingh Onnes have suggested independently that it might be possible to liquefy hydrogen by allowing it to do work by expanding in a heat-engine driven backwards (see Chap. VIII.). The mechanical difficulties would, however, be very great.

There is another method, however, which, though thermodynamically far less efficient, is, owing to its simplicity, well adapted to the purpose. It was shown by Joule and Sir William Thomson in 1852 that when a gas expands without doing external work it is slightly cooled, except in the case of hydrogen, which is warmed. This phenomenon is known as the Joule - Kelvin effect. Hampson in England and Linde in Germany first suggested that this property might be made use of for the liquefaction of air. In 1900 Prof. Dewar [1] showed that hydrogen when at a sufficiently low temperature is also cooled by free expansion.[2] In this way he obtained liquid hydrogen in quantity. Air can be liquefied by the Hampson-Linde process without previous cooling below normal temperatures. *Cooling by free expansion.*

The essential parts of the improved form of apparatus used by Dr. Travers [3] for the liquefaction of hydrogen are shown in Fig. 144. Hydrogen is generated on a large scale in the usual way from sulphuric acid and zinc. The gas is compressed by a pump to about 150 atmospheres, and the heat developed during compression is

---

[1] *Chemical News,* March 1900.

[2] Olszewski found that hydrogen must be cooled to below − 80° C. in order that further cooling may take place, when the pressure is reduced by free expansion from about 110 atmospheres to one atmosphere (see Art. 366).

[3] *Phil. Mag.,* April 1901 ; *Nature,* vol. lxvii. p. 443, 1903.

removed by passing it through coils immersed in water.   After being
purified by passing through a water-separating cylinder and a cylinder

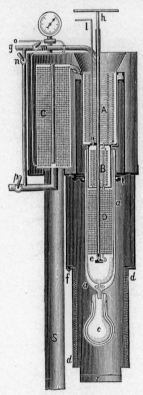

Fig. 144.

filled with caustic potash, it enters the
liquefier at o, its temperature being that of
the atmosphere.   The tube o leads to the
bottom of a regenerator-coil C, which consists of a great length of narrow copper
tubing coiled in layers of flat spirals.   As
the interstices between the coils are filled
with a descending current of the cooled
hydrogen which is issuing from the apparatus, the entering gas, as it passes up through
the coil C, is cooled to about $-170°$ C., and
at this temperature it enters the refrigerating coil in the vessel A, which is kept continually replenished with liquid air, the
temperature being here reduced to $-190°$ C.
The hydrogen then passes through a second
refrigerating coil in the chamber B, which
is closed and connected with an exhaust
pump by the pipe g; liquid air flows continuously from A to B through a pin-hole
valve controlled by the lever l, and, boiling
under a pressure of 100 mm. of mercury,
lowers the temperature to $-200°$ C.   The
gas now passes into the regenerator-coil
D ; it escapes at the valve e, expanding
suddenly and lowering the pressure to one
atmosphere, and passes up through the interstices of the coil D, then
through an annular space surrounding the chambers B and A, and
finally flows downwards through the interstices of the regenerator-coil
C, cooling the entering portion as already mentioned, and, issuing at
p, returns to the compressor at a temperature only two or three
degrees below that of the atmosphere.

The sudden expansion at e cools the gas still further below $-200°$,
and as it passes upward it lowers the temperature of the next portion
coming down the coil D, which in its turn is cooled to a still lower
temperature by expansion, and exerts a stronger cooling effect on the
next portion.   This goes on till finally the gas partially liquefies in
the vacuum-vessel a.   In order to collect the liquid another vacuum-
vessel c is supported below a within the vessel dd.   The latter is a
brass cylinder with two glass windows placed opposite each other, and

is lined with glass cylinders to shield the receiver c from external heat; it is secured to the upper section of the casing by nuts and screws f which compress a rubber washer between the flanges of the joint. The vessel dd being thus rendered gas-tight, the flow of liquid hydrogen into c can be regulated by a stop-cock (not shown in the figure) which controls the pressure in dd. The flow of liquid hydrogen into c can be watched through the windows. At first, a small quantity of white solid is deposited on the inside of a, probably consisting of air and arseniuretted hydrogen, but the gas becomes purer after circulating once or twice through the apparatus. The hydrogen is filtered through a piece of baize in the bottom of a, and flows out in a fairly rapid stream into c as a clear colourless liquid. To withdraw c, the gas-tight stopper r in the bottom of dd is removed, and c is lowered.

Very good heat-insulation is necessary for the success of this experiment. A and B are kept cool by the cold hydrogen passing up round them, outside which are two vessels packed with sheep's wool. B and D are protected by the vacuum-vessel aa. These vacuum-vessels are double-walled glass tubes, the annular space between the two walls being highly exhausted.

The valve e is of a special construction to prevent clogging with solid impurities. It is regulated by turning the milled head h.

Before commencing the experiment it is necessary to cool the regenerator-coil D to the temperature of liquid air. This is done by closing the stop-cock p and putting the interior of the apparatus in connection with the exhaust pump by opening the cock n; liquid air is then drawn through the coils till they are sufficiently cooled.

The temperature of liquid hydrogen is $-252°\cdot8$ C. By causing Solid it to boil under reduced pressure Professor Dewar succeeded in hydrogen. freezing it to a foam-like solid. A further quantity of the liquid contained in a tube and immersed in the boiling hydrogen was frozen to a transparent ice.

The only substance which is not solidified at the temperature of Helium. liquid hydrogen is helium. This gas does not liquefy even when cooled to about $10°$ lower by surrounding it with solid hydrogen evaporating under reduced pressure and suddenly diminishing the pressure as in Cailletet's experiments. It was liquefied by Kamerlingh Onnes[1] in 1908. Its boiling point at atmospheric pressure is $-268°\cdot6$ C.

[1] An account of the experiments (taken from the *Proceedings* of the Royal Academy of Amsterdam) is given in *Nature*, Aug. 1908.

Onnes tried to solidify helium by evaporating the liquid, and thus cooling it to the solidifying point. Although he reached a temperature as low as $-272°$, the liquid did not solidify. It was afterwards solidified by Keesom,[1] who applied pressure to liquid helium which was contained in a tube surrounded by the same liquid, which was cooled by rapid evaporation. The pressure required to produce solidification depended on the temperature. At the lowest temperature reached, a pressure of 26 atmos. was required.

241. On the State of Matter near the Critical Point.—The question now arises for consideration as to the state of a body at or a little above its critical point. Is it gaseous or liquid, or a mixture of the two states? When carbon dioxide gas is compressed at temperatures above $31°$ C. no visible evidence of liquefaction is obtained, even when the compression is pushed up to the point at which the liquid volume is attained. In this case, then, does the substance continue throughout in the gaseous state, or does it liquefy in the whole or in part, or are we presented with a new state of matter? Such are the questions raised by Andrews, and since they were first proposed they have been the subject of much discussion and inquiry. If carbon dioxide gas at $100°$ C., for example, or any higher temperature, is compressed, few would hesitate to declare that the gaseous state is maintained throughout the compression, just as when hydrogen or nitrogen is subjected to great pressures at ordinary temperatures.

On the other hand, when the experiment is made with carbon dioxide at temperatures a little above $31°$ C., the rapid change of volume which occurs during a certain period of the experiment would lead to the conjecture that liquefaction, total or partial, actually takes place, although optical tests fail to detect it. Against this view it might be urged that during this period of rapid change of volume, increase of pressure is always necessary for diminution of volume, and this is opposed to the ordinary laws of the liquefaction of saturated vapours. Furthermore, the higher the temperature the less marked this period of rapid change becomes, until it ultimately disappears.

In the opinion of Andrews, the answer to the question is to be found in the intimate relations which exist between the gaseous and liquid states of matter. These he regards as only widely separated forms of the same condition of matter, which may be made to pass into one another by a series of gradations so gentle that the passage shall nowhere present any interruption or breach of continuity. Thus at high temperatures and low pressures the substance approximates to the condition of an ideal gas obeying Boyle's law. Increase of pressure

[1] *Proc. R. Academy of Amsterdam*, vol. xxix. p. 1136, 1926.

and reduction of temperature decrease the mean free path and kinetic energy of the molecules, and the substance begins to deviate sensibly from Boyle's law. It commences to acquire the properties of the liquid, and gradually loses the distinctive properties of the so-called perfect gas. The gas and liquid then are, in the opinion of Andrews, "only distant stages of a long series of continuous physical changes."

242. On the Determination of the Critical Constants.—The physical constants which characterise the critical state of matter have become of considerable importance in the determination of the mathematical functions which represent the thermal and mechanical properties of fluids, and which establish the relations between the liquid and gaseous states. The accurate determination of the three critical constants for various substances is consequently a matter of importance. Of these the critical temperature is the most easily determined, for by employing as heaters the vapours of pure liquids boiling under a constant pressure, which can be adjusted at pleasure, the temperature can be regulated with considerable nicety and is easily measured.

The critical pressure may also, as a rule, be determined without very much difficulty, provided that the substance is obtained perfectly pure—a matter of prime importance. In the case of substances which attack mercury at high temperatures the ordinary method of operation requires modifications, which render the calculations more laborious, but otherwise the difficulty is not greatly increased.

The estimation of the critical volume, even when the substance is perfectly pure and without action on mercury, is a matter of much greater difficulty. In order to secure a correct reading of the critical volume it is necessary that the substance should be exactly at the critical temperature. A very small alteration of temperature, such as $0°\cdot1$ C., at, or just below, the critical point, produces a considerable alteration in the volume, and for this reason a small error in the temperature leads to a considerable error in the volume. The main object is therefore to bring the substance exactly to the critical temperature. Professor Sidney Young [1] takes the substance to be in this state when, on rapidly increasing the volume somewhat above the critical volume, the fall of temperature due to expansion causes a momentary separation of the liquid and vapour. In order to determine the critical volume, this temporary mark of division is noted and the volume then slightly diminished. After a few minutes the temperature becomes constant, and the volume is again increased

[1] S. Young, *Phil. Mag.* vol. xxxiii. p. 181, 1892.

slightly but rapidly, and the position of the mark of division of liquid and vapour again noted, this being now nearer the top of the tube. Proceeding in this way, it is possible, under favourable conditions, to make the substance occupy such a volume that a very slight but rapid expansion gives a temporary mark of division of liquid and vapour almost exactly at the top of the tube. This volume Professor Young takes as the critical volume.

Case of water.

In the case of substances, such as water, which attack glass at high

Steam line for water.

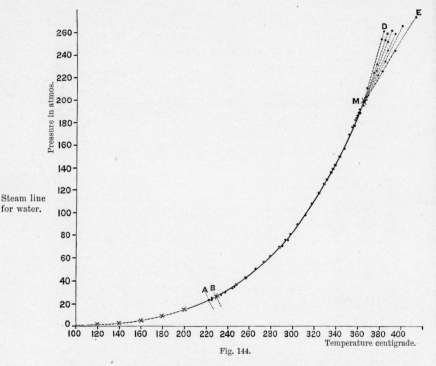

Fig. 144.

temperatures, these methods cannot be applied. The method adopted by MM. Cailletet and Colardeau[1] in the case of water was founded on the observation of the vapour pressure curve when the liquid was enclosed in a strong steel tube. If a suitable quantity of the liquid be taken in the tube the vapour pressure will be unique up to the critical point, but beyond this point the course of the curve will depend on the quantity of liquid present when the critical point is approached (Fig. 144). By starting with different quantities of

[1] Cailletet et Colardeau, *Comptes rendus*, tom. cxii. p. 563, 1891 ; and *Ann. de Chimie et de Physique*, 6e sér., tom. xxv. p. 519.

liquid in the tube, the point at which the vapour pressure curve begins to branch can be determined, and the critical constants thence deduced. The same method may be employed to determine the critical constants of any other substance, the inside of the tube being coated with platinum, or some other substance, to avoid attack.

The apparatus of Cailletet and Colardeau is shown in Fig. 145. The tube FD which contained the water was made of steel sufficiently

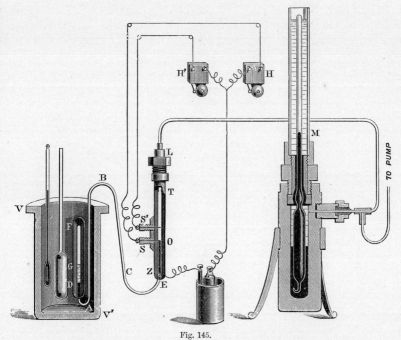

Fig. 145.

strong to resist the pressures experienced during the experiments. This tube was heated directly in a bath VV′, and by means of a flexible steel tube ABC it communicated with another similar and equal steel tube ET, which communicated with a hydrogen manometer M and a pump by which water was forced into both. The pressure of the vapour in FD is transmitted to the manometer by means of this water and the thread of mercury in the tube DABCE. An insulated platinum wire penetrates the wall of the tube ET at S, and when the mercury rises to this level, so as to come into contact with it, an electric circuit is closed and an electric bell is set ringing. By this means the level of the mercury in ET can be kept exactly at S, and consequently the space DF occupied by the liquid and vapour can be kept constant. When the temperature rises the vapour pressure increases, and the mercury is forced through ABCE and rises into contact with the platinum wire at S, and sets the bell in motion. The pump is then placed in action till the ringing just ceases. A second platinum wire penetrates the wall of TE, insulated at S′, some centimetres above S, and this is in connection with another bell, so that if the expansion of the vapour is rapid, or the action of the pump too slow, the mercury rises to S′ and the second bell rings. This gives warning that the vapour is on the point of expelling all the mercury from the reservoir, and this of course must be avoided.

The liquid first employed in the bath was mercury, the boiling point of which is below the critical temperature of water. For higher temperatures a bath of equal parts of the nitrates of soda and potash was used. This mixture is notably more fusible than either constituent, becoming liquid at 220° C., and can be used easily up to above 400° C. The bath was heated by a gas-burner, which was controlled so as to give a stationary temperature. The following results were obtained for the pressure of saturated water vapour :—

Temperature.	Pressure.	Temperature.	Pressure.
°C.	atmos.	°C.	atmos.
225	25·1	300	86·2
230	27·5	305	92·2
235	30·0	310	99·0
240	32·8	315	106·1
245	35·5	320	113·7
250	39·2	325	121·6
255	42·9	330	130·0
260	46·8	335	138·8
265	50·8	340	147·7
270	55·0	345	157·5
275	59·4	350	167·5
280	64·3	355	178·2
285	69·2	360	188·9
290	74·5	365	200·5
295	80·0	...	...

The curve of vapour pressure branches at 365° C., which is therefore the critical temperature of water substance, the corresponding pressure being 200·5 atmos. (see Fig. 144).

243. Distinction between Gases and Vapours.—Previous to the experiments of Andrews there was no clear distinction between gases and vapours. In general, substances which assumed the gaseous condition at ordinary temperatures were termed gases, while those

which assumed the condition of a liquid at the ordinary temperatures of the air were termed vapours when in the gaseous state. Thus ether in the gaseous state was termed a vapour, whereas sulphur dioxide was called a gas; yet these substances, from the present point of view, are both vapours—one derived from a liquid boiling at 35° C., and the other from a liquid boiling at − 10° C. The distinction between gases and vapours was thus determined by the trivial circumstance of the boiling point of the liquid being lower or higher than the ordinary temperature of the atmosphere. Such a distinction may have advantages for ordinary reference, but it is without scientific value. A criterion for scientifically distinguishing between a gas and a vapour is afforded, as Andrews pointed out, by the critical temperature. Thus a substance can exist partly in the liquid and partly in the gaseous state, or as a liquid and vapour in contact, only at temperatures below the critical temperature. Above the critical temperature it is impossible to compress the substance so that part of it may visibly assume the liquid state while the remainder exists as a vapour. For this reason a vapour may be defined as a gaseous substance which may be in the whole or in part compressed into the liquid state—that is, a gaseous substance at a temperature lower than the critical temperature. On the other hand, a gas is a substance at a temperature higher than its critical temperature.

According to this definition, any substance may be a gas or a vapour according to its temperature. A gas cannot be changed into a liquid by pressure alone, but a vapour may be changed by pressure into the liquid state, and may exist in presence of its own liquid. Thus carbon dioxide is a gas above 31° C., and a vapour at lower temperatures.

244. Critical Point of a Mixture.—In his later experiments Andrews [1] proved that the presence of a so-called permanent gas, such as air, lowered in a marked manner the critical temperature of a liquefiable gas, such as carbon dioxide. Thus when three volumes of carbon dioxide gas were mixed with four of nitrogen no liquefaction took place at any pressure until the temperature was reduced to − 20° C. The addition of even $\frac{1}{10}$ of its volume of air or nitrogen to carbon dioxide lowers the critical temperature several degrees.

An extremely important observation was made by M. Cailletet [2] in this department. A mixture of five parts of carbon dioxide with one of air was compressed at such a temperature that liquefaction was

[1] Andrews, *Proc. Roy. Soc.* vol. xxiii. p. 514, 1875.
[2] Cailletet, *Comptes rendus*, tom. xc. p. 210 ; and *Journal de Physique*, 1ʳᵉ sér., tom. ix. p. 192, 1880.

produced. On gradually increasing the pressure at constant temperature the meniscus of the liquid faded, and at a certain pressure disappeared. On diminishing the pressure again the liquid reappeared, and the pressure at which this occurred was lower the higher the temperature, as shown by the following table :—

Pressure (atmos.) . .	132	124	120	113	110
Temperature . . .	5°·5 C.	10°	13°	18°	19°

At 21° C., however, the gas did not liquefy under a pressure of 400 atmospheres.

The disappearance of the liquid carbon dioxide on increasing the pressure is very plausibly explained from Cailletet's point of view that the solubility in the liquid of the gas, or mixture of gas and vapour, occupying the upper part of the tube, increases with the pressure, and at a certain pressure they will mix in all proportions, and the surface of separation will disappear at this point.[1]

Further investigations of the critical point of mixtures have been made by Ramsay, Pawlewski, Ansdell, and Dewar. According to Pawlewski,[2] the critical point of a mixture of two substances belonging to the same class of organic compounds should be intermediate between that of the constituents, and divide the interval between the critical temperatures of the constituents in a proportion measured by the percentage composition of the mixture. Thus Sir W. Ramsay found that the critical temperature of a mixture of equal weights of pure benzene and ether was half-way between those of the constituents. According to the experiments of Mr. G. Ansdell,[3] this law is not accurately fulfilled by mixtures of hydrochloric acid and carbon dioxide. If the law held generally, then the critical temperature of any substance, such as hydrogen or nitrogen, could be determined by noting the critical temperature of a definite mixture of it with some other substance, such as carbon dioxide, whose critical temperature is known.

In the experiments of Professor Dewar[4] on mixtures of carbonic acid with other substances, liquefaction appeared to set in at temperatures above the critical temperature of the gas. The presence of the

---

[1] This question has been attacked thermodynamically by M. Duhem (*Journal de Physique*, tom. vii. p. 158, 1888), who shows that the experimental results follow from the thermodynamic potential of the system.

[2] *Berichte*, No. IV., 1882.

[3] G. Ansdell, *Proc. Roy. Soc.* vol. xxxiv. p. 113, 1882.

[4] James Dewar, *Proc. Roy. Soc.* vol. xxx. p. 538, 1880.

second substance thus appeared to raise the critical point.   This may perhaps arise from the formation of some new compound under particular conditions of temperature and pressure.   These experiments are very interesting.   Thus carbon dioxide in presence of bisulphide of carbon liquefied under 49 atmos. at 19° C., and floated on the convex surface of the bisulphide.   At 35° C., liquefaction took place under 78 atmos., and at 40° C., under 85 atmos.   At 58° C., liquefaction seemed to occur at 110 atmos.   On keeping the temperature at 47° C. and gradually increasing the pressure, the upper surface of the liquid carbon dioxide disappeared under 110 atmos., as in Cailletet's experiment, and reappeared on reducing the pressure to 75 atmos.

In presence of chloroform at 28° C., the carbon dioxide liquefied under a pressure of 25 atmos., and on increasing the pressure to 50 atmos. the two liquids mixed completely.   At 35° C., liquefaction set in under a pressure of 55 atmos., and the carbon dioxide mixed rapidly with the chloroform on standing.

In presence of benzene the carbon dioxide liquefied at 18° C., and a pressure of 25 atmos.; and at the moment of liquefaction the surface of the benzene was violently agitated, the liquid carbon dioxide falling through it in an oily stream, and mixing with it completely up to a certain point.   It then collected on the surface in a distinct layer as further condensation proceeded; but on standing for about five minutes the line of separation disappeared, and the two liquids formed an apparently homogeneous mixture.   On releasing the pressure the carbon dioxide boiled away rapidly from the benzene.   At 35° liquefaction occurred under 35 atmos.; but in this case the liquid carbon dioxide did not fall through the benzene as before or appear to be nearly so soluble in it.   At 52° C. and 70° C. liquefaction occurred under 60 and 85 atmos. respectively, and in each case the two liquids mixed—in the former on standing, and in the latter rapidly. Similar results were obtained in presence of ether and nitrous oxide.

In the case of camphor, some small pieces were fused so as to adhere to the sides of the tube near its upper end, and the tube was then filled with carbon dioxide gas.   The temperature being 12° C., the camphor began to melt when pressure was applied, and ran down the sides of the tube before the mercury appeared in sight.   On suddenly releasing the pressure when the tube was full of liquid at 50° C., the sides of the tube became coated with crystals of camphor, and these rapidly dissolved again when the pressure was increased.

Other substances were investigated with similar results, and in the opinion of Professor Dewar, the carbon dioxide behaves throughout as if it formed an unstable compound with the other substance present, and this compound is decomposed and reconstituted according to the conditions of temperature and pressure.

245. Liquid and Vapour Densities up to the Critical Point.— When a vapour is compressed to liquefaction in a tube, a means of determining the density of both the liquid and saturated vapour is afforded. By this method the saturated vapour density and other physical constants of hydrochloric acid were deduced by Mr. G. Ansdell.[1] A tube, such as that used by Andrews, was filled with the gaseous substance, and its mass became known by observation of the initial volume, pressure, and temperature. The pressure was then increased till the condensing point was reached, and the volume was then noted. This volume gives the density of the saturated vapour, and may be determined by taking the mean of two observations— one at the point where the volume diminishes and the manometer ceases to show increase of pressure, and the other in the reverse operation, when the volume is allowed to increase and its value is observed at the point where the manometer shows a slight decrease of pressure.

The mercury was then caused to rise in the tube till the whole gas was liquefied. The liquid now filled the top of the tube and its volume was observed, the tube being already carefully calibrated. This volume gave the density of the liquid. From the results of the experiments it appears that the density of the saturated vapour steadily increases as the temperature rises up to the critical point, while that of the liquid diminishes, and near the critical point the two approximate to equality. In Fig. 146 the volume of the saturated vapour—that is, the whole volume occupied when the gas is just at the condensing point—is plotted for various temperatures along the curve AC, while the liquid volumes at the same temperatures are shown by the curve BC. A mutual union of the two curves is indicated at the critical point, but experiments could not be made nearer than $0°\cdot25$ C. to this point on account of the rapid change of volume. This equality of volume or density at the critical volume is what would be naturally expected, and it is in accordance with similar experiments by MM. Cailletet and Mathias.

In the experiments of MM. Cailletet and Mathias[2] the method of determining the density of the liquid differed from that adopted by Ansdell. The mercury was not forced up till liquefaction was

[1] G. Ansdell, *Proc. Roy. Soc.* vol. xxx. p. 117, 1879–80.
[2] Cailletet and Mathias, *Journal de Physique*, 2e sér., tom. v. p. 549, 1886.

completed and the upper end of the tube filled with liquid alone, but the gas tube and compression pump were connected to a piece of apparatus like that shown in Fig. 147. This consists of a tube ABC, the two arms of which are united at D and communicate through the tube DE with the gas tube and compression pump. The lower part of the tube contains some mercury AB. On cooling the tube and gradually increasing the pressure, liquefaction takes place in both arms. After a small quantity of liquid is thus obtained in each arm the condensation in A is stopped and the arm BCD is alone cooled, and condensation is allowed to proceed in it till a

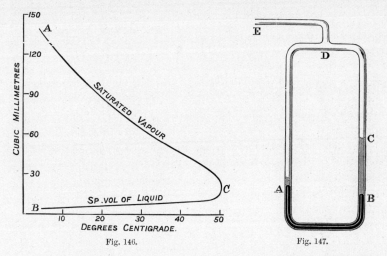

Fig. 146.   Fig. 147.

column of liquid BC of a convenient height is obtained. The difference of level of the mercury in the two arms gives the weight of the column of liquid above B diminished by that above A. The object of having liquid in both arms is to correct for the difference of surface tension which would exist if the mercury at A were in contact with the gas and that in B with the liquid.

By this means the density of the liquid is ascertained, and the results of the experiments were found to be represented by the following formulæ :—

For nitrous oxide from − 20°·6 C. to + 24° C.—

$$\rho = 0 \cdot 342 + 0 \cdot 00166\theta + 0 \cdot 0922 \sqrt{36 \cdot 4 - \theta}.$$

For carbon dioxide between − 34° C. and + 22° C.—

$$\rho = 0 \cdot 350 + 0 \cdot 0035\theta + 0 \cdot 101 \sqrt{31 - \theta},$$

and for ethylene at − 21° C., − 3°·7, 4°·3, and 6°·2 respectively, the density of the liquid was 0·414, 0·353, 0·332, and 0·31.

The saturated vapours were studied in a manner similar to that employed by Ansdell, namely, by noting the volume at the point of liquefaction. The formulæ obtained were :—

For nitrous oxide (saturated vapour)—

$$\rho = 0 \cdot 5099 - 0 \cdot 00361\theta - 0 \cdot 0714 \sqrt{36 \cdot 4 - \theta}.$$

For ethylene—

$$\rho = 0 \cdot 1929 - 0 \cdot 00188\theta - 0 \cdot 0346 \sqrt{9 \cdot 2 - \theta},$$

and for carbon dioxide—

$$\rho = 0 \cdot 5668 - 0 \cdot 00426\theta - 0 \cdot 084 \sqrt{31 - \theta}.$$

These formulæ belong to the general type

$$\rho = a + b\theta + c \sqrt{\theta_c - \theta},$$

where θ_c is the critical temperature, and if a curve be constructed with ρ and θ as co-ordinates it will be an arc of a parabola. Such a formula, of course, cannot be expected to be more than roughly approximate.

In a later investigation M. Amagat[1] employed a somewhat different method. In the method employed by Ansdell the saturated vapour density is estimated by observing the volume occupied by the substance in a graduated tube when the pressure is increased just to the point of liquefaction. It is, however, very difficult to determine the exact point at which the first traces of liquid appear, or at which the last traces disappear; and a small trace of air retards the liquefaction considerably, and then it takes place at a pressure notably superior to the maximum pressure of the pure vapour. It is only when some of the substance has been condensed that liquefaction takes place at the normal pressure. For this reason M. Amagat adopted the following method. The gaseous substance was compressed till part of it, say $\frac{1}{10}$ the total mass, was liquefied. When equilibrium was thoroughly established the volumes of the liquid and vapour were observed. The condensation was then proceeded with till $\frac{2}{10}$ or $\frac{3}{10}$ were liquefied, and the new volumes were observed. If Δv and $\Delta v'$ denote the increase of liquid and the decrease of vapour when we pass from the first stage to the second, ρ and ρ' the densities of the liquid and saturated vapour respectively, then the mass of vapour condensed is

$$\rho' \Delta v' \text{ or } \rho \Delta v ;$$

---

[1] E. Amagat, *Comptes rendus*, tom. cxiv. p. 1093, May 1892.

hence

$$\frac{\Delta v}{\Delta v'} = \frac{\rho'}{\rho}.$$

But if v and v' denote the total volumes of liquid and vapour, we have

$$\rho v + \rho' v' = m,$$

where m is the whole mass of the substance. From these two equations we obtain the quantities ρ and ρ' at once.

In this method the effect of the variation of the meniscus with temperature is eliminated, as it has no influence on the ratio of Δv to $\Delta v'$. The difficulty of the observations, however, increases rapidly as the critical point is approached, the instability of the substance rendering it difficult to obtain the meniscus in a steady position.

While carrying out these experiments M. Amagat noticed some interesting effects which had not been previously recorded. Thus by slow compression the meniscus disappeared at a temperature inferior to that of the critical point (at $30°\cdot5$ C., for example, in the case of carbon dioxide). As long as the meniscus existed the interior generators of the tube appeared broken at its level (on account of the difference of refractive index) in such a way as to produce the appearance of a sudden diminution of internal diameter of the tube. At the moment of vanishing of the meniscus the breach in the generators disappeared and was replaced by two curves joining very regularly the two portions of each generator, the density at the same time appearing to pass in a continuous manner through all values from ρ to ρ'. This appearance was very transitory. An opaque horizontal band, resembling a thick emulsion, suddenly sprang up towards the middle of the curvature and then disappeared. The meniscus then vanished with the broken generators, and a shower of fine drops fell upon the surface of the liquid and agitated it violently. In some cases the rain of droplets resembled the bubbles of vapour rising in a boiling liquid, and sometimes bubbles rose while the droplets fell, both phenomena occurring simultaneously.

These facts show how difficult it is to make measurements at within two or three tenths of a degree of the critical point. M. Amagat was, however, able to obtain good results by this method up to $31°$ C. with carbon dioxide. The results of his experiments are shown in Fig. 148, where the saturated vapour and liquid densities are represented by a curve having the densities for ordinates and the corresponding temperatures for abscissæ. This curve, like those of MM. Cailletet and Mathias, resembles a parabola having its axis somewhat inclined to the axis of temperature. The locus of the middle

points of its chords is accurately a right line,[1] but the summit of the
curve is much flatter than that of a true parabola, the densities of
the liquid and vapour rapidly approaching equality at the critical
temperature. At this temperature the two branches of the curve
unite.

On the same diagram is represented the curve of vapour pressure,
having the same temperatures for abscissæ, and the corresponding

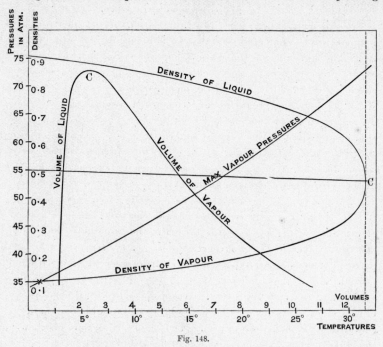

Fig. 148.

pressures as ordinates. The intersection of this curve with the
ordinate at the critical temperature gives the critical pressure. All
the critical constants are thus determined. For carbon dioxide
M. Amagat finds

$$\theta_c = 31°\!\cdot\!35 \text{ C.}, \quad p_c = 72\!\cdot\!9 \text{ atmos.}, \quad \rho_c = 0\!\cdot\!464.$$

The remaining curve shows the water line and steam line—that is,
the border curve or locus of points at which the substance is all liquid
or all saturated vapour. The pressures being ordinates and the
volumes abscissæ, it gives the volume of the substance when it is all
saturated vapour or all liquid at any temperature up to the critical
point.

[1] This fact is generally referred to as the law of ectilineal diameters.

246. James Thomson's Hypothesis.—Two years after the publication of Andrews's experiments on the isothermals of carbon dioxide, Professor James Thomson [1] supplemented these curves by an ingenious speculation suggested by the shape of the isothermals immediately above the critical temperature, as well as by the idea of continuity of transformation so much insisted on by Andrews.   Thus in Fig. 149 the broken line ABCDE represents the ordinary isothermal of a substance passing from the liquid to the gaseous state.   The part AB refers to the liquid state, and is approximately a straight line parallel to the axis of pressure.   At B the vapour pressure is equal to the external pressure, and the substance begins to separate into a mixture of saturated vapour and liquid.   The quantity of vapour increases at the expense of the liquid till D is reached, and here the substance is all converted into saturated vapour.   While this transformation is in progress the pressure remains constant, and the line BD, representing the isothermal of the mixture, is parallel to the axis of volume. Beyond D the substance is a non-saturated vapour, and the isothermal approximates more and more closely to that of a perfect gas.   In the whole isothermal there are breaches of continuity at B and D if the temperature is below that of the critical point, but no such discontinuity appears in the case of an isothermal above the critical temperature.   Here the curvature of the isothermal undergoes no sudden change at any point.   The whole curve is continuous and unbroken throughout its course.   The same remarks apply to the state of the substance.   Along the line AB the whole mass is liquid and homogeneous throughout.   At B discontinuity of state sets in, one portion being liquid and the other portion vapour.   At D the simultaneous existence of the two states ceases, and the whole mass again assumes a uniformity of state, being entirely converted into vapour.

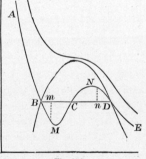

Fig. 149.

In order to complete the continuity which exists above the critical temperature, and extend it to transformations below that temperature, Thomson put forward the suggestion that AB and DE are portions of the same continuous curve, and are joined by some ideal branch, such as BMCND, along which the substance might pass continuously from the liquid to the gaseous condition without any separation into two distinct states simultaneously existing in

[1] J. Thomson, *Proc. Roy. Soc.*, 1871.

contact with each other. This part of the curve is very interesting, for along the portion BM the condition of superheated liquids, as exemplified in the experiment of Donny and Dufour (Art. 194), finds representation, and along the portion DN the condition of super-saturated vapours finds place. Thus the abnormal conditions of both liquids and vapours are embraced by Thomson's curve, and the so-called *difficulty* of commencement of change of state is merely the passage of the substance along the curve BMCND for some distance beyond B or D.

The condition of the substance at any point along this curve is one of uniformity throughout the mass, but it is essentially one of unstable equilibrium for any considerable displacement. Thus the vapour at N is what we have termed supersaturated, and if the equilibrium be disturbed, condensation will set in; and if the temperature be kept constant, the point representing the state of the substance will fall with a decrease of volume to n, where the mass is partly liquid and partly vapour. In the same manner, at M the condition is that of a uniform superheated liquid, and if the equilibrium be disturbed a sudden formation of vapour with explosive violence takes place; and the condition of stable equilibrium for the same temperature is assumed at m, where the substance is partly liquid and partly vapour.

Along the portion between M and N the curve slopes upwards, indicating that the volume and pressure increase simultaneously, an unstable condition which is not easily conceived, and which can never be realised in a homogeneous mass. Experimental evidence of this part of the curve cannot therefore be expected, unless perhaps, as J. Thomson himself suggested, it may exist in passing through the thin surface film of a liquid in contact with its own vapour.

If the isothermal curves for any substance be traced, each on a separate sheet of cardboard, the upper portion of the cards being cut away along the curves, and if these cards be placed with their planes parallel and at distances equal to the corresponding difference of temperature, they will form the characteristic surface of the substance, and exhibit the relation between p, v, and θ. Thomson constructed such a model for carbon dioxide from the curves of Fig. 149. This surface exhibits very clearly the remarkable changes of volume at and near the critical point, and it assists in giving a clear view of the nature and meaning of the continuity of the liquid and gaseous states.

The p, v, θ model.

Although the whole mass of a substance passing from the state of vapour at D to the liquid state at B cannot be made to pass continuously along the curved path DNCMB, yet during the process of liquefaction states corresponding to various points on this line may exist, and the passage under constant pressure from vapour to liquid along the straight line DCB may be the result of the passage of small portions of the substance, variously located throughout the mass, through the states represented by some such curve as that suggested by James Thomson. Thus, although the transformation as a whole appears discontinuous, the continuity may be present in various parts of the mass while the transformation is being conducted.

The question now arises as to how the line BD is situated with respect to the hypothetical curve BMND; in other words, being given the curve, find the position of the line, or the pressure of normal ebullition, at the temperature of this isothermal. The answer to the question appears to be that the right line must be drawn so that the area BMC is equal to the area CND. The reasoning by which Maxwell[1] arrived at this conclusion is as follows. Suppose the substance to pass from B to D along the hypothetical curve in a state always homogeneous throughout, and to return to B from D along the straight line DB in the form of a mixture of liquid and vapour. Since the temperature is constant throughout, no work, on the whole, can have been converted into heat (Second Law, see p. 47). But the external work done by the substance in the first part of the process is represented by the area enclosed by the curve and the ordinates at B and D with the axis of volume; while that done on the substance in the second is represented by the area enclosed by the line BD with the same ordinates and axis. Hence these areas must be equal and opposite; or, in other words, the area BMC is equal[2] to the area

---

[1] Maxwell, *Nature*, vol. xi., 1875.

[2] The equality of these areas has been deduced by Clausius (*Wied. Ann.* vol. ix. p. 337, 1880) from the algebraic statement of the Second Law. Assuming the cycle composed of the curve BMND and the line DB to be reversible, we have for the whole cycle (see Art. 330)

$$\int \frac{dQ}{T} = 0 ;$$

but throughout the cycle the temperature is constant, therefore

$$\int dQ = 0,$$

or no heat is, on the whole, given to the substance or taken from it during the process, and consequently as before the areas are equal. Thus, Maxwell's proof rests ultimately on the same axiom as that of Clausius, viz. on the second law of thermodynamics. Both, however, apply principles derived from experience to a case which cannot be realised experimentally, namely, the passage through the states represented by the curve, and which consequently casts doubt on the legitimacy of the conclusions. A proof of the theorem can also be derived from the theorems of Gibbs on the thermodynamic surface (Gibbs on the Equilibrium of Heterogeneous Substances, Chap. VIII. sec. vi.).

It may be remarked that the internal energy of the mixture of liquid and satu-

CND. The value of either area, of course, cannot be determined, and the shape of the curve between B and D cannot be determined until some general relation between the pressure, volume, and temperature has been established.

Passing along the right line BD, the substance is partly liquid and partly vapour, but in passing from the state of liquid, at B, to that of saturated vapour, at D, along the curve suggested by Thomson, the substance is at each point of the path homogeneous throughout. The equality of areas just mentioned may therefore be stated in either of the following ways :—" The pressure of the saturated vapour is such that the external work done during vaporisation is the same as that which would be performed if the substance increased its volume by the same amount, while at each stage of the transformation it remained homogeneous throughout," or " The pressure of a saturated vapour is equal to the *mean pressure* of the substance while receiving an increase of volume corresponding to complete vaporisation, and remaining at each stage of the process homogeneous throughout."

A method of plotting the unrealisable, or James Thomson, part of the isothermal curve has been described by Professors Ramsay and Young.[1] The relation between temperature and pressure is determined by drawing vertical lines (constant volume) across the isothermal curves, cutting them in points which correspond to certain definite pressures, which may be determined from a properly constructed diagram. A series of equi-volume curves may thus be plotted out by using the temperatures as ordinates and the pressures as abscissæ. All such curves were found to be straight lines, the relation between pressure and temperature at constant volume being linear and of the form [2]

$$p = b\Theta - a,$$

where a and b are constants depending on the volume chosen, and varying with it. The values of a and b being found by experiment for any volume at temperatures above the critical point, extrapolation was then applied to temperatures below the critical point, and the relation between pressure and temperature determined along the unrealisable part of the curve. Experimentally the pressure may be cautiously reduced below the point at which boiling occurs, and simi-

---

rated vapour at the point C, where the James Thomson curve is cut by the right line BD (Fig. 149), is not the same as the internal energy of the mass at the same point when in the hypothetical homogeneous state, but the internal energies in the two states at C differ by the area of either loop BCM or CDN.

[1] *Nature*, vol. xliv. p. 276 and p. 608, 1891.

[2] The equation of Van der Waals is of this form (see p. 480).

larly a part of the curve on the other side can be realised by having the vapour in a space free from dust, so that condensation does not begin, although the temperature is below that of condensation.

The equality of the areas of the curve above and below the horizontal vapour line, as already referred to, was tested and verified by tracing the curve in this manner on tin plates, and cutting out the segments and weighing.

SECTION VII

ON EQUATIONS RELATING TO THE FLUID STATE OF MATTER

247. Early Experiments on Boyle's Law.—A perfect gas has been referred to already as an ideal substance which rigorously obeys Boyle's law. The substances which are ordinarily termed gases and vapours obey this law only more or less approximately. Within fairly wide limits the volume of any ordinary gas varies very approximately in the inverse ratio of the pressure to which it is subject. This law was discovered by Robert Boyle in 1660, and in 1661 he presented to the Royal Society his work, "Touching the Spring of Air and its Effects." With respect to the experiments on air he says : "'Tis evident that as common air when reduced to half its natural extent obtained a spring about twice as forcible as it had before, so the air, being thus compressed, being further crowded into half this narrow space, obtained a spring as strong again as that it last had, and consequently four times as strong as that of common air."

According to the dynamical theory of gases, Boyle's law is a consequence of the comparatively very wide separation of the molecules. When the molecules are widely separated, so that they possess free paths, during which they move in right lines, and are free from mutual influences, the time spent in mutual influence becomes vanishingly small compared with the time spent in traversing the free path, and as a consequence the mutual effect of the molecules on each other becomes negligible, at least in a first approximation. The nature of the molecules and their mutual actions when near each other are thus eliminated from consideration. Such perfect freedom of a system of molecules from mutual influence is only attainable ideally as a limiting case. In the gases found in nature the time spent by any molecule in its collisions with the others is not vanishingly small compared with the whole period, and for this reason the effect of the mutual interactions of the molecules becomes sensible, and deviations from the law of Boyle of greater or less magnitude are exhibited.

Boyle himself does not appear to have considered this law to possess the wide generality afterwards attributed to it.   He believed that for pressures above four atmospheres the compression of air was less than the amount deduced from the law, and Muschenbroek [1] appears to have arrived at the same conclusion.

Sulzer and Robison [2] both obtained the opposite result, and found that when the pressure was increased in the ratio of 7 to 1, the density increased in the greater ratio of about 8 to 1.   This indicated a very wide divergence from the law, and must be attributed to faulty apparatus and the mode of observation, for later experiments by Oersted and Swendsen,[3] with improved apparatus, gave results which were very consistent with the law, although, on the whole, the density appeared to increase somewhat faster than the pressure.   This, however, they attributed to errors of observation.

The next series of experiments was by Despretz.[4]   The direct object of this investigation was to determine if all gases were equally compressible.   It consequently was not ascertained if any particular gas obeyed Boyle's law, but rather that the different gases were compressed by different amounts when subjected to the same increase of pressure ; and hence, if any one of the gases examined obeyed the law accurately, the deviations of the others from it could be deduced. The method of experiment was to enclose different gases in barometer tubes standing in the same cistern.   The tubes were all of the same length, and the quantity of gas in each was so adjusted that initially the mercury stood at the same level in all the tubes.   The system was then placed in a tall cylinder filled with water and fitted with a screw, by which the pressure could be increased at pleasure.   It was then found that when the pressure was increased the previous equality of volume of the various gases became destroyed, and that the level of the mercury stood higher in some of the tubes than in others.   It was thus found that such gases as carbonic acid and ammonia were more compressible than air, and that when the pressure exceeded 15 atmos. hydrogen exhibited an opposite effect.   Up to 15 atmos. no difference of behaviour between air and hydrogen could be detected, but at higher pressures the hydrogen possessed a sensibly greater volume.   This showed that of all the gases examined hydrogen was the least compressed at high pressures, or that the product pv was greater for air than for any other gas except hydrogen.   If the values

[1] See the introduction to Regnault's Memoir on the compressibility of gases (*Mém. de l'Acad.* tom. xxi.).

[2] Robison, *Mechanical Philosophy*, vol. iii. p. 637.

[3] *Edin. Journal of Science*, vol. iv., 1826.

[4] Despretz, *Ann. de Chimie et de Physique*, 2° sér., tom. xxxiv. pp. 335, 443 ; 1827.

of pv were tabulated from such an experiment, while the temperature was maintained constant, the extent to which the various gases deviated from Boyle's law would be placed in evidence; and if every precaution has been taken to obtain them perfectly free from aqueous vapour, and all other impurities, the discrepancies must be attributed to an actual difference of compressibility of the various gases.

The research was next taken up by Pouillet,[1] who followed the method of Oersted and Despretz. He compared the compressibility of two gases contained in tubes about 2 m. long, and he concluded that oxygen, hydrogen, and nitrogen were equally compressible up to 100 atmos., and that sulphurous acid, carbonic acid, ammonia, etc., were notably more compressed than the former under high pressures. It still remained, however, to test the obedience of any single gas to Boyle's law ; it was still believed that air obeyed the law, and the investigation of this point was taken up by Dulong and Arago.[2] Their experiments ranged up to 27 atmos., and within these limits they found that the observed volume was always slightly less than that calculated by the law. From an inspection of the numbers furnished by their experiments it appears that the difference between the observed and calculated volumes did not increase but rather diminished as the pressure increased. The difference, however, was always very small, and fluctuated a good deal in magnitude, so that it could not be concluded with confidence that any deviation from Boyle's law had been proved. For this reason the whole matter was investigated by Regnault[3] in a much more comprehensive manner. The method of experiment adopted was to enclose the gas under examination in a glass tube of accurately determined capacity, and surrounded by a bath kept at a uniform temperature. The gas filled

---

[1] Pouillet, *Éléments de Physique*, tom. i. p. 327.

[2] Dulong et Arago, *Ann. de Chimie et de Physique*, 2e sér., tom. xliii. p. 74, 1830.

[3] Regnault, *Mém. de l'Acad.* tom. xxi. p. 329.

In Regnault's experiments on Boyle's law the divergence of pv could not have been due to errors of observation. The differences would have required an error of reading of the pressure of from 2 to 118 mm.

Regnault represented the results of his experiment by a formula—

$$\frac{p_0 v_0}{pv} = 1 \pm A\left(\frac{v_0}{v} - 1\right) \pm B\left(\frac{r_0}{v} - 1\right)^2.$$

In his second memoir he proposed the formula (p being expressed in metres of mercury)—

$$\frac{0\cdot76 v_0}{pv} = 1 \pm A(p - 0\cdot76) \pm B(p - 0\cdot76)^2.$$

For air and nitrogen A was negative and B positive ; for carbonic acid both A and B were negative ; and for hydrogen both were positive.—*Relation des expériences*, tom. ii. p. 237, etc.

the tube initially, and its pressure p_0 was registered by means of an open-air mercury manometer. The pressure was then increased by forcing the mercury to rise from a cistern below into the manometer tube, and this was continued till the volume of the gas was reduced to half its initial volume, or very approximately so. Thus if Boyle's law is obeyed, and if $v_0 = 2v$, then we should have $p = 2p_0$. In practice it was more convenient to bring the final volume v approximately to the value $\frac{1}{2}v_0$, and then observe the pressure p, when the initial pressure p_0 was varied by admitting different quantities of gas into the tube. The following table contains the results of Regnault's experiments on air, nitrogen, hydrogen, and carbon dioxide. It will be observed that in no case was the product pv found to be constant, but that the quotient p_0v_0/pv exceeds unity in

Air.		Nitrogen.		Carbon Dioxide.		Hydrogen.	
p_0.	p_0v_0/pv.	p_0.	p_0v_0/pv.	p_0.	p_0v_0/pv.	p_0.	p_0v_0/pv.
mm.		mm.		mm.		mm.	
738·72	1·001414	753·46	1·000988	764·03	1·007597	...	...
2112·53	1·002765	4953·92	1·002952	3186·13	1·028698	2211·18	0·998584
4140·82	1·003253	8628·54	1·004768	4879·77	1·045625	5845·18	0·996121
9336·41	1·006366	10981·42	1·006456	9619·97	1·155865	9176·50	0·992933

the case of all the gases except hydrogen, and notably in the case of carbonic acid. In the case of hydrogen, however, the quotient was less than unity, and the inference was that within the limits of these experiments the product pv diminishes as the pressure increases for all the gases examined except hydrogen. In the case of this gas the deviation is in the opposite direction, the product pv increases, and the compressibility is less than that deduced from Boyle's law. This apparently peculiar and unexpected behaviour drew from Regnault the ironical remark that hydrogen was a "gaz plus que parfait."

Later experiments have, however, shown that this property is not characteristic of hydrogen, but is exhibited by all other gases under high pressures, provided they remain in the gaseous state under these pressures. The general law seems to be that the product pv at first General diminishes as the pressure is increased, and after attaining a minimum law. value it begins to increase steadily with the pressure. The exact course of the variations of pv is, however, modified to a considerable extent by the temperature at which the experiments are made. This

2 H

is placed in evidence by the following important investigations of
M. Amagat :—

248. Amagat's Experiments.— The experiments of Regnault
proved conclusively that Boyle's law is not rigorously obeyed by any
gas in nature, and that in the case of all the gases examined, except
hydrogen, the product pv diminished. Within the limits of these
experiments it appeared that pv continued to diminish as the pressure
increased. That this diminution of pv does not go on indefinitely,
but that after decreasing for some time a value of the pressure was
ultimately reached beyond which the product pv increased, as in the
case of hydrogen, was first discovered by Natterer while endeavouring
to liquefy the so-called permanent gases—oxygen, hydrogen, and air.
Although the ground thus broken by Natterer[1] was of the highest
interest and importance, nearly twenty years elapsed before the
subject was taken up and examined more thoroughly. This was done
simultaneously by Cailletet and Amagat in 1870 ; and the experiments of the latter[2] especially advanced the knowledge of the subject
in a marked degree. The method of experiment consisted essentially
in the comparison of two manometers—one containing nitrogen, and
the other containing the gas under examination. The latter was
placed in a bath, the temperature of which could be varied at pleasure,
and also maintained uniform during a series of observations. A
previous investigation of the compressibility of nitrogen, made with
the greatest care (the pressure being directly determined by means of

[1] J. Natterer, *Wiener Ber.*, 1850, 1851, 1854 ; *Pogg. Ann.* vol. lxii. p. 139 ; vol.
xciv. p. 436.

[2] Amagat, *Ann. de Chimie et de Physique*, 4ᵉ sér., tom. xxix. ; 5ᵉ sér., tom. xxiii.
p. 353. *Comptes rendus*, tom. lxxiii. p. 183 ; tom. lxxv. p. 479 ; tom. cxv. p. 638,
etc., 1892.

Amagat (*Comptes rendus*, tom. xcix. p. 1153) gives the following table for the
product pv for nitrogen and air at the ordinary temperature of 16° C., by which the
correct reading of an ordinary air manometer may be determined at ordinary
temperatures :—

Pressure in Metres of Mercury.	Nitrogen. pv.	Air. pv.	Pressure in Metres of Mercury.	Nitrogen. pv.	Air. pv.
0·76	1·0000	1·0000	45	0·9895	0·9815
20	0·9930	0·9901	50	0·9897	0·9808
25	0·9919	0·9876	55	0·9902	0·9804
30	0·9908	0·9855	60	0·9908	0·9803
35	0·9899	0·9832	65	0·9913	0·9807
40	0·9896	0·9824	...	...	...

The pressure was determined by a column of mercury in a tube attached to a tower
65 metres in height.

an open-air manometer), furnished the means of determining the actual pressure by means of the nitrogen manometer. Thus in the present investigation the volume and temperature of the gas under examination were directly observed, and the pressure was determined by the nitrogen manometer. All the quantities, p, v, and θ, are thus known, and the variations of any function of these quantities may be determined. M. Amagat represented the variation of the product pv at constant temperature by tracing curves, of which the ordinates were the values of pv, and the abscissæ the corresponding values of p. An inspection of these curves shows that all the gases examined may be divided into two groups. Hydrogen is typical of the first group,

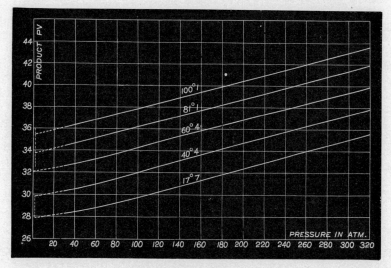

Fig. 150.—Hydrogen.

and in this (Fig. 150) the curves are sensibly straight lines within the limits of the experiments. The lines corresponding to different temperatures are parallel to each other, but inclined to the axis of pressure in such a manner as to indicate that pv increases uniformly with the pressure. Carbon dioxide and ethylene are typical of the second group. In this case pv diminishes to a minimum, and then increases indefinitely with the pressure.

If Boyle's law were rigorously obeyed the curve connecting pv and p would be a right line, parallel to the axis of pressure, and the curve connecting p and v at constant temperature would be an equilateral hyperbola. Hence in the case of carbon dioxide and other substances of this group, the curve connecting p and v is at first steeper than the hyperbola, and afterwards becomes less steep, and is not asymptotic to the axis of pressure.

The behaviour of nitrogen is shown in Fig. 151. At low pressures the product pv diminishes as the pressure increases, but after reaching a minimum the product begins to increase, and the curve rises like that of hydrogen. The figure shows the curves for experiments conducted at $17^{\circ}\cdot7$, $30^{\circ}\cdot1$, $50^{\circ}\cdot4$, $75^{\circ}\cdot5$, $100^{\circ}\cdot1$.

The curves for ethylene are shown in Fig. 152. In this case the variation of pv is much more marked. The curve falls rapidly at first and is concave towards the axes. It then turns and rises almost uniformly. It will be observed that as the temperature increases the

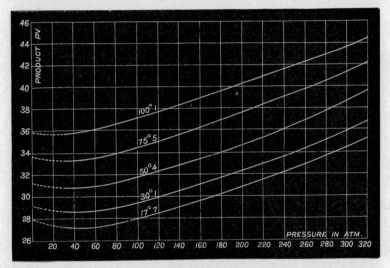

Fig. 151.—Nitrogen.

marked drop in the curve as well as the concavity disappears, and it is to be surmised that above a certain temperature the curve would, like that belonging to hydrogen, show only an upward slope. The fact that the product pv always increases for hydrogen is, then, a sequence of the fact that at ordinary temperatures it is farther from its critical temperature than the other gases, or at least it is so far removed from it that the initial downward slope has disappeared from the curve. At low temperatures it is to be expected that the hydrogen curve would show a sag like that of nitrogen, and at very low temperatures like those of ethylene and carbon dioxide.

The curves for carbon dioxide are shown in Fig. 153, and resemble generally those of ethylene. Near the critical point the variation of the product pv is very rapid, but as the temperature becomes more elevated constancy is more nearly approached, and the point of the curve where pv is least gradually recedes from the origin.   Thus, for

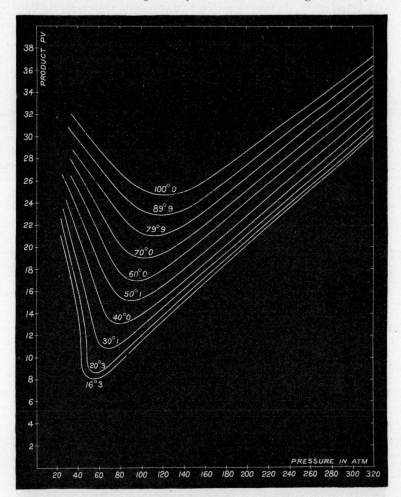

Fig. 152.—Ethylene.

ethylene at $16°·3$ C. the minimum value of pv corresponds to a pressure of 55 atmospheres, while at $50°$ C. the corresponding pressure is 88 atmos., and at $100°$ it is 120 atmos.   In the case of carbon dioxide the minimum values of pv at the temperatures recorded in Fig. 153 were found by M. Amagat [1] to occur at the following pressures :—

_____

[1] Amagat, *Comptes rendus*, tom. cxiii. p. 450, 1891.

Temp.	Pressure.	Temp.	Pressure.	Temp.	Pressure.	Temp.	Pressure.
°C.	Atmos.	°C.	Atmos.	°C.	Atmos.	°C.	Atmos.
0	35	30	76	60	143	100	211
10	45	40	101	70	162	137	247
20	57	50	124	80	179	198	255
...	...	...	...	90	196	258	218

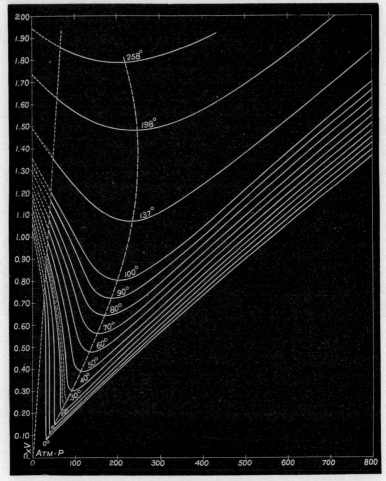

Fig. 153.—Carbon dioxide.

It appears from Fig. 153 that these minimum points advance to the right as the temperature rises, but that this displacement ceases at high temperatures, and a retrogade motion sets in, so that the (dotted)

curve passing through these points possesses a parabolic form.   This is
shown more clearly in Fig. 154, which exhibits the left-hand portion
of Fig. 153 enlarged.   The parabolic form of the dotted curve,
passing through the minimum points, is here strongly brought out, as
well as a second parabolic dotted curve, which appertains to temperatures below the critical point, and passes through those points at
which condensation begins as well as those at which it is completed

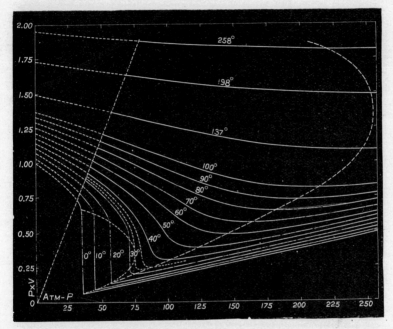

Fig. 154.—Carbon dioxide.

(cf. Fig. 148).   The two dotted isothermals correspond to the
temperatures 32° and 35° C.

The parabola of minimum values of pv can be found from Van der
Waals's equation (Art. 251) by writing $p = x$, $pv = y$, and obtaining the
locus of minimum values of y.

For very high pressures the curves become for all substances a
system of sensibly straight and parallel lines, and the equation of any
one of these lines will obviously be

$$pv = ap + \beta,$$

or

$$p(v - a) = \beta.$$

The quantity a depends on the nature of the substance, while β

depends on the temperature.   When $v = a$ the pressure is infinite, and a is therefore the least volume into which the substance can be compressed.   With this meaning then the above equation would be interpreted by saying that at high pressures the law of Boyle is obeyed by all substances at temperatures above the critical point, if we take as the volume of the gas the whole space in which it is enclosed, diminished by the least volume of the substance—that is, if the volume of the gas be considered as the space $v - a$ rather than the whole space v in which it is enclosed.

For the ratio a/v under a pressure of 760 mm. M. Amagat finds—

Hydrogen.	Carbonic acid.	Ethylene.
$\dfrac{a}{v} = 0 \cdot 00078$	$0 \cdot 00170$	$0 \cdot 00231$

Difficulties at low pressures.

In all such experimental investigations the gas is compressed in a tube over mercury, and in testing the truth of Boyle's law a correction for the pressure of the mercury vapour must be applied.   This correction has an insignificant effect at high pressures, but at low pressures it leads to great trouble and doubt.   For this reason a new series of experiments was undertaken by Amagat[1] on the compressibility of air, hydrogen, and carbon dioxide in a rarefied condition.   The same question had been previously treated by Mendeléeff,[2] Kirpitschoff, and Hemilian, by Siljerström[3] and Amagat.[4]   The results of these investigations differ considerably, and are attended by certain unavoidable sources of error, which become more and more accentuated as the pressure is diminished.   At low pressures the deviation from Boyle's law is exceedingly small, and at very feeble pressures it becomes so shrouded by the errors of experiment that it is impossible to be certain either of its magnitude or the direction in which it takes place. The method of experiment adopted by Amagat consisted in allowing the gas, enclosed in a glass cylinder of volume v and at pressure p, to expand into another glass cylinder of sensibly equal volume v'.   Both the cylinders were immersed in an oil bath kept at a constant temperature.   After expansion the new volume of the gas was $v + v'$, and its pressure p' was measured.   The quantities vp and $(v + v')p'$ could thus be compared, and the deviations from Boyle's law, if any, were determined.   In the case of air no sensible deviation was found at low pressures, but carbon dioxide yielded a product pv which diminished

[1] Amagat, *Ann. de Chimie et de Physique*, 5e sér., tom. xxii. p. 397, 1881 ; and tom. xxviii., 1883.

[2] Mendeléeff and Kirpitschoff, *Ann. de Chimie et de Physique*, 5e sér., tom. ii. p. 427 1874 ; and tom. ix., 1876.

[3] P. A. Siljerström, *Pogg. Ann.* vol. cli. p. 451, 1874.

[4] Amagat, *Ann. de Chimie et de Physique*, 5e sér., tom. viii., 1876.

continuously as the pressure increased. This method of experiment, though apparently very simple, presents considerable experimental difficulties, and condensation of the gas on the walls of the enclosing vessel seems to be unavoidable.

The isothermal curves for hydrogen were later investigated by Holborn,[1] and those for nitrogen, oxygen, and helium by Holborn and Otto. These experiments show that the curves can be well represented by an equation of the form

$$pv = A + Bp + Cp^2.$$

The following table gives the values obtained for the constants A, B, C :—

Gas.	Temp.	A.	B × 10³.	C × 10⁶.
Hydrogen	0°	0·99918	0·82094	0·3745
	50°	1·18212	0·89000	...
	100°	1·36506	0·91400	...
Nitrogen	0°	1·00057	− 0·58100	4·76327
	50°	1·18368	− 0·02500	3·80816
	100°	1·36682	0·36057	3·15102
Oxygen	0°	1·00130	− 1·30143	0·46452
	50°	1·18456	− 0·63543	0·27755
	100°	1·36782	− 0·20357	0·22571
Helium	0°	0·99930	0·69543	...
	50°	1·18223	0·68887	...
	100°	1·36518	0·66804	...

The pressure in these experiments varied from 20 to 100 atmospheres.

The compressibility of air at low temperatures was determined indirectly by Witkowski,[2] making use of Amagat's values for air at 16° C., and of his own experiments on the coefficient of dilatation of air (Art. 122). If v is the volume of a mass of air at pressure p and temperature θ, v_t its volume at the same pressure and at temperature t, v_0' its volume at standard pressure and temperature t, and v_0 its volume at standard pressure and temperature, then we may put

$$pv = \eta p_0 r_c,$$

$$pv_t = \epsilon p_0 v_0',$$

---

[1] Also a large number of experiments were carried out at the Leyden laboratory by Onnes and Hyndman, Schalkwijk, Onnes and Braak, Dorsman and Holst, and Crommelin and Smid (see *Proc. R. Acad. of Amsterdam*, 1901, 1902, 1907, 1915).

[2] *Phil. Mag.*, April 1896.

where η is an unknown function of p and θ, but ϵ is known for all pressures from Amagat's experiments. If a volume v_0 be heated under constant atmospheric pressure to t°, its new volume will be $v_0' = v_0(1 + at)$, a being the mean coefficient of dilatation at atmospheric

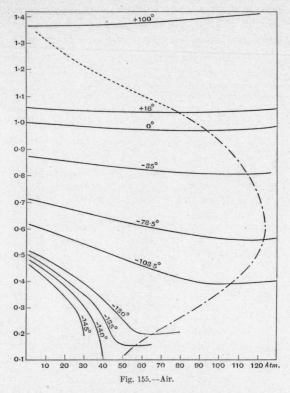

Fig. 155.—Air.

pressure which is practically independent of the temperature. If the pressure be now raised to p, the volume becomes

$$v_t = \frac{\epsilon p_0 v_0'}{p} = \frac{\epsilon p_0 v_0 (1 + at)}{p},$$

and if its temperature be now raised to θ° at constant pressure p, its volume will be

$$v = \frac{\epsilon p_0 v_0 (1 + at)}{p} \cdot \frac{1 + a_{p\theta}\theta}{1 + a_{pt}t} = \frac{\eta p_0 v_0}{p},$$

therefore

$$\eta = \epsilon(1 + at)\frac{1 + a_{p\theta}\theta}{1 + a_{pt}t}.$$

In Fig. 155 the ordinates are the values of pv, which is proportional to η, for given temperatures and varying pressure.

249. Compressibility of Gases under High Pressures.—The compressibility of gases under very high pressures has also been investigated by M. Amagat.[1] The method employed was that used for studying the compressibility of liquids [2] within the same limits of pressure, but the difficulty was far greater, arising chiefly from the smallness of the volume which a gas occupies when it is highly compressed.   After numerous trials, perfectly regular and concordant results were obtained by using for gauging the tubes the method of reading by electrical contacts, which then served to estimate in the same tubes the volumes successively occupied by the compressed gas.

For the same reduction of volume Amagat found far higher pressures than those obtained by Natterer.   This difference can be easily accounted for by the inevitable errors inherent in the method pursued by the latter.   The following results refer to high pressures. For pressures below 1000 atmos. it was proposed to employ an apparatus which would enable the temperature to be raised far higher than it previously had been with these very high pressures, where it was only possible to work between 0° and 50°.   The table gives, for the pressures specified in the first column, the volumes occupied at 15° by a mass of the gas which occupied unit volume at 15° and 760 mm.

Atmos.	Air.	Nitrogen.	Oxygen.	Hydrogen.
750	0·002200	0·002262	...	...
1000	0·001974	0·002032	0·001735	0·001688
1500	0·001709	0·001763	0·001492	0·001344
2000	0·001566	0·001613	0·001373	0·001161
2500	0·001469	0·001515	0·001294	0·001047
3000	0·001401	0·001446	0·001235	0·000964

It is interesting to compare the compressibility of strongly compressed gases with that of liquids.   In order to facilitate this comparison the following table from 750 atmos. to 3000 atmos. contains their coefficients of compressibility as usually defined, viz. $- dv/vdp$:—

Limits of Pressure.	Air.	Nitrogen.	Oxygen.	Hydrogen.
Between 750 and 1000 atmos.	0·000411	0·000407	...	...
,, 1000 ,, 1500 ,,	0·000268	0·000265	0·000258	0·000408
,, 1500 , 2000 ,,	0·000167	0·000170	0·000160	0·000272
,, 2000 ,, 2500 ,,	0·000123	0·000122	0·000115	0·000197
,, 2500 ,, 3000 ,,	0·000093	0·000091	0·000091	0·000158

[1] Amagat, *Comptes rendus*, tom. cvii. p. 523, 1888.
[2] *Ibid.* tom. cxv. p. 638, etc., 1892–93.

It is thus seen that at high pressures the three first gases have pretty much the same compressibility, and that it is of the same order as that of liquids. In fact, at 3000 atmos. it is virtually equal to that of alcohol at normal pressure. Hydrogen, however, has a much larger (almost double) compressibility at 3000, and it is almost equal to that of ether about the normal pressure. These compressibilities, like those of liquids, increase with the temperature, as is shown in the following table for hydrogen :—

Limits of Pressure in Atmos.	At 0°.	At 15°·4.	At 47°·3.
Between 1000 and 1500	...	0·000408	0·000416
,,　　 1500　,,　 2000	0·000263	0·000272	0·000280
,,　　 2000　,,　 2500	0·000196	0·000197	0·000208
,,　　 2500　,,　 3000	0·000156	0·000158	0·000158

The apparent densities are easily deduced from the apparent volumes given in the foregoing table, and if we assume the ordinary value of the compressibility of glass, the following results are obtained for the real densities at 3000 atmospheres :—

Densities at 3000 Atmos. compared with Water.

Oxygen	1·0972 (apparent)	1·1054 (real)
Air	0·8752　　 ,,	0·8817　 ,,
Nitrogen . . .	0·8231　　 ,,	0·8293　 ,,
Hydrogen . . .	0·0880　　 ,,	0·0887　 ,,

The curves obtained by measuring p along the axis of abscissæ and pv along the ordinates are nearly straight lines, but all present a slight concavity towards the axis of abscissæ.

250. The Properties of Vapours.—At a time when it was supposed that the so-called permanent gases rigorously, or with an extreme degree of proximity, obeyed Boyle's law, it had been found that vapours near their condensing points deviated considerably from the law. The experiments of Cagniard de la Tour (1822), Cahours[1] (1845), and Bineau[2] (1846) proved that as the pressure of an unsaturated vapour was increased the product pv diminished up to the condensing point, or that the coefficient of expansion of a vapour decreases from the condensing point, ultimately falling to that of a perfect gas as the temperature of the unsaturated vapour is raised. In the experiments of M. Cahours the coefficient of expansion appeared at first to increase to a maximum, and then to decrease gradually to that of a perfect gas as the vapour was gradually heated from the

---

[1] Aug. Cahours, *Comptes rendus*, tom. xx. p. 51, 1845 ; and tom. xxi. p. 625.

[2] Bineau, *Ann. de Chimie et de Physique*, 3ᵉ sér., tom. xviii. p. 226, 1846.

point of saturation.   This peculiarity was explained on the supposition that at the saturation point condensation occurred on the walls of the enclosing vessel, and that as the vapour was heated this condensed layer evaporated and led to an abnormally high coefficient of expansion.   According to Regnault's [1] experiments, it appears that unsaturated water vapour may be regarded as practically obeying Boyle's law until the pressure reaches $\frac{4}{5}$ of the maximum vapour pressure.

The specific volume of a vapour, or its vapour density at the point of saturation, is of great importance, as this quantity enters into many thermodynamic equations.   The first experiments which established the influence of temperature and pressure on the densities of vapours were those of Fairbairn and Tate in 1860.   These experiments (as well as those of Hirn [2] and Wüllner [3]) proved that the density of a saturated vapour is always greater than the value deduced on the supposition that Boyle's law is obeyed up to the point of saturation. Their method also admitted of the investigation of the behaviour of non-saturated vapours, for by superheating the enclosed vapour the difference of level of the mercury surfaces and the volume of the enclosed vapour could be observed; and in this method the errors arising in the estimation of the volume are not greater than those which ordinarily accompany the determination of the temperature, and the method is consequently favourable to the correct calculation of the specific volume of the saturated vapour.

An elaborate series of investigations on the compressibility of vapours and variations of the product pv near the condensing point was executed by Herwig [4] in 1868, but the method was not good for the determination of the specific volume of the saturated vapour.   The vapour under examination was enclosed in one arm of a graduated glass tube in which the volume could be read off.   The other arm of the tube communicated with a manometer which registered the pressure, and also with an air-pump by means of which the pressure could be varied at pleasure.   The vapour tube was immersed in a bath so that the temperature could be varied at pleasure, and the behaviour of the saturated vapour studied at various temperatures and pressures. The saturation point was determined by observing when the pressure commenced to diminish as the volume was gradually increased, and the sensitiveness of the method depends on whether an appreciable change of pressure is caused by a small change of volume at this point.   This,

---

[1] Regnault, *Mém. de l'Acad.* tom. xxvi. p. 200.
[2] Hirn, *Théorie mécanique de la chaleur.*
[3] Wüllner, *Lehrb. d. exp. Phys.* vol. iii. p. 664.
[4] Herwig, *Pogg. Ann.* vol. cxxxvii., 1869 ; vol. cxli., 1870.

however, is not the case, for the value of v corresponding to the exact point of saturation is very ill-defined, the rectilinear part of the isothermal merging gradually into the hyperbolic, and large changes of volume giving rise to small changes of pressure.

251. Influence of Intermolecular Actions and the Magnitude of Molecules on the Characteristic Equation of the Fluid State.—It appears conclusively established by the foregoing investigations that no substance in nature accurately obeys Boyle's law, but that, as a general rule, the deviations from this law take place in such a manner that at first the augmentation of pressure with diminution of volume is not sufficiently great, and after a certain pressure is reached (which varies with the temperature) the opposite effect sets in, and there is a universal preponderance of increase of pressure. We shall now consider how these two opposite effects may be accounted for by the dynamical theory when the size and mutual influence of the molecules are taken into account. In order that the simple equa-
Conditions. tion $pv = R\Theta$ may be obeyed, it is necessary (1) that the space actually filled by the molecules of the gas may be vanishingly small compared with the whole volume of the enclosure in which it is contained ; (2) the time spent in a collision must be negligible compared with the average interval between two successive impacts ; and (3) the influence of the molecular forces must be vanishingly small at the mean distance of the molecules. These conditions merely express the supposition that all intermolecular influence may be neglected.

If these conditions are not fulfilled, deviations in various directions from the simple gaseous laws take place, which become more and more considerable as the molecular state of the gas corresponds less and less to these conditions. As the space occupied by a given mass of gas is diminished, the length of the mean free path becomes shorter, and the number of molecules in encounter at any instant bears a larger proportion to the number describing free paths. The exact nature of the effect of an encounter is unknown, but it is to be expected that when the number of encounters largely increases, the properties of the substance will be determined more by the nature of the mutual action between two molecules when in collision (*i.e.* within the sphere of each other's action) than by the motion of the molecules when describing their free paths, and for this reason deviations from the simple laws of gases may be anticipated. As the condensation increases, the behaviour of the substance will become more complicated, and its state of aggregation may change, the mass passing partly or altogether into the liquid state ; but the theoretical investigation of its general characteristics cannot be proceeded with until we know the nature of the action between molecules when they are so closely packed that each is constantly subject to the influence of the others. The experimental data for the study of this action are to be obtained from the study of the relations between density, pressure, and volume, such as that furnished by the work of Regnault, Andrews, Amagat, and Cailletet, and besides this, in another direction, by the study of the rate of diffusion and the viscosity of fluids.

Attempts have been made by several physicists to deduce a general equation connecting the pressure, volume, and temperature which will express the characteristic properties of any substance throughout the fluid state from the condition of a perfect gas to that of a liquid. In forming an equation which shall replace $pv = R\theta$, the first consideration that presents itself is the manner in which the molecular attraction affects the pressure and volume of the mass. It is clear that the result of this attraction will be to increase the pressure inside the mass, or produce what is termed a capillary pressure ϖ due to the surface layer, so that if the pressure on the walls of the enclosure is p, the pressure in the interior of the mass will be $p + \varpi$ where ϖ is some function to be determined.[1] In the second place, when the size of the molecules is taken into account the volume v becomes reduced by some quantity ϕ, and the first step is to replace the equation $pv = R\theta$ by the more general equation—

$$(p + \varpi)(v - \phi) = R\theta.$$

In this form the equation agrees with that constructed by Hirn,[2] in

[1] The mutual attraction of the molecules diminishes the pressure on the walls of the enclosure, for each molecule in passing through the surface layer is acted on by an attractive force directed towards the interior of the mass by which its impact on the wall of the vessel is diminished. This capillary pressure seems to exist in steam in the form of clouds, and in tobacco smoke, as appears from the researches of Bosscha. In wet capillary tubes clouds show a meniscus like mercury, and are depressed in the same way. It probably rises into importance in the case of highly compressed gases and vapours near the condensing point. The smaller the volume the larger this internal pressure becomes, so that it may ultimately equal or even exceed the pressure which the substance would exert on the walls of the vessel by the unobstructed motion of its molecules if molecular attraction did not exist ; when this limit is reached no external pressure will be necessary to keep the substance within the enclosure ; or, in other words, the gas has liquefied. Whether this occurs or not depends evidently on the magnitude of ϖ compared with the kinetic energy of the molecules, and if the latter is large—that is, if the temperature is high—no possible diminution of volume will render ϖ sufficiently great, and the gas cannot be liquefied. In other words, the critical temperature has been passed. A liquid might, therefore, be defined as a fluid substance in which the average kinetic energy of the molecules is unable to counterbalance the internal or capillary pressure caused by their mutual attraction.

[2] Hirn, *Théorie mécanique de la chaleur*, 3rd edit., tom. ii. p. 211.

which ϕ is the sum of the volumes of the molecules and ϖ the sum of the internal actions, or the internal pressure. In his further treatment of this equation, however, in which he seeks to determine the quantities ϖ and ϕ, he makes inferences which seem difficult to justify, and the results of which do not seem to agree with experiment.

The most celebrated equation of this kind was developed by J. D. van der Waals in 1879, and in it the effects of the size and the mutual attraction of the molecules are taken into account. This equation may be derived from the foregoing, from the consideration that the attraction between any two elements of the mass is proportional to their product, and hence in a homogeneous fluid to the square of the density. At any given temperature, therefore, the capillary pressure ϖ will vary as the square of the density or inversely as the square of the volume. The quantity ϕ, on the other hand, is the value of the volume at any given temperature when the pressure is infinite, or the least volume into which it is possible to compress the fluid. This, in the case of a system of particles in motion, has been taken as four times the sum of the volumes of the particles.[1] Denoting this by b and the quantity ϖ by a/v^2, where a is for the present considered as a constant, we obtain the equation of Van der Waals—

$$\left(p + \frac{a}{v^2}\right)\ (v - b) = R\Theta.$$

This equation gives isothermal curves agreeing closely with the earlier experiments of Andrews on carbon dioxide, and exhibiting also the characteristic differences of form above and below the critical temperature. On comparison, however, with later experiments the equation has been found not to represent the facts sufficiently, and cannot be brought into accordance with them by altering the constants. Tait has pointed out that Van der Waals's equation does not hold for any real liquid.

This arises from the limited considerations on which the term a/v^2 is introduced. The capillary pressure ϖ will obviously be influenced by other circumstances besides change of density. Van der Waals assumed it as self-evident that the mutual attraction of the molecules does not depend on the temperature, so that the quantity ϖ is a function of the volume only, and the molecular attraction remains

---

[1] The quantity b is called the co-volume, and is generally considered as proportional to the space u actually occupied by the molecules in a unit volume, so that $b = ku$ where k is the same for all gases. Van der Waals finds $k = 4$ from considerations based on the theory of probability, and the same result has been obtained in a different way by Boltzmann and Jeans (Jeans' *Dynamical Theory of Gases*, pp. 139, 172).

unaltered when the substance is heated at constant volume. This might be true if the motion of a molecule at different temperatures differed only in the quantity of its mean kinetic energy but took place in all other respects in exactly the same way, the paths and the ratio of its velocities at different stages of the paths being exactly the same. In the case of a perfect gas it may be assumed that every pair of molecules separate immediately after collision; but when a gas is near its condensing point, it may happen that two molecules may not separate after collision, but that the molecules may collect in little groups and oscillate about each other. The number of such groups will increase as the temperature falls; and consequently, if this happens, the mean strength of the mutual attraction, or the pressure function ϖ, will increase as the temperature falls.

It would appear, therefore, that the quantity a in the formula of Van der Waals very probably varies with the temperature. In its present form no universal or rigorous validity can be ascribed to it, and although Van der Waals obtains it as the ultimate result of an elaborate and ingenious mathematical investigation, yet the assumptions introduced in the various stages of the work render the final equation little more than a first approximation to the truth. The essay of Van der Waals is, nevertheless, a bold and promising attack on an exceedingly difficult problem. He starts [1] with the theorem of Clausius that in stationary motion the mean kinetic energy of a system is equal to the mean virial, or (p. 93)

$$\tfrac{1}{2}\Sigma(m\mathrm{V}^2) = \tfrac{3}{2}pv + \tfrac{1}{2}\Sigma r\phi(r),$$

the final term representing the virial of the intermolecular forces. He then assumes that the temperature of a substance is measured by the mean kinetic energy of the molecules, but although this may be true for gases, it may not hold for liquids, or vapours near their condensing points, or for highly compressed gases. Assuming, however, for the present, that the mean kinetic energy is proportional to the temperature, the virial equation becomes

$$pv = \mathrm{R}\Theta - \tfrac{1}{3}\Sigma r\phi(r),$$

which shows the deviation from Boyle's law when the virial exists.

Van der Waals assumes the molecules to be elastic spheres which attract each other when not in contact, and he considers the effect of the size of the molecules in diminishing the length of the free path, and finds this effect, in the case of a rarefied gas, to be the same as if the volume of the enclosure had been diminished by four times

---

[1] *Die Continuität des gasförmigen und flüssigen Zustandes.* The Memoir of Van der Waals has been translated into English by Richard Threlfall and John F. Adair, *Physical Memoirs, Physical Society of London,* vol. i. part iii.

the sum of the volumes of the molecules. At a constant temperature the effect of the molecular attraction is to diminish the pressure
on the walls of the enclosure by a quantity varying as the square
of the density, so long as the encounters take place, on the whole,
between two molecules at a time and not between three or more.

The failure of the equation of Van der Waals to sufficiently represent the facts led Clausius [1] to construct an equation, which appeared
to him to retain all that was correct in previous formulæ, and which
also made allowance for the variation of molecular attraction with
temperature.   This equation gives the pressure in terms of the temperature and volume in the form

$$p = \frac{R\Theta}{v-a} - \frac{c}{\Theta(v+\beta)^2},$$

where R, c, a, β are constants. This equation, like that of Van der
Waals, gives a cubic for v for any given values of the temperature
and pressure. As every cubic equation has either one or three real

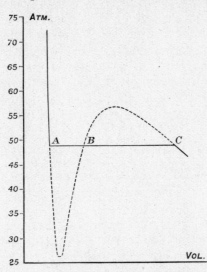

roots, both these equations
furnish either one or three
real values of v for any given
condition of temperature and
pressure. The one real root
applies to the gaseous condition where a definite volume
exists for every value of p and
Θ. The three real roots apply
to that region in which for
given values of p and Θ the
substance can exist either
wholly as a saturated vapour,
or altogether as a liquid, or as
a mixture of the two. The
latter volume does not exist
as a definite volume, but the
root corresponding to it is represented on the diagram (Fig.

Fig. 156.—Curve for carbonic acid, after Clausius.
Temperature 13°·1.

156) by the point in which the rectilinear part of the isothermal,
parallel to the horizontal axis, meets the curved or hypothetical part
of the isothermal suggested by James Thomson.

The equation of Clausius embraces four constants, to be determined
by comparison with the results of four experiments on the values of
p and v at four different temperatures. The equation of Van der

[1] Clausius, *Wied. Ann* vol. ix. p. 337, 1880.; *Phil. Mag.*, June 1880.

Waals, on the other hand, embraces only three constants, which can be determined by three experiments.   Hence, if both be regarded merely as empiric formulæ, a greater range and more general agreement with experiment would be expected from the equation of Clausius.

In the case of carbon dioxide the values of the constants deduced by Clausius were, using the kilogramme and metre as units—

$$R = 19 \cdot 273, \quad c = 5533, \quad a = 0 \cdot 000426, \quad \beta = 0 \cdot 000494.$$

The tables calculated by this formula show in general a satisfactory, and in some cases a strikingly good accordance with the results of experiment.

M. Sarrau [1] has further shown that the formula of Clausius represents the results of Amagat's experiments very satisfactorily in the case of hydrogen, nitrogen, and methane; but for carbonic acid and ethylene the range of accordance is much more limited.

This equation was constructed by Clausius [2] to represent the experiments of Andrews on carbon dioxide, under the supposition that it would apply to other substances by changing the constants only.   On trial, however, it was found that the equation, in this form, would not yield a satisfactory agreement with the results obtained from experiments on other substances; and in order to meet this deficiency, Clausius changed the quantity c/Θ in the final term of the equation (p. 482) into a general function of the temperature.

If we write Clausius's equation in the form

$$p(v - a) = R\Theta - \frac{c(v - a)}{\Theta(v + \beta)^2},$$

and neglect a and β in the last term, which is small, we get

$$p(v - a) = R\Theta - \frac{c}{\Theta v},$$

and substitute $R\Theta/p$ for v in the last term, we have

$$p(v - a) = R\Theta - \frac{pc}{R\Theta^2},$$

or

$$v = \frac{R\Theta}{p} - \frac{c}{R\Theta^2} + a,$$

a modification of Clausius's equation which has been used by Love and Callendar.

Another form of the characteristic equation of a gas has been

[1] Sarrau, *Comptes rendus*, tom. xciv. pp. 639, 718, 845, 1882.
[2] Clausius, *Wied. Ann.* vol. xiv. p. 279, 1881 ; *Ann. de Chimie et de Physique*, 5ᵉ sér., tom. xxx. p. 433, 1883.

proposed by C. Dieterici.[1] Dieterici observes that if we calculate the values of the critical constants v_c, p_c, and Θ_c from Van der Waals's equation (see next article), and if we put $v_o = R\Theta_c/p_c$, so that v_o is the value of the critical volume derived from the equation of a perfect gas by substituting the values of the other constants, then $v_o/v_c = \frac{8}{3} = 2\cdot67$. But the value of v_o/v_c obtained for a considerable number of organic substances by using the observed values of the critical constants lies between $3\cdot67$ and $3\cdot95$, so that Van der Waals's equation gives too small a value. By an argument based partly on the kinetic theory, Dieterici arrives at the formula

$$p = \frac{R\Theta}{v-b} e^{-\frac{a}{R\Theta v}},$$

an equation which, like Van der Waals's, contains only two arbitrary constants, and from which the value $3\cdot695$ is obtained for v_o/v_c. This equation agrees with Van der Waals's to the first order of small quantities, for if we put

$$e^{\frac{a}{R\Theta v}} = 1 + \frac{a}{R\Theta v} \text{ approx.}$$

$$= 1 + \frac{a}{pv^2} \text{ approx.}$$

we get

$$p\,(v-b)\,e^{\frac{a}{R\Theta v}} = \left(p + \frac{a}{v^2}\right)(v-b) = R\Theta,$$

which is Van der Waals's equation. Dieterici's equation seems to accord with the experimental facts over a wider range than Van der Waals's equation.

Another equation, given by Keyes,[2] is

$$p = \frac{R\Theta}{v-\delta} - \frac{a}{(v+b)^2},$$

where a and b are constants, and $\delta = \beta e^{-\frac{a}{v}}$, where α and β are constants. This equation was used by L. B. Smith and R. S. Taylor[3] to express the equation of state for nitrogen. Their experiments extended from $0°$ to $200°$ C., and from 30 to 330 atmos., and the results agreed closely with this formula.

252. The Critical Constants.—The critical constants, or the pressure, volume, and temperature at the critical point, may be easily obtained in terms of the constants which appear in the equation of

[1] *Wied. Ann.* 69, p. 685, 1899.

[2] *Journ. Amer. Chem. Soc.* vol. xliii. p. 1452, 1921.

[3] *Ibid.* vol. xlv. p. 2107, 1923.

Van der Waals.   Writing this equation as a cubic in v, thus

$$pv^3 - (bp + R\Theta)v^2 + av - ab = 0,$$

then at the critical point the three roots of this equation are equal, and hence the critical constants are determined by the equations

$$3v_c p_c = bp_c + R\Theta_c,$$
$$3v_c^2 p_c = a,$$
$$v_c^3 p_c = ab.$$

From the two last of these it follows at once, by division, that

$$v_c = 3b.$$

Hence

$$p_c = \frac{a}{27b^2},$$

and

$$\Theta_c = \frac{8a}{27 R b}.$$

In this manner Van der Waals, having determined the constants a and b from Regnault's experiments on the compressibility of carbonic acid, found for this substance $\theta_c = 32°\cdot 5$ C., the close agreement of which with the experimental result of Andrews is remarkable.

Taking one atmosphere as unit pressure, and the volume occupied by the gas at zero centigrade and one atmosphere pressure as unit volume, the values of the constants were

$$273R = 1\cdot 00646, \quad a = 0\cdot 00874, \quad b = 0\cdot 0023.$$

253. Corresponding States.—A deduction of Van der Waals's from his equation concerns what may be termed corresponding states of matter.   If the pressure, volume, and temperature of a substance be expressed as multiples of their critical values—that is, if we write

$$p = \lambda p_c, \quad v = \mu v_c, \quad \Theta = \nu \Theta_c,$$

then any other substance will be in a corresponding state when its pressure, volume, and temperature are the same multiples λ, μ, ν of their critical values.   Substituting in the equation

$$\left(p + \frac{a}{v^2}\right)(v - b) = R\Theta,$$

and replacing p_c, v_c, Θ_c by their values in terms of a, b, R, we have

$$\left(\lambda + \frac{3}{\mu^2}\right)(3\mu - 1) = 8\nu,$$

an equation in which everything depending on the nature of the substance has disappeared, and which should apply to all substances, just as $pv = R\Theta$ applies to all perfect gases.   Hence if pressures, volumes, and temperatures be expressed in terms of their critical values, the isothermals become the same for all substances.

At the time when Van der Waals published his work sufficient experimental data were not available to test the accuracy of these deductions, and since that time they have been subject to much criticism, both favourable and adverse.[1] From the experiments of Dr. S. Young,[2] it appears that the conclusions of Van der Waals are very approximately true for the halogen derivatives of benzene, or at least that these substances show very much smaller deviations than the others examined. The law, therefore, seems to be not quite, but very nearly, true for these substances; but in the case of the other substances examined the majority of the generalisations were either only roughly true or else altogether departed from.

[1] A discussion of this equation, in which Lord Rayleigh, Professor P. G. Tait, and Professor Korteweg took part, appeared in *Nature*, vols. xliv. and xlv., 1891-92.

[2] S. Young, *Phil. Mag.* vol. xxxiii. p. 153, 1892.

CHAPTER VI

RADIATION AND ABSORPTION

SECTION I

GENERAL THEORETICAL CONSIDERATIONS

254. Propagation of Heat.—There are three methods commonly recognised by which heat may be propagated or conveyed from one place to another. The first of these is that which we are about to consider at present, and is termed *radiation*. It is by this method that heat and light reach us from the sun, or from a lamp or fire, and during the period of transit the heat is spoken of as radiant heat, or simply as radiation, this term embracing light as well as heat. This method of propagation is distinguished from the other two, known as convection and conduction, in which the transfer of heat is effected wholly or largely by the agency of matter. In the former the heat is carried from place to place by the matter with which it is associated, so that the flow of heat depends altogether on the motion of matter. It is by this method that heat is conveyed through buildings heated by hot-water pipes, and it is chiefly in this way that uniformity of temperature is established in unequally heated fluids.

The process of conduction, on the other hand, does not depend on any visible motion of matter. It is by this method that temperature equilibrium is established in solids, and that heat passes from the warmer to the colder parts of the same solid. Thus if one end of an iron bar be placed in a furnace and the other in a vessel of ice, a flow of heat will take place along the bar from the furnace to the ice; and if radiation from the sides of the bar be prevented as far as possible, the rate at which the ice melts will afford a rough measure of the flow of heat along the bar. This method of conveying heat from one place to another is usually attributed to molecular action or propagation by contact, the warmer molecules heating the colder by contact or otherwise. This process, however, will be considered in fuller

487

detail in the next chapter ; at present we shall confine our attention
to the process of radiation, which does not appear to depend in any
way on the presence of matter, but which takes place through the
best vacua, and through interstellar spaces, and is further distinguished
from the comparatively slow processes of convection and conduction
by advancing with the enormous velocity of 300,000,000 metres per
second.

In approaching the study of such a subject as the nature of
radiant heat, and the process by which it is emitted and propagated
through space, the most philosophic method of procedure is to
determine as far as possible the laws which govern its propagation
through different media, as well as its passage from one medium to
another, before any hypothesis is framed as to the nature of the
emission or the mechanism by which it is propagated.   Thus, without
any hypothesis, the laws of its reflection and refraction, and the
manner in which its intensity varies with the distance from the source,
may be examined and determined.   Whatever the mechanism may be
by which radiant heat is emitted and propagated, we have the most
complete experimental evidence that the process is precisely the same
as that employed in the propagation of light, and any evidence which
can be adduced in favour of the supposition that light is a wave
motion propagated through a medium can also be stated with regard
to radiant heat.   Radiation in this sense consists essentially in the
propagation of a wave motion through the ether.   What is propagated
and radiated in all cases is energy, and all phenomena connected with
it are to be explained as the consequences of the interchange of energy
between the ether and matter, and it is purely as the recipients or
donors of such that we ourselves become sensible of heat and cold.

255. On the Formation of a Theory.—The phenomena of radiant
heat and light having been proved to be subject to the same laws of
reflection, refraction, polarisation, and interference—in fact, the two
being reducible to, and merely different effects of, the same physical
agency—a definite hypothesis is framed, and the investigation proceeds
from the direct study of the phenomena to the elaboration of a connected theory which accounts for the facts and exhibits their sequence
and relations. The existence of atoms and molecules of matter is
first admitted, and a medium is then assumed in which they vibrate
and generate waves, or a periodic disturbance of some sort,
travelling with the velocity of 300,000,000 metres per second.   In
this manner a mental picture is formed of the unknown process by
which energy is emitted by a body and propagated through the space
around it—a picture which has proved of enormous advantage in

grappling with the investigation of the phenomena, but which may, or may not, have a similitude to the processes actually in action.

In forming such a picture, or in framing any hypothesis as to the mode of propagation of radiant heat and light, we fall back upon analogous phenomena which we can thoroughly examine, and with the ideas formed in the study of the latter we approach the investigation of the former.   We thus proceed to the interpretation of the unknown processes in terms of well-conceived analogies derived from the known. The ideas by which we picture and conceive of the propagation of heat and light are derived from the study of the phenomena of sound.   A sounding body is the source of an influence which is radiated from it in all directions through the surrounding medium with a definite velocity.   When this phenomenon is examined, it is found that the sounding body is in rapid vibration, and that these vibrations are communicated to the air ; that sound waves are thus generated in the air which spread out from the vibrating body and break upon the ear, causing the impression which we call sound.   Here the vibrating body is recognised as the source of an influence which is radiated from it in all directions with a definite velocity, and which causes a certain impression on one of our organs of sense.   With the knowledge thus gained, we proceed to the explanation of the phenomena of heat and light, and make the very promising and attractive assumption that they too are due to wave motion propagated through a hypothetical medium named the ether.

In this case, however, as the nature of the medium is entirely unknown, as well as the exact character of the waves, we consider it prudent in the present state of knowledge to stop at this stage of the hypothesis, and we hesitate to ascribe any particular type or character to the vibrations and wave motion.   In one respect, however, the study of light seems to restrict the character of these waves. It appears from the consideration of certain phenomena that they cannot be propagated by longitudinal vibrations, as in the case of sound, or at least that such vibrations do not play an essential part in the production of light or vision.   With this one restriction, we make no further hypothesis, except for particular purposes of explanation and illustration.   We have distinct evidence that the propagation is that of a periodic disturbance or a periodic change of some property of a medium ; but beyond this no other assumption is warranted by the facts, except for the purposes of working out some particular theory, and the extra assumptions thus introduced should be clearly laid down as the hypotheses on which the theory is built, and these are justified only in so far as all the deductions following from the theory are substantiated by direct appeal to experiment.

256. Dynamical Analogy.——Let us now consider the radiation and absorption of sound, in order that we may approach the analogous phenomena of light and heat with a distinct mental picture which will be exceedingly convenient and fruitful, but which at any stage may be modified or entirely discarded when it is found to be misleading or inconsistent with the new facts. Let us suppose that we have two mounted tuning-forks of the same pitch placed in air and at a distance from each other. If one of the forks is set in vibration, the waves which it radiates through the air fall upon the other, and set it also in vibration, because they are of the same period as those waves which it would itself emit when sounding. Thus, while one is losing energy the other is gaining it, or as we might put it with reference to the other radiation, while one is growing colder the other is growing warmer. That the second fork absorbs the radiation emitted by the first may be distinctly placed in evidence by stopping the vibration of the first, in which case the sound emitted by the second can be distinctly heard, although at the beginning of the experiment it was silent. It has consequently been set in vibration by the waves emitted by the other fork. Here, then, we have a distinct case of radiation and absorption of sound, the essential condition for absorption being that the pitch of the absorbing fork should be the same as that of the emitting. This single principle permeates the whole science of radiation and absorption, and is embraced in the general statement that a body absorbs waves which are of the same period as those which it emits when it is itself in vibration.

In order to apply this idea more comprehensively to the case of radiant heat and light, it is necessary to take into account the supposed molecular structure of matter. We must, from this point of view, not merely regard a radiating body as analogous to a single tuning-fork, but rather as a swarm of tuning-forks, each molecule corresponding to a fork in vibration and emitting waves peculiar to itself. If the forks of such a swarm be relatively fixed and not entangled, the waves radiated from the system will depend only on the periods of free vibration of the forks ; but if the forks be not relatively fixed, but have motions of translation amongst each other such as those ascribed to the molecules of a fluid, the waves radiated will be influenced both by the motion of the forks and by their mutual collisions—the pitch of those forks which are moving at any instant towards the observer will be somewhat raised, while that of those which are moving away from the observer will be lowered. For this reason, if the forks are all identical and possess the same free period, the sound emitted by the moving system will not be a pure tone, of a single wave-length, but will consist rather of a group of waves lying within certain limits determined by the velocity of motion of the forks, some of the waves being longer and some shorter than that emitted by a single fork at rest.   It is in this manner that the finite width of the spectral lines of an incandescent gas has been explained.[1]   Instead of having a line representing a single wave-length of light, we are presented with well-defined narrow bands arising from the broadening of the lines already referred to by the motions of translation of the molecules of the radiating substance.   The same motion promotes the absorption of groups of waves rather than of waves of a single period, so that the absorption bands are also of finite width.

If now the radiation from such a system of vibrating forks falls upon another system in silence, any waves which are of the same period as those peculiar to the second system will be absorbed by it, and the forks of this system will be set in vibration.   This absorption will continue till an equilibrium is established between the rate at which the energy is absorbed and emitted by the second system.   This corresponds exactly to the method by which a cold body is supposed to become warmed in the presence of a hot one.   The temperature of one falls by radiation, while that of the other rises by absorption, until an equilibrium is established between the radiation and absorption of each.   From this point of view every body at a stationary temperature must be regarded as radiating energy at a constant rate; but since the temperature remains stationary, it must be regarded as also absorbing energy at the same rate—so that, on the whole, the loss by radiation is exactly compensated by absorption from other sources. The equilibrium here attained is not one of rest but rather one of activity, such as exists between a liquid and its saturated vapour in a closed space when the stage is reached at which as many molecules return to the liquid per second as are projected from its surface. In this case, too, there is an equilibrium; but there is also constant evaporation balanced by an equal condensation, and matters remain as if the equilibrium were one of death rather than one of active life.

It may be remarked here that a large swarm of similar tuning-forks, such as we have just considered, would be highly opaque to a note or sound wave of the same period as themselves, for they rapidly absorb such a wave, and it would be almost completely used up before it had penetrated far into the system.

----

[1] See the author's *Theory of Light*.

In analogy to this, it was discovered by De la Roche, and abundantly confirmed by Melloni and others, that when radiant heat is passed through one screen the transmitted beam is almost completely transmitted by another screen of the same material, and it has also been established that all substances are highly opaque to their own radiation.

257. The Theory of Exchanges.—The foregoing considerations prepare us to grant that each body whose molecules are in vibration is a source of radiation in the ether, and that the amount of radiation thrown off in this manner by any body depends only on the nature and temperature of the body itself. Returning again to the system of vibrating tuning-forks, we may admit that the sound-radiation from each fork takes place independently of all the others. Each fork is in vibration, and must be regarded as the centre of a system of waves as if all the others were at rest. The rate at which any fork parts with its energy may be, however, considerably modified. Thus if two or more of the forks happen to be of the same pitch, each will absorb part of the energy emitted by the other and will thus recruit its stock, so that the energy lost per second by any fork will now be only the difference between that radiated through its own vibration and that absorbed from the others. When these two parts are equal the energy of the fork remains constant ; but still we regard it as radiating at a constant rate, while it absorbs at the same rate, and it is in this sense that the radiation of any body at any temperature is said to be equal to its absorption at the same temperature.

In this manner we are led to believe that the equilibrium of temperature which ultimately becomes established among a system of bodies contained in an enclosure impervious to heat, and which contains no source of heat, is attained not merely by the warmer bodies radiating to the colder, but by a mutual process of radiation and absorption, all the bodies being supposed to radiate simultaneously, each to an amount depending on its constitution, surface-condition, and temperature. Further, when the equilibrium of temperature is once attained, the process of radiation is not supposed to cease, but to continue as actively as before, equilibrium being maintained by simultaneous radiation and absorption.

From this point of view there is a continual interchange of energy between the bodies within the enclosure, while at the same time the energy of each remains constant. Before equilibrium is reached the hotter bodies radiate more than they absorb, while the colder absorb more than they radiate ; the quantity which each radiates per second at any stage is, however, independent of whether its temperature happens to be rising or falling, and is supposed to be determined by the nature and temperature [1] of the body.

This view was introduced by Prévost,[2] of Geneva, in 1792, when endeavouring to explain the supposed radiation of cold.[3] According to Prévost's line of thought, any body is not merely regarded as radiating heat when its temperature is falling, or absorbing heat when its temperature is rising. What it is wished to express is that both processes are continually and simultaneously going on, the radiation depending only on the body itself, while the absorption depends on the nature of the body itself as well as on the condition of neighbouring bodies.

In order to illustrate this point let us consider the case of a thermometer suspended in a warm room at a steady temperature. In this case all the bodies in the room are radiating heat, part of which is absorbed by the thermometer, and if the temperature of the thermometer is stationary, the quantity of heat absorbed by it is balanced by an equal radiation. If now a cold body be brought into the room and placed in the vicinity of the thermometer, this body will screen the thermometer from some of the radiation which previously fell upon it, and will not itself radiate an equal supply. The total radiation received by the thermometer will consequently be diminished. The equilibrium which previously existed will thus be broken, and the temperature of the thermometer will fall to that point at which its emission is precisely equal to its absorption under the new circumstances. This is a case of what was designated as the radiation of cold. It illustrates how equilibrium is reached and maintained, not merely by the warmer bodies radiating and the colder absorbing, but rather by the mutual process of simultaneous emission and absorption.

It also illustrates how largely the indications of a thermometer depend on the nature of the radiation of the bodies around it as well as on the temperature of the medium in which it is immersed. The indication of a thermometer may differ very much from the temperature of the air at the point where it is suspended. If the waves emitted by any neighbouring body are such as the thermometer can absorb, it will be influenced by them in a corresponding degree ; but if they are such as it does not absorb—that is, if they are dissimilar to

[1] On this point see *Phil. Mag.*, October 1881, p. 261, Arthur Schuster.

[2] Prévost, *Sur l'équilibre du feu*, Genève, 1792 ; *Du calorique rayonnant*, Gen., 1809.

[3] The experiment illustrating the reflection of cold was revived by Pictet, but was originally made some centuries before by Plempius, and the Academicians del Cimento.—Young's *Lectures*, p. 489.

those which it emits, then they will be without influence on the indications of the instrument. Whether a thermometer detects a certain class of waves or not depends on the nature of the material; thus if the thermometric substance absorbs only waves of a certain length, then it will respond only to these waves, and although it may be traversed by copious radiation of other wave-lengths, its indication might still be the same. The indication of a thermometer is thus determined by the resultant effect of all the various waves which influence it.

The indication of a thermometer is found to be ultimately the same in all parts of an enclosure impervious to heat, and which contains no source of heat ; and it is in this statistical sense that we assert that all parts of, and all objects in, such an enclosure ultimately come to the same temperature. The indication of the thermometer is independent of the shape or material of the walls of the enclosure, and if the bulb be coated with lamp-black, or silver-foil, or any other substance, the temperature recorded will remain the same. Now, of the whole radiation falling upon the thermometer in such a case, part is absorbed and part is reflected either regularly or irregularly. The reflected part when the bulb is silvered is enormously greater than when it is coated with lamp-black, and consequently the absorbed portion must be so much less in the former case than in the latter. But since the temperature of the thermometer is the same whatever it be coated with, it follows that the heat absorbed by it when coated with any substance must be exactly the same as that emitted, and hence the emission of any substance at any temperature must be exactly equal to its absorption at the same temperature. If we confine our attention to a body A, then when the flow of heat takes place from the surrounding space B into A, we say that A is absorbing heat from B ; but if the flow takes place from A to B, we say that A is radiating, or, if we like, that B is absorbing heat from A. The direction of the flow, then, determines whether we say that a body is emitting or absorbing heat, and the assertion of the equality of the emitting and absorbing powers assumes that for the same infinitesimal difference of temperature the flow will be the same whether it takes place from A to B or from B to A, across the surface of separation.[1]

258. Emissivity or Surface Conductivity.—It was established by Sir John Leslie, by his researches in radiant heat, that some substances emit heat under the same conditions much more copiously than others. For this reason it is customary to speak of the emissivity or emissive power of a substance or of the surface of a body. The radiating

---

[1] The terms emissive and absorbing powers are used in a somewhat different sense in section v.

body employed by Leslie was a cubical vessel of block-tin, filled with hot water, the sides of which could be coated with any substance whose emissivity it was desired to study. This vessel is known as Leslie's cube. It is constructed so that it may be rotated round a vertical axis, and any face can be brought into action when desired. If the cube be filled with hot water, and if one side be coated with a thin sheet of gold, another with polished silver, a third with copper, and the fourth with varnish, it is found, when these faces are allowed to radiate in succession against the face of a thermopile or other delicate radiometer, that the faces coated with the metals radiate only very feebly; but when the varnished face is turned towards the pile, the indication of the instrument shows that the radiation from this face is very copious. The polished metals are consequently much less efficient as radiators than the varnish. It is for this reason that hot liquids contained in polished metal vessels retain their heat much longer than when the surface is unpolished. The reflection at the surface increases with the polish, and this whether the radiation is passing from the inside outwards or from the outside inwards. The polished surface is a good reflector, and therefore a poor radiator.

Without adopting any hypothesis as to the process by which radiation occurs, or as to the nature of heat or the structure of matter, the *surface emissivity* of a body may be defined as measured by the quantity of heat which the body loses per unit surface per unit time under given conditions—such, for example, as when its temperature is 1° C. higher than that of the enclosure in which it is situated, and when the air in this enclosure is at a definite pressure or entirely removed. This definition does not involve reference to the radiation of any other body, nor does it involve any hypothesis as to the law of variation of emissivity with temperature, but leaves its dependence on temperature and other circumstances to be determined by direct experiment.

This quantity is also termed the *surface conductivity*, and sometimes the *external conductivity*, as distinguished from the internal conductivity or property by which heat is conveyed through solids from places of higher to places of lower temperature. In practice all we can determine is the rate at which a body loses heat when cooling under given conditions, so that the so-called coefficients of emission which have been as yet determined are only rough measurements involving what might be termed the emissivity proper of the substance as well as the internal conductivity of the material and other quantities depending on the nature of the enclosure.

SECTION II

COOLING

259. Empirical Laws of Cooling.—When a hot body is suspended in the air it is easily determined that the cooling proceeds by two very distinct processes which act simultaneously. One of these is the radiation already considered, which takes place equally in all directions, and the other arises in the convection and conduction of the air surrounding the body. The air in immediate contact with the body becomes heated and rises through the colder and denser air above. In this manner an ascending current of air is established around the body, and fresh supplies are continually brought into contact with it beneath, which become heated in turn, and rising carry off part of its heat. This is the process termed convection, and the amount of heat carried off in this manner will depend on the pressure and nature of the air or gas in which the body may be immersed. The rate of cooling will consequently be determined by the sum of two functions, one of which represents the loss of heat by radiation, and the other that lost by the convection and conduction of the surrounding medium.

For the sake of simplicity we shall first consider the case of a body suspended in an enclosure which is free from air or other gas, so that the cooling takes place by radiation to the walls of the enclosure alone. If the temperature of the body be θ, the heat lost per second by radiation will be some function of the temperature θ; and if the walls of the enclosure be maintained at some temperature θ_0, then by the considerations reviewed in the last section a mutual process of radiation and absorption takes place between the body and the walls of the enclosure. The heat absorbed per second by the body will be a function of the temperature θ_0 of the walls of the enclosure, and this quantity will be the same as that which would be radiated by the body at θ_0, for at this temperature there would be equilibrium of temperature between the body and the enclosure. Hence, if $f(\theta)$ denotes the heat lost per second by radiation when the

496

body is at the temperature θ, the same function will represent the heat gained by absorption when in an enclosure at the same temperature, since by the theory of exchanges the radiation at any temperature is equal to the absorption at the same temperature. Hence, if $f(\theta)$ represents the rate of loss by radiation, $f(\theta_0)$ will represent the rate of gain by absorption,[1] and their difference

$$f(\theta) - f(\theta_0)$$

will determine the rate of cooling of the body.

Newton seems to have been the first to consider the law of cooling of a body subject to any constant cooling action—such, for example, as the influence of a uniform current of air. In such cases he supposed that the rate of cooling was proportional to the excess of the temperature of the body above that of the medium in which it was immersed. This admission amounts to assuming $f(\theta) = A\theta + B$ in the foregoing expression, or if the temperature be measured from the absolute zero, then $B = 0$, and the assumption is that the total radiation of a body is proportional to its absolute temperature. In this case we have for the rate of cooling—

$$f(\theta) - f(\theta_0) = A(\theta - \theta_0),$$

or since the rate of cooling is $-\dfrac{d\theta}{dt}$,

we may write

$$\frac{d\theta}{dt} = -E(\theta - \theta_0),$$

where E is a coefficient depending on the nature of the body and its surface condition. This formula has been found to represent the facts fairly well for small differences of temperature, and may be used to determine the radiation correction in such experiments as ordinarily occur in calorimetry, where the excess of θ over θ_0 never exceeds a few degrees centigrade. For differences exceeding $40°$ or $50°$ C., this law was found even by such early experimenters as Martine,[2] Kraft, Richmann, Leslie, and Dalton to deviate seriously from the truth when temperature is measured in the ordinary way by a mercurial thermometer, and Dalton for this reason proposed a new scale of temperature, according to which the law of Newton would be exact.

In consequence of these discrepancies Dulong and Petit undertook an elaborate series of experiments on the cooling of thermometers in an enclosure maintained at a constant temperature, and which could be either exhausted or filled with a gas at any pressure desired. From the results of these experiments they were led to propose the

---

[1] This is the assumption.   [2] *Dissertations sur la chaleur*, 1740.

formula $Aa^\theta + B$ for $f(\theta)$, the rate of radiation of a surface at temperature θ. In this formula θ may be taken as the absolute temperature
if desired, as the effect is only to alter the value of the coefficient A.
If the absolute temperature be chosen, then the radiation will be zero
when $\theta = 0$ and we shall have $B = -A$. By the same reasoning as
before it will follow that the absorption from the walls of the enclosure at θ_0 will be $Aa^{\theta_0} + B$, so that the rate of cooling will be

$$f(\theta) - f(\theta_0) = A(a^\theta - a^{\theta_0}),$$

or

$$\frac{d\theta}{dt} = -E(a^\theta - a^{\theta_0}).$$

In the same memoir [1] Dulong and Petit have investigated the rate
of cooling under the simultaneous action of radiation and convection,
and have represented it by an empirical formula of a highly artificial
character. The term representing the loss by radiation is the
same as that given above, while that which represents the loss by
convection and conduction depends on the pressure of the gas, being
jointly proportional to a power of the pressure varying with the nature
of the gas and a power of the temperature excess which is the same
for all gases. The formula of Dulong and Petit seems to apply with
considerable accuracy through a much wider range of temperature
difference than that of Newton. We shall consequently review the
experiments by which they were led to the law which bears their
name.

DULONG AND PETIT'S EXPERIMENTS

260. Principles of the Research.—In their classical investigations of the laws of cooling, MM. Dulong and Petit operated entirely
by observing the rate of cooling of large liquid-in-glass thermometers
under various conditions. In studying the influence of the nature of
the surface on the rate of cooling the advantage of using a liquid which
is a good conductor is twofold. In the first place, when the temperature of the outside layer falls, convection currents are set up which
equalise the temperature of the mass, and the greater the conductivity
of the liquid the more rapidly will this equality be attained. For
this reason the temperature of a good conducting liquid like mercury
will be approximately the same throughout, and the rate of cooling
will depend chiefly on the nature of the surface of the bulb, and this
can be varied at pleasure.

The thermometers employed by Dulong and Petit in this research

[1] Dulong and Petit, *Ann. de Chimie et de Physique*, 2ᵉ sér., tom. vii. pp. 225
and 337, 1817.

were constructed after the fashion represented in Fig. 157. Each
was provided with a large bulb E and a wide stem CD joined together
by a tube DE of capillary bore, which
prevented convection currents passing
between the liquid in the bulb and that
in the stem.   In making an experiment
the bulb alone was heated, while the
stem was screened, so as to be always as
nearly as possible at the temperature of
the air, and on account of the width of
the upper portion of the stem, the bulb,
even though large, could be heated if
necessary almost to the boiling point of
mercury.   During the process of cooling,
the cold mercury from the stem enters
the bulb and lowers the temperature of
the mass within the bulb, so that the
apparent velocity of cooling is rendered
too high.   Hence all observations had
to be corrected for this inequality of
temperature.

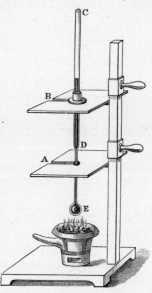

FIG. 157.

The main object of the inquiry was
to determine the velocity of cooling of any body under given conditions as a function of the temperature.   Thus, if the rate of cooling
be expressed by the equation

$$-\frac{d\theta}{dt} = f(\theta) \qquad . \qquad . \qquad . \qquad . \qquad . \qquad . \qquad (1)$$

the object is to determine the form of the function f, the temperature
of the enclosure being given.   From an experimental point of view,
however, it is easier to express the temperature of the body at any
time as a function of the time.   Thus, if we have

$$\theta = \phi(t) \qquad . \qquad . \qquad . \qquad . \qquad . \qquad . \qquad (2)$$

then by differentiating (2) and comparing with (1), we see that

$$f(\theta) = -\phi'(t),$$

or the velocity of cooling is the first derived of the function ϕ.

In order to determine this function, Dulong and Petit, having
heated the thermometer, placed it under the conditions in which its
cooling was to be studied, and they observed its temperatures

$$\theta_0, \ \theta_1, \ \theta_2, \ \theta_3, \quad . \quad . \quad . \quad \theta_n,$$

at the times

$$0, \ t_1, \ t_2, \ t_3 \quad . \quad . \quad . \quad t_n.$$

From these observations they concluded that the temperature at any time could not be found by the simple formula of Newton, but by the more general expression

$$\theta = \theta_0 a^{at+\beta t^2} \quad . \quad . \quad . \quad . \quad . \quad . \quad (3)$$

where θ is the excess of the temperature of the thermometer over that of the enclosure at the time t, θ_0 the excess at the beginning of the experiment, $t = 0$, and a, α, β are constants which can be determined by a knowledge of any three values of θ at the corresponding times.

Differentiating (3) we have

$$\frac{d\theta}{dt} = \theta(\alpha + 2\beta t) \log a \quad . \quad . \quad . \quad . \quad . \quad (4)$$

and by eliminating t between (3) and (4) the velocity of cooling is determined as a function of the temperature excess θ.

In order to diminish the time of observation in this investigation two thermometers were used. The larger, having a bulb of 6 cm. diameter, was used at high temperatures, and the smaller, with a bulb of 2 cm. diameter, was employed for the lower temperatures, the observations with the smaller being commenced at a temperature somewhat above that at which those with the larger were stopped.

261. Preliminary Experiments.—The various circumstances which may influence the rate of cooling of a thermometer placed in a vacuum are : the form and extent of the surface of the bulb as well as its nature or coefficient of emission, the total mass and nature of the liquid enclosed in the bulb, and finally the temperature θ_0 of the enclosure, as well as the excess $\theta - \theta_0$ of the thermometer. If, however, the thermometer be suspended in a gas, the rate of cooling will be influenced by the conduction and convection of the gas. In this case, then, the whole velocity of cooling will be the sum of two functions, one of which determines the cooling by radiation to the walls of the enclosure, and the other the cooling action of the gas. The latter will be influenced by all the circumstances mentioned above, and in addition by the nature and pressure of the gas. Besides this, the rate of cooling will depend on the magnitude and shape of the enclosure, as well as upon the nature of its walls, and the rate of cooling for one species of radiation may, in a given enclosure, be very different from that for another. These considerations have not, however, been investigated by Dulong and Petit.

Writing the total velocity of cooling in the form

$$V = f(M, N, S, E, \theta_0, \theta - \theta_0) + \phi(M, N, S, E, \theta_0, \theta - \theta_0, p, G),$$

where M and N refer to the mass and nature of the liquid respectively,

S the area of the surface of the bulb, and E its coefficient of emission, θ_0 the temperature of the enclosure, and θ that of the thermometer, p the pressure, and G the nature of the gas, Dulong and Petit proceeded by some preliminary experiments in air to test how far the rate of cooling was influenced by the mass M and nature N of the liquid, and by the surface S of the bulb. By taking thermometers whose bulbs were of different sizes in one series of experiments, of different shapes (spherical and cylindrical) in another series, and filled with different liquids in a third series, they found that for equal excesses of temperature the rates of cooling bear constant ratios to each other.

These experiments show that the total rate of cooling may be expressed as the sum of two functions, one a function of E, θ, $\theta - \theta_0$, and the other a function of these quantities, as well as of p and G, both of these functions being also multiplied by the same quantity A, which is itself a function of the mass and nature of the liquid, and of the surface S of the bulb. The expression for the rate of cooling thus becomes simplified into the following form:—

$$V = Af(E, \theta_0, \theta - \theta_0) + A\phi(E, \theta_0, \theta - \theta_0, p, G).$$

The remaining variables do not submit to the same simplification.

262. Experiments in a Vacuum and in a Gas.—In the general expression for the rate of cooling the function ϕ expresses the cooling effect of the gas within the enclosure, and consequently if the enclosure be exhausted so that the thermometer cools in a vacuum, the function ϕ disappears from the expression for V, and we have simply

$$V = Af(E, \theta_0, \theta - \theta_0).$$

The observations under these conditions will therefore lead to the determination of the function f. It must be remembered, however, that we know nothing as yet of the properties of any space totally devoid of matter—all that has ever been obtained is a partial vacuum.

The apparatus employed in these experiments consisted of a large copper globe (Fig. 158), about 30 cm. in diameter, and blackened on the inside. This globe formed the cooling chamber or enclosure in which the cooling of the thermometer was observed. It was immersed in a large water bath which could be kept at any desired temperature θ_0 by means of a regulated current of steam. The dimensions of the thermometer were previously calculated, so that observations on its cooling could be commenced at about 300° C. The thermometer, when heated to about 350°, was placed with

its bulb at the centre of the enclosure, which was then rapidly
exhausted, and the rate of cooling noted.   A small correction

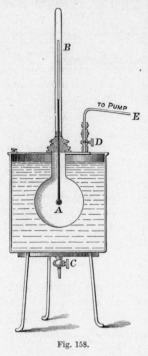

Fig. 158.

was still necessary for the cooling effect
of the residue of air left in the cooling
chamber, the exhaustion being seldom
pushed beyond 3 or 4 mm.   The rates of
cooling, V_1, V_2, etc., were observed, corresponding to the temperatures $0°$, $20°$,
$40°$, $60°$, and $80°$ at which the chamber
was kept.

When the quantities V_1, V_2, etc., at
the different temperatures of the enclosure
walls were compared, it was found that
the ratios V_2/V_1, V_3/V_2, etc., were approximately the same ($1·16$) for all values of
the excess.

Hence, if we consider the influence
of the temperature θ_0 of the chamber, we
see that the rates of cooling for the same
excess $\theta - \theta_0$ with different values of θ_0,
viz. $0°$, $20°$, $40°$, $60°$, increasing in arithmetical progression, are such that the ratios
V_1/V, V_2/V_1, V_3/V_2 are equal to each
other, and we consequently conclude that,
for the same excess of temperature, *if the
temperature of the chamber be increased in an arithmetical progression, the
velocity of cooling will increase in a geometrical progression.*

It follows, therefore, that the velocity of cooling for a given excess
can be represented in the form

$$V = A a^{\theta_0},$$

where A is a function of the excess $\theta - \theta_0$.

But by the theory of exchanges the velocity of cooling must be
of the form

$$V = f(\theta) - f(\theta_0),$$

and the final form arrived at by Dulong and Petit, which satisfies
both these conditions, is

$$V = k(a^{\theta - \theta_0} - 1) . a^\theta$$

or

$$V = k(a^\theta - a^{\theta_0}).$$

When the observed values of V were compared with their
corresponding values calculated by this formula, the close agree-

ment exhibited showed that the equation is capable of representing the facts with considerable accuracy. On the whole, however, it cannot be regarded as having any sound theoretical basis, but must be looked upon merely as an empirical formula of wider range than Newton's. Its simplicity might lead us to fancy that it could be obtained theoretically, but until we possess more information about the mechanism of emission we have no ground on which to base a theory.

To terminate their vacuum experiments, Dulong and Petit observed the effect of varying the surface of the thermometer bulb. They found that the rate of cooling when the surface was naked differed from that when it was coated with silver-foil or any other substance. The quantity a was found, however, to remain unaltered, so that it does not depend on the surface emissivity, or on the mass or nature of the liquid, and the coefficient k alone was found to vary with the nature of the surface.

A series of experiments on the cooling of a thermometer in a vacuum having been completed, a further series on the cooling of the same thermometer in the same chamber when occupied by a gas will furnish the data necessary to the calculation of the cooling influence of the gas. In this case we have already written the general expression for the velocity of cooling in the form

$$V = A f(E, \theta_0, \theta - \theta_0) + A\phi(E, \theta_0, \theta - \theta_0, p, G),$$

and since the first term of the left-hand member of this equation represents the cooling in a vacuum, it may be replaced by the quantity $k(a^\theta - a^{\theta_0})$, and if the velocity V be observed we have then for ϕ

$$A\phi = V - k(a^\theta - a^{\theta_0}).$$

The first point investigated by Dulong and Petit[1] was the influence of the nature of the surface of the bulb on the cooling function ϕ of the gas. Having determined the rate of cooling in a vacuum when the bulb was naked, and also when it was silvered, they repeated the same experiments in air and other gases, and the results showed that the cooling power of the gas did not depend on the nature of the surface ; or, in other words, the coefficient E of the surface does not enter into the function ϕ.

This result appears to have been first remarked in a general way by Sir J. Leslie, and is a fact of great importance in the study of the conductivity of gases.

The influence of the temperature θ_0 of the enclosure on the cooling power of the gas was next examined. The pressure being kept

---

[1] *Ann. de Chimie et de Physique*, 2e sér., tom. vii. p. 337, 1817.

constantly at 720 mm., the temperature of the enclosure was brought successively to 20°, 40°, 60°, 80°, with the result that the cooling effect of the air for a given excess was found to be the same for all values of θ_0.

As a result of these experiments, the formula obtained for the velocity of cooling was

$$\mathrm{V} = k(a^\theta - a^{\theta_0}) + mp^c(\theta - \theta_0)^{1\cdot233},$$

where p is the pressure of the gas, and k is a constant which depends on the nature of the surface, while the constants m and c depend on the nature of the gas. Such is the general expression to which the experiments of Dulong and Petit have led. The first term relates to the radiation alone, while the second deals with the cooling effect of the ambient gas. The whole, however, must be regarded simply as an empirical formula founded on one of the most elaborate series of experiments ever conducted.

263. Experiments of De la Provostaye and Desains.—The range of applicability of the formula of Dulong and Petit was made the subject of a careful investigation by MM. De la Provostaye and Desains.[1] The result of the new researches proved that the formula could be applied only within a limited range, like all other empirical formulæ, in the neighbourhood of the experiments from which the various constants happened to be determined. Thus the quantity k was found to be only approximately constant. Its value varied little with a naked-bulbed thermometer, but with a silvered bulb it changed from 0·0087 at 150° C. to 0·0109 at 63° C. The constant m was also found to depend to some extent on the emissivity E, being greater for a metallic surface than for the naked glass. But perhaps the most important result of the investigation was that the cooling power of the gas was found not to be proportional to a power of the pressure (p^c) when the pressure was feeble. The experiments appear to show that as the pressure diminished from 760 mm., the cooling power decreased at first, and then remained constant from a value p_1 to a value p_2 of the pressure, after which it augmented with reduction of pressure. These limiting pressures p_1 and p_2 were further found to be more elevated and more widely separated the smaller the dimensions of the enclosure. This behaviour is to be attributed to the effect of the diminution of pressure and of the smallness of the chamber on the convection currents. Under these circumstances the cooling effect due to convection will be almost entirely eliminated,

---

[1] F. De la Provostaye et P. Desains, *Ann. de Chimie et de Physique*, 3e sér., tom. xvi. p. 337, 1846.

and the cooling due to the gas takes place entirely by molecular convection.

Emissivity in Absolute Measure

264. M'Farlane's Experiments.—The first trustworthy experiments, yielding emissivities in absolute measure, were those made by Dr. Donald M'Farlane[1] in Glasgow, under the direction of Lord Kelvin. The method adopted consisted in observing the cooling of a copper sphere about 4 cm. in diameter. This sphere was suspended inside a double-walled tin-plate vessel, which had its interior coated with lamp-black and the space between its walls filled with water at the temperature of the atmosphere. Its temperature was taken by means of a thermo-electric couple, one junction of which was situated at the centre of the sphere, and the other junction was in metallic contact with the outside of the tin-plate vessel, the circuit being completed through the coil of a sensitive mirror galvanometer. One junction was thus kept at a constant temperature of about 14° C., while the other had the gradually diminishing temperature of the centre of the sphere.

In making an experiment the copper ball was heated in the flame of a spirit-lamp till its temperature was considerably above that required to throw the spot of light off the galvanometer scale. It was then placed in position within the tin-plate water jacket, and as soon as the spot of light came within range, the deflections from the zero position were noted at intervals of one minute until the change of deflection was reduced to about two scale divisions per minute.

Two series of experiments were made in this way. In the first the surface of the ball was bright, and in the second it was coated with a thin covering of soot from a lamp flame, and in both the air was kept moist by a saucer of water placed inside the enclosure. The heat emitted per second was calculated by the formula $Q = a + b\theta + c\theta^2$, where θ is the difference of temperature.

The couple was standardised by tying its ends to the bulbs of two previously compared thermometers, placed in two vessels of water, one at the temperature of the air and the other heated by small additions of hot water.

The following table gives the results obtained for the heat emitted from the copper ball in calories per square centimetre of surface, per second, per degree difference in temperature, when the temperature of the surrounding vessel was about 14° C. :—

[1] D. M'Farlane, *Proc. Roy. Soc.* vol. xx. p. 90, 1871.

Difference of Temperature.	Heat emitted.		Ratio of Emissive Power of Polished to that of Blackened Surface.
	Polished Surface.	Blackened Surface.	
5°	·000178	·000252	0·707
10°	·000186	·000266	0·699
15°	·000193	·000279	0·692
20°	·000201	·000289	0·695
25°	·000207	·000298	0·694
30°	·000212	·000306	0·693
35°	·000217	·000313	0·693
40°	·000220	·000319	0·693
45°	·000223	·000323	0·690
50°	·000225	·000326	0·690
55°	·000226	·000328	0·690
60°	·000226	·000328	0·690

265. Bottomley's Experiments.—The same subject was also attacked by Dr. J. T. Bottomley.[1]   In this investigation the radiating body was a platinum wire stretched inside a long copper tube which was blackened on the inside and kept cool by a water-jacket.   The wire was heated by an electric current, and its surface might be bright and polished or might be coated with lamp-black, platinum-black, oxide of copper, or some other material.

Two methods of estimating the electric energy were employed. One consisted in measuring the current and the difference of potential between two chosen points on the radiating wire; the other consisted in measuring the current and determining simultaneously the resistance of the wire by means of a specially designed Wheatstone's bridge. The resistance when known gives the temperature of the wire.   The energy supplied to the wire by the electric current is lost through radiation and by conduction at its ends, but the latter source of loss is negligible, and when the dimensions of the wire are known the area of its surface is known, and the rate of loss of heat per unit area becomes determined at any temperature.

In order to obtain data for the elimination of the cooling effect of the air, the copper tube was connected with a five-fall Sprengel pump, so that the air pressure could be reduced, and in the extreme vacuum it was measured by a M'Leod's gauge.

A long and very complete series of determinations was made in this manner at various constant pressures and at different gradually increasing temperatures.   Several series of observations were also taken at constant temperature while the pressure was gradually diminished.   This mode of procedure proved by far the most

[1] J. T. Bottomley, *Phil. Trans.*, 1887, p. 429.

appropriate to the purpose in hand, and required the use of a special current-meter. On reducing the pressure it was found that a point was reached at which further exhaustion did not affect the emission. In this way a condition seems to be gradually reached in which the radiation is independent of everything removable by a Sprengel pump.

The temperature of the envelope being 15° C., the value of the emission per square centimetre of a bright platinum wire was in water-gramme-centigrade units—

$$\text{At } 408° \text{ C.} \quad . \quad . \quad . \quad . \quad . \quad . \quad 378 \cdot 8 \times 10^{-4}$$
$$,, \ 505° \text{ C.} \quad . \quad . \quad . \quad . \quad . \quad . \quad 726 \cdot 1 \times 10^{-4}$$

Dr. Bottomley considered that these experiments do not support the fourth power law of Stefan (Art. 277) and that a similar series of experiments by Schleiermacher[1] contradicts this law in the same manner.

Some interesting results obtained by Mr. Evans[2] as to the energy necessary to maintain a given candle-power in an incandescent lamp were confirmed during this investigation. The object of Evans's experiments was to compare the radiation of the carbon filaments of incandescent lamps having a bright polished surface with that from those having a dull surface like lamp-black, and he was led to an important practical conclusion as to the superior light-giving efficiency of the bright-looking filaments. If it be allowed that the temperature of a carbon filament can be measured by its resistance (this diminishing as the temperature increases), it follows from Evans's results that the temperature to which a filament must be raised, in order that it may furnish light of a definite candle-power, is higher when the surface is dull than when it is in the brilliant metallic-looking state. This result was so unexpected that Bottomley put it to the test of direct experiment. The result confirmed the conclusions derived from the experiments of Evans, and showed that the temperature which produces red-heat (for example) is very much higher when the surface of the heated body is dull than when it is bright and polished. Thus in the case of two platinum wires contained in vacuum tubes, one wire being bright and the other dulled with a thin film of smoke, when at the same dull red-heat the glass tube which contained the bright wire was not unpleasantly warm to the hand, while that containing the other wire was hot enough to blister the skin. The ratio of the

Evans's experiments.

---

[1] Schleiermacher, *Wied. Ann.* vol. xxvi. p. 237, 1885. Stefan's law is only true for the radiation within a closed space at uniform temperature. These conditions are not here fulfilled.

[2] M. Evans, *Proc. Roy. Soc.* vol. xl. p. 207, 1886.

resistances of the wires in this state was as 130 : 93, so that their difference of temperature must have been considerable.[1]

[1] Sir W. Crookes (*Proc. Roy. Soc.* vol. xxi. p. 239, 1881) has given a valuable comparative determination of the loss of heat from the same surface (the bulb of a mercury-in-glass thermometer) at different pressures, varying from one atmosphere down to two-millionths of an atmosphere.

SECTION III

DIATHERMANCY OF SOLIDS AND LIQUIDS

266. Melloni's Experiments.—Substances like glass which transmit light are said to be transparent, and in a similar manner those which permit radiant heat to pass through them are said to be diathermanous. At first sight it might be surmised that those bodies which most freely transmit light also most copiously transmit the non-luminous rays, such as the radiation from hot-water pipes, and that substances which are opaque to light are also opaque to radiant heat; but a little consideration will prepare any one possessing a knowledge of the fundamental principles of the wave theory to expect that different substances may behave very differently in their transmission of non-luminous radiation. The marked difference of behaviour in the transmission of light is detected at once by the eye, and may be more closely studied by an examination of the spectrum of the transmitted light. Thus blue glass and sulphate of copper transmit only the blue end of the spectrum, and red glass intercepts this end and transmits only the red; and the striking feature of these cases is the powerful effect of an almost infinitesimal amount of colouring matter on the transmission of light.

A solution of permanganate of potash intercepts the middle portion of the spectrum and transmits both ends, the mixture of red and blue giving rise to the gorgeous colour of the solution. Various substances are thus proved to possess what is termed selective absorption as regards the waves of light, singling out certain waves for destruction, while they permit others to pass. Hence if the non-luminous radiation, like the luminous, be a wave motion in the ether, we are prepared to find that transparency to light does not necessarily imply transparency to radiant heat, and that a substance which is opaque to light may freely transmit non-luminous radiation, and further, that a substance which is transparent to the radiation from one source may be practically opaque to that of another.

When light and radiant heat were considered to be essentially different, however, this view was not so easily entertained. Those who espoused the caloric theory found it very difficult to admit that heat could be transmitted through any substance in the same manner as they conceived light to be. All cases in which heat appeared to be so transmitted were explained by supposing that the heat was first absorbed by the substance, and afterwards radiated by it when it became hot. That heat can be transmitted almost instantaneously like light seems to have been discordant with the ideas of the calorists, and the point was combated by them for some time after the conclusive experiments of De la Roche and Melloni.

The transmission of heat and the property of selective absorption by bodies for the dark rays was first established by De la Roche, who concluded from this that radiant heat consists of a mixture of different rays, or, as we should now say, a multitude of waves of different lengths, just as white light is a mixture of different waves or differently coloured rays.

The work of De la Roche was subsequently confirmed by the elaborate researches of Melloni[1] with the thermopile. The method of analysis adopted may be briefly described as follows. The source of heat was placed at one side of a screen provided with an aperture, and the thermopile was placed at the other, so that the radiation, after passing through the aperture, fell upon it either unobstructed or after passing through a thin plate of the material under examination. In this manner Melloni found that rock-salt was exceedingly diathermanous, transmitting over 90 per cent of the incident radiation, whereas plates of alum and pure water of the same thickness scarcely transmitted the tenth part of the radiation from a lamp flame, and an inappreciable amount of the radiation from low temperature sources, such as a blackened copper ball heated to 390° C., or a Leslie's cube.[2]

[1] Melloni, *Ann. de Chimie et de Physique*, 2e sér., tom. liii. p. 5, 1833, and tom. lv.

[2] Rock-salt transmits a very large percentage of the radiation from all the sources, whereas alum transmits, according to Melloni, only the luminous rays (this, however, is not quite correct). Hence if, as Melloni supposed, the rock-salt transmits all the radiation, the difference between the quantities transmitted by a plate of rock-salt and a plate of alum should give the value of the obscure radiation as compared with the luminous. Tested in this way Melloni found the following proportions for the three sources employed :—

Source.	Luminous.	Obscure.
Oil flame	10	90
Incandescent platinum . . .	2	98
Flame of spirit-lamp . . .	1	99

The results of experiments with four different sources of heat
are contained in the following table, which exhibits not only the
difference of diathermancy of different substances for the radiation
from the same source, but also the difference of behaviour of the same
substance towards the radiation from different sources.   The numbers
represent the percentages of the incident radiation transmitted by the
various substances.   Four sources of heat were employed: (1) a
Locatelli lamp without a glass chimney ; (2) a platinum spiral heated
to incandescence in the flame of a spirit-lamp ; (3) a copper plate
heated to nearly 400° C. by a spirit-lamp ; (4) a thin copper vessel
blackened on the outside and filled with boiling water.

Thickness 2·6 mm.	Locatelli Lamp.	Incandescent Platinum.	Blackened Copper heated to 390°.	Blackened Copper heated to 100°.
Rock-salt (clear) . . .	92	92	92	92
Fluate of lime (clear) . .	78	69	42	33
Rock-salt (dull) . . .	65	65	65	65
Iceland spar.	39	28	6	0
,, ,, ...	38	28	5	0
Mirror glass	39	24	6	0
,, ,, ...	38	26	5	0
Rock-crystal (clear) . .	38	28	6	0
,, ,, (smoky) . .	37	28	6	0
Acid chromate of potash .	34	28	15	0
Sulphate of barytes (pure) .	24	18	3	0
Sulphate of lime . . .	14	5	0	0
Alum	9	2	0	0
Ice (very pure) . . .	6	0	0	0

This table shows how different substances differ in diathermancy,
and it also shows that, with a single exception, the diathermancy of
each substance varies with the nature of the source of heat.   Rock-
salt alone appears to be equally transparent to the radiation from all
sources.   Melloni supposed this substance to be perfectly transparent
to all kinds of radiation, and that the 8 per cent deficit in the foregoing table arose from reflection at the surfaces of the plate and not
from absorption in the interior.   More recent experiments, however,
by MM. Provostaye and Desains have proved that rock-salt does
exhibit selective absorption, and Balfour Stewart demonstrated that
it is particularly opaque to the radiation from a heated piece of the
same substance.

In the case of liquids the diathermancy was examined by enclosing
them in a glass cell with parallel faces.   The source of heat was an
Argand lamp furnished with a glass chimney, so that in considering
the results of the following table it must be remembered that the

diathermancy of the liquid is for the radiation of the lamp in question after passing through glass :—

Liquids, thickness 9·21 mm.				Rays transmitted.
No screen	.	.	.	100
Mirror glass (same thickness as liquid)	.	.	.	53
Carburet of sulphur (colourless)	.	.	.	63
Naphtha (rectified, colourless)	.	.	.	26
Sulphuric ether (colourless)	.	.	.	21
Pure sulphuric acid (colourless)	.	.	.	17
Hydrate of ammonia (colourless)	.	.	.	15
Nitric acid (pure and colourless)	.	.	.	15
Alcohol (absolute and colourless)	.	.	.	15
Hydrate of potassium (colourless)	.	.	.	13
Acetic acid (rectified, colourless)	.	.	.	12
Alum water (colourless)	.	.	.	12
Distilled water	.	.	.	11

This table shows that pure water is exceedingly opaque to radiant heat, and that the solution of a salt in it increases rather than diminishes its diathermancy. The position of a solution of alum is worthy of remark in this respect, for it seems to have been very generally supposed that this solution is practically opaque to non-luminous heat. The above table shows that Melloni found it more diathermanous than pure water, and this conclusion has been verified by Mr. Shelford Bidwell.[1] The ordinary supposition may perhaps have arisen from the fact that a plate of alum is highly opaque to thermal radiation (but not so much so as sugar-candy or ice), and it may have been inferred that its solution would also be highly opaque.

Alum cell.

Sifting.

The diathermancy of any body to radiation which has already passed through another was also examined by Melloni. Some of the results are contained in the following table. It appears that any substance is particularly transparent to radiation which has already been sifted by a plate of that substance. Thus a plate of alum which only transmitted 9 per cent of the heat from a naked lamp transmitted 90 per cent of that which had already passed a plate of this material. The same remark applies to the other substances, so that all are capable of sifting heat in such a manner that a second plate will transmit a large portion of the heat which has already passed through a plate of the same material. This, of course, is what we should expect theoretically, for when the radiation passes through a plate of any substance the emergent beam consists chiefly of those waves which the substance freely transmits, and this will be almost entirely transmitted by a second plate of the same substance.

[1] *Brit. Assoc. Report*, p. 309, 1886.

Examples of athermanous combinations are also contained in the table, just as red and green glass together make a combination opaque to light. Thus rays which have passed through alum are very feebly transmitted by black mica or black glass.

Plates not specially indicated were 2·6 mm.	Rays from Lamp.	Rays from Alum, thickness 2·6 mm.	Rays from Sulphate of Lime, thickness 2·6 mm.	Rays from Chromate of Potash, 2·6 mm.	Rays from Green Glass, 1·85 mm.	Rays from Black Glass, 1·85 mm.
Rock-salt	92	92	92	92	92	92
Fluate of lime	78	90	91	88	90	91
Iceland spar	39	91	89	56	59	55
Glass (0·5 mm.)	54	90	85	68	87	80
,, (0·8)	34	90	82	47	56	45
Rock-crystal	38	91	85	52	78	54
Chromate of potash . . .	34	57	53	71	28	24
Sulphate of barytes . . .	24	36	47	25	60	57
Black opaque mica (0·9) . .	20	0·4	12	16	38	43
Sulphate of lime	14	59	54	22	9	15
,, ,, thick (12 mm.) .	10	56	45	17	5	0·4
Alum	9	90	47	15	0·2	0·3

267. Influence of the Temperature of the Source.

It was for some time supposed that the transmissibility of heat through diathermanous substances augmented with the temperature of the source. Knoblauch [1] was the first to prove that this is not the case, but that the passage of radiant heat through any substance is determined alone by the nature of the substance. He showed in these researches that the heat emitted by an alcohol flame was more absorbed by certain substances than the heat emitted by a platinum wire placed in the flame, and he argued that the temperature of the flame cannot be lower than that of the spiral. Thus a plate of transparent glass placed between the incandescent platinum spiral and the thermopile transmitted a greater percentage of the radiation than when the source of heat was the flame alone without the spiral. This showed that the heat from the spiral, or source of lower temperature, was best transmitted, and this result was afterwards verified by Melloni.

Transparent glass allows the luminous or shorter waves to pass Glass. freely through it, but it is highly opaque to the longer, or ultra red-waves, that is to the obscure or non-luminous radiation. Reference to the foregoing tables shows that a plate of glass of the kind employed by Melloni, and only one-tenth of an inch thick, intercepts

[1] Knoblauch, *Pogg. Ann.*, 1847 ; and Taylor's *Scientific Memoirs.*

2 L

all the radiation from a source at 100° C., and transmits only 6 per cent of the heat emitted by a source at 400° C. It is for this reason that a glass plate is often used as a fire-screen. Now, the radiation from the flame of a spirit-lamp is nearly all non-luminous, but when a platinum spiral is plunged in the flame the luminosity is largely increased. The spiral becomes incandescent, absorbing the non-luminous waves of the flame, and emitting in return a copious supply of the shorter luminous waves. In this manner the percentage of waves which are easily transmitted by glass, is increased, and the presence of the spiral augments the transmissibility of the radiation. Thus Melloni found that a glass plate transmitted 41·2 per cent of the radiation from the flame alone, and 52·8 per cent of that from the flame and spiral. A plate of selenite transmitted in the same way 4·4 per cent from the flame, and 19·5 from the spiral.

In the case of substances which are opaque to the waves of higher refrangibility, the presence of the spiral would be expected to produce an opposite effect and reduce the transmissibility, for in this case the action of the spiral is to increase that portion of the radiation which is not transmitted by the substance. This was also verified by Melloni. Thus for black glass he found a transmission of 52·6 per cent from the flame, and only 42·8 from the spiral, and for black mica a transmission of 62·8 from the flame, and 52·5 from the spiral.

DIATHERMANCY OF GASES AND VAPOURS

268. Tyndall's Experiments.—The first successful experiments on the transmission of radiant heat through gases were made by Professor Tyndall at the Royal Institution in 1859. Previous to that date no experimenter had been able to detect any absorption of radiant heat by gaseous matter, and it was generally supposed that matter in the gaseous state transmitted perfectly all kinds of radiation. In approaching this investigation, either of two distinct methods of attack may be adopted : (1) the thermopile and the source of heat may be both placed in the chamber containing the gas under consideration ; or (2) either or both may be situated outside the space enclosing the gas. The first method has been employed by Magnus and others, and will be considered later on. It is subject, as Tyndall[1] pointed out, to

---

[1] Previous to the work of Tyndall, no doubt, many experimenters had investigated the action of air upon radiant heat ; otherwise the conviction that air perfectly transmitted radiant heat could not have become so universal, but that all other gases were supposed to behave in a like manner proves that experiments on them could scarcely have been seriously attempted.

Dr. Franz of Berlin (*Pogg. Ann.* vol. xciv. p. 342) with a sensitive thermopile

errors arising from convection currents and conduction of heat, and for this reason Tyndall adopted the second mode of experiment.

In making a preliminary experiment by this method, a tube about 4 feet long and 3 inches in diameter was fitted air-tight with rock-salt plates at the ends and furnished with two stop-cocks, so that it could be exhausted or filled with air or any other gas. The source of heat was placed opposite one end, and the thermopile faced the other, so that the radiation, after traversing the tube, fell upon it and produced a deflection of the galvanometer needle. The tube was first exhausted and the deflection of the galvanometer noted when the radiation fell upon the pile after traversing the empty space. Pure dry air was then admitted, and the deflection was found to remain unaltered, so that the radiation seemed to be transmitted as freely through the air as through a vacuum. The first inference is that either air does not absorb radiant heat at all, or else to such a small extent that this mode of experiment fails to detect it. Or it might happen that rock-salt and air absorb the same kind of rays, and that the radiation, after passing through the first plate of salt, is so sifted that no waves of the particular kind absorbed by air remain.

Rock-salt was chosen to close the ends of the tube, because it is by far the most diathermanous substance we know of. It is not particularly necessary to have a transparent substance, for gases, we know, freely transmit the luminous waves, and if they possess any marked absorbing power, it must be for waves below the red or beyond the violet. The essential thing then is to stop the ends of the tube with plates of some substance which freely transmits the longer waves below the red, and rock-salt is the best yet found for this purpose.

Tyndall, however, did not rest satisfied with this negative reply to his inquiry. He was fully convinced that air probably did absorb some of the radiant heat, but such a small fraction that the apparatus failed to detect it. He consequently exercised his ingenuity to render the apparatus more and more delicate, so that even the very feeblest absorption might be fully placed in evidence. This required a strong source of heat, so that a small fraction of it might not be infinitesimal,

---

had discovered a supposed absorption by dry air in a 3-foot tube of 3·54 per cent ; but this was attributed by Tyndall to the fact that Franz employed glass plates to close the ends of the tube, and as glass largely absorbs the non-luminous radiation, the plates soon become warm and radiate heat to the pile. In this situation of affairs, when the cool gas is admitted into the tube it rapidly lowers the temperature of the radiating glass plates both by conduction and convection, so that the total radiation to the pile is reduced just as if the gas exercised a true absorption of the radiant heat.

and it also required the galvanometer needle to be kept in the most sensitive position. A strong source of heat produces a large deflection of the needle, and in this part of the scale the instrument is not very sensitive to small changes of heat. The problem to be solved then was to work with small deflections and a strong source.

This difficulty was overcome by Tyndall in the following manner. The indications of the thermopile depend not so much on the temperature of either face as on their difference of temperature, and when the two faces are brought to the same temperature the deflection of the galvanometer is reduced to zero. The solution of the difficulty is now obvious. For if a strong beam of radiant heat be employed, which, falling on one face of the pile, produces a large deflection of the needle, then by bringing up a second source of heat opposite the other face of the pile, the action of the first source may be counterbalanced by the second, and the galvanometer deflection may be reduced to zero if desired. Let us now suppose that this has been effected, and that the needle stands at zero and in equilibrium under the joint action of the two sources of heat; and let us further suppose that the experimental tube already described has been exhausted and placed in the path of one of the beams of heat, so that the beam of radiant heat, falling upon one of the faces of the pile, passes through the empty tube. Now let us suppose air or any other gas to be introduced into the tube. Then if this gas absorbs any small fraction of the heat, the previous equilibrium will be broken and the needle will move to a new position of rest. The deflection of the needle will be, within certain limits, proportional to the quantity of heat absorbed, and this for a substance of given absorbing power will be proportional to the intensity of the beam passing through the tube. Hence, the stronger the beam of radiant heat employed, the greater the ultimate indication of the galvanometer, and by the foregoing device it is rendered possible to use a beam of any strength desired. The preliminary difficulty being thus overcome, Tyndall again approached the inquiry, and with marked success, as will appear from what follows.

The type of apparatus finally adopted is sketched in Fig. 159. The experimental tube SS′ was a hollow brass cylinder, polished within, and closed air-tight at the ends S and S′ with plates of rock-salt. The length of this tube was about 4 feet, and the source of heat C was a cube of cast copper filled with water, which was kept boiling by a lamp. The cube C was not isolated but brazed to a short cylinder F of the same diameter as the experimental cylinder, and capable of being connected air-tight with the latter at S. Thus between the source of heat and the experimental tube there was a front chamber F which could be exhausted, so that the radiation from C might enter the experimental tube unsifted by air. In order to avoid conduction of heat from C to the rock-salt plate at S, the front chamber F passed through a vessel V, in which a stream of cold water continually circulated. The experimental tube and the front chamber F were connected, independently, with the air-pump, so that either of them

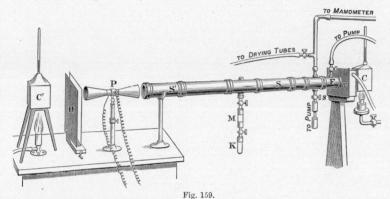

Fig. 159.

might be filled or exhausted without interfering with the other. The thermopile P was furnished with a conical reflector at each end, and the compensating cube C′ was used to neutralise the radiation from C. An adjusting screen H, capable of a very fine motion to and fro, was employed to bring about exact compensation.

As the very slightest traces of impurity largely affect the diathermancy of air, the strictest precautions were necessary in order to ensure that the sample admitted into the experimental tube was perfectly pure and dry. For this purpose it was passed through U-tubes filled with pure glass broken into small fragments and moistened with pure sulphuric acid. It was also found necessary to cover each column of the U-tube with a layer of dry glass fragments ; for the smallest trace of dust from the corks, or a fragment of sealing-wax not more than the twentieth part of a pin's head in size, was sufficient to vitiate the results if it reached the acid. The carbonic acid was removed by passing the air through another set of U-tubes filled with pure broken Carrara marble moistened with caustic potash.

The front chamber F and the experimental tube SS′ being both exhausted, the rays of heat from the source C were allowed to fall upon the face of the pile, and the effect of this radiation was compensated by the cube C′, the needle standing at zero. Pure dry air was then allowed to enter the cylinder, but no appreciable motion of the needle could be observed.

The absorption of heat by air is therefore so small that even this delicate test fails to detect it. Oxygen, hydrogen, and nitrogen, when carefully purified, and treated in the same way, showed, like air, no sensible absorption of the radiant heat. The compound gases, on the other hand, especially ammonia and olefiant gas, exhibited a very marked effect. The absorption increased with the pressure of the gas, but not according to any simple law. For very small pressures, however, the absorption was found, as we should expect, to be very approximately proportional to the pressure.

The results for various gases are collected in the following table:—

Substance.	Absorption at 1 Atmo.	Substance.	Absorption at 1 Atmo.
Air	1	Carbonic acid . .	90
Oxygen . . .	1	Nitrous oxide . .	355
Nitrogen . . .	1	Sulphide of hydrogen.	390
Hydrogen . . .	1	Marsh gas . . .	403
Chlorine . . .	39	Sulphurous acid .	710
Hydrochloric acid .	62	Olefiant gas . .	970
Carbonic oxide . .	90	Ammonia . . .	1195

Vapours. The examination of vapours was conducted by placing some of the liquid in a test-tube K fitted with a screw-tap carefully cemented on (Fig. 159). By this means it could be attached to a stop-cock, and thus connected with the experimental tube. The liquid being introduced, the tube K was connected with an air-pump, and the air was completely removed, so that nothing but the liquid and its vapour remained. The stop-cock was then shut, and K was attached to the experimental tube. The latter being completely exhausted, and the needle of the galvanometer standing at zero, the tap attached

Substance.	Pressures.		
	0·1.	0·5.	1·0.
Bisulphide of carbon . . .	15	47	62
Iodide of methyl	35	147	242
Benzole	66	182	267
Chloroform	85	182	236
Methylic alcohol	109	390	590
Amylene	182	535	823
Sulphuric ether	300	710	870
Alcohol	325	622	...
Formic ether	480	870	1075
Acetic ether	590	980	1195
Propionate of ethyl . . .	596	970	...
Boracic ether	620	...	...

to K was opened. The vapour was thus allowed to enter the experimental tube silently, and without the slightest commotion, while the manometer attached to the apparatus was carefully observed. In this manner the absorptions of the vapours mentioned in the preceding table were examined at pressures of 0·1, 0·5, and 1 inch respectively.

The influence of the temperature of the source on the transmission of radiant heat by vapours was very marked. By raising the radiating spiral from a barely visible heat to an intense white heat, the absorption of bisulphide of carbon and chloroform was reduced to less than one-half, and corresponding reductions took place with the other vapours. In some cases even a reversal of the order of their absorbing powers was exhibited.

Experiments on ozone showed so marked an absorption of radiant heat by this substance that it takes rank with olefiant gas and boracic ether as an absorber.

The diathermancies of several volatile liquids and of their vapours were also examined by Tyndall, in order to determine if the state of aggregation is of paramount importance, or if the absorption depends chiefly on the nature of the individual molecules, and if their deportment towards radiant heat remains characteristic of the molecule throughout all states of aggregation. Of the liquids examined, water showed the greatest absorption. *Effect of state of aggregation.*

It appeared from these experiments that in the main the molecules maintain their characteristics as absorbers of radiant heat, although the state of aggregation changes, and if any inference be allowed we should expect that aqueous vapour would be exceedingly opaque to thermal radiation, for, as we have already seen, pure water stands at the bottom of the list as a transmitter of radiant heat.

This anticipation as to the opacity of aqueous vapour seems to have been fully verified by the experiments of Tyndall, but subsequent investigations by Magnus and others by different methods brought the matter into warm dispute, for, while Tyndall with one form of apparatus found the absorption of aqueous vapour to be enormously greater than that of dry air, Magnus with another found no such difference of absorbing power.

The low diathermancy of pure water prepared Tyndall to expect that aqueous vapour would also prove itself highly opaque to radiant heat, and this expectation was surprisingly confirmed. Pure dry air being admitted into the experimental cylinder, a deflection of scarcely 1° was observed. Making a similar experiment with the undried air of the room the needle moved through 48°. This corresponded to an absorption of 72—that is to say, the aqueous vapour contained in the air absorbs 72 times the quantity of heat absorbed by the air itself. This figure is rendered all the more surprising when we remember that the quantity of vapour in the air amounts to less than one-half per cent.

This result, if true, is of such importance in the science of meteorology that it ought to be subjected to the most careful examination, and the closest scrutiny of the whole matter seems to have been carried out by Tyndall. Rock-salt is a hygroscopic substance, and it might be supposed that the aqueous vapour condenses on the faces of the rock-salt plates which close the ends of the experimental tube, and that in this manner a thin film of aqueous salt solution is formed, which, as appears from Melloni's tables, is highly opaque to radiant heat, though not more opaque than pure water. The question, therefore, arises whether in the foregoing experiment the absorption observed is not in reality due to thin films of moisture deposited on the plates.

With regard to this objection, Tyndall took effective precautions to prevent the deposition of moisture, such that, on examining the plate, even with a lens, no trace of moisture could be detected on it, the polish remaining perfect throughout.

Further, the plates of rock-salt were dispensed with entirely, and the experimental tube was left open at both ends, the arrangement of the apparatus being as shown in Fig. 160. In order to avoid agita-

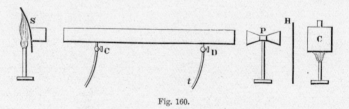

Fig. 160.

tion of the surrounding atmosphere while the air was being introduced into the open tube, it was arranged that dry air should be allowed to enter the tube slowly through the tap C, while D was connected with an air-pump which was slowly worked, so that the dry air was drawn from C towards D. Thus throughout the central portion of the tube a column of moist air could be displaced by dry air, and *vice versa*.

In making an experiment with this apparatus the tube was at first filled with the common air of the laboratory, and the needle was brought to zero by the compensating cube. Dry air was then allowed to enter slowly and displace the moist air which initially occupied the tube. As soon as the dry air was allowed to enter, the needle com-

menced to move and finally stood at a deflection of 45°. When the
supply of dry air was cut off, the deflection commenced to fall, but
with great slowness, indicating a slow diffusion of the aqueous vapour
through the dry air of the tube. If the pump was worked the dry
air was removed more quickly and the needle sank rapidly to zero.

The result of all these experiments
was, therefore, to confirm the conclusion already arrived at by Tyndall as to the high absorptive power
of aqueous vapour for radiant heat.

Humid air was also tested at
various pressures, and the results
verified the anticipation that the
absorption varies directly as the
quantity of vapour present.

**269. Experiments of Magnus
and of Lecher and Pernter.**—
The experiments of Professor Magnus[1]
on the diathermancy of gases were
conducted chiefly with the apparatus
shown in Fig. 161. This consisted of
two glass vessels having their bottoms
fused together, one being much larger
than the other. The smaller one, C,
stood upright, and acted as the source
of heat, being partly filled with water
which was kept at the boiling point
by a current of steam passed through
the tube pp. The larger vessel BF
was turned mouth downwards, and
had its mouth FF ground down so
that it could be placed like an ordinary
receiver on the plate of an air-pump
and exhausted, while, by means of
the cocks H and K, it could be

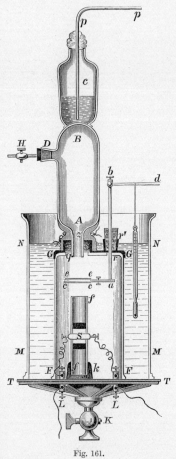

Fig. 161.

filled with any gas desired. It was surrounded by a water bath,
MM, kept at 15° C. Within this experimental space a thermopile S,
with its axis vertical, was attached to the plate of the air-pump,
and one face was directed towards the common surface of the two
vessels which had been fused together. This surface was heated to
100° C. by the hot water and acted as the radiator. The pile could

[1] Magnus, *Pogg. Ann.* vol. cxii. p. 531; *Phil. Mag.* vol. xxii., 1861.

be exposed to the radiation or protected from it at pleasure by means of a movable screen, *ce*, and the entire space between the pile and the radiating surface could be rendered a vacuum or filled with a gas.

Experimenting in this way, Magnus found that air and oxygen intercepted over 11 per cent of the heat radiated by the source, while hydrogen cut off more than 14 per cent. Tyndall, on the other hand, after using every precaution, found that these gases were practically vacua to radiant heat. With the more powerful compound gases, on the other hand, Tyndall found a considerably stronger action than Magnus. Thus with olefiant gas Magnus found an absorption of less than 54 per cent, whereas Tyndall obtained more than 72. This result, however, was to be expected, as the length of gas traversed by the radiant heat in the experiments of the former was under 15 inches, whereas in those of the latter it was 33.

Aqueous vapour.

We now come to the case of aqueous vapour. With both the gas-flame and the boiling water as sources of heat, Magnus found the effect of dry air to be precisely the same as that of moist air saturated with vapour. He concluded from his experiments " that the water present in the atmosphere at 16° C. exercises no perceptible influence on the radiation." The vast difference obtained by Tyndall in the behaviour of moist and dry air to radiant heat has been already noticed, and as these discrepancies were attributed by Magnus to condensation on the interior surface of Tyndall's experimental tube and on the rock-salt plates, so Tyndall in turn attributed them to sources of error inherent in Magnus's method of experiment. Thus, Magnus in his first apparatus (Fig. 161) avoided the use of plates of any kind ; but in order to do this he was compelled to bring his gas into direct contact with his source of heat. Convection currents may in this manner be set up within the experimental chamber, and Tyndall held that the results obtained by Magnus were largely affected by this source of error, the greater convection of hydrogen also accounting for the difference obtained by Magnus between this gas and air. So also Magnus used glass plates to close his experimental tube, and these, according to Tyndall, become heated and radiate to the pile as secondary sources. On the introduction of a gas, however, the plates become cooled by convection and conduction, and the effect of this cooling on the pile is the same as if a true absorption took place within the gas.

More recently a series of experiments on the absorption of radiant heat by gases and vapours was published by Ernst Lecher and Joseph Pernter;[1] but these new investigations, instead of settling the question

---

[1] Lecher and Pernter, *Sitzb. der k. Akad. der Wissensch. in Wien*, July 1880 ; *Phil. Mag.*, January 1881.

in dispute between Tyndall and Magnus as to the comparative absorptions of dry and moist air, placed the whole matter in a state of greater uncertainty. For whereas Tyndall found an exceedingly low absorption for dry, and a high absorption for moist air, while Magnus found the same absorption for both, and that tolerably high, the results of the experiments of Lecher and Pernter show practically no absorption for either ; or, in other words, both dry and moist air act as a vacuum towards radiant heat.

The method adopted in these investigations was similar to that employed by Magnus, the source of heat and the thermopile being in the same chamber as the gas under examination. In order to avoid convection currents, however, a special heating arrangement was adopted, whereby the radiating surface was suddenly brought to 100° C. by directing a jet of steam against it. The apparatus was for this reason a considerably modified form of that of Magnus.

It is now fully established that pure air is highly diathermanous, but that the aqueous vapour and carbon dioxide present in ordinary air possess a well-marked absorbing power. The whole subject of absorption is best studied as a branch of physical optics, being closely connected with dispersion and selective reflection. In the experiments above described, no attempt was made to employ radiation of a definite wave-length, hence the existence of absorption bands or lines characteristic of each substance could not reveal themselves.

270. The Differential Thermometer.—In the preceding investigations on the laws of cooling, the temperatures were registered by ordinary liquid-in-glass thermometers. The general study of radiation, however, required some much more sensitive temperature-registering apparatus, and the great advances in this subject followed the invention of more and more delicate instruments for the detection of feeble radiation. All the most valuable of these instruments depend in principle on the thermo-electric properties of matter.

The first instrument specially invented for the study of radiant

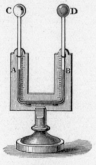

Fig. 162.

Fig. 163.

heat was a species of air thermometer designed by Sir J. Leslie, and in his hands this instrument (which is now of little more than historic interest) rendered important service. In Leslie's form of the apparatus (Fig. 162) two equal bulbs, C and D, filled with air are connected, as shown in the diagram, by a narrow bent tube which contains some non-volatile liquid, such as sulphuric acid. When the two bulbs are at the same temperature, the liquid stands at the same level in the two arms of the tube; but if one of the bulbs is heated, the pressure of the air within it increases, and the liquid is forced towards the cooler bulb by the expanding air in the warmer. The level of the liquid in the arm to which the warmer bulb is attached will thus be lower than the level in the other arm, and from the difference of level the difference of temperature may be estimated.

Thus since the bulbs are equal, and the liquid stands at the same level in the arms when the temperature is the same, it follows that the mass of air in one bulb is the same as that in the other. If the zero mark of the scale be the point at which the level of the liquid stands when the two bulbs have the same temperature, and if v denotes the volume of each scale division of the tube, then when the surface of the liquid stands n divisions below the zero mark in one arm, and n divisions above it in the other, the volumes occupied by the air in these arms will be V and $V + 2nv$ respectively, and the corresponding temperatures of the bulbs will be Θ and $\Theta + \Delta\theta$. In addition, the pressure in the colder bulb will be P, and if the pressure due to the weight of each scale division of the liquid be p, the pressure in the warmer bulb will be $P + 2np$, and consequently applying the equation $PV = R\Theta$ to each arm we have

$$\frac{PV}{\Theta} = \frac{(P + 2np)(V + 2nv)}{\Theta + \Delta\theta} = \frac{2nPV}{\Delta\theta}\left(\frac{p}{P} + \frac{v}{V}\right),$$

since p/P and v/V are both small, the final member being obtained by subtracting the numerator and denominator of the first from the corresponding terms of the second. The equality of the first and third members gives at once

$$\Delta\theta = 2n\Theta\left(\frac{p}{P} + \frac{v}{V}\right).$$

If the colder bulb be at zero centigrade, then $\Theta = \frac{1}{a}$, and further, if the volume V be replaced by V_0, the volume of either bulb up to the zero mark, and P by P_0, the pressure when the liquid stands at the same level in the two arms, we have the approximate equation

$$\Delta\theta = \frac{2n}{a}\left(\frac{p}{P_0} + \frac{v}{V_0}\right).$$

A modified form of Leslie's apparatus was designed by Count Rumford, which possesses much greater delicacy than the original. In Rumford's form (Fig. 163) the liquid column is reduced to a simple index moving along the horizontal part of the tube which joins the bulbs, so that the pressure in one bulb is always equal to that in the other.

If the index be displaced n divisions from the zero mark, we have in this case

$$\frac{V}{\Theta} = \frac{V + 2nv}{\Theta + \Delta\theta} = \frac{2nv}{\Delta\theta},$$

where V is the volume, and Θ the temperature of air in the colder arm.
Hence

$$\Delta\theta = 2n\Theta\frac{v}{V},$$

or approximately

$$\Delta\theta = \frac{2n}{a}\frac{v}{V_0}.$$

A modified form of the differential thermometer has also been devised by Matthiessen, which can be used conveniently with liquids. For this object the arms to which the bulbs are attached are bent round twice at right angles, so that the bulbs hang downwards, and can be easily dipped into liquids, and the difference of temperature of two liquids can thus be registered. The differential thermometer, when employed as a radiometer, is less sensitive than a simple air thermometer, for when the index moves under the expansion of the air in one of the bulbs an increase of pressure is set up in the other, and this reduces the displacement of the index which would otherwise occur.

271. The Thermopile.—The thermopile is probably the most celebrated instrument ever designed for the study of radiant heat, for although it has been surpassed in delicacy and quickness of action by more recent forms of apparatus, yet it is to the services of the thermopile that we owe the researches of Melloni and Tyndall, as well as many of the advances that have since been made in the study of radiation. This instrument was invented by Nobili, and in its action is based on a discovery made by Seebeck about 1820, that when two wires of different metals are joined end to end so as to form a closed circuit, then when one of the junctions is heated, or cooled, an electric current passes round the circuit, and this current continues to flow as long as any difference of temperature exists between the two junctions.

The most elementary form of such an apparatus is shown in Fig.

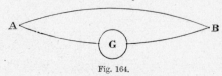

Fig. 164.

164, where A and B are the junctions of two dissimilar wires, the wires being soldered together at these points, and one of them being in circuit with a galvanometer G. As long as A and B are at different temperatures, a current passes round the circuit and deflects the needle of the galvanometer. When the two junctions are at the same temperature, as when they are both immersed in the same bath, there is no current, and the galvanometer needle remains steady, but as the difference of temperature increases the current strength increases, and the deflection of the needle augments accordingly.

We have here, therefore, a means of estimating differences of temperature, and on this property a scale of temperature might be founded by saying arbitrarily that the current strength in the circuit is proportional to the difference of the temperatures of the two junctions just as legitimately as on the expansion of mercury

or any other liquid. We have, however, already chosen the air
or perfect gas thermometer as our standard of reference, and, understanding temperature to be measured in this way, it is found that
the current strength in a thermo-electric circuit is not exactly proportional to the difference of the temperatures of the two junctions,
but for small differences it is nearly so. The electromotive force
gradually increases with the difference of temperature; but, as
Cumming discovered, if one junction is kept at a constant temperature, while the temperature of the other is gradually raised, the
current strength does not go on continually increasing, but ultimately
reaches a maximum, after which it decreases and ultimately falls to
zero again, and becomes reversed, so that the deflection of the
galvanometer vanishes, not only when the two junctions have the
same temperature, but also again when they are at very different
temperatures. The mean of the temperatures of the two junctions
when the latter occurs is found to be always the same for the same
pair of metals, and is called their neutral [1] temperature. The
existence of this phenomenon utterly disqualifies the thermo-electric
couple as a standard of measurement of temperature, and for all
purposes of measurement the instrument must be empirically graduated
by a direct comparison of its indications with those of some standard
instrument.

The thermopile, as usually constructed, consists not of a single
pair of wires, but of several pairs arranged in such a way that a
given difference of temperature produces a much more marked
deflection of the galvanometer than that which would be caused by
a single pair. This arrangement is indicated in Fig. 165, which shows
a system of pairs of little bars of two different metals soldered
together, and arranged so that the alternate bars are of the same
metal, and thus at each junction two dissimilar metals are soldered
together. If the system is in circuit with a galvanometer G, and if
all the lower junctions are at one temperature, while all the upper
junctions are at another, then the electromotive force of the system
will be equal to that of a single pair multiplied by the number of
pairs.

In practice about twenty-five pairs, each consisting of a small

---

[1] Since the electromotive force vanishes when the temperatures θ_1 and θ_2 of the
two junctions are equal, it follows that $\theta_1 - \theta_2$ must be a factor of the expression for
the electromotive force. In the same way, if the neutral temperature be θ_0, then the
electromotive force vanishes when $\frac{1}{2}(\theta_1 + \theta_2) = \theta_0$, and, therefore, $\theta_0 - \frac{1}{2}(\theta_1 + \theta_2)$ must
also be a factor. The expression for the electromotive force must therefore be of
the form

$$A(\theta_1 - \theta_2)\{\theta_0 - \tfrac{1}{2}(\theta_1 + \theta_2)\}.$$

bar of antimony soldered to a similar bar of bismuth, are arranged, as shown in Fig. 166, in the form of a rectangular parallelepiped, the pieces being carefully insulated from each other by some insulating material, such as thin paraffined paper.

In conjunction with a thermopile it is necessary to use a galvanometer, and in constructing a delicate instrument it is necessary to pay due attention to the proper construction of the latter. With a given pile the best galvanometer to work with is one whose resistance is equal to that of the pile, and in constructing a galvanometer of some predetermined resistance, what is required is to wind it with as many turns of wire as possible, especially near the inside, where each turn produces the greatest effect. The question also arises as to what number of couples will be most advantageous in a thermopile. Now, it is clear that the face of the pile need not exceed the area on which the radiation can be concentrated, and if the number of bars

Thermo-
pile.

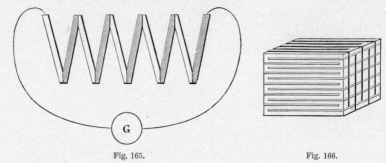

Fig. 165.   Fig. 166.

in a given area be doubled the electromotive force will be doubled, but the resistance of the pile will be increased four times, for not only are there twice the number of bars, but the cross-section of each is halved, so that if the resistance of the galvanometer be made four times as great by winding twice the number of turns of wire in the same space, the resistance of the whole circuit will be four times as great, and, consequently, the current will be half as great; but as it circulates round the needle twice as often, the deflection will be the same as before. Hence the deflection will be the same with one pair and a corresponding galvanometer as with many pairs filling the same space. This is true only so long as the resistances of the connecting wires can be neglected, and as it is often necessary to work with the pile at some distance from the galvanometer, the number of pairs in the pile should be considerable, for, as they are increased, the effect of the connecting wires becomes less and less. Another point of practical importance in favour of a large number of pairs is, that in this case the electromotive force is large, and the disturbing effects of accidental electromotive forces are of smaller consequence—such, for example, as the thermo-electric effects which may occur at binding screws subject to accidental changes of temperature by handling, etc., or by connecting wires moving in the earth's magnetic field.

The difficulties attending the use of the thermopile as a sensitive and accurate radiometer arise from the comparative slowness of its indications and the length of time required for it to return to zero. These defects unfit it for many delicate experiments.

272. The Bolometer.—An instrument depending on the change of electric resistance with temperature, and surpassing the thermopile in delicacy and merit as a radiometer, was brought out in 1881 by Professor Langley,[1] and named the bolometer or actinic balance. This instrument was designed for the study of the distribution of heat in the solar spectrum, and in the hands of the inventor it has proved itself a fruitful means of investigation in this department, not merely detecting the presence of very feeble radiation, but also, as its name indicates, furnishing a measure of its amount (Fig. 167).

The working part of the instrument consists of a thin strip of steel, platinum, or palladium foil, resembling a grating or system of parallel elements of the same metal joined so as to form a continuous circuit. This system of strips, or grating as we shall call it, is punched from a thin sheet of the foil, giving strips about 1 cm. long, $\frac{1}{2}$ mm. wide, and $\frac{1}{100}$ to $\frac{1}{500}$ mm. thick, this process being preferable to that of soldering the ends of the strips together. The grating is exposed to the radiation, and is placed in one of the arms of a Wheatstone's bridge, and a similar grating, screened from all radiation, is placed in another arm of the bridge, and used as a counterbalancing resistance. This arm also includes a resistance which can be varied, so that exact balance may be obtained in the galvanometer circuit. A current from a battery of one or more Daniell's cells divides itself between the two systems, one-half passing through each. When

---

[1] Langley, *Proc. American Acad. of Arts and Sciences*, vol. xvi. p. 342, 1881.

The earliest account of an instrument, depending on change of electrical resistance, for measuring or detecting heat appears to be that of Svanberg (*Pogg. Ann.* vol. xxiv. p. 416, 1851), who, for this purpose, introduced a flat spiral of blackened copper wire into one of the arms of a Wheatstone's bridge. Dr. Baur has published two papers on the Bolometer (*Proc. Berlin Phys. Soc.*, March 3, 1882 ; *Ann. der Ph. und Ch.* vol. xix. p. 12, 1883). He constructed his gratings of tinfoil, blackened with platinic chloride, and this sensitive surface acquires its final temperature almost instantaneously. The two resistances are placed side by side, so that, by the movement of a shutter, the radiation may be allowed to fall on one or the other alternately, and thus double the effect.

the two currents are equal, the needle of the galvanometer remains motionless, but when heat falls upon the exposed system, the resistance of that set increases, and the current passing through it is diminished, with a consequent deflection of the galvanometer. By this means a change of temperature of so little as $\frac{1}{10000}$ of a degree centigrade or less may be measured; and from the excessive thinness of the strips, they take up and part with heat almost instantaneously, so that this instrument is much more prompt in its action than the thermopile. It is also much more accurate, for Professor Langley estimates the error of a single measure with it at less than 1 per cent.

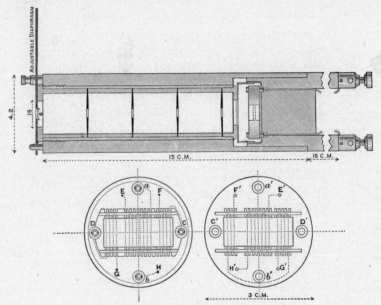

Fig. 167.

To protect the grating from air currents and sudden changes of temperature it is enclosed in a chamber lined with copper to secure an equable distribution of temperature. This chamber is contained in a long cylinder of wood or ebonite, which is also furnished with four or more coaxial cardboard diaphragms pierced with apertures 6 mm. in diameter, and separated by ebonite rings, which form a succession of drum-like chambers through which the radiation passes, and which effectually stop air currents from without. The mouth of this cylinder is furnished with a revolving cardboard disc with suitable stops which admit or shut out the radiation at pleasure. At the back of the copper-lined chamber containing the strips is a layer of solid non-conducting material through which the connecting wires pass to binding screws, and behind this is a chamber containing the adjustable resistance by which the two arms of the bridge may be counterbalanced to perfect equality. It is advisable to have the two arms as equal as possible at first, since, if unequal, the increment of resistance of the larger caused by a general rise of temperature exceeds that of the smaller, necessitating a frequent readjustment of the variable resistance, and producing a " drift " of the galvanometer needle, which slowly changes its direction according as the temperature of the room rises or falls. A similar drift, due to different causes, also affects the thermopile when the galvanometer is very delicate.

The requirements of the instrument necessitate in the construction of the grating the use of a metal of high electrical resistance, and the resistance of which changes considerably with change of temperature. At the same time the metal requires to be tenacious as well as ductile, and not liable to become oxidised or changed by exposure to the air. The metals which seem to best meet these requirements are steel, platinum, and palladium.

The bolometer has been applied by Tschqlieeff [1] in the measurement of dielectric constants, and in the detection of Hertzian waves.

It seems difficult to believe that an instrument such as the bolometer, which depends in its action on the change of resistance of a wire with temperature, a variation which is always comparatively small, could be made to surpass or even approach in delicacy as a radiometer a properly designed and carefully constructed instrument such as the thermopile, which depends on the thermo-electromotive force developed by difference of temperature at the junctions of two dissimilar metals. If an instrument of the latter class could be constructed as delicately as Langley's bolometer, a better result ought to be obtained. The one point, however, in which the bolometer has a great advantage is the smallness of the mass of the part to be heated, whereas in the thermopile, however delicate the bars may be, the mass is so large that the rate of heating and the ultimate rise of temperature must be comparatively small. A thermopile cannot be made with bars of antimony and bismuth as thin as the wires of the bolometer, and such a construction would be necessary in order to use the thermo-electromotive force with the same advantage as the variation of resistance is in the bolometer. If the connecting wires had no resistance, no advantage would be gained by having more than a single pair of bars in the pile, provided the galvanometer were properly

---

[1] Tschqlieeff, *Journal de la Société Physico-Chimique Russe*, 1890, p. 115.

proportioned, and the mass of the instrument would be greatly diminished. The problem on hand is then reduced to the invention of some delicate method of detecting the current in a single couple, and the solution of this problem has been given by Professor C. V. Boys in the beautiful instrument named the radio-micrometer.

273. The Radio-Micrometer.—The active part of the instrument devised by Professor Boys[1] (the radio-micrometer) consists of a very light circuit (Fig. 168) composed of a single loop of fine bare copper wire, to the lower ends of which a pair of very light bars of antimony and bismuth[2] are soldered. These bars form a thermo-electric couple, and the circuit is completed by soldering them side by side at their lower ends to a very small disc of thin copper, or (if the instrument is intended for spectrum analysis) to a very narrow strip of copper foil on which the radiation is received. When radiation falls on this disc the lower junction of the couple becomes heated and a current traverses the circuit, and in order to detect this the circuit is suspended in a strong magnetic field (Fig. 169), in which it is deflected, as in the case of Thomson's siphon recorder, or the moving coil galvanometer.[3] It thus possesses all the advantages of an ideal thermopile of exceedingly small mass, while the current is detected without the aid of a separate galvanometer.

The circuit is suspended by being attached to the lower end of a very thin capillary glass tube, 5 cm. long, which is suspended by a quartz fibre made by the bow-and-arrow process.[4] Close to the top of the tube a very light galvanometer mirror is fastened, so that any heat which may fall upon it has no influence on the circuit below. The circuit of copper wire hangs in a narrow hole within a mass of

[1] C. V. Boys, *Phil. Trans.* vol. clxxx., A, p. 159, 1888–89 ; *Journ. Soc. Arts*, 11th October 1889.

[2] Alloys of these metals are preferable. Thus, as Professor Boys points out, $32 Bi + 1 Sb$ is better than Bi in the ratio $10 : 9$, and $12 Bi + 1 Sn$ is better than Sb, or again $10 Bi + 1 Sb$ and Sb and Cd in equivalent proportions are still better, but the latter alloy is troublesome to work. The dimensions of the circuit employed were : Thermo-electric bars $\frac{1}{3} \times \frac{1}{60} \times \frac{1}{200}$ inch ; No. 36 copper wire made into a circuit 1 inch long and about $\frac{1}{10}$ inch wide ; a copper heat-receiving surface about $\frac{1}{10}$ inch diameter, and blackened on the side exposed to the radiation ; mirror $\frac{1}{10}$ inch square and $\frac{1}{200}$ inch thick. The quartz fibre was 4 inches long and $\frac{1}{8000}$ inch thick, and the weight of the complete circuit was half a grain.

[3] This principle of fixed magnet and movable coil appears to have been employed by Sturgeon as early as 1836, and M. D'Arsonval, on 5th February 1886, exhibited, at a meeting of the Physical Society of France, an instrument called by him the thermo-galvanometer, with which the radio-micrometer of Boys was identical in all essential respects. In detail, however, the two instruments differ essentially ; but when Professor Boys became acquainted with the work of D'Arsonval, he at once fully admitted the claim of the latter to priority.

[4] See *Phil. Mag.*, June 1887.

brass situated between the pole-pieces, NS, of a powerful permanent
steel magnet, and the little bars of antimony and bismuth (or alloy)
hang below within a cavity drilled out of a mass of soft iron, where
the radiation falls upon the junction through a transverse aperture
(Fig. 169).   Thus, while the circuit hangs in a strong magnetic field,
the central mass of soft iron (shaded dark in Fig. 169) screens the
antimony and bismuth, and prevents any trouble arising from dia-
magnetism.   Such disturbances have been so completely overcome
that a strong magnet may be moved about close to the instrument
without affecting it.

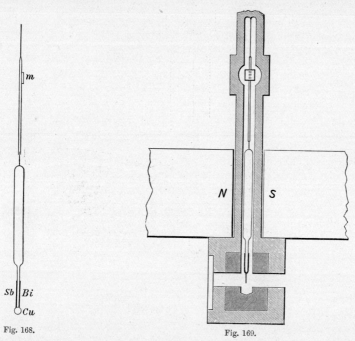

Fig. 168.

Fig. 169.

Fig. 170 shows the whole instrument enclosed within a thick
wooden cover (dotted outline), which prevents external radiation and
draughts from falling upon and unequally warming the metal cavity.
Attached to this wooden cover is a paper tube, which projects in front
of the chamber containing the thermo-electric pair.   The radiation
enters through this tube, and it is fitted with a series of diaphragms
such as Langley used with his bolometer.   A glass window closes the
back of the chamber, so that it is possible to see whether the radiation
falls upon the copper disc as intended, while the glass protects the
junction from the dark heat of the eye.

Besides its extreme quickness of action and delicacy, the advantages claimed for this instrument are its freedom from extraneous thermal and magnetic influences, the circuit being suspended in a cavity within a mass of metal. It has also a constant and definite zero, given by the control of the suspending fibre, and this being of quartz, the difficulties caused by the uncertain behaviour of silk under varying conditions of temperature and humidity are obviated. The sensibility of the apparatus may also be varied at pleasure, and it may be rendered "dead beat," or its logarithmic

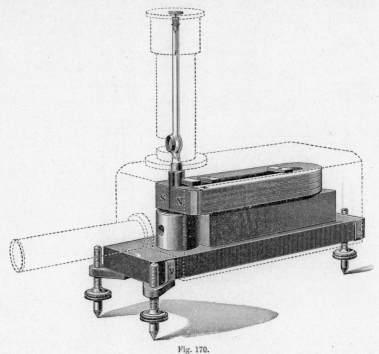

Fig. 170.

decrement may be varied at will. A further advantage is that in spectroscopic work the radiation may be limited by a narrow slit without seriously reducing the sensibility of the instrument. On the other hand, it must, like the galvanometer, be kept in a fixed position, and cannot be handled or pointed in other than a horizontal direction, so that in this respect it is less convenient than thermopile or bolometer.

The radio-micrometer may be used differentially by placing a second couple in the upper end of the circuit, and this may be furnished with a separate window, so that the radiation from one source may fall on one couple, and the other may be exposed at the same time to the radiation from any other source.

Besides being vastly more sensitive than the thermopile, the radio-micrometer has a further advantage, which is most important in astronomical work, for a measure can be effected with it in a few seconds instead of the several minutes necessary to the older apparatus. So great was the delicacy of the apparatus constructed by Boys that the radiation received by the mirror of a telescope of 16 inches aperture from a candle situated at a distance of between 2 and 3 miles was distinctly observable, and an amount of heat of about $\frac{1}{150000}$ of that received from the full moon could be detected with certainty. It was, therefore, legitimately hoped that this instrument would settle the question as to whether or not any radiation from the fixed stars had yet been perceived. Experiments in this direction had been made in 1869 by Huggins [1] with the thermopile; but although the results did not prove con- Stellar radiation. clusively that the thermopile was capable of detecting such feeble radiation, yet they made it exceedingly probable that the effects observed were really due to stellar radiation. A year later Mr. Stone,[2] using the great equatorial at Greenwich and a single couple, found that at night every slight change in the sky, even though invisible to the eye, so disturbed the galvanometer that it was impossible to distinguish between effects due to the stars and those caused by the varying clearness of the sky. This difficulty was largely obviated by placing in the focal plane of the object glass two thermo-electric pairs so connected that the heating of the exposed face of one would produce an effect opposite in kind to that produced by the heating of the exposed face of the other. Under these conditions a change in the sky affected the two faces equally or nearly so, and the galvanometer was not disturbed by variations of the sky ; but if a star were allowed to shine first on one face and then on the other, cor-responding deflections in opposite directions ought to be obtained. This arrangement had been employed previously by Lord Rosse [3] in his experiments on the heat of the moon. Mr. Stone concluded from his experiments that the radiation from Arcturus heated the face of the pile through about $\frac{1}{50}$ of a degree Fahrenheit, a quantity which might be registered by any well-constructed liquid-in-glass thermometer !

With the radio-micrometer, however, which is vastly more sensitive than the thermopile, and which would detect with certainty a radiation

[1] Wm. Huggins, *Proc. Roy. Soc.* vol. xvii. p. 309, 1869.

[2] E. J. Stone, *Proc. Roy. Soc.* vol. xviii. p. 159, 1869.

[3] Lord Rosse, *Proc. Roy. Soc.* vol. xvii. p. 436, 1869.

enormously less than that of the full moon, Boys[1] could find no
radiation effect from Arcturus or any other star or planet, and he
has consequently proved that no heating effect from the stars has
yet been observed.

274. Lummer and Kurlbaum's Bolometer.—An improved form
of bolometer has been constructed and used by Profs. Lummer and
Kurlbaum[2] for the purpose of studying the laws of radiation.   As in
Langley's instrument, the conductor exposed to the radiation consists
of a zig-zag strip of platinum cut from a single thin sheet of metal,
but instead of one such grating, four are used, all prepared in exactly
the same way; these form the four branches of the Wheatstone's
bridge.   The advantage of this arrangement is that, all four branches
being exactly similar, a slight change in the temperature of the
apparatus produces an equal effect on all the branches, so that the
balance is not disturbed, and the troublesome drift of the zero point
is avoided.   Besides, two gratings belonging to opposite arms of the
bridge are placed one immediately behind the other, so that the strips
of the one cover the gaps of the other, and both being exposed to the
same radiation, the effect is doubled.

In order to obtain four gratings of exactly the same character,
neither gold-leaf nor tin-foil nor platinum-foil could be used.   Tin-
foil or platinum-foil would be too thick for a very delicate instrument,
and gold-leaf is not sufficiently uniform in thickness.   The gratings
were constructed of platinum in the following way.

A sheet of platinum was attached by heat to a sheet of silver ten

Fig. 171.

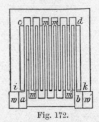

Fig. 172.

times as thick, and the whole rolled out till the thickness of the
platinum was reduced to 0·0005 of a millimetre or less.   Four similar
gratings of the shape shown in Fig. 171 were cut from the composite
sheet and fastened, by means of a solution of colophonium in ether,
to square frames of slate, as exhibited in Fig. 172.   When the grating
had been adjusted in a symmetrical position, the ether was driven off
by heat.   The ends a, b of the strip were soldered to copper contact

[1] C. V. Boys, *Proc. Roy. Soc.* vol. xlvii. p. 480, 1890.
[2] *Ann. der Physik*, Bd. 46, p. 204, 1892.

pieces w and w', and these, as well as the broad elbows of the strip $m\,m'$, covered with japan lacquer. The silver was dissolved off the parts not protected by the lacquer by means of nitric acid. After careful washing and drying, the platinum strips were blackened on one side by the smoke of a specially constructed lamp. In the later forms platinum black was used. Fig. 173 shows the appearance of the reverse side of the frame, which is exposed to the radiation. The slate is bevelled along the edges to which the grating is fastened.

Fig. 174 gives a diagrammatic representation of the connections. B is the battery, W an adjustable resistance, rr' a sliding-contact resistance or rheochord for obtaining an exact balance, and K_1, K_2, etc.,

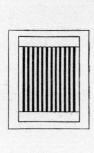

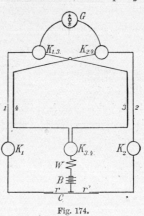

Fig. 173.   Fig. 174.

the copper contact pieces of the gratings. The gratings are numbered 1, 2, 3, 4, and it will be noticed that the opposite arms of the bridge are arranged together. Each bolometer grating has a resistance of about 60 ohms.

The complete instrument is represented in Fig. 175. The frames are fixed in pairs in india-rubber casings, h, h', which have openings ss to allow free passage of air between the frames. Part of one of the casings is removed in the figure, as well as a portion of each grating, so as to show the arrangement. The points K_1, K_2, $K_{3.4}$ are the same as in Fig. 174. A blackened metal plate g between the stands h and h' prevents any rays which penetrate between the strips of both gratings being reflected or allowed to fall on the other pair.

The platinum strips, being very thin, have a large surface compared to their mass, and hence, when exposed to radiation, equilibrium is attained in less than 4 seconds. Their relatively large cooling surface also admits of the use of a current density 40 times as great as is usual with thick resistances. The silver not being removed from the angles of the gratings, these have a small resistance, and the resistance of the exposed parts constitutes nearly the whole resistance of the arm of the bridge. The inventors claim that an accuracy of about 0·01 per cent can be attained with this instrument.'

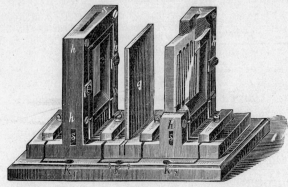

Fig. 175.

This bolometer is designed for the purpose of measuring the total radiation from a source. In order to measure the distribution of energy in a spectrum, a *line* bolometer must be used. In such an instrument, instead of a grating a single narrow strip of platinum is used. This should be made as thin as possible, if the delicacy of the instrument is to be preserved.

Line
bolometer.

SECTION V

DISTRIBUTION OF ENERGY IN THE SPECTRUM OF A BLACK BODY

275. Radiation in an Enclosure at Uniform Temperature.—
Let us now consider the nature of the radiation within an enclosure,
the walls of which are maintained at a uniform temperature. For convenience, we may suppose the temperature to be a red or white heat,
and that there is a small opening in the heated vessel through
which we can introduce various bodies and watch what is going on
inside.

If we introduce pieces of different coloured substances, such as red
or green glass, polished platinum or gold, etc., we shall find that these
bodies lose their distinctive appearance as soon as they have attained
the temperature of their surroundings; in fact, they will be indistinguishable from the walls of the enclosure. In the same way, it is
not easy to see bodies placed in the middle of a good fire, where the
above conditions are approximately realised.

This phenomenon is due to the equality of the radiation and
absorption of a body at a uniform temperature. The green glass, for
instance, powerfully absorbs the red rays coming from the back of the
enclosure, but it emits an equal quantity of red rays on its own
account, owing to its high temperature. This could be proved by
rapidly taking it out of the white-hot vessel and examining it in the
dark, when it would be seen to glow with a red light. A piece of red
glass under similar circumstances would glow with a greenish light.
For a somewhat similar reason molten copper shines with a greenish
blue light, and molten gold with a bluish green light. A piece of
polished metal placed in the enclosure would stop the rays coming
from the back of the enclosure, but would reflect those falling on its
surface, so that in this case also it would appear of exactly the
same colour as its surroundings. Common salt, being highly diathermanous, emits very little radiation when heated. If melted in a
crucible at a bright red heat it appears as bright as the crucible, but

when poured out, it looks almost like water, though there is a faint red glow on solidification.   Thus we see that, within a vessel at a uniform temperature, all bodies radiate in a similar way, if we include in their radiations the rays which they transmit, reflect, or scatter.

If we assume the principle that the radiations given out by a body depend only on its temperature and the nature of its substance, and not at all on the radiations which it receives,[1] we can show that the radiation within an enclosure at uniform temperature is independent, both as regards its character and intensity, of the nature of the material of which the walls of the vessel are made.   Suppose that we have within the enclosure two plates of the same material A and B (Fig. 176), and that A is receiving radiations from the external envelope

Fig. 176.

E.   If A and B are at the same constant temperature, equal amounts of energy will be radiated from A to B and from B to A.   A is therefore neither gaining nor losing energy on the side towards B; and as its temperature is not changing, it must be radiating towards E an amount of energy equal to that which it receives.   As, by the above principle, the radiation of A is the same on both sides, it must be sending to B the same quantity of energy which it receives from E.   And the *quality* as well as the *quantity* of the radiation which B receives from A must be similar to that of the radiation which A receives from E; for since the coefficient of absorption of a material depends on the quality (wave-length, etc.) of the incident radiation, B would not absorb the same proportion of the incident rays as A if the two radiations differed in character, which it must do, as it is at the same constant temperature.

We conclude, therefore, that a body in temperature equilibrium with its surroundings emits radiations precisely similar to those which it receives.   The radiations within an enclosure at uniform temperature will accordingly not be changed in character by altering the material of the walls either in part or in whole.

It ought to be borne in mind that such bodies as glass lose their characteristic radiating peculiarities only while they remain in such an enclosure, for when taken out of it and viewed in the dark, they resume those peculiarities; thus colourless glass gives out very little light, coal and black porcelain a great deal.   Indeed, it is only the light from a black body that represents by itself the brightness of the

---

[1] The rays given out by fluorescent and phosphorescent bodies depend on the radiations which they receive.   All such bodies are therefore to be excluded from the present discussion.

enclosure, and such a body when taken out and hastily examined in the dark, without allowing it time to cool, will be found to give out rays having a brightness in all respects the same as that of the enclosure in which it was placed, because, being opaque and non-reflective, all the light which it gave out in the enclosure was proper to itself, none having passed through its substance or been reflected from its surface ; it therefore retains this light when taken into the dark, provided its temperature is not in the meantime allowed to fall.

By considerations of this kind Kirchhoff was led to form the conception of a *perfectly black body*, *i.e.* a body which absorbs all the radiations which fall upon it, of whatever wave-length they may be. The radiation given out by such a body would possess a character independent of the property of any particular substance, for it would be the same as the radiation within an enclosure at uniform temperature.   We know of no substance which is perfectly black in this sense, but we can study the radiation within a uniformly heated enclosure, and thus investigate the properties of a perfectly black body.

Perfectly black body.

The important fundamental principle, proved above, and upon which the conception of a perfectly black body is based,—namely, that the radiation within a uniformly heated enclosure depends on the temperature of the enclosure and on nothing else,—was arrived at independently by Balfour Stewart and Kirchhoff about the year 1858.   In the discussion here given Balfour Stewart's line of reasoning is followed.[1]

Kirchhoff expressed the conviction that the laws governing the radiations within an enclosure at uniform temperature would be found to be of a simple character, like all known relations which do not depend on the specific properties of bodies.[2]

276. Emissive and Absorptive Powers—Kirchhoff's Law.—If radiations of a given wave-length λ fall on the surface of any body, then the absorptive power of the body for that wave-length, which we may denote by a_λ, is defined by Kirchhoff to be the *ratio of the radiant energy absorbed to the total incident radiant energy*.   Since a perfectly black body absorbs all the radiations which fall upon it, the value of a_λ for such a body is unity, whatever the wave-length may be ; but for all actual substances the absorptive power is a proper fraction, the value of which depends on the nature of the body, on its temperature, and on the wave-lengths of the incident radiation.   The more closely a body realises the conditions of a black body, the more nearly will the value of a_λ approach unity for all values of λ.

---

[1] See *Edin. Phil. Trans.*, March 1858 ; also Balfour Stewart's *Lessons in Elementary Physics.*

[2] *Pogg. Ann.* Bd. cix. p. 292, 1860.

If $e_\lambda d\lambda$ is the radiant energy comprised between wave-lengths λ and $\lambda + d\lambda$ which is given out per second by unit surface of any body, then, when $d\lambda$ is made infinitely small, the quantity e_λ is called the *emissive power* [1] of the body for the wave-length λ. The emissive power of a body is also a function of the wave-length, temperature, and the nature of the body. The *absolute* emissive power of a body is the emissive power of the body at a temperature of $1°$ absolute, *i.e.* the energy of wave-length λ radiated per second by unit surface to a surrounding enclosure at absolute zero.

Suppose that we have a heated chamber at uniform temperature, within which are pieces of different substances. As has been shown in the preceding article, the radiation within the chamber will be uniform and independent of the nature of the walls or enclosed bodies. Thus if dQ is the quantity of energy between wave-lengths λ and $\lambda + d\lambda$ received in one second by unit surface of any of the bodies, dQ will be the same for all bodies. Of this energy any body whose absorptive power is a_λ will absorb a fraction $a_\lambda dQ$, while the remainder $(1 - a_\lambda)dQ$ will be reflected or transmitted. If e_λ is the emissive power of the body for wave-length λ, the energy emitted will be $e_\lambda d\lambda$, if we consider only the emission proper to the body in virtue of its temperature. The total energy sent out by unit surface of the body is then $(1 - a_\lambda)dQ + e_\lambda d\lambda$, and this is equal to the energy received, so that

$$(1 - a_\lambda)dQ + e_\lambda d\lambda = dQ.$$

In the case of a perfectly black body, $a_\lambda = 1$, so that if E_λ is its emissive power we have

$$E_\lambda d\lambda = dQ,$$

therefore

$$(1 - a_\lambda)E_\lambda + e_\lambda = E_\lambda \quad . \quad . \quad . \quad . \quad . \quad (1)$$

or

$$e_\lambda = a_\lambda E_\lambda,$$

Kirchhoff's law.
so that, *for radiations of the same wave-length and the same temperature, the emissive power divided by the absorptive power is the same for all bodies and is equal to the emissive power of a perfectly black body.* This is known as Kirchhoff's law.

In the case of bodies like metals, which transmit none of the radiations, the energy which is not absorbed is reflected, so that we may put

$$R_\lambda = 1 - a_\lambda,$$

where R_λ is the *reflecting power* for wave-length λ. Equation (1) of

---

[1] See an article by O. Lummer in the *Rapports présentés au Congrès International de Physique*, Paris, 1900. The definitions of absorptive and emissive powers here given are not those usually followed.

this article may then be written

$$E_\lambda = e_\lambda + E_\lambda R_\lambda,$$

which expresses the fact that if we restore to any body the radiations which escape it by reason of its reflecting power, it will radiate as a black body.

In what precedes the radiation spoken of must be understood to be completely diffused, that is, the rays are travelling equally in all directions.

If we consider a small element of area ds of a radiating surface, and confine our attention to rays of wave-lengths included within the limits λ and $\lambda + d\lambda$, we see that the quantity of energy radiated per second within a small solid angle $d\omega$ in a direction perpendicular to ds may be expressed in the form $i_\lambda ds d\omega d\lambda$, where i_λ is a constant for each wave-length λ, and depends only on the nature of the body and its temperature.

The energy emitted per second in a direction OA (Fig. 177), making an angle θ with the normal to ds, and comprised within a small solid angle $d\omega$, is, by the law of cosines, equal to $i_\lambda \cos\theta\, ds\, d\omega\, d\lambda$. To find the total energy per second, draw a hemisphere of radius r round O as centre ; then the area of the ring-element of area ABB′A′ is $2\pi r^2 \sin\theta\, d\theta$,

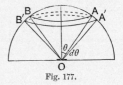

Fig. 177.

and the solid angle which it subtends at O is $2\pi \sin\theta\, d\theta$, so that the energy per second emitted within this solid angle is

$$2\pi i_\lambda \sin\theta \cos\theta\, ds\, d\lambda\, d\theta \qquad . \quad . \quad . \quad . \quad (2)$$

and we have, by integration, since the total energy emitted in all directions is $e_\lambda ds d\lambda$,

$$e_\lambda ds d\lambda = 2\pi i_\lambda ds d\lambda \int_0^{\frac{\pi}{2}} \sin\theta \cos\theta\, d\theta,$$

or

$$e_\lambda = \pi i_\lambda \qquad . \quad . \quad . \quad . \quad . \quad (3)$$

We can also express the density of the energy in a space uniformly filled with radiations in terms of the emissive power. For if we draw a plane AB (Fig. 178) parallel to a radiating plane XY at a distance h

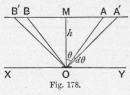

Fig. 178.

from it ; then the energy radiated per second by an element of surface ds is, for the same solid angle, $2\pi i_\lambda \sin\theta \cos\theta\, ds\, d\lambda\, d\theta$ by (2). Now the distance OA is $h \sec\theta$, therefore if c is the velocity of light, the time taken to reach A is $h \sec\theta / c$, and the energy sent out in this time, that is, the energy which fills the small space described by the revolution of OAA′ round

Density of energy.

OM, is

$$2\pi i_\lambda \frac{h}{c}\sin\theta\, ds d\lambda d\theta.$$

If we suppose h very small, then we may integrate for θ from 0 to $\frac{\pi}{2}$, therefore the energy between the planes due to ds is

$$2\pi i_\lambda \frac{h}{c}ds d\lambda \int_0^{\frac{\pi}{2}}\sin\theta\, d\theta = 2\pi i_\lambda \frac{h}{c}ds d\lambda.$$

But if $d\psi$ is the energy per unit volume, the space between the planes, at a distance from their edges, contains for every element ds a quantity of energy $d\psi h ds$, therefore

$$d\psi = \frac{4\pi i_\lambda}{c}d\lambda = \frac{4e_\lambda}{c}d\lambda \quad . \quad . \quad . \quad . \quad . \quad (4)$$

where the expression is doubled, so as to include the equal number of rays which are travelling *towards* XY.

Intensity.   For a perfectly black body $d\psi = \dfrac{4\mathrm{E}_\lambda}{c}d\lambda$. We shall call the quantity $4\mathrm{E}_\lambda/c$ the *intensity* of black-body radiation for the wave-length λ.

The total emission S from unit surface for all radiations is given by the equation

$$S = \int_0^\infty e_\lambda d\lambda = \pi \int_0^\infty i_\lambda d\lambda = \frac{\psi c}{4},$$

where ψ is the density for all radiations in an enclosed space at uniform temperature.

If for any body the value of the absorptive power a_λ were a constant for all values of λ, we should have

$$S = \int_0^\infty a_\lambda \mathrm{E}_\lambda d\lambda = a_\lambda \int_0^\infty \mathrm{E}_\lambda d\lambda.$$

A body of this nature would be called a *perfectly grey body*, and its radiation would be, for all wave-lengths, proportional to that of a perfectly black body. No systematic search has been made for such a substance.

277. Stefan's Law.—In 1879 J. Stefan [1] suggested the law that the total radiation of any body is proportional to the fourth power of its absolute temperature. He was led to this conclusion by the result of an experiment of Tyndall's in which the radiations of a platinum wire at a white heat ($1200°$ C.) and at a red heat ($525°$ C.) were in the ratio $11·7$. Stefan noticed that the ratio $\dfrac{(1200+273)^4}{(525+273)^4}$ is equal to $11·6$. On testing the law by the results of Dulong and Petit's

[1] *Wien. Akad. Sitz.* Bd. lxxix. p. 391, 1879.

experiments, he found that it was well satisfied. Other observers found considerable deviations from this law. We shall see presently (Art. 279) that for the radiation of a black body Stefan's law has been verified by Lummer and Pringsheim. It is not strictly true for other bodies. In using this law we must take account of the radiation received by the black body. Thus if its absolute temperature is Θ, and it radiates to surroundings at $0°$ C., the energy lost per second by unit area is

$$S = \sigma(\Theta^4 - 273^4),$$

where σ is a constant.

This law has been theoretically deduced by L. Boltzmann[1] from the principles of thermodynamics and the electromagnetic theory of light, and hence is often referred to as the Stefan-Boltzmann law (see Art. 281).

278. Distribution of Energy in the Spectrum. — The earlier experiments on the distribution of energy in the spectrum were made on the spectrum of the sun. In 1800 Herschel discovered the existence of the invisible infra-red rays by observing the heating effect on a thermometer placed beyond the red end of the solar spectrum. Herschel found the maximum of energy to be situated in the infra-red. Before him Landriani, Rochon, and Sennebier had found the maximum energy in the yellow or red. Later still Seebeck, employing prisms of different materials to produce the spectrum, found that with flint glass the maximum calorific effect was in the infra-red; with crown glass, in the red; and with water and other substances, in the yellow. Melloni showed that these differences could be accounted for by the absorption of the rays by the material of the prism. Using the most diathermanous substance, rock-salt, he found the maximum energy to be in the infra-red.

It is obvious that the distribution of energy will depend on the dispersion of the prism as well as on its selective absorption. The normal spectrum obtained by the use of a diffraction grating was first employed by Draper. His experiments indicated that the maximum heating effect in the solar spectrum was situated in the yellow. The diffraction grating does not appear, however, to give very satisfactory results. The spectra overlap, the dark part of the first spectrum being superposed on the visible part of the second, and so on.

The best way to determine the law of distribution in the normal spectrum is to find the distribution in an ordinary refraction spectrum and calculate the corresponding distribution in the normal spectrum,

[1] *Wied. Ann.* Bd. xxii pp. 31 and 291, 1884.

knowing the relative dispersion. Lundquist, employing Cauchy's formula of dispersion, first adopted this method. He also made allowance for the width of the thermopile.

The results so far obtained were not of a high order of precision, as the thermopile, which was the instrument used for measuring the energy of the radiations, is not, in its ordinary form, capable of very great accuracy. But after the invention of the bolometer by Langley, great progress began to be made in these measurements.

279. Experiments of Lummer and Pringsheim.[1] — The laws governing the radiations within an enclosed space at uniform temperature have been experimentally studied by a number of physicists, amongst whom Professors Lummer and Pringsheim hold an important place. We shall describe here the method of investigation pursued by

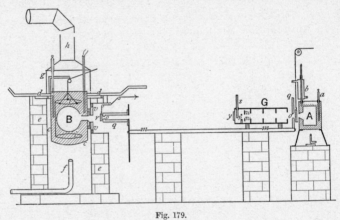

Fig. 179.

them in studying the variation with temperature of the total radiation from such an enclosure, and the distribution of energy in its spectrum. In future it will be generally convenient, when speaking of the radiation within a uniformly heated enclosure, to refer to such an enclosure as a " black body ".

The experiments on the total radiation from a black body were carried out for a range of temperature between 100° and 1300° C. The apparatus is shown in Fig. 179.

A is a double-walled vessel of sheet copper blackened inside. The space between the walls contains water which is kept boiling. A condenser b prevents the escape of steam into the room. The temperature of the water is given by the thermometer a. The vessel A is used to standardise the instrument which measures the radiation.

---

[1] *Ann. der Physik*, Bd. lxiii. p. 395, 1897.

Between the temperatures 200° and 600° C. a copper sphere B, coated inside with platinum black, was used. It was enclosed in an iron vessel *cc* filled with a mixture of sodium and potassium nitrates which melts at 219° C. It was heated by a burner *f*, which was supplied with a regulated supply of gas and air, so that the temperature could be kept constant. To secure uniformity in heating, the gases of combustion passed all round *cc*, and a stirrer *ii* was used to equalise the temperature of the nitre bath. The temperature was measured by a high-pressure mercury thermometer and by a thermo-element. The opening of B was surrounded by a vessel *vv* through which a current of water at atmospheric temperature flowed. At each end of the bench *mm* was fixed a diaphragm *q* with a movable shutter *r*, through both which a current of water at atmospheric temperature also flowed. The temperature of the water could be accurately

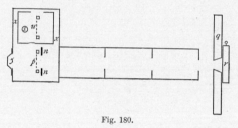

Fig. 180.

regulated. The water-filled vessels *vv* and *q* protected the bolometer from radiation from the outside of the heated chamber.

The radiant energy was measured by means of a Lummer-Kurlbaum bolometer G, represented on a larger scale in Fig. 180. Its distance from the black body could be varied by running it along the bench *mm* (Fig. 179). The two pairs of gratings of the bolometer (see Art. 274) are shown at *p* and *u*. The radiation reaches *p* through a number of stops, the narrowest one, *ww*, being just in front of the grating. The inside of the casing and the surfaces of the stops were covered, partly with felt and partly with black velvet. The other pair of gratings *u* were further protected from extraneous radiation by being enclosed in a cardboard box *xx*, in which a thermometer *s* is placed. The door *y* is for the purpose of putting the instrument in alignment with the direction of the radiation.

For temperatures between 600° and 1300° C. an iron cylinder (Fig. 181) was substituted for the copper sphere B. It was coated within with platinum black. A porcelain tube containing a Le Chatelier thermo-element passed through from side to side. The cylinder was enclosed in a double-walled gas-furnace. The temperatures were reduced to the scale of the nitrogen thermometer from the results of Holborn and Day's comparisons.[1]

In making an observation, the shutter r was raised, allowing the radiation to fall on the surface of the bolometer. As soon as the galvanometer needle had reached the end of its swing the shutter was closed, the point reached by the spot of light on the galvanometer scale being noted. In some experiments at high temperatures, the needle did not completely return to its original position; the mean of the initial and final positions was then taken as the zero.

In order to show that the deflection of the spot of light was proportional to the energy of the incident radiation, the bolometer G was placed facing the black body A, and the deflection at various distances along the bench was noted. It was found that the law of inverse squares was satisfied, *i.e.* that the deflection was inversely

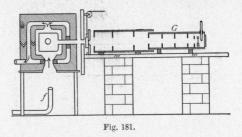

Fig. 181.

proportional to the square of the distance of the bolometer grating from the diaphragm aperture of the black body.

It was arranged that the deflection of the spot of light should be about 300 mm. for all temperatures. This was managed in any one of three ways : (1) by altering the sensitiveness of the instrument by means of a variable resistance which regulated the current from the battery through the Wheatstone's bridge ; (2) by altering the distance of the bolometer from the black body ; and (3) by varying the size of the aperture of the stop *ww*. The last method was, however, not adopted finally.

In using the boiling-water vessel as a standard of reference, its temperature was taken to be 100° C. and that of the shutter as 17° C., or 373° and 290° absolute respectively. The small variations in these temperatures were corrected for by assuming Stefan's law (see Art. 277); thus, to take a particular case, the swing of the galvanometer needle was 336·9 scale divisions when the absolute temperatures of the boiling water and shutter were 373·1° and 287·1° respectively. The

[1] L. Holborn and A. Day, *Ann. der Physik*, Bd. ii. p. 505, 1900.

corrected swing x was then calculated from the formula

$$\frac{x}{336\cdot9} = \frac{373\cdot0^4 - 290\cdot0^4}{373\cdot1^4 - 287\cdot1^4},$$

whence

$$x = 328\cdot9.$$

All the observations were reduced to a standard condition in which the distance was 633 mm., the shutter temperature 17° C., and the variable resistance 100 ohms. The diameter of the stop ww was 16 mm. in all experiments.

Assuming Stefan's law, that the total radiation of a black body is proportional to the fourth power of the absolute temperature, we have the equation

$$\delta = \sigma(\Theta^4 - 290^4) \qquad . \quad . \quad . \quad . \quad . \quad (1)$$

when δ is the deviation of the needle, and σ a constant. In the following table given by Lummer and Pringsheim the temperatures calculated in the fourth column are got by putting for σ in the above equation its mean value 123·8 and computing the values of Θ.

Temperature (absolute).	Deviation (reduced).	$\sigma \times 10^{10}$.	Θ (calculated).	Θ obs. — Θ calc.
°			°	°
373·1	156	127	374·6	− 1·5
492·5	638	124	492·0	+ 0·5
723	3320	124·8	724·3	− 1·3
745	3810	126·6	749·1	− 4·1
810	5150	121·6	806·5	+ 3·5
868	6910	123·3	867·1	+ 0·9
1378	44700	124·2	1379	− 1
1470	57400	123·1	1468	+ 2
1497	60600	120·9	1488	+ 9
1535	67800	122·3	1531	+ 4

In this table three results have been omitted which showed a discrepancy of more than 10°. These were all performed with the iron cylinder at temperatures better suited for the nitre bath. When the combustion in the furnace was not sufficiently rapid, equilibrium of temperature was only imperfectly realised.

It will be seen that the value of σ shows no systematic variation, and consequently the truth of Stefan's law may be regarded as established.

If in equation (1) we put S for δ where S is the total loss of energy of unit surface (see Art. 277), then σ is the absolute emission of a black body. Kurlbaum found the value of σ to be $5\cdot32 \times 10^{-5}$ in C.G.S. units. For later determinations see Art. 286.

280. Distribution of Energy in the Spectrum of a Black Body.—

Experiments were also made by Lummer and Pringsheim[1] to determine the distribution of energy in the spectrum of a black body. For this purpose the spectrum was produced by refraction through a prism of fluor-spar, which is very transparent to infra-red radiations. It has indeed two strong absorption bands in the extreme infra-red (see Art. 284), but these are beyond the range of Lummer and Pringsheim's experiments, which extended from wave-lengths of 6μ up to about the beginning of the visible spectrum.[2] As the use of lenses would be inadmissible, the image of the slit was formed by means of a concave mirror.   The extent of the part of the spectrum used was

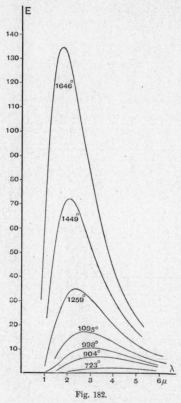

Fig. 182.

55 times the width of the image of the slit. The radiations were produced by means of an electrically heated cylindrical chamber, the temperature of which was measured by a thermo-element. A Lummer-Kurlbaum linear bolometer was employed to measure the radiant energy, the width being ·6 mm. and the thickness 0·001 mm.; its resistance for a length of 10 mm. was 16 ohms. The results were reduced to those for the normal spectrum by employing the Ketteler-Helmholtz formula of dispersion, the constants of which for fluor-spar have been determined by Paschen.[3]

As the platinum strip of the bolometer has a certain width, it will measure the energy of the radiation for a finite, though small, range comprised between certain wave-lengths λ and $\lambda + \delta\lambda$. It does not therefore strictly measure the intensity of emission for a definite wave-length, but its mean value over a small range.   Also as the image of the slit has a finite width, the

[1] *Verh. der Deutsch. Phys. Ges.*, Feb. 1899 ; *Ann. der Physik*, Bd. vi. p. 192, 1901.

[2] A *micron* or ·001 mm. is generally denoted by μ. The range of the visible spectrum is from about $0\cdot7\mu$ (red) to $0\cdot4\mu$ (violet).

[3] *Wied. Ann.* Bd. liii. p. 301, 1894.

spectrum is not quite pure. A method of correcting for the width of the slit and of the bolometer is given in Art. 287.

The results of Lummer and Pringsheim's observations are exhibited in Fig. 182, where the ordinates are intensities or emissive powers (which are proportional), and the abscissæ are wave-lengths. The total energy of radiation for a given temperature is represented by the area between the curve and the horizontal axis. This area increases according to the fourth power of the absolute temperature, according to Stefan's law.

Experiments have also been carried out by several observers on the visible part of the spectrum, using a photometer instead of a bolometer, as the energy is very small. These, as well as the curves of Fig. 182, will be discussed subsequently.

281. Boltzmann's Proof of Stefan's Law.—According to the *Pressure of radiation.* electromagnetic theory of light, when light is incident perpendicularly on a plane surface which is perfectly reflecting, it exerts a pressure on the surface equal to the density of the energy of the radiation.[1] If, instead of a parallel beam, the light is incident in all directions, then the pressure is equal to one-third of the density of the energy (compare the case of the pressure of a gas, Art. 55). If then a reflecting surface be moved against incident radiation, work must be done. The demonstration of Stefan's law depends on the application of this principle to an imaginary process suggested by Bartoli.

Let AC (Fig. 183) be a cylinder of unit section and of length a, whose sides are perfectly reflecting, but the end AB is a perfectly black body at absolute temperature Θ. The cylinder is closed by a perfectly reflecting piston P. Let P be at any distance x from AB. Then the space between P and AB, whose volume is x, is filled with diffused radiations of a density ψ corresponding to

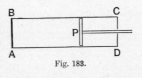

Fig. 183.

the temperature Θ of AB. When equilibrium is established, let the temperature of AB be changed to $\Theta + d\Theta$, and let the piston be drawn out a distance dx and equilibrium restored; then writing down the thermodynamic equation of work (see Art. 321)

$$dQ = dU + dW,$$

which expresses the fact that the total energy dQ supplied is expended partly in increasing the internal energy of radiation by an amount dU, and partly in doing external work dW, we have, since $U = x\psi$ and $dW = p\,dx = \frac{1}{3}\psi\,dx$,

[1] See Clerk Maxwell's *Electricity and Magnetism*, vol. ii. p. 440.

$$dQ = d(x\psi) + \tfrac{1}{3}\psi \, dx$$

$$= x\, d\psi + \tfrac{4}{3}\psi \, dx.$$

If ϕ is the entropy (Art. 331) of the radiation,

$$d\phi = \frac{dQ}{\Theta} = \frac{x}{\Theta}\, d\psi + \frac{4\psi}{3\Theta}\, dx,$$

and, as $d\phi$ is a perfect differential, we have

$$d\phi = \frac{\partial \phi}{\partial \psi}\, d\psi + \frac{\partial \phi}{\partial x}\, dx.$$

Comparing this equation with the previous one, we get

$$\frac{\partial \phi}{\partial \psi} = \frac{x}{\Theta}, \quad \frac{\partial \phi}{\partial x} = \frac{4\psi}{3\Theta},$$

whence

$$\frac{\partial^2 \phi}{\partial \psi \partial x} = \frac{\partial}{\partial x}\left(\frac{x}{\Theta}\right) = \frac{4}{3}\frac{\partial}{\partial \psi}\left(\frac{\psi}{\Theta}\right),$$

and as Θ is independent of x, being a function of ψ only, the last equation becomes

$$\frac{1}{\Theta} = \frac{4}{3}\left(\frac{1}{\Theta} - \frac{\psi}{\Theta^2}\frac{d\Theta}{d\psi}\right),$$

or

$$\frac{d\psi}{\psi} = \frac{4\, d\Theta}{\Theta},$$

the integral of which is

$$\psi = b\Theta^4$$

where b is a constant. This proves Stefan's law.

282. Permanence of Black-body Radiation during Adiabatic Expansion—Change of Wave-length.—If a chamber whose walls are perfect reflectors is filled with radiations, then the wave-length of any ray is not altered by reflection at the boundary as long as the reflecting surface is at rest. If, however, the volume is increased, as in the case considered in the last article, then, by Doppler's principle, the wave-length is increased when reflection takes place at the moving surface. Similarly, the wave-length would be diminished if reflection took place at a surface which was moving towards the incident beam. The density of the energy of the radiation also changes on expansion, partly because it is distributed over a larger volume and partly because some of the energy is expended in doing work. The question then arises whether, if the vessel were originally filled with black-body radiation, it would still be black-body radiation after the expansion. Let us suppose, if possible, that after expansion or compression, the radiation does not correspond to that of a black body. Let a cylinder whose sides are perfectly reflecting be divided into two parts D, E by a piston (Fig. 184), and let one end of the cylinder be in communication with a black-body reservoir at temperature T_2, while the other end is in communication with a black body at a

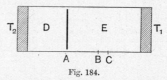

Fig. 184.

lower temperature T_1. We shall suppose that the piston is perfectly reflecting and has a hole in it which can be left open, or closed by a perfectly reflecting shutter, or covered by a diaphragm of selectively transmitting material, also that T_1 can be shut off at will by a perfectly reflecting shutter. At starting, let the piston be at A and reflect perfectly and let T_1 be uncovered. Then D and E are filled with radiations corresponding to the temperatures T_2 and T_1 respectively. Then the following cycle of operations can be performed :—

(1) T_1 is shut off and the piston allowed to advance to B, till the pressure is the same on both sides. E is now filled with radiations which have the same density of energy as those in D but are, by hypothesis, differently distributed, some kinds of radiation being in excess and some in defect. Let the material of the diaphragm in the piston be so chosen that it will transmit those radiations which are in excess and not those which are in defect.

(2) The diaphragm in the piston is exposed, so that some radiations pass back into D. The piston is advanced to C till the pressures are again equalised.

(3) The hole in the piston is opened, and the radiations allowed to mix. The piston is drawn back to B. No work is done, since the pressure is the same on both sides.

(4) The piston is made perfectly reflecting once more, and drawn back to A. Since the pressure depends on the density of the energy only, and not on its distribution, the work done on the system in this stage is equal to the work done by it in (1). T_1 is uncovered again, and the radiation in E recovers its original distribution.

When T_1 is uncovered at the end of the cycle the density of energy in E is the same as it was at the first (though its distribution is not), it therefore neither receives energy from nor gives energy to T_1. In this cycle we have obtained useful work in (2) at the expense of the black body T_2 only. As this is contrary to the second law of thermodynamics, we infer that the original assumption was false, and that if an enclosure, bounded by perfectly reflecting walls, is filled with black radiation, *i.e.* with radiation corresponding to that of a black body at a definite temperature, and if the volume is changed adiabatically, then the radiation will still be black radiation corresponding to some new definite temperature.[1]

To find the change in wave-length suffered by a ray reflected at a moving surface, suppose the mirror AX (Fig. 185) to be moving

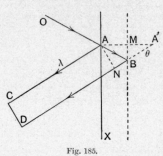

Fig. 185.

with a velocity u in the direction AA′ perpendicular to itself, and let the ray OA be incident at an angle θ. Draw AC in the direction of the reflected ray, and equal to the wave-length λ. When any wave-crest has reached C after reflection at A, the succeeding one will be at A, but instead of being reflected at A it will, since the mirror has moved, go on in the direction OA, and overtake the mirror at some point B, being then reflected along BD parallel to AC. The distance of the second wave-crest behind the first is thus increased from AC to AB + BD, and the increase $\delta\lambda$ in the wave-length is consequently AB + BN, where AN is perpendicular to BD. If A′ is the image of A in the second position of the mirror, AB + BN = A′N = AA′ cos θ. The time taken by the ray to travel over AC and the mirror to recede from A to M is the same,[2] therefore AM/u = λ/c, when c is the velocity of light, so that we get

$$\delta\lambda = 2\text{AM} \cos\theta = \frac{2\lambda u \cos\theta}{c} \qquad . \qquad . \qquad . \qquad . \qquad (1)$$

[1] The mode of presenting the argument is that given in O. W. Richardson's *Electron Theory of Matter*, p. 337. It may be instructive to compare the process with the following, which does not contradict the second law of thermodynamics. Replace the black bodies T_1 and T_2 by reservoirs containing mixtures of hydrogen and nitrogen at temperatures T_1 and T_2 respectively, the reservoir at the lower temperature containing a larger proportion of hydrogen. Let the pressures be such that either can be reduced to the temperature and pressure of the other by adiabatic compression or expansion. For the selectively transmitting diaphragm substitute a sheet of palladium which transmits hydrogen but not nitrogen. For perfectly reflecting read non-conducting. The process above described can then be imitated, work being obtained apparently at the expense of T_2, since neither the energy nor the amount of gas in T_1 is altered. But the process is not a true cycle, because the hydrogen in T_1 is being exchanged for nitrogen from T_2. In the radiation process the black body T_1 need not be a reservoir, it may be supposed as small as we please. We assume, of course, that by the theory of exchanges a black body placed in contact with radiations of an energy-density corresponding to its own temperature will adjust the distribution also to correspond.

[2] Neglecting the time taken by the second ray to traverse AB, *i.e.* neglecting the square and higher powers of u/c, which is always a very small quantity.

283. Wien's General Formula for the Distribution of Energy.[1]
—Let us consider now the case of a perfectly reflecting chamber
which is filled with black-body radiation and is expanding.
The change in wave-length of any ray in a given time depends on
the number of reflections and the angle of incidence at each reflection. Thus, if the chamber is a cylinder with a moving piston, it is
clear that of all rays having a wave-length λ, the wave-length will
increase more rapidly for those which strike the piston at a small
rather than at a large angle of incidence, for the change will not
only be greater at each reflection, but also the reflections will occur
at shorter intervals. It will be more convenient for our purpose to
suppose that the shape of the chamber is irregular, and that it
expands in such a way that if we trace the path of any particular
ray we shall find that the angle of incidence is sometimes small and
sometimes large, and that the path between two successive reflections is sometimes long and sometimes short, and in fact that the
average history of any ray during a definite period is the same,
whatever ray we take.

By formulæ (2) and (3), Art. 276, the energy emitted in time
dt by an element of surface ds of a black body is, for radiation of
wave-length between λ and $\lambda + d\lambda$, whose angle of emission lies
between θ and $\theta + d\theta$,

$$2\mathrm{E}_\lambda \sin \theta \cos \theta \, ds \, d\lambda \, d\theta \, dt,$$

and this is therefore the amount of energy of the same angle of
incidence, and the same wave-length incident in time dt on an element
of surface ds of the chamber. But by formula (4) of the same article,
if V is the volume of the chamber, the whole energy for which the
wave-length lies between λ and $\lambda + d\lambda$ is

$$\frac{4\mathrm{E}_\lambda \mathrm{V}}{c} d\lambda,$$

therefore the fraction of this energy which suffers a change of wave-
length in time dt is

$$\frac{c \sin \theta \cos \theta \, ds \, d\theta \, dt}{2\mathrm{V}}.$$

Multiplying by the value of $\delta\lambda$ given in (1) of the last article, we
see that the average change of wave-length is

$$\frac{\lambda u \sin \theta \cos^2 \theta \, d\theta \, ds \, dt}{\mathrm{V}}.$$

Now, if $\delta\mathrm{V}$ is the total change in volume, $\delta\mathrm{V} = dt \int u \, ds$, therefore,

---

[1] W. Wien, *Rapports présentés au Congrès International de Physique*, Paris,
1900, vol. i. ; *Ann. der Physik*, Bd. lviii. p. 662, 1896. As Wien's demonstration
is open to objection, a modified form of the proof of his theorem, due to Professor
W. M'F. Orr, is here given.

summing the changes due to every element of surface and every angle of incidence, we get for the average change of wave-length $\delta\lambda$

$$\delta\lambda = \lambda\frac{\delta V}{V}\int_0^{\frac{\pi}{2}}\sin\theta\cos^2\theta d\theta = \tfrac{1}{3}\lambda\frac{\delta V}{V},$$

or

$$\frac{\delta\lambda}{\lambda} = \tfrac{1}{3}\frac{\delta V}{V},$$

whence

$$\lambda V^{-\frac{1}{3}} = \text{const.}$$

or

$$\frac{\lambda^3}{\lambda^3_0} = \frac{V}{V_0},$$

where λ_0 and V_0 are the original and λ and V the final values. We may express this result by saying that when the chamber expands without altering its shape the change in wave-length is proportional to the linear dimension. Thus, if r_0 is the original value of any linear dimension and r its final value,

$$\frac{\lambda}{\lambda_0} = \frac{r}{r_0} \quad . \quad . \quad . \quad . \quad . \quad (1)$$

To find the change in the energy-density ψ, we observe that the loss of energy is equal to the work done, or, since $V\psi$ is the total energy,

$$d(V\psi) = -dW = -pdV = -\tfrac{1}{3}\psi dV \quad . \quad . \quad . \quad \text{(Art. 281)}$$

whence

$$Vd\psi + \tfrac{4}{3}\psi dV = 0,$$

which on integration gives

$$\frac{\psi}{\psi_0} = \left(\frac{V_0}{V}\right)^{\frac{4}{3}} = \left(\frac{r_0}{r}\right)^4 = \left(\frac{\lambda_0}{\lambda}\right)^4 \quad . \quad . \quad . \quad . \quad (2)$$

But, by Stefan's law,

$$\frac{\psi}{\psi_0} = \left(\frac{\Theta}{\Theta_0}\right)^4,$$

therefore

$$\frac{\Theta}{\Theta_0} = \frac{\lambda_0}{\lambda},$$

or

$$\lambda\Theta = \text{const.} \quad . \quad . \quad . \quad . \quad . \quad . \quad (3)$$

Wien's displacement law.

This important equation expresses the fact that if radiation of a particular wave-length whose intensity corresponds to a definite temperature is adiabatically altered to another wave-length, then the temperature changes in the inverse ratio. This is known as Wien's displacement law.

We should arrive also at the same result if we supposed the enclosure to be of such a shape and to expand in such a manner that the greater change in wave-length of a ray incident at a small angle is exactly compensated for by the length of path described between successive reflections. Thus if the enclosure is a sphere which expands uniformly, then a ray whose angle of incidence is θ has travelled a distance $2r\cos\theta$ since its last reflection, where r is the radius of the sphere. If t is the time taken to describe this path, $t = 2r\cos\theta/c$, therefore since the wave-length changes by $2\lambda u \cos\theta/c$ in time t, the change per second is $\delta\lambda = \lambda u/r$. But if δr is the increase of radius per second, $\delta r = u$, therefore $\delta\lambda/\lambda = \delta r/r = \frac{1}{3}\delta V/V$ as before. This is the case considered by Wien.

Again, we may take the chamber to be a rectangular box which expands so as always to be similar to itself. Let three sides be kept fixed in position, and let δx, δy, δz (supposed small) be the increments per second of the dimensions x, y, z of the box. Then if α, β, γ are the direction angles of any ray, the number of reflections per second on the moving face perpendicular to the axis of x is $c\cos\alpha/2x$ and the increase of λ at each is $2\lambda\cos\alpha\,\delta x/c$, therefore the increase of wave-length per second is

$$\delta\lambda = \lambda\left(\frac{\delta x}{x}\cos^2\alpha + \frac{\delta y}{y}\cos^2\beta + \frac{\delta z}{z}\cos^2\gamma\right) = \lambda\frac{\delta x}{x},$$

since $\delta x/x = \delta y/y = \delta z/z$ by hypothesis. But $V = xyz$, therefore $\delta V/V = \delta x/x + \delta y/y + \delta z/z = 3\delta x/x$, so that $\delta\lambda/\lambda = \frac{1}{3}\delta V/V$ as before.

In the chamber which we have been considering there exist radiations of all wave-lengths. These are perfectly independent of each other, and all have their wave-lengths altered in the same ratio by equation (1). The intensity I_λ and emissive power E_λ vary as the fifth power of the absolute temperature. For let $r/r_0 = k$, then if we confine our attention to radiations of wave-lengths comprised between the values λ_0 and $\lambda_0 + d\lambda_0$, these limits become altered to λ and $\lambda + d\lambda$, and as $\lambda = k\lambda_0$, and $\lambda + d\lambda = k(\lambda_0 + d\lambda_0)$ by (1) we have $d\lambda = kd\lambda_0$. If $d\psi_0$ is the original density of these radiations, this changes to $d\psi$, where $d\psi_0 = k^4 d\psi$ by (2). But $d\psi$ is proportional to $E_\lambda d\lambda$ (Art. 276), therefore

$$\frac{E_\lambda d\lambda}{E_{\lambda_0} d\lambda_0} = \frac{d\psi}{d\psi_0} = \frac{1}{k^4},$$

therefore

$$\frac{E_\lambda}{E_{\lambda_0}} = \frac{1}{k^5} = \frac{\Theta^5}{\Theta_0^{\,5}}.\qquad\cdot\qquad\cdot\qquad\cdot\qquad\cdot\qquad\cdot\qquad(4)$$

Combining (3) and (4), we obtain

$$E_\lambda \lambda^5 = \text{const.} = Cf(\lambda\Theta),$$

or

$$E_\lambda = C\lambda^{-5}f(\lambda\Theta) \qquad . \qquad . \qquad . \qquad . \qquad (5)$$

where C is an absolute constant.

Equation (5) is a general formula for the distribution of energy in the spectrum. It contains, however, an unknown function of $\lambda\Theta$. In the next article we shall discuss the various forms which have been suggested for this function. But whatever the form given to the function, the equation satisfies Wien's displacement law and Stefan's law, provided that $\int_0^\infty z^{-5}f(z)dz$ is finite. For the total energy S, which is equal to $\int_0^\infty E_\lambda d\lambda$, must be finite, and putting $\lambda\Theta = z$, we have $dz = \Theta d\lambda$, and therefore

$$S = C\int_0^\infty \lambda^{-5}f(\lambda\Theta)d\lambda$$

$$= C\int_0^\infty \frac{\Theta^5}{z^5}f(z)\frac{dz}{\Theta}$$

$$= C\Theta^4\int_0^\infty z^{-5}f(z)dz \qquad . \qquad . \qquad . \qquad . \qquad (6)$$

Wien's displacement law has been verified by Lummer and Pringsheim and others. If we suppose the change from one temperature to a higher one to take place by means of an adiabatic compression, then, by Wien's law, the new curve of distribution (Fig. 182) is got from the first one by shifting each ordinate towards the origin in the ratio of distances $\Theta_0 : \Theta$, and increasing its height in the ratio $\Theta^5 : \Theta_0^5$. Thus to a maximum ordinate E_{m_0} in the first curve corresponds the maximum ordinate E_m of the second; and therefore if λ_m is the abscissa of a maximum ordinate,

$$\lambda_m\Theta = \text{const.} = A \text{ (say)},$$

$$E_m\Theta^{-5} = \text{const.} = B.$$

The following table exhibits the results of Lummer and Pringsheim's experiments. The temperatures given in the sixth column were calculated by putting the *mean* value of B ($= 2188 \times 10^{-17}$) in the formula.

[TABLE

Abs. Temp. (observed).	λ_m.	E_m.	$A = \lambda_m \Theta$.	$B = E_m \Theta^{-5}$ ($\times 10^{17}$).	$T = \sqrt[5]{\dfrac{E_m}{B}}$	Diff.
621·2	4·53	2·026	2814	2190	621·3	+0·1
723	4·08	4·28	2950	2166	721·5	−1·5
908·5	3·28	13·66	2980	2208	910·1	+1·6
998·5	2·96	21·50	2956	2166	996·5	−2·0
1094·5	2·71	34·0	2966	2164	1092·3	−2·2
1259·0	2·35	68·8	2959	2176	1257·5	−1·5
1460·4	2·04	145·0	2979	2184	1460·0	−0·4
1646	1·78	270·6	2928	2246	1653·5	+7·5

Since the wave-length is measured in microns (see footnote, p. 550) the mean value of $\lambda_m \Theta$ is 0·2940 in C.G.S. units.

284. Formulæ for the Law of Distribution.—We shall now give the principal formulæ which have been proposed for the law of distribution of energy in the spectrum of a black body. All such formulæ must conform to Wien's general law expressed by equation (5), p. 558, which we shall now write

$$E = C\lambda^{-5} f(\lambda\Theta) \quad . \quad . \quad . \quad . \quad . \quad (1)$$

where E may be taken to be either the emissive power or the intensity of black radiation, the difference consisting only in the factor $4/c$, which may be included under C (see Art. 276).

In 1887 Michelson deduced a formula from certain assumptions based on Maxwell's law of distribution of velocities amongst the molecules of a gas. As Michelson's formula does not satisfy equation (1) we shall not further consider it; his idea of making use of Maxwell's law was, however, adopted by Wien,[1] who imagines the radiation to be produced in the following way :— Wien's formula.

Let A be a chamber whose internal surface is perfectly reflecting, and B a perfectly transparent vessel within A. Suppose the space between these filled with a gas capable of absorbing and emitting radiations. If the temperature of the gas is uniform the space within B, which we may take as vacuous, will be filled with black radiation. Wien makes the following assumptions :—

(1) Each molecule sends out rays whose wave-length depends only on the velocity of the molecule, and of which the intensity is a function of this velocity. Since the wave-length is a function of the velocity, the velocity may be regarded as a function of the wave-length.

(2) The energy of radiation of wave-length between limits λ and

[1] *Ann. der Physik*, Bd. lviii. p. 662, 1896.

$\lambda + d\lambda$ is proportional to the number of molecules sending out waves of this period and to a function of the molecular velocity v.

Now on the kinetic theory the number of molecules whose velocities lie between the limits v and $v + dv$ is

$$v^2 e^{-\frac{v^2}{a^2}} dv,$$

where a is a constant given by the equation

$$\overline{v^2} = \frac{3}{2} a^2,$$

$\overline{v^2}$ being the mean square of velocity of all molecules. Therefore, expressing v as a function of λ, and remembering that $\overline{v^2}$ is proportional to the absolute temperature, we may write the number of molecules as

$$c' f(\lambda) e^{-\frac{f(\lambda)}{\Theta}} d\lambda,$$

and as the energy is proportional to this expression and to some other function of λ, we get

$$E = F(\lambda) e^{-\frac{f(\lambda)}{\Theta}}.$$

A comparison of this equation with the general form (1) gives Wien's formula

$$E = C\lambda^{-5} e^{-\frac{a}{\lambda\Theta}} \quad . \quad . \quad . \quad . \quad . \quad (2)$$

where a and C are constants.

This equation makes E vanish for $\lambda = 0$, or $\lambda = \infty$, as it should do. If $\Theta = \infty$ E is finite.

Wien's assumptions are by no means obviously true, and the experiments of Lummer and Pringsheim described in Art. 280 show that the formula does not accord well with the facts. Equation (2) gives for a constant wave-length λ

$$\log E = \gamma_1 - \gamma_2 \frac{1}{\Theta},$$

where γ_1 and γ are independent of Θ. If then curves are plotted for given wave-lengths, taking $\log E$ as ordinate and Θ^{-1} as abscissa, these curves (isochromatics of Nichols) should be straight lines. They exhibited, however, a distinct curvature near the axis of ordinates, that is for high temperatures.

Paschen and Wanner found that Wien's formula was well satisfied by the results of their experiments, which were made on the visible rays, using a photometer instead of a bolometer. We shall see presently how these divergent results can be reconciled.

Lord Rayleigh [1] has argued that it is unlikely that E should tend to a finite value for infinite values of Θ, and also that as, according to the Maxwell-Boltzmann law of partition of energy, the energy of a system which can vibrate in several modes is equally divided amongst the modes, and as this law is probably true for the graver modes at least, there should, for waves of low frequencies, be equable partition of energy between temperature heat and radiation; and as temperature energy is proportional to the temperature, the radiation for long waves should vary ultimately as the temperature.   He proposed the formula

Lord Rayleigh's formula.

$$E = C\lambda^{-4}\Theta e^{-\frac{a}{\lambda\Theta}} . \qquad . \qquad . \qquad . \qquad . \qquad (3)$$

which satisfies equation (1).   It does not, however, agree well with experimental results except for long waves and high temperatures.

Thiesen [2] suggested the formula

$$E = C\lambda^{-4}(\lambda\Theta)^{\frac{1}{2}}e^{-\frac{a}{\lambda\Theta}} \qquad . \qquad . \qquad . \qquad . \qquad (4)$$

which agrees better with experiment, and also makes E become infinite with Θ.   But it has no theoretical justification.

The three formulæ (2), (3), and (4) can all be included under the more general form

$$E = C\lambda^{-\mu}(\lambda\Theta)^{5-\mu}e^{-\frac{a}{\lambda\Theta}},$$

Lord Rayleigh's, Thiesen's, and Wien's equations being obtained by giving μ the values 4, 4·5, and 5 respectively.

Jahnke [3] proposed the empirical formula

$$E = C\lambda^{-4}\Theta e^{-\frac{a}{(\lambda\Theta)^\nu}} \qquad . \qquad . \qquad . \qquad . \qquad (5)$$

which agrees well with experiment on putting $\nu = 1\cdot3$.

The most satisfactory formula on theoretical as well as experimental grounds is one given by Planck :— [4]

Planck's formula.

$$E = \frac{C\lambda^{-5}}{e^{\frac{a}{\lambda\Theta}} - 1} \qquad . \qquad . \qquad . \qquad . \qquad (6)$$

This equation is in close accord with the results of the experiments

[1] *Phil. Mag.*, June 1900.   [2] *Verh. d. Deutsch. Phys. Ges.*, Feb. 1900.
[3] Lummer and Jahnke, *Ann. der Physik*, Bd. iii. p. 283, 1900.
[4] *Ann. der Physik*, Bd. iv. p. 553, 1901.   The outlines of Planck's method are as follows.   He imagines a space bounded by perfectly reflecting surfaces and which contains a number of tuned Hertzian resonators, to be filled with monochromatic waves of the same period.   These are being continually absorbed and emitted by the resonators.   Borrowing from the kinetic theory of gases the definition of entropy as the logarithm of the probability of the existing distribution of energy, and making use of (*a*) Wien's law given by equation (1) above, (*b*) an expression for the intensity of radiation of a Hertzian resonator obtained by means of the electromagnetic theory, and (*c*) the thermodynamic relation between temperature, entropy,

of Lummer and Pringsheim, and also agrees with those of Paschen. For small values of λ and Θ it approximates to Wien's formula (2), and for large values of λ and Θ, in which the higher terms in the

expansion of $e^{\frac{a}{\lambda\Theta}}$ may be neglected, it approximates to Lord Rayleigh's formula (3). This explains how Paschen, experimenting with short waves, verified Wien's formula, while Lummer and Pringsheim, working with long waves and high temperatures, found deviations from that formula. Lummer and Pringsheim subsequently carried out a series of experiments on the visible spectrum, using a Lummer-Brodhun photometer, and confirmed the results of Paschen and Wanner, as well as Planck's equation.

Rubens and Kurlbaum's experiments.

Planck's formula makes E infinite when Θ is infinite, and also fulfils Lord Rayleigh's condition that for long waves and high

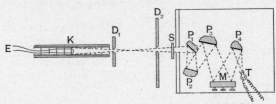

Fig. 186.

temperatures E should vary ultimately as Θ. This condition has been experimentally verified by Rubens and Kurlbaum,[1] using a method due to Beckmann. There are many substances which possess the property of *selective reflection* (commonly associated with anomalous dispersion), that is, that they powerfully reflect rays of a particular wave-length. The rays which are most strongly reflected for incident light are those which are most strongly absorbed for transmitted light, that is, they are rays for which the substance has a very large coefficient of absorption.[2] It has been mentioned that fluor-spar freely transmits infra-red rays, but there are two bands in the infra-red spectrum produced by refraction through fluor-spar; these correspond to wave-lengths of 24μ and $31\cdot6\mu$ respectively. Rays of these wave-lengths are strongly reflected by fluor-spar. By means of four successive reflections from fluor-spar surfaces Beckmann succeeded in

---

and energy, he calculates an expression for the entropy of the system in terms of the energy and frequency of a single resonator, and hence obtains the formula given above.

[1] *Sitz. der Preuss. Akad. der Wiss. Berlin*, p. 929; Oct. 1900. *Ann. der Physik*, Bd. iv. p. 649; 1901.

[2] The coefficient of absorption of a substance must not be confounded with its absorptive power. Polished metals have a small absorptive power, but a very large coefficient of absorption, *i.e.* they are highly opaque to transmitted light.

obtaining these rays of considerable purity. The experiments of Rubens and Kurlbaum were made with black bodies ranging in temperature from − 188° C. to 1500°. The apparatus is represented in Fig. 186. K is the black body, of which four kinds were used, one of which could be surrounded with liquid air, another with a mixture of solid carbon dioxide and ether, and the third with steam, while the fourth could be heated electrically. E is the thermo-element giving the temperature. D_1 and D_2 are screens with small apertures, and S the shutter of the measuring apparatus, all these three being filled with water at air temperature. P_1, P_2, P_3, and P_4 are four reflecting surfaces of fluor-spar ; M is an adjustable mirror, and T a thermopile. It is obvious that this instrument furnishes a method of measuring the intensity of radiation of a given wave-length for various temperatures. The results obtained agreed well both with Jahnke's and Planck's formula, but showed considerable deviation from Wien's.

Other substances possessing the same property of selective reflection for infra-red radiation are sylvine ($\lambda = 60\mu$), rock-salt ($\lambda = 51 \cdot 2\mu$), and quartz ($\lambda = 8 \cdot 85\mu$). Rubens and Kurlbaum also experimented with the two latter and confirmed their previous results.

Subsequent investigations by Rubens and by Michel[1] gave somewhat different values for the wave-lengths selectively reflected by some of the crystals just mentioned. The following table is taken from Michel's paper :—

Substance.	Wave-lengths selectively reflected.	
	Rubens.	Michel.
Fluor-spar . . .	22·3	22·4
,, . . .	32·8	33·0
Aragonite . . .	39	38·9
Rock-salt . . .	51·7	52·3
Sylvine . . .	64·8	64·0

Planck's formula was also verified by Rubens and Michel[2] using the same method as Rubens and Kurlbaum, but with more elaborate apparatus. In these experiments the value obtained for Wien's constant[3] a was 1·430.

285. The Quantum Theory.[4]—We shall begin the consideration

[1] Zeit. für Physik, vol. ix. p. 285, 1922.

[2] Sitz. der Preuss. Akad. (Berlin), p. 590, 1921.

[3] Wien's constant a is the same, or nearly the same, as Planck's constant a, since Wien's formula is derived from Planck's by neglecting the second term in the denominator.

[4] See J. H. Jeans' Report on Radiation and the Quantum Theory.

of this theory by an illustration from the kinetic theory of gases. Suppose we have a gas containing two kinds of molecule, viz. a relatively small number of massive molecules and a very large number of very small molecules. In this case, by the doctrine of equipartition of energy, the average kinetic energy of a molecule of either kind is the same (assuming that each molecule has the same number of degrees of freedom). It follows that the energy of the system is nearly all resident in the small molecules, simply because they are relatively much more numerous. If, again, we replace the small molecules by a continuous medium capable of exchanging energy with the first set of molecules, this medium consequently possessing an infinite number of degrees of freedom, then, when equilibrium is attained, *all* the energy will have passed into the medium. Now, if we suppose a hot body to be placed in a perfectly reflecting enclosure, we know that when equilibrium is attained, most of the energy will remain in the body and only a small part will exist in the form of those etherial waves which constitute radiant energy. In the electromagnetic theory the ether is treated as a continuous medium, and even if we assume that this is not strictly true, we must still regard it as extremely fine-grained when compared to the atoms of matter or even to the constituent electrons of such matter. Thus, if we admit the law of equipartition of energy, we are led to expect that all or very nearly all the energy will pass out of the body into the ether, which is directly contrary to experience.

Again, let us imagine a rectangular box with perfectly reflecting walls to be filled with black-body radiation corresponding to some definite temperature, and let us calculate the distribution of energy according to the ordinary mechanics. In Art. 168 we have calculated the number of possible modes of vibration, of frequency lying between the limits ν and $\nu + \delta\nu$, of unit mass of an elastic solid in the form of a rectangular block. The number of possible modes of vibration for the ether in the rectangular box comprised between the same limits of frequency is calculated in exactly the same way, but we must omit v, since we are dealing with unit volume, and we also omit the first term, because there are no compressional waves. Putting c for the velocity of light, the number of vibrations is $8\pi\nu^2\delta\nu/c^3$. Now, if λ is the wave-length, $\lambda\nu = c$, therefore $\nu = c/\lambda$, $\delta\nu = -c\lambda^{-2}\delta\lambda$; therefore, omitting the negative sign, which merely means that $\delta\nu$ and $\delta\lambda$ are of opposite sign, we see that the number of possible modes of vibration whose wave-length lies between λ and $\lambda + \delta\lambda$ is

$$8\pi\lambda^{-4}\delta\lambda \quad . \quad . \quad . \quad . \quad . \quad . \quad (1)$$

By the kinetic theory of gases (see Art. 375) the average energy for each degree of freedom of the molecule is $\frac{1}{2}R_0\Theta$, when R_0 is the universal gas-constant; therefore, by the law of equipartition of energy, if the radiation is at a temperature Θ, *i.e.* is in temperature equilibrium with a gas at that temperature, this will be the kinetic energy corresponding to each mode of vibration of the ether. And the energy is half kinetic and half potential, therefore the total energy between wave-lengths λ and $\lambda + \delta\lambda$ is

$$8\pi R_0\Theta\lambda^{-4}\delta\lambda \quad . \qquad . \qquad . \qquad . \qquad . \qquad (2)$$

This formula was given by Lord Rayleigh and by J. H. Jeans in 1900 as being the formula which ought, on the Newtonian mechanics, to govern the partition of energy in the spectrum. It cannot be the true law, for the total energy obtained by integrating from $\lambda = 0$ to $\lambda = \infty$ would be infinite for any finite value of Θ. And if the total energy were finite the only possible value for Θ would be $\Theta = 0$.

This, in fact, is the prediction of the classical mechanics as to the final steady state. We are led to expect that all the energy of the matter will be dissipated away into radiation in the ether, as in the analogy given above.

It was in the effort to devise a radiating system which would accord with the known facts that Planck originated the conception that changes of energy may take place, not continuously, but by multiples of a certain unit or quantum. Perhaps the simplest way of introducing the idea of quanta is that given by Jeans [1] in the following manner. In the kinetic theory of gases the probability that a system shall have its co-ordinates $(p_1, p_2, \ldots)$ and momenta $(q_1, q_2, \ldots)$ within a range $dp_1 dp_2 \ldots dq_1 dq_2 \ldots$ is found to be of the form

$$Ae^{-2hE}dp_1 dp_2 \ldots dq_1 dq_2 \ldots$$

when E is the energy of the system in this configuration, A is a constant, and h is given by $2hR_0\Theta = 1$. Hence if ϵ is any amount of energy, the probabilities of the system having energies 0, ϵ, 2ϵ, $\ldots$ will stand in the ratios

$$1 : e^{-2h\epsilon} : e^{-4h\epsilon} : \text{etc.}$$

Strictly speaking, the probabilities we are discussing are not those of the system having energies 0, ϵ, 2ϵ, $\ldots$ but of its co-ordinates

[1] In Planck's line of reasoning, which is different from Jeans', the quanta occur in the distribution of energy between his resonators. It is impossible to arrive at Planck's law of radiation without the introduction of a discontinuity somewhere in the emission or absorption of energy. For a simple and strict proof of Planck's formula, see a paper by Eddington (*Phil. Mag.* vol. l. p. 803, 1925). This is based on Einstein's proof of Planck's law (*Phys. Zeitschr.* vol. xviii. p. 121, 1917).

lying within equal infinitesimal ranges of values $dp_1 dp_2$ . . . $dq_1 dq_2$ . . . surrounding these energies, but this complication is immaterial for our present purpose.

Suppose that we are considering a very great number, M, of vibrations, and suppose that of these N have zero energy. Then the number which may be expected to have energy ϵ will be $Ne^{-2h\epsilon}$, the number which may be expected to have energy 2ϵ will be $Ne^{-4h\epsilon}$, and so on. If we suppose that all of the M vibrations have their energies equal to one or other of the values o, ϵ, 2ϵ, . . . then we must have

$$M = N\,(1 + e^{-2h\epsilon} + e^{-4h\epsilon} + e^{-6h\epsilon} + \ldots) = \frac{N}{1 - e^{-2h\epsilon}} \quad . \quad . \quad (3)$$

The total energy of all these vibrations must be

$$\epsilon Ne^{-2h\epsilon} + 2\epsilon Ne^{-4h\epsilon} + 3\epsilon Ne^{-6h\epsilon} + \ldots$$

$$= N\epsilon e^{-2h\epsilon}\,(1 + 2e^{-2h\epsilon} + 3e^{-4h\epsilon} + \ldots)$$

$$= \frac{N\epsilon e^{-2h\epsilon}}{(1 - e^{-2h\epsilon})^2}$$

$$= \frac{M\epsilon}{e^{2h\epsilon} - 1}, \text{ by the relation (3).}$$

If the particular vibrations are those of wave-length between λ and $\lambda + \delta\lambda$ in a unit volume of ether, then, by formula (1) the value of M must be taken to be $8\pi\lambda^{-4}\delta\lambda$, and the total energy is

$$8\pi\lambda^{-4}\frac{\epsilon}{e^{2h\epsilon} - 1}\delta\lambda,$$

or, putting for h its value $1/2R_0\Theta$, the expression for the energy corresponding to wave-lengths between λ and $\lambda + \delta\lambda$ is

$$\frac{8\pi\lambda^{-4}\epsilon}{e^{\frac{\epsilon}{R_0\Theta}} - 1}\delta\lambda \quad . \quad . \quad . \quad . \quad . \quad (4)$$

which may also be written in the form

$$8\pi R_0\Theta\lambda^{-4}\frac{x}{e^x - 1}\delta\lambda,$$

where x is put for $\epsilon/R_0\Theta$.

This expression becomes identical with Planck's formula for $E\delta\lambda$ if we put

$$\epsilon = h\nu \quad . \quad . \quad . \quad . \quad . \quad (5)$$

where ν is the number of vibrations per second and h is a universal physical constant now generally known as Planck's constant. Writing $h\nu$ or hc/λ for ϵ, we get

$$E = \frac{8\pi hc\lambda^{-5}}{e^{\frac{a}{\lambda\Theta}} - 1} \quad . \quad . \quad . \quad . \quad . \quad (6)$$

where $a = hc/R_0$. By comparing this with equation (6), Art. 284, we see that $C = 8\pi hc$. The meaning attached to h by Planck in this formula requires that E should be the intensity of black radiation, not the emissive power of a black body. The latter is obtained by multiplying by $\frac{1}{4} c$.

It will be seen that, according to this theory, exchanges of energy take place by integral multiples of $h\nu$, as if, in some transformations at any rate, light-energy were atomic in character. The size of the quantum depends, however, on the frequency ν. The dimensions of Planck's constant h are not those of energy but of action or angular momentum (energy × time). In Bohr's theory of the structure of the atom (Art. 58) the angular momentum of the electron round the centre of its orbit (assuming the latter to be circular) is an integral multiple of $h/2\pi$. In the innermost, most stable, orbit the angular momentum is $h/2\pi$.

The great objection to Planck's theory is that it is impossible, as far as we can see, to reconcile it with the classical mechanics and with the undulatory theory of light. Any attempt to explain such phenomena as interference and diffraction seems to demand that light-energy is infinitely divisible. On the other hand, the phenomena of radiation, of the line-spectra of the elements, the photo-electric effect and the specific heats of metals at low temperatures, seem to require that interchanges of energy take place by quanta.

A further objection is in the mode in which the theory is put forward. Planck does not propound a new system of mechanics, but makes use of the ordinary mechanics, superposing the quantum hypothesis on it, although the two are apparently inconsistent. Similarly in Bohr's constitution of the atom, the electron in the steady state is supposed to describe its orbit according to the Newtonian laws, while the quantum theory is brought in to account for the emission of energy in passing from one orbit to another.

In recent years, owing to the researches of Heisenberg, Schrödinger, and many others, important advances have been made in the application of the theory of quanta to the elucidation of spectra and atomic physics generally. It seems fairly well established that the Newtonian laws of mechanics do not hold for the atom, though for certain classes of phenomena they may be statistically true for large assemblages of atoms. The fact that the quantum theory is most successful just where the ordinary dynamics fail must be regarded as a strong argument in its favour. The surprisingly accurate quantitative results that have been obtained by its means seem to indicate that though it may need modification, it will, in its essential features, survive all the criticism that has been directed against it, and that an ultimate reconciliation between the two opposing theories may be effected.

286. Constants of Radiation.—The constants occurring in the various radiation formulæ are not only connected with each other but also with the other universal physical constants. Thus we have seen that Planck's formula (6, Art. 285) involves the velocity of light and the gas-constant, the only new constant introduced being Planck's constant h. A very careful determination of the charge e of an electron has been made by R. A. Millikan,[1] from which he has deduced the values of a number of other physical constants including the radiation constants, which agree very closely with recent determinations by more direct methods. The following are Millikan's values for some of these constants :—

Charge of an electron . . . . $e = 4 \cdot 774 \times 10^{-10}$
Number of molecules in 1 c.c. of a gas at 0° C. and 760 mm.
　　press. . . . . $N = 2 \cdot 705 \times 10^{19}$
Mass of an atom of hydrogen in grammes . . . $m = 1 \cdot 662 \times 10^{-24}$
The gas-constant . . . . $R_0 = 1 \cdot 372 \times 10^{-16}$
Stefan's constant of total radiation . . . . $\sigma = 5 \cdot 72 \times 10^{-5}$
Wien's constant . . . . $\lambda_m \Theta = 0 \cdot 2883$
Planck's constant . . . . $h = 6 \cdot 547 \times 10^{-27}$

The only one of these which differs very considerably from the earlier accepted values is Stefan's constant, which is about $7\frac{1}{2}$ per cent greater than Kurlbaum's value. The earlier direct determinations of σ agree well with the latter, but later measurements have tended to higher values, and Millikan's figure has been experimentally obtained by Coblentz.

A great many other determinations of radiation constants have been made. The probable value of the Stefan-Boltzmann constant σ is discussed by Gerlach,[2] who regards $5 \cdot 752 \times 10^{-5}$ as that which best agrees with the values of related constants. The value of the constant a occurring in Wien's and Planck's formulæ is of importance in optical pyrometry. Coblentz found the value $1 \cdot 432$ in C.G.S. units. Rubens and Michel[3] give $1 \cdot 430$. These are for Wien's formula, that is, the value of a which makes the right-hand side of equation (2), Art. 284, most nearly constant. Michel states, however, that if Planck's law is assumed exact, then the value of a which agrees best with the observations is not $1 \cdot 430$ but $1 \cdot 427$.

The probable value of Planck's constant h has been discussed by

---

[1] *Phil. Mag.*, July 1917, p. 1.
[2] *Zeit. für Physik*, vol. ii. p. 76, 1920.
[3] *Phys. Zeitschr.* vol. xxii. p. 569, 1921.

R. T. Birge.[1] The mean value derived from the results of a number of experimenters employing seven different methods is $6 \cdot 554 \times 10^{-27}$. This figure depends on Millikan's value for e.

In the examples given below, some of the other physical constants are calculated from the experimental values of the radiation constants of Stefan and Wien.

287. Correction for width of Bolometer and Slit.[2]—Let XPY (Fig. 187) be a portion of the true curve connecting intensity and wave-length in the spectrum of a black body, and suppose that a correction is to be applied for the width of the bolometer only. If AB is the width of the bolometer on the spectrum, then the instrument, instead of giving the true intensity MP for the middle point M of AB, gives the *mean* intensity MP′ between A and B ; in other words, it measures the energy represented by the area AXPYB, which, divided by AB, gives MP′. The curve thus obtained will be the dotted curve X′P′Y′ ; the problem is then how to obtain the true curve from the plotted curve X′P′Y′.

We may, with close approximation, suppose the true curve XPY to be coincident with a parabola drawn through X and Y with its axis vertical, and having its tangents at X and Y coincident with those of XPY. By the geometry of the parabola, the area of XPYX is $\frac{2}{3}$ NP × AB ; but this area is NP′ × AB by definition, therefore NP′ = $\frac{2}{3}$ NP. Now, for a very short distance along the curve, we may assume that the difference of the ordinates of the two curves is changing at a uniform rate, that is, that PP′ is a mean between XX′ and YY′. But NN′ is the mean of XX′ and YY′, therefore NN′ = PP′, therefore PP′ = $\frac{1}{3}$ P′N′. Thus we obtain the following rule—Draw a chord X′Y′, the difference of whose abscissæ AB represents the width of the bolometer. Erect the middle ordinate MP′, and add to it one-third of the length P′N′ intercepted between the curve and the chord. This gives the point P on the true curve.

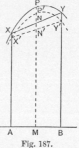

Fig. 187.

A second application of the same process would furnish a correction for the width of the slit, taking AB as the width of the image of the slit.

If the curvature is a maximum at P, the difference of ordinates PP′ is also a maximum, so that in this case PP′ would be greater than either XX′ or YY′ ; thus with very peaked curves there is a tendency for the corrected curve to be still a little too flat at the peak, unless the deviation from the parabolic form happens to be such as to correct for this. In any case, the error in practice would be negligible.

EXAMPLES

1. Find a relation between the constants of Planck's equation and that of Stefan's.

{Taking the total radiation to surroundings at absolute zero,

$$S = \sigma \Theta^4 = \int_0^\infty E d\lambda = C \int_0^\infty \lambda^{-5} \left(e^{\frac{a}{\lambda \Theta}} - 1 \right)^{-1} d\lambda.$$

On putting u^{-1} for λ, this transforms to

$$S = C \int_0^\infty u^3 e^{-\frac{au}{\Theta}} \left(1 - e^{-\frac{au}{\Theta}} \right)^{-1} du.$$

[1] *Phys. Review*, vol. xiv. p. 361, 1919.
[2] This method is adapted from a paper by Lord Rayleigh (*Phil. Mag.* vol. xlii. p. 441, 1871).

Expanding by the binomial theorem, and integrating term by term, we obtain

$$S = \frac{6C}{a^4} \Theta^4 \left(\frac{1}{1^4} + \frac{1}{2^4} + \frac{1}{3^4} + \ldots \right) = \frac{\pi^4 C}{15 a^4} \Theta^4,$$

therefore $$\sigma = \frac{\pi^4}{15} \cdot \frac{C}{a^4}.\Big\}$$

2. Find the values of the constants a and C in Planck's equation, assuming that $\lambda_m \Theta = \cdot 2883$ in centimetre-degrees, and that $\sigma = 5 \cdot 72 \times 10^{-5}$ in ergs per sq. cm. per sec. per (degree)[4].

{If E is a maximum for a given temperature, $d\mathrm{E}/d\lambda = 0$; therefore, differentiating Planck's expression, regarding Θ as constant, we get

$$\frac{a}{\lambda_m \Theta} = 5 \left(1 - e^{-\frac{a}{\lambda_m \Theta}} \right).$$

As a first approximation, put $a/\lambda_m \Theta = 5$, and then substitute ; the second approximation gives $4 \cdot 966$, and a third gives $4 \cdot 965$, therefore

$$a = 4 \cdot 965 \times \cdot 2883 = 1 \cdot 431.$$

Making use of the result of the preceding example,

$$C = 15 \times \left(\frac{1 \cdot 431}{\pi} \right)^4 \times 5 \cdot 72 \times 10^{-5} = 3 \cdot 69 \times 10^{-5}$$

in ergs $\times$ cm.[2] per sec.}

3. Taking c the velocity of light as 3×10^{10} cm. per sec., the gas-constant R_0 (Art. 375) as $1 \cdot 372 \times 10^{-16}$, and Planck's constant h as $6 \cdot 554 \times 10^{-27}$, calculate all the radiation constants.

{Since $a = hc/R_0$ and $C = 2\pi h c^2$ when Planck's formula refers to emissive power, we get

$$\sigma = 5 \cdot 706 \times 10^{-5}, \quad a = 1 \cdot 433, \quad C = 3 \cdot 706 \times 10^{-5}, \quad \lambda_m \Theta = 0 \cdot 2886.\}$$

4. Calculate the charge of an electron given that the quantity of electricity required to liberate half a cubic centimetre of hydrogen in electrolysis is $0 \cdot 433$ in absolute electromagnetic units.

{$Ne = 0 \cdot 433$, therefore $e = 1 \cdot 60 \times 10^{-20}$ in electromagnetic units, or, multiplying by c, $4 \cdot 80 \times 10^{-10}$ in electrostatic units.}

SECTION VI

MEASUREMENT OF TEMPERATURE BY RADIATION

288. Radiation Scale of Temperature.—It follows from the principles explained in the preceding section that the radiation within an enclosure whose walls are at a uniform temperature is unique in character, and that the density of energy is uniform. If then we define the temperature of such an enclosure by means of the formula

$$\Theta = k\psi^{\frac{1}{4}},$$

when k is some constant, and ψ the density of radiant energy, we are furnished with a new scale of temperature, which does not depend on the specific properties of any body, and which is therefore an *absolute* scale in the same sense as Lord Kelvin's thermodynamic scale. If we assume that a body at the absolute zero of Lord Kelvin's scale does not emit any radiations, then the zeros of the two scales are identical. By giving a suitable value to k we may make the two scales coincide at one other given temperature, *e.g.* at $0°$ C. The scales will then coincide at all other temperatures if Stefan's law is rigidly true.

It will be noticed that this method of defining temperature enables us to speak of the temperature of a vacuum, by which we mean the temperature characteristic of the radiation which fills it. If the density of the energy is given, then its temperature is given uniquely, provided that the radiation is completely diffused. If the radiation is not diffused, then its temperature will not be the same as that of diffused radiation of the same density. Thus the temperature of the sun's rays as they reach the earth's atmosphere is effectively that of the sun himself. The earth's surface is not, however, raised to a high temperature by these rays; this is because the earth is receiving energy from the direction of the sun only and radiating it to all parts of the heavens. We can, by means either of a lens or parabolic mirror, increase the solid angle virtually subtended by the sun at an absorbing surface without increasing the emitting surface, and in this way very high temperatures may be attained. A small body placed at the focus of a parabolic mirror whose aperture, as viewed from the focus, is less than the sun's angular diameter, would be raised to the temperature of the sun, if no absorption took place in the atmosphere or at the surface of the mirror. Any directed quality in radiation increases its temperature and thermodynamic availability. Thus polarised light is of a higher order of availability than ordinary light of the same intensity.

The application of the laws of radiation to the practical measurement of temperature is especially suited to the determination of high temperatures, since there is no limit to the temperature which the instruments are capable of measuring, and there is no objection to the use of the method beyond the limits of the gas thermometer, since the laws on which it is based are themselves founded on theoretic principles and not on empirical results. We may find the temperature of a chamber which radiates as a black body by means of a standardised bolometer, using any one of the four formulæ—

$$S = \sigma(\Theta^4 - \Theta_0^4) \qquad \qquad (1)$$
$$\lambda_m \Theta = \text{const.} \qquad \qquad (2)$$
$$E_m \Theta^{-5} = \text{const.} \qquad \qquad (3)$$
$$E_\lambda = \frac{C\lambda^{-5}}{e^{\frac{a}{\lambda\Theta}} - 1} \qquad \qquad (4)$$

the first being Stefan's law, the two next contained in Wien's law, and the last Planck's law. Of these, Stefan's law is theoretically the simplest to use, as the spectroscope is not required. The second formula does not lend itself to accurate work, as the wave-length λ_m for which E is a maximum cannot be fixed precisely. The maximum value E_m can, however, be accurately estimated, and as it increases enormously with the temperature, the third formula, like the first, is especially suited for measuring high temperatures. It is, however, inconvenient to have to find out in what part of the spectrum the intensity of radiation is a maximum, and there are other objections to the third formula, which accordingly has been little used.

Planck's formula has the disadvantage that the temperature can only be obtained from it by the method of successive approximations. Of course it would be possible to draw up a table giving the value of Θ for a number of successive values of E_λ, but it is more usual to employ Wien's formula. If λ is small, within the range of the visible spectrum for instance, Wien's formula gives substantially the same result as Planck's, except at very high temperatures, when a small correction may be necessary. Wien's equation is

$$E_\lambda = C\lambda^{-5}e^{-\frac{a}{\lambda\Theta}},$$

from which we derive

$$\Theta = \frac{a}{\lambda \left(\log_e C - \log_e E_\lambda - 5 \log_e \lambda\right)}.$$

The only serious objection to the use of the radiation method is that it is only strictly applicable to the measurement of the temperature of a black body. Thus it would be the appropriate method to use in finding the temperature of the interior of a Bessemer converter after the blow, or of any other chamber at a fairly uniform temperature and with a small aperture. But for measuring the temperature of an incandescent burner or of the electric arc it is not so suitable. It will, however, enable us to assign a lower limit to such temperatures.

Another method may be employed, which is applicable to high temperatures only. This consists in comparing the *brightness* of the heated body with that of a source at known temperature by means of a photometer. This method, on account of the selective emission of bodies, is also only strictly applicable to black bodies. Melted platinum reflects light well, which shows that it cannot be a perfect radiator, and the same is true of other substances.

The question naturally arises here whether the temperature scale fixed by a radiation pyrometer standardised at one temperature will be found to agree experimentally with the thermodynamic or perfect gas scale. Since the radiation constants discussed in the preceding section have been found to be constants as the result of a large number of experiments conducted over a wide range of temperature, and since in these experiments the temperature was of course determined by methods previously in existence, we see at once that the measure of agreement to be expected between the two scales will depend on the degree of constancy exhibited by the coefficients σ, a, etc., which occur in the radiation formulæ. The later determinations of any one constant show a tendency to agree more and more closely, and no systematic variation with temperature seems to have been exposed. We may therefore anticipate that the readings of a radiation pyrometer will not differ from those of a corrected gas thermometer by a greater amount than is indicated by the uncertainty of the exact values of the constants employed.

The agreement between the two scales was tested by Mendenhall and Forsythe [1] in the following way. A black body was constructed of a design very similar to that described in the next article. Both the black body and the bolometer which received the radiations were enclosed in a chamber filled with nitrogen at a low pressure. The gas was constantly pumped away and renewed at the same time, while

---

[1] *Phys. Review*, vol. iv. p. 62, 1914.

the pressure was maintained constant. This was done in order to prevent contamination by gases given off by the heated carbon, which would alter the absorption of the radiation on its way to the bolometer. It was arranged that the black body could be kept steadily at either of two known temperatures, viz. the melting point of gold (1336 K.) or the melting point of palladium (1822 K.). The end of the chamber containing the bolometer was shut off by a water-filled screen having two small apertures, through one of which the radiation was admitted to the bolometer, the other being used to observe the black body with an optical pyrometer, and ensure that its temperature was the same as that of the melting point of gold or palladium previously observed with the same instrument. By moving a lever, a rotating sector could be brought up in front of the bolo-meter aperture so as to cut down the radiation in a predetermined ratio. This rotating sector consisted of a pair of brass discs mounted close together on the same axis, with corresponding open-ings cut out of the two discs. The object in using a second disc was to prevent any heat which might be absorbed and re-radiated by the first disc from reaching the bolometer. This pair of discs was rotated rapidly by a motor. Thus the proportion of radiation trans-mitted was in the ratio of the angle of the sector cut out to four right angles ; this ratio was made to be $(1336 \div 1822)^{\frac{1}{4}}$. When the black body was at the melting point of gold, the bolometer was exposed to the full radiation, but when it was at the higher temperature the rotating sector was interposed. Now, the figures taken as the melting points of gold and palladium are those fixed by Day and Sosman with the nitrogen gas thermometer, so that if Stefan's law is to provide the same scale as the gas thermometer, the resistance of the bolometer should be exactly the same in the two cases. This was found to be very nearly so, the mean ratio of the galvanometer deflections being 1·001, which is very nearly unity.

Mendenhall and Forsythe used the same apparatus to test whether the optical and total radiation pyrometers gave consistent readings, and found differences of less than 0°·5 at 1750° C., and about 4° at 2820° C. They also used it to determine the melting point of platinum, which they found to be 1753° C.

Hoffmann and Meissner [1] used a König-Martens spectral photo-meter to measure the relative brightnesses of a black body at the melting points of gold and palladium. Two series of experiments were made, and in one of these the black body was immersed in the liquid metal at its melting point. The relative brightness of melting

[1] *Ann. der Physik*, vol. lx. p. 201, 1919.

palladium and gold was found to be 81·5 for wave-length 0·6563μ. Taking the constant a of Planck's formula to be 1·430, and the melting point of gold to be 1063° C., this makes the melting point of palladium to be 1557° C., which is 8° higher than Day and Sosman's figure.

289. Lummer and Pringsheim's Experiments.[1]—In order to prove the efficiency of the radiation laws for the measurement of temperature, Lummer and Pringsheim made a series of determinations of the

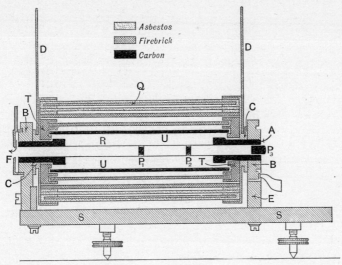

Fig. 188.

temperature of a specially constructed black body, using three different methods—formulæ (1) and (3) above, and the photometer method—and thus tested the agreement between them.

The radiating chamber was represented by a carbon tube R (Fig. 188) with a wall 1·2 mm. thick, 34 cm. long, and an internal diameter of 1 cm.   In the manufacture of this tube, care was taken to secure an accurate cylindrical form and even thickness of wall.   The ends were slightly conical and covered with copper by electro-deposition.   Over these conical ends thicker carbon cylinders A were fitted; these were copper-plated within and without, and rested in strong metallic clamps B which conveyed the current.   The back wall of the radiating cavity was formed by the plug P_1, fitted in the centre of the carbon tube and closing as air-tight as possible.   The form of plug shown was chosen so as to reduce as far as possible the

---

[1] *Sitz. der Deutsch. Phys. Gesell.*, Jan. 1903.   *Electrician*, Aug. 7, 1903.

unavoidable inequality of electrical heating produced by it.   Behind P_1 was placed a second plug P_2, which diminished the harmful effect of any gap between the first plug and the wall of the tube.   A third plug P_3 closed the end of the tube hermetically, in order to cut off the oxygen of the atmosphere.   To protect the carbon from burning, the hot tube was surrounded by a system of enclosures, whose mounting may be seen from the figure.   Since the porcelain carriers T were firmly mounted on the thick carbon cylinders A, and were pressed tight against the projecting noses of the carbon cylinders by means of the copper rings C, the air could not directly reach the outside of the heating tube.   The innermost protecting tube U was of carbon, which had the double advantage of being capable of withstanding the high temperature and of freeing any air from oxygen.   The other tubes were partly of porcelain and partly of asbestos, and one tube Q of nickel. At the high temperature used, even the thick metallic clamps became red-hot.   To prevent this, large copper discs D were fitted on.   They fitted tight on the copper rings C, and conducted the heat outwards.

With a current of 160 amperes a temperature of about 2300° absolute was reached, and this could be maintained fairly constant for some hours.   The tube was gradually destroyed by oxidation at the open end, but it was found that the combustion could be considerably retarded by allowing a current of nitrogen to pass slowly through the cap F mounted in front of the opening.

In order to determine the temperature by various methods in quick succession, the carbon body was mounted on a carriage rolling on iron rails.   Along the railway the various measuring instruments were so mounted and adjusted that by a simple displacement of the carriage the black body could be brought into the right position in front of each.

For the determination of the total radiation a Lummer-Kurlbaum surface bolometer was used.   Of the two gratings exposed to the radiation the slits of the first were exactly covered by the strips of the second, so that it formed a bolometer wall which stopped all the radiation.   The instrument could be displaced along a scale, and measurements were made at distances of 90 cm., 60 cm., and 40 cm. from the measuring diaphragm.   These showed that the law of distance was fulfilled.

For the determination of the energy curves a linear Lummer-Kurlbaum spectrum bolometer was used, which was built into a case of metal and glass nearly air-tight.   To get rid of the absorption lines of steam and carbon dioxide, the air in the case was freed from these as carefully as possible.   The adjustment and reading of the angles could be done from outside. The slit projecting from the case was closed by a fluor-spar plate and was protected by water-bathed diaphragms. The refracting prism was also of fluor-spar.

The measures of brightness were made with a Lummer-Brodhun spectrum photometer, and were made on different portions of the luminous spectrum, that part being chosen for which the observation plates used were least selective. Five absorption plates were necessary to reduce the light, and together they reduced it to the eight-thousandth part.

The different measuring instruments were calibrated with the help of an electrically heated black porcelain body, the temperature of which was measured with a Le Chatelier thermo-element.

The carbon body was used in various states of incandescence, and in all cases the differences between the measurements made by the various methods remained within the limits of errors of observation. The following table gives the results for the highest temperature in the order in which they were obtained :—

No.	Method.	Absolute Temp.	90 cm.	60 cm.	0·62 μ.	0·59 μ.	0·55 μ.	0·51 μ.	0·49 μ.
1	Brightness . .	2310			2294	2315	2300	2312	2320
2	Total radiation .	2325	2317	2335					
3	Brightness . .	2320			2307	2307	2315	2331	2339
4	Total radiation .	2330	2330	2330					
5	Maximum energy	2330							
6	Brightness . .	2330			2325	2327	2325	2339	2333
7	Total radiation .	2345	2348	2339					
8	Maximum energy	2320							

The agreement between results obtained by methods so different is a strong confirmation of the laws made use of.

290. Féry's Radiation Pyrometer.—The first practical form of pyrometer making use of total radiation was invented by Féry.[1] The instrument is shown in section in Fig. 189. The radiation from the hot body is focussed by means of the concave mirror on to a sensitive thermocouple mounted at D ; the electromotive force generated by the couple is indicated on a galvanometer connected to the terminals BB.

In a second and later form of the instrument Féry has replaced the thermocouple and galvanometer by a bi-metallic (nickel-steel and brass) spiral placed in the focus of the mirror. When heated,

---

[1] "La mesure des températures élevées et la loi de Stefan," C. Féry, *Comptes rendus de l'Académie des Sciences*, vol. 134, p. 977 ; 1902.

the spiral uncoils and carries an aluminium pointer over a dial divided in degrees of temperature, thus dispensing with the galvanometer.

Mr. R. S. Whipple,[1] in conjunction with Professor Féry, has

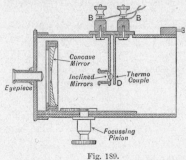

Fig. 189.

introduced a modification of the radiation pyrometer, in which the mirror is focussed on to the inside end of a long closed tube, Fig. 190, thus rendering the instrument's readings independent of the nature of the furnace or material into which the tube is placed. This pyrometer is particularly suitable for determining the temperature of

Fig. 190.

molten metal in a crucible, the tube being plunged directly into the metal.

291. Optical Pyrometers.—In the case of bodies which are so hot as to be self-luminous, the temperature may be determined by measuring the brightness of the heated body. Before the invention of high temperature measuring instruments it was the practice, in smelting works and wherever furnaces were used, to depend on the skill of the workman in estimating the temperature of a furnace from its brightness as judged by the eye alone. A more reliable estimate could obviously be formed if the brightness were directly compared by eye with that of a subsidiary hot body maintained at some known temperature. Greater accuracy as well as greater convenience are

[1] "Modern Methods of Measuring Temperature," Robert S. Whipple, *Proceedings of the Institution of Mechanical Engineers in Cambridge,* 29th July 1913.

secured if the comparison source and the object whose temperature is to be measured are viewed through a telescope in such a way that the two images are seen side by side. If the cone of rays which enters the eye-piece has always the same angular magnitude, then the amount of light entering the eye is independent of the distance of the observing telescope from the hot body. An optical pyrometer is an instrument by means of which the temperature of a luminous source is measured by comparing it in this way with a standard source—usually a filament lamp. The comparison lamp may be standardised once for all by matching its brightness with that of a black body at a succession of known temperatures and ascertaining the current required to produce the brightness corresponding to any given temperature of the black body. If light of all wave-lengths were employed, the colour of the light from the two sources would in general be different, and it would not be possible to make an exact match. This difficulty is got over by only admitting to the eye light which is nearly monochromatic, that is, whose wave-length lies between narrow limits. The use of a spectroscope for this purpose would not be suitable in practical work. A much simpler device, which is generally used, is to place a sheet of a special kind of red glass in front of the eye-piece. This serves as a monochromatic screen to cut off all the rays of the visible spectrum except a narrow band in the red. Green or blue glasses are sometimes used, but there is an advantage in using red glass, as the red part of the spectrum becomes visible at lower temperatures than the green or blue, and, besides, red glasses can be manufactured more nearly monochromatic than green or blue.

If the comparison lamp is a tungsten filament lamp it can be used to measure temperatures by direct comparison up to about 1600° C., but if operated at a higher temperature there is a risk of producing alterations which will make it unreliable as a standard. When, therefore, it is required to measure higher temperatures, the intensity of the light from the observed source must be reduced in some known ratio when the comparison is made. One way of effecting the reduction is by means of a rotating sector such as that described in Art. 288. Another way is to polarise the light from the two sources by some suitable optical arrangement in such a way that two semi-circular patches of light, one from each source, are seen in the field of view, these being polarised in planes at right angles. If these are viewed through a Nicol prism, their intensities are changed by rotating the prism. When the prism has been adjusted so that the two appear equally bright, their relative intensities can be deduced from the angle through which the prism has been rotated. If the light from the observed source is already polarised, incorrect results may be obtained, unless the instrument is rotated about the line of sight, and observations taken in different positions. A third device, simpler than either of the foregoing, is to reduce the intensity by interposing a screen of dark neutral-tinted glass. Glasses can be made which will cut down the intensity in a nearly constant ratio, whatever the temperature of the source may be.

The simplest type of optical pyrometer, and one which is in very general use, is known as the disappearing filament pyrometer. An early form of this instrument was patented by Morse in the United States in 1902. Fig. 191 gives a diagrammatic representation of

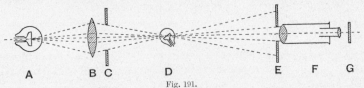

A   B C   D   E   F   G

Fig. 191.

Holborn and Kurlbaum's disappearing filament pyrometer. The instrument is sighted on the body whose temperature is to be measured. In the figure this is a filament lamp A. The rays are focussed by means of the objective B on the comparison lamp D. C and E are fixed screens which limit the cones of light. F is the eye-piece and G is a red glass monochromatic screen. The filament of the bulb D is seen against the background of the observed body A. The current in D is then adjusted till a particular part of the filament D disappears from view owing to its brightness being exactly the same as that of the background. The appearances seen during adjust-

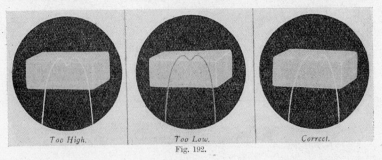

Too High.   Too Low.   Correct.

Fig. 192.

ment are represented in Fig. 192 [1] (with a different background). The temperature is then deduced from the current in D given by an ammeter. If a wire filament is used, then the position of the part

    [1] The third section of the figure is not quite correct—the filament is still a little brighter than the background.

which is to be matched with the background is indicated by a bend as in Fig. 192. If a ribbon filament is used, then the comparison point may be indicated by a small nick in the ribbon.

As already stated, the comparison lamp may be standardised by observations on a black-body chamber at a number of successive known temperatures. This is a difficult process and requires special equipment. A simpler method is to set up a black body, electrically heated, containing a Le Chatelier thermo-element and also a short length of gold or palladium wire held between two platinum wires. The temperature is gradually raised, and as soon as the gold or palladium melts, the black body is kept steadily at the temperature indicated by the thermocouple. The pyrometer is then standardised for this one temperature. All other temperatures are calculated by comparing the brightness at the known temperature with that at the required temperature, and applying Wien's law. In making the comparison, the brightness of the observed source must be reduced to equality with that of the standard lamp by a rotating sector or absorbing glass. By using a number of sectors or absorbing glasses with different transmissions, points can be obtained for drawing a curve showing the relation between temperature and current.

By Wien's law, if E and E' are the brightnesses at temperatures Θ and Θ', of which the lower temperature Θ' is known,

$$\mathrm{E} = C\lambda^{-5} e^{-\frac{a}{\lambda\Theta}}, \quad \mathrm{E}' = C\lambda^{-5} e^{-\frac{a}{\lambda\Theta'}},$$

so that

$$\log_e \frac{\mathrm{E}}{\mathrm{E}'} = \frac{a}{\lambda}\left(\frac{1}{\Theta'} - \frac{1}{\Theta}\right).$$

In this equation, λ is the effective wave-length of the light transmitted by the red glass, that is, it is that wave-length which has been found to accord best with the application of Wien's law. The ratio E'/E is the fraction of light of effective wave-length λ which is transmitted by the particular absorbing glass used; this also has been determined for a number of special glasses.[1] Wien's constant a is taken as 14330 by some, and 14300 by others (in micron degrees, as λ is usually measured in microns). Hence, as Θ' is known, Θ can be calculated.

---

[1] A large amount of work has been done in testing various monochromatic glasses (red, green, and blue), and in studying the absorption of special smoky glasses. See articles by Hyde, Cady, and Forsythe (*Astrophys. Journ.* vol. xlii. p. 294, 1915); Forsythe (*ibid.* vol. xlix. p. 237, 1919; *Journ. Opt. Soc. of America*, vol. iv. p. 305, 1920). It is stated by Hoffmann (*Zeit. für Physik*, vol. xvii. p. 1, 1923) that the Jena smoky glass F7839 has a constant transmission for all temperatures between 1100° and 4000° C. for wave-length $\lambda = 0·656\mu$, which is the effective wave-length of Jena red glass F4512.

The disappearing filament pyrometer can be used from about 600° C. up to 1550° C. without the use of an absorbing screen. With absorbing glasses the highest temperatures may be estimated.

If a heated body which does not radiate as a black body is observed through an optical pyrometer and the temperature calculated as if it were a black body, then the temperature so estimated will be less than the true temperature. To obtain the true temperature, the emissivity of the body must be known for the particular wave-length of the light transmitted. A considerable amount of work has been done in the way of determining the emissivities of various substances.[1]

292. Various Temperature Measurements.—Experiments have been made by several observers in order to determine the laws of radiation in the case of bodies which do not fulfil the condition of being black radiators. Paschen studied the radiation of polished platinum and of lamp-black, and stated as the result of his experiments that it could be represented by the formula

$$E = C\lambda^{-a}e^{-\frac{a}{\lambda\Theta}},$$

where a is a constant depending on the nature of the substance. He gave the values $a = 6\cdot42$ and $a = 5\cdot53$ for polished platinum and lamp-black respectively. If the above formula is true, then Paschen's results imply that the total radiation from these substances is proportional to Θ^{a-1}, the value of the exponent being $5\cdot42$ for platinum and $4\cdot53$ for lamp-black.

Lummer and Kurlbaum surrounded the heated body with a box of polished platinum having a small aperture opposite which the bolometer was placed. This constitutes an approximation to the condition of a black body. They found that the total radiation varied as the following powers of the temperature—5 for polished platinum, $4\cdot5$ for oxide of iron, and nearly 4 for lamp-black and for platinum-black. This shows that the two latter substances in a reflecting enclosure radiate approximately as black bodies.

Lummer and Pringsheim investigated the distribution of energy in the spectrum of heated platinum, and using the platinum box mentioned above, found that the maximum emissive power E_m varied as the sixth power of the temperature. This accords with the results of Lummer and Kurlbaum for the total radiation, assuming Paschen's equation. Paschen found that $\lambda_m\Theta$ is constant for polished platinum,

---

[1] For a detailed account of the various methods and instruments used in pyrometry and the results obtained, see *Methods of Measuring Temperature*, by E. Griffiths (1925).

and this result was confirmed by Lummer and Pringsheim, who gave the value 2630 for this constant, λ_m being measured in microns.

Assuming that the radiation from the following sources is intermediate between that of platinum and that of a black body, Lummer and Pringsheim gave the limits of their temperatures as in the table.

	$\lambda m.$	$\Theta_{max}.$	$\Theta_{min}.$
Electric arc	0·7	4200° abs.	3750° abs.
Nernst lamp	1·2	2450	2200
Auer lamp	1·2	2450	2200
Incandescent lamp	1·4	2100	1875
Candle	1·5	1960	1750
Argand lamp	1·55	1900	1700

Violle, by a calorimetric method, evaluated the temperature of the electric arc at 3900° abs.; Wilson and Gray, by extrapolating the curve of emission of copper oxide, found the value 3600°; Abney and Festing gave, for the electric arc, $\lambda_m = 0·73\mu$, which, by the method given above, corresponds to the limits 4000° and 3600°; Wanner, by prolonging the isochromatic lines for the incandescent lamp, obtained the values 3700° for the negative and 3850° for the positive carbon of the electric arc.

Other determinations are contained in the following table:—[1]

Observer.	Date.	Temperature °C.	Method.
Wanner	1900	3430—3630	Wien's law.
Very	1899	3330—3730	$\lambda_m\Theta = $ const.
Féry	1902	3490	Stefan's law.
	...	3880	Wien's law.
Waidner and Burgess	1904	3400—3450	Wien's law.
Reich	1906	3430	Wien's law.

Many experiments have been made by various physicists with the object of fixing the melting points of refractory metals. In order to realise black-body conditions as nearly as possible, Mendenhall[2] used the device of folding a ribbon of the metal lengthways, so that the cross-section was in the shape of a narrow V. The ribbon was heated by an electric current up to its melting point, while the pyrometer was sighted on the inner apex of the V. Mendenhall calculated that, under these conditions, the conditions for a black body were nearly fulfilled. Another method is to bore a hole along the axis of a rod of the metal, and observe the inner wall through a small transverse hole. The melting point of molybdenum was estimated at

[1] *Methods of Measuring Temperature*, E. Griffiths, p. 186, 1925.
[2] *Astrophys. Journ.* vol. xxxiii. p. 91, 1911.

2840° K. by Pirani and Alterthum,[1] and that of tungsten at 3660° K.
Worthing[2] estimated the melting point of tungsten at 3655° K. The
mean of estimations of the melting point of tantalum by several
observers is about 3120° K.

Methods for estimating the temperature of the sun are given in
Art. 294.

We have seen that the value of the constant $\lambda_m \Theta$ is 2940 for black
bodies and 2630 for platinum. This indicates that the maximum E_m
of the emissive power is nearer the luminous part of the spectrum in
the case of platinum than of a black body, so that the radiation of
heated platinum appears to be less deficient in short than in long
waves. This seems to be the case with other substances, for Becquerel
found that the light-intensity of glowing bodies does not depend much
on their nature. This is an argument in favour of the use of the
photometric method for the measurement of temperature, when the
conditions of a black body cannot be realised.

293. The Solar Constant.[3]—The quantity of heat received in one
minute from the sun at his mean distance from the earth, by one
square centimetre of a perfectly absorbing surface presented normally
towards the sun, and supposed to be situated just outside our atmosphere, is known as the *solar constant*. It is very probable that this
quantity is not in reality constant, for it cannot be assumed that the
successive portions of the sun's surface which are presented to us have
all the same radiating power ; and further, there is reason to believe
that the heating effect of the sun undergoes a periodical variation
corresponding to the variation in the area of sun-spots, the period
being roughly about 35 years.

The method usually adopted for finding the value of the solar
constant is to find the rate at which heat is received at the earth's
surface during successive periods of the same day. The thickness of
atmosphere traversed may be then taken to be proportional to the
secant of the sun's zenith distance. Applying then Biot's formula for
the intensity I' of radiation transmitted through a thickness t of a
medium whose coefficient of absorption is k, we have

$$I' = I e^{-kt},$$

where I is the intensity of the incident beam. As we do not know k,
and as t refers to thicknesses of varying density, it will be convenient
to write this equation $\qquad S = S' a^{\sec z}$ . . . . (1)

---

[1] *Zeit. für Elektrochemie*, vol. xxix. p. 5, 1923.

[2] Forsythe and Worthing, *Astrophys. Journ.* vol. lxi. p. 146, 1925.

[3] See the Report by M. A. Crova, *Rapports présentés au Congrès International de Physique*, vol. iii. p. 453, 1900.

where S is the solar constant and S′ the fraction transmitted by the atmosphere, a a constant called the *transmission coefficient*, not yet determined, and z the sun's zenith distance, t being proportional to *sec z*. If now we give to a such a value as will make S constant for all the observations, then we may take this as the true value of a. The formula then gives S.

There are many objections to this method. In the first place, a large number of rays of very short wave-length are probably *completely* absorbed by the upper layers of the air, and no allowance for these is possible. Again, the rays have to pass through a proportionately greater thickness of the lower layers when the incidence is very oblique, owing to the earth's curvature ; also, the varying amount of reflection from the different layers is unknown. To eliminate as far as possible the errors due to atmospheric absorption, it is advisable (a) to select those series of experiments which have been performed on the most favourable days, and (b) to carry out the observations at as high an altitude as possible. The best days for experiment are not always those which appear best to the eye. Generally speaking, the days on which the sky is bluest and scatters the greatest amount of polarised light are the most favourable. On this account the cyanometer and polarimeter are of great use in forming an opinion. M. Crova found that, at Montpellier, only four or five days in the year were fully satisfactory. If the ground is at all moist, the best time for observing is before noon. Towards noon the observed radiation falls off, owing to the air becoming charged with moisture by evaporation. If the soil is very dry the observations are liable to be affected by hot currents arising from the heated ground. It is obviously difficult to carry out an experiment at a high altitude and at the same time to secure a favourable day. M. Crova performed a number of experiments on Mont Ventoux and some on Mont Blanc.

Besides the formula above given, many others have been suggested ; some of these are based on a calculation of the *mass* of air traversed, and when applied to the observations obtained on those days on which the observed heating-effect is a maximum, give very consistent values for the solar constant at various hours of the day.

The instruments used to measure the rate at which heat is received at the earth's surface are called actinometers or pyrheliometers. These are small calorimetric apparatus, blackened externally, and exposed alternately in the sunshine and in shade. If the air is not perfectly calm, it is necessary to enclose them in a sheltering envelope. The temperature is measured by a thermo-electric junction. It is advisable to allow the temperature to rise only a little above that of the surrounding air, as Newton's law can then be used for the cooling correction. Since only small differences of temperature are observed, these can be estimated to nearly $0°·001$ C. The heat-capacity of the blackened body being known, the heat received per minute is determined from the rate of rise of temperature. One of the best forms of instruments of this type is the Ångström pyrheliometer.[1] The principle employed is simple. Two thin metal strips[2] (20 mm. long, 1·5 mm. wide, and ·02 mm. thick) are alternately exposed to the radiation to be measured. When one strip is being heated by the radiation falling upon it, the other strip, which although shielded is close to the exposed strip, is heated to the same temperature by an electric current passing through it. Equality of temperature is indicated by a sensitive galvanometer connected to a pair of copper-constantan thermo-junctions, attached to the back of the receiving strips, but insulated from them by thin silk paper and shellac varnish.

It is then assumed that the energy expended in the electrically heated strip is equal to the radiant energy absorbed by the exposed strip.

The amount of energy absorbed by each particular instrument depends on three factors, which must be accurately known, viz. the width and resistance of the strips and the coefficient of absorption of the smoke-black film on the strips.[3]

Knowing these values, the absolute value of the radiation may be determined.

The radiated energy absorbed by unit length of the strips $= qab$, where

$q =$ the radiation in C.G.S. units,
$a =$ the coefficient of absorption, $0·98$,
$b =$ the width of the strip in centimetres.

Again, if i be the intensity of the current and r the resistance of unit length, then the electrical power used to balance the radiated energy is ri^2 watts.

Accordingly

$$qab = ri^2 \quad \text{and} \quad q = \frac{ri^2}{ab}.$$

This formula gives the strength of the radiation in watts per sq. cm.

[1] R. S. Whipple, "Instruments for the Measurement of Solar Radiation," *Transactions of the Optical Society*, London, 1915. A full description of the various instruments used in measuring solar radiation will be found in this paper.

[2] As originally constructed by Ångström the strips were of platinum, but Callendar having shown that the temperature coefficient of this metal was a serious source of error, strips of manganin are now employed.

[3] The absorption coefficient is generally given at 98 per cent in a new instrument—the evidence seems to show that the black deteriorates in time, the absorption coefficient becoming smaller.

Fig. 193[1] shows a section of Abbott and Fowle's absolute pyrheliometer, which is composed of a black-body receiver combined with a flow calorimeter, the chief innovation being the adoption of a hollow absorbing chamber to receive the solar rays. Such a chamber has approximately the properties of a perfect black body, and is

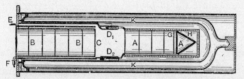

Fig. 193.—Water-flow Pyrheliometer.

almost a perfect absorber.[2] Consequently no correction is needed for the reflection of rays from the receiving surface.

AA is a chamber of about 3·5 cm. inside diameter, whose walls are hollow, and adapted for the circulation of a stream of water. The stream enters at E and bathes the walls and rear of the chamber and the cone-shaped receiver of rays H, and passes off at F, carrying away the heat developed by the solar rays which entered the chamber by the measured orifice C. At D_1 and D_2 are platinum coils adapted to measure the rise of temperature of the water due to the heating. The vestibule BB through which the rays pass is bathed by the outflowing water which escapes at F. The water flows in a spiral channel round and round the vestibule B, so that it is effectually kept at a constant temperature. The circulation of the inflowing water in the walls of the chamber AA is also effected by means of a spiral channel cut from the front to the back, thence by a spiral of decreasing radius down to the centre of the back of the chamber, then by a spiral on the cone-shaped piece H until it emerges into the tube which leads to D_2. In order to prevent outside temperature influences from vitiating the observation, the whole apparatus is enclosed in the Dewar vacuum flask KK, and to prevent the breakage of the flask it is enclosed in a brass tubular receptacle. Reference should be made to the original paper for information as to the construction of the resistance thermometer coils, the method of maintaining the water-flow constant, etc. On the back of the receiving-cone H a coil of manganin wire is wound, forming a heating coil by means of which a definite quantity of electrical energy can be dissipated in the instrument. In this way a direct comparison may be made between the temperature-rise in the outflowing water caused by solar radiation and that caused by a known quantity of electrical energy.

[1] *Annals of the Astrophys. Obs. of the Smithsonian Institution*, vol. ii. p. 40.
[2] R. S. Whipple, *loc. cit.* p. 51.

Besides these, recording actinometers are also used. In these the blackened thermo-electric junction is continuously exposed to the sun and has a very small heat-capacity, so that it can take up a temperature of equilibrium very rapidly. A continuous record of the change of temperature is given by allowing the spot of light from the galvanometer mirror to fall on a uniformly moving strip of photographic paper or similar device. These instruments must be standardised by comparison with one of the former kind.

The results of observation vary a good deal. Violle obtained 2·5 calories on Mont Blanc ; Langley 3 calories on Mount Whitney ; Savélief 2·81 and 3·4 calories at Kief. The latter figure was got under especially favourable circumstances, the ground being covered thickly with snow, while the maximum temperature during the day was $-18°$ C. ; the air was consequently very clear and free from moisture. Ångström, introducing into his calculation a term to correct for absorption of carbon dioxide, obtained 4 calories at Ixelö ; Houdaille 2·9 calories on Mont Ventoux ; and Hansky 3·0 and 3·4 calories on Mont Blanc. Several of these observers used a form of instrument designed by M. Crova. The latter physicist obtained values as high as 1·6 and 1·7 calories at Montpellier, without allowing for atmospheric absorption ; the solar constant must be greater than this, and he was of opinion that it is not less than 3 calories per square centimetre per minute. This estimate is now regarded as much too high, the most approved value being that obtained for the period 1904–9 by C. G. Abbott,[1] Director of the Astrophysical Observatory, Smithsonian Institution, Washington, viz. 1·925 calories per square centimetre per minute.

294. Effective Temperature of the Sun.[2]—The temperature which must be assigned to the sun in order that his total radiation should have its actual value, on the assumption that he radiates as a black body, is called the effective temperature of the sun. If we know the value of the solar constant S, we can calculate his temperature. Let R be the radiation per square centimetre at the sun's surface, s his radius, and r the distance of the earth, then the total radiation over the sun's surface is $4\pi s^2 R$, and this must be equal to the radiation $4\pi r^2 S$ over a sphere of radius r with the sun as centre ; therefore

$$R = \frac{r^2}{s^2} S = \left(\frac{9 \cdot 23 \times 10^7}{4 \cdot 3 \times 10^5} \right)^2 S = 46,000 \text{ S}.$$

---

[1] *Annals of the Astrophys. Obs. of the Smithsonian Institution*, vol. iii. p. 166, 1910 ; *Nature*, June 1911.

[2] See a paper by J. H. Poynting, *Phil. Trans.* vol. ccii. A, p. 525, 1903. Prof. Poynting prefers to use the term "full radiator" instead of "black body", owing to the incongruity in applying the latter expression to luminous bodies.

Poynting considered, for a reason that will be explained presently, that the best of the various values given for S is 2·5 calories, as deduced by Wilson and Gray from Rosetti's calculations.   This gives

$$R = 46,000 \times 0\cdot175 \times 10^7 = 0\cdot805 \times 10^{11}.$$

On putting, in accordance with Stefan's law,

$$R = \sigma\Theta^4,$$

and adopting Kurlbaum's value for σ, namely, $5\cdot32 \times 10^{-5}$, we get

$$\Theta = 6200° \text{ absolute}$$

as a probable value for the sun's temperature.

Wilson compared the radiation from the sun with that from a black body, and assuming the same percentage absorption in the atmosphere, deduced as the result of his experiments,

$$\Theta = 5773° \text{ abs.}$$

Somewhat higher values have been obtained by other observers. C. G. Abbott estimates the temperature at 5840° absolute.

Poynting calculated the temperature of a planet in temperature equilibrium at the distance of the earth from the sun, and, comparing the result with the actual mean temperature of the earth, used it to discriminate between the various numbers given for the solar constant.   As, according to Langley, the moon reflects about $\frac{1}{8}$ of the radiation received, it is not likely that the earth reflects more than $\frac{1}{10}$, as the atmosphere increases the absorbing power.   If the earth reflects less than this, it will not make much difference in the result of the calculation, as the value arrived at for the temperature depends on the fourth root of the absorptive power, and $\sqrt[4]{0\cdot9} = 0\cdot974$, which is not much less than unity.

The following assumptions are made to simplify the calculation. The planet is supposed to be rotating about an axis perpendicular to the plane of its orbit.   This will make the temperature of the poles too low and that of the equator too high, and thus give a mean temperature which is a little too low, but the difference may be neglected for our purpose.   It is also assumed that the effect of the atmosphere is to keep the temperature constant day and night in any given latitude, which is approximately true for the earth.   It is further assumed that no conduction of heat takes place from one latitude to another, and that the surface and the atmosphere over it at any point have one effective temperature as a full radiator. Making these suppositions, let us consider a band of the surface

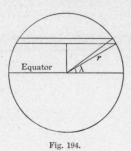

Fig. 194.

between latitudes λ and $\lambda + d\lambda$. The area receiving heat from the sun at any instant, if projected normally to the stream of solar radiation, is (Fig. 194)

$$2r \cos \lambda \,.\, rd\lambda \cos \lambda = 2r^2 \cos^2 \lambda d\lambda,$$

where r is the radius of the planet. The amount of energy absorbed per second by this band is, if S is the solar constant and a the absorptive power,

$$a\text{S}\,.\,2r^2 \cos^2 \lambda d\lambda.$$

But the band all round the globe is radiating equally, so that the radiating area is

$$2\pi r \cos \lambda \,.\, rd\lambda = 2\pi r^2 \cos \lambda d\lambda \;;$$

and as, on the assumption of temperature equilibrium, all the heat received by this area is radiated by it again, we have, as the radiation per square centimetre,

$$\frac{a\text{S}\,.\,2r^2 \cos^2 \lambda d\lambda}{2\pi r^2 \cos \lambda d\lambda} = \frac{a\text{S} \cos \lambda}{\pi}.$$

If the effective temperature for this latitude is Θ_λ, then, applying Stefan's law,

$$\Theta^4_\lambda = \frac{a\text{S} \cos \lambda}{\pi\sigma},$$

and the average temperature over the globe, being the same as for one hemisphere, is

$$\overline{\Theta} = \frac{1}{2\pi r^2} \int_0^{\frac{\pi}{2}} \Theta_\lambda \,.\, 2\pi r^2 \cos \lambda d\lambda$$

$$= \left(\frac{a\text{S}}{\pi\sigma}\right)^{\frac{1}{4}} \int_0^{\frac{\pi}{2}} \cos^{\frac{5}{4}} \lambda d\lambda$$

$$= \frac{\sqrt{\pi}}{2} \,.\, \frac{\Gamma(\frac{9}{8})}{\Gamma(\frac{5}{8})} \,.\, \left(\frac{a\text{S}}{\pi\sigma}\right)^{\frac{1}{4}}.$$

Evaluating this expression, we get

$$\overline{\Theta} = 290° \text{ absolute.}$$

Tempera-
tures of
planets.

This is about the mean temperature of the earth's surface, and hence Poynting adopted the value of S which leads to this result, in preference to other values which give higher temperatures. It should be remembered, however, that we have assumed Stefan's law for the earth's radiation. We have also further assumed that the earth is radiating energy at the same rate as it receives it, *i.e.* that its surface is in temperature equilibrium with the sun's radiation. The surface of the earth must be at a somewhat higher temperature than this, since it is continually receiving heat from the interior. Joly [1] calculates that the amount of heat coming to the surface is about 0·000075 of a calorie per sq. cm. per minute.

However, if we regard the assumptions as approximately true, and if we suppose the planets to be in a state of similar temperature equilibrium, then we may calculate their mean temperatures by the simple formula

$$\frac{\Theta_p}{\Theta_e} = \sqrt{\frac{r_e}{r_p}},$$

where Θ_p is the temperature of the planet, and r_p its distance from the sun, Θ_e and r_e being corresponding quantities for the earth. For the temperature is proportional to the fourth root of the radiation, and the radiation is inversely proportional to the square of the distance from the sun. Poynting gives 69° C. as the mean temperature of Venus determined in this way, and the temperature of Mars as being near the freezing point of mercury. The corresponding figure for. Neptune is about – 200° C. Langley calculated that the surface of the full moon is only a few degrees above the freezing point of water ; Poynting, however, gives a higher estimate.

Example

1. Find the temperature of equilibrium of a perfectly black disc exposed normally to the sun's rays at the distance of the earth ; supposing that it has a non-conducting backing, so that it can radiate only to a hemisphere of space.

{Let ψ_s and ψ_e be the densities of the sun's radiant energy at his surface and at the distance of the earth, r the radius of the sun, R the distance of the earth, and Θ_s the effective temperature of the sun, then

$$\frac{\psi_e}{\psi_s} = \frac{r^2}{R^2}.$$

For equilibrium, the disc must be emitting energy at the same rate as it receives it, therefore the density of the emitted energy in the immediate neighbourhood of the disc is ψ_e (neglecting the falling-off at the edges of the disc). This shows that the temperature of the disc does not depend on whether the incident radiation is *directed* or *diffused*. We may therefore apply Stefan's law, and put, if Θ_e is the required temperature,

$$\frac{\Theta_e}{\Theta_s} = \sqrt[4]{\frac{\psi_e}{\psi_s}} = \sqrt{\frac{r}{R}}.$$

If we assume $\Theta_s = 6200°$, $r = 430,000$ miles, R $= 93,000,000$ miles, this gives

$$\Theta_e = 422° \text{ abs.} = 149° \text{ C.}$$

If we supposed the disc to radiate on both sides, we should have to put $\frac{1}{2}\psi_e$ for ψ_e, so that the result would be divided by $\sqrt[4]{2}$, or $\Theta_e = 81°$ C.}

[1] *Radioactivity and Geology*, p. 75.

CHAPTER VII

CONDUCTION

SECTION I

ON THE CONDUCTIVITY OF SOLIDS

295. Preliminary Considerations.—One of the three processes by which heat is transferred from one body to another, or from one part of a body to another, is termed conduction; the other two have been considered already, and are known as convection and radiation. In the case of radiation the propagation takes place with the velocity of light, and, except in the case of absorbing media, when radiant energy is transmitted through any body, it leaves the intermediate parts apparently unaffected.

The propagation of heat by conduction, on the other hand, is comparatively a very slow process, and the heat, in travelling through a body by this method, increases the temperature of the intermediate parts, and remains partly lodged in them, at least until a stationary condition is attained. When one end of a metal rod is placed in a lamp-flame, a gradual rise of temperature is noticed along the bar, the parts nearest the flame being warmer than those more remote. For some time the temperature at each point of the bar gradually increases, but ultimately a stationary condition is reached, and the temperature at each point remains permanently the same. In this stationary state, however, there is still a flow of heat along the rod, and the temperature has become steady, merely because the heat is radiated from the surface of the rod as fast as it is supplied at the end.

The process of conduction is usually regarded as essentially different from that of radiation, and it is sometimes described as the passage of heat from one body to another, or from one part of a body to another, "by contact", so that the heat passes from one layer to another while the matter remains at rest. This mode of passage might be intelligible

592

if heat were regarded as a fluid, but from any other point of view it is without meaning. In the process of radiation heat is propagated as a free-wave motion in the ether, but in the process of conduction the action of the matter through which the heat travels becomes of prime importance. Each molecule as it becomes heated may affect those around it, either by direct radiation or by forcing into vibration those with which it may come into contact. On consideration, therefore, it will appear that no entirely new process is essentially involved in the conduction of heat, but that all equalisation of temperature may be effected either by convection or by a process of intermolecular radiation and absorption.

Let us return to the molecular theory, and assimilate the molecules of a body to tuning-forks, or other vibrating systems, each having one or more definite periods of vibration, and, bearing in mind what has been already stated in Art. 256, let us consider the propagation of heat along a bar heated at one end. For greater clearness let us suppose that the end of the bar is heated by being placed very close to a hot radiating surface, such as a white-hot metal ball, and let the molecules of the bar be supposed free to vibrate independently— that is, spaced in the ether so that they may vibrate freely. The ball is then to be regarded merely as a source of waves in the ether, which, when emitted, fall upon the end of the bar. These waves are at first chiefly used up in setting in vibration a thin layer of molecules at the end of the bar. This layer (which we may say is a few millions of molecules deep) absorbs the waves at first almost completely, and protects those behind from disturbance. Very soon, however, the front molecules are set in active vibration, and become sources of disturbance themselves, radiating waves in the ether, so that new molecules in the rear begin to be set in motion, and the disturbance is thus gradually propagated along the bar by a process of absorption and subsequent radiation (by the molecules) of the waves from the source of heat.[1]

So far we have no contact considerations whatever, the whole process is simply the propagation of wave motion through an absorbing system. Of course the molecules may be in contact, at least some of them may, and jangling may take place, so that when one molecule is disturbed it forces the vibrations of others close to it. The supposition of actual contact is, however, not absolutely necessary to the intelligible explanation of the phenomenon, as will perhaps be more clear from the following illustration.

Let us suppose that a vast number of boats are moored in a

[1] See Art. 306 for Drude's theory of heat conduction.

2 Q

large harbour, and let each boat floating on the water correspond to a molecule of matter in the ether. Now let a storm arise at some distance out at sea, and let the waves travelling to shore approach the harbour, and be of such a period that the boats absorb them and are thus set vibrating. The first waves which arrive will be almost entirely absorbed by the front row of boats, so that those nearer land are quite protected from disturbance. After a little, however, the front ranks are in violent oscillation, and cease to absorb any sensible fraction of the waves which fall upon them; or, regarded from the other point of view, they radiate as much as they absorb. The waves are now able to penetrate farther, and gradually reach the boats in the rear, so that the disturbance is thus gradually *conducted* through the whole system.

The propagation of a disturbance in this manner would be expected to be a fairly slow process, such as we actually observe in nature, the rate of propagation being determined by the rate at which the waves are absorbed by the molecules and by the molecular capacities —that is, by the whole period of absorption of any molecule, or the interval of time between the commencement of absorption by a molecule and the stage at which it radiates as much as it absorbs. This interval will, of course, depend on the nature of the molecules, and the conductivity may be expected to vary considerably in different substances.[1] The simplest experiments show us that different bodies vary enormously in conducting powers. For example, a silver spoon placed in a cup of hot tea soon becomes heated throughout its length, while a glass rod placed in the same cup will scarcely ever show any perceptible increase of temperature at its farther end ; but although we have substances like glass which are bad conductors of heat, yet we have no non-conductors of heat as we have non-conductors of electricity. This is a serious disadvantage, and is much felt in almost every department of practical life.

COMPARISON OF CONDUCTIVITIES

296. Ingen-Hausz's Experiment.—One of the earliest methods of *comparing* the conductivities of different bodies for heat was suggested by Franklin, and the comparison was carried out by Ingen-Hausz.[2]

[1] Pictet supposed that heat ascends in a solid more rapidly than it descends, but the observations which led him to this opinion were probably influenced in a considerable degree by upward air currents. For even in the so-called vacuum of an air-pump sufficient air remains to explain his experiments. Ascending currents are produced in the neighbourhood of the hot body, and for this reason cold air continually approaches its lower parts, so that the heat is carried upwards.

[2] Ingen-Hausz (Jean): "Sur les métaux comme conducteurs de la chaleur," *Journ. de Phys.* tom. xxxiv. pp. 68, 380 ; 1789.

Bars of the various substances were prepared and coated with bees-wax. Their ends were then immersed in a bath A of hot oil (Fig. 195), and after standing some time it was observed that the wax was melted off the different bars to different lengths.   On some of the bars the wax is melted off more rapidly, and on some to greater distances, than on others, but it does not hold that those from which the wax is melted most
rapidly at first are those from which
it will be furthest melted on prolonged
immersion.   If all the bars had the
same conducting power—that is, allowed
the same flow of heat per unit time—
then when the wax is melting the
temperature at any point of the bar
will be less the greater the specific
heat, so that on those of the lowest

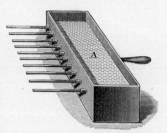

Fig. 195.—Ingen-Hausz's Experiment.

specific heat the wax will melt most rapidly ; but on prolonged im-mersion the temperature of the bar reaches a permanent state, and all the heat which enters it by conduction leaves it by radiation.

It has been demonstrated by Professor Tyndall that the tempera-ture wave travels faster in bismuth than in iron, though the conductivity of bismuth is much less than that of iron.   The specific heat becomes of no account when the stationary state is attained, and the length of wax melted will be greater as the conductivity is greater.   The length melted off when the permanent state is arrived at will not, however, be in the simple ratio of the conductivities, but if the bars have the same cross-section and the same coefficients of emission, we shall show further on that the conductivities k and k' of any two on which the lengths ultimately melted off are l and l' are related by the equation

$$\frac{k}{k'} = \frac{l^2}{l'^2}.$$

To secure the same coefficient of emission the bars may be electro-plated and polished.   The rate of melting of the wax on any bar measures the rate at which a wave of temperature travels along it, but this is not the conductivity.   The relative conductivities are determined alone from the lengths melted off when the *permanent stage* is arrived at.

Another form of the experiment consists in attaching small pellets to the lower sides of the bars by means of wax.   The temperature at which the wax is sufficiently softened to allow the pellets to fall off travels along the bars at different rates, but if the balls be equally spaced the conductivities will be as the squares of the numbers of balls melted off when the permanent state is attained.

Rectilinear Flow of Heat—Conduction through an Infinite Wall

297. Precise Definition of Conductivity.—The first to give a thoroughly scientific definition of conducting power was Fourier, who, in his *Théorie analytique de la chaleur* (1822), treated the subject of the propagation of heat with a power and completeness which left little room for extension or improvement, and suggested or rendered possible almost all later developments.[1]

In order to obtain an exact notion of conduction, let us consider the case of a plane lamina or wall, with parallel faces, one of which is kept at a fixed temperature θ_1, while the other is maintained at θ_2. Here there will be established a permanent state and a uniform flow of heat from the hotter to the colder face, and the temperature may be taken to fall uniformly from θ_1 at one face to θ_2 at the other, if the wall be throughout of the same material, and if the conducting power does not depend on the temperature. Hence, if we consider any plane drawn in the wall parallel to the faces, it is clear that the same quantity of heat will pass across every such plane per second when the permanent state is established.

In estimating this quantity of heat the first principle that we make use of is, that the quantity of heat which flows through such a wall is directly proportional to the difference of temperature $(\theta_1 - \theta_2)$ of its faces. This we may regard as established by experiment. From this it will follow that for walls of the same substance and of different thicknesses, whose faces have the same temperature difference $(\theta_1 - \theta_2)$, the flow will be in the inverse ratio of the thickness. For since the difference of temperature between the faces is the same for all the walls, then the fall per unit thickness is inversely as the thickness, and consequently the flow through a plate of unit thickness of any wall, which is the same as the flow through the wall, will be inversely as the thickness of the wall. Further, the quantity of heat which flows through an area A of such a wall in a time t will be proportional to A and also to t. We consequently have for the quantity which flows through a plate of area A and thickness e in a time t—

[1] With respect to Fourier's work, Professor Tait says: "Its exquisitely original methods have been the source of inspiration of some of the greatest mathematicians; and the mere application of one of its simplest portions to the conduction of electricity has made the name of Ohm famous."

$$Q = K\frac{\theta_1 - \theta_2}{e}At.$$

The coefficient K is a quantity depending on the nature of the substance, and is called the *conductivity* of the substance. Taking the case of a wall of unit thickness, with unit difference of temperature between its faces, we find that the conductivity K *is numerically equal to the quantity of heat which flows per unit time through unit area of a plate of unit thickness, having unit difference of temperature between its faces.*

If we suppose the lamina to have an infinitely small thickness dx and an infinitely small temperature difference $d\theta$ between its faces, the quantity of heat which flows through it in a small time dt will be

$$Q = KA\frac{\theta - (\theta + d\theta)}{dx} = -KA\frac{d\theta}{dx}dt.$$

The quantity $d\theta/dx$ is the *gradient of temperature* at any point—that is, the change of temperature per unit thickness—and the above expression for Q, which is of fundamental importance in the theory of

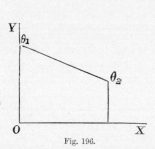

Fig. 196.

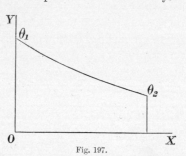

Fig. 197.

conduction, expresses that the flow through unit area per unit time is equal to the conductivity K multiplied by the temperature gradient.

We have so far considered the substance homogeneous—that is, that each layer of the wall possesses the same conducting power, so that the temperature falls uniformly from one face to the other, and the temperature gradient is uniform. The curve representing the relation between the temperature θ at any point and the distance x of the point from one face will therefore be a right line (Fig. 196)—

$$\theta = a + bx.$$

The constants a and b are easily determined, for when $x = 0$ we have $\theta = \theta_1$, therefore $a = \theta_1$; and when $x = e$ we have $\theta = \theta_2$, therefore $\theta_2 = \theta_1 + be$ or $b = (\theta_2 - \theta_1)/e$. The temperature at any point of the wall is consequently

$$\theta = \theta_1 - \frac{\theta_1 - \theta_2}{e}x.$$

If, however, the various layers of the wall have different conductivities the temperature gradient will not be uniform, and the relation between θ and x will not be linear. When the conductivity is good the slope of temperature will be small, but the reverse will hold when the conductivity is bad. Fig. 197 would represent the temperature curve for a wall in which the conductivity gradually improved from the face θ_1 to the face θ_2. Something like this may actually hold in nature, for the quantity K, instead of being a constant for a given kind of matter, will in general depend upon its physical state as regards temperature and pressure. We know that electrical conductivity diminishes as the temperature rises, and the evidence as to thermal conductivity points in the same direction. In general, those substances which are the best conductors of electricity are also the best conductors of heat, and anything which affects one may also influence the other. In the case of the wall considered above, the temperatures of the layers near the face θ_1 are higher than those near the face θ_2; consequently, if the conductivity at high is less than at low temperatures, the slope of temperature will be steeper near the face θ_1 than near the face θ_2.

In all such cases, however, when the steady state is established, the quantity of heat which passes each layer is the same, and we have therefore

$$\mathrm{K}\frac{d\theta}{dx} = \text{constant}.$$

Hence if K be given as a function of x and θ, the above differential equation determines the form of the temperature curve and the gradient at each point of the wall.

Ex. 1. If K varies as θ, then—

$$\theta^2 = ax + b,$$

and the temperature curve is consequently a parabola.

Ex. 2. If K varies inversely as x, we have

$$\theta = ax^2 + b,$$

and the temperature curve is again a parabola.

Ex. 3. If K is proportional to x, we have

$$\theta = a\int\frac{dx}{x} = a\,\log\,x + b,$$

or

$$x = \mathrm{A}e^{\frac{\theta}{a}},$$

and the temperature curve is consequently logarithmic.

298. Steady Flow of Heat through a Long Bar.—Let us now consider the case of a long bar heated steadily at one end. For some time after the first application of heat at the end the temperature at each point of the bar will gradually rise, but ultimately each point will acquire a stationary temperature and a steady flow will take place along the bar. Theoretically it would require an infinite time to reach this steady state, but it is practically attained in a comparatively short time, depending on the nature of the bar. Supposing this stage to have been attained, let θ be the temperature of the surface at a distance x from the hot end, measured along the axis of the bar. Then if we suppose the temperature gradient to be uniform over the cross-section A of the bar at this point, or if its mean value over the section be $d\theta/dx$, the flow of heat per unit time across this section will be

$$- KA\frac{d\theta}{dx}.$$

But the temperature at an adjacent point, $x + \delta x$, will be $\theta + \frac{d\theta}{dx}\delta x$, since $d\theta/dx$ is the rate at which the temperature rises along the bar, and this multiplied by δx will be the rise of temperature in passing from the point x to $x + \delta x$, if δx be taken so small that the temperature gradient is sensibly constant between the two points. Hence the flow of heat across the section at the point $x + \delta x$ will be

$$- KA\frac{d}{dx}\left(\theta + \frac{d\theta}{dx}\delta x\right),$$

and consequently the excess of what flows in at one face of the element over what flows out at the other will be [1]

$$KA\frac{d^2\theta}{dx^2}\delta x.$$

Now, in the steady state this excess must be entirely radiated from the surface of the element, and denoting the perimeter of the bar by p, the area of this surface is $p\delta x$, so that if θ be measured from the temperature of the surrounding medium—that is, if θ is the excess of the temperature of the surface of the element over that of the sur-

---

[1] This is on the assumption that K is a constant. If K is a function of the temperature, let Q be the flow of heat per second across a section whose distance is x from the point of reference. Then the heat-flow per second across a section whose distance is $x + \delta x$ will be $Q + \frac{dQ}{dx}\delta x$, and since $Q = - KA\frac{d\theta}{dx}$, the excess of heat which flows in at one face of the element over that which flows out of the other face is

$$\frac{d}{dx}\left(KA\frac{d\theta}{dx}\right)\delta x,$$

or

$$A\frac{d}{dx}\left(K\frac{d\theta}{dx}\right)\delta x.$$

If K is constant, this reduces to the expression in the text.

rounding medium, the heat radiated by the element will be $Ep\theta\delta x$, assuming Newton's law, where E is the surface emissivity of the bar. Hence in the steady state we have [1]

$$KA\frac{d^2\theta}{dx^2} = Ep\theta,$$

or

$$\frac{d^2\theta}{dx^2} = \mu^2\theta,$$

where for brevity we have written

$$\mu^2 = \frac{Ep}{KA}.$$

It may be easily verified by substitution that the solution of this equation is

$$\theta = Me^{\mu x} + Ne^{-\mu x},$$

where M and N are constants to be determined by the conditions of the problem.

Cor. *Ingen-Hausz's Experiment.*—In this case the wax is melted off a bar to a distance l, and the temperature here is the melting point of the wax. We also suppose that the bars are very long, so that their extremities are at the temperature of the surrounding medium ; in this case we have the excess $\theta = 0$, when $x = \infty$, therefore

$$0 = Me^{\mu\,\infty} + Ne^{-\mu\,\infty} = Me^{\mu\,\infty},$$

consequently

$$M = 0.$$

---

[1] This equation may also be written in the form

$$k\frac{d^2\theta}{dx^2} = -\frac{d\theta}{dt},$$

where $-d\theta/dt$ is what Forbes termed the statical rate of cooling—that is, the rate at which the element would cool if isolated from the rest of the bar, and $k = K/c$, where c is the thermal capacity of the substance per unit volume. For if we consider the element isolated and to lose heat by its surface $p\delta x$ only, then the rate of loss is, by Newton's law, $Ep\theta\delta x$, but this must be counterbalanced by a fall of temperature, so that if the rate of fall of temperature of the element be $-d\theta/dt$ we have

$$Ep\theta\delta x = -cA\delta x\frac{d\theta}{dt},$$

so that

$$\frac{Ep}{A}\theta = -c\frac{d\theta}{dt},$$

therefore, etc.—See further, *Phil. Mag.*, March 1879, pp. 198, 251, Dr. O. J. Lodge.

But when $x = 0$ the excess of temperature is that of the source θ_0, therefore

$$\theta_0 = N,$$

and therefore we have in general for the excess of temperature θ, at any distance x,

$$\theta = \theta_0 e^{-\mu x}.$$

Now if on any bar a length l_1 of the wax is melted off, we have

$$\theta_1 = \theta_0 e^{-\mu l_1},$$

where θ_1 is the melting point of the wax, measured from the temperature of the surrounding medium, and hence

$$\mu l_1 = \log\left(\frac{\theta_0}{\theta_1}\right).$$

Now for all the bars θ_1 and θ_0 are the same, therefore if the wax is melted off to distances l_1, l_2, l_3, etc., we have

$$\mu_1 l_1 = \mu_2 l_2 = \mu_3 l_3 = \ldots \text{ constant.}$$

For any two bars we have consequently

$$\frac{l_1}{l_2} = \frac{\mu_2}{\mu_1},$$

or

$$\frac{l_1{}^2}{l_2{}^2} = \frac{E_2 p_2}{K_2 A_2} \cdot \frac{E_1 p_1}{K_1 A_1}.$$

Hence if the bars have the same cross-section, perimeter, and coefficient of emission, we shall have

$$\frac{K_1}{K_2} = \frac{l_1{}^2}{l_2{}^2},$$

or

$$\frac{K_1}{l_1{}^2} = \frac{K_2}{l_2{}^2} = \frac{K_3}{l_3{}^2} = \text{etc.}$$

299. Comparison of Conductivities by Means of Three Temperatures at Equal Distances.—Let the temperatures of the bar (Fig. 198) at distances x, $x + a$, $x + 2a$, be θ_1, θ_2, θ_3, then we have

$$\theta_1 = Me^{\mu x} + Ne^{-\mu x} = a + b, \text{ suppose.}$$
$$\theta_2 = Me^{\mu(x+a)} + Ne^{-\mu(x+a)} = ae^{\mu a} + be^{-\mu a}.$$
$$\theta_3 = Me^{\mu(x+2a)} + Ne^{-\mu(x+2a)} = ae^{2\mu a} + be^{-2\mu a}.$$

Eliminating a and b from these equations we have

$$\begin{vmatrix} \theta_1 & \theta_2 & \theta_3 \\ 1 & e^{\mu a} & e^{2\mu a} \\ 1 & e^{-\mu a} & e^{-2\mu a} \end{vmatrix} = 0,$$

or

$$\theta_1(e^{\mu a} - e^{-\mu a}) - \theta_2(e^{2\mu a} - e^{-2\mu a}) + \theta_3(e^{\mu a} - e^{-\mu a}) = 0.$$

Dividing by $e^{\mu a} - e^{-\mu a}$ we have

$$\theta_1 - \theta_2(e^{\mu a} + e^{-\mu a}) + \theta_3 = 0,$$

that is

$$e^{2\mu a} - \frac{\theta_1 + \theta_3}{\theta_2} e^{\mu a} + 1 = 0.$$

Denoting $\dfrac{\theta_1 + \theta_3}{\theta_2}$ by $2n$ we have the quadratic

$$e^{2\mu a} - 2n e^{\mu a} + 1 = 0,$$

or

$$e^{\mu a} = n + \sqrt{n^2 - 1},$$

the positive sign being taken with the radical, because in the experiment of Art. 300, $\theta_1 + \theta_3$ is greater than $2\theta_2$, and n is greater than unity, therefore $n - \sqrt{n^2 - 1}$ is less than unity. But $e^{\mu a}$ is greater than unity, hence we have finally

$$\mu a = \log\,(n + \sqrt{n^2 - 1}),$$

and for two bars of the same perimeter, section, and coefficient of emission we have, taking a the same in both—

$$\sqrt{\frac{K_1}{K_2}} = \frac{\mu_2}{\mu_1} = \frac{\log\,(n_2 + \sqrt{n_2{}^2 - 1})}{\log\,(n_1 + \sqrt{n_1{}^2 - 1})}.$$

Hence,[1] by reading the temperatures of three thermometers placed at

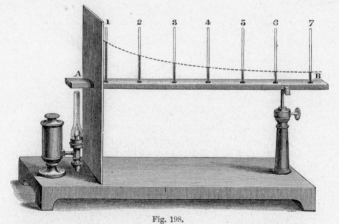

Fig. 198.

equal distances from each other in bars of various substances, their conductivities may be compared—that is, the specific or relative conductivity of any bar may be obtained, but the absolute conductivity as defined in Art. 297 remains still unknown.

---

[1] This equation suggests a method of comparing the emissivities of the surface of a bar when coated with different substances, or when in different states of polish. For when n_1 and n_2 are determined for the same bar in two different surface conditions, we know the ratio of μ_1 to μ_2—that is, of E_1 to E_2.

300. Despretz's Experiments.—The principles of the foregoing article were made use of by Despretz[1] in a series of experiments on the relative conductivities of bars of various metals. The bar under experiment was heated at one end by a steady lamp, and the temperatures at various points of the bar were determined by means of thermometers which were inserted in small holes sunk into the axis of the bar (Fig. 198). The thermometers are brought into intimate contact with the bar by having their bulbs surrounded by a little mercury, or in the case of high temperatures by a fusible alloy, placed in the holes into which they are inserted. By this means the temperature curve along the entire length of the bar can be plotted, and this curve, if the principles assumed in Art. 298 are accurately fulfilled, should be logarithmic. The conditions assumed in the theory are, however, only approximately fulfilled in practice, and the curve is found on trial to be only approximately logarithmic. The logarithmic curve between any two points is found to lie above the experimental curve, so that the latter has a greater sag towards the bar than the former.

In order to compare the conductivities of two bars by the method of the foregoing article it is necessary that they should have the same surface emissivity, and this may be secured, at least approximately, by coating them with lamp-black, or a black varnish, or by electro-plating, or more simply by covering them with white paper pasted on. If, in addition, the cross-sections and perimeters of the bars under comparison be the same, the conductivities of any pair are compared by the formula[2]

$$\sqrt{\frac{K_1}{K_2}} = \frac{\log (n_2 + \sqrt{n_2{}^2 - 1})}{\log (n_1 + \sqrt{n_1{}^2 - 1})},$$

where, if θ_1, θ_2, θ_3 are the temperature excesses registered by three equidistant thermometers, then $2n = (\theta_1 + \theta_3)/\theta_2$. Despretz verified the theoretic deduction of the foregoing article, viz. that the temperature

---

[1] Despretz, *Ann. de Chimie et de Physique*, 2e sér., tom. xix. p. 97, 1822 ; and tom. xxxvi. p. 422, 1827.

[2] As a result of experiments by Jakob and Erk (*Zeit. für Physik*, vol. xxxv. p. 670, 1926) it was found that very considerable errors are introduced by the assumption that the surface conductivity is independent of the difference in temperature between the surface of the rod and the air. This objection applies both to Despretz's experiments and to those of Wiedemann and Franz (Art. 301). According to Jakob and Erk, the equation in the text should be written

$$\sqrt{\frac{K_1}{K_2}} = \sqrt{\frac{a_1}{a_2}} \cdot \frac{\log (n_2 + \sqrt{n_2{}^2 - 1})}{\log (n_1 + \sqrt{n_1{}^2 - 1})},$$

where a_1 and a_2 are different coefficients, and they show how a_1 and a_2 may be determined from the observations.

excesses of a series of equidistant thermometers along the same bar were related, by the equations

$$\frac{\theta_1 + \theta_3}{\theta_2} = \frac{\theta_2 + \theta_4}{\theta_3} = \frac{\theta_3 + \theta_5}{\theta_4} = \text{etc.}$$

Objections have been raised to this method of experiment on the ground that the thermometer holes sunk in the bar introduce a discontinuity into the material, which alters both the distribution of temperature and the flow of heat. The error introduced in this manner will, however, be inappreciable if the widths of the cavities be fairly small compared with the diameter of the bar. For example, a cavity 2 mm. wide cannot produce any sensible effect on the flow of heat through a bar from 1 to 2 centimetres thick, especially when the cavities are filled up with a fluid metal.

In order to secure the same surface emissivity Despretz coated the bars with lamp-black, but this so increased the emissivity that the temperature fell very rapidly along the bar, and in many cases it became very difficult to observe the difference of temperature between two thermometers even at a short distance from the heated end.

Any want of homogeneity in the bars will also introduce considerable difficulty and uncertainty into such experiments as these, and perfectly homogeneous bars, free from all impurities, are perhaps not to be obtained. For such reasons, therefore, differences are to be expected between the results obtained by different observers from experiments made on different specimens of the same substance, and discrepancies of a more or less serious aspect are not surprising. In ordinary laboratory experiments it is better to use short bars, and for accurate determinations bars artificially cooled at the end.

301. Experiments of Wiedemann and Franz.—In order to examine the accuracy of the results obtained by Despretz, a new series of experiments was undertaken by Wiedemann and Franz.[1] The principle of the method adopted was the same as that of Despretz, but the apparatus employed differed in some important respects. The bars employed were about half a metre long and 6 mm. in diameter, and in order to secure the same surface emissivity they were electroplated.

The bar under examination was fixed horizontally in the centre of a glass vessel (Fig. 199) which was air-tight, and could be exhausted so that experiments could be made in a vacuum as well as in air. This vessel was immersed in a water-bath, the temperature of which could be determined and kept constant. The end of the bar was heated by a current of steam, and its temperature was thus kept approximately at 100° C. The temperatures at various points along the bar were

[1] Wiedemann and Franz, *Ann. de Chimie*, 3e sér., tom. xli. p. 107, 1854.

determined by means of a thermopile, the leading wires of which
passed through a glass tube which could be protruded into the interior
of the inner vessel at will, so that the pile could slide along the bar
and register the temperature at its various points. The pile was

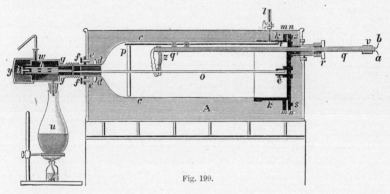

Fig. 199.

graduated by direct experiments made by heating, within the apparatus
itself, a hollow tube of steel filled with mercury and containing a
thermometer.[1] The results of these experiments are contained in the
following table :—

RELATIVE CONDUCTIVITIES

	In Air.	In Vacuum.
Silver	100	100
Copper	73·6	74·8
Gold	53·2	54·8
Brass	{ 23·1 { 24·1	{ 25·0 { 24·0
Tin	14·5	15·4
Iron	11·9	10·1
Steel	11·6	10·3
Lead	8·5	7·9
Platinum . . .	6·3	7·3
Rose's alloy . . .	2·8	2·8
Bismuth	1·8	...

**302. On the Experimental Determination of Absolute Con-
ductivities.**—The definition of conductivity stated in Art. 297 sug-

[1] Langberg (*Pogg. Ann.* Bd. lxxxix. p. 1, Sept. 1853) introduced the method of
thermo-electric couples instead of the thermometers used by Despretz. The junction
was applied against the bar. Wiedemann and Franz employed the same method, but
adopted many precautions neglected by Langberg. The principal objection to Langberg's work is the neglect of making the same closeness of contact with the couple
in all cases, and in employing wires instead of bars the errors due to air-currents and
accidental causes were greatly magnified. The possibility of a definite difference of
temperature between the bar and the junction is a serious objection raised by Verdet.

gests at once a method of estimating it in absolute measure, for if the
two faces of a plate of known thickness and area be maintained at
fixed temperatures, and if the difference of these be accurately known,
as well as the quantity of heat which flows through the plate per second,
then all the quantities necessary for the estimation of K will be known.
Thus, if steam be blown against one face of the plate, and if melting ice or
water be placed in contact with the other, the flow of heat may be ascertained by the amount of steam condensed on one side, or by the amount
of ice melted on the other, or by the change of temperature of the water.

A great difficulty attending this method arises, however, in the
determination of the exact temperatures of the faces of the plate, for
the hot face is certainly colder than the vapour, and the cold face is
undoubtedly warmer than the water or ice in contact with it.   The
difference of temperature between the faces of the plate will therefore
be much less than the difference of temperature between the steam on
one side and the water on the other.   To proceed on the supposition
that the hot face is at the temperature of the steam, or very approximately so, and that the cold face is also very nearly at the temperature
of the melting ice or water, is to assume conditions which are very far
from the truth.   This is shown clearly by the results obtained in this
manner by Clément and Péclet,[1] the number obtained by the former
for the conductivity of copper being about 200 times too small, and
that of the latter 6 times too small.[2]   This means that, if the other
quantities be supposed to have been correctly observed, the difference
of temperature between the faces of the plate was with the former
200 times and with the latter 6 times less than was supposed.

The change of temperature in passing through a thin film of water
in contact with the plate may, in such an experiment, be much greater
than the whole difference between the faces of the plate, so that
although the face of the plate is essentially at the same temperature
as the surface of the adjacent film, yet it may differ largely from
the temperature registered by any ordinary thermometer placed close
to it, nor does it seem likely that the difficulty could be quite got rid
of by taking the temperature of the face by means of thermo-electric
junctions.   Péclet seems to have been alive to this source of error in
Clément's experiments, for he vastly improved his apparatus by placing
a special stirrer in the water so that fresh layers were constantly
brought into contact with the face of the metal plate ; but even this
only partially removed the error, for the surface film adheres to the
plate, and no process of stirring would remove it with sufficient

---

[1] Péclet, *Ann. de Chimie et de Physique*, 3e sér., tom. ii. p. 107, 1841.
[2] See art. "Heat," *Ency. Brit.* (Lord Kelvin).

rapidity to keep the face of the plate at anything like the mean temperature of the liquid.

The only hopeful method, then, is to take temperatures in the metal itself and not outside it.   Thus, if the plane faces of the plate be supposed vertical, then small vertical holes should be drilled in the plate, one near each face, and the temperatures of the metal at these points may be taken either by small thermometers placed in the holes or by some thermo-electric method.   By this means the temperatures of the two faces of a layer of known thickness of the plate are known, and all the quantities required for the determination of K may be obtained with tolerable accuracy.   This amounts practically to what we shall describe as the guard-ring method.

Another method was devised by Forbes in 1850, and although it is very simple in principle, yet it is exceedingly tedious and laborious in practice.   The object of the method is to determine K by estimating the quantity of heat that flows through any section of a bar, heated at one end, as in the experiments of Despretz.   When the stationary stage is attained, the whole heat that crosses any section of the bar is radiated from the surface between the section and the cool end of the bar. If, therefore, the temperatures be known at all points along the bar, and if the emissivity of the surface be also determined for all temperatures by separate observations on a similar bar, or on part of the same bar, then the whole quantity of heat radiated per second by the surface between any cross-section and the cold end can be calculated. This with the temperature gradient at the section in question gives the conductivity.   The temperature gradient is found from the temperature curve, being the trigonometrical tangent of the angle which the tangent line at the corresponding point of the curve makes with the axis of x.   Hence when the temperature curve is plotted, we can find the temperature gradient at any point of the bar.

A third method has also been devised and employed with success. This method was introduced by Ångström and depends on the observation of the periodic flow of heat in a bar alternately heated and cooled at one end or at some point of its length.   We shall consider this method fully later on ; at present we shall describe the experiments of Forbes, as they were the first to yield trustworthy results.

303. Forbes's Method.—As already mentioned, the experimental method of Forbes [1] consists essentially of two distinct observations—

---

[1] Forbes, James D., *Phil. Trans. Roy. Soc. Edinburgh*, vol. xxiii. p. 133, April 1862.   The experiments described in this paper were made ten years previous to its publication, and a brief account of them was communicated to the British Association at Belfast in 1852.

one, the determination of the temperature curve, and thence the
estimation of the temperature gradient at all points along a bar heated
steadily at one end, and the other the determination of the rate of
cooling of a similar bar uniformly heated, and then left to cool in the
open air under the same conditions as the first bar. The first was
termed by Forbes the *statical*, and the second the *dynamical*, or cooling,
experiment. In the former the observations are made on a bar when
the steady state has been acquired, and it is steady temperatures that
are taken, whereas in the latter the observations are made on the rate
of cooling of a bar, and the temperatures registered are those of a
cooling body. The two bars may therefore be referred to, for brevity,
as the *statical* and *dynamical* bars respectively.

The Statical Experiment.—In this experiment a bar of wrought iron
8 feet long and $1\frac{1}{4}$ inch square section was used. One end was heated
by being fixed into a cast-iron crucible, which was finely adjusted to it,
and contained molten lead or solder. This was kept in the fluid state
and at as uniform a temperature as possible by means of a powerful
gas furnace. By adjusting the gas-flame, and by placing pieces of the
solid metal in the fluid, the temperature of the heated end could be
regulated with considerable exactness, and kept constantly at the melting point of lead or solder. This, however, was a very laborious process, as the experiment lasted from six to eight or even ten hours.
The iron bar was so long that the temperature of the farther end was
not sensibly raised during the experiment, and it was employed in two
surface conditions—one in which the surface was bright, and the other
in which it was covered with thin white paper,[1] applied with the least
possible quantity of paste, so that the conductivity of the same bar
might be determined when the surface emissivity was greatly changed
(in the ratio 1 : 8, according to Leslie).

The temperature curve was determined by means of ten thermometers placed in small holes (0·28 inch diameter) drilled in the
bar. The holes in the colder part of the bar were filled with mercury,
while those near the hot end were filled with a fusible metal in a
semi-fluid state, as it was found that when mercury was used in the
warmer holes the surface became hotter, by convection, than the
central part of the hole, contrary to the law of distribution of heat in
a solid bar, and consequently an undue (though perhaps hardly sensible) amount of heat was thereby dissipated. It was also ascertained

[1] The paper might also be used to render the surfaces of different bars alike,
and for this purpose it would no doubt be much better than a black varnish, the
difficulties arising from the use of which have been already noticed as a source of
considerable trouble to Despretz.

by direct experiment that the boring of several additional holes between the extreme holes did not sensibly disturb the flow of heat when the intermediate holes had thermometers surrounded by mercury inserted in them.

The temperature curve must be determined by readings of all the thermometers in the steady state, and this is extremely difficult to secure in practice, for the instant has to be seized when the casual fluctuations become inappreciable simultaneously on all the thermometers, and although the source of heat may appear quite steady for a time, yet the temperature wave arising from some antecedent irregularity may still be travelling along some more remote portion of the bar.   Experience, and the patient entry of a number of successive observations of all the thermometers, can alone secure the desired precision.[1]

The Dynamical Experiment.—The dynamical or cooling experiment was made on an iron bar in all respects similar to that employed in the statical experiment, except that it was only about 20 inches long.   A small hole was bored at the centre of one side (Fig. 200) in which a thermometer could be placed with an amalgam round it, as in the previous experiment.   At first a high uniform temperature was communicated to this bar by immersing it in a cylindrical vessel containing a heated fusible metal (4 parts lead + 3 tin + 3 bismuth).   The bar was first wrapped in several folds of paper to prevent any sudden chill of the fluid metal on its first immersion, and it was completely immersed and withdrawn a few times, each end being alternately lowest, so as to equalise its temperature as much as possible throughout.   When thoroughly heated it was withdrawn, and the paper cover was rapidly cut off.   The naked bar was then placed horizontally on

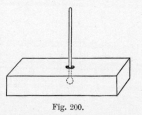

Fig. 200.

two blunt-edged props, so as to cool under the same circumstances as the statical bar.   Mercury, previously heated, was placed in the hole, or holes (there were usually two or three near the centre of the bar),

---

[1] One good thermometer might be used to take all the readings by the *stepping method*, and the necessity of having a large number of accurate thermometers may be thus avoided.   For if a single accurate thermometer be possessed, it may be placed at first in the hottest hole, and then in the others successively, after being allowed to cool, until it has very approximately attained the temperatures of the thermometers in the other holes in succession.   All the readings may be thus made with one good thermometer.

It is also worthy of note that the form of the temperature curve may be sensibly influenced by convection currents.

and thermometers were inserted. The temperatures were then read
off from minute to minute, and the rate of cooling determined, the
object of the experiment being to determine the rate at which any
element of surface of the statical bar loses heat, ascertained in terms
of the temperature registered by a thermometer sunk in the bar at
that point.[1]

Calculation of the Flux of Heat.—From the results of these two
experiments the flow of heat across any section of the statical bar
may be evaluated in the steady state. The temperature curve being
plotted, tangents were drawn at its various points, and the ordinates
MP (Fig. 201) and subtangents MN measured. The ratio of these
gave the value of $d\theta/dx$, the temperature gradient at each point along
the bar. The results derived from the dynamical experiment were also
represented graphically, the temperatures being taken as ordinates, and

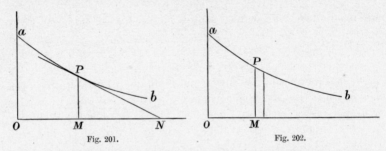

Fig. 201.   Fig. 202.

the corresponding times as the abscissæ of a curve. Tangents were
drawn to this curve, and the corresponding subtangents measured.
The ratio of these at any point of the curve gave the rate of cooling
$- d\theta/dt$ at the corresponding temperature. These rates having been
tabulated, another curve was constructed, having the rates of cooling
for ordinates, and the corresponding lengths along the statical bar for
abscissæ. The ordinate of this curve (Fig. 202) being $- d\theta/dt$, it follows

---

[1] At temperatures approaching 200° C. a difficulty arose which could not be
completely overcome. When a bar has been heated uniformly the distribution of
heat over any cross-section is not the same as when the bar in the statical experiment has attained the permanent state, nor is it the same as when the bar under
experiment has cooled to a certain extent. In fact, it has been shown by Fourier
that in the early stages of cooling of a body which has been uniformly heated, the
expression for the temperature at any point includes certain circular functions
which, in the case of good conductors, rapidly become evanescent. Such oscillations
of temperature affect the rate of cooling, and are perceptible in the higher part of
the scale, their general tendency being to make the rate of cooling of a thermometer
sunk in the axis of the bar at first too small, for the bar is at first only superficially
cooled. These irregularities at temperatures approaching 200° C. are mentioned by
Forbes as the greatest difficulty met with in the inquiry.

that the element of area between two very close ordinates at a distance dx will be proportional to the quantity of heat radiated by the element per second, and hence the area of this curve between the ordinate corresponding to the point x and infinity (the cold end of the bar) represents the total loss of heat from the surface of the bar beyond the section; or, in other words, the flow of heat across this section. This curve is approximately logarithmic, and the area between any two ordinates can be calculated with sufficient exactness, or it can be found by means of a planimeter.

If we integrate the equation given in the footnote, p. 600, with respect to x, from x to ∞, we get

$$k\frac{d\theta}{dx} = \int_x^\infty \frac{d\theta}{dt}dx,$$

and as $\dfrac{d\theta}{dx} = -\dfrac{\text{MP}}{\text{MN}}$ (Fig. 201), and the integral is given by the area of the curve (Fig. 202) from x to ∞, by substituting the computed values of these quantities, we obtain k, and hence K.

The following table contains the results of the experiments :—

CONDUCTIVITY OF WROUGHT IRON (1¼-INCH BAR)

Temperature .	0°	25°	50°	75°	100°	125°	150°	175°	200°
Conductivity . (Centimetre, Minute, and Centigrade Degree Units.)	12·36	11·80	11·15	10·59	9·94	9·38	8·73	8·18	7·62

The great merit of Forbes's method is that it seeks to determine the conductivity directly in terms of its definition instead of through a solution of Fourier's equation, which is founded on the hypothesis of constant conductivity, and on Newton's law of cooling. The experiments have been repeated by Professor Tait,[1] with Forbes's iron bar, and they were also extended to other metals with the object of testing in what manner the thermal conductivity varied with temperature, and to determine if the variations of thermal and electrical conductivity followed the same laws. For this purpose copper and lead were chosen, because they can be obtained pure and are not excessively expensive. Two specimens of copper were used—one (Crown) of the highest, and the other (C.) of the lowest electrical conductivity. An alloy (German silver) was also examined because the electrical conductivity of this substance varies little with temperature.

Tait's experiments.

[1] Tait, *Trans. Roy. Soc. Edin.* vol. xxviii. p. 717, 1879.

In such an investigation as this a considerable range of temperature is essential, and at high temperatures the experimental difficulties become enormously increased.   The end of the bar was kept at a high uniform temperature, not by Forbes's method of melting solder, which requires constant watching, but by a special gas-burner, furnished with a regulator devised by Dr. Crum Brown, which supplied the gas to the burner at a constant pressure.   In practice the working of this arrangement was found to be almost perfect.   Another difficulty arose in the displacement of the zero on the thermometers when exposed to high temperatures, and an uncertainty always attends the correction to be applied, on account of the portion of mercury which occupies the stem not being at the same temperature as that in the bulb.   In the case of copper, and even with German silver, a further difficulty arose at high temperatures in the oxidation of the surface.   The coating of oxide promotes radiation, and at different temperatures the surface becomes oxidised to different degrees, so that each set of experiments with the short bar can be strictly compared only with one part of the long bar.   The heating of the short bar for the dynamical experiment was effected by placing it over a row of gas-jets while it was rotated round its axis, so as to become uniformly heated on all sides.   Other methods, such as a hot air bath, were tried and abandoned, and it was found that in heating the bar it was more important to avoid oxidation than to secure absolute uniformity of temperature.

When the statical cooling curves were constructed, they were found to be not even approximately logarithmic, except for small intervals, and even then the axis was not usually asymptotic to the curve.   In reckoning the area between the curve and the axis, a great difficulty arose in determining how much should be allowed for the portion (in theory, infinitely long but of finite area) which extended beyond the lowest temperature observed, and the error arising from this uncertainty becomes more important the lower the temperature.   This difficulty did not arise, however, in the case of copper, for on account of the high conductivity of this substance the further end of the bar was kept in a large vessel of gutta-percha, through which cold water constantly circulated, so that its temperature was below that of the surrounding air, and the temperature gradient $d\theta/dx$ was nowhere very small.   In all such experiments a small temperature gradient and slow flow of heat should be avoided, and for this reason the surface of a good conductor, such as a copper bar, should be smoked.

The conductivity of cast iron was determined by Callendar and

Nicolson, using Forbes's method.[1] To avoid the uncertainties of surface loss of heat a large bar was used, and the surface loss of heat was reduced to one quarter by lagging the bar like a steam-pipe to a

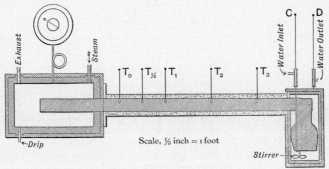

Fig. 203.

depth of 1 inch. The apparatus is shown in Fig. 203. The bar was heated by steam at one end and cooled by a stream of water flowing through a calorimeter at the other. It was 4 inches in diameter and 4 feet long between heater and calorimeter. The heat transmitted was measured calorimetrically. The temperature gradient near the entrance to the calorimeter was deduced from observation with five thermometers placed at suitable intervals along the bar. The results obtained (for a temperature of $40°$ C.) varied from $0·116$ to $0·118$ in C.G.S. units from observations on different days, and were probably more accurate than those obtained by the cylinder method (Art. 304).

304. The Guard-Ring Method.—It has been already pointed out (Art. 302) that the absolute conductivity of a substance may be determined by what has been called the wall method—that is, by keeping the two faces of a plate of the substance at two known temperatures, and noting the quantity of heat which flows through a known area per second. The great difficulty of determining the exact temperatures of the faces of the plate, however, placed this method in disrepute, and the determinations of conductivity have been chiefly based upon the bar method, either by the method of steady flow already described, or by the variable or periodic process introduced by Ångström (Art. 309). Another difficulty in the guard-ring method is the measurement of the area of the surface through which the heat measured is transmitted.

If, however, a very thick plate of the material be employed, the temperature may be taken at various points of its interior, and the

[1] H. L. Callendar, *Ency. Brit.* 11th edition, art. "Conduction of Heat."

uncertainty of the surface temperature may be avoided. An outline
of an experiment conducted on this principle is roughly represented
in Fig. 204. The plate under examination is ABCD. One face, AB,
forms the end of a chamber filled with steam, and the other face, CD,
forms the end of another chamber filled with ice. When the steady
flow of heat is established, the lines of flow of the heat will be straight

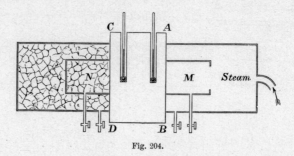

Fig. 204.

lines, perpendicular to the faces AB and CD, or, at any rate, this will
be the case around the centre of the plate. Hence, if a known area
of the central portion be isolated, and if the temperatures at any two
points within the plate be determined by inserting thermometers (or
couples), as shown in the figure, and if the quantity of heat which
flows through this isolated portion be also determined, the conductivity
of the plate will be known. By varying the thickness of the plate and
noting the corresponding changes in the flow of heat, it could be
ascertained if the differences of temperature of the faces AB and CD
remained the same. To isolate the central portion a cylindrical
chamber M may be fixed against the face AB. The steam, which
condenses in M, can be drained off and weighed, and this will afford
a measure of the quantity of heat which flows through the isolated
section. Another measure of the same quantity may be obtained by
fixing a similar cylinder N against the face CD, which, if filled with
ice, will afford a measure of the flow by the quantity of ice melted per
second. This may be roughly measured by allowing the water to
drain off from N as the ice melts, and weighing it; but a much more
accurate plan will be to make N the bulb of a Bunsen's ice calorimeter,
and thus measure the quantity of ice melted by the diminution of
volume.

This method has been applied by M. Berget [1] with considerable
success to mercury and some other metals. The apparatus adopted
in the case of mercury is shown in Fig. 205. A cylindrical column of

[1] Alphonse Berget, *Journal de Physique*, tom. vii. p. 503, 1888.

mercury AB, contained in a glass tube, was surrounded by another column of mercury, as shown in the figure, which acted as a guard-ring and prevented loss of heat by lateral radiation, so that the central column could be regarded as part of an infinite wall heated at its two faces to two constant temperatures, and if the conductivity does not vary with the temperature the distribution of temperature along the column will be linear.   The essential part of the apparatus Berget's was a Bunsen's ice calorimeter, into which the column AB protruded. experiments. The mercury guard-ring rested on a sheet-iron plate, which in turn

rested on the ice surrounding the bulb of the calorimeter. The mercury was heated at the top by steam, introduced by tubes, as shown in the figure. Through four apertures pierced in the side of the vessel which contained the mercury, thermo-electric junctions 1, 2, 3, 4 were inserted.   These were simply four threads of iron wire, so that each pair of them, with the column of mercury between their ends, formed a thermo-pile which measured the differ-ence of temperature between the ends of the pair.

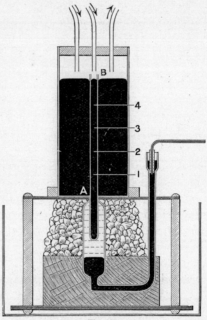

Fig. 205.

The greatest care was taken in reading the temperatures indicated by these couples, and the results proved that the dis-tribution of temperature along the column was linear.   The mean value of K for mercury was found in this manner to be 0·02015 C.G.S. units.   In all cases it was found that the times necessary for the establishment of the steady flow were proportional to the squares of the lengths of the column, which is a consequence of Fourier's theory.

The same method was also applied to metals, and the conductivity of copper was found to be 1·04050, of iron 0·1587, and of brass 0·2625.

A method which may be called the cylinder method was em-ployed by Callendar and Nicolson.[1]   The cylinders used were 2 feet long and 5 inches in diameter, with 1-inch axial holes.   The central

[1] *Ency. Brit., loc. cit.* ; *Brit. Assoc. Report*, 1897.

hole was heated by steam under pressure, and the total flow of
heat was measured by finding the amount of steam condensed in a
given time. The outside was cooled by water circulating rapidly in
a spiral tube. A difficulty in this method arises from the fact that
the temperature gradient has to be measured by thermometers or
thermocouples sunk in holes bored parallel to the axis, so that the

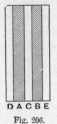

exact thickness of the cylinder wall between two thermometers cannot be measured very accurately. Callendar
and Nicolson found 0·109 for cast iron and 0·119 for
mild steel at about 60° C.

DACBE

Fig. 206.

The conductivity of a number of substances which
are not very good conductors of heat was measured by
Lees,[1] using a method which may be regarded as a
modification of the wall method. The theoretical form
of the apparatus (not that actually adopted) is represented in Fig. 206. A and B are two discs of the material to be
tested. D, C, and E are similar discs of a good conductor such as
copper, the middle disc C being electrically heated. The heat supplied
is measured by a wattmeter, and the temperatures of the three
metallic discs measured by thermo-electric contacts. Some heat is
lost at the curved surfaces of the discs, and, to enable this quantity
to be determined directly by experiment, the whole of the heat
supplied to the discs must be lost in the same way, i.e. by conduction and radiation through air. To satisfy this condition, the
collection of discs should be placed in an air-bath kept at a constant
temperature. The heat lost from the curved surfaces of the discs
then follows with sufficient closeness the same law as that lost from
the flat surfaces of the outer discs, and the relative amounts of the
two can be determined from a knowledge of the areas and temperatures of the various surfaces, if the surfaces have the same emissivity,
an equality which is easily secured by varnishing them.

Once the method of surrounding the discs by an enclosure at
constant temperature is adopted, a further simplification of the
arrangement of discs is possible. If one of the discs (A) of the
substance under test and one of the outer discs (D) were removed,
the relative amounts of heat lost by the heating disc C by conduction
and radiation directly to the air from its exposed surfaces, and by
conduction through the disc B of material experimented on, partly to
the air directly by conduction and radiation from the surface of B,
and partly by conduction to the outer metallic disc E and by radiation
from its surfaces, could still be calculated, and, the total heat supplied

[1] *Phil. Trans.*, 1898, p. 399.

being known, the conductivity of the material determined. As it
required only one disc of the material, this method was adopted.

This modified arrangement is shown in Fig. 207. S is the disc
of the substance operated on. M is the outer good-conducting disc,
0·320 cm. thick. C and U are also good-conducting
discs, respectively 0·103 and 0·312 cm. thick. P is a thin
flat coil of silk-covered platinoid wire insulated by mica
and shellac, the total thickness of coil and mica being
0·110 cm. The dark lines indicate the mica insulation.
Thus the combination C, P, and U correspond to the
heating disc C of Fig. 206. The discs C, U, and M were
made of copper and all the discs were 4 cm. in diameter.
The various thicknesses of the copper discs were chosen

Fig. 207.

so as to make the temperature-differences suitable for thermo-electric
measurement. Glycerine was used to secure good thermal contact
between the discs. Platinoid and copper wires were soldered to opposite ends of a diameter of each copper disc, and by this means the
temperature was measured thermo-electrically. The set of discs was
varnished and placed in a thermostat air-chamber. The observations
were made when a steady state was attained. Corrections were made
for loss of heat by conduction along the wires, also for conduction along
the coil wires. For the calculation of the conductivity from the data
of the experiment, reference must be made to the original paper.
Lees found that the conductivity of solids which are not very good
conductors decreases with rise of temperature (in the neighbourhood
of 40° C.). Glass was found to be an exception to this rule. The
appended table contains some of the conductivities determined.

Solid.	Conductivity.	Percentage Charge per Degree C.
Glass . .	·00245	+ 0·0025
Sulphur .	·00067	− 0·0036
Ebonite. .	·00042	− 0·0019
Shellac . .	·00058	− 0·0055

A simple method[1] of measuring the conductivities of metals
consists in heating a short rod of the material by an electric current,
the ends of the rod being kept at a constant temperature by means
of solid copper blocks provided with a water circulation, the whole
being surrounded by a jacket at the same temperature, which is
taken as the zero of reference. The current is so adjusted that the
external loss of heat from the surface of the rod is compensated by

[1] H. L. Callendar, *loc. cit.*

the increase of resistance of the rod with rise of temperature.   For if R_0 is the resistance of unit length of the rod at the temperature of reference, and R the resistance at θ degrees above this temperature, we may put

$$R = R_0(1 + a\theta),$$

where a is the temperature coefficient of electrical resistance. Then the heat generated per second in a length dx of the rod is $C^2R_0(1 + a\theta)dx$, where C is the current.   The excess of heat entering the portion dx by conduction over that leaving it is, by Art. 298, $KAd^2\theta/dx^2 . dx$, and the heat lost by radiation is $Ep\theta dx$.   The heat developed according to the Thomson effect is very small[1] and is eliminated by keeping the two ends at the same temperature.   The equation for a steady state is therefore

$$C^2R_0(1 + a\theta) + KA\frac{d^2\theta}{dx^2} - Ep\theta = 0.$$

If C is so chosen that $C^2R_0a = Ep$, the equation reduces to

$$\frac{d^2\theta}{dx^2} = -\frac{C^2R_0}{KA} = \text{const.}$$

so that

$$\theta = a + \beta x + \gamma x^2,$$

where a, β, and γ are constants, and $2\gamma = -C^2R_0/KA$.   If we measure x from the centre of the rod, $\beta = 0$, since the temperature gradient is symmetrical about the centre.   If $2l$ is the length of the rod, $\theta = a + \gamma x^2$ and $0 = a + \gamma l^2$; subtracting these, we get

$$\theta = -\gamma(l^2 - x^2) = \frac{C^2R_0}{2KA}(l^2 - x^2).$$

The mean value of θ along the rod is

$$\theta_m = \frac{1}{l}\int_0^l \theta dx = \frac{C^2R_0l^2}{3KA}.$$

But if R_m is the mean resistance per unit length, the observed resistance is $2R_ml = 2lR_0(1 + a\theta_m)$, therefore

$$K = \frac{C^2R_0{}^2l^2a}{3A(R_m - R_0)}.$$

If the dimensions of the rod are suitably chosen, the distribution of temperature is always very nearly parabolic, so that it is not necessary to determine the critical current $C^2 = Ep/R_0a$ very accurately, as the correction for external loss is a small correction in any case.   The

---

[1] If an alternating current is used, the Thomson effect is avoided altogether.

chief difficulty is that of measuring the small change of resistance accurately, and of avoiding errors from accidental thermo-electric effects. Using this method, the conductivity of very pure copper was found by Duncan to be 1·007 at 33° C.

305. Lees' Experiments on Metals.[1]—A series of experiments was made by Lees to determine the conductivity of a number of pure metals over a wide range of temperature. The previous work of Lorenz and especially of Jaeger and Diesselhorst had indicated that there is a slight decrease of conductivity with rise of temperature, and this is confirmed on the whole by Lees' experiments, although he did not always find that the maximum conductivity occurred at the lowest temperatures. The method consisted in heating a thin rod at one end by an electric current flowing in a coil fitting on the rod, the heat being measured electrically and the difference of temperature at two points on the rod determined by a platinum thermometer.

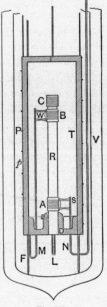

Fig. 208.

The apparatus is shown in Fig. 208. The rods of metal were in the form of circular cylinders 7 or 8 cm. long and 0·585 cm. in diameter. The lower end of the rod fitted into a copper disc D which in its turn fitted accurately into the lower end of a copper cylinder T closed at the top. Three thin brass sleeves, A, B, C, fitted on the rod and could be easily slid by the fingers. C carried the heating coil of silk-covered platinoid wire; A and B carried similar coils of platinum. L, M, and N are the copper leads of these coils. The silk thread s wound round sleeve, wires, and the wooden disc W was for the purpose of obviating stress on the fine wires. The copper enclosure was supported on a wire frame F by means of which it could be placed in the Dewar vessel V. Around the outside of the copper tube was wound an insulated platinoid wire p of the same resistance as the heating coil C, and whenever the current was switched off C it was switched on to p, so that the heat supplied to the apparatus should be the same throughout an experiment. A further coil P was also wound on the tube to allow the temperature to be rapidly raised, if necessary. Olive oil in the joints excluded air and made good thermal contacts. The distance apart of the three sleeves was measured to 0·01 cm.

---

[1] *Phil. Trans.*, 1908, p. 381.

When all was in the Dewar vessel, the current was sent round C and adjusted to get a suitable difference of resistance of A and B. The current was then switched to p and, after five or ten minutes, the difference of resistance of A and B and the actual resistance of the lower one (A) was measured. The difference of resistance found when the heating current flowed round the rod, less the mean difference of resistance when the current flowed round the tube (before and after), gives, so long as the rate of rise of temperature of the apparatus is uniform, the difference of resistance which would be produced if the heating current was supplied to the rod and the temperature of the tube kept constant. The experiments were started at liquid air temperature and carried up to somewhat above room temperature, using the supplementary heating coil if necessary.

Corrections were made for the difference of temperature of rod and coils, the effect of the sleeves and conduction along the various leads. The emissivity was measured in a subsidiary experiment. Terms involving the emissivity affected the result only to a small extent. The effect of the variable state of temperature was very small.

Lees found the following conductivities amongst others (in calories per cm. per degree per second) :—

Temp. .	$-170°$	$-160°$	$-150°$	$-125°$	$-100°$	$-75°$	$-50°$	$-25°$	$0°$	$18°$
Copper .	1·112	1·079	1·054	·996	·973	·958	·944	·932	·924	·916
Silver . .	·996	·998	1·000	1·005	1·008	1·004	·997	·997	·981	·974
Zinc . .	·280	·278	·276	·270	·271	·269	·268	·269	·269	·268
Aluminium .	·524	·514	·508	·491	·492	·493	·496	·499	·502	·504
Lead . .	·093	·092	·091	·089	·087	·085	·085	·084	·084	·083
Iron . .	·151	·152	·153	·154	·152	·150	·148	·147	·147	·147
Steel . .	·113	·113	·113	·113	·114	·115	·116	·116	·116	·115

306. Thermal and Electric Conductivities—Variation of Thermal Conductivity with Temperature.—It was first remarked by Forbes that the order of the thermal and electric conductivities of metals was the same—that is, that those metals which have the lowest electric resistance also conduct heat best. The analogy was pushed further by Wiedemann and Franz, who, from their experiments (Art. 301), concluded that not only were the thermal and electric conductivities in the same order, but that they were sensibly in the same proportion, so that the ratio of the thermal to the electric conductivity is the same for all metals. The truth of this conclusion has been the subject of many subsequent investigations, some of which appear to disprove the law. The more recent experiments of Lees and also those of Jaeger and Diesselhorst show that it is approximately true for pure metals. Lorenz also, on theoretical grounds, put forward the law that the ratio of the thermal to the electric conductivity is proportional to the absolute temperature. This law is well confirmed, for some pure metals at any rate, by the experiments referred to, but not so well for alloys.[1] In 1900 Drude [2] propounded the following theory of electrical and heat conduction in metals. The positive electricity in a metallic atom is to be regarded as fixed to the atom of matter, but every metal contains a large number of free electrons, which are conceived to partake of the heat-motion of the atoms. According to the law of equipartition of energy, the mean kinetic energy is the same for an atom of matter and a free electron. Owing to the relatively very small mass of the electron, we may treat the atoms as if they were at rest, the electrons moving with very high velocities and rebounding from the atoms like elastic spheres. An electric force will tend to produce a flow of electrons in a direction opposite to the force, that is, an electric current. A temperature gradient in the metal will tend to produce a flow of heat-energy just as in a gas, according to the kinetic theory of heat conduction in a gas. The rate of transmission of electricity or heat is controlled by the collisions of the electrons with the atoms. Applying the methods of the kinetic theory, Drude arrived at the formula [3]

$$\frac{K}{\sigma} = 3\left(\frac{R_0}{e}\right)^2 \frac{O}{J},$$

which agrees well with experimental results. Drude did not, however, allow for the effect of Maxwell's law of distribution of velocities, and Lorentz [4] showed, by a more rigorous deduction from the kinetic theory, that the formula should be

$$\frac{K}{\sigma} = 2\left(\frac{R_0}{e}\right)^2 \frac{\Theta}{J},$$

which does not agree well with experiment, though it is of the right order of dimensions. The weak point in the argument is in the use of the law of equipartition of energy, which is discredited by the quantum theory (Art. 285), though it may safely be applied in the case of a mixture of gases, where the velocities are not so high.[5]

[1] For a table of the experimental values of $K/\sigma\Theta$ where σ is the electrical conductivity, see Lees, *loc. cit.*

[2] *Ann. der Physik;* i., 1900, p. 566.

[3] σ is the electrical conductivity, R_0 is the universal gas constant (see Art. 375), e is the charge of an electron, and J is Joule's equivalent.

[4] H. A. Lorentz, *Theory of Electrons*, Note 29.

[5] See Jeans' *Dynamical Theory of Gases*, p. 427.

307. Flow of Heat in a Bar before the Steady State is acquired.
—In the case of a bar heated at one end before the permanent state
of steady flow is reached, a preliminary stage is passed through, in
which the temperature of each element of the bar gradually rises.
During this stage the difference between the quantities of heat which
flow in at one face and out at the other face of a short length δx of
the bar is not all radiated from the surface of the element; but if the
mean temperature of the element rises by an amount $d\theta$ in a time dt,
a quantity of heat

$$\mathrm{A}c\frac{d\theta}{dt}\delta x$$

is spent per second in raising the temperature of the bar, where c is
the thermal capacity per unit volume—that is, the specific heat multiplied by the density of the substance. The equation of propagation
therefore becomes

$$\mathrm{A K}\frac{d^2\theta}{dx^2}=\mathrm{E}p\theta+\mathrm{A}c\frac{d\theta}{dt}.$$

If the bar be surrounded by a guard-ring, or be coated with a non-
conducting material, we may write $\mathrm{E}=0$, and the equation becomes

$$\frac{\mathrm{K}}{c}\frac{d^2\theta}{dx^2}=\frac{d\theta}{dt},$$

or

$$k\frac{d^2\theta}{dx^2}=\frac{d\theta}{dt},$$

where k is written for K/c, and has been termed the *diffusivity* of the
material by Lord Kelvin. The same quantity has also been named
the *thermometric conductivity* of the substance by Clerk Maxwell, since
it measures the change of temperature which would be produced in a
unit volume of the substance by the quantity of heat which flows in
unit time through unit area of a layer of unit thickness having unit
difference of temperature between its faces.

It is this quantity that chiefly determines the effect of the heat
conducted across any part of a body in heating the substance on one
side, or cooling it on the other, and when this effect is to be reckoned
it is convenient to measure the thermal conductivity in terms of this
special unit, rather than of the ordinary water gramme unit of heat.

It may be remarked that the diffusivity k is of the dimensions l^2/t,
and is consequently to be reckoned in units of area per unit time. In the
C.G.S. system it is therefore expressed in square centimetres per second.

COR.—In the case of an infinite wall heated uniformly over one
face, or a bar heated at one end and furnished with a guard-ring, when
the flow of heat becomes steady, the foregoing equation reduces to—

$$\frac{d^2\theta}{dx^2}=0, \quad \text{or} \quad \theta=ax+b,$$

that is, the temperature curve is a right line, if a and b are constants.

308. Periodic Flow of Heat through a Long Bar.—If a long bar be periodically heated and cooled at one end, a thermometer sunk in it at any point will exhibit corresponding variations of temperature. When the end of the bar is heated a temperature wave travels along it, and the indication of the thermometer gradually rises. In the same way, when the end of the bar is cooled, the temperature registered by the thermometer will gradually fall, so that if the temperature of the end of the bar be varied periodically, the temperature at every point of the bar will also vary in a corresponding periodic manner, and when the periodic variation of temperature has been maintained for a sufficient time, the oscillations of temperature at any point of the bar will attain a fixed character, so that the mean temperature at each point remains steady.

If the periodic variation of temperature be a simple harmonic variation, then the variations of temperature at any point of the bar may be represented by a sine curve, $\theta = a \sin (at + \beta)$, where θ is the temperature, measured from the mean, and t the time. If, however, we consider the fluctuations of temperature at the various points of the bar, we find that the amplitude of the temperature variations at any point will diminish as the distance from the hot end increases, and at a certain distance along the bar the variations of temperature will be insensible, and the temperature of the bar will remain constantly equal to that of the surrounding medium (Fig. 209). The mean temperature at all points will not, however, be the same, but will diminish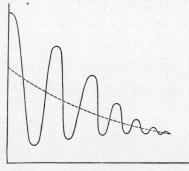

Fig. 209.

as we recede from the heated end, the curve of mean temperature being logarithmic, and similar to the temperature curves obtained by Despretz and Forbes. The fluctuations of temperature at each point will be periodic, but the variation of temperature near the heated end will be much greater than at some distance along the bar, the temperature waves gradually dying out as they proceed along the bar. These conclusions will appear clearly in the following analysis :—

Let us take the case of a bar surrounded by a non-conducting jacket, and let a simple harmonic variation of temperature be applied to one end. In this case the temperature at any point is determined by the equation

$$k\frac{d^2\theta}{dx^2} = \frac{d\theta}{dt} \qquad . \qquad . \qquad . \qquad . \qquad . \qquad (1)$$

and a simple harmonic solution of this is

$$\theta = ae^{-\alpha x}\sin(\omega t + \beta x + \gamma) \qquad . \qquad . \qquad . \qquad . \qquad (2)$$

if the constants ω, a, β be properly chosen. Differentiating (2) and substituting directly in (1) we find at once that in order that (1) may be satisfied by (2) we must have the relations

$$\alpha^2 = \beta^2, \quad \text{and} \quad 2a\beta k = -\omega \qquad . \qquad . \qquad . \qquad (3)$$

Now it is clear that if we confine our attention to a definite point of the bar, so that x remains the same while t and θ vary, then θ will vary periodically, being the same when t increases by any multiple of $2\pi/\omega$. Hence, if the end of the bar be heated and cooled in a simple harmonic manner, the complete period of a heating and cooling being T, we have

$$\omega = \frac{2\pi}{T},$$

and consequently ω measures the frequency of the alternations of temperature.

Let us now examine the time at which a thermometer placed in the bar at a distance x_1 from the origin will reach its highest or lowest temperature. This will happen when $\sin(\omega t + \beta x + \gamma)$ attains its greatest or least value—that is, when it is ± 1; or, in other words, the temperature will be a maximum at the point x_1 at the time t_1 given by the equation

$$\omega t_1 + \beta x_1 + \gamma = (2n + \tfrac{1}{2})\pi,$$

and the maximum temperature at a point x_2 will be reached at a time t_2, given by the equation

$$\omega t_2 + \beta x_2 + \gamma = (2n + \tfrac{1}{2})\pi,$$

the minima temperatures at the same points being reached when the values are $(2n - \tfrac{1}{2})\pi$. Hence by subtraction we obtain

$$\omega(t_1 - t_2) + \beta(x_1 - x_2) = 0,$$

or

$$\frac{x_2 - x_1}{t_1 - t_2} = \frac{\omega}{\beta}.$$

Now, if the points x_1 and x_2 be so chosen that the maxima or minima of temperature occur at them simultaneously, we shall have $t_2 - t_1$, equal to the periodic time T, and the difference of distance $x_2 - x_1$ will be the length of the temperature wave λ, so that the last equation becomes

$$-\lambda = \frac{\omega}{\beta}T = \frac{2\pi}{\beta}.$$

Hence, in our original equation (2) for θ the quantities α and β are determined by the equation

$$\alpha = -\beta = \frac{2\pi}{\lambda}; \qquad \qquad \qquad (4)$$

But the second equation of condition (3) gives

$$k = \frac{-\omega}{2\alpha\beta};$$

consequently, by substituting for α, β, and ω, we have the relation

$$k = \frac{\lambda^2}{4\pi T} \qquad \qquad \qquad (5)$$

and when λ and T are known, we are furnished with the value of k.

This expression for k may also be written in the form

$$4\pi k = \lambda v,$$

where v is the velocity of temperature wave propagation (λ/T) along the bar, so that k is jointly proportional to the wave-length and the velocity of propagation.

The equation (2) for θ may now be written in the form

$$\theta = ae^{-\frac{2\pi x}{\lambda}} \sin 2\pi \left(\frac{t}{T} - \frac{x}{\lambda} + \frac{\gamma}{2\pi} \right).$$

Thus the amplitude of the temperature variation at any point x is proportional to $e^{-\frac{2\pi x}{\lambda}}$, so that the amplitudes go on decreasing as we recede from the heated end of the bar, and the mean temperature at any point diminishes in the same way.

In order to determine the diffusivity by this method, it is consequently only necessary to measure the wave-length λ corresponding to simple harmonic variation of temperature of known period T, and the conductivity may then be calculated in absolute measure when the thermal capacity of the substance per unit volume is determined.

If, however, the bar be not furnished with a guard-ring, but if radiation takes place from its surface, as in the experiments of Despretz and Forbes, the equation of propagation is

2 s

$$\mathrm{A}\mathrm{K}\frac{d^2\theta}{dx^2}=\mathrm{A}c\frac{d\theta}{dt}+\mathrm{E}p\theta,$$

or

$$k\frac{d^2\theta}{dx^2}=\frac{d\theta}{dt}+\mu\theta,$$

where $\mu = \mathrm{E}p/\mathrm{A}c$.

A solution of this, which expresses simple harmonic variations of temperature in a long bar heated and cooled at one end, is again

$$\theta = ae^{-ax}\sin(\omega t + \beta x + \gamma);$$

but in this case the relations connecting the constants are found by substitution to be

$$a^2 - \beta^2 = \frac{\mu}{k}, \quad \text{and} \quad 2a\beta = \frac{-\omega}{k},$$

from which it follows that

$$a = \sqrt{\frac{1}{2k}\left\{(\omega^2+\mu^2)^{\frac{1}{2}}+\mu\right\}}$$

$$\beta = \sqrt{\frac{1}{2k}\left\{(\omega^2+\mu^2)^{\frac{1}{2}}-\mu\right\}}$$

as before $\omega = 2\pi/\mathrm{T}$, while a is the rate of diminution of the Napierian logarithm of the temperature range, and β is the rate of retardation of phase reckoned in radians per unit length of the bar.

If the variation of temperature be not a simple harmonic variation it may be expressed as a sum of such variations if it be periodic, and the more general solution of the equation—

$$k\frac{d^2\theta}{dx^2}=\frac{d\theta}{dt}+\mu\theta,$$

which applies to any regularly periodic variation of temperature, will be

$$\theta = a_0e^{-a_0x} + a_1e^{-a_1x}\sin(\omega t + \beta_1 x + \gamma_1) + a_2e^{-a_2x}\sin(2\omega t + \beta_2 x + \gamma_2) + \text{etc.},$$

if the constants be properly chosen.[1] Differentiating and substituting this value of θ in the equation, we find that in order that it may be satisfied we must have

$$a^2_0 = \frac{\mu}{k}, \quad k(a^2_n - \beta^2_n) = \mu, \quad 2ka_n\beta_n = -n\omega.$$

From which we derive

$$a_n = \sqrt{\frac{1}{2k}\left\{(\mu^2+n^2\omega^2)^{\frac{1}{2}}+\mu\right\}}$$

$$\beta_n = \sqrt{\frac{1}{2k}\left\{(\mu^2+n^2\omega^2)^{\frac{1}{2}}-\mu\right\}}$$

where as before $\omega = 2\pi/\mathrm{T}$.

---

[1] This is the case represented in Fig. 209, the dotted line being given by $\theta = a_0e^{-a_0x}$.

309. Ångström's Experiments.—The first experimental determination of conductivities by the periodic method was made by the Swedish philosopher Ångström.[1] Long bars were employed, and the periodic heating and cooling was effected by enclosing a short portion of the middle of the bar in a vessel CD, as shown in Fig. 210, through

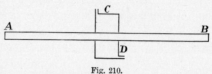

Fig. 210.

which could be alternately passed a current of steam and a current of cold water.[2] When this heating and cooling had been continued for some time, the temperature at each point of the bar became steadily periodic, and the mean value of the temperature at any point became constant. Rigorously speaking, however, an infinite time is required to reach this stage. The bars were perforated at intervals of 50 mm. by cavities 2·25 mm. in diameter, which contained the bulbs of thermometers provided with arbitrary scales.

In making an experiment the heating was applied for twelve minutes and the cooling for the same time, so that the periodic time T was twenty-four minutes. The temperature at a given point of the bar was observed for each minute during one or more of these periods; and since at a given point the only variable in the general expression for θ is the time, the equation for θ may be written in the form

$$\theta = A_0 + A_1 \sin(\omega t + \delta_1) + A_2 \sin(2\omega t + \delta_2) + A_3 \sin(3\omega t + \delta_3) + \text{etc.},$$

in which, from the observations of θ, corresponding to various values of t, the constants A_0, A_1, etc., δ_1, δ_2, δ_3, etc., can be calculated. In practice the series may be limited to the first three or four terms, as the coefficients A_1, A_2, A_3, etc., decrease rapidly. Let us now suppose that similar observations are carried out at another point of the bar, and that the temperature at this point is given at the time t by the series

$$\theta' = A'_0 + A'_1 \sin(\omega t + \delta'_1) + A'_2 \sin(\omega t + \delta'_2) + \text{etc.}$$

If the first series corresponds to a point x and the second to a point x', we have, using the notation of the foregoing article,

$$A_1 = a_1 e^{-a_1 x}, \quad \text{and} \quad A'_1 = a_1 e^{-a_1 x'},$$

with similar expressions for the other coefficients, so that if the distance $x' - x$ between the two points be denoted by l, we have

---

[1] Ångström, *Phil. Mag.* vol. xxv. p. 130, 1863 ; and vol. xxvi. p. 161 ; *Pogg. Ann.* Bd. cxiv. p. 513, 1861 ; and *Ann. de Chimie et de Physique*, 3e sér., tom. lxvii. p. 379.

[2] This was adopted with the copper bar, but the iron bar was cooled simply by radiation.

$$\frac{A_1}{A'_1} = e^{a_1 l}, \quad \text{while} \quad \delta'_1 - \delta_1 = \beta_1 l,$$

therefore

$$a_1 l = \log (A_1 / A'_1),$$

and consequently

$$a_1 \beta_1 l^2 = (\delta'_1 - \delta_1) \log (A_1 / A_1').$$

But we have already found that

$$-a_1 \beta_1 = \frac{\omega}{2k} = \frac{\pi}{kT},$$

and hence

$$k = \frac{\pi l^2}{T(\delta_1 - \delta'_1) \log (A_1 / A'_1)}.$$

In the same manner, if we had employed the terms involving A_n and A'_n, we should have had

$$A_n = a_n e^{-a_n x}, \quad \text{and} \quad A'_n = a_n e^{-a_n x'}.$$

Therefore

$$\frac{A_n}{A'_n} = e^{a_n l}, \quad \text{and} \quad \delta'_n - \delta_n = \beta_n l,$$

consequently

$$a_n \beta_n l^2 = (\delta'_n - \delta_n) \log (A_n / A'_n).$$

But

$$2k a_n \beta_n = -n\omega,$$

therefore

$$k = \frac{n\pi l^2}{T(\delta_n - \delta'_n) \log (A_n / A'_n)}.$$

Thus each pair of terms leads to an independent determination of the quantity k, but the value obtained from the first pair is most reliable. The accuracy of the obtained value of k may also be controlled by altering the period of heating and cooling.[1]

Ångström's first experiments were made with square bars 570 mm. long and 23·75 mm. side, and the values found for the conductivity of copper and iron at the mean temperature of 50° C. were—

---

[1] The value of k may also be deduced, without using β, when a is known for two different periods. For the general expression for a is

$$2k a^2 = (\mu^2 + n^2 \omega^2)^{\frac{1}{2}} + \mu,$$

or

$$4 k^2 a^4 - 4 k a^2 \mu = n^2 \omega^2.$$

Similarly for a different period ω' we have

$$4 k^2 a'^4 - 4 k a'^2 \mu = n^2 \omega'^2.$$

Therefore, eliminating μ, we obtain

$$k = \frac{n}{2 a a'} \sqrt{\frac{\omega^2 a'^2 - \omega'^2 a^2}{a^2 - a'^2}}$$

$$\text{For copper .   .   .   .   .   } K = 54\cdot62$$
$$\text{For iron   .   .   .   .   .   } K = 9\cdot77$$

the units employed being the centimetre, gramme, and minute.

A subsequent series of experiments [1] on bars 1178 mm. long and 35 mm. thick, furnished with thermometers at intervals of 200 mm., and in which the heating apparatus was so modified that different mean temperatures could be obtained, gave in the same units—

$$\text{For copper   .   .   . } K = 58\cdot94 \ (1 - 0\cdot001519\theta)$$
$$\text{For iron .   .   .   . } K = 11\cdot927 \ (1 - 0\cdot00214\theta)$$

This method when applied with proper precautions is undoubtedly capable of furnishing good results. In practice, however, the use of ordinary mercury thermometers is not advisable in the determination of rapidly varying temperatures, as they are always tardy in their indications and liable to work by sudden starts. For the measurement of temperatures in all such cases the employment of thermoelectric couples would be much superior.

The method of variable temperature was used also by Callendar, employing the apparatus of Fig. 203. The steam pressure in the heater was varied by gauge in such a manner as to produce an approximately simple harmonic oscillation of temperature, the cool end being kept at a steady temperature. The amplitudes and phases of the temperature waves were observed by taking readings of the thermometers at regular intervals. Periods of 60, 90, and 120 minutes were severally employed, and distances of 6 and 12 inches between the thermometers. In some experiments the bar was lagged, in others bare. The heat loss never exceeded 7 per cent with the bar bare. The variation of c was determined by a special series of experiments. Callendar obtained 0·1113 and 0·1144 for cast iron at 102° C. and 54° C. respectively.

310. Conductivity of the Earth's Crust—Underground Temperatures.—The method of determining conductivities by periodic heating and cooling may be applied directly to the estimation of the conductivity of the earth's crust at any place. For by day the surface of the earth is heated and by night it is cooled, so that a series of heat waves are propagated into the interior, and if the length of the wave and the periodic time are known we have the data required for the calculation of k. There is also a general aggregate heating of the surface during the summer with a corresponding cooling during the winter, so that in addition to the diurnal waves, which are lost at a depth of 3 or 4 feet, there is an annual wave which may be traced to a much greater

[1] Ångström, *Phil. Mag.* vol. xxvi. p. 161, 1863.

depth, but at a depth of 50 feet or more the temperature at each point remains sensibly constant throughout the year.

If, however, the mean temperatures at different depths be compared, they are found to increase as we descend to the greatest depths yet penetrated. The amount of this increase varies much with the locality and the nature of the strata in which the observations are made, being largely affected by water-percolation and other circumstances, so that in some places it is as much as 1° F. for 30 or 40 feet, whereas in others an increase of 1° F. corresponds to a descent of 120 or 130 feet. Roughly speaking, however, the rate at which this increase takes place in this country is about 1° F. for every 60 feet of descent. This gradual increase of temperature as we descend proves that there must be a flow of heat from the interior through the surface, and the amount of heat which escapes from the earth per annum in this manner may be estimated when the conductivity of the crust is known. Having calculated the present rate of loss, we can calculate backwards what the temperature of the earth must have been in time past, and in this manner Lord Kelvin[1] argued that it cannot be more than 200,000,000 years since the earth was a molten mass, on which a solid crust was just beginning to form.

This mode of calculating the age of the earth is invalidated by the discovery that the temperature gradient in the earth's crust can be accounted for, wholly or in part, by the existence of radium in the igneous rocks. Lord Kelvin mentioned the possibility of chemical action of some kind, but dismissed it as extremely improbable, though not impossible. He considered the case of an infinite solid bounded by a plane (for the purposes of this calculation, the error in treating the earth's surface as plane is insensible), the whole solid being at a uniform high temperature to begin with, the surface being then brought to a lower temperature (which we may take as the zero of reference) and kept constant at that temperature. The appropriate solution of equation (1) of Art. 308 is

$$\theta = \frac{2\theta_0}{\sqrt{\pi}} \int_0^{x/2\sqrt{kt}} e^{-z^2} dz,$$

where θ_0 is the original temperature. For, when $t = 0$, the upper limit of integration is infinite, and $\theta = \theta_0$ for all values of x. When $x = 0$, $\theta = 0$ for all values of t. The expression for θ is seen by differentiation to be a solution of the equation.

If the crust at any place be supposed homogeneous, and if the periodic variations of temperature be regarded as uniform, then the problem of the propagation of heat-waves through it is the same as that of an infinite wall periodically heated and cooled over one face, or the same as that of a bar periodically heated at one end and coated with a non-conducting material or a guard-ring. If, therefore, a number of thermometers be buried with their bulbs at different depths

[1] Sir William Thomson, *Trans. Roy. Soc.* Edin. vol. xxiii., 1862.

below the surface, the inward progress of the annual wave may be
determined and the wave-length estimated.   In the case of a simple
harmonic variation of temperature we have (Art. 308)

$$k = \frac{\lambda^2}{4\pi \mathrm{T}},$$

which, with the thermal capacity per unit volume of the material,
determines the absolute conductivity K.

The diurnal waves become insensible at so small a depth that in
most localities the inequalities of the soil and drainage prevent any
satisfactory observations on their inward propagation being carried out.
At depths exceeding 3 feet the daily variations become insensible,
and the changes observed are due to daily averages (varying from
day to day) which constitute the annual wave.   If the annual variation
were truly periodic, a complex harmonic function could be determined
which would represent for all time the temperature at depths below
3 feet.   But the annual variation is by no means perfectly periodic,
since there are differences in the annual average temperatures and
continual irregularities in the progress of the variation within each
year.   Sources of such disturbances are the unequal percolation of
water and irregularities on the surface and within the crust.

If, however, the temperature be supposed periodic and be expressed as a complex harmonic function, and if the constants of the
series be determined by observations on a thermometer buried at a
certain depth, and if the constants of another series representing the
varying temperature at another depth be determined in the same way
by observations on another thermometer, then the comparison of each
term of one series with the corresponding term of the other furnishes
a determination of the conductivity, and all the values derived in this
manner should agree perfectly if the data are accurate and if the
assumed conditions are fulfilled—that is, if the isothermal surfaces are
parallel planes, and if c and k are constant throughout the material.

These conditions, however, are not strictly fulfilled, and the first
thing to be tested is how far the different determinations agree, and
to learn accordingly how far the theory may be applied.[1]

[1] This method (Sir William Thomson, *Trans. Roy. Soc. Edin.* vol. xxii. p. 405)
differs from that followed by Forbes in substituting the consideration of the
separate terms of a complex harmonic function for the examination of the whole
variation unanalysed, which he conducted according to the plan laid down by
Poisson.   This plan consisted in using the formula for a simple harmonic variation, as approximately applicable to the actual variation.   At great depths the
amplitudes of the second and higher terms of the complex harmonic series become
so much reduced that they do not sensibly influence the variation, which may
consequently be expressed with sufficient accuracy by a single harmonic term of

This difficult and laborious test has been applied by Lord Kelvin to the observations of Professor Forbes[1] on thermometers buried at different depths and in different soils near Edinburgh, and the analysis has proved that serious discrepancies from the theoretic formula existed, but these appeared to be attributable rather to irregularities in the form and constitution of the surface than to variations in the conductivity and specific heat of the material.   Probably also thermometric errors considerably influenced the results, since there was necessarily some uncertainty in the corrections which must be applied to the stem in order to estimate the temperature of the bulb.

The following table contains the final results, the unit of length being one foot :—

Substance.	Diffusivity.			Conductivity.		
	Per Ann.	Per 24 Hr.	Per Second.	Per Ann.	Per 24 Hr.	Per Second.
Trap rock of Calton Hill	267·0	0·7310	·000008461	141·1	0·3863	·000004471
Sand of Experimental Garden .	295·0	0·8100	·000009374	88·9	0·2435	·000002818
Sandstone of Craigleith Quarry . .	784·5	2·1478	·00002486	362·7	0·9929	·00001149

Much valuable information concerning the observations which have been made on the rate of increase of underground temperature downwards is contained in the Reports of the Committee of the British Association appointed for this purpose.   A summary of the results contained in the first fifteen Reports (1868–81) has been drawn up by Professor J. D. Everett, the Secretary to the Committee, in which the general questions affecting such observations are discussed.   Two kinds of thermometers have been used—slow-acting thermometers and maximum thermometers.   A slow-acting thermometer consists of an ordinary thermometer having its bulb embedded in stearine or tallow, the whole instrument being hermetically sealed within a glass jacket.   These were placed in holes a few feet deep bored in newly opened rock, such as is presented in mine works or tunnels.   The holes were carefully plugged and made air-tight to exclude the influence of the external air.   After the lapse of a few days the thermometers were withdrawn and read, the slow action permitting this to be done

yearly period ; but at the greatest depths, for which continuous observations had been made, Lord Kelvin found that the second term had a very sensible influence, and the third and fourth terms were by no means without effect on the variations at 3 and 6 feet from the surface.

[1] Forbes, *Trans. Roy. Soc. Edin.* vol. xvi. part ii., 1846.

without any appreciable change taking place in its indication during the operation. The maximum thermometers employed were of two types—the Phillips and the Inverted Negretti—both being sealed in strong glass jackets to prevent the bulbs from being affected by pressure when lowered to a great depth in water.

The thermo-electric method of Becquerel was also tested by Dr. Everett, and from the result of some laboratory experiments it was concluded that the method could not be relied on to yield satisfactory results. The following table contains some of the results, the depth stated in each case being that of the deepest observation utilised :—

	Depth in Feet.	Feet for 1° F.
Bootle Waterworks (Liverpool) . .	1392	130
Przibram Mines (Bohemia) . . .	1900	126
St. Gothard Tunnel[1]	5578	82
Mont Cenis Tunnel[1]	5280	79
East Manchester Coal-field . .	2790	77
Paris Artesian Wells . . .	1312	56·7
London Artesian Wells (Kentish Town) .	1100	55
Yakutsk, frozen ground (Siberia) .	540	52
Sperenberg, boring in salt (Berlin) .	3492	51·5
St. Petersburg, well (Russia) . .	656	44
Carrickfergus, shaft of salt mine .	770	43
,, ,, ,,	570	40
Slitt Mine, Weardale (Northumberland) .	660	34

Interesting observations have been made in a very deep bore (4500 feet) in Wheeling, West Virginia, by Mr. Hallock.[2] Beginning at a depth of 1591 feet (the upper portion of the bore was cased with iron tubes), the first 244 feet showed a gradient of 1° F. in 92 feet, the next 651 feet gave 1° in 84·5 feet, the next 746 feet gave 1° in 80·6, the next 643 feet gave 1° in 62·4, and the next 587 feet gave 1° in 58·1. The mean gradient for the whole 2871 feet (1591 to 4462) being 1° F. in 71·8 feet. At a depth of 4492 feet the mean temperature of some water in the bottom of the well was found to be 110·36° F.

---

[1] In the sixteenth Report it is mentioned that these numbers were derived from a conjectural correction for the convexity of the mountain surfaces. Dr. Stapff's calculations lead, however, to the conclusion that a much larger allowance must be made under this head. He deduces 1° F. in 85 feet as the average rate of increase from the surface above to the tunnel, and he calculates that at a depth below the tunnel, sufficient to make the isothermal surfaces sensibly plane, the increase is 1° F. in 57·8 feet.

[2] W. Hallock, *American Journal of Science and Art*, March 1892.

The conductivity of some igneous rocks has been measured by Poole[1] over a considerable range of temperature. The conductivity of granite falls from about 6×10^{-3} C.G.S. units at ordinary temperatures to under 4×10^{-3} at $500°$ C., and rises again to about $4·7 \times 10^{-3}$ on cooling. The change in conductivity was attributed to the formation of minute cracks in the rock on heating. The conductivity of basalt rises slightly with temperature up to about $270°$, above which it is constant up to $600°$ and nearly equal to 4×10^{-3}. There is a small permanent lowering of conductivity caused by heating the rock.

311. The General Equations of Conduction.—So far we have confined our attention chiefly to the propagation of heat along bars, or parallel to a single direction. The general case, however, in which the flow may take place in any manner may be treated by a similar method, and the general equations which determine it may be obtained without further difficulty. Thus if three mutually rectangular axes OX, OY, OZ (Fig. 211) be chosen as axes of reference, and if a small

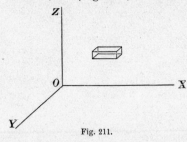

Fig. 211.

rectangular parallelepiped, having its edges parallel to the axes of reference, be considered, and if the lengths of the edges be δx, δy, δz, then confining our attention to the pair of faces perpendicular to the axis OX, it is clear that if the temperature at the central point of the parallelepiped be θ, the temperatures of the two faces under consideration will be

$$\theta + \tfrac{1}{2}\frac{d\theta}{dx}\delta x, \quad \text{and} \quad \theta - \tfrac{1}{2}\frac{d\theta}{dx}\delta x,$$

for $d\theta/dx$ is the rate at which the temperature changes parallel to the axis OX—that is, the change of temperature per unit length in this direction, consequently

$$\tfrac{1}{2}\frac{d\theta}{dx}\delta x$$

is the difference of temperature between the centre of the parallelepiped and either end. It is of course understood that the element of volume is taken so small that the temperature over each face is sensibly uniform, and that the rate of change of temperature may be taken uniform along each edge.

[1] *Phil. Mag.* vol. xxvii. p. 58, 1914.

The influx at the first face per second is consequently

$$-K\delta y\delta z\frac{d}{dx}\left(\theta - \tfrac{1}{2}\frac{d\theta}{dx}\delta x\right),$$

while the efflux at the opposite face is

$$-K\delta y\delta z\frac{d}{dx}\left(\theta + \tfrac{1}{2}\frac{d\theta}{dx}\delta x\right),$$

and hence it follows that the differences between the influxes and effluxes per unit time for the pairs of opposite faces are

$$K\frac{d^2\theta}{dx^2}\delta x\delta y\delta z, \qquad K\frac{d^2\theta}{dy^2}\delta x\delta y\delta z, \qquad \text{and} \qquad K\frac{d^2\theta}{dz^2}\delta x\delta y\delta z.$$

The sum of these three quantities must consequently remain lodged in the element, so that if the thermal capacity per unit volume be c, this sum must be equal to

$$c\frac{d\theta}{dt}\delta x\delta y\delta z,$$

for $d\theta/dt$ is the rate of change of temperature of the element—that is, the change of temperature per unit time. We have consequently the general equation—

$$K\left(\frac{d^2\theta}{dx^2}+\frac{d^2\theta}{dy^2}+\frac{d^2\theta}{dz^2}\right)=c\frac{d\theta}{dt}.$$

If the temperature has become permanent at each point, so that a steady flow is established, we have $d\theta/dt = 0$, and the equation of steady flow is therefore

$$\frac{d^2\theta}{dx^2}+\frac{d^2\theta}{dy^2}+\frac{d^2\theta}{dz^2}=0,$$

or, as it is generally written,

$$\nabla^2\theta = 0.$$

To determine θ as a function of x, y, z, t, it is necessary to know the manner in which the heat enters or leaves the body at the various points of its surface—that is, we want an accurate knowledge of the surface conditions. We might suppose, for example, that one part of the surface is kept in contact with a medium at uniform temperature θ_1, while the remainder of the surface is kept in contact with another medium at a different temperature θ_2. If θ_1 be higher than θ_2, then in the stationary state heat will enter the surface in contact with the first medium and escape by the surface in contact with the second, the quantity which enters being equal to that which escapes.

Thus if dn be an element of the normal to the element of surface dS, and h_1 and h_2 the coefficients of *exterior* conductivity for the first and second media, then we have the quantity of heat which passes through $d\text{S}$ equal to

$$-\text{K}\frac{d\theta}{dn}d\text{S} = h_1(\theta_1 - \theta)d\text{S},$$

and for an element in contact with the second medium we have

$$-\text{K}\frac{d\theta}{dn}d\text{S} = h_2(\theta_2 - \theta)d\text{S}.$$

These equations express the surface conditions necessary to the complete determination of the flow of heat and distribution of temperature.

312. Isothermal Surfaces, Lines, and Tubes of Flow.—In the general case the temperature at any point of a body will be a function of the co-ordinates x, y, z, of the point and of the time t, so that the general expression for θ at any point will be of the form

$$\theta = f(x, y, z, t).$$

Hence, if we write

$$f(x, y, z, t) = a,$$

where a is a constant, we obtain the locus of all the points at which the temperature has the same value a at the time t. These points lie on a surface, determined by the function f, and named an *isothermal surface* because it is one of equal temperature. When the flow has become steady, the temperature at any point remains steady, and therefore does not involve the time. In this case, then, the isothermal surfaces are fixed in shape and position, each separating those parts of the body which are hotter than a certain temperature from those which are colder. In the variable state, on the other hand, the shape and position of an isothermal surface corresponding to a definite temperature will in general vary with the time.

If a system of such surfaces be supposed drawn within the body, the temperature of each differing, by 1° suppose, from that which immediately precedes or follows it, the whole body will then be divided into a system of layers or shells such that the temperature of one face of each layer exceeds that of the other by 1°, and a flow of heat will proceed through the shell from the hotter face to the colder. The direction of the flow at each face will also be perpendicular to the surface, for since the temperature is constant all over each isothermal, it follows that there can be no flow along such a surface.

It follows then that the direction of the resultant flow at any point of a body is along the normal to the isothermal surface passing through that point, so that if a line be drawn cutting the whole system of surfaces orthogonally, the direction of the flow at every point of this line will be along the line. For this reason a line drawn so as to cut each of the system of surfaces at right angles is termed a *line of flow.*

The whole body may thus be imagined to be divided into a system of infinitely thin shells by a system of isothermal surfaces, and the infinite system of lines which can be drawn cutting these shells orthogonally are the lines of flow.

One property of these systems is that no two isothermal surfaces, or no two lines of flow, can intersect each other, for no point can possess two different temperatures at the same time, nor can the flow at any point be at once in two different directions.

If now we consider any closed curve drawn in the body, say a curve traced on an isothermal surface, and if we imagine the lines of flow passing through each point of this curve to be drawn, then these lines will form a tube having the lines of flow lying in its surface. Such a tube is termed a *tube of flow,* and is such that there is no flux of heat across its walls, for it is bounded entirely by lines of flow, and no two such lines can intersect.

In the steady state it is clear that the total flow of heat across any isothermal surface is the same as that across any other, that these surfaces cut the tubes of flow orthogonally, and that the quantity of heat which crosses any section of such a tube per second is the same wherever the section be made. In fact, any heat that is once within a tube of flow must for ever remain within it, as there can be no flow across its walls.

Again, if we take two close isothermal surfaces, enclosing a thin shell, and if we consider two equal elements of area dS on different parts of the surface of this shell, then if $d\theta$ be the difference of temperature between the two faces, and dn the normal thickness of the shell at one of the chosen points, and dn' that at the other, the flows of heat per second through the two elements will be

$$Q = -K\frac{d\theta}{dn}dS \quad \text{and} \quad Q' = -K\frac{d\theta}{dn'}dS$$

respectively. Hence it follows that

$$\frac{Q}{Q'} = \frac{dn'}{dn};$$

or, in other words, the flow per unit area at any point of the shell is inversely as the thickness of the shell, so that where the shell is thinnest the flow is most rapid. In the same way it follows, from what has been stated concerning tubes of flow, that the flow per unit area through any cross-section of a tube of flow varies inversely as the area of the section, and combining these results, it follows that the tubes of flow are narrowest where the isothermal surfaces are closest, and *vice versa*. All this, however, follows at once from our definitions (Art. 297).

In the above equation we have supposed the conductivity of the material to be the same at each of its points; if this be not the case we have $Q/Q' = K dn'/K' dn$, so that the more general statement will be that the flow per unit area at any point of a shell bounded by two isothermal surfaces is directly proportional to the conductivity and inversely proportional to the thickness of the shell at this point.

Examples

1. A sphere is uniformly heated and then left to cool in a medium of uniform temperature.

In this case the isothermal surfaces are a system of concentric spheres, and the lines of flow are right lines passing through their common centre, while the tubes of flow are cones having a common vertex at the centre of the sphere. The lines and tubes of flow remain fixed while cooling proceeds, but the radius of the isothermal surface corresponding to a given temperature gradually contracts, the surface moving in towards the centre.

2. The centre of a sphere is kept at a constant temperature by a source of heat, while the surface is immersed in a medium of uniform lower temperature.

In Example 1 the temperature at each point gradually falls, and no state of steady flow is attained. In this case, however, there is a supply at the centre, and a state of steady flow from the centre towards the surface is established. Here the isothermal surfaces, as before, are spheres, but now they remain fixed in the body, and the total quantity of heat that flows across any surface per second is the same as that which flows across any other. Supposing the conductivity uniform, we have for this quantity

$$- K \frac{d\theta}{dr} 4\pi r^2 = Q,$$

and since Q is the same for all values of r, we have

$$- r^2 \frac{d\theta}{dr} = a,$$

where a is a constant.

Hence

$$\theta = - \int \frac{a dr}{r^2} = \frac{a}{r} + b,$$

which gives the temperature at any distance r from the centre.

3. Two surfaces of a uniform spherical shell are kept at constant temperatures θ_1 and θ_2.

Let the radii of the two surfaces be r_1 and r_2. Then the temperature at any intermediate distance r is given by the equation of Example 2. The constants a and b are determined by the two surface conditions—

$$\theta_1 = \frac{a}{r_1} + b, \quad \text{and} \quad \theta_2 = \frac{a}{r_2} + b.$$

Therefore

$$a = \frac{(\theta_1 - \theta_2)r_1 r_2}{r_2 - r_1}, \quad b = \frac{\theta_1 r_1 - \theta_2 r_2}{r_1 - r_2};$$

consequently

$$\theta = \frac{1}{r_1 - r_2}\left\{ \theta_1 r_1 - \theta_2 r_2 - \frac{(\theta_1 - \theta_2)r_1 r_2}{r} \right\};$$

while the quantity of heat which flows across any isothermal surface per second is $4\pi Ka$, and the same quantity of heat would flow per second through an area $4\pi r^2$ of a wall of the same thickness as the shell and having its faces at the same difference of temperature $(\theta_1 - \theta_2)$, if r is the geometric mean of r_1 and r_2.

4. The internal and external surfaces of a long hollow circular cylinder are kept at fixed temperatures θ_1 and θ_2.

In this case the isothermal surfaces are coaxial cylinders, and the tubes of flow are wedges having their edges on the axis of the cylinder. The cross-section of any one of these wedges by a plane parallel to its edge is a rectangle of constant length, and a breadth which varies directly as the distance from the axis. The area of the section consequently varies directly as its distance from the axis, and therefore the flow per unit area, in the steady state, varies inversely as the distance. Taking K constant, the equation of flow may therefore be written in the form, if the inner surface be hottest,

$$-\frac{d\theta}{dr} = \frac{a}{r},$$

where a is a constant ; and hence

$$\theta = -a \log r + b.$$

The constants a and b are determined by means of the surface conditions

$$\theta_1 = -a \log r_1 + b, \quad \text{and} \quad \theta_2 = -a \log r_2 + b.$$

So that

$$a = \frac{\theta_1 - \theta_2}{\log (r_2/r_1)}, \quad \text{and} \quad b = \frac{\theta_2 \log r_1 - \theta_1 \log r_2}{\log (r_1/r_2)}.$$

The temperature at any distance r is consequently given by the equation

$$\theta = \frac{\theta_1 - \theta_2}{\log (r_1/r_2)} \log r + \frac{\theta_2 \log r_1 - \theta_1 \log r_2}{\log (r_1/r_2)},$$

or

$$\theta = \frac{\theta_1 \log (r/r_2) - \theta_2 \log (r/r_1)}{\log (r_1/r_2)}.$$

The quantity of heat which flows per second across a length l of the cylinder will be

$$Q = -2\pi r l K \frac{d\theta}{dr} = 2\pi a K l$$

$$= \frac{2\pi K l (\theta_1 - \theta_2)}{\log (r_2/r_1)}.$$

If e be the thickness of the cylinder, we have $e = r_2 - r_1$, and hence

$$\log \frac{r_2}{r_1} = \log \left(1 + \frac{e}{r_1}\right) = \frac{e}{r_1}$$

if e be small. Hence for a thin cylindrical tube of radius r we have approximately

$$Q = 2\pi K l (\theta_1 - \theta_2)\frac{r}{e}.$$

ON THE CONDUCTIVITY OF CRYSTALS

313. Propagation of Heat in Æolotropic Substances.—In the previous investigations we have had under consideration the propagation of heat in isotropic substances—that is, in substances possessing the same physical characteristics not only in every part, but also in every direction around any point. When heat is supplied at any point of an isotropic body, the flow takes place equally in all directions around the point, and the isothermal surfaces are concentric spheres surrounding the heated point as centre. On the other hand, when any point of a heterogeneous substance is heated, the flow of heat in any direction, and the shape of the isothermal surfaces, will depend upon the characteristics of the substance, or the manner in which its physical properties vary from point to point and from one direction to another. If the substance be homogeneous, however, but not isotropic, then although its properties may be different in different directions around any point, yet the properties of the substance along any line are the same as those along any parallel line, so that when any two points are compared, the thermal conductivity and other properties of the substance along any line drawn from one point will be the same as along a parallel line drawn through the other. It follows, therefore, that when any point of a homogeneous substance is supplied with heat, the isothermal surfaces around it will be independent of the position of the point ; or, in other words, those around one heated point will be similar, and similarly situated, to those around any other point. We shall see immediately that in general these surfaces are systems of similar ellipsoids, which become spheres, as a particular case, when the substance is isotropic.

The first experiments which established a difference of conductivity in different directions seem to be those of MM. de la Rive and de Candolle.[1] These philosophers proved that wood conducted heat along the fibre better than at right angles to it, and this conclusion has been confirmed by the subsequent investigations of Tyndall[2] and Knoblauch.[3] The conductivities in different directions were compared by the method adopted by Despretz (Art. 300), blocks of wood being cut with pairs of opposite faces perpendicular to the fibre, parallel to the fibre, and perpendicular to the ligneous layers, and parallel to both the fibre and the ligneous layers, respectively. In all cases the conductivity was best along the fibre and worst in the direction perpendicular to the fibre and parallel to the ligneous layers—that is, perpendicular to the radius from the centre to the bark of the tree.

This result is confirmed by the experiments of E. Griffiths and Kaye,[4] who measured the conductivities of a number of timbers and

[1] De la Rive and de Candolle, *Bibliothèque universelle de Genève*, tom. xxxix.
[2] Tyndall, *Phil. Mag.*, 4th Series, vols. v. and vi. ; and *Heat a Mode of Motion.*
[3] Knoblauch, *Pogg. Ann.* vol. cv. p. 623.
[4] *Proc. R. Soc.* vol. civ. p. 71, 1923.

other poor conductors by the plate method. An electrically heated copper disc was placed between two discs of the material, and outside these again were two water-cooled copper discs. Temperatures were measured with copper-constantan thermocouples. A few of the results are contained in the following table, the conductivities being in C.G.S. units, and the mean temperature 20° C. :—

CONDUCTIVITIES OF WOODS

(cal. cm.$^{-1}$ deg.$^{-1}$ sec.$^{-1}$)

Name of Wood.	Percentage of Moisture.	Parallel to Fibre.	Perp. to Fibre and Radial.	Perp. to Fibre and to Radius.
Ash	15	0·00073	0·00042	{0·00039
Spruce . . .	16	0·00053	0·00029	0·00025
Oak	14	...	...	0·00028
Balsa	13	...	...	0·00011

A similar difference of conductivity along and perpendicular to the planes of cleavage of laminated rocks which are not crystallised has been detected by Jannettaz,[1] the conductivity being best parallel to the planes of cleavage and worst perpendicular to them. The same difference along and perpendicular to the planes of cleavage of bismuth has also been found by Svanberg and Matteucci. This difference in the case of laminated rocks shows that underground temperatures may be considerably modified by the inclination of the strata to the horizon.

314. Experiments of M. de Senarmont.—The first extended experimental investigation of the conductivity of crystals was that of M. de Senarmont.[2] The method adopted consisted in cutting a thin plate, with parallel faces, in any desired direction from the crystal. The surfaces of the plate were coated with a thin film of white wax, and heat was applied at one point, from which it was conducted in all directions through the plate. As the plate became warm the wax melted around the point, and the inequalities of conductivity in different directions were indicated by the shape of the bounding line of the melted wax.

In the case of isotropic substances, such as glass or cubic crystals, this curve was always a circle, and it was also a circle when the plate was cut in certain directions from crystals which did not belong to the cubic system, but in general with a plate cut in any other direction from a crystal the curve was elliptical, or at least an oval curve very

---

[1] Édouard Jannettaz, *Journal de Physique*, tom. v. p. 150 ; and *Ann. de Chimie*, 4ᵉ sér., tom. xxix. p. 5, 1873.

[2] De Senarmont, *Ann. de Chimie et de Physique*, 3ᵉ sér., toms. xxi. xxii. xxiii., 1847–48.

approximately an ellipse. This line remained visible on the wax after the plate had cooled, and its eccentricity and the position of the axes of the curve could be determined. It would thus appear that the isothermal surfaces around a heated point of a crystal are in general a system of concentric ellipsoids.

It was also found that the axes of these ellipsoids, or the thermic axes, coincided with the crystallographic axes of symmetry, so that, for example, in crystals of the cubic system the propagation of heat took place as in uncrystallised media, and in crystals of the rhombohedral system the axis of the crystal was an axis of thermic symmetry, the isothermal surfaces being ellipsoids of revolution around it. It was found in this manner that quartz and calc-spar conduct heat best along the axis of symmetry, and equally in all directions perpendicular to this axis, while idocrase and tourmaline conduct heat best at right angles to the axis.

One method of heating the crystalline plate is shown in Fig. 212.

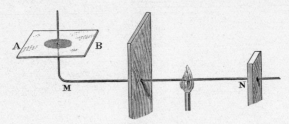

Fig. 212.

A small hole having been drilled through the plate AB, a copper or silver wire (being good conductors) was passed through it, and the lower portion MN was bent at right angles and heated by a lamp, the direct radiation of the lamp being carefully screened off. The wire soon becomes heated, and being a good conductor, the heat is carried to the plate, the wax melts around the hole, and an isothermal line corresponding to the melting point of the wax is left imprinted on it.

In M. de Senarmont's experiments it was not a simple wire that was used, but a fine silver tube, so that when it became heated an ascending current of hot air flowed through it, and heat was carried to the plate both by the conduction of the metal and by the convection of the heated air. Two other methods of heating the plate were also employed. In one the rays of the sun were concentrated by a lens of short focus to a point on the surface of the plate, and in the other a wire was passed through the hole and heated by an electric

current. The former method possesses an advantage in that the
drilling of a hole is avoided, and no discontinuity is introduced into
the plate, and in the latter method caution is necessary in heating the
wire, for if the temperature be raised too suddenly the plate may be
fractured.

When the plate is fairly thick, and heated by a wire passing
through a hole at right angles to its faces, the curves on its two faces
are in general not true ellipses, but egg-shaped ovals, such as are
shown in Fig. 213, having their more obtuse ends turned in opposite
directions on the two faces.   This arises from the fact that the plate
is not heated at a single point, but along a line, and when the source
of heat is a line, the curves on the two faces will be similar ellipses
only when the line is in the direction of the diameter of the thermic
ellipsoid, which is conjugate to the direction of the faces of the plate.
This point will be brought out in the theoretical investigation which
follows.

Later experiments by Von Lang[1] and Jannettaz extended
the results obtained by De Senarmont to a great number of

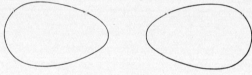

Fig. 213.

crystals, but they brought to light no new or more general relations.

A determination of the absolute conductivities of crystals in
different directions was made by Lees,[2] according to a plan suggested by Sir Oliver Lodge.[3]   This method consists in placing
a slice of the crystal between the ends of two bars of metal
placed end to end with their lengths in the same straight line.
The crystalline lamina thus forms part of a compound bar which
may be treated experimentally, either by the method of Forbes or
by that of Ångström.

In order to secure good contact between the bars and the crystal,
a metal (brass) was used which would amalgamate, and the contact
given by the amalgamated ends was found to be extremely good.
The temperature curve along the bars was determined by means of

[1] Victor von Lang, *Pogg. Ann.* vol. cxxxv. p. 29, 1868.

[2] Charles H. Lees, *Memoirs and Proc. of the Manchester Phil. and Lit. Soc.* vol.
iv. p. 17, 1890–91 ; *Phil. Trans.*, 1892.

[3] O. J. Lodge, *Phil. Mag.* (5) vol. v. p. 110, 1878.

thermo-electric couples of iron and German silver soldered into the bars. The compound bar was packed in sawdust, and one end was heated by steam, while the other was immersed in cold water. When the temperature curve was plotted, the value of $d\theta/dx$ could be determined for each face of the crystalline plate ;[1] and when the absolute conductivity of the brass bars is known, that of the crystal can be deduced. The absolute conductivity of the brass was determined by Forbes's method. Lees found that the value of K for quartz is 0·0299 parallel to the optic axis, and 0·0158 perpendicular to it.

Kaye and Roberts,[2] using the same apparatus as that of Griffiths and Kaye mentioned in the preceding article, measured the conductivity of single crystals of bismuth. The metal crystallises in the rhombohedral system. At 18° C. the conductivity parallel to the trigonal axis was 0·0159, and perpendicular to the axis 0·0221.

315. Theory of Conduction in Crystals.—The theory of thermal conduction in crystalline media was attacked as early as 1828 by Duhamel,[3] who from the hypothesis of molecular radiation deduced the general expressions for the flow of heat, and subsequently obtained a number of general consequences which applied directly to the experiments of M. de Senarmont. In 1851 the theory was presented by Stokes [4] in a form independent of any hypothesis of molecular radiation, the only assumption made being the general one that the quantity of heat is conserved, and, by means of an auxiliary solid, problems relating to crystalline conduction were reduced to corresponding problems concerning isotropic bodies.

Thus if we consider the flow of heat across an elementary plane area, drawn in a given direction, through any point P of the body, then if f be the flux of heat per unit area, per second, across this plane, the flow across the element dS in the time dt will be $f.dS.dt$, and the value of f will depend on the direction in which the plane is drawn, and also on the time and the position of the point. For the present we shall consider the time and position given, so that f will depend only on the direction of the plane.

Let three rectangular planes of reference be chosen, and let f_x, f_y, f_z be the fluxes across them. Then if the elementary plane dS be supposed to approach indefinitely close to the origin, it will, with the

---

[1] A correction for the thin layer of mercury between the metal and the crystal was determined by a special experiment.

[2] *Proc. R. Soc.* vol. civ. p. 98, 1923.

[3] Duhamel, *Journal de l'École polytechnique*, toms. xxi. xxxii. See also Lamé, *Leçons sur la théorie analytique de la chaleur*, Paris, 1861.

[4] G. G. Stokes, *Cambridge and Dublin Mathematical Journal*, vol. vi. p. 215, 1851.

planes of reference, enclose a small tetrahedron whose faces are dS, λdS, μdS, νdS respectively, where λ, μ, ν are the direction cosines of the normal to dS. Now, if the steady stage has been reached, as much heat flows into this tetrahedron as flows out; and even if this stage has not been attained, the difference between what flows in and what flows out will be vanishingly small compared with either, for it is proportional to the thermal capacity of the element and the rate of rise of temperature, but the former is proportional to the cube of the linear dimensions of the element of volume, whereas the fluxes across the faces vary as their areas or the squares of the linear dimensions. We may therefore equate the sum of the flows across any three faces to that across the fourth, so that we have the flow $f.dS$ per second across the base dS equal to the sum of the flows $f_x.\lambda dS$, $f_y.\mu dS$, $f_z.\nu dS$ across the other faces; or

$$f = \lambda f_x + \mu f_y + \nu f_z \qquad . \qquad . \qquad . \qquad . \qquad (1)$$

This equation shows that if the fluxes of heat across the planes of reference be represented by three vectors, as in the case of forces or velocities, the flux across any other plane will be represented by the sum of the resolved parts of these vectors along the perpendicular to the plane. For some plane through P the flux of heat is greater than for any other, and the flux of heat across any other plane is this maximum flux multiplied by the cosine of the angle between the planes.

Let θ be the temperature at P, and let us consider an elementary parallelepiped of sides δx, δy, δz. The flow of heat per second through the face $\delta y \delta z$ is $f_x.\delta y \delta z$, and the flow through the opposite face is $(f_x + \frac{df_x}{dx}\delta x)\delta y \delta z$, and so on for the other pairs of faces, so that the gain of heat per second is

$$-\left(\frac{df_x}{dx} + \frac{df_y}{dy} + \frac{df_z}{dz}\right)\delta x \delta y \delta z.$$

But if the rate of change of temperature be $d\theta/dt$, and if the thermal capacity per unit volume be c, this must be equal to $c\delta x \delta y \delta z d\theta/dt$, and we have

$$\frac{df_x}{dx} + \frac{df_y}{dy} + \frac{df_z}{dz} = -c\frac{d\theta}{dt} \qquad . \qquad . \qquad . \qquad . \qquad (2)$$

These formulæ are perfectly general, and apply whether the substance be homogeneous or not. We shall now suppose the material homogeneous, and that c is constant.

At this point a distinct assumption is made—namely, that the flow of heat at P depends not on the absolute temperature, but only on the variation of temperature in its vicinity. In fact, it is assumed that the flux across any plane is a linear function of the rates of change of temperature $d\theta/dx$, $d\theta/dy$, $d\theta/dz$, parallel to the axes, so that we may write

$$\left.\begin{aligned} -f_x &= a_1\frac{d\theta}{dx} + \beta_1\frac{d\theta}{dy} + \gamma_1\frac{d\theta}{dz} \\ f_y &= a_2\frac{d\theta}{dx} + \beta_2\frac{d\theta}{dy} + \gamma_2\frac{d\theta}{dz} \\ -f_z &= a_3\frac{d\theta}{dx} + \beta_3\frac{d\theta}{dy} + \gamma_3\frac{d\theta}{dz} \end{aligned}\right\} \qquad . \quad . \quad . \quad . \quad (3)$$

Substituting these values of f_x, f_y, f_z in equation (2) we have

$$a\frac{d^2\theta}{dx^2} + b\frac{d^2\theta}{dy^2} + c\frac{d^2\theta}{dz^2} + 2f\frac{d^2\theta}{dydz} + 2g\frac{d^2\theta}{dzdx} + 2h\frac{d^2\theta}{dxdy} = c\frac{d\theta}{dt} \qquad . \quad . \quad (4)$$

where $a = a_1$, $2f = \gamma_2 + \beta_3$, etc.

Now there is a certain set of rectangular axes—namely, the axes of the quadric—

$$ax^2 + by^2 + cz^2 + 2fyz + 2gzx + 2hxy = 1 \qquad . \quad . \quad . \quad (5)$$

for which the equation (4) takes the form

$$A\frac{d^2\theta}{dx^2} + B\frac{d^2\theta}{dy^2} + C\frac{d^2\theta}{dz^2} = c\frac{d\theta}{dt} \qquad . \quad . \quad . \quad . \quad (6)$$

for if new axes of reference Ox', Oy', Oz' be chosen, making angles with the old axes Ox, Oy, Oz, whose direction cosines are l, m, n; l', m', n'; l'', m'', n''; then

$$x' = lx + my + nz,$$

and

$$\frac{d}{dx'} = l\frac{d}{dx} + m\frac{d}{dy} + n\frac{d}{dz},$$

and since the symbols of differentiation combine with each other according to the same law as factors, it follows that the equation (4) will be transformed by a change of axes exactly as if the symbols of differentiation were replaced by co-ordinates x, y, z. When the principal axes of the surface (5), or any three conjugate diameters of it, are taken as the axes of reference, the equation (4) takes the form (6). These axes are termed the *thermic axes* of the crystal.

Taking the thermic axes as the axes of co-ordinates, the general expressions (3) for the flux of heat become simplified. The expressions (3) for f_x, f_y, f_z contain nine arbitrary constants; but when we substitute (2) and compare the result with (6) it follows at once that $\beta_1 = -a_2$, $\gamma_1 = -a_3$, $\gamma_2 = -\beta_3$, so that the expressions may be written in the form

$$-f_x = \quad A\frac{d\theta}{dx} - H\frac{d\theta}{dy} + G\frac{d\theta}{dz}$$

$$-f_y = \quad H\frac{d\theta}{dx} + B\frac{d\theta}{dy} - F\frac{d\theta}{dz} \qquad \cdots \quad (7)$$

$$-f_z = -G\frac{d\theta}{dx} + F\frac{d\theta}{dy} + C\frac{d\theta}{dz}$$

If the substance be symmetrical with respect to two rectangular planes, the coefficients F, G, H must vanish,[1] for the planes of symmetry must contain the thermic axes, and if these planes be taken as those of xz and yz, the expression for f_x must change sign with x, while f_y and f_z remain unaltered. Similarly f_y must change sign with y, while f_x and f_z remain unaltered, and referring to equation (7) this requires F, G, H to vanish, so that

$$f_x = -A\frac{d\theta}{dx}, \quad f_y = -B\frac{d\theta}{dy}, \quad f_z = -C\frac{d\theta}{dz} \qquad \cdots \quad (8)$$

The constants A, B, C are thus the conductivities of the substance in the directions of the thermic axes, and are termed the principal conductivities of the crystal.

Now, in the case of an isotropic substance the equation which determines the distribution of temperature is (Art. 311)

$$K\left(\frac{d^2\theta}{dx^2} + \frac{d^2\theta}{dy^2} + \frac{d^2\theta}{dz^2}\right) = c\frac{d\theta}{dt} \cdot \qquad \cdots \quad (9)$$

and equation (6), which applies to a crystalline body, will be transformed into an equation of the same form as (9) if the co-ordinates x, y, z be altered in the ratios $\sqrt{A/K}$, $\sqrt{B/K}$, and $\sqrt{C/K}$ respectively, or (9) will be transformed into (6) by altering the co-ordinates in the inverse ratio. And if we take $K^3 = ABC$, any volume of one will be strained by this transformation into an equal volume of the other. Hence the distribution of temperature in an isotropic solid, arising from any given conditions of heat-supply at one or more points, being determined, the corresponding distribution and the isothermal surfaces in a crystal may be deduced by straining the co-ordinates in the manner just indicated.

Derived solid.

Thus if heat be supplied at one point of an infinite isotropic solid according to any law, the isothermal surfaces will be spheres, and if the source be taken as the origin of co-ordinates, any one of these spheres will be given by the equation

$$x^2 + y^2 + z^2 = r^2 \qquad \cdots \quad (10)$$

where r is the radius of the sphere. This surface becomes strained by the above transformation of co-ordinates into the ellipsoid

---

[1] Stokes, in the paper referred to, gives reasons for the supposition that F, G, H vanish in the general case.

$$\frac{x^2}{A} + \frac{y^2}{B} + \frac{z^2}{C} = \frac{r^2}{K} \quad . \quad . \quad . \quad . \quad . \quad (11)$$

which is the corresponding isothermal surface in a crystal, the axes of reference being taken in the directions of the thermic axes of the crystal.

Hence in an infinite crystalline medium, if heat be introduced at a single point, the isothermal surfaces will be a system of concentric and similar ellipsoids, the axes of any one of which are directly proportional to the square roots of the three principal conductivities of the substance. Again, in the isotropic medium the flow of heat at any point takes place along the radius of the sphere, and varies inversely as the distance from the source, and the same result holds in the crystal. The flow across any plane touching the thermic ellipsoid is consequently in the direction conjugate to that plane.

Now, if an infinite isotropic plate be considered, and if heat be supplied at any point or any number of points along a normal to the plate, the isothermal surfaces will be surfaces of revolution round the normal, and the isothermal curves on the face of the plate will be circles. Hence, if a corresponding crystalline plate be heated at any point or at any number of points along a line (the line of sources) taken in the direction conjugate to the faces of the plate with respect to the thermic ellipsoid (11), any particular isothermal surface will be the surface generated by an ellipse moving with its plane parallel to the faces of the plate, its centre on the line of sources, and its principal axes parallel and proportional to those of the ellipse in which the thermic ellipsoid is cut by a plane parallel to the faces.

In the particular case in which the faces of the plate are cut parallel to the circular sections of the thermic ellipsoid, the isothermal curves on the faces will be circles, but the line joining the centres of the systems on the two faces will not be normal to the faces. In order, then, to procure ellipses on the faces of a plate in De Senarmont's experiment, it is necessary that the hole in the plate should be drilled in the direction conjugate to the faces with respect to the thermic ellipsoid.

In the same manner when a crystalline bar is heated at one end, the isothermal surfaces are not planes at right angles to the length of the bar, but are planes parallel to the diametral plane of the thermic ellipsoid, which is conjugate to the direction of the length of the bar.

Again, the flow of heat across any element of area in the crystal is equal to the flow across the corresponding element of the derived isotropic solid. For the flow across an element of area $dydz$ perpendicular to the axis of x in the crystal is $-A\frac{d\theta}{dx}dydz$, and if $K^3 = ABC$, this is equal to the flow across the corresponding area in the derived solid.

If we denote by Δ_x, Δ_y, Δ_z, the differences between the expressions (7) and (8), we have

$$\frac{d\Delta_x}{dx} + \frac{d\Delta_y}{dy} + \frac{d\Delta_z}{dz} = 0,$$

which is analogous to the equation of continuity of an incompressible fluid.

ON THE CONDUCTIVITY OF FLUIDS

316. Conductivity of Liquids—Despretz's Method.—When the lower strata of a liquid are heated expansion occurs, and the consequent diminution of density causes the heated portions of the liquid to rise to the surface, while the colder parts sink to the bottom. In this manner convection currents are set up which transport the heat from one part of the liquid to another, and tend to bring about a uniformity of temperature throughout the mass. On the other hand, when the upper surface of the liquid is heated the warmer layers remain *in situ*, and the lower strata can become heated only by radiation and conduction proper, or by the process of diffusion or molecular convection—that is, by the individual molecules of the liquid becoming heated at the top and afterwards travelling into the lower strata, carrying their heat with them, and gradually parting with it to the colder molecules below by radiation or by contact, or by both processes simultaneously.[1]

When heat is supplied at the upper surface of a liquid the flow of heat downwards is in general exceedingly slow, except in the case of mercury or other metals in the liquid state. In illustration of this we may cite the fact that the upper strata of water contained in a tube, at the bottom of which some ice is fixed, may be boiled without melting the ice below. Such a very feeble flow of heat might reasonably lead to the suspicion that in liquids the transport is mainly effected by molecular diffusion and convection rather than by that process of conduction which takes place in solids.

The earliest experiments of any note on the conductivity of liquids

[1] Molecular diffusion of energy in fluids is regarded as conduction, since it is immaterial whether a moving molecule exchanges energy with another molecule or not. Convection, on the other hand, implies the existence of currents in the fluid, and depends on some external force (usually gravity) and also on the freedom of motion allowed by the containing vessel.

are those of Despretz,[1] the method adopted being analogous to the
process applied to the determination of the conductivity of metal bars.
In operating on water a cylindrical wooden vessel B (Fig. 214) was
employed, about 1 metre high and 20 cm. in diameter. At intervals
of 5 cm. holes were drilled in the walls of the cylinder, and in these
thermometers were inserted with their bulbs placed vertically over one
another along the axis of the cylinder. The vessel was filled with
water, and on the top of the liquid a copper box A was placed, which
was kept filled with hot water, renewed every five minutes. When
this was continued for some time the upper thermometers were
observed to show a gradual
increase of temperature,
and the wave of tempera-
ture proceeded slowly
downwards, as long as
thirty-six to forty hours
being required before the
stationary state was at-
tained.   This elevation of
temperature could not be
attributed to conduction
of heat down through
the sides of the feebly-
conducting vessel, for

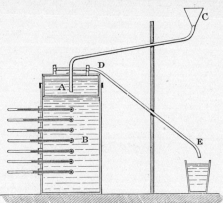

Fig. 214.—Despretz's Apparatus.

Despretz, by means of other thermometers placed in the liquid, with
their bulbs near the walls of the vessel, found that the temperature
was higher along the axis than near the sides of the cylinder. Near
the top the temperature did not vary much over a horizontal cross-
section, but lower down this variation was considerable. It was thus
proved that the propagation of heat takes place through the liquid
either by molecular diffusion or by conduction proper, or by both
processes.

   Despretz specially observed the temperatures in the stationary
condition, and he found that the distribution of temperature along the
axis of the cylinder followed the same law as that in a long metal bar
heated at one end and cooling by radiation in the open air.   In this
case we have already seen that the temperature curve is logarithmic
and given by the formula

$$\theta = ae^{-\mu x},$$

[1] Despretz, *Comptes rendus*, 1838, p. 933 ; *Ann. de Chimie et de Physique*, vol.
lxxi. p. 216, 1839.   Earlier experiments on the passage of heat downwards through
liquids were made by Murray (Nicholson's *Journal*, vol. i., 1802) and by Rumford
(Nicholson's *Journal*, vol. xiv., 1806).

so that the relative conductivities of liquids may be determined in this manner like those of solids. Thus for liquids of conductivities K_1, K_2, K_3, etc., if lengths l_1, l_2, l_3, etc., correspond to equal differences of temperature, we have, as in the experiment of Ingen-Hausz,

$$\frac{K_1}{l_1{}^2} = \frac{K_2}{l_2{}^2} = \frac{K_3}{l_3{}^2} = \text{etc.}$$

By a comparison of cylinders of the same material, Despretz found that μ varied inversely as the square root of the diameter of the cylinder, and this relation holds also for metals. The method, however, does not appear to be suited to give very accurate results, and the interest attaching to these experiments is chiefly historical.[1]

The same method was subsequently adopted by Paalzow,[2] in a slightly modified form, in an investigation of the relation, if any, between the electric and thermal conductivities of various liquids, and his observations prove that no relation exists between these quantities. For it appeared that water and sulphuric acid conduct heat almost equally, the former being somewhat the better.[3]

317. More Recent Investigations.—The methods which have been since applied to the determination of the conductivities of liquids belong chiefly to two classes : one in which a layer of the liquid under examination is contained between two horizontal discs having their centres in the same vertical line, and the other in which the liquid is contained in the annular space between two coaxial cylinders.

The first method, which may be termed the flat disc method, was adopted by Professor Guthrie[4] in 1869, and later by Weber,[5] Christiansen,[6] Wachsmuth,[7] and by Milner and Chattock.[8]

Lundquist[9] used a method in which a glass cylinder of water was alternately heated and cooled, thus resembling Ångström's method for solids. Other methods were used by Graetz,[10] Chree,[11] R. Weber,[12] and Goldschmidt.[13]

[1] A valuable historical account of the conduction of heat in liquids has been given by Dr. C. Chree in the *Philosophical Magazine* for July 1887, vol. xxiv. p. 1.

[2] Paalzow, *Pogg. Ann.* vol. cxxxiv. p. 618, 1868.

[3] The sulphuric acid is highly ionised, which accounts for its electrical conductivity.

[4] Guthrie, *Phil. Mag.* vol. xxxvii. p. 468, 1869.

[5] H. F. Weber, *Wied. Ann.* vol. x. pp. 103, 304, 472 ; vol. xi. p. 347, 1880.

[6] C. Christiansen, *Wied. Ann.* vol. xiv. p. 23, 1881.

[7] R. Wachsmuth, *Wied. Ann.* vol. xlviii. p. 158, 1893.

[8] S. R. Milner and A. P. Chattock, *Phil. Mag.* vol. xlviii. p. 46, 1899.

[9] G. Lundquist, *Upsala Universitats Årsskrift*, p. 29, 1869.

[10] L. Graetz, *Wied. Ann.* vol. xviii. p. 79, 1883 ; vol. xxv. p. 337, 1885.

[11] C. Chree, *Proc. R. Soc.* vol. xlii. p. 300 ; vol. xliii. p. 30, 1887.

[12] R. Weber, *Ann. der Physik*, vol. xi. p. 1047, 1903.

[13] R. Goldschmidt, *Phys. Zeitschr.* vol. xii. p. 417, 1911.

Experiments by the coaxial cylinder or annular space method have been made by Winkelmann [1] and Beetz.[2]

Winkelmann's results, expressed in centimetre, gramme, and minute units, are, for temperatures between 10° and 18° C. :—

Water	0·092
Salt solution	0·1605
Alcohol	0·0904
Bisulphide of carbon . . .	0·1186
Glycerine	0·0449

The determinations of the conductivities of poor conductors by Lees (Art. 304) were extended by him to liquids also. Fig. 215 shows the form of the apparatus. C, U, M, and L are nickel-plated copper discs, these being termed the cover, upper, middle, and lower discs respectively. P is the heating coil. G is a glass disc of known conductivity used to measure the transmission of

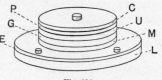

Fig. 215.

heat. E is an ebonite ring which confined the liquid between the discs M and L. To find the heat conducted through the ebonite ring, an experiment was made with air instead of liquid, the small amount conducted through the air being calculated. The whole apparatus was enclosed in an air-bath. Lees found a decrease in conductivity with rise of temperature. He states also that the conductivity of a substance does not always change abruptly at the melting point. The following table contains some of his results for liquids at 25° C. :—

Liquid.	Conductivity.	Mean Percentage Change per Degree C.
Water . . .	·00136	− 0·0055
Glycerine . .	·00068	− 0·0044
Methyl alcohol .	·00048	− 0·0031
Ethyl alcohol . .	·00043	− 0·0058

In the experiments on the conductivity of water made by the various physicists mentioned above, no large range of temperature was investigated. In all cases where the experiments indicated a temperature coefficient, this coefficient was found to be positive, except in the case of Lees' experiments. These latter measured the conductivity relatively to that of glass, and are therefore less

[1] A. Winkelmann, *Pogg. Ann.* vol. cliii. p. 481, 1874.
[2] W. Beetz, *Wied. Ann.* vii. p. 435, 1879.

reliable than direct determinations. The point was settled by the experiments of Jakob,[1] who investigated the conductivity of water between 0° C. and 80° C. with the apparatus shown in Fig. 216. The plate method was used, K_1 and K_2 being two copper discs of the same diameter separated by three small pieces of glass plate whose thickness (2·248 mm. at 14°) was accurately measured. All the rest of the space between the discs was filled with water, which was

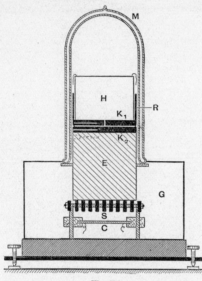

Fig. 216.

retained in position by surface tension at the edges. The small hole through the centre of the upper disc was for the introduction of the water. In each disc a narrow hole (seen in the figure) was bored parallel to the surface and nearly reaching the centre. These holes received the thermo-elements which gave the temperatures. A fairly thick-walled brass ring R rested on the upper disc, and inside this was a copper vessel H containing a heating coil immersed in oil. The bottom of this vessel (of brass) and the surfaces of the copper discs were made as truly plane as possible. The object of the brass ring R was to intercept radiation from the heater H. Thermo-elements were soldered to the ring R and were used for the purpose of determining the loss of heat by lateral radiation. The lower copper disc K_2 rested on a coppered cylindrical iron block E, which had a hole bored laterally near its upper end for the reception of a thermo-couple, and had projections from its sides which supported a vacuum vessel M, which was inverted over the apparatus. The block E rested on an iron grid S, standing in a vessel G, beneath which was a disc of cork. The whole apparatus rested on a plate with levelling screws.

For experiments at the lowest temperatures, G was filled with ice and there was also a ring-shaped vessel containing ice round the mouth of the vacuum vessel. Between 20° and 40° a stream of cold water flowed through G and kept its temperature steady. At higher temperatures G was filled with oil and heated by a coil C.

[1] *Ann. der Physik*, vol. lxiii. p. 537, 1920.

From the definition of conductivity in Art. 297 we have

$$K = \frac{(Q-q)e}{A(\theta_1 - \theta_2)},$$

where e is the thickness of the film of water, A its area, θ_1 and θ_2 the temperatures of its upper and lower faces ; Q the heat generated per unit time in the heater H, which was measured electrically ; and q the heat lost per unit time, *i.e.* which does not pass through the water. For the calculation of q the original paper must be consulted. As aids in its determination, it was arranged that a subsidiary heater could be substituted for the block E, and thus the amount of heat passing through the water reduced to zero. Also, experiments were made with air between the plates.

The results of these experiments were well represented by the formula

$$K = 0 \cdot 001325(1 + 0 \cdot 002984\theta),$$

which shows that the conductivity of water increases uniformly with the temperature between 0° C. and 80° C.

Conductivity of Gases

318. Andrews's Experiment—Conductivity of Hydrogen.—Difficult as the practical determination of the conductivity of liquids may be, the investigation becomes more complicated and perplexing in the case of gases, for here the phenomenon is masked by direct radiation, and it is almost impossible to determine how far the effects are due to convection and diffusion. For these reasons the determination of the thermal conductivity of gases is an investigation of extreme difficulty.

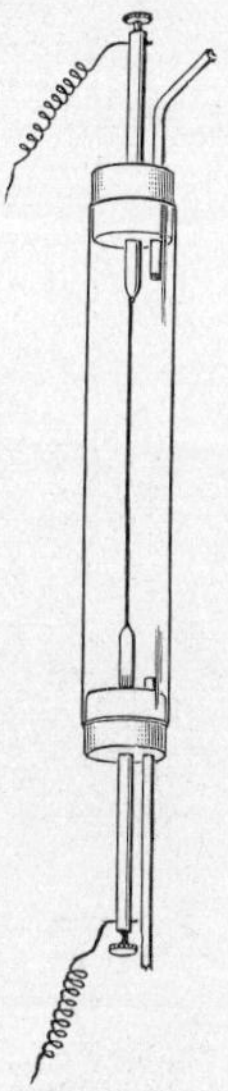

Many familiar facts, however, render it certain that heat is not conveyed with facility through air or other gases except by radiation. Thus the presence of interstices and cavities filled with air renders such materials as felt, wool, furs, etc., very bad conductors of heat. Such substances when compressed, so as to reduce the air cavities, conduct heat much better, and consequently become less warm when used as articles of clothing, but whether heat is propagated through the material more freely when the cavities are filled with air than when they are completely empty or filled with other gases, must be tested by experiment.

The experimental evidence on this subject points consistently to hydrogen as being a much better conductor of heat than any other gas, or at least indicates that heat is much more freely propagated by this gas than by any other. A celebrated

Fig. 217.

experiment on this subject is that described by Dr. Andrews,[1] and usually attributed to Grove. A thin platinum wire (Fig. 217), through which an electric current could be passed, was stretched within a glass tube. When the tube was filled with air, or any gas other than hydrogen, while the wire was raised to incandescence by the electric current, it was found that the brightness remained, though less vivid, when the tube was exhausted.[2] On the other hand, when hydrogen was passed into the tube, the brightness of the wire was greatly diminished, or altogether annulled.

The experiment was varied by Grove,[3] who passed the same current through two similar wires stretched in different tubes, which

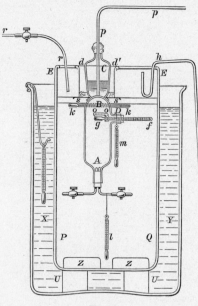

Fig. 218.

could be filled with different gases. When one of the tubes contained hydrogen the wire in that tube was not luminous, although the wire in the other was vividly bright. This effect was found by Magnus to be very decided, even when the wires were stretched in very narrow tubes only 1 mm. in diameter, so that the layer of gas was very thin, and convection currents could scarcely occur.

319. Experiments of Magnus.—The first notable investigation of the relative conductivities of gases was that published by Magnus[4] in 1860. The apparatus employed is shown in Fig. 218, and was similar to that already described in Art. 269. The investigation of the diathermancy of gases, in fact, developed out of the present inquiry concerning their conductivities. The gas under

[1] Andrews, *Proc. Roy. Irish Academy*, vol. i. p. 465, 1840.

[2] The vacua mentioned in this and the following article could not have been high. The extreme vacua produced by the more efficient methods of the present day are the best of all heat-insulators.

[3] Grove, "Bakerian Lecture," *Phil. Trans.*, 1847 ; and *Phil. Mag.* vol. xxvii. p. 445.

[4] Magnus, *Pogg. Ann.* vol. cxii. pp. 351, 497. Translated, *Phil. Mag.* vol. xxii. p. 1, 1861.

examination was contained in a very thin glass vessel AB, which was 160 mm. high and 56 mm. wide. The upper vessel C was fixed to AB by fusion, and contained water kept near the boiling point by a current of steam. This formed the source of heat, and in order to compare the indications of the thermometer when different gases were used, it was necessary that the vessel AB should be kept in an enclosure at constant temperature. For this purpose it was placed inside a cylinder PQ, which was surrounded by a bath of water XY, as shown in the figure. By this means the temperature of the inner enclosure was kept constantly at 15° C. A thermometer fg was fixed horizontally, and protected by a screen oo from the direct radiation of the source of heat above. In the earlier experiments a cork screen was used, but it was afterwards found that one of polished metal (silvered copper-foil) was much more efficient as a protection. This arises from the fact that the polished metal, although a better conductor than cork, is yet a much more feeble radiator and absorber. The following results give an idea of the difference in the indications of the thermometer when protected and unprotected in this manner in air at the pressure of one atmo. :—

Cork Screen 2 mm. Thick. 23° C.	Two Copper-foils 1 mm. Distant. 21°·5	No Screen. 25°·5

When the steam is allowed to enter the vessel C the temperature indicated by the thermometer fg gradually rises, and in about half an hour becomes stationary—the time varying with the nature and pressure of the gas. This temperature depends on several circumstances, such as the conducting and radiating powers of the glass vessel AB, on the thickness and radiating power of the screen, and finally on the conductivity of the gas, and more or less on its diathermancy. The results of the experiments are, however, comparatively simple. When the pressure of the gas was reduced to 15 mm. or less, the stationary temperature of the thermometer was sensibly the same for all gases, and differed little from the temperature in vacuo. Denoting this latter by 100 (it was 11°·7 C. with a cork screen 2 mm. thick, and 7°·8 with a metal screen [1]), the corresponding numbers for the various gases at atmospheric pressure were as follows :—

---

[1] The temperatures were counted from that of the surrounding medium, which was 15° C.

[TABLE

2 U

Substance.	Thermometer.	Substance.	Thermometer.
Vacuum . . .	100	Protoxide of nitrogen .	75·2
Air	82·0	Marsh-gas . . .	80·3
Oxygen . . .	82·0	Olefiant gas . .	76·9
Hydrogen . . .	111·1	Ammonia . . .	69·2
Carbonic acid . .	70·0	Cyanogen . . .	75·2
Carbonic oxide . .	81·2	Sulphurous acid . .	66·6

It appears from this table that the stationary temperature of the thermometer is higher in a vacuum than in any gas except hydrogen. The heat, therefore, travels through all these gases (except hydrogen) with less facility than through a vacuum. Further, the temperature of the thermometer rises as the gases are more rarefied, except in the case of hydrogen, for here the opposite effect was exhibited, the temperature falling as the hydrogen became more rare. This has been supposed to demonstrate the true conductivity of hydrogen, and to prove that the other gases possess no appreciable conducting power. It is, however, evident from the results that the other gases exercised quite as decided an effect as hydrogen, but in the opposite direction. The only certain inference we seem able to make is that the flow of heat to the thermometer, or the heat-carrying power of the space, is increased by hydrogen and diminished by the other gases, and there are no *a priori* grounds for the supposition that hydrogen possesses a conducting power similar to metals more than any other gas.

320. Absolute Conductivity of a Gas.—If a plane be imagined drawn through a mass of gas, then, according to the kinetic theory, the molecules are continually crossing from one side to the other of this plane, and by this process of interchange the properties of the gas tend to become equalised on both sides of the plane. Equalisation of temperature may thus be brought about by molecular diffusion, and the transport of heat through a gas by conduction is merely the transport of kinetic energy by molecular diffusion. The absolute conductivity of a gas might then be defined as the quantity of heat, or kinetic energy, transported per second through a layer of the gas 1 cm. thick, 1 square cm. area, and having 1° C. difference of temperature between its faces, the transport being effected by molecular motions alone and not by the motion of large portions of the gas, such as takes place in convection currents.

To measure the conductivity of a gas consequently requires the study of its cooling under conditions in which the effects of convection currents are negligible.

This line of investigation has been followed by Kundt and War-burg[1] among others. When a thermometer is allowed to cool in a gas it loses heat by radiation, and also by conduction, but the effect due to the latter is completely masked by that arising from con-vection currents unless the pressure is small. When the pressure is diminished to a certain value the effects of convection currents become insensible, and the rate of cooling of the thermometer at any given temperature remains constant, until a stage of exhaustion is reached at which the mean free path of a molecule is not vanishingly small compared with the dimensions of the enclosure. This constancy of the rate of cooling is in accordance with the kinetic theory, from which it follows that the conductivity of a gas up to this limit is independent of the pressure.

Kundt and Warburg operated with three different enclosures, and found that with air the rate of cooling of the thermometer remained constant for pressures between 150 mm. and about 1 mm., and for hydrogen between 150 mm. and about 9 mm. Within these limits the action of convection currents was therefore insensible, and the observations lead to the conductivity of the gas when the cooling arising from direct radiation is determined. For this purpose the enclosure was exhausted as completely as possible after being thoroughly desiccated at a temperature of 200° C. In this state the rate of cooling was found to be independent of the shape of the enclosure, which showed that the effect of conduc-tion by the residual gas was negligible. The radiation being thus known, the cooling produced by conduction was determined by difference.

By this means it was found that the conductivity of hydrogen was 7·1 times that of air, while the corresponding ratio for carbonic acid was 0·59. The former agrees with the theoretic deductions of Maxwell, but the latter is sensibly less than the value (0·7) obtained theoretically. The theoretic coefficient for carbonic acid is, however, unsatisfactory, as it depends on the ratio of the two specific heats, which varies with the temperature, and the theory does not take this into account.

The estimation of the absolute values of the conductivities required a knowledge of the thermal capacity of the thermometer, and, as this was not accurately determined, numerical results were not deduced. The value for air was, however, set down at 0·000048 in the C.G.S. system of units.

[1] Kundt and Warburg, *Pogg. Ann.* vols. clv. and clvi. ; and *Journal de Physique*, vol. v. p. 118, 1876.

Stefan [1] observed the cooling of a thermometer furnished with a double envelope of copper and brass. The air between the two envelopes was thus heated by the interior and cooled by the exterior surface. The temperatures of these surfaces being known, and the rate of cooling being determined, the flow of heat through the layer of air can be deduced and the conductivity evaluated. The number found in this manner for air was 0·000056, which is 20,000 times less than that of copper. The dynamical theory led Maxwell to the number 0·000055. Stefan also found that, in accordance with theory, the conductivity was independent of the pressure, and that the conductivity of hydrogen was seven times greater than that of air. The effect of radiation is, however, neglected in the foregoing, and this renders the value of K somewhat too high.

The value deduced by Winkelmann [2] was 0·000052, and the variation with temperature was expressed by the formula

$$K = K_0 (1 + 0·00277\theta).$$

According to theory, however, the conductivity should vary as the square root of the absolute temperature,[3] and this result in itself is obvious, for under given circumstances the quantity of energy transported across any stratum of the gas will be proportional to the average velocity of translation, and, as we have already seen, this is proportional to the square root of the absolute temperature.

Andrews's method of heating a wire immersed in a gas by means of an electric current has been made the basis of a measurement of the conductivity of a gas by Schleiermacher,[4] Eucken,[5] Weber,[6] Schneider,[7] and others. In Eucken's experiments the conductivities of various gases were compared with that of air, which was taken as 0·0000566. To prevent convection currents, the pressure of the gas was reduced to 30 or 40 cm. of mercury, and the tubes were very narrow. He used fine platinum wires stretched along the axes of silver tubes 1 mm. in bore. The loss by radiation was determined by exhausting the apparatus, and was only 1 per cent of the heat conducted. The temperature of the wire was deduced from its

[1] Stefan, *Sitzungsberichte der Wiener Akademie*, vol. lxv. p. 42 ; and *Journal de Physique*, tom. ii. p. 147, 1873.

[2] A Winkelmann, *Pogg. Ann.* vol. clvi. p. 497, 1875 ; vol. clix. p. 177, 1876.

[3] This is on the assumption that the molecules are elastic spheres, and could not be expected to be true for gases which are not monatomic.

[4] A. Schleiermacher, *Wied. Ann.* vol. xxxiv. p. 623, 1888.

[5] A. Eucken, *Phys. Zeitschr.* vol. xii. p. 1101, 1911 ; vol. xiv. p. 324, 1913.

[6] S. Weber, *Ann. der Physik*, vol. liv. pp. 325, 437 ; 1917.

[7] E. Schneider, *Ann. der Physik*, vol. lxxix. p. 177, 1926 ; vol. lxxx. p. 215, 1926.

resistance.   In this method the calculation of corrections for loss of
heat at the ends, etc., is difficult.[1]   A table of results is given in
Art. 383.   Weber's values are given in the following table :—

CONDUCTIVITY OF GASES

Air.	Hydrogen.	Helium.	Neon.	Argon.
0·0000568	0·0004165	0·0003438	0·0001089	0·0000385

Nitrogen.	Oxygen.	Methane.	Carbon Dioxide.	Nitrous Oxide.
0·0000566	0·00005768	0·0000720	0·00003393	0·0000353

The plate method was used by Hercus and Laby[2] to measure
the conductivity of air.   A, B, and C (Fig. 219) are three copper
discs, silvered and polished, B being surrounded by a guard-ring D.
A, B, and D are heated electrically to the
same temperature, and C is cooled by a stream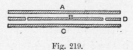
of water.   The heat-energy given to B was
measured.   A correction has to be made for
Fig. 219.
the heat radiated to C, and this was estimated from the results of
separate experiments on Dewar flasks with silvered walls.   The value
obtained for the conductivity of air at 22° C. was 0·0000574.
Using a formula of Sutherland's[3] to calculate the variation with
temperature, they deduce the value 0·0000540 at 0° C.

[1] See a paper by H. Busch (*Ann. der Physik*, vol. lxxx. p. 33, 1926) in which
the calculation of corrections is discussed.

[2] O. Hercus and T. H. Laby, *Proc. R. Soc.* vol. xcv. p. 190, 1918.

[3] This formula is also used by Eucken.   It applies to the variation of viscosity
with temperature, and as the ratio of conductivity to viscosity is nearly constant,
it may be used to reduce the conductivity also to standard temperature.

CHAPTER VIII

THERMODYNAMICS

SECTION I

THE FIRST FUNDAMENTAL PRINCIPLE

321. The First Law and the Energy Equation.—The modern science of thermodynamics is based on two fundamental principles, both of which relate to the conversion of heat into work. The first of these is the principle of equivalence established by Joule, and is represented algebraically by the equation

$$W = JH.$$

This principle, which is known as the *first law of thermodynamics*, asserts that when work is spent in producing heat, the quantity of work spent is directly proportional to the quantity of heat generated, and conversely, that when heat is employed to do work a quantity of heat disappears which is the equivalent of the work done. This conception is derived from the dynamical theory, according to which heat is regarded as a form of energy, and consequently, when work is done by thermal agencies, or heat generated by the expenditure of work, the quantity expended of either is the equivalent of the quantity generated of the other in accordance with the general principle of the conservation of energy.

Let us now consider the various departments in which a quantity of heat, when communicated to any body, may expend itself. In the first place, a portion of it, but not necessarily all, may be employed in raising the temperature of the body. This portion is spent, according to the dynamical theory, in increasing that energy known as the sensible heat of the body. The increase of temperature is in general accompanied by increase of volume, and as a consequence work will be expended in two departments. For if the body be subject to external forces, work will be done by or against these forces while the volume

is changing. This is termed the *external work*. For example, if the
body be subject to a uniform pressure p, the work done against this
external pressure during an expansion dv will be pdv. So also work will
be done against internal forces, such as molecular attractions, while
the volume or state is changing ; and the amount of heat expended in
the performance of this *internal work*, as it is called, may be a considerable portion of the whole. Under the head internal work may
also be placed the first-mentioned increase of molecular energy or
increase of sensible heat of the body.

Thus if the internal energy of the body be denoted by U, and if
this embraces both the kinetic and potential energies of the molecules,
the heat supplied to the body will be expended in two departments—
one in doing external work, and the other in altering the internal
energy of the body. Hence, if the external work done is dW, and if
the change of internal energy is dU, when a quantity of heat dQ is
given to a body, we have

$$dQ = dU + dW \quad . \quad . \quad . \quad . \quad . \quad (1)$$

—the symbol J being avoided by expressing dQ in work units (ergs).

The quantity of heat dQ is regarded as positive when given to the
body, and negative when taken from it. Under these circumstances
the work dW must be regarded as positive when done by the body,
and negative when done on it, in accordance with equation (1). When
the external work is introduced by ordinary mechanical reactions, External
resistance to distortion, etc., the expression for dW takes the usual work.
form of stress multiplied by strain, but work may be done by a system
in many other ways. For example, a liquid, in altering the area of
its surface, is subject to capillary forces, and if T denotes the surface
tension, and dS an element of surface, the expression for dW in this
case is TdS. So also work may be done in consequence of electric or
magnetic forces when electrified or magnetised matter is moved from
places of lower to places of higher potential. Thus, if a quantity dq
of electricity is moved from a place of zero potential to a place at
potential V, the expression for dW is Vdq. If, however, energy be
given to external systems only by work done against a uniform
normal pressure p, then $dW = pdv$, and the energy equation becomes

$$dQ = dU + pdv . \quad . \quad . \quad . \quad . \quad (2)$$

Prof. W. M'F. Orr has suggested the following statement of the
first law. "If a body or system undergoes any *cycle* of operations,
i.e. one such that the initial state and the final state are the same,
the total amount of heat taken in, algebraically, in the cycle by the
system from external bodies is proportional to the amount of work

done (algebraically) by the system on external bodies." The advantage of this form of statement is that the possibility of work being gained or lost owing to a change in the internal energy of the system is eliminated (see Art. 324). It might be added that if energy (not work) in any other form than heat enters or leaves the system, it must be reckoned in terms of heat energy.

322. Remarks on the Energy Equation—Cyclic Transformations. —In general for every substance there is some characteristic equation connecting the volume, pressure, and temperature, so that when any two of these quantities are known, the third is completely determined. For this reason, when the condition of a substance is represented graphically, as in Art. 67, the pressure and volume being known, the temperature corresponding to any point A (Fig. 219) becomes determinate, and the state represented by the point is unique.[1] Hence we may assume that the internal energy U, which appears in the

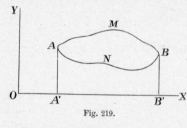

Fig. 219.

energy equation, is completely determined for any state by the co-ordinates of the point which represents that state in the diagram.

This is expressed by saying that the internal energy U corresponding to any state A is a function of the co-ordinates which define the state, and consequently the change of internal energy in passing from any state A to another state B will depend only on the points A and B, and in no way on the nature of the transformation by which the body may pass from A to B. In other words, if a substance be brought from any state A to any other state B, through any series of transformations represented by the path AMB, the change of internal energy depends only on the co-ordinates of A and B, being independent of the nature of the path AMB. The assumption made here is merely that if a body, after passing through any series of transformations, be brought back again to its initial condition, its internal energy will be the same at the end of the cycle as at the beginning, whether it returns to its initial condition by the same path, AMB, as it set out, or by a different, ANB. This amounts to saying that U at any point is a single valued function of the co-ordinates of the point, or that dU is *a perfect differential*.

[1] An ambiguity arises when more than one value of the temperature can exist for the same values of the pressure and volume ; so also in the case of a liquid and its saturated vapour, the pressure is a function of the temperature alone, and the volume within certain limits is independent of both.

On the other hand, the external work done during any transformation depends not only on the initial and final conditions of the substance, but also on the nature of the intermediate operations. For, as has been shown (Art. 67), the external work performed in passing from the state A to the state B along the path AMB is represented by the area AMBB'A', so that the external work is not known unless the shape of the curve AMB, or the relation connecting the volume and pressure throughout the transformation, is known. In other words, W is not determined by the initial and final co-ordinates, and dW *is not a perfect differential.* The work done during any transformation depends on the nature of the transformation from beginning to end, and in order to estimate it we require not only a knowledge of the initial and final states, but also some subsidiary relation, such as $f(p,v) = 0$, connecting the volume and pressure throughout the transformation.

It thus appears that the quantity of heat supplied to a body in passing from the state A to the state B depends on the nature of the transformation by which it is brought from A to B as well as on the positions of these points. This quantity of heat consequently cannot be expressed, like the internal energy, in terms of the co-ordinates of A and B, but requires a knowledge of the subsidiary relation $f(p,v) = 0$, that is the shape of the path AMB. Hence dQ *is not a perfect differential.* In the language of the differential calculus this is expressed by saying that, in the case of the internal energy U, we have

$$\frac{d}{dx}\left(\frac{d\text{U}}{dy}\right) - \frac{d}{dy}\left(\frac{d\text{U}}{dx}\right) = 0,$$

where x and y are the independent variables chosen to determine the condition of the body. But in the case of the quantity of heat Q, we have

$$\frac{d}{dx}\left(\frac{d\text{Q}}{dy}\right) - \frac{d}{dy}\left(\frac{d\text{Q}}{dx}\right) \gtrless 0.$$

According to the caloric theory, however, which regarded heat as indestructible, the quantity of heat supplied to a body in passing from any state A to any other state B must depend only on the initial and final states, and not on the nature of the intermediate transformations. According to this theory, then, dQ would be a perfect differential, and the external work would be derived from the heat, not by using up an equivalent quantity of it, but by transferring it, unaltered in quantity, from bodies of higher to bodies of lower temperatures, in a manner somewhat analogous to the way in which work is obtained by allowing water to descend from places of higher to places of lower level.

The fact that dQ is not a perfect differential according to the dynamical theory arises therefore from the principle of equivalence, according to which, when any substance passes through any cycle of transformations, an amount of heat disappears which is the equivalent of the work done, and if the substance be brought back to its initial condition after passing through a complete cycle of transformation, a quantity of heat represented by the area of the cycle is destroyed, or generated, according to the direction in which the cycle is passed through.

323. Integrating Factor of the Energy Equation.—If x and y be any two independent variables which determine the condition of a body, it follows that dQ may be expressed in the form

$$dQ = Xdx + Ydy \qquad . \qquad . \qquad . \qquad . \qquad . \qquad (1)$$

where X and Y are each functions of x and y; but since dQ is not a perfect differential, dX/dy will not be equal to dY/dx. The left-hand side of this equation, however, may be made an exact differential by multiplying it by a factor μ, which is some function of x and y. The quantity μdQ will then be a perfect differential, and we shall consequently have

$$\frac{d}{dx}\Big(\mu Y\Big) = \frac{d}{dy}\Big(\mu X\Big),$$

or

$$\mu\Big(\frac{dY}{dx} - \frac{dX}{dy}\Big) = X\frac{d\mu}{dy} - Y\frac{d\mu}{dx},$$

an equation which expresses the integrating factor μ in terms of X and Y.

The relation between X and Y may be deduced by comparing (1) with the energy equation. For since U and W are supposed expressible in terms of x and y, we have

$$dU = \frac{dU}{dx}dx + \frac{dU}{dy}dy, \text{ and } dW = X'dx + Y'dy.$$

But by the energy equation we have

$$dQ = \Big(\frac{dU}{dx} + X'\Big)dx + \Big(\frac{dU}{dy} + Y'\Big)dy,$$

and therefore

$$X = \frac{dU}{dx} + X', \text{ and } Y = \frac{dU}{dy} + Y'.$$

Hence, since dU is a perfect differential, it follows that we must have

$$\frac{d}{dx}\Big(Y - Y'\Big) = \frac{d}{dy}\Big(X - X'\Big),$$

or

$$\frac{dY}{dx} - \frac{dX}{dy} = \frac{dY'}{dx} - \frac{dX'}{dy}.$$

In the particular case when the only external force is a uniform normal pressure p, and in which the independent variables which determine the condition of the body are p and v, we have

$$dQ = Ldv + Mdp,$$

where L is the heat of dilatation or the quantity of heat absorbed by the body under constant pressure while its volume changes by unity, and M is the quantity of heat required to change the pressure by unity when the volume is kept constant.   Hence if μ is the integrating factor

$$\frac{d}{dp}\left(\mu L\right) = \frac{d}{dv}\left(\mu M\right) \quad . \quad . \quad . \quad . \quad . \quad (2)$$

But by the energy equation

$$dQ = \frac{dU}{dp}dp + \frac{dU}{dv}dv + pdv.$$

Therefore

$$L = \frac{dU}{dv} + p, \quad \text{and} \quad M = \frac{dU}{dp}.$$

Hence, since U is a perfect differential, we have

$$\frac{dL}{dp} - \frac{dM}{dv} = 1 \quad . \quad . \quad . \quad . \quad . \quad (3)$$

as the relation between L and M.

Using this result equation (2) becomes

$$\mu = M\frac{d\mu}{dv} - L\frac{d\mu}{dp},$$

which expresses μ in terms of L and M.

COR. In the case of a perfect gas an integrating factor is the reciprocal of the temperature Θ measured from the zero of the perfect gas thermometer.   For in the case of a perfect gas the energy equation is (Art. 160)

$$dQ = C_v d\theta + pdv.$$

Therefore

$$\frac{dQ}{\Theta} = C_v\frac{d\theta}{\Theta} + R\frac{dv}{v},$$

and the right-hand member of this equation is obviously an exact differential.   Hence dQ/Θ is a perfect differential.

Examples

1. If there is one integrating factor of dQ, show that there are an infinite number.

{If μ is an integrating factor of dQ, then

$$\mu dQ = d\phi.$$

But if Φ be any function of ϕ, we have

$$\Phi = f(\phi), \text{ and } d\Phi = f'(\phi)d\phi,$$

consequently

$$\mu f'(\phi)dQ = f'(\phi)d\phi = d\Phi,$$

so that the factor $\mu f'(\phi)$ also renders dQ a perfect differential.}

2. Denoting the specific heats at constant pressure and constant volume by C_p and C_v respectively, prove that in dynamical units

$$C_v = \left(\frac{dU}{d\theta}\right)_v, \text{ and } C_p = \left(\frac{dU}{d\theta}\right)_p + p\left(\frac{dv}{d\theta}\right)_p.$$

{Since U is completely determined by the variables v and θ, we have

$$dQ = \left(\frac{dU}{d\theta}\right)_v d\theta + \left(\frac{dU}{dv}\right)_\theta dv + pdv.$$

Hence, as is otherwise directly obvious,

$$\left(\frac{dQ}{d\theta}\right)_v = C_v = \left(\frac{dU}{d\theta}\right)_v,$$

and similarly by taking p and θ as independent variables we obtain the second relation.

In the case of a perfect gas U is a function of θ alone, and hence

$$\left(\frac{dU}{d\theta}\right)_p = \left(\frac{dU}{d\theta}\right)_v = C_v,$$

so that the second relation becomes $C_p - C_v = R.$}

3. A gas changes its volume from v_1 to v_2 at constant temperature, find the quantity of heat absorbed.

{Since the temperature is constant, the energy equation $dQ = C_v d\theta + pdv$ becomes

$$dQ = pdv = R\Theta\frac{dv}{v}.$$

Hence the heat absorbed is (in dynamical units)

$$Q = R\Theta \log (v_2/v_1).$$

From this relation it follows that if the isothermal changes of a gas are such that the quantities of heat absorbed or evolved form an arithmetical progression, the corresponding changes of volume form a geometrical progression.[1]

The above equation may also be written in the form

$$Q = p_1 v_1 \log (v_2/v_1),$$

so that if this refers not to unit mass of the gas, but to that quantity which assumes a volume v_1 under a pressure p_1, the equation contains nothing depending on the nature of the gas. This equation was employed by Joule in one of his determinations of J.}

4. Determine the work done when a gas is compressed adiabatically from $p_1 v_1$ to $p_2 v_2$.

{We have

$$W = \int_{v_2}^{v_1} pdv = p_1 v_1{}^\gamma \int \frac{dv}{v^\gamma} = \frac{p_1 v_1}{\gamma - 1}\left[\left(\frac{v_1}{v_2}\right)^{\gamma-1} - 1\right] = \frac{p_2 v_2 - p_1 v_1}{\gamma - 1}.\}$$

---

[1] This result was arrived at by Carnot, *Motive Power of Heat*, p. 81, English edition.

5. Prove that the areas included between the adiabatic lines of a perfect gas and the axis of volume are equal if measured from the points where they are intersected by any isothermal.

{This follows from the property that the internal energy of a perfect gas is a function of the temperature only.}

6. If μ is an integrating factor of dQ, prove that taken round any closed cycle

$$\int \mu dQ = 0.$$

{Since $\mu dQ = d\phi$, it follows that the value of the integral taken along any curve joining two points $p_1 v_1$ and $p_2 v_2$ is simply $\phi_1 - \phi_2$ where ϕ_1 is the value of ϕ at $p_1 v_1$, and ϕ_2 its value at $p_2 v_2$. When the cycle is closed $\phi_1 = \phi_2$.}

7. If a substance has attained its maximum density under a given pressure, prove that the tangent plane to the characteristic surface at the corresponding point is parallel to the axis of temperature.

{If the characteristic equation be $f(p, v, \theta) = 0$, then under constant pressure we have

$$\frac{df}{d\theta} + \frac{df}{dv}\frac{dv}{d\theta} = 0.$$

But if the density is a maximum $dv/d\theta = 0$; therefore at the corresponding point we have $df/d\theta = 0$, which was to be proved.

The locus of these points is a curve on the characteristic surface which obviously divides it into two parts, such that the projection of one on the plane pv is the same as that of the other. Hence it follows that every curve on the characteristic surface which cuts this locus projects on the plane pv into a curve touching the projection of the locus, and consequently two curves which intersect on it project into two which touch each other.}

SECTION II

324. The Work of Sadi Carnot.—At the time when Sadi Carnot wrote his celebrated essay (1824) on "The Motive Power of Heat,"[1] the works of Rumford and Davy had been completed, and the undulatory theory of light was regarded as established by weighty arguments in every department, yet the caloric theory of heat still held its ground, and the scientific world remained to be converted to the new doctrine. The introduction of the steam-engine, and the great industrial revolution which accompanied it, attracted attention to the manner in which work may be produced by heat; and it was in seeking to discover the general laws which govern the action of heat-engines that Carnot was led to some of those forms of reasoning which are still continually employed in the dynamical theory.

Before the time of Carnot no relation seems to have been suspected between the work performed by a steam-engine and the heat drawn from the furnace. In seeking to establish this relation Carnot based his work on the doctrine of the conservation of energy, or the impossibility of perpetual motion; and although in conjunction with this he espoused the doctrine of the conservation of caloric, yet in much of his work the latter is not essential, and many of his conclusions remain true on any theory and require but little modification to adapt them to the dynamical theory. It is, besides, in this work that we find the first examples of cyclic operations in which a working substance, after passing through any series of transformation, is brought back again to its initial condition; and it is only for such a cycle, Carnot informs us, that we are entitled to reason upon the relation between the external work done and the heat employed in its production.

In fact, as we have already mentioned, if a substance be allowed to

---

[1] Sadi Carnot, *Réflexions sur la puissance motrice du feu et sur les moyens propres à la développer* (translated by R. H. Thurston, 1890. London: Macmillan and Co.).

expand, doing external work, it is not legitimate to assert that the heat spent is the equivalent of the work done unless the substance in its final state is in exactly the same condition as at the beginning ; but when the substance has been brought back to its initial state, we are entitled to assert that, on the whole, it has neither lost nor gained energy, and we are then in a position to reason upon the external processes that have taken place, and to determine the condition of equivalence among them.

Besides this conception of complete cycles, the other grand idea introduced by Carnot was the principle of reversibility—namely, that by the expenditure of an equal quantity of work the heat may be taken from the condenser and restored again to the source.

In spite of his adoption of the caloric theory,[1] Carnot seems to have been by no means confident of its truth, and in his later writings (which unfortunately remained unpublished until recent times) he showed that he was thoroughly convinced that it was false, as he not only espoused the dynamical theory, but also planned several experiments to determine the equivalent relation between heat and work, and deduced a value of that equivalent probably from the very data employed by Mayer in 1842. That Carnot was finally convinced of the truth of the dynamical theory, and that he had also conceived the great principle of the conservation of energy in its general form, is distinctly proved by the following passages taken from his notes, written when the wave theory of light had just triumphed :—

"At present light is generally regarded as a vibratory motion of the ethereal fluid. Light produces heat, or at least accompanies the radiating heat, and moves with the same velocity as heat. Radiating heat is then a vibratory movement. It would be ridiculous to suppose that it is an emission of matter while the light which accompanies it could be only a movement.

"Could a motion (that of radiating heat) produce matter (caloric) ?

"No, undoubtedly ; it can only produce a motion. Heat is then the result of a motion.

"It is then plain that it could be produced by the consumption of motive power, and that it could produce this power.

"Heat is simply motive power, or rather motion which has changed form. It is a movement among the particles of bodies. Wherever there is a destruction of motive power, there is at the same time production of heat in quantity exactly proportional to the quantity of motive power destroyed. Reciprocally, whenever there is destruction of heat, there is production of motive power.

"We can then establish the general proposition that motive power is in quantity

---

[1] It is interesting to note that of the two principles adopted by Carnot, viz. the impossibility of perpetual motion and the conservation of caloric, the former was by no means generally received at the time, while the latter was generally admitted as true. At present the former is universally admitted as true, while the latter is as generally believed to be false.

invariable in nature—that it is, correctly speaking, never either produced or destroyed. It is true that it changes form—that is, it produces sometimes one sort of motion, sometimes another, but it is never annihilated."

These words prove that some time before his death (in 1832) he was not only convinced of the truth of the dynamical theory of heat, but that he had also grasped the law of conservation of energy in its widest form. "Motive power," he says, "is in quantity invariable in nature; it is, correctly speaking, never either produced or destroyed."

Working on the caloric theory, however, he postulated that in the steam-engine and other heat-engines the work is performed not by an actual consumption of caloric, which was opposed to the doctrine of the materiality of heat, but " to its transportation from a hot body to a cold body." Thus by the fall of heat from a higher to a lower temperature he supposed work to be done in a manner in some way analogous to that in which work is obtained by allowing water to fall from a higher to a lower level. In the latter case the quantity of water which reaches the lower level is the same as that which leaves the higher; none of the water is destroyed in performing any work which it may be employed to do. It is the motion acquired in falling that is used up in doing work. The work derived from a heat-engine was supposed to be produced in a somewhat similar manner, the quantity which reached the condenser being supposed the same as that which left the source. Thus the work was done by the caloric in flowing from a hot to a cold body, and in doing the work it was supposed, like the water, to be wholly or partially brought to rest. This Carnot speaks of as "the re-establishment of equilibrium in the caloric."

One of the chief points, however, is the recognition by Carnot of the necessity in all engines by which work is continuously derived from thermal agencies, of two bodies at different temperatures—that is, a source and a condenser, or the passage of heat from one body to another at a lower temperature.

325. Carnot's Cycle.—Carnot's work failed to attract attention until ten years after its publication, when it was brought into prominence by Clapeyron,[1] who cleared up most of what remained obscure in Carnot's reasoning, and exhibited it in a more elegant form by representing the various transformations geometrically by means of indicator diagrams. The cycle which Carnot supposed his working substance to traverse when geometrically represented consists of a four-sided figure, ABCD (Fig. 220), bounded on two opposite sides,

---

[1] Clapeyron, *Journal de l'École polytechnique*, tom. xiv., 1834. Translated in Taylor's *Scientific Memoirs*, part iii.

AD and BC, by isothermal lines, and on the remaining pair by adiabatic lines.

The working substance is taken in the state represented by the point A, and being contained in a non-conducting vessel, is allowed to expand adiabatically—that is, without thermal communication with other bodies—until it reaches the state B. During this operation, external work represented by the area ABB'A' is done by the substance, and its temperature falls from θ to θ'. The next operation is an isothermal compression along the curve BC to some arbitrary point C. During this stage, work represented by the area BCC'B' is done on the

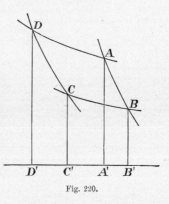

Fig. 220.

substance, and as the temperature is supposed to be kept constant, the heat developed by the compression must be removed as fast as it is generated. Let the quantity thus removed be Q'. The third operation is an adiabatic compression of the substance from C to D until the substance regains its original temperature θ, so that D is on the isothermal line which passes through A. During this operation, work represented by the area CDD'C' has been done on the substance, while its temperature has been raised from θ' to θ. The fourth and last operation is the isothermal expansion of the substance from D to the starting-point A. During this transformation the substance expands, doing external work represented by the area DAA'D', while in order to keep its temperature constant a quantity of heat Q must be absorbed from some external source. This quantity, if no hypothesis be made concerning the nature of heat, may be either equal to or different from the quantity Q' evolved by the substance during the isothermal compression BC.

If the caloric theory be admitted, then Q must be equal to Q', and regarding the cycle as a whole, an amount of work represented by the area DABB'D' has been done by the substance, while DCBB'D' has been done on it, leaving a balance represented by the area of the figure ABCD as the work gained during the cycle.

So far the whole process is independent of any theory of heat,[1] and

[1] The cycle described here is virtually that given by Carnot in his original essay. He begins it with the adiabatic operation AB, and terminates with the isothermal DA. As usually described it would appear as if Carnot's account required correction and modification to adapt it to the dynamical theory. The cycle described by Carnot is independent of all theory ; he merely describes a series of transformations

must stand intact whatever theory be adopted. The substance has simply passed through a cycle of operations, and has now returned to its initial condition. If $Q = Q'$, as Carnot taught, the work has been obtained simply by the flow of a quantity Q of heat from a temperature θ to a lower temperature θ'. If, on the other hand, the dynamical theory be adopted, a quantity of heat, equivalent to the work performed during the cycle, must have disappeared. In other words, Q is greater than Q', and the difference $Q - Q'$ has been converted into work represented by the area of the cycle. This conclusion is in strict accord with all experimental investigation, and the direct verification in the case of the steam-engine has been already noticed (p. 45).

In order to realise such a cycle it would be necessary to enclose the working substance, say a gas, in a non-conducting cylinder fitted with a non-conducting piston and a perfectly-conducting bottom. We must also be provided with two bodies which can be maintained at constant temperatures θ and θ'.

In the first operation the cylinder must be placed on a non-conducting support, and the substance, supposed to be initially at the temperature θ, is allowed to expand without loss or gain of heat until its temperature falls to θ'. The cylinder is then removed from the support and placed with its conducting bottom in contact with the body at temperature θ'. The second operation is now commenced, and the substance is compressed while its temperature is maintained constantly at θ'.

In any actual operation, of course, the temperature of the working substance would exceed that of the body to which it yields its heat, but by compressing very slowly this difference can be made as small as we please. Again, the working substance is supposed to yield its heat to a body constantly at the same temperature θ', and this would require the body to have an infinite capacity for heat, or else to be maintained in some way constantly at the same temperature θ' by internal or external transformations. The second transformation of the cycle is consequently like the first, only an ideal limit which may be approached but not attained in practice. This, however, will not invalidate the adoption of such a cycle in our reasoning

---

through which the working substance passes. It is in the subsequent deductions, founded on some postulate as to the manner in which work is obtained from heat, that the theory comes in. The corrections to Carnot's work introduced by James Thomson and Maxwell are consequently not only unnecessary, but are an injustice to the illustrious author of *The Motive Power of Heat*, and no doubt they were proposed at a time when Carnot's work was learned by report rather than by consultation of the original.

concerning heat-engines. It merely furnishes us with an ideal type to which we can only approximate in practice.

The third operation is conducted like the first by placing the cylinder on the non-conducting stand and compressing until the original temperature θ is regained. The cylinder is then placed in contact with the other body or source of heat at temperature θ, and the working substance is allowed to expand while heat is supplied to it as required in order to keep its temperature constant.

The characteristic of the cycle, which must be carefully kept in view in order that it may be reversible, is that the working substance parts with heat to, and takes in heat from, bodies at the same temperature as itself. There is no passage of heat by conduction from one body to another at a lower temperature. The transference of heat between the working substance and any other body is such that this substance and the body in question are at the same temperature while the transference is taking place.

Further, all the heat absorbed by the working substance is taken in at one temperature and all the heat given out is ejected at another. There are thus only two temperatures involved, and this renders the cycle the simplest possible representation of a heat-engine, just as the simplest representation of an engine worked by water power would be the case in which the water is all received at one level and all ejected at another—for example, the case of a water-wheel in which there is no leakage.

An examination of the foregoing cycle shows that it is *reversible*— that is, if the working substance be made to traverse it in the opposite direction, the operations will be all repeated in the inverse order and opposite sense. Thus a quantity of heat Q will be evolved at θ by the working substance in passing from A to D, and a quantity Q' will be absorbed at θ' in passing from C to B, while during the complete cycle an amount of work represented by the area of the cycle is done on the substance. In other words, by the expenditure of work a quantity of heat is taken in at the lower temperature θ', and another quantity is evolved at a higher temperature θ, or heat is transported from a cold body to a hot body by the expenditure of work, just as water may be transported from a low level to a higher.

Reversible cycle.

The process by which heat is converted into work is said to be reversible when the series of changes can be performed in the reverse order, the forces remaining the same, but the velocities being of opposite sign. The first condition of reversibility, of course, is the possibility of causing the substance to pass back again from its final to its initial state successively, and in the reverse order through all the stages passed

through in the direct process.   A *reversible engine* is one in which the
working substance passes through a reversible cycle.   When it is not
possible to repeat the transformations in the reverse order, or, when
reversed, if the forces are not equal in magnitude to those which occur
at the same point in the direct process, the transformation is said to
be *irreversible*.

326. Efficiency of a Reversible Engine—Carnot's Theorem.   If
we define the efficiency of a heat-engine as the ratio of the quantity
of work W done during a complete cycle to the quantity of heat Q
drawn from the source, we can easily show that the efficiency of all
reversible engines must be the same, and that this is the major
limit to the efficiency of any engine.   In other words, no engine can
be constructed having an efficiency greater than that of a reversible
engine.   For let us suppose that it is possible to construct an engine
B, which has a greater efficiency than a given reversible engine A.
Then if A draws a quantity Q of heat from the source, and performs
an amount of work W during each stroke of the piston, it will
restore a quantity Q of heat to the source when worked backwards
by the expenditure of a quantity of work W, since it is supposed
reversible.   Now let the engine B draw a quantity Q of heat from
the source during each stroke (this can be made the same as the
quantity drawn by A by simply altering the quantity of working
substance in the cylinder), and let this engine perform, if possible,
a quantity of work $W' > W$.   Then B may be employed to drive
A backwards, and in addition we shall have a quantity of work
$W' - W$ at our disposal, which can be employed in any manner.
Now B draws Q from the source, and A, being worked backwards,
restores Q to it.   Consequently the compound engine, consisting of
A and B working together, furnishes us with a quantity of work
$W' - W$ at every stroke, while no heat is drawn from the source.
According to the caloric theory, the body at lower temperature,
that is, the condenser, will also be unaffected, so that we have an
engine which would supply us constantly with work without compensation of any kind—that is, we have perpetual motion.   In this
manner, by assuming the impossibility of perpetual motion, Carnot
proved that no engine can have a greater efficiency than a reversible
engine.   This, then, is the major limit to the efficiency of any heat-
engine, and it follows as a corollary that no reversible engine can have
a greater efficiency than any other reversible engine; or, in other
words, all reversible engines working between the same limits of
temperature must have the same efficiency.[1]

[1] It is by no means, however, evident *a priori* that the efficiency of a reversible

The same result holds also, according to the dynamical theory, when a suitable hypothesis is made concerning the conditions under which work may be derived from heat. Carnot's hypothesis was, as we have already seen, that work is obtained by simply letting heat pass, unaltered in quantity, from a hot body to a cold body. The corresponding hypothesis necessary under the dynamical theory is easily deduced, and was arrived at almost simultaneously by Clausius and Lord Kelvin in slightly different but equivalent forms.

Thus, as before, let us suppose that an engine B is more efficient than some reversible engine A, and let B work A backwards. Then, according to the dynamical theory, the quantity which either draws from the source, when working direct, exceeds that which it yields to the condenser by an amount which is the equivalent of the work done during the cycle. Hence, if A and B be so constructed, by suitably arranging the quantity of the working substance, that they draw the same quantity of heat from the source during each stroke of the piston, then if B does more work than A, it must yield less heat to the condenser, so that when A and B are coupled up (A working backwards) the source will remain unaffected, but A will draw more heat from the condenser than B yields to it. There will thus be a quantity of work $W' - W$ derivable from the compound engine and a corresponding withdrawal of heat from the condenser. This amounts to obtaining work continuously by using up the heat of the colder of two bodies. That this is impossible was the form in which Lord Kelvin stated the hypothesis. In other words, this hypothesis asserts that the manner in which work is derived from heat is by using up the heat of the hotter of two bodies, a quantity Q being drawn from this body, and in part converted into work, while the remainder is yielded to the colder body.

It is not, however, *a priori* evident that work cannot be derived by using up the heat of a single body, or by using up the heat of the coldest of a system of bodies. That all engines which have been con-

engine should be independent of the nature of the working substance. Thus ether boils at 35°, and the tension of its vapour at 90° is equal to that of water at 150°, while to produce a gramme of ether vapour requires five times less heat than a gramme of water vapour ; therefore ether at the expense of much less heat places a far greater pressure at the disposal of the workman. What compensation does water offer ? Carnot was satisfied to assert that any incomplete compensation would involve the possibility of perpetual motion. Without entering into a full discussion of the question, we may state that complete compensation does take place : that although a much greater pressure for the same expenditure of heat is obtained with ether vapour, yet more work cannot be obtained—for work requires expansion, and this produces cooling and consequent condensation, so that in this operation the compensation is effected.

structed to work in complete cycles do work by using up the heat
of the hotter body, or source, is true ; but if at any time we should
obtain the means of dealing with the molecules individually, and not
as now in the aggregate, it is not impossible that all the molecular
motion of a single body should be used up in doing work, or be
transferred to another body, so that work might be obtained by
using the heat of a single body or of the coldest body of a system,
or all the heat of one body might be transferred to another at a higher
temperature.

Another method of regarding the question leads to the form in
which the hypothesis was stated by Clausius. Thus we have seen
that in Carnot's cycle work can be performed by drawing heat from
a source and giving at the same time heat to the condenser, the latter
quantity being related to the former by some hypothesis concerning
the nature of heat. So in the reverse process by the performance
of work heat may be drawn from the condenser and restored to the
source.

Hence, if we employ the excess $W' - W$ of work furnished by
the engines A and B, when working as already indicated, to drive
another engine working in the reverse manner between the same
source and refrigerator, this third engine will transfer heat from
the colder body to the warmer—that is, on the whole, without the
expenditure of any work the heat could be continually transferred
from the colder to the warmer of two bodies. If this be admitted as
impossible, the second fundamental principle may be stated in either
of the following forms for a cyclic process.

Second
law.

"It is impossible for a self-acting machine, unaided by any
external agency, to convey heat from one body to another at a
higher temperature, or heat cannot of itself (that is, without compensation) pass from a colder to a warmer body " (Clausius).

The equivalent statement by Lord Kelvin is that "it is impossible
by means of inanimate material agency to derive mechanical effect
from any portion of matter by cooling it below the temperature of the
coldest of surrounding objects."

In making these statements it must be remembered that they
apply only to the continued performance of useful work—that is, to
engines working in complete cycles. Without this limitation it
might be objected, for example, that work could be derived from a
highly compressed gas by simply allowing it to expand. During the
expansion it would do work against external pressure ; this work
would be derived from the heat of the gas alone, no condenser
being required, and the substance might be thus cooled much below

the temperature of the surrounding bodies. If, however, a complete cycle be performed, so that the substance is left in its initial condition, then the principle applies in either of the forms given above.

The following two modes of stating the second law have been suggested by Prof. W. M'F. Orr. They are equivalent to Lord Kelvin's and Clausius' forms respectively, but are more precise.

(1) "If a system interchanges heat with external bodies *at one assigned temperature only*, then it is impossible that *in a cycle* it should, on the whole, receive heat from external bodies, and (as a necessary consequence by the first law), on the whole, do work on external bodies.

(2) "If a system undergoes any cycle of processes in which the total amount of work done on it is algebraically zero (the statement is also true if it is negative), and if it interchanges heat with external bodies at two assigned temperatures only, then it is impossible that, on the whole, it should receive heat at the lower temperature and (as a consequence by the first law) give out heat at the higher temperature."

It is easy to prove that if either of these is true, the other must be true also. Further, these statements will be found most convenient in making applications of the second law or in discussing apparent violations of it.[1]

It follows from the second law that it is impossible to produce Maxwell's demon. any difference of temperature or pressure in an isolated mass at uniform temperature and pressure throughout without the expenditure of work, and to the statement in this form Maxwell[2] has devised an ingenious but illusory violation. He takes the case of a mass of gas at uniform temperature and pressure throughout, and he then imagines a being capable of dealing with the individual molecules of the gas. According to the ordinary theory, these molecules are moving with velocities which differ considerably, so that if a partition be supposed erected in the enclosure, the imaginary being may sift the molecules so as to accumulate the faster-moving molecules in one region and the slower molecules in the other. By this means inequalities of temperature and pressure might be introduced without the expenditure of any work.

It must be remembered, however, that to this being the gas is by

[1] In former editions of this book, examples were given of apparent violations of the second law. In all these it will be found that the working substance does not undergo a *cycle* of transformations.
[2] *Theory of Heat*, 3rd edition, p. 328.

no means a uniformly heated mass. The faster-moving molecules are hot and the slower cold, and the whole mass to him is made up of discrete parts at very different temperatures, and this sifting of the molecules is no more a violation of the second law than would be the collection by an ordinary being of the warmer members of a system of bodies into one region of space and the colder into another.

The point then appears to be that a clear understanding of the meaning of the word *body* should be obtained in stating the second law, for, without this, apparent violations can be easily manufactured by a confusion of terms.

327. Determination of the Efficiency.—The efficiency of a heat-engine working between two given temperatures has been defined as the ratio of the quantity of work performed to the quantity of heat drawn from the source, and in the case of a reversible engine we have seen that this efficiency is independent of the nature of the working substance. It must, therefore, be determined completely by the two temperatures between which it works. This is expressed by saying that the efficiency is some function of the temperatures of the source and condenser, or, algebraically expressed,

$$\frac{W}{Q} = f(\theta, \theta').$$

According to the dynamical theory, W may be replaced by $Q - Q'$, the difference between the quantity of heat drawn from the source and that yielded to the condenser, and the expression for the efficiency becomes

$$\frac{Q - Q'}{Q} = f(\theta, \theta').$$

From this it follows that Q/Q' is a function of θ and θ', and therefore, if Q_1 and Q_2 be the quantities of heat taken in and ejected by a reversible engine working between the temperatures θ_1 and θ_2, we have

$$\frac{Q_1}{Q_2} = F(\theta_1, \theta_2),$$

when $F(\theta_1, \theta_2)$ is some function of θ_1 and θ_2.

Now, returning to Carnot's cycle (Fig. 220), it is clear that Q_1, the quantity of heat absorbed along the isothermal DA, can depend only on the temperature θ_1, the nature of the working substance, and its pressure and volume in the initial and final states—that is, on the co-ordinates of D and A. Hence we may write

$$Q_1 = f\theta_1, N, p, v),$$

where N refers to the nature of the working substance. Similarly we have

$$Q_2 = f(\theta_2, N, p, v).$$

Hence

$$\frac{Q_1}{Q_2} = \frac{f(\theta_1, N, p, v)}{f(\theta_2, N, p, v)},$$

and this must be independent of everything except θ_1 and θ_2, and consequently $f(\theta_1 N, p, v,)$ must be of the form $Kf(\theta_1)$, where K involves everything depending on N, p, and v, so that we have [1]

$$\frac{Q_1}{Q_2} = \frac{Kf(\theta_1)}{Kf(\theta_2)} = \frac{f(\theta_1)}{f(\theta_2)}.$$

Now Q_1 is always greater than Q_2, hence $f(\theta_1)$ is always greater New scale. than $f(\theta_2)$ if θ_1 is greater than θ_2. The function $f(\theta)$ is consequently such that its magnitude increases as the temperature θ increases, and we might therefore form a new scale of temperature by tabulating the values of this function (if once determined) for all values of the centigrade measure θ. The values of this function might therefore be used to denote the corresponding temperatures on the new scale. So that if we denote $f(\theta)$ by τ we shall have

$$\frac{Q_1}{Q_2} = \frac{\tau_1}{\tau_2}, \quad \text{or} \quad \frac{Q_1}{\tau_1} = \frac{Q_2}{\tau_2},$$

---

[1] This relation may also be established as follows :—We have, for an engine working between the limits θ_1 and θ_2,

$$\frac{Q_1}{Q_2} = F(\theta_1, \theta_2),$$

and, in the same manner for an engine working between the limits θ_2 and θ_3, we have

$$\frac{Q_2}{Q_3} = F(\theta_2, \theta_3).$$

Consequently by multiplication we find

$$\frac{Q_1}{Q_3} = F(\theta_1, \theta_2)F(\theta_2, \theta_3).$$

But Q_1/Q_3 must be equal to $F(\theta_1, \theta_3)$, therefore

$$F(\theta_1, \theta_3) = F(\theta_1, \theta_2)F(\theta_2, \theta_3) ;$$

that is, θ_2 must disappear from the right-hand member. In order that this may happen, the function F must be of the form

$$F(\theta_1, \theta_2) = \frac{f(\theta_1)}{f(\theta_2)},$$

and consequently we have

$$\frac{Q_1}{Q_2} = \frac{f(\theta_1)}{f(\theta_2)}.$$

and the new scale of temperature will be such that any two temperatures on it bear to each other the same ratio as the quantities of heat
taken in and ejected by a reversible engine working between these
temperatures as source and condenser. The efficiency of such an
engine will consequently be

$$\frac{Q_1 - Q_2}{Q_1} = \frac{\tau_1 - \tau_2}{\tau_1}.$$

328. Carnot's Function.—In the case of an engine working between two infinitely
near temperatures, τ and $\tau + d\tau$ (or θ and $\theta + d\theta$), the efficiency is obviously

$$\eta = \frac{d\tau}{\tau} \quad . \quad . \quad . \quad . \quad . \quad (1)$$

Now in this case the efficiency must be some function of θ, since it depends only on
θ and $\theta + d\theta$, and Carnot consequently wrote it in the form

$$\eta = \mu d\theta \quad . \quad . \quad . \quad . \quad . \quad (2)$$

where μ is a function of θ to be determined, and is known as *Carnot's function*.
Comparing (1) and (2) we find

$$\mu = \frac{1}{\tau}\frac{d\tau}{d\theta} = \frac{d}{d\theta}(\log \tau).$$

Hence if $d\tau/d\theta = 1$, Carnot's function is numerically equal to the reciprocal of the
absolute temperature. In general, with the foregoing notation, we have

$$\mu = \frac{f'(\theta)}{f(\theta)}.$$

329. Absolute Temperature and Absolute Zero.—The remarkable
proposition established in the foregoing article was seized upon by
Lord Kelvin [1] as early as 1848, and made the basis of a scale of
absolute temperature—absolute in the sense of being independent of
the properties of any particular substance.

We have seen that if Q_1 and Q_2 be the quantities of heat taken in
and ejected by a reversible engine working between the limits of
temperature θ_1 and θ_2, then the ratio Q_1/Q_2 is independent of the
nature of the working substance, and depends only on the temperatures
θ_1 and θ_2. Now the numbers expressing θ_1 and θ_2 will depend on the
nature of the thermometric substance and on the system of thermo-
metry adopted, and the ratio of θ_1 to θ_2 will depend in general on the
system chosen; but, on the other hand, the quantities τ_1 and τ_2 are
such that their ratio is independent of the nature of the working
substance or of the system of thermometry adopted in the measurement
of θ_1 and θ_2. If therefore the numbers expressing τ_1 and τ_2 are taken
to represent the temperatures at which the heat is taken in and ejected

---

[1] Wm. Thomson, *Proc. Cambridge Phil. Soc.*, or *Phil. Mag.*, 1848; and *Trans.
Roy. Soc. Edin.*, 1854.

by a reversible engine, we can assert that the ratio of any two temperatures on this scale is equal to the ratio of the quantities of heat taken
in and ejected by a reversible engine working between these limits,
and is independent of the properties of any particular substance.

This mode of reckoning temperature leads us to the notion of an
absolute zero of temperature, for if the heat Q_2 ejected by an engine
be zero, then τ_2 will be zero also, and the efficiency of the engine will
be unity. All the heat Q_1 taken in from the source will be converted
into work ; and since we cannot suppose that more heat can be converted into work than that which is drawn from the source, it is
impossible for τ to be negative, and hence the temperature corresponding to $\tau = 0$ is the lowest possible temperature conceivable. The zero
of this scale is consequently an absolute zero of temperature independent of the properties of any particular substance, for when the
efficiency of one reversible engine is unity, the efficiency of every
other reversible engine working between the same source and condenser will also be unity, and hence,
if τ is zero for one substance, it will
also be zero for every other. This
zero is therefore absolute.

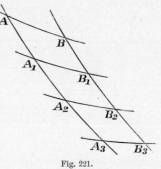

Fig. 221.

Lord Kelvin's system of reckoning temperatures is exhibited graphically as follows :—Let AA_1A_2 and
BB_1B_2 (Fig. 221) be any pair of
adiabatic lines for any substance
chosen at random. These lines correspond to the state of the body
before and after some arbitrary quantity of heat has been added to
it. Let AB be any isothermal line for the same substance, and let
A_1B_1, A_2B_2, etc., be other isothermals drawn, so that the areas of the
cycles ABB_1A_1, $A_1B_1B_2A_2$, $A_2B_2B_3A_3$, etc., are equal to each other.
In this case we have

$$Q - Q_1 = Q_1 - Q_2 = Q_2 - Q_3 = \text{etc.,}$$

and hence, since $Q/\tau = Q_1/\tau_1$, we must have

$$\tau - \tau_1 = \tau_1 - \tau_2 = \tau_2 - \tau_3 = \text{etc. ;}$$

in other words, the isothermals have been drawn so as to correspond
to equal differences of temperature, so that if $\tau - \tau_1$ be the unit of
temperature, $\tau - \tau_2$ will be two units, $\tau - \tau_3$ three units, and so on.
Lord Kelvin's method of graduating the scale of temperature is consequently equivalent to saying that the number of degrees between the

temperature τ corresponding to the isothermal AB and the temperature τ' corresponding to any other isothermal A'B' is to be taken proportional to the area ABB'A'.

The absolute zero of temperature being that which corresponds to $Q = 0$, the only thing which yet remains arbitrary is the size of the degree, and this may be chosen so that the number of degrees between two standard temperatures on our new scale is the same as that on one of the ordinary scales—for example, so that there may be 100 degrees between the freezing and boiling points of water. As soon as the number corresponding to one of these points has been determined, the numerical value of every other temperature is settled in a manner independent of the laws of expansion of any particular substance. To determine the number on the absolute scale which corresponds to the freezing point or boiling point of water requires a special investigation of the behaviour of some particular substance. The simplest case is that of a perfect gas—that is, an ideal substance which obeys Boyle's law at all temperatures.

Case of a perfect gas.   If the working substance be a perfect gas, the characteristic equation of which is

$$pv = R\Theta,$$

where Θ is the temperature measured from the zero of a thermometer filled with this substance, as indicated in Art. 89, then the quantity of heat Q taken in by the substance while passing from A to B along an isothermal is, in dynamical units,

$$Q = \int_{v_1}^{v_2} p\,dv = R\Theta \int_{v_1}^{v_2} \frac{dv}{v} = R\Theta \log \frac{v_2}{v_1},$$

and the quantity Q' ejected in returning along A'B', the lower isothermal Θ' of a Carnot's cycle, is

$$Q' = \int_{v_4}^{v_3} p\,dv = R\Theta' \int_{v_4}^{v_3} \frac{dv}{v} = R\Theta' \log \frac{v_3}{v_4}.$$

Hence we have

$$\frac{Q}{Q'} = \frac{\Theta \, \log \, (v_2/v_1)}{\Theta' \, \log \, (v_3/v_4)} \qquad . \qquad . \qquad . \qquad . \qquad . \qquad (1)$$

But since A and A' are on the same adiabatic, we have, if the ratio of the specific heats is constant,

$$p_1 v_1{}^\gamma = p_4 v_4{}^\gamma, \quad \text{and similarly } p_2 v_2{}^\gamma = p_3 v_3{}^\gamma,$$

and consequently

$$\frac{p_2 v_2{}^\gamma}{p_1 v_1{}^\gamma} = \frac{p_3 v_3{}^\gamma}{p_4 v_4{}^\gamma} \qquad . \qquad . \qquad . \qquad . \qquad . \qquad (2)$$

But $p_1 v_1 = p_2 v_2$, and $p_3 v_3 = p_4 v_4$ by the isothermal conditions, therefore (2) becomes

$$\frac{v_2}{v_1} = \frac{v_3}{v_4},$$

and equation (1) becomes

$$\frac{Q}{Q'} = \frac{\Theta}{\Theta'}.$$

But $Q/Q' = \tau/\tau'$ on the absolute scale, therefore we have finally

$$\frac{\tau}{\tau'} = \frac{\Theta}{\Theta'};$$

or, in other words, the absolute zero on Lord Kelvin's scale is the same as the zero of the perfect gas thermometer. Now the coefficient of expansion of a gas has been found to be $\frac{1}{273}$ on the centigrade scale, so that when the interval between the freezing and the boiling points of water is divided into 100 equal parts, the zero of the perfect gas thermometer will be 273 degrees below the freezing point of water, and this is what is meant by saying that the absolute zero is $-273°$ C., or that on the absolute scale the freezing point of water is $273°$, and the boiling point $373°$.

As no ordinary gas rigorously obeys the laws of a perfect gas, the number 273 obtained by observation of the expansion of air requires correction in respect to the deviations of air from the supposed ideal condition, and these deviations can only be determined by special experiment. For this reason a special examination of the properties of air was made by Joule and Thomson by a method which we shall consider subsequently (sec. viii.).

Examples

1. Prove that an adiabatic curve cannot intersect an isothermal in more than one point, and therefore cannot touch it.

{If an adiabatic and an isothermal intersected in two points, they would form a closed cycle, and work could be performed with a single source at the temperature of the isothermal.}[1]

2. In passing along an adiabatic, prove that the temperature must always change in the same sense.

{Otherwise the same temperature would exist at two or more points on the same adiabatic.}

3. In the same manner the quantity dQ must always have the same sign in passing along an isothermal.

4. Of all the cycles that a mass of gas can pass through between given extreme temperatures, the cycle of Carnot gives the maximum ratio of the work performed to the heat spent.

---

[1] The touching here spoken of refers to two-point contact. It is possible for an adiabatic to have three-point contact with an isothermal, i.e. to touch it and cross it at the same time. This is actually the case with water at 4° C.

5. If an isothermal and an adiabatic intersect at a point M (Fig. 222), making angles A, B, C, D, show that in passing to any other state M'—

(1) If M' lies in A there is heating accompanied by a subtraction of heat.

(2) If M' lies in B there is heating accompanied by a communication of heat.

(3) If M' lies in C there is cooling accompanied by a communication of heat.

(4) If M' lies in D there is cooling accompanied by a subtraction of heat.

6. In general, if two adiabatic tangents be drawn at A and A' (Fig. 223), and

Fig. 222.   Fig. 223.

two isothermal tangents at B and B' to any closed cycle, there will be a communication of heat in passing along ABA', and a subtraction of heat in passing back along A'B'A, while there will be a fall of temperature in passing along BA'B' and a rise of temperature in passing along B'AB.

SECTION III

330. Extension of Carnot's Cycle—The Theorem of Clausius.— In the case of a simple Carnot's cycle the quantities of heat taken in and ejected during the isothermal transformations at absolute temperatures τ_1 and τ_2 are connected with these temperatures by the equation

$$\frac{Q_1}{\tau_1} = \frac{Q_2}{\tau_2} \, ;$$

or, if quantities of heat taken in be regarded as positive, while quantities given out are considered negative, this relation may be written in the form

$$\frac{Q_1}{\tau_1} + \frac{Q_2}{\tau_2} = 0.$$

Now in the case of a general transformation, represented graphically by a curve of any form, the heat is not all taken in at the same temperature and given out at another, but is taken in and given out

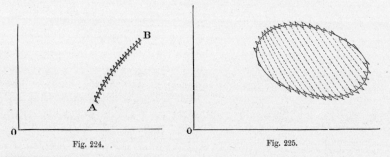

Fig. 224.   Fig. 225.

at temperatures which vary continuously. The above relation may, however, be extended to any reversible transformation by the following simple method suggested by Clausius :—[1]

Let the curve AB (Fig. 224) represent any reversible transformation whatever, which brings the working substance from the state A

---

[1] Clausius, *Mechanical Theory of Heat*, p. 88.

to the state B. This whole transformation may be considered as
made up of an immense number of very small transformations, which
are alternately isothermal and adiabatic, as shown by the zigzag line
overrunning AB, the successive elements of which are alternately
elements of isothermal and adiabatic curves. The smaller the elements
of this zigzag line, the more closely will it coincide with the continuous
curve AB, and the coincidence will be indefinitely close when the
elements are taken indefinitely small. Hence, if the continuous
transformation AB is replaced by the zigzag of alternate isothermals
and adiabatics, the effect on the quantities of heat, and the corresponding temperatures at which they are taken in or ejected, will be
vanishingly small.

From these considerations it follows that any reversible cycle
represented by any closed curve may be broken up into an infinite
number of indefinitely small Carnot cycles, as shown in Fig. 225.
For each of these cycles we have, if $d\mathrm{Q}_1$ be the quantity of heat
absorbed at τ_1 and $-d\mathrm{Q}_2$ the quantity ejected at τ_2—

$$\frac{d\mathrm{Q}_1}{\tau_1}+\frac{d\mathrm{Q}_2}{\tau_2}=0 \; ;$$

and by taking the sum of these for all the cycles, we have for any
cyclic reversible transformation whatever

$$\int\frac{d\mathrm{Q}}{\tau}=0.$$

In Carnot's cycle the working substance is supposed to take in
heat at the temperature of the hot body, and eject it at the tempera-

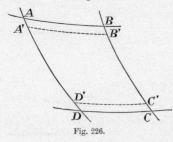

Fig. 226.

ture of the cold body. In practice,
however, the working substance must
be somewhat colder than the source
when taking in heat, and warmer than
the refrigerator when giving it out.
Hence, if ABCD (Fig. 226) be the
cycle of Carnot in the ideal limit, the
practical cycle will be represented by
the dotted figure [1] A′B′C′D′. The
area of the latter will be less than that of the former, so that the
efficiency in practice will be less than that of the ideal case. Consequently, if Q_1 and Q_2 are the quantities of heat taken in and ejected,
and τ_1 and τ_2 the absolute temperatures of the source and refrigerator,
we have

---

[1] When the operation is reversed, A′B′ will be above AB, and C′D′ below CD,
and the area of the reverse cycle will exceed that of the direct.

$$\frac{Q_1 - Q_2}{Q_1} < \frac{\tau_1 - \tau_2}{\tau_2},$$

which gives at once $Q_1/\tau_1 < Q_2/\tau_2$, or

$$\frac{Q_1}{\tau_1} - \frac{Q_2}{\tau_2} < 0.$$

If, however, τ_1 and τ_2 denote the absolute temperatures of the working substance when taking in and giving out heat, we have still

$$\frac{Q_1}{\tau_1} - \frac{Q_2}{\tau_2} = 0 \; ;$$

and that the left-hand member is less than zero when τ_1 and τ_2 denote the absolute temperatures of the hot and cold bodies, follows at once from the fact that in this case the temperature of the source is higher than that of the working substance, while that of the condenser is lower; and as a consequence, Q_1/τ_1 is diminished, while Q_2/τ_2 is increased.

In the same manner, if in any closed cycle the working substance be not at the same temperature as the body from which it absorbs, or to which it ejects heat, then we have

$$\int \frac{dQ}{\tau} = 0,$$

when the temperature τ is that of the working substance when it takes in or ejects the quantity of heat dQ;[1] but if τ be the temperature of the body to which the working substance yields heat or from which it abstracts it, then the positive constituents of this integral are all diminished, while the negative are increased, and we have

$$\int \frac{dQ}{\tau} < 0.$$

331. Entropy.—The interpretation of the theorem of the preceding article is, that the value of the integral for any reversible transformation which brings a body from a condition represented by any point A to that represented by any other point B depends only on the initial and final conditions, or is a function of the co-ordinates of A and B.   For if ϕ be the value of the integral taken along any path AMB (Fig. 219), and ϕ' its value when the transformation is effected along any other path ANB joining the same pair of points, then the pair of paths AMB and ANB form a closed reversible cycle, and for the whole cycle the value of the integral must vanish; therefore $\phi - \phi' = 0$, or $\phi = \phi'$.   The meaning of this is that the value of ϕ at

---

[1] dQ is the whole quantity of heat gained either from external or internal agencies.

any point depends only on the co-ordinates of the point, or that dQ/τ is a perfect differential—that is, the complete differential of some function ϕ, so that

$$\frac{dQ}{\tau} = d\phi,$$

and the value of the integral taken along any path joining the points whose co-ordinates are $p_1 v_1$ and $p_2 v_2$ is

$$\int_2^1 \frac{dQ}{\tau} = \phi_1 - \phi_2,$$

where ϕ_1 is the value of the function ϕ at the point $p_1 v_1$, and ϕ_2 its value at $p_2 v_2$.

By working along an isothermal line τ remains constant, and the value of ϕ changes by an amount Q/τ, where Q is the quantity of heat added to or taken from the substance during the transformation. This suggests the measurement of ϕ from a zero at which the substance contains no heat, but in practice it is with the changes of ϕ rather than with its absolute value that we are mainly concerned, so that we may measure ϕ (as we measure potential in dynamics) from any assumed origin; and the value of the integral taken along any path drawn from this origin to any other point may be written in the form

$$\int \frac{dQ}{\tau} = \phi.$$

The function ϕ has been termed the *entropy* of the substance by Clausius;[1] and it is clear that throughout any adiabatic transformation the entropy of a body at the same temperature throughout remains constant; for if $dQ = 0$, we have $d\phi = 0$, and this means that ϕ remains constant. The adiabatic lines of any substance are consequently lines of constant entropy, and for this reason they have been also named *isentropics*. If, however, any body be subject to operations which produce inequalities of temperature in the mass, there will be a transference of heat from the warmer to the colder parts by conduction and radiation, and although the body may neither receive heat from nor give it out to other bodies (so that the transformation is adiabatic throughout), yet on account of the inequalities of temperature, the entropy of the mass will increase as explained below (Art. 334), and under these circumstances the transformation will not be isentropic.

It has been already pointed out (Art. 322) that the quantity of

[1] R. Clausius (*Pogg. Ann.* vol. cxxv. p. 390) introduced the idea of a transformation equivalent of a quantity of heat, and dQ/τ is the transformation equivalent of the quantity dQ. The name entropy was consequently chosen from the Greek word τροπή, signifying transformation.

heat absorbed or given out by a body in passing from one condition
to another is not determined completely by the initial and final conditions, that Q is not expressible in terms of the initial and final
co-ordinates, or that dQ is not a perfect differential.   But we have
just seen that dQ/τ is a perfect differential, and this means that τ is
the integrating divisor of dQ, or $1/\tau$ is its integrating factor.

An interesting interpretation of the term entropy, as applied to a gas, has been
given by Boltzmann.[1] The expression "distribution of velocities", employed in
Art. 369 with reference to the molecules of a gas, might be understood in either of
two senses.   In the first place, we might take it to mean a complete definition of
the velocity in magnitude and direction of each individual molecule ; we shall call
a distribution given in this way an *arrangement*.   But by a given distribution of
velocities we ordinarily mean that we are given the number of molecules corresponding to each velocity, and we do not concern ourselves with the identity of the
molecules which possess this velocity, nor with their direction.   Such a statistical
distribution may be referred to as a *complexion*. The restriction being made that
the total energy of the gas is given, we see that a large number of complexions might
be supposed possible, and each complexion will include a large number of possible
arrangements.   If we assume that all arrangements are equally probable, then the
most probable complexion is that which contains the greatest number of possible
arrangements.[2]   This complexion will be the stable distribution of Art. 373.

Taking the simplest case, that of a gas whose molecules behave like perfectly
elastic smooth spheres, if we calculate an expression for the entropy as defined by
Clausius, we find that by suitably choosing the constant of integration, we can make
it proportional to the *logarithm of the probability* of the complexion of the gas.   If
one portion of gas has a complexion whose probability is P and another portion has
a complexion whose probability is P', then the probability for the two taken together
is PP', since the chance that two events should both happen is the product of the
separate chances.   Now log PP' = log P + log P', therefore the entropy of the whole
of a mass of gas is the sum of the entropies of its parts, as it should be.

According to this view, in its most general form, every transformation is in a
sense reversible.   If we could reverse the velocity of every particle of mass in the
universe, then events would proceed backwards, and things would revert to, and
pass through all their former stages.   Thus when a weight falls from a height, its
kinetic energy, on impact with the ground, is converted into diffused molecular
motion, or heat.   If the velocities were all reversed, then it would come about that
at a particular instant the molecules would conspire in a common motion to produce
an impulse which would project the weight up to its original level.   The number of
arrangements in the most probable complexion is, however, so enormously pre-
ponderant, that the chance of even a slight departure from the stable condition is
vanishingly small.

332. Clausius's Theorem considered as the Second Law.—The
theorem of Clausius that in any closed reversible cycle we have

$$\int \frac{dQ}{\tau} = 0 \qquad . \qquad . \qquad . \qquad . \qquad . \qquad . \qquad (1)$$

---

[1] See *Vorlesungen über Gastheorie*, by L. Boltzmann, vol. i.

[2] As an illustration of what is meant, we may take the case of a mixture of two
powders.   Every arrangement of grains is equally probable, but the most probable
complexion is a uniform mixture.

or, in other words, that the change of entropy of a system subject to any reversible transformation depends only on the initial and final conditions of the system, has been deduced merely as a generalisation of the equation

$$\frac{Q_1}{\tau_1} + \frac{Q_2}{\tau_2} = 0 \qquad . \qquad . \qquad . \qquad . \qquad . \qquad (2)$$

which applies to a simple Carnot's cycle. This latter equation depends on the theorem of Carnot that the efficiency of a reversible engine depends only on the temperatures of the source and refrigerator; and in deducing this theorem from the point of view of the dynamical theory, the only principle made use of is the second law in any one of the forms stated in Art. 326. It follows, therefore, that equation (1) is only a mathematical representation of the second law, and it has consequently been customary with many writers to write down equation (1) as the second law of thermodynamics. We have avoided this because it appears preferable to state the main axiom in its primitive form as the second law rather than any mathematical disguise of it, for the fundamental postulate is by this means kept more prominently in view.

Since equation (1) contains the second law, it ought to be possible to deduce this law from it. Thus, starting with (1)—that is, that the entropy of a body is the same at the end as at the beginning of any closed reversible cycle of operations—let us suppose that the body has returned to its initial condition, so that the entropy has now attained its initial value. Now, if any exchange of heat has taken place during the cycle between the working substance and other bodies, for example, if dQ_1 has been taken in by the working substance at τ_1, and if dQ_2 has been given out at τ_2, then, in order that the entropy may remain unaltered, this exchange must take place in such a way that

$$\frac{dQ_1}{\tau_1} = \frac{dQ_2}{\tau_2}.$$

Hence if τ_2 is less than τ_1, it follows that dQ_2 is less than dQ_1, or the quantity of heat gained by the cold body is less than that lost by the hot body, so that work is done during the cycle by drawing heat from the warmer of two bodies and giving it in part to the colder.

333. Entropy of a System.—The entropy of a body being taken arbitrarily as zero in some standard condition A (Fig. 227), defined by some standard temperature and pressure (or volume), the entropy in any other state B is the value of $\int \frac{dQ}{\tau}$ taken along any reversible path by which the body may be brought to B from the standard state A.

The path may obviously be an arc AC (Fig. 227) of an isothermal line passing through the point defining the standard state, together with the arc BC of the adiabatic line passing through B.   The entropy in the state B may consequently be measured thus.   Let the volume be changed adiabatically until the standard temperature τ is attained, and then change the volume isothermally until the standard pressure is attained.   If the quantity of heat imparted during the latter operation be Q, the entropy in the state B is

$$\phi = \frac{Q}{\tau}.$$

In this operation the temperature and pressure are supposed uniform throughout the body ; and if the mass in this case be unity, it is clear that the quantity of heat imparted when the mass is m will be mQ, so that the entropy of a mass m in the state B will be $m\phi$ where ϕ is the entropy per unit mass. This amounts to saying that the entropy of two units of mass in a given condition is twice that of one unit.

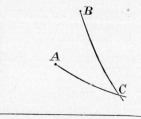

Fig. 227.

Hence, if we have a system of bodies at different temperatures τ_1, τ_2, etc., and masses m_1, m_2, etc., the entropy of the system will be the sum of the entropies of its parts or

$$\Phi = m_1\phi_1 + m_2\phi_2 + m_3\phi_3 + \ . \ . \ . \ \text{etc.} = \Sigma(m\phi),$$

where ϕ_1, ϕ_2, etc., are the entropies per unit mass of m_1, m_2, etc.   The average entropy of the system per unit mass might therefore be defined as

$$\frac{\Phi}{\Sigma(m)} = \frac{\Sigma(m\phi)}{\Sigma(m)},$$

just as the whole volume of a system is $V = \Sigma(mv)$, and the average volume per unit mass may be taken as $\Sigma(mv)/\Sigma(m)$.

334. Increase of Entropy caused by Equalisation of Temperature.—All processes, such as radiation, convection, and conduction, by which the temperatures of the various parts of a system become equalised, change the entropy of the system, and it is easily shown that the result of such operations is to increase the entropy.   For if a quantity of heat dQ leaves a body at temperature τ_1, the entropy of this body will be diminished by an amount $d\phi_1 = d$Q$/\tau_1$, and if this same quantity passes into a body at a lower temperature τ_2, its increase of entropy will be $d\phi_2 = d$Q$/\tau_2$.   Consequently the increase of entropy of the pair will be

$$d\phi_2 - d\phi_1 = dQ\left(\frac{1}{\tau_2} - \frac{1}{\tau_1}\right);$$

and this is a positive quantity, since τ_2 is less than τ_1.

Since such processes as radiation and conduction tend to reduce, rather than to exaggerate, differences of temperature, it follows that the entropy of the material universe, as we know it, must be continually increasing—that is, the entropy of the universe is growing towards a maximum value which will be attained when all temperature difference ceases to exist.

335. Available Energy or Motivity.—When an engine working between any source and refrigerator draws a quantity of heat Q from the source, we have seen that the whole of this quantity is not converted into work but only a fraction of it—viz. ηQ, where η is the efficiency of the engine. The remainder is given to the refrigerator ; and if the refrigerator is the coldest body of the system, this quantity remains unavailable for the purposes of work. If τ_0 be the temperature of the coldest body of a system, and if this body be used as the refrigerator of an engine describing Carnot's cycle, then when a quantity dQ of heat is drawn from a source at temperature τ, the fraction of this which can be converted into work is

$$\frac{\tau - \tau_0}{\tau}dQ.$$

This available fraction of dQ has been termed its *motivity* by Lord Kelvin ;[1] and it follows that a quantity of heat is wholly available for conversion into work only when the refrigerator is at the absolute zero of temperature, and in this case the motivity of a quantity of heat is equal to the whole quantity.

The motivity of any quantity is simply its practical value, and it is only when the refrigerator is at absolute zero that the motivity becomes equal to the dynamical value dQ.

336. Dissipation of Energy.—If τ_0 be the temperature of the coldest body of a system, the motivity of a quantity of heat dQ at temperature τ is

$$\left(1 - \frac{\tau_0}{\tau}\right)dQ.$$

If the quantity dQ be taken in by an engine describing Carnot's cycle, and if the quantity dQ' be ejected at the temperature τ' by the same engine, the motivity still remaining in dQ' is

$$\left(1 - \frac{\tau_0}{\tau'}\right)dQ',$$

---

[1] W. Thomson, *Phil. Mag.* and *Proc. Roy. Soc. Edin.*, 1852.

so that the change of motivity of the system is

$$d\mathrm{Q} - d\mathrm{Q}' - \tau_0\left(\frac{d\mathrm{Q}}{\tau} - \frac{d\mathrm{Q}'}{\tau'}\right);$$

and consequently if the working substance describes any closed cycle, the change of motivity is

$$\mathrm{Q} - \mathrm{Q}' - \tau_0\!\int\!\frac{d\mathrm{Q}}{\tau},$$

where Q is the whole quantity of heat taken in and Q′ the whole quantity given out by the working substance during the cycle. If the cycle be reversible, the loss of motivity will be simply Q – Q′, so that for a reversible cycle the integral vanishes; but if the cycle be not reversible, the loss of motivity will be greater than Q – Q′, and consequently the integral taken round such a cycle must have a negative value. There is thus a waste of motivity or a dissipation of energy of the positive value

$$\mathrm{D} = -\tau_0\!\int\!\frac{d\mathrm{Q}}{\tau}.$$

If a quantity of heat Q passes from a body at temperature τ_1 to another at a lower temperature τ_2, the loss of availability is

$$\tau_0\mathrm{Q}\left(\frac{1}{\tau_2} - \frac{1}{\tau_1}\right),$$

that is, the loss of availability or the dissipation is measured by the product of τ_0 and the increase of entropy.

As has been already pointed out, the efficiency of every engine falls short of the ideal limit of the reversible engine, so in practice when it is attempted to transform energy, a part of it is necessarily dissipated. Further, as the energy of the universe is constantly undergoing transformation, there is a constant dissipation in operation, and a constant degradation to the final unavailable state of uniformly diffused heat. The statement, therefore, that the entropy of the universe is tending towards a maximum, amounts to saying that the available energy of the universe is tending towards zero.

337. Graphic Representations.—The condition of a substance being determined by the co-ordinates of any point A (Fig. 228), we may speak of the whole energy of the substance in this state, although this is a quantity which we have no means of ascertaining experimentally. We cannot deprive a body of all its heat, and in the case of bodies which assume the gaseous condition, we cannot allow the volume of the containing vessel to increase sufficiently to obtain all the work derivable from the expansion of the substance, and so we cannot determine the whole energy. Nevertheless, when a body passes from

any state A to any other B, by means of any transformation represented graphically by the curve AB, we can determine how much
energy the body receives or loses, and in practice this is all we want.

Thus, if AP and BQ represent the adiabatic curves passing through
A and B, and if PQ be a fictitious curve representing the zero isothermal, then the area APQB (Art. 67) is the equivalent of the heat lost
by the body in passing from A to B (when B is below the line AP
the heat will be lost).   So, also, the area ABNM represents the
external work done by the body during the transformation (when B is
to the right of A the body expands and does external work).   Hence,
in passing from A to B the whole energy lost by the body will be
represented by the area APQBNM, and this area is independent of

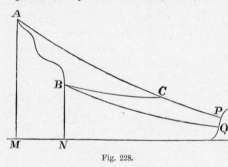

the form of the curve AB.
It is to be noted, on the
other hand, that the area
ABNM and the area APQB
both depend on the shape
of the curve, and conse-
quently, although the ex-
ternal work done and the
quantity of heat emitted
both depend on the nature
of the transformation, the

Fig. 228.

change of energy of the substance is completely determined by the
co-ordinates of the initial and final states (cf. Art. 322).

Hence,

Area APQBNM $= U - U_0 =$ change of energy.

Area ABMN $=$ $W = \int p dv.$

Area APQB $=$ $Q = \int \tau d\phi.$

If the temperature corresponding to B—that is, the temperature
τ_0 of the isothermal BC—be the lowest available temperature (for
example, if the body be surrounded by a medium at this temperature),
then in passing from A to B the temperature of the body cannot fall
below τ_0, and no part of the curve AB can descend below BC, and
since the body receives no heat from outside, the curve AB cannot
rise above AP.   The supposed conditions consequently constrain the
path AB to lie within a certain region, and under these conditions it is
clear that when it coincides with the limiting path ACB, made up of
the arc AC of an adiabatic and the arc BC of the isothermal through
B, the quantity of heat lost will be least and the quantity of external
work done by the body will be greatest.   The path ACB is consequently the path of least loss of heat, and the area ACBNM repre-

Path of
least heat.

sents the maximum amount of work that can be derived by bringing the substance from A to B under the supposed conditions. This area, therefore, represents the whole energy available for transformation into work. The quantity of heat given out along this path is obviously

$$Q = \tau_0(\phi - \phi_0) = \text{area CPQB},$$

where ϕ_0 is the entropy in the state B and ϕ the entropy in the state A. It appears, therefore, that if U and U_0 be the whole energies in the states A and B respectively, then the work done during the transformation cannot exceed the area ACBNM, or

$$U - U_0 - \tau_0(\phi - \phi_0).$$

This, then, is the energy available for mechanical purposes under the circumstances, and it follows that the greater the original entropy of the body the less the available energy (see further, sec. vii.).

Examples

1. If a system of bodies at different temperatures and pressures be contained within an adiabatic enclosure of constant volume, prove that the quantity of energy converted into work will be greatest when the system is reduced to thermal and mechanical equilibrium as follows :—

(a) Change the volume of each body adiabatically till they all attain the same temperature.

(β) The bodies being all at the same temperature, let those under higher pressure expand isothermally and compress those under lower pressure until the pressures of all are equal.

{The entropy of the system remains the same throughout this process, since there is no communication of heat except between bodies at sensibly the same temperature, and the work gained is consequently greatest.}

2. In a Carnot's cycle bounded by two isothermals τ_1 and τ_2, and two isentropics ϕ_1 and ϕ_2, prove that the area is

$$(\tau_1 - \tau_2)(\phi_1 - \phi_2).$$

{We have $Q_1 = \tau_1(\phi_1 - \phi_2)$ and $Q_2 = \tau_2(\phi_1 - \phi_2)$, and the area is $Q_1 - Q_2$ $\therefore$, etc.}

3. The area of a Carnot's cycle, bounded by two infinitely close isothermals and two infinitely close isentropics, is

$$d\tau d\phi.$$

4. A series of isothermals corresponding to absolute temperatures in arithmetical progression, and a similar arithmetic series of isentropics, form a network, the meshes of which are of equal area.

5. If the absolute temperature and the entropy be taken as co-ordinates to represent the state of a working substance, the area of any cycle represents the heat absorbed, or ejected.

{This follows from the relation $dQ = \tau d\phi$.}

6. The whole area between two isentropics and an isothermal is

$$\tau(\phi_1 - \phi_2).$$

7. In the case of a perfect gas, determine the entropy and prove directly that for a closed cycle

$$\int \frac{dQ}{\tau} = 0.$$

{In the case of a perfect gas we have (Art. 160)

$$\frac{dQ}{\tau} = C_v \frac{d\tau}{\tau} + R \frac{dv}{v},$$

$$\therefore \ \phi_1 - \phi_2 = C_v \log \frac{\tau_1}{\tau_2} + R \log \frac{v_1}{v_2} = C_v \log \frac{p_1}{p_2} + C_p \log \frac{v_1}{v_2}.\Big\}$$

8. Assuming the specific heat s of a liquid to be constant, determine the entropy per unit mass.
{Here $dQ = s\,d\tau$, $\therefore \ \phi_1 - \phi_2 = s \log (\tau_1/\tau_2)$.}

9. A unit mass of liquid at τ is converted into saturated vapour at the same temperature; determine the change of entropy.
{Here we have

$$\phi_1 - \phi_2 = \int \frac{L\,dm}{\tau} = \frac{L}{\tau}.$$

Hence, if a unit mass of liquid at τ_0 be raised to τ and vaporised at this temperature, the change of entropy is

$$s \log \frac{\tau}{\tau_0} + \frac{L}{\tau},$$

and if in addition the vapour be superheated to a temperature τ', the change of entropy will be, assuming the superheated vapour to obey the laws of gases,

$$s \log \frac{\tau}{\tau_0} + \frac{L}{\tau} + C_v \log \frac{\tau'}{\tau} + R \log \frac{v'}{v}.$$

The entropy, like the internal energy, depends only on the initial and final conditions, and consequently the foregoing expression should be independent of the temperature τ of ebullition, so that

$$(s - C_v) \log \tau + L/\tau - R \log v = 0.\}$$

10. If a body describes a closed isothermal and if it is reversible its area is zero, consequently it consists of two or more loops (cf. p. 459).

11. If the internal energy of a body be a function of the temperature only, prove that its characteristic equation is of the form

$$p = \tau f(v).$$

{In this case we have $dQ = \frac{dU}{d\tau} d\tau + p\,dv$, therefore $d\phi = \frac{1}{\tau} \frac{dU}{d\tau} d\tau + \frac{p}{\tau} dv$, and consequently $\frac{p}{\tau} dv$ must be a perfect differential—that is, p/τ must be a function of v.}

12. If a substance be such that U increases uniformly with τ when v is constant, and uniformly with v when τ is constant, and if C_p be constant, find the characteristic equation.
{Evidently we must have $dU = a\,d\tau + b\,dv$, where a and b are constants. Therefore

$$dQ = \tau\,d\phi = dU + p\,dv = a\,d\tau + (b + p)dv \qquad . \qquad . \qquad . \quad (1)$$

But since $d\phi$ is a perfect differential it follows that $(b+p)/\tau$ must be a function of v, or

$$b+p=\tau f(v) \quad . \quad . \quad . \quad . \quad . \quad (2)$$

Hence if p and τ be taken as independent variables, we have by (1) and (2)

$$dQ=\left[a+(b+p)\frac{dv}{d\tau}\right]d\tau+(b+p)\frac{dv}{dp}dp=\left(a-\frac{f^2}{f'}\right)d\tau+\frac{f}{f'}dp.$$

Therefore

$$C_p=\left(\frac{dQ}{d\tau}\right)_p=a-\frac{f^2}{f'}.$$

Hence

$$(a-C_p)\frac{df}{f^2}=dv, \quad \text{or} \quad C_p-a=(v+c)f,$$

where c is a constant. But $f=(b+p)/\tau$, therefore the required relation is

$$(p+b)(v+c)=(C_p-a)\tau.\}$$

13. If C_p and C_v be both constant, show that U may be expressed as a linear function of τ and v.

14. Two non-conducting vessels of volumes v_1 and v_2 are connected by a tube furnished with a tap. The vessels are filled with gas at the same temperature and at pressures p_1 and p_2 respectively. The tap is opened and the gas is allowed to fill both vessels; find the change of entropy, prove that it is positive, and explain why there is any change of entropy (cf. Art. 331).

15. If a substance obeys Boyle's law, and if its internal energy be a function of the temperature only, prove that its characteristic equation is

$$pv=R\tau$$

where R is a constant.

{If the substance obeys Boyle's law, then the function $f(v)$ of Ex. 11 must be simply a constant divided by v. Therefore, etc.}

16. If the characteristic equation of a substance be $pv=R\tau$, prove that the internal energy depends on the temperature only.

{We have

$$d\phi=\frac{dU}{\tau}+\frac{pdv}{\tau}=\frac{dU}{\tau}+R\frac{dv}{v}.$$

The final term being a perfect differential, it follows that dU/τ is a perfect differential, but dU is also a perfect differential, $\therefore$ etc.}

17. A unit mass of gas expands from a volume v_1 to a volume v_2 without doing external work (e.g. into an empty vessel); find the loss of motivity.

[*Ans.* $\tau_0 R \log (v_2/v_1)$.]

SECTION IV

338. Fundamental Differential Equations.—In general, the condition of a substance is completely determined by any pair of the quantities p, v, τ, ϕ, U, and in solving any thermodynamic problem, the pair most suitable for the purpose in hand must be chosen as independent variables. The quantities among which relations are most commonly established by the theory of heat are p, v, τ, ϕ, the two specific heats, and the latent heats of change of state. These variables are connected by two distinct equations

$$dQ = dU + dW . \qquad \cdots \qquad \cdots \qquad (1)$$

and

$$dQ = \tau d\phi \qquad \cdots \qquad \cdots \qquad (2)$$

furnished by the first and second fundamental principles of thermodynamics. When two distinct equations are obtained between any number of variables, we can proceed by known methods to deduce other relations among the variables which are often very useful and remarkable.

Thus, starting from equations (1) and (2), we obtain by equating their right-hand members

$$\tau d\phi = dU + dW \qquad \cdots \qquad \cdots \qquad (3)$$

or, in the case in which the only external force is a uniform normal pressure p, we have

$$dU = \tau d\phi - p dv \qquad \cdots \qquad \cdots \qquad (4)$$

We shall deal at present with this simpler case, and proceed to express (4) in terms of any two independent variables x and y which determine the condition of the body. These symbols may be subsequently replaced by any pair of the quantities p, v, τ, ϕ at pleasure. Now since ϕ and v are supposed to be expressible in terms of x and y, we have

$$d\phi = \frac{d\phi}{dx} dx + \frac{d\phi}{dy} dy, \quad \text{and} \quad dv = \frac{dv}{dx} dx + \frac{dv}{dy} dy.$$

Therefore equation (4) becomes

$$dU = \left(\tau \frac{d\phi}{dx} - p\frac{dv}{dx} \right) dx + \left(\tau\frac{d\phi}{dy} - p\frac{dv}{dy} \right) dy.$$

Consequently it follows that the coefficients of dx and dy in this equation are the differential coefficients of U with respect to x and y respectively, or

$$\frac{dU}{dx} = \tau\frac{d\phi}{dx} - p\frac{dv}{dx}, \text{ and } \frac{dU}{dy} = \tau\frac{d\phi}{dy} - p\frac{dv}{dy}.$$

But since dU is a perfect differential, we have

$$\frac{d}{dy}\left(\frac{dU}{dx} \right) = \frac{d}{dx}\left(\frac{dU}{dy} \right);$$

that is,

$$\frac{d}{dy}\left(\tau\frac{d\phi}{dx} - p\frac{dv}{dx} \right) = \frac{d}{dx}\left(\tau\frac{d\phi}{dy} - p\frac{dv}{dy} \right),$$

or finally, we are furnished with the elegant relation

$$\frac{d\tau}{dx}\frac{d\phi}{dy} - \frac{d\tau}{dy}\frac{d\phi}{dx} = \frac{dp}{dx}\frac{dv}{dy} - \frac{dp}{dy}\frac{dv}{dx} \qquad . \quad . \quad . \quad . \quad (5)$$

the direct geometrical interpretation of which is that corresponding elements of area are equal whether referred to p and v, or τ and ϕ, as rectangular co-ordinates.

By choosing x and y as any pair of the four quantities p, v, τ, ϕ, this equation yields at once the following thermodynamic relations, connecting thermometric and calorimetric phenomena.

339. First Relation.—If ϕ and v be chosen as independent variables in the fundamental equation (5) of the preceding article, we obtain, replacing x by ϕ and y by v, and noticing that consequently $d\phi/dx = 1$, and $dv/dy = 1$, and that, in addition, since ϕ and v are supposed independent, we must have $d\phi/dy = 0$ and $dv/dx = 0$, so that (5) reduces to

$$\left(\frac{d\tau}{dv} \right)_\phi = -\left(\frac{dp}{d\phi} \right)_v \qquad . \quad . \quad . \quad . \quad (I)$$

In this equation $d\tau$ is the change of temperature experienced by the substance in passing along an element of an adiabatic line (ϕ constant), and the left-hand member is the rate of change of temperature when the volume varies adiabatically, or the change of temperature per unit change of volume during an adiabatic transformation. In the right-hand member dp is the change of pressure caused by change of heat while the volume is kept constant, and the right-hand member is the change of pressure per unit change of entropy at constant volume.

The relation then asserts that during an adiabatic expansion the fall of temperature per unit increase of volume is equal to the increase of pressure per unit increase of entropy at constant volume ; or equal to the absolute temperature multiplied by the increase of pressure per (dynamical) unit increase of heat at constant volume, since $dQ - \tau d\phi$, and consequently the relation may be written in the form

$$\left(\frac{d\tau}{dv}\right)_\phi = -\tau\left(\frac{dp}{dQ}\right)_v.$$

340. Second Relation. — Choosing τ and v for independent variables, we have in the general equation (5) $x = \tau$, $y = v$, and

$$\frac{d\tau}{dx} = 1, \quad \frac{dv}{dy} = 1, \quad \frac{d\tau}{dy} = 0, \quad \frac{dv}{dx} = 0,$$

and consequently the equation reduces to

$$\left(\frac{d\phi}{dv}\right)_\tau = \left(\frac{dp}{d\tau}\right)_v \quad \cdot \quad \cdot \quad \cdot \quad \cdot \quad \cdot \quad \text{(II)}$$

which, being interpreted as before, means that the change of entropy per unit change of volume at constant temperature is equal to the change of pressure per unit change of temperature at constant volume ; or writing it in the form

$$\left(\frac{dQ}{dv}\right)_\tau = \tau\left(\frac{dp}{d\tau}\right)_v,$$

we find that the change of heat per unit change of volume at constant temperature, or the latent heat of isothermal expansion, is equal to the absolute temperature multiplied by the change of pressure per unit change of temperature at constant volume.

For example, in the case of a body changing state at constant temperature, if L be the quantity of heat necessary to change unit mass of the substance from the first state into the second, and if v_1 and v_2 be the corresponding specific volumes of the substance, the whole change of volume is $v_2 - v_1$ (supposing the volume to be greater in the second condition than in the first), and hence the change of heat per unit change of volume is $L/(v_2 - v_1)$, and the equation becomes

$$\frac{L}{v_2 - v_1} = \tau\left(\frac{dp}{d\tau}\right)_v.$$

341. Third Relation. — Choosing p and ϕ for independent variables, we have $x = p$, $y = \phi$,

$$\frac{dp}{dx} = 1, \quad \frac{d\phi}{dy} = 1, \quad \frac{d\phi}{dx} = 0, \quad \frac{dp}{dy} = 0,$$

and equation (5) reduces to

$$\left(\frac{d\tau}{dp}\right)_\phi = \left(\frac{dv}{d\phi}\right)_p \quad \cdot \quad \cdot \quad \cdot \quad \cdot \quad \cdot \quad \text{(III)}$$

which asserts that the change of temperature per unit increase of pressure during an adiabatic transformation is equal to the change of volume per unit increase of entropy under constant pressure. Or writing the relation in the form

$$\left(\frac{d\tau}{dp}\right)_\phi = \tau\left(\frac{dv}{dQ}\right)_p,$$

we find that the adiabatic rate of change of temperature with pressure is equal to the absolute temperature multiplied by the increase of volume per unit of heat supplied under constant pressure.

This relation also leads to the final equation of the preceding article.

342. Fourth Relation.—If we now take τ and p as independent variables, we have $x = \tau$, $y = p$,

$$\frac{d\tau}{dx} = 1, \quad \frac{dp}{dy} = 1, \quad \frac{d\tau}{dy} = 0, \quad \frac{dp}{dx} = 0,$$

and the fundamental equation reduces to

$$\left(\frac{d\phi}{dp}\right)_\tau = -\left(\frac{dv}{d\tau}\right)_p \quad . \qquad . \qquad . \qquad . \qquad . \qquad \text{(IV)}$$

which implies that the decrease of entropy per unit increase of pressure during an isothermal transformation is equal to the increase of volume per unit increase of temperature under constant pressure—that is, the expansion av. Writing the relation in the form

$$\left(\frac{dQ}{dp}\right)_\tau = -\tau\left(\frac{dv}{d\tau}\right)_p = -\tau v a,$$

we see that the heat given out by the substance per unit increase of pressure at constant temperature is equal to the continued product of the absolute temperature, the volume, and the expansibility.

From this formula it follows that if a is positive—that is, if the substance expands with heating—then dQ/dp must be negative; or, in other words, a quantity of heat must be taken away from the body in order to keep its temperature constant when the pressure is increased. It follows, therefore, that increase of pressure is accompanied by a development of heat in the case of bodies which expand on being heated, and similarly increase of pressure will produce a lowering of temperature in the case of bodies which contract when heated.

These theoretical conclusions have been confirmed by many experiments. Thus Joule [1] found that water when suddenly compressed at temperatures above 4° C. showed an increase of temperature, while

---

[1] Joule, *Phil. Trans.*, 1859 ; *Scientific Papers*, p. 474.

at temperatures below 4° the opposite effect was produced. The liquid was enclosed in a strong vessel furnished with a cylinder in which a piston worked, and the pressure could be suddenly changed by loading the piston with weights. The change of temperature was measured by a thermo-electric couple of copper and iron wires, one junction of which was placed in the middle of the liquid under examination, and the other in a bath of water. Sperm oil was also examined, and the experimental results in all cases were in close accord with the numbers derived from theory.

The effect of suddenly placing a wire or a bar of any substance under tension is the same as suddenly reducing the pressure (a tension being a negative pressure), so that wires of such substances as iron, copper, lead, etc., when suddenly stretched, show a cooling effect, while vulcanised india-rubber and wet bay wood were found by Joule to exhibit a heating effect.

343. Fifth and Sixth Relations.—The foregoing thermodynamic equations are generally known as "the four thermodynamic equations." Two other relations may be obtained immediately from equation (5) by choosing p and v, or τ and ϕ, for independent variables. Thus, if p and v be chosen, we have

$$\frac{dp}{dx}=1, \quad \frac{dv}{dy}=1, \quad \frac{dp}{dy}=0, \quad \frac{dv}{dx}=0,$$

and the fundamental equation (5) becomes

$$\left(\frac{d\tau}{dp}\right)_v\left(\frac{d\phi}{dv}\right)_p - \left(\frac{d\tau}{dv}\right)_p\left(\frac{d\phi}{dp}\right)_v = 1 \quad . \quad . \quad . \quad . \quad \text{(V)}$$

In like manner, if τ and ϕ be chosen as independent variables, we have

$$\frac{d\tau}{dx}=1, \quad \frac{d\phi}{dy}=1, \quad \frac{d\tau}{dy}=0, \quad \frac{d\phi}{dx}=0,$$

and equation (5) reduces to

$$\left(\frac{dp}{d\tau}\right)_\phi\left(\frac{dv}{d\phi}\right)_\tau - \left(\frac{dp}{d\phi}\right)_\tau\left(\frac{dv}{d\tau}\right)_\phi = 1 \quad . \quad . \quad . \quad \text{(VI)}$$

an equation which may be directly deduced from (V) by substituting in it from the four thermodynamic relations.

344. The Four Thermodynamic Formulæ.—The four thermodynamic formulæ deduced above as particular cases of the general equation of Art. 338 may also be deduced directly by writing the equation

$$dU = \tau d\phi - p dv \quad . \quad . \quad . \quad . \quad . \quad \text{(1)}$$

in the equivalent forms—

$$d(U - \tau\phi) = -\phi d\tau - pdv \quad . \quad . \quad . \quad . \quad (2)$$
$$d(U + pv) = \tau d\phi + vdp \quad . \quad . \quad . \quad . \quad (3)$$
$$d(U - \tau\phi + pv) = vdp - \phi d\tau \quad . \quad . \quad . \quad . \quad (4)$$

Thus, from (1), it follows that

$$\left(\frac{dU}{d\phi}\right)_v = \tau, \text{ and } \left(\frac{dU}{dv}\right)_\phi = -p \quad . \quad . \quad . \quad . \quad (5)$$

the first of which expresses that the absolute temperature measures the increase of internal energy per unit change of entropy at constant volume, or that the change of internal energy at constant volume is equal to the heat received, and the second expresses that the pressure measures the decrease of internal energy per unit increase of volume during adiabatic expansion. Differentiating the first of the equations (5) with respect to v, and the second with respect to ϕ, we have

$$\left(\frac{d\tau}{dv}\right)_\phi = -\left(\frac{dp}{d\phi}\right)_v \quad . \quad . \quad . \quad . \quad \text{(I)}$$

which is the first thermodynamic relation.

Similarly, from equation (2), if we write $U - \tau\phi = \mathscr{F}$, we have

$$\left(\frac{d\mathscr{F}}{d\tau}\right)_v = -\phi, \text{ and } \left(\frac{d\mathscr{F}}{dv}\right)_\tau = -p, -$$

with corresponding interpretations, and from these it follows that

$$\left(\frac{d\phi}{dv}\right)_\tau = \left(\frac{dp}{d\tau}\right)_v \quad . \quad . \quad . \quad . \quad \text{(II)}$$

which is the second relation.

So also, if we write $U + pv = \mathscr{F}'$, equation (3) gives us

$$\left(\frac{d\mathscr{F}'}{d\phi}\right)_p = \tau, \text{ and } \left(\frac{d\mathscr{F}'}{dp}\right)_\phi = v.$$

Hence

$$\left(\frac{d\tau}{dp}\right)_\phi = \left(\frac{dv}{d\phi}\right)_p \quad . \quad . \quad . \quad . \quad \text{(III)}$$

which is the third relation.

Finally, writing $U - \tau\phi + pv = \Phi$, we have from equation (4)

$$\left(\frac{d\Phi}{dp}\right)_\tau = v, \text{ and } \left(\frac{d\Phi}{d\tau}\right)_p = -\phi,$$

therefore

$$\left(\frac{dv}{d\tau}\right)_p = -\left(\frac{d\phi}{dp}\right)_\tau \quad . \quad . \quad . \quad . \quad \text{(IV)}$$

which is the fourth thermodynamic relation.

345. General Equations.—In the foregoing investigations the

2 z

only external force acting on the body was supposed to be a uniform normal pressure p. In the general case the energy equation will be

$$dQ = dU + dW . \quad . \quad . \quad . \quad . \quad (1)$$

which, with the relation $dQ = \tau d\phi$, may be written in the form

$$dU = \tau d\phi - dW \quad . \quad . \quad . \quad . \quad . \quad (2)$$

Now if x and y be any two independent variables which determine the condition of the body, we have

$$d\phi = \left(\frac{d\phi}{dx}\right)_y dx + \left(\frac{d\phi}{dy}\right)_x dy,$$

and

$$dW = \left(\frac{dW}{dx}\right)_y dx + \left(\frac{dW}{dy}\right)_x dy.$$

It is to be remembered, however, that dW is not a perfect differential, and that consequently $\frac{d}{dx}\left(\frac{dW}{dy}\right)$ is not equal to $\frac{d}{dy}\left(\frac{dW}{dx}\right)$.

Substituting for $d\phi$ and dW in equation (2), we have

$$dU = \left(\tau \frac{d\phi}{dx} - \frac{dW}{dx}\right)dx + \left(\tau \frac{d\phi}{dy} - \frac{dW}{dy}\right)dy,$$

consequently

$$\frac{dU}{dx} = \tau \frac{d\phi}{dx} - \frac{dW}{dx}, \text{ and } \frac{dU}{dy} = \tau \frac{d\phi}{dy} - \frac{dW}{dy} \quad . \quad . \quad . \quad (3)$$

But dU is a perfect differential, therefore

$$\frac{d}{dy}\left(\tau \frac{d\phi}{dx} - \frac{dW}{dx}\right) = \frac{d}{dx}\left(\tau \frac{d\phi}{dy} - \frac{dW}{dy}\right),$$

which, since $d\phi$ is also a perfect differential, reduces to

$$\frac{d\tau}{dx}\frac{d\phi}{dy} - \frac{d\tau}{dy}\frac{d\phi}{dx} = \frac{d}{dx}\left(\frac{dW}{dy}\right) - \frac{d}{dy}\left(\frac{dW}{dx}\right).$$

The right-hand member of this equation is termed by Clausius [1] "the work difference referred to xy," and is denoted by the symbol D_{xy}.

This may be regarded as the general differential equation for ϕ, and when the only force is a uniform external pressure it reduces to the equation of Art. 338.

In the same manner, by eliminating ϕ from equations (3), we obtain a general differential equation for U. Thus

$$\frac{d\phi}{dx} = \frac{1}{\tau}\left(\frac{dU}{dx} + \frac{dW}{dx}\right), \text{ and } \frac{d\phi}{dy} = \frac{1}{\tau}\left(\frac{dU}{dy} + \frac{dW}{dy}\right),$$

and consequently, since $d\phi$ is a perfect differential, we have

$$\frac{d}{dy}\left(\frac{1}{\tau}\frac{dU}{dx} + \frac{1}{\tau}\frac{dW}{dx}\right) = \frac{d}{dx}\left(\frac{1}{\tau}\frac{dU}{dy} + \frac{1}{\tau}\frac{dW}{dy}\right),$$

---

[1] Clausius, *Mechanical Theory of Heat*, p. 114.

which reduces to

$$\frac{d\tau}{dx}\frac{dU}{dy_i} - \frac{d\tau}{dy}\frac{dU}{dx} = \tau^2\left[\frac{d}{dx}\left(\frac{1}{\tau}\frac{dW}{dy}\right) - \frac{d}{dy}\left(\frac{1}{\tau}\frac{dW}{dx}\right)\right].$$

When the only external force is a uniform pressure p, this becomes

$$\frac{d\tau}{dx}\frac{dU}{dy} - \frac{d\tau}{dy}\frac{dU}{dx} = \tau^2\left[\frac{d(p/\tau)}{dx}\frac{dv}{dy} - \frac{d(p/\tau)}{dy}\frac{dv}{dx}\right];$$

and when the variables are p and v, this becomes

$$\tau - p\frac{d\tau}{dp} = \frac{d\tau}{dp}\frac{dU}{dv} - \frac{d\tau}{dv}\frac{dU}{dp}.$$

Examples

1. Apply the relation (5) to prove that the difference of the specific heats of any substance may be expressed in the form

$$C_p - C_v = \tau\left(\frac{dp}{d\tau}\right)_v\left(\frac{dv}{d\tau}\right)_p = -\frac{\tau\left(\dfrac{dp}{d\tau}\right)_v^2}{\left(\dfrac{dp}{dv}\right)_\tau}.$$

{We have

$$C_p - C_v = \tau\left[\left(\frac{d\phi}{d\tau}\right)_p - \left(\frac{d\phi}{d\tau}\right)_v\right]$$

$$= \tau\left(\frac{dp}{d\tau}\right)_v\left(\frac{dv}{d\tau}\right)_p\left[\left(\frac{d\tau}{dp}\right)_v\left(\frac{d\phi}{dv}\right)_p - \left(\frac{d\tau}{dv}\right)_p\left(\frac{d\phi}{dp}\right)_v\right],\text{ therefore, etc.}\}$$

2. Prove that the ratio of the adiabatic and isothermal elasticities of any substance is the same as the ratio of the two specific heats.

{We have

$$E_\phi = -v\left(\frac{dp}{dv}\right)_\phi, \text{ and } E_\tau = -v\left(\frac{dp}{dv}\right)_\tau.$$

Hence

$$\frac{E_\phi}{E_\tau} = \frac{\left(\dfrac{dp}{d\tau}\right)_\phi\left(\dfrac{d\tau}{dv}\right)_\phi}{\left(\dfrac{dp}{d\phi}\right)_\tau\left(\dfrac{d\phi}{dv}\right)_\tau} = \frac{\left(\dfrac{d\phi}{dv}\right)_p\left(\dfrac{dp}{d\phi}\right)_v}{\left(\dfrac{d\tau}{dv}\right)_p\left(\dfrac{dp}{d\tau}\right)_v}$$

in virtue of the thermodynamic relations.

Hence

$$\frac{E_\phi}{E_\tau} = \frac{\left(\dfrac{d\phi}{d\tau}\right)_p}{\left(\dfrac{d\phi}{d\tau}\right)_v} = \frac{\left(\dfrac{dQ}{d\tau}\right)_p}{\left(\dfrac{dQ}{d\tau}\right)_v} = \frac{C_p}{C_v}.\}$$

3. Prove that

$$dQ = C_p\left(\frac{d\tau}{dv}\right)_p dv + C_v\left(\frac{d\tau}{dp}\right)_v dp.$$

{The first member of the right-hand side is the quantity of heat required to be added to the substance while its temperature changes by $d\tau$, and the volume changes by dv under constant pressure. Similarly the second member is the quantity of heat required to be added while the volume is kept constant. The sum of the two is the whole quantity required when both volume and pressure vary.

Otherwise thus

$$dQ = \left(\frac{dQ}{dv}\right)_p dv + \left(\frac{dQ}{dp}\right)_v dp = \left(\frac{dQ}{d\tau}\frac{d\tau}{dv}\right)_p dv + \left(\frac{dQ}{d\tau}\frac{d\tau}{dp}\right)_v dp$$

$$= C_p\left(\frac{d\tau}{dv}\right)_p dv + C_v\left(\frac{d\tau}{dp}\right)_v dp.$$

In the case of a perfect gas $pv = R\tau$, and we have

$$\frac{dQ}{\tau} = C_p\frac{dv}{v} + C_v\frac{dp}{p},$$

which, when $dQ = 0$, gives $pv^\gamma = $ const.}

4. Substituting this value of dQ in the equations $dQ = dU + pdv$, and $dQ = \tau d\phi$, show that, p and v being independent variables,

$$\frac{d}{dv}\left(C_v\frac{d\tau}{dp}\right) = \frac{d}{dp}\left(C_p\frac{d\tau}{dv} - p\right),$$

$$\frac{d}{dv}\left(\frac{C_v}{\tau}\frac{d\tau}{dp}\right) = \frac{d}{dp}\left(\frac{C_p}{\tau}\frac{d\tau}{dv}\right).$$

Hence deduce the relation

$$C_p - C_v = \tau\left(\frac{dp}{d\tau}\right)_v\left(\frac{dv}{d\tau}\right)_p.$$

5. If dQ be the quantity of heat absorbed during an isothermal expansion, prove that

$$dQ = (C_p - C_v)\left(\frac{d\tau}{dv}\right)_p dv.$$

{This follows from the above expression for dQ, Ex. 3, together with the isothermal condition

$$d\tau = \left(\frac{d\tau}{dp}\right)_v dp + \left(\frac{d\tau}{dv}\right)_p dv = 0.\}$$

6. Assuming Clapeyron's equation for an isothermal transformation

$$dQ = \frac{1}{f(\theta)}\left(\frac{dp}{d\theta}\right)_v dv,$$

where $f(\theta)$ is some unknown function of the temperature centigrade, we have, by equating this value of dQ to that of Ex. 5,

$$(C_p - C_v)\left(\frac{d\tau}{dv}\right)_p = \frac{1}{f(\theta)}\left(\frac{dp}{d\theta}\right)_v.$$

But by Ex. 1,

$$(C_p - C_v)\left(\frac{d\tau}{dv}\right)_p = \tau\left(\frac{dp}{d\tau}\right),$$

therefore

$$f(\theta) = \frac{1}{\tau}\frac{d\tau}{d\theta},$$

and

$$dQ = \tau\left(\frac{dp}{d\tau}\right)_v dv,$$

which is the second thermodynamic relation.

7. Writing the equation for dQ in the form

$$dQ = C_v d\tau + ldv,$$

where l is the latent heat of isothermal expansion, prove that

$$l = \tau \frac{dp}{d\tau}, \quad \text{and} \quad \frac{dC_v}{dv} = \tau \frac{d^2p}{d\tau^2}.$$

{The equation is equivalent to

$$d\phi = \frac{1}{\tau}(C_v d\tau + l\,dv),$$

and consequently

$$\frac{d}{dv}\left(\frac{C_v}{\tau}\right) = \frac{d}{d\tau}\left(\frac{l}{\tau}\right);$$

also

$$dU = C_v d\tau + l\,dv - p\,dv,$$

therefore

$$\frac{dC_v}{dv} = \frac{d}{d\tau}(l - p);$$

consequently by comparison we obtain the relations in question. For a unit mass of liquid converted at constant temperature into vapour we have

$$\left.\frac{L}{v_2 - v_1} = \tau \frac{dp}{d\tau}.\right\}$$

8. Prove that

$$dQ = C_v d\tau + (C_p - C_v)\frac{d\tau}{dv}\,dv.$$

{We have by Ex. 3

$$dQ = C_v \frac{d\tau}{dp}dp + C_p \frac{d\tau}{dv}dv.$$

But

$$d\tau = \frac{d\tau}{dp}dp + \frac{d\tau}{dv}dv;$$

therefore by substituting for $\frac{d\tau}{dp}dp$ we obtain the relation in question.

This relation compared with that of the preceding example shows us that

$$l = (C_p - C_v)\frac{d\tau}{dv} = \tau \frac{dp}{d\tau}. \quad \text{See Ex. 1.}\}$$

9. Writing the equation for dQ in the form
$$dQ = C_p d\tau + l'dp,$$

prove that

$$l' = -\tau \frac{dv}{d\tau} = -\tau v a, \quad \text{and} \quad \frac{dC_p}{dp} = -\tau \frac{d^2v}{d\tau^2}.$$

10. Prove by direct transformation that the equation

$$\frac{dC_v}{dv} = \tau \frac{d^2p}{d\tau^2}$$

is equivalent to

$$C_p - C_v = \tau \left(\frac{dp}{d\tau}\right)_v \left(\frac{dv}{d\tau}\right)_p.$$

11. In the case of a saturated vapour the pressure is independent of the volume, and consequently the equation

$$\frac{dC_v}{dv} = \tau \frac{d^2p}{d\tau^2}$$

leads to the equation

$$C_v = \tau v \frac{d^2 p}{d\tau^2} + f(\tau).$$

12. Show that the relations

$$\frac{d}{d\tau}\left(\frac{dQ}{dv}\right) - \frac{d}{dv}\left(\frac{dQ}{d\tau}\right) = \frac{dp}{d\tau},$$

$$\frac{d}{d\tau}\left(\frac{dQ}{dv}\right) - \frac{d}{dv}\left(\frac{dQ}{d\tau}\right) = \frac{1}{\tau}\frac{dQ}{dv},$$

$$\frac{d}{dv}\left(\frac{dQ}{d\tau}\right) = \tau \frac{d^2 p}{d\tau^2}$$

are equivalent forms of the second thermodynamic relation.

13. In the same manner prove that

$$\frac{d}{d\tau}\left(\frac{dQ}{dp}\right) - \frac{d}{dp}\left(\frac{dQ}{d\tau}\right) = -\frac{dv}{d\tau},$$

$$\frac{d}{d\tau}\left(\frac{dQ}{dp}\right) - \frac{d}{dp}\left(\frac{dQ}{d\tau}\right) = \frac{1}{\tau}\frac{dQ}{dp},$$

$$\frac{d}{dp}\left(\frac{dQ}{d\tau}\right) = -\tau \frac{d^2 v}{d\tau^2}$$

are equivalent forms of the fourth relation.

14. Show that

$$\frac{d}{dp}\left(\frac{dQ}{dv}\right) - \frac{d}{dv}\left(\frac{dQ}{dp}\right) = 1 = \frac{1}{\tau}\left(\frac{d\tau}{dp}\frac{dQ}{dv} - \frac{d\tau}{dv}\frac{dQ}{dp}\right)$$

are equivalent forms of the fifth relation.

15. If

$$D_{xy} = \frac{d}{dx}\left(\frac{dW}{dy}\right) - \frac{d}{dy}\left(\frac{dW}{dx}\right),$$

and

$$D_{\xi\eta} = \frac{d}{d\xi}\left(\frac{dW}{d\eta}\right) - \frac{d}{d\eta}\left(\frac{dW}{d\xi}\right),$$

prove that

$$D_{\xi\eta} = \left(\frac{dx}{d\xi}\frac{dy}{d\eta} - \frac{dx}{d\eta}\frac{dy}{d\xi}\right)D_{xy},$$

and similarly if

$$\Delta_{xy} = \tau^2\left[\frac{d}{dx}\left(\frac{1}{\tau}\frac{dW}{dy}\right) - \frac{d}{dy}\left(\frac{1}{\tau}\frac{dW}{dx}\right)\right],$$

prove that

$$\Delta_{\xi\eta} = \left(\frac{dx}{d\xi}\frac{dy}{d\eta} - \frac{dx}{d\eta}\frac{dy}{d\xi}\right)\Delta_{xy}.$$

16. Prove that when the only force is a uniform external pressure

$$dQ = \frac{\tau}{C_p - C_v}\left[C_p\left(\frac{dp}{d\tau}\right)_v dv + C_v\left(\frac{dv}{d\tau}\right)_p dp\right].$$

{We have

$$dQ = \left(\frac{dQ}{d\tau}\right)_v d\tau + \left(\frac{dQ}{dv}\right)_\tau dv = C_v d\tau + \tau\left(\frac{dp}{d\tau}\right)_v dv$$

by the second thermodynamic relation.

Similarly

$$dQ = \left(\frac{dQ}{d\tau}\right)_p d\tau + \left(\frac{dQ}{dp}\right)_\tau dp = C_p d\tau - \tau\left(\frac{dv}{d\tau}\right)_p dp$$

by the fourth thermodynamic relation.

Eliminating $d\tau$ by means of these two equations, we obtain the expression in question.

In the case of a perfect gas the corresponding equations are

$$dQ = C_v d\tau + \frac{R\tau}{v} dv,$$

$$dQ = C_p d\tau - \frac{R\tau}{p} dp,$$

$$dQ = \frac{C_p}{C_p - C_v} p\, dv + \frac{C_v}{C_p - C_v} v\, dp. \Big\}$$

17. Find the relation between the specific heats of a gas, if the quantity of heat Q required for a transformation of a gas depends only upon the initial and final states.

{We have the foregoing equation

$$(C_p - C_v)dQ = C_v v\, dp + C_p p\, dv.$$

Hence if dQ is the complete differential of a function of p and v, we have

$$\frac{d}{dv}\left(\frac{C_v v}{C_p - C_v}\right) = \frac{d}{dp}\left(\frac{C_p p}{C_p - C_v}\right) \quad . \quad . \quad . \quad . \quad (1)$$

This equation cannot be satisfied if C_p and C_v are different constants, but if they be considered as unknown functions of p there is an infinite number of solutions.

One of historic importance is found in the supposition that $C_p - C_v = \text{const.} = R$, then equation (1) becomes

$$v\frac{dC_v}{dv} - p\frac{dC_v}{dp} = R,$$

or

$$C_v = R \log (v) + F(pv) \quad . \quad . \quad . \quad . \quad . \quad (2)$$

$F(pv)$ being an arbitrary function of pv, and consequently of the temperature τ. Hence, if for the same temperature each of the two specific heats (the difference of which is supposed const.) increases proportionately to the logarithm of the volume, then heat may be regarded as a substance, the presence of which in greater or less quantity determines the thermal state of a body. Accepting this hypothesis, which is contradicted by all the facts, we may calculate the quantity of heat in the gas.

Thus writing $F(pv) = \phi'(pv)$ for facility, we have

$$C_v = R \log v + \phi'(pv),$$

$$C_p = C_v + R = R + R \log v + \phi'(pv).$$

Therefore

$$R\,dQ = C_v v\, dp + C_p p\, dv$$

$$= \phi'(pv)(v\,dp + p\,dv) + Rp\,dv + R \log v(v\,dp + p\,dv) ;$$

hence

$$RQ = \phi(pv) + Rpv \log v,$$

or

$$Q = \psi(\tau) + R\tau \log v,$$

the function ψ being left indeterminate.

Carnot regarded heat as a substance, and consequently admitted that the specific heats increased as the logarithm of the volume. This, however, remained to be tested by experiment.}

18. Show that the quadrilateral area between the lines $\tau = a$, $\tau = a + da$ and $\phi = \beta$, $\phi = \beta + d\beta$ is

$$\frac{da\,d\beta}{\dfrac{d\tau}{dp}\dfrac{d\phi}{dv} - \dfrac{d\tau}{dv}\dfrac{d\phi}{dp}},$$

and hence show that when quantities of heat are measured in thermal units

$$\frac{d\tau}{dp}\frac{d\phi}{dv} - \frac{d\tau}{dv}\frac{d\phi}{dp} = \frac{1}{J}.$$

{Cf. equation (5), p. 701.}

19. Employ the equation of Ex. 3 to prove that

$$C_p - C_v = \tau \left(\frac{dp}{d\tau}\right)_v \left(\frac{dv}{d\tau}\right)_p.$$

{Dividing both sides by τ we have

$$\frac{d\phi}{dp} = \frac{C_v}{\tau}\frac{d\tau}{dp}, \quad \frac{d\phi}{dv} = \frac{C_p}{\tau}\frac{d\tau}{dv},$$

which, by means of the final equation of the preceding example, reduces as required.}

20. Prove that if a be the coefficient of expansion, the element of heat communicated to a body may be expressed in the form

$$dQ = C_p d\tau - av\tau dp.$$

{We have

$$dQ = \left(\frac{dQ}{d\tau}\right)_p d\tau + \left(\frac{dQ}{dp}\right)_\tau dp,$$

and by the fourth thermodynamic relation this transforms into the required expression.}

21. Prove that

$$d(U + pv) = C_p d\tau + v(1 - a\tau)dp.$$

22. Deduce the relations—

$$\frac{dp}{dU} = \frac{d\tau}{dU}\frac{d\phi}{dv} - \frac{d\tau}{dv}\frac{d\phi}{dU},$$

$$\frac{dv}{dU} = \frac{d\phi}{dU}\frac{d\tau}{dp} - \frac{d\phi}{dp}\frac{d\tau}{dU},$$

$$\frac{d\tau}{dU} = \frac{dp}{dU}\frac{dv}{d\phi} - \frac{dp}{d\phi}\frac{dv}{dU},$$

$$\frac{d\phi}{dU} = \frac{dv}{dU}\frac{dp}{d\tau} - \frac{dv}{d\tau}\frac{dp}{dU}.$$

{These follow from equation (5), p. 701, by taking as independent variables U and one of the quantities v, p, ϕ, τ.}

23. Find the rate at which heat has to be supplied to a liquid film in order to keep the temperature constant, when the area is increased.

The energy equation in this case is, if T denotes surface tension,

$$dU = dQ + TdS,$$

or

$$d(U - \phi\tau) = -\phi d\tau + TdS,$$

therefore

$$-\left(\frac{d\phi}{dS}\right)_\tau = \left(\frac{dT}{d\tau}\right)_s,$$

therefore

$$\left(\frac{dQ}{dS}\right)_\tau = -\tau\left(\frac{dT}{d\tau}\right)_s,$$

or, the latent heat of extension is equal to the absolute temperature multiplied by the rate of decrease of surface tension with temperature. According to experiments by Lord Kelvin, the heat required to keep the temperature constant is equivalent to nearly half the work done in stretching the film.

24. Find an expression for the difference between the specific heat of a substance at constant pressure p and at constant atmospheric pressure.

By the fourth thermodynamic relation

$$\left(\frac{d\phi}{dp}\right)_\tau = -\left(\frac{dv}{d\tau}\right)_p,$$

therefore

$$\frac{d^2\phi}{dpd\tau} = -\left(\frac{d^2v}{d\tau^2}\right)_p,$$

or

$$\tau\frac{d}{dp}\left(\frac{d\phi}{d\tau}\right) = -\tau\left(\frac{d^2v}{d\tau^2}\right)_p,$$

therefore

$$\frac{dC_p}{dp} = -\tau\left(\frac{d^2v}{d\tau^2}\right)_p;$$

therefore

$$C_p - C_1 = -\tau\int_1^p \left(\frac{d^2v}{d\tau^2}\right)_p dp.$$

25. Show that the difference of the specific heats of a solid can be represented by the equation

$$C_p - C_v = \frac{9\lambda^2 v\tau}{K},$$

where λ is the coefficient of linear expansion, and K the compressibility.

We have (see Art. 107)

$$3\lambda = a = \frac{1}{v}\left(\frac{dv}{d\tau}\right)_p, \quad K = -\frac{1}{v}\left(\frac{dv}{dp}\right)_\tau,$$

therefore

$$\frac{9\lambda^2}{K} = -\frac{1}{v}\left(\frac{dv}{d\tau}\right)_p^2 \left(\frac{dp}{dv}\right)_\tau,$$

and, dividing the second thermodynamic equation by the fourth,

$$\left(\frac{dp}{dv}\right)_\tau = -\left(\frac{d\tau}{dv}\right)_p\left(\frac{dp}{d\tau}\right)_v,$$

therefore

$$\frac{9\lambda^2 v\tau}{K} = \tau\left(\frac{dv}{d\tau}\right)_p\left(\frac{dp}{d\tau}\right)_v$$

$$= C_p - C_v \qquad . \quad . \quad . \quad . \quad \text{(Ex. 1)}$$

26. Prove the relation

$$\frac{C_p}{C_v} - 1 = -\frac{\left(\frac{dQ}{dp}\right)_\tau}{\left(\frac{dQ}{dp}\right)_v}.$$

By Ex. 1,

$$C_p - C_v = \tau\left(\frac{dp}{d\tau}\right)_v\left(\frac{dv}{d\tau}\right)_p$$

$$= -\left(\frac{dp}{d\tau}\right)_v\left(\frac{dQ}{dp}\right)_\tau \quad . \quad . \quad . \quad \text{(4th rel.)}$$

from which the result follows immediately.

SECTION V

CHANGE OF STATE

346. The Fundamental Equations.—The general phenomena attending the change of state of matter have been described in Chapter V., and we shall now consider them from the point of view of the thermodynamic theory, and deduce the laws applying to the passage of matter from any one of its three typical states to any other. Our results apply alike to the passage from the liquid to the solid state, or from either of these states to the condition of saturated vapour ; but for the sake of definiteness we may keep in view one particular change of state, say that of a liquid into its saturated vapour. The characteristic of such a transformation is that the pressure depends on the temperature alone, and not on the volume, so that p and τ cannot be chosen as independent variables defining the condition of the substance.

Let us take the case of a unit mass of any substance existing partly in one state (say liquid) and partly in another (saturated vapour), and let v_1 and v_2 be the specific volumes of the substance in the first and second states respectively. Then if the quantity of matter in the second state be m, the quantity in the first state will be $1 - m$, and the whole volume of the mixture will be

$$v = (1 - m)v_1 + mv_2.$$

When v and p, or v and τ, are known, v_1 and v_2 can be expressed in terms of them, and the quantity m can be determined. When a further quantity dm of the mass changes state, the quantity of heat necessary to effect the transformation is $dQ = L\,dm$, where L is the latent heat of change of state, and in this case the pressure is supposed constant, so that the volume v of the mass changes accordingly. If, however, the whole volume v be kept constant, the transformation of dm will entail a change of temperature and a corresponding change of pressure throughout the mass ; so that if s_1 be the specific heat of the substance in the first state, and s_2 that in

714

the second, as explained below, the transformation of a small quantity dm of the substance will produce a small change of temperature $d\tau$ throughout the whole mass, and the quantity of heat necessary to the operation will be

$$dQ = L dm + \{s_1(1-m) + s_2 m\} d\tau \quad . \quad . \quad . \quad . \quad (1)$$

But $dQ = \tau d\phi$, and consequently

$$d\phi = \frac{L}{\tau} dm + \frac{s_1(1-m) + s_2 m}{\tau} d\tau \quad . \quad . \quad . \quad (2)$$

We have thus the otherwise obvious relations [1]

$$\left(\frac{d\phi}{dm}\right)_\tau = \frac{L}{\tau}, \text{ and } \left(\frac{d\phi}{d\tau}\right)_m = \frac{s_1(1-m) + s_2 m}{\tau} \quad . \quad . \quad (3)$$

Now $d\phi$ is a perfect differential, and therefore these equations give us

$$\frac{d}{dm}\left\{\frac{s_1(1-m) + s_2 m}{\tau}\right\} = \frac{d}{d\tau}\left(\frac{L}{\tau}\right);$$

that is,

$$s_2 - s_1 = \tau \frac{d}{d\tau}\left(\frac{L}{\tau}\right) \quad . \quad . \quad . \quad . \quad (4)$$

The first of the equations (3) is merely a statement of the fact that under constant pressure (or temperature) $dQ = L dm$, and it at once leads to another fundamental equation. For since the whole change of volume per unit mass in passing from one state to the other is $v_2 - v_1$, we have for the change of volume, when the quantity dm is transformed under constant pressure, $dv = (v_2 - v_1) dm$. Hence the first of the equations (3) gives

$$(v_2 - v_1)\left(\frac{d\phi}{dv}\right)_\tau = \frac{L}{\tau},$$

or by the second thermodynamic relation (Art. 340),

$$\frac{L}{\tau} = (v_2 - v_1)\left(\frac{dp}{d\tau}\right)_v \quad . \quad . \quad . \quad . \quad (5)$$

If the change of state takes place in such a way that p is independent of v, the suffix may be omitted in $dp/d\tau$.

Equations (4) and (5) are the fundamental thermodynamic formulæ applying to the passage of a substance from any one of the three states of matter to any other, whether it be liquefaction, vaporisation, or sublimation. The quantities s_1 and s_2 are the specific heats of the substance in the two states under the conditions of pressure and volume at which the transformation takes place, and in the operation considered above they agree neither with the specific heat at constant volume nor with that under constant pressure; but in the case of the liquid or solid the specific heat under constant pressure may be used without serious

---

[1] Obvious, since when τ is constant $dQ = L dm = \tau d\phi$, which is the first relation, and when m is constant $dQ = s_1(1-m)d\tau + s_2 m d\tau = \tau d\phi$, which is the second.

error, as the dilatation and external work are small. In the case of the saturated vapour, however, the specific heat employed here is the quantity of heat required to raise the temperature of unit mass of the saturated vapour one degree, while the pressure is so varied that the mass is kept at the saturation point throughout the operation. This quantity will be considered more fully later on (Art. 348).

If the specific heats of the substance be known in both states, then equation (4) furnishes us with a knowledge of the variations of the latent heat with temperature, or if the specific heat in one state be known, and if the latent heat be known as a function of the tempera-ture, the equation may be employed to determine the specific heat of the substance in the other state.

On the other hand, if the pressure of the saturated vapour be known in terms of the temperature, equation (5) yields the specific volume (or density) of the saturated vapour at all temperatures when the density of the liquid and the latent heat are known.[1]   So also, since L and τ are both positive, it follows that if v_2 is greater than v_1, then dp and $d\tau$ must have the same sign; but if v_2 be less than v_1, then dp and $d\tau$ must have opposite signs.   In other words, if a substance passes from one state to another in which the specific volume is greater, then an increase of pressure raises the temperature at which this transformation will take place.   This happens in the case of liquids passing into vapour, or in the case of solids which expand in melting, and is expressed by saying that increase of pressure raises the boiling point or melting point.   If, however, the substance contracts in passing from the first state to the second, then if dp be positive $d\tau$ will be negative, and an increase of pressure will lower the tempera-ture at which the transformation can occur.   A notable example of this occurs in the case of ice (Art. 183), which, we have seen, contracts in melting, and consequently has its melting point lowered by increase of pressure.   The dynamical theory thus leads us to anticipate all the phenomena treated of in Art. 184.

---

[1] Clausius has deduced the values of the specific volume (or density) of saturated steam at various temperatures by this method, and has shown that grave errors are introduced when the density of a saturated vapour is deduced from that of the superheated vapour, under the supposition that it obeys the laws of a perfect gas (*Mechanical Theory of Heat*, p. 143).   In this formula L is measured in work units, so that if all the quantities involved have been determined experimentally, the formula yields the value of the dynamical equivalent, L being known in thermal units.   In this manner M. Pérot (*Ann. de Chimie*, 6e sér., tom. xiii. p. 145, 1888), having determined the densities of saturated water vapour and ether vapour, deduced the value 424 for J, thus verifying the formula.   In a similar manner it has been verified by M. Mathias (*Ann. de Chimie*, 6e sér., tom. xxi. p. 69, 1890).   For another mode of verification, see Bertrand's *Thermodynamics*, p. 155.

When $v_2 = v_1$ the equation shows that either $L = 0$ or else $dp/d\tau$ is infinite. The former condition is approached in the case of a liquid passing into vapour when the temperature approaches that of the critical point ; and in the case of fusion, where $v_2 - v_1$ is small, the coefficient of increase of pressure with temperature is large, and the latter condition is approached.

Examples

1. Find the lowering of the freezing point of water per atmosphere increase of pressure, taking the latent heat of ice to be 80, the specific volume of ice being 1·087, and that of water at 0° C. being unity.
{Here we have $v_2 - v_1 = 0.087$, $\tau = 273$, $dp = 1033$ grammes, while L expressed in dynamical units is 80×42700, hence

$$\frac{80 \times 42700}{273} = 0.087 \frac{1033}{d\tau},$$

or

$$d\tau = \frac{1033 \times 273 \times 0.087}{80 \times 42700} = 0.0072.\}$$

2. In the case of paraffin the latent heat in thermal units is 35.35, $v_2 - v_1 = 0.125$, $\tau = 325.7$, find the change of temperature per atmosphere in the melting point.
[Ans. $d\tau = 0.028$.
Experiments on this substance gave M. Battelli[1] a mean change of 0°·03 C. per atmosphere.
3. In the case of naphthalene, if the latent heat in thermal units $= 35.46$, $v_2 - v_1 = 0.146$, $\tau = 352.2$, find the change in the melting point per atmosphere.
[Ans. $d\tau = 0.035$.

As the equations (4) and (5) are of fundamental importance, the following instructive method of deducing them is added :—

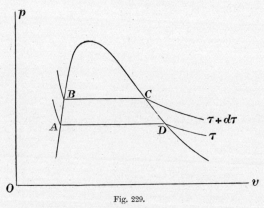

Fig. 229.

Let AD and BC (Fig. 229) represent the isothermal lines corre-

[1] A. Battelli, *Journal de Phys.* tom. vi. p. 90, 1887.

sponding to two infinitely close temperatures τ and $\tau + d\tau$. Along the line AB the substance is all in the liquid state, and along the line CD it is all in the condition of saturated vapour. Now if a unit mass of the substance be supposed to describe the cycle ABCD, the quantity of heat absorbed in passing from A to B will be $s_1 d\tau$, and the quantity given out in passing from C to D will be $s_2 d\tau$, so that if L be the latent heat at the temperature τ, that at the temperature $\tau + d\tau$ will be

$$L + \frac{dL}{d\tau} d\tau,$$

and the total quantity of heat absorbed during the cycle will be

$$dQ = s_1 d\tau + L + \frac{L}{d\tau} d\tau - s_2 d\tau - L = \left(s_1 - s_2 + \frac{dL}{d\tau} \right) d\tau.$$

But dQ is the equivalent of the external work done—that is, of the area of the cycle, the length of which is $v_2 - v_1$, and the breadth $\left(\frac{dp}{d\tau} \right)_v d\tau$.

Hence

$$dQ = (v_2 - v_1) \left(\frac{dp}{d\tau} \right)_v d\tau.$$

Consequently we have

$$s_1 - s_2 + \frac{dL}{d\tau} = (v_2 - v_1) \left(\frac{dp}{d\tau} \right)_v \qquad . \quad . \quad . \quad . \quad (6)$$

Further, the change of entropy must be zero, since the substance has returned to its initial condition, therefore

$$\Sigma \frac{dQ}{\tau} = \frac{s_1 d\tau}{\tau} + \frac{L + \dfrac{dL}{d\tau} d\tau}{\tau + d\tau} - \frac{s_2 d\tau}{\tau} - \frac{L}{\tau} = 0,$$

or

$$s_2 - s_1 = \frac{dL}{d\tau} - \frac{L}{\tau} = \tau \frac{d}{d\tau} \left(\frac{L}{\tau} \right),$$

which is the same as equation (4). Combining this with (6) we obtain (5), or

$$\frac{L}{\tau} = (v_2 - v_1) \frac{dp}{d\tau} = s_1 - s_2 + \frac{dL}{d\tau},$$

which expresses the two fundamental equations.

347. Internal and External Latent Heats.—When change of state occurs with change of volume the heat necessary to the transformation is the sum of two parts : one the equivalent of the external work done while the volume changes ; and the other, which is sometimes called the " true latent heat," is spent in altering the internal energy of the substance. If the transformation takes place under a uniform pressure p, the heat spent in external work, or the *external* latent heat, is

$$L_e = p(v_2 - v_1),$$

and consequently the heat spent in doing internal work, or the *internal latent heat*, is

$$L_i = L - p(v_2 - v_1) = \tau(v_2 - v_1)\left(\frac{dp}{d\tau} - \frac{p}{\tau}\right),$$

or

$$L_i = \tau^2(v_2 - v_1)\frac{d}{d\tau}\left(\frac{p}{\tau}\right).$$

Thus for water at $100°$ C., $L_e = 40\cdot21$, and $L_i = 496\cdot29$.

348. Specific Heat of Saturated Vapour.—We now return to the consideration of the fundamental equation (4), which connects the difference of the specific heats with the temperature and the latent heat of change of state. In the case of the liquid and solid states the specific heats commonly considered are positive quantities, and the ordinary specific heat under constant pressure of the solid or liquid at the temperature in question may be used without appreciable error in dealing with this equation. In the case of the saturated vapour, however, the specific heat involved is neither that at constant pressure nor yet that at constant volume, but is the quantity of heat supplied to a unit mass of the saturated vapour when its temperature is raised $1°$ C., while at the same time the pressure and volume are varied in such a manner that the whole mass remains saturated.

Under such conditions the quantity of heat supplied will depend upon the amount of work done on or by the substance while its volume is varied under pressure so as to keep it saturated, and, as already pointed out (Art. 132), the specific heat under such circumstances may have any value, positive or negative, depending on the nature of the substance and the temperature in question. We must not be surprised, therefore, if we find that the specific heats of some saturated vapours are positive while others are negative, or that the specific heat of the same saturated vapour is positive at some temperatures and negative at others.

The meaning of the specific heat of a substance under certain conditions being positive is that, in order to change the temperature of unit mass of the substance $1°$ C. under the given conditions, a certain quantity of heat must be communicated to it while external work is done on or by the substance according to the nature of the given conditions; while if the specific heat is negative, the external work which must be done on the substance in consequence of the given conditions is more than sufficient to raise the temperature of the mass $1°$ C., and therefore heat must be taken from the substance in order that the temperature may not rise above the required point.

Consequently, when it is said that the specific heat of a saturated vapour of some given substance is negative, it is to be inferred that the work spent in compressing any mass of the saturated vapour to the volume which the same mass would occupy when existing as saturated vapour at a temperature 1° higher, would if converted into heat be more than sufficient to raise the temperature of the mass 1° C. In other words, the internal energy of a unit mass of the vapour at θ exceeds the internal energy of a unit mass at a temperature 1° lower by a quantity which is less than the work required to compress the mass at the lower temperature into the volume occupied at the higher.

Our fundamental equation

$$s_2 = s_1 + \frac{d\mathrm{L}}{d\tau} - \frac{\mathrm{L}}{\tau}$$

shows us that s_2 may be either positive or negative according to the magnitudes of the quantities involved in the right-hand member, and if we use the equation of Ex. 20, p. 712,

$$d\mathrm{Q} = \mathrm{C}_p d\tau - a v \tau dp,$$

we are led to the same conclusion, for in the case of a saturated vapour p is a function of τ alone, and consequently we may write

$$dp = \frac{dp}{d\tau} d\tau,$$

so that we have for the specific heat

$$\frac{d\mathrm{Q}}{d\tau} = \mathrm{C}_p - a v \tau \frac{dp}{d\tau},$$

a quantity which may be either positive or negative.

As an example we shall consider the important and interesting case of water vapour. For this substance Regnault found, as explained in Art. 201, for the total heat Q at any temperature θ

$$\mathrm{Q} = \mathrm{L} + \int_0^\theta s d\theta = 606 \cdot 5 + 0 \cdot 305 \theta \quad . \quad . \quad . \quad . \quad (1)$$

where s is the mean specific heat of water between 0° and θ°. Hence

$$\mathrm{L} = 606 \cdot 5 + 0 \cdot 305 \theta - \int_0^\theta s d\theta,$$

and for water

$$s = 1 + 0 \cdot 00004 \theta + 0 \cdot 0000009 \theta^2,$$

therefore [1]

$$\mathrm{L} = 606 \cdot 5 - 0 \cdot 695 \theta - 0 \cdot 00002 \theta^2 - 0 \cdot 0000003 \theta^3.$$

---

[1] Clausius uses the shorter expression

$$\mathrm{L} = 607 - 0 \cdot 708 \theta,$$

and hence

$$s_2 = 0 \cdot 305 - \frac{607 - 0 \cdot 708 \theta}{273 + \theta},$$

But by (1), if $d\tau$ be taken equal to $d\theta$ in accordance with the equation $\tau = 273 + \theta$ (Art. 329), we have

$$\frac{d\text{L}}{d\tau} + s = 0 \cdot 305,$$

and hence by substitution in the fundamental formula we find for the saturated vapour

$$s_2 = 0 \cdot 305 - \frac{606 \cdot 5 - 0 \cdot 695\theta - 0 \cdot 00002\theta^2 - 0 \cdot 0000003\theta^3}{273 + \theta},$$

which is obviously negative for any moderate value of θ.

The following table contains the specific heats of the under-mentioned saturated vapours, as deduced by Clausius from the results of Regnault's experiments, using the fundamental formula (4):—

Temperature	0° C	50°	100°	150°
Water vapour	− 1·916	− 1·465	− 1·133	− 0·676
Ether	+ 0·1057	+ 0·1222	+ 0·1309	+ 0·1344
Bisulphide of carbon .	− 0·1837	− 0·1600	− 0·1406	− 0·1325
Chloroform	− 0·1079	− 0·0549	− 0·0153	+ 0·0155
Bichloride of carbon .	− 0·0442	− 0·0219	− 0·0066	− 0·0015
Acetone	− 0·1482	− 0·08832	− 0·0515	− 0·0223

The foregoing table shows that the specific heat of saturated water vapour is negative [1] at all moderate temperatures, and that within the same range the specific heat of ether vapour is positive.

or

$$s_2 = 1 \cdot 013 - \frac{800 \cdot 3}{273 + \theta},$$

which gives values agreeing closely with those deduced from the longer expression.

[1] The fact that the specific heat of saturated water vapour is a negative quantity was discovered simultaneously by Rankine and Clausius in 1850. Previously the subject had been treated from the point of view of the caloric theory, according to which the so-called total heat (that is, the quantity of heat taken in by a body in passing from a given initial to a given final condition) depends only on the initial and final states, and may therefore be expressed completely as a function of the variables which define the condition of the body, depending in no way upon the manner in which the substance passes from the initial to the final state. This is

The numbers further show that the value of this quantity approaches zero in the case of water vapour as the temperature rises, and in the case of ether as the temperature falls. We are thus led to suspect that for each of these substances there is a temperature at which the specific heat of the saturated vapour vanishes, and that

Inversion. probably beyond this temperature an inversion occurs and the specific heat changes sign, becoming positive in the case of water vapour and negative in the case of ether. This inversion is shown to occur actually in the case of chloroform, the specific heat of the vapour being positive above and negative below the temperature $123°$ C. We may therefore conclude that the specific heat of the saturated vapour of any substance may be either positive or negative according to the temperature. When the specific heat of a saturated vapour is negative,

Effect of adiabatic expansion. adiabatic expansion will be accompanied by partial condensation, for if we suppose the mass to expand until its temperature falls by any given amount, a quantity of heat must be added to it, in order that it may remain just saturated at the lower temperature, and if this quantity be not supplied, condensation must take place. In the same manner it follows that when the specific heat of a saturated vapour is positive, heat must be taken away from it, in order that it may

---

expressed by saying that dQ is a perfect differential, and hence, from equation (1), Art. 346, we have

$$\frac{d\mathrm{L}}{d\tau} = \frac{d}{dm}\{s_2 m + s_1(1 - m)\} = s_2 - s_1,$$

which gives

$$s_2 = s_1 + \frac{d\mathrm{L}}{d\tau} \quad . \quad . \quad . \quad . \quad . \quad (1)$$

Now, Watt, who was the first to publish any distinct views on this subject, was led by his experiments to the conclusion that the sum of the free and latent heats is constant (Watt's law, p. 363), and this is expressed by the equation

$$\mathrm{L} + \int s_1 d\tau = \text{const.}, \quad \text{or} \quad \frac{d\mathrm{L}}{d\tau} + s_1 = 0 . \quad . \quad . \quad (2)$$

This combined with (1) leads to the conclusion that s_2 is zero, a result which was long believed to be true, and was expressed by saying that if a saturated vapour changes its volume in a vessel impermeable to heat it always remains saturated. Regnault's experiments (Art. 197), however, proved that Watt's law was false, and that

$$\frac{d\mathrm{L}}{d\tau} + s_1 = 0\cdot305,$$

which, combined with (1), led to the conclusion that for water vapour $s_2 = 0\cdot305$, a positive quantity. Hence the idea arose that if saturated steam is compressed, heat must be supplied to it in addition to that generated by the compression, in order that it may remain throughout at the saturation point, and conversely, if saturated steam be allowed to expand in order to cool it, so that it may remain saturated during the expansion, a positive quantity of heat must be abstracted from it.

remain saturated as it cools, consequently during adiabatic expansion the vapour must become superheated.

The fact that the specific heat of water vapour is negative is of particular interest on account of its importance in the theory of the steam-engine, and in 1862 Hirn verified experimentally that the sudden adiabatic expansion of dry saturated steam is accompanied by condensation. He allowed steam to pass gently from a boiler, in which it was generated under a pressure of 5 atmos., into a long copper cylinder, the ends of which were closed with parallel plates of glass. The steam was allowed to enter this cylinder until all the air and condensed water were driven out and the walls had attained the temperature of the steam. The exit tap of the cylinder was then shut and connection with the boiler was cut off. The cylinder was thus filled with dry saturated vapour at a pressure of 5 atmos., and when looked through from end to end appeared quite clear. The exit tap being suddenly opened, the pressure at once fell, and a dense cloud formed within the cylinder, which rendered it opaque to an observer looking through from end to end. This cloud, however, soon disappeared as the vapour, now at 100° C., rapidly absorbed heat from the walls of the cylinder (previously at 152° C.). No such condensation could be obtained when ether vapour was treated in the same way ; but, on the other hand, this substance exhibited condensation when suddenly compressed.

These experiments were subsequently repeated with an improved form of apparatus by M. Cazin.[1] The cylinder was connected with another in which a piston worked, and the whole was placed in an oil-bath, the temperature of which could be varied at pleasure. By this arrangement saturated vapour in one cylinder could be allowed to expand suddenly into the other, or, when occupying both, could be suddenly compressed by moving the piston. A cloud was always formed by expansion in the case of steam but never by compression, and the same result was obtained with bisulphide of carbon. On the other hand, ether vapour always condensed during compression but never during expansion, showing that its temperature of inversion, as in the case of steam, was not within the limits of the experiments. In the case of chloroform the temperature of inversion appeared to be between 130° and 136° C., and in the case of benzene between 115° and 130° C.

From some experiments on the latent heats of the easily liquefiable gases—carbon dioxide, sulphurous acid, and protoxide of nitrogen—

[1] Cazin, *Ann. de Chimie et de Phys.*, 4e sér., tom. xix. ; *Comptes rendus*, tom. lxii. p. 56, 1866.

(margin note: Experiments of MM. Hirn and Cazin.)

M. Mathias [1] concludes that, as the temperature approaches that of
the critical point, the specific heat of every saturated vapour becomes
negative, and increases indefinitely in absolute value. For the substances examined it appeared that the latent heat of vaporisation
decreases as the temperature rises, and ultimately vanishes, as would
be expected, at the critical point, so that if a curve be constructed,
having latent heats for ordinates and temperatures for abscissæ, this
curve will cut the axis of abscissæ at a point corresponding to the
critical temperature. It was further found that this curve intersects
the axis at right angles in all the cases examined, and consequently at
the critical point we have

$$L = 0, \quad \text{and} \quad \frac{dL}{d\tau} = -\infty.$$

Hence it follows from the equation

$$s_2 = s_1 + \frac{dL}{d\tau} - \frac{L}{\tau}$$

that, at the critical temperature, we have $s_2 = -\infty$.

If all substances behave in this way, then, in the neighbourhood
of the critical point, the specific heat is negative for all saturated
vapours. Now in all known cases s_2 increases with rise of temperature,
and by the foregoing it decreases to $-\infty$ at the critical point, and
must therefore pass through a maximum value at some temperature
below the critical point. Consequently, if there be a point of inversion
at ordinary temperatures at which s_2 passes from negative to positive
values, there must also be a second point of inversion below the
critical temperature at which it changes from positive to negative.
There may then be two points of inversion, but if only one point of
inversion exists it must be the latter.

Two inver-
sions.

The negative value of the specific heat of steam, and the consequent condensation of this vapour when allowed to expand, appeared
at first sight inconsistent with the long-known paradox that high-
pressure steam escaping from a small orifice into the air will not burn
the hand, or even the face ; while, on the contrary, low-pressure
steam (which is consequently at a lower temperature) inflicts horrible
burns. This difficulty was explained by Lord Kelvin thus : [2] " The
steam, in rushing through the orifice, produces mechanical effect which
is immediately wasted in fluid friction, and consequently reconverted
into heat, so that the issuing steam at the atmospheric pressure would
have to part with as much heat to convert it into water at the temperature of 100°, as it would have had to part with to have been

[1] Mathias, *Ann. de Chimie et de Phys.*, 6ᵉ sér., tom. xxi. p. 69, 1890.
[2] *Dynamical Theory of Heat.*

condensed at the high pressure, and then cooled down to 100°, which, for a pound of steam initially saturated at the temperature t, is by Regnault's modification of Watt's law ·305 $(t-100)$ more heat than a pound of saturated steam at 100° would have to part with to be reduced to the same state ; and the issuing steam must, therefore, be above 100° in temperature, and dry." The thermal effect of fluid friction alluded to in this statement is considered in Art. 364.

349. The Triple Point.—When an enclosure is filled by a substance which is partly liquid and partly in the state of saturated vapour, the pressure is a function of the temperature alone, and when the equation connecting them is known in some form, such as

$$p=f(\theta),$$

the relation between pressure and temperature may be represented graphically by a curve, such as that shown in Fig. 144. This curve gives the pressure corresponding to any temperature when the liquid and vapour are in contact, and in stable equilibrium together. It is the curve of maximum vapour pressure, and is termed *the steam line*.[1]

In the same manner, if an enclosure be filled by a substance partly liquid and partly solid, and if the two states are in stable equilibrium together, the temperature of the mixture is that at which the solid melts under the pressure within the enclosure. This pressure is also completely determined by the temperature, and the relation connecting them may be represented graphically by a curve. This curve is the line of fusion and is called *the ice line*.

So also a solid may exist in stable equilibrium with its vapour, and we have thus a third curve which connects the temperature and pressure of a substance when existing partly in the solid state, and partly in the condition of vapour. This curve is called the *hoar-frost line* (Fig. 230).

From his experiments on the pressures of the saturated vapours of water substance above and below 0° C., Regnault[2] concluded that in passing from the vapour of the liquid to that of the solid there is no appreciable change in the vapour-pressure curve, and that consequently the hoar-frost line is simply a continuation of the steam line. The

---

[1] The term steam line has also been applied to the curve (Fig. 148, curve C) which represents the relation between the pressure and specific volume of the saturated vapour. This need not lead to any confusion, as one connects pressure and volume, while the other connects pressure and temperature. The former is the projection on the plane p, v, and the latter the projection on the plane p, θ, of the real steam line on the characteristic surface.

[2] Regnault, *Mém. de l'Acad.* tom. xxvi. p. 751.

difference between the vapour pressures of water and ice at 0° C. is, however, much too small to be placed in evidence by these experiments, and it was subsequently shown by Kirchhoff[1] that the steam line and the hoar-frost line are not continuous, but are distinct curves, and intersect each other at an angle.   Professor James Thomson[2] then announced the theorem that the point of intersection of these curves is situated on the ice line; or, in other words, that the three curves intersect in a common point, and this was afterwards proved by M. Moutier to follow as a consequence of the principles of thermodynamics (Art. 355).

This theorem is merely the statement of the fact that there is a temperature and pressure for which the three states—solid, liquid,

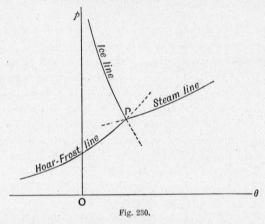

Fig. 230.

and vapour—can exist simultaneously together in equilibrium.   For example, there is a certain temperature and pressure at which water substance may exist partly as ice, partly as water, and partly as vapour, so that the lower part of a closed vessel containing the mixture will be filled with water in which ice floats, while the upper part is filled with saturated vapour, the pressure within the vessel being that of water vapour at the temperature of the mixture—a temperature which exceeds 0° C. by a small fraction of a degree.   This temperature and pressure are those which determine the triple point, and at this temperature the pressure of the saturated vapour of the liquid is the same as that of the solid, but at no other.

The three curves shown in Fig. 230 roughly represent the two vapour-pressure lines intersecting at a point P on the line of fusion. This point is the triple point for the substance to which the curves

[1] Kirchhoff, *Pogg. Ann.* tom. ciii., 1858.
[2] J. Thomson, *Phil. Mag.* (5) vol. xlvii. p. 447.

belong, and its co-ordinates are the temperature and pressure of the triple point. In order to prove that these curves are distinct, it is only necessary to show that the tangents to them at P are inclined at different angles to the axis $O\theta$, thus denoting the three states—solid, liquid, and vapour—by the suffixes 1, 2, 3 respectively, and denoting the difference of the specific volumes by u, so that $u_{23} = (v_3 - v_2)$, we have by formula (5), Art. 346, if τ be the absolute temperature of the triple point,

$$\left(\frac{dp}{d\tau}\right)_{12} = \frac{L_{12}}{\tau u_{12}}, \quad \left(\frac{dp}{d\tau}\right)_{23} = \frac{L_{23}}{\tau u_{23}}, \quad \left(\frac{dp}{d\tau}\right)_{31} = \frac{L_{31}}{\tau u_{31}}.$$

But $dp/d\tau$ is the trigonometrical tangent of the angle which the tangent to the curve makes with the axis $O\theta$, and as the latent heats and differences of specific volume are in general different for the three changes of state, it follows that the three curves are inclined to each other at definite angles at P. Thus the difference of the trigonometrical tangents of the inclinations of the hoar-frost line and the steam line at P to the axis $O\theta$ is

$$\left(\frac{dp}{d\tau}\right)_{13} - \left(\frac{dp}{d\tau}\right)_{23} = \frac{1}{\tau}\left(\frac{L_{13}}{u_{13}} - \frac{L_{23}}{u_{23}}\right).$$

Now at the triple point, and nowhere else (see p. 741),

$$L_{13} = L_{12} + L_{23},$$

while $u_{13} = u_{12} + u_{23}$, but since u_{12} is small compared with u_{13} and u_{23} we may write $u_{13} = u_{23}$, and we obtain

$$\left(\frac{dp}{d\tau}\right)_{13} - \left(\frac{dp}{d\tau}\right)_{23} = \frac{L_{12}}{\tau u_{23}}.$$

Exercises

1. Determine the entropy ϕ and internal energy U of a mixture of liquid and saturated vapour.

{Let there be unit mass partly liquid and partly saturated vapour, and let ϕ_0 be the entropy of the mass when it is all liquid at the point A, Fig. 231. At any point M let the mass of vapour be m, while that of liquid is $1 - m$, then the change of entropy in passing from A to M (considering the path ABM) is obviously [1]

$$\phi - \phi_0 = \int \frac{dQ}{\tau} = \int_{\tau_0}^{\tau} \frac{s_1 d\tau}{\tau} + \frac{Lm}{\tau} \quad . \quad . \quad . \quad . \quad (1)$$

---

[1] This equation may also be deduced directly from the equation of Art. 346. For we have

$$dQ = m s_2 d\tau + (1 - m)s_1 d\tau + L dm = s_1 d\tau + \tau \frac{d}{d\tau}\left(\frac{Lm}{\tau}\right) d\tau$$

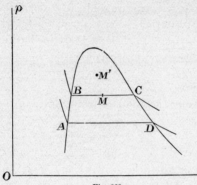

Fig. 231.

where s_1 is the specific heat of the liquid state along AB and τ the temperature of the isothermal BMC. If ϕ be supposed constant the point M will trace out an adiabatic line, and the differential equation of these lines will be

$$\frac{s_1}{\tau}+\frac{d}{d\tau}\left(\frac{\mathrm{L}m}{\tau}\right)=0 \ . \qquad (2)$$

The change of entropy of the mass in passing from the condition M to any other condition M' will consequently be

$$\phi'-\phi=\int_{\tau}^{\tau'}\frac{s_1 d\tau}{\tau}+\frac{\mathrm{L}'m'}{\tau'}-\frac{\mathrm{L}m}{\tau} \qquad . \quad . \quad . \quad . \quad (3)$$

and if M and M' lie on the same adiabatic, the right-hand member of this equation is equal to zero.

To determine the internal energy we have, for the quantity of heat absorbed in passing from A to M along the path ABM,

$$\mathrm{Q}=\int_{\tau_0}^{\tau}s_1 d\tau+\mathrm{L}m \qquad . \quad . \quad . \quad . \quad . \quad (4)$$

while the external work done during this transformation is

$$\mathrm{W}=\int_{\tau_0}^{\tau}p\,dv_1+p(v-v_1) \qquad . \quad . \quad . \quad . \quad (5)$$

where v_1 is the specific volume of the liquid and v the whole volume of the mixture at M, τ the temperature at M, and τ_0 the temperature at A, the integral being taken along the line AB. Hence

$$\mathrm{U}-\mathrm{U}_0=\mathrm{Q}-\mathrm{W}=\int_{\tau_0}^{\tau}s_1 d\tau-\int_{\tau_0}^{\tau}p\,dv_1+\mathrm{L}m-p(v-v_1) \qquad . \quad . \quad . \quad (6)$$

But since v_1 is practically independent of the pressure we may write $dv_1=\frac{dv_1}{d\tau}d\tau$, and since $v=(1-m)v_1+mv_2$, we have

$$v-v_1=m(v_2-v_1)=m\mathrm{L}/\tau\frac{dp}{d\tau},$$

consequently (6) becomes

$$\mathrm{U}-\mathrm{U}_0=\int_{\tau_0}^{\tau}\left(s_1-p\frac{dv_1}{d\tau}\right)d\tau+\mathrm{L}m\left(1-p/\tau\frac{dp}{d\tau}\right) \qquad . \quad . \quad . \quad (7)$$

which is Clausius's expression.

---

by the fundamental equation

$$s_2-s_1=\tau\frac{d}{d\tau}\left(\frac{\mathrm{L}}{\tau}\right).$$

Hence

$$d\phi=\frac{s_1 d\tau}{\tau}+\frac{d}{d\tau}\left(\frac{\mathrm{L}m}{\tau}\right)d\tau.$$

If, however, we integrate by parts, (5) becomes

$$W = pv - p_0v_0 - \int_{\tau_0}^{\tau} v_1 dp \qquad . \qquad . \qquad . \qquad . \qquad (8)$$

where p_0, v_0 refer to the point A, and p, v to the point M. Hence, for the change of internal energy, we have

$$U - U_0 = Q - W = Lm - (pv - p_0v_0) + \int_{\tau_0}^{\tau} \left(s_1 + v_1 \frac{dp}{d\tau} \right) d\tau \qquad . \qquad . \qquad (9)$$

and the change of the internal energy in passing from M to any other condition M′ is

$$U' - U = L'm' - Lm - (p'v' - pv) + \int_{\tau}^{\tau'} \left(s_1 + v_1 \frac{dp}{d\tau} \right) d\tau.$$

If M and M′ lie on the same adiabatic $Q = 0$, and the right-hand member of this equation represents the external work done.}

2. Prove that an adiabatic increase of temperature will diminish or increase the quantity of vapour in a mixture of liquid and vapour ; or, in other words, cause condensation or vaporisation, according as the quantity

$$s_1(1 - m) + s_2$$

is positive or negative, m being the mass of vapour per unit mass of the mixture.

{Taking the mass of the mixture to be unity, we have for any small transformation

$$dQ = \{(1 - m)s_1 + ms_2\} d\tau + Ldm,$$

and since the transformation in question is adiabatic we have $dQ = 0$, and consequently

$$\left(\frac{dm}{d\tau} \right)_\phi = -\frac{1}{L}\{(1 - m)s_1 + ms_2\}.$$

Hence, if the quantity within the bracket is positive dm and $d\tau$ have opposite signs, but if this quantity is negative dm and $d\tau$ have the same sign. That is, m increases with τ when $(1 - m)s_1 + ms_2$ is negative and decreases as τ increases if this quantity is positive.}

3. A mixture of liquid and vapour expands adiabatically, determine the change in the relative proportions of the liquid and vapour.

{Since the entropy is constant, equation (3) of Ex. 1 gives, since s_1 is practically constant,

$$\frac{m'L'}{\tau'} = \frac{Lm}{\tau} - s_1 \log \frac{\tau'}{\tau} \qquad . \qquad . \qquad . \qquad . \qquad (1)$$

Now if v be the volume of the mixture at τ we have

$$v = (1 - m)v_1 + mv_2 = v_1 + m(v_2 - v_1) = v_1 + m\frac{L}{\tau} \Big/ \frac{dp}{d\tau},$$

so that

$$\frac{Lm}{\tau} = (v - v_1)\frac{dp}{d\tau} \qquad . \qquad . \qquad . \qquad . \qquad (2)$$

and equation (1) becomes

$$(v' - v_1')\left(\frac{dp}{d\tau} \right)' = (v - v_1)\frac{dp}{d\tau} - s_1 \log \frac{\tau'}{\tau} \qquad . \qquad . \qquad . \qquad (3)$$

when p and v_1 are known as functions of τ, this equation gives the new temperature τ' in terms of the new volume v', the original volume v, and the original temperature τ.

If the latent heat at τ be given, the first term of the right-hand member of (3) may be used in its original form mL/τ.}

4. A unit mass of saturated steam is allowed to expand adiabatically, determine when the maximum condensation has taken place.

{By Ex. 2 condensation will cease when the mass m of vapour remaining satisfies the equation

$$(1 - m)s_1 + ms_2 = 0,$$

or

$$m = \frac{s_1}{s_1 - s_2} = \frac{s_1 \tau}{L - \tau \dfrac{dL}{d\tau}}.$$

This result may also be obtained from equation (3) of Ex. 1 by expressing that ϕ is constant and m a maximum. In the case of steam, if

$$\dot{L} = 800 - 0 \cdot 705\tau,$$

we find for the maximum condensation

$$m = \frac{\tau}{800}.\}$$

5. A mixture half water and half steam at 150° C. is enclosed within a non-conducting cylinder and allowed to expand, pushing back a piston, determine what happens.

{If m be the mass of vapour present at any instant, the whole mass of the mixture being unity, then evaporation or condensation will occur according as

$$s_1 + m(s_2 - s_1)$$

is positive or negative. Now for water vapour we have the formula

$$L = 800 - 0 \cdot 705\tau.$$

Therefore

$$s_2 - s_1 = \tau \frac{d}{d\tau}\left(\frac{L}{\tau}\right) = -\frac{800}{\tau},$$

so that at the temperature 150° C. we have, taking $s_1 = 1$, and $m = \frac{1}{2}$,

$$s_1 + m(s_2 - s_1) = 1 - \frac{400}{423} = 0 \cdot 054,$$

which is a positive quantity, consequently evaporation takes place as the expansion proceeds.

This might also be seen at once from the final equation of the preceding example. For the amount of vapour present when the maximum condensation has taken place at 150° C. is $m = \frac{423}{800} = \cdot 529$, and this exceeds the quantity in our problem.

Hence more vapour will form on expansion, until its quantity is $m' = \frac{\tau'}{800}$. Substituting this in equation (1), Ex. 3, we obtain an equation which gives τ' the temperature at which evaporation ceases and condensation begins. This temperature is about 120° C. Condensation then takes place, and the ratio of the vapour to the liquid will again become unity at a temperature of about 91° C.}

6. Show that when the specific heat of a saturated vapour is negative the adiabatic lines intersect the steam line (Fig. 148), passing downwards across it from right

to left, and when the specific heat is positive they pass across it from left to right, their upper parts lying to the left and their lower to the right.

7. Prove that the external latent heat L_e (Art. 347) is related to the latent heat L by the equation

$$\frac{L}{L_e} = \frac{\tau}{p}\frac{dp}{d\tau}.$$

8. If the latent heat of vaporisation can be expressed in the form

$$L = a - b\tau,$$

prove that the difference of the specific heats of the liquid and the saturated vapour varies inversely as the absolute temperature.

{We have

$$s_2 - s_1 = \frac{dL}{d\tau} - \frac{L}{\tau} = -\frac{a}{\tau}.\}$$

9. In the same case prove that the variation of the specific heat of a saturated vapour per degree of temperature is inversely proportional to the square of the absolute temperature.

{Neglecting the variations of the specific heat of the liquid, we have by Ex. 8

$$\frac{ds_2}{d\tau} = \frac{a}{\tau^2}.\}$$

10. Supposing the latent heat of vaporisation of water to be given by the formula

$$L = 800 - 0{\cdot}705\tau,$$

calculate the temperature of inversion.[1]

{Taking the specific heat of water to be unity we find

$$s_2 = 1 - \frac{800}{\tau},$$

consequently the temperature of inversion $(s_2 = 0)$ is $527°$ C. ; cf. Arts. 201, 238.}

11. Calculate the difference between the trigonometrical tangents of the angles which the tangents to the hoar-frost line and the steam line at the triple point make with the axis of abscissæ in the case of water substance.

{Taking the latent to be 80, $J = 42700$, $\tau_0 = 273$, $u_{23} = 209400$ c.c., we find

$$\left(\frac{dp}{d\tau}\right)_{13} - \left(\frac{dp}{d\tau}\right)_{23} = 0{\cdot}059,$$

the pressure being measured in grammes per square centimetre.}

12. Deduce the ratio of the quantities $\left(\dfrac{dp}{d\tau}\right)_{13}$ and $\left(\dfrac{dp}{d\tau}\right)_{23}$ in terms of the latent heats of fusion and evaporation. Calculate their numerical values for water substance, and compare the calculated values with the results of Regnault's experiments.

---

[1] The linear formula for latent heat is widely departed from at high temperatures, hence the result here obtained differs considerably from the true temperature, as determined by experiment.

CHARACTERISTIC FUNCTIONS AND THERMODYNAMIC POTENTIAL

350. Characteristic Functions—Formulæ of M. Massieu.—The two fundamental principles of thermodynamics furnish two equations connecting the three unknowns which determine the state of a body, viz.

$$dQ = dU + dW = \tau d\phi.$$

Hence, in order to determine all the coefficients relating to the substance, it is necessary to have some other equation connecting the variables which define its state. We are consequently led to expect that although these various coefficients and the state of the body cannot be determined in absence of this third equation, yet it should be possible to express them in terms of some function of the variables. That is what M. Massieu [1] has shown, and the function from which the various quantities may be derived he terms the *characteristic function* of the body. It depends upon the pair of independent variables chosen, having one form when τ and v are chosen, and another when τ and p are taken.

Thus, if we write, as in Art. 344,

$$\mathcal{J} = U - \tau\phi,$$

then the equation

$$dU = \tau d\phi - p dv. \qquad \qquad (1)$$

Variables τ and v.

may be written in the equivalent form

$$d\mathcal{J} = -\phi d\tau - p dv \qquad \qquad (2)$$

Consequently we have

$$\phi = -\left(\frac{d\mathcal{J}}{d\tau}\right)_v, \text{ and } p = -\left(\frac{d\mathcal{J}}{dv}\right)_\tau. \qquad (3)$$

while

$$U = \mathcal{J} + \tau\phi = \mathcal{J} - \tau\left(\frac{d\mathcal{J}}{d\tau}\right)_v. \qquad (4)$$

---

[1] F. Massieu, *Comptes rendus*, tom. lxix. pp. 858, 1057, 1869 ; *Journal de Physique*, tom. vi. p. 216, 1877.

Further the specific heat at constant volume is given by the equation

$$C_v = \left(\frac{dU}{d\tau}\right)_v = -\tau \frac{d^2\mathscr{F}}{d\tau^2} \quad . \quad . \quad . \quad . \quad (5)$$

while for the difference of the specific heats we have (p. 707)

$$C_p - C_v = -\tau\left(\frac{dp}{d\tau}\right)^2 \bigg/ \frac{dp}{dv} = \tau\left(\frac{d^2\mathscr{F}}{d\tau dv}\right)^2 \bigg/ \frac{d^2\mathscr{F}}{dv^2} \quad . \quad . \quad . \quad (6)$$

therefore

$$C_p = -\tau \frac{d^2\mathscr{F}}{d\tau^2} + \tau\left(\frac{d^2\mathscr{F}}{d\tau dv}\right)^2 \bigg/ \frac{d^2\mathscr{F}}{dv^2} \quad . \quad . \quad . \quad (7)$$

In like manner the isothermal elasticity and the coefficient of increase of pressure are given by the equations

$$-v\left(\frac{dp}{dv}\right)_\tau = v\frac{d^2\mathscr{F}}{dv^2} \quad . \quad . \quad . \quad . \quad (8)$$

and

$$\frac{1}{p}\left(\frac{dp}{d\tau}\right)_v = \frac{d^2\mathscr{F}}{d\tau dv} \bigg/ \frac{d\mathscr{F}}{dv} \quad . \quad . \quad . \quad . \quad (9)$$

Thus, when the temperature and volume are taken as independent variables, all the other quantities appertaining to the condition of the substance U, p, ϕ, C_p, C_v, etc., can be expressed in terms of the function $\mathscr{F}$, and its partial differential coefficients.

In the same way, if the pressure and temperature be chosen as independent variables, equation (1) may be thrown into the form $d(U - \tau\phi + pv) = vdp - \phi d\tau$.

Hence, if we write

$$U - \tau\phi + pv = \Phi,$$

we have

$$d\Phi = vdp - \phi d\tau \quad . \quad . \quad . \quad . \quad . \quad (10)$$

Variables τ and p.

and consequently

$$v = \left(\frac{d\Phi}{dp}\right)_\tau, \quad \text{and} \quad \phi = -\left(\frac{d\Phi}{d\tau}\right)_p \quad . \quad . \quad . \quad (11)$$

while

$$U = \Phi + \tau\phi - pv = \Phi - \tau\left(\frac{d\Phi}{d\tau}\right)_p - p\left(\frac{d\Phi}{dp}\right)_\tau \quad . \quad . \quad (12)$$

For the specific heat at constant pressure we have $dQ = dU + pdv$, or

$$C_p = \left(\frac{dU}{d\tau}\right)_p + p\left(\frac{dv}{d\tau}\right)_p = -\tau\frac{d^2\Phi}{d\tau^2} \quad . \quad . \quad . \quad (13)$$

and for the specific heat at constant volume we have

$$C_v = C_p + \tau\left(\frac{dv}{d\tau}\right)^2 \bigg/ \frac{dv}{dp} = -\tau\frac{d^2\Phi}{d\tau^2} + \tau\left(\frac{d^2\Phi}{d\tau dp}\right)^2 \bigg/ \frac{d^2\Phi}{dp^2} \quad . \quad . \quad (14)$$

The coefficient of expansion and the compressibility may also be expressed in terms of Φ, thus

$$\frac{1}{v}\left(\frac{dv}{d\tau}\right)_p = \frac{d^2\Phi}{d\tau dp} \bigg/ \frac{d\Phi}{dp} \quad . \quad . \quad . \quad . \quad (15)$$

and

$$-\frac{1}{v}\left(\frac{dv}{dp}\right)_\tau=\frac{d^2\Phi}{dp^2}\Big/\frac{d\Phi}{dp}\quad\cdot\quad\cdot\quad\cdot\quad\cdot\quad\cdot\quad(16)$$

Hence, when the pressure and temperature are chosen as independent variables, the function Φ enables us to express all the other quantities.

Examples

1. Calculate the characteristic functions $\mathscr{F}$ and Φ in the case of a perfect gas.

{Here we have the relation $pv=R\tau$, while the internal energy is a function of the temperature only, and is given by the equation

$d\mathrm{U}=\mathrm{C}_v d\tau$.   Hence if C_v be regarded as constant, $\mathrm{U}-\mathrm{U}_0=\mathrm{C}_v(\tau-\tau_0)$.   (1)

Further, $d\mathrm{Q}=\mathrm{C}_v d\tau+pdv$, and therefore

$$d\phi=\mathrm{C}_v\frac{d\tau}{\tau}+\mathrm{R}\frac{dv}{v}.$$

Hence

$$\phi-\phi_0=\mathrm{C}_v\log\frac{\tau}{\tau_0}+\mathrm{R}\log\frac{v}{v_0}=(\mathrm{C}_v+\mathrm{R})\log\frac{\tau}{\tau_0}-\mathrm{R}\log\frac{p}{p_0}\quad\cdot\quad\cdot\quad(2)$$

and therefore

$$\mathscr{F}=\mathrm{U}-\tau\phi=\mathrm{U}_0-\mathrm{C}_v\tau_0-\tau\phi_0+\mathrm{C}_v\tau\left(1-\log\frac{\tau}{\tau_0}\right)-\mathrm{R}\tau\log\frac{v}{v_0}\quad\cdot\quad\cdot\quad(3)$$

while

$$\Phi=\mathrm{U}_0-\mathrm{C}_v\tau_0-\tau\phi_0+\tau(\mathrm{C}_v+\mathrm{R})\left(1-\log\frac{\tau}{\tau_0}\right)+\mathrm{R}\tau\log\frac{p}{p_0}\quad\cdot\quad\cdot\quad(4)$$

These expressions may be verified by applying the formulæ of the preceding article. Thus

$$\frac{d\mathscr{F}}{dv}=-\frac{\mathrm{R}\tau}{v}=-p,\text{ and }\frac{d\Phi}{dp}=\frac{\mathrm{R}\tau}{p}=v,\text{ etc.}$$

In these expressions for $\mathscr{F}$ and Φ the quantity R may be replaced by k/ρ, where k is a constant, the same for all gases, and ρ is the normal density of the gas. See p. 141.}

2. Express the various coefficients of a substance in terms of the quantity $\mathscr{F}'=\mathrm{U}+pv$.

351. Condition of the Possibility of a Transformation.—When a system passes through any cycle of transformations, if $d\mathrm{Q}$ be the quantity of heat taken in by the system along any element of the cycle, and τ the absolute temperature of the source which yields the heat, then if the cycle be reversible, we have

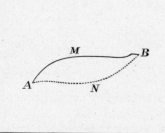

$$\int\frac{d\mathrm{Q}}{\tau}=0.$$

But if the conditions of reversibility be not fulfilled, we have (Art. 331)

$$\int\frac{d\mathrm{Q}}{\tau}<0.$$

Fig. 232.

The interpretation of this is that if a system passes from a state A to another state B, then the value of the above integral taken along any path joining A and B is greatest when the operation is reversible.   In other words, $\phi_B - \phi_A$ is the same for all reversible paths joining A and B, and is greater than the integral of dQ/τ for any path between A and B which is not reversible. Thus if AMB (Fig. 232) is a reversible path, while ANB is not reversible,[1] then considering the whole cycle ANBMA we have

$$\int_{ANB} \frac{dQ}{\tau} + \phi_A - \phi_B < 0,$$

and therefore

$$\int_{ANB} \frac{dQ}{\tau} < \phi_B - \phi_A . \qquad \qquad (1)$$

We conclude therefore that no transformation from the state A to the state B is possible which would give the integral a value greater than $\phi_B - \phi_A$, while a transformation which would give the integral a smaller value is possible, but not reversible.

The inequality (1) is consequently the condition that a transformation from any state A to another state B may be possible. For an infinitely small change it becomes

$$dQ < \tau d\phi \qquad \qquad (2)$$

or the quantity of heat absorbed is greatest when the operation is reversible. This is also directly obvious from the reasoning of Art. 331.

When the system is isolated, $dQ = 0$, and the above inequalities (1) and (2) mean that for every possible transformation $d\phi$ must be positive; or, in other words, every possible change of the system is attended by an increase of entropy.

It follows as a corollary that in any isolated system stable equilibrium will be attained when the entropy has reached its maximum value. For in this case the entropy cannot increase, and therefore no change can take place in the system.

352. Thermodynamic Potential.—The preceding inequality which tests the possibility of a transformation may be expressed in terms of either of the characteristic functions of M. Massieu. When an elementary transformation is reversible we have

$$dQ = \tau d\phi,$$
$$d\mathcal{F} = -\phi d\tau - p dv,$$
$$d\Phi = v dp - \phi d\tau,$$

and when the operation does not satisfy the conditions of reversibility, we must have

$$dQ < \tau d\phi \qquad \qquad (1)$$
$$d\mathcal{F} < -\phi d\tau - p dv \qquad \qquad (2)$$
$$d\Phi < v dp - \phi d\tau \qquad \qquad (3)$$

The reversibility, or otherwise, depends not on the particular path, but on the conditions under which it is traversed.

Thus by applying the inequality (1) we obtain (2) and (3) immediately. For

$$d\mathcal{F} = d(\mathrm{U} - \tau\phi) = d\mathrm{U} - \tau d\phi - \phi d\tau,$$

consequently (since $d\mathrm{Q}$ is less than $\tau d\phi$) we have

$$d\mathcal{F} < d\mathrm{U} - d\mathrm{Q} - \phi d\tau.$$

But $d\mathrm{U} - d\mathrm{Q} = -pdv$ if the only external force is a uniform normal pressure. Therefore we have

$$d\mathcal{F} < -\phi d\tau - pdv \quad . \quad . \quad . \quad . \quad (2)$$

In the same way

$$d\Phi = d(\mathrm{U} - \tau\phi + pv) = d\mathcal{F} + pdv + vdp,$$

and therefore by (2) we have

$$d\Phi < vdp - \phi d\tau \quad . \quad . \quad . \quad . \quad (3)$$

Consequently (1), (2), (3) express the same condition of possibility.

We shall now consider two particular cases. In the first place, if the temperature and volume of the system remain constant, then if any transformation of the system were possible under these conditions, it must take place in such a way that we have (by 2)

$$d\mathcal{F} < 0.$$

That is, $d\mathcal{F}$ must be negative, or the transformation is possible only if it takes place in such a way as to decrease $\mathcal{F}$.

On the other hand, if the pressure and temperature remain constant, as when fusion and vaporisation are in progress, then (3) gives us

$$d\Phi < 0,$$

so that $d\Phi$ is negative, and any transformation that may be possible under these conditions [1] must be such that the function Φ decreases.

We conclude therefore that—

(α) If v and τ remain constant in any system (not isolated) the function $\mathcal{F}$ cannot increase.

(β) If p and τ remain constant in any system (not isolated) the function Φ cannot increase.

(γ) If a system be isolated the entropy cannot decrease.

From (α) we infer that when the function $\mathcal{F}$ is a minimum it is impossible for any change to take place, and consequently the system under the conditions (α) is in stable equilibrium. While from (β) we infer that the system will be in stable equilibrium when Φ is a minimum. Now in rational mechanics the equilibrium of a system is

[1] J. W. Gibbs, *Trans. Connecticut Acad.* vol. iii. pp. 108-248, 343-524, 1875-78; *Silliman's Journal*, vol. xvi. pp. 441-458, 1878; *American Journal of Arts and Sciences*, vol. xviii., 1879.

stable when the potential energy, or the force function, is a minimum, and consequently the functions $\mathcal{F}$ and Φ here play a part corresponding to that of the force function in mechanics, and the function $\mathcal{F}$ has been accordingly named [1] by M. Duhem *the thermodynamic potential at constant volume*, while the function Φ is termed *the thermodynamic potential at constant pressure.*[2]

353. Thermodynamic Potential of a Heterogeneous Mass.—When the mass under consideration is not homogeneous throughout, but consists of masses m_1, m_2, m_3, etc., of different qualities or in different states, the thermodynamic potential of the whole is the sum of the thermodynamic potentials of the constituents. For if U_1, U_2, U_3, etc., be the internal energies of the constituents per unit mass, then the whole internal energy is

$$U = m_1 U_1 + m_2 U_2 + m_3 U_3 + \text{etc.},$$

and in the same way if ϕ_1, ϕ_2, ϕ_3, etc., be the entropies per unit mass of the parts, then the whole entropy is

$$\phi = m_1 \phi_1 + m_2 \phi_2 + m_3 \phi_3 + \text{etc.}$$

Consequently we have for the whole mass, if the temperature be the same throughout,

$$\mathcal{F} = U - \tau\phi = \Sigma m_1 U_1 - \tau \Sigma m_1 \phi_1 ;$$

that is,

$$\mathcal{F} = m_1 \mathcal{F}_1 + m_2 \mathcal{F}_2 + m_3 \mathcal{F}_3 + \text{etc.}$$

In the same way, if the pressure be the same throughout, we have $v = m_1 v_1 + m_2 v_2 + m_3 v_3 +$ etc., and the thermodynamic potential at constant pressure is

$$\Phi = m_1 \Phi_1 + m_2 \Phi_2 + m_3 \Phi_3 + \text{etc.}$$

Thus for a unit mass, a part m of which is in the state of saturated vapour, the remainder $1 - m$ being liquid, we have

$$\Phi = (1 - m)\Phi_1 + m\Phi_2.$$

354. Change of State.—In illustration of the preceding principles let us consider the case of a unit mass of any substance existing in two different states of aggregation. For instance, let a fraction m of it be in the state of vapour, and the remainder $1 - m$ in the liquid state. Now if a further quantity dm of the liquid becomes vapour, the pressure remaining constant, the thermodynamic potential of the liquid diminishes by an amount $\Phi_1 dm$, while that of the vapour increases by the amount $\Phi_2 dm$, where Φ_1 and Φ_2 are the thermodynamic potentials per unit mass of the liquid and vapour respectively, and

---

[1] P. Duhem, *Le Potentiel thermodynamique*, Paris, 1886.

[2] $\mathcal{F}$ has been called by v. Helmholtz the *free energy* of the system. It represents the part of the energy which, in reversible isothermal processes, can be converted into work. For if τ is constant $d\mathcal{F} = -pdv$ (equation 2, Art. 350).

evidently remain constant under the supposed conditions.   Hence the change of the thermodynamic potential of the mixture is

$$d\Phi - (\Phi_2 - \Phi_1)dm.$$

But for the possibility of any such transformation $d\Phi$ must be negative, and consequently if Φ_2 be greater than Φ_1, then dm must be negative, and condensation alone is possible, whereas if Φ_2 be less than Φ_1, dm must be positive, and vaporisation alone is possible.   When Φ_2 is equal to Φ_1, either transformation is possible and reversible.

Hence, when the change of state is reversible, we have

$$\Phi_1 - \Phi_2 = 0 \quad . \quad . \quad . \quad . \quad . \quad . \quad (1)$$

and as Φ_1 and Φ_2 are functions of the temperature and pressure, this equation is a relation connecting the temperature and pressure of the mass when the change of state takes place in a reversible manner. Now the pressure of a mass changing state is a function of the temperature alone, and we cannot have two equations connecting p and τ, otherwise they would be completely determined, therefore the equation (1) must be the functional relation connecting the temperature and pressure during change of state ; in other words, it is the equation of the steam line, the ice line, or the hoar-frost line, according to the states to which Φ_1 and Φ_2 are supposed to refer.   Hence if Φ_1, Φ_2, Φ_3 refer to the solid, liquid, and gaseous states respectively, the transformation from one state to another will be reversible along any one of the lines

(Steam line) . . . . . . $\Phi_2 - \Phi_3 = 0$ . . . . (1)
(Hoar-frost line) . . . . . $\Phi_3 - \Phi_1 = 0$ . . . . (2)
(Ice line) . . . . $\Phi_1 - \Phi_2 = 0$ . . . . (3)

When the supposed transformation does not take place along one of these curves it is not reversible, and it will be impossible if it would

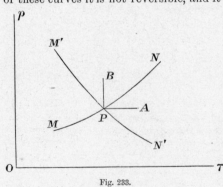

Fig. 233.

entail an increase of Φ.   We can easily examine, with regard to any one of the curves, the region in its plane for which the transformation is possible and for which impossible.   Thus any curve $f(x, y) = 0$ divides its plane into two regions, such that the co-ordinates of any point in one of them makes $f(x, y)$ a positive quantity, while any

point in the other renders it negative.   The curve itself is the line of demarcation between the two regions, and any point on it makes $f(x, y)$ zero.   Thus if the equation of the curve MN (Fig. 233) be

$$\Phi_1 - \Phi_2 = 0,$$

the co-ordinates of any point A not situated on the curve will not satisfy the equation of the curve, and we propose to determine whether it yields a positive or a negative value.   For this purpose draw AP parallel to the axis $O\tau$, and let the co-ordinates of P be p and τ while those of A are p and $\tau + d\tau$, then the change of $\Phi_1 - \Phi_2$ in passing from P to A will be, using Massieu's formulæ,

$$\left(\frac{d\Phi_1}{d\tau} - \frac{d\Phi_2}{d\tau}\right)d\tau = (\phi_2 - \phi_1)d\tau = \frac{L}{\tau}d\tau,$$

and this is a positive quantity.   Therefore A is in the positive region.

Similarly, if we take a point B whose co-ordinates are τ and $p + dp$, we have for the value of $\Phi_1 - \Phi_2$ at this point

$$\left(\frac{d\Phi_1}{dp} - \frac{d\Phi_2}{dp}\right)dp = (v_1 - v_2)dp,$$

and this will be negative if v_1 is less than v_2.   Consequently we infer that if the latent heat is positive, and if the change of volume is also positive in passing from the state (1) to the state (2), then the curve $\Phi_1 - \Phi_2 = 0$ passes between the points A and B as shown in the figure, A lying in the positive region and B in the negative.   If, however, the change of volume be negative, as in the fusion of ice, then the curve will not pass between A and B, but will be situated like M'N', so that the two points lie on the same side of it.   In the former case increase of temperature is accompanied by increase of pressure, whereas in the latter increase of temperature is accompanied by decrease of pressure.

Let us now return to the equation

$$d\Phi = (\Phi_2 - \Phi_1)dm,$$

and consider the transformation PA (Fig. 233).   In this case the value of $\Phi_2 - \Phi_1$ at A is $-Ld\tau/\tau$, a negative quantity if the transformation from the state (1) to the state (2) is accompanied by absorption of heat—that is, if L is positive.   In this case dm can only be positive, and we conclude that at every point on the right-hand side of the curve the only transformation possible is one in which dm is positive and entails an absorption of heat.   In the same way the only transformation possible to the left-hand side of the curve is one in which dm is negative and entails an evolution of heat.[1]

[1] J. Moutier, *Bulletin de la Société Philomathique*, 6e sér., tom. xiii., 1876 ; 7e sér., toms. i. ii. iii. iv.

Similarly, if we consider the transformation PB, we find that the value of $\Phi_2 - \Phi_1$ at B is $(v_2 - v_1)dp$, and therefore if v_2 is greater than v_1 the only transformation possible in the region above the curve (dp positive) is one in which dm is negative—that is, one in which there is a decrease of volume,—whereas in the region below the curve (dp negative) the only transformation possible is one which entails an increase of volume.[1]

Thus if the pressure of a mixture of water and its saturated vapour could be increased without condensation or change of temperature, the new condition would be unstable. In this state the water cannot evaporate, but there is a likelihood of sudden liquefaction. On the other hand, if the pressure happened to diminish without evaporation or change of temperature the vapour cannot condense, but there is danger of explosive ebullition.

Along the curve of reversible transformation $\Phi_1 - \Phi_2 = 0$, we have

$$\left(\frac{d\Phi_1}{d\tau} - \frac{d\Phi_2}{d\tau}\right)d\tau + \left(\frac{d\Phi_1}{dp} - \frac{d\Phi_2}{dp}\right)dp = 0.$$

That is

$$(\phi_2 - \phi_1)d\tau = (r_2 - v_1)dp,$$

or

$$\frac{L}{\tau} = (v_2 - v_1)\frac{dp}{d\tau}.$$

355. The Triple Point.—The preceding theory may be applied at once to deduce the theorem of the triple point (Art. 349), viz. that the two vapour-pressure curves (the steam line and the hoar-frost line) intersect on the line of fusion or ice line. For the equation of the steam line is

$$\Phi_2 - \Phi_3 = 0 \quad . \quad . \quad . \quad . \quad . \quad . \quad (1)$$

and along this the liquid and vapour are in equilibrium. The equation of the hoar-frost line is

$$\Phi_3 - \Phi_1 = 0 \quad . \quad . \quad . \quad . \quad . \quad . \quad (2)$$

and along this the vapour and solid are in equilibrium. Now by adding (1) and (2) together we obtain the equation of a curve which must pass through all the points in which (1) and (2) intersect each other, but the sum of (1) and (2) gives

$$\Phi_1 - \Phi_2 = 0 \quad . \quad . \quad . \quad . \quad . \quad . \quad (3)$$

But this is the equation of the ice line, and we therefore conclude that every point of intersection of any two of these curves lies on the third.

From this it follows at once that if two of these curves coincide in any region the third must coincide with them all along their common part, or if two of them coincide completely, the three become one

[1] Gustave Robin, *Bulletin de la Société Philomathique*, 7e sér., tom. iv. p. 21.

and the same curve, and the substance can exist in only two states. Now in the case of water the steam line and the ice line are obviously distinct, and therefore the hoar-frost line must also be a distinct curve, and cannot merge into the steam line as Regnault thought, but cuts it at an angle at the triple point.

The co-ordinates of this point obviously satisfy the equations

$$\Phi_1 = \Phi_2 = \Phi_3,$$

so that at the triple point the thermodynamic potential is the same (to a constant) for all three states.

To determine the angles at which the three curves intersect at the triple point we have, taking the steam line,

$$\left(\frac{d\Phi_2}{dp} - \frac{d\Phi_3}{dp}\right)dp + \left(\frac{d\Phi_2}{d\tau} - \frac{d\Phi_3}{d\tau}\right)d\tau = 0,$$

which by Massieu's formulæ gives at once

$$(v_2 - v_3)dp = (\phi_2 - \phi_3)d\tau ;$$

therefore, for the inclination of the tangent to the axis of abscissæ, we have

$$\left(\frac{dp}{d\tau}\right)_{23} = \frac{\phi_2 - \phi_3}{v_2 - v_3}, \quad \left(\frac{dp}{d\tau}\right)_{31} = \frac{\phi_3 - \phi_1}{v_3 - v_1}, \quad \left(\frac{dp}{d\tau}\right)_{12} = \frac{\phi_1 - \phi_2}{v_1 - v_2}.$$

Hence the trigonometrical tangents of the angles are obviously connected by the relation

$$(v_2 - v_3)\left(\frac{dp}{d\tau}\right)_{23} + (v_3 - v_1)\left(\frac{dp}{d\tau}\right)_{31} + (v_1 - v_2)\left(\frac{dp}{d\tau}\right)_{12} = 0.$$

And this by the fundamental formula of Art. 346 gives

$$L_{23} + L_{31} + L_{12} = 0.$$

Hence, at the triple point, we have

$$L_{13} = L_{12} + L_{23}.$$

Writing this equation in the form

$$(v_1 - v_2)\left[\left(\frac{dp}{d\tau}\right)_{12} - \left(\frac{dp}{d\tau}\right)_{31}\right] = (v_3 - v_2)\left[\left(\frac{dp}{d\tau}\right)_{23} - \left(\frac{dp}{d\tau}\right)_{31}\right],$$

we see that if v_1, v_2, v_3 are in ascending order of magnitude, so that $v_1 - v_2$ and $v_3 - v_2$ have opposite signs, then the differences

$$\left(\frac{dp}{d\tau}\right)_{12} - \left(\frac{dp}{d\tau}\right)_{31} \quad \text{and} \quad \left(\frac{dp}{d\tau}\right)_{23} - \left(\frac{dp}{d\tau}\right)_{31}$$

must have opposite signs. In other words, if the value of v_2 is intermediate between those of v_1 and v_3, then the magnitude of $\left(\frac{dp}{d\tau}\right)_{31}$ lies between those of $\left(\frac{dp}{d\tau}\right)_{12}$ and $\left(\frac{dp}{d\tau}\right)_{23}$. Hence the curve (13), which corresponds to the greatest change of volume, can be placed with reference to the other two, for the angle which the tangent to it at the triple point makes with the axis of abscissæ is intermediate in magnitude between the angles which the tangents to the other two make with the same axis. Consequently, if an ordinate be drawn cutting the three curves, the point of section with the curve (13) will lie between those with (12) and (23).

356. Applications.—The principles of thermodynamic potential have been applied with much success to the problems presented in the theory of solutions, dissociation, and thermo-electric phenomena.[1]

As an illustration let us take the case of a compound which dissociates into two simple substances at a certain temperature and under constant pressure. Then if at any instant the mass of the compound present in the mixture be m_3, while the masses of the dissociated elements are m_1 and m_2, and if Φ_1, Φ_2, Φ_3 be the corresponding thermodynamic potentials per unit mass respectively, we have for the whole mass of the mixture

$$\Phi = m_1\Phi_1 + m_2\Phi_2 + m_3\Phi_3.$$

Hence, if the masses m_1, m_2, m_3 be supposed to change by amounts dm_1, dm_2, and dm_3, under the pressure p and temperature τ, we have

$$d\Phi = \Phi_1 dm_1 + \Phi_2 dm_2 + \Phi_3 dm_3 \qquad \dots \quad \dots \quad (1)$$

But dm_1, dm_2, dm_3 are connected by the equation $dm_1 + dm_2 + dm_3 = 0$; so that if w_1, w_2, w_3 denote the molecular weights of the compound and its constituents respectively, we have

$$\frac{dm_1}{w_1} = \frac{dm_2}{w_2} = \frac{-dm_3}{w_1 + w_2} \qquad \dots \quad \dots \quad \dots \quad (2)$$

and consequently (1) becomes

$$(w_1 + w_2)d\Phi = [(w_1 + w_2)\Phi_3 - w_1\Phi_1 - w_2\Phi_2]dm_3.$$

Consequently, if the quantity

$$(w_1 + w_2)\Phi_3 - w_1\Phi_1 - w_2\Phi_2$$

is positive, a change in which dm_3 is negative is alone possible, whereas if this quantity be negative the only change possible is one in which m_3 increases. If the transformation is reversible, then

$$(w_1 + w_2)\Phi_3 - w_1\Phi_1 - w_2\Phi_2 = 0,$$

and this equation represents the curve of dissociation pressure. The dissociation pressure is thus a function of the temperature only, and is independent of the quantity m_3 of the original compound present, and of all such circumstances.

---

[1] A full exposition of the theory of thermodynamic potential and its applications will be found in M. Duhem's work, *Le Potentiel thermodynamique et ses applications*, Paris, 1886.

357. Plane Diagrams.—The advantage of the graphic method of representing the state of a substance by means of a point in a plane diagram, and the elegance of the method in concisely representing the whole history of a transformation, have been already illustrated in many cases. The particular case of Watt's indicator diagram (Art. 66), in which the co-ordinates of the point are taken as the pressure and volume of the substance, is that which has hitherto been most commonly employed, but evidently any pair of the five quantities p, v, τ, ϕ, U, which determine the condition of the substance, may be used for the same purpose, and it may happen that for one problem the representation may be most simply represented by one pair, while for another problem simplicity and elegance will be most easily secured by choosing another pair.

Thus when p and v are taken, as in Watt's method, the lines of constant volume (*isometrics*) and the lines of constant pressure (*isopiestics*) are systems of right lines parallel to the two axes of reference respectively, while the lines of constant temperature (*isothermals*), the lines of constant entropy (*isentropics*), and the lines of constant internal energy (*isodynamics* or *isenergics*) are each a system of curved lines of some particular form depending on the nature of the substance.

The other quantities which require to be represented on the diagram, and which depend on the nature of the transformation rather than on the nature of the substance, are the external work W performed by the body, and the quantity of heat Q supplied to it in passing from one state to another through some intermediate series of states. In the case of a pv diagram the work is represented very simply by the area enclosed by the path of the body, the ordinates at its extremities, and the axis of abscissæ, but the quantity Q is not so simply represented, as it depends not only on the area representing the work, but also on the change of internal energy. Thus, while p, v, τ, ϕ, U are functions of the state of the body, the quantities W and Q are determined, not by the state of the body at any instant, but by the whole series of states through which the body passes from one condition to another.

On the other hand, if τ and ϕ be taken as co-ordinates, the isothermals and isentropics will be systems of right lines parallel to the axes of reference, and the isometrics, isopiestics, and isodynamics will be curves of some particular character depending on the nature of the body. The quantity Q on this diagram will be represented (like the quantity W on the pv diagram) by the area included between the path, the ordinates at its extremities, and the axis of abscissæ, for we have $d\mathrm{Q} = \tau d\phi$, or

$$\mathrm{Q} = \int \tau d\phi,$$

while W will depend on this area, and also on the change of internal energy experienced by the substance in passing from its initial to its final condition.

It is clear, therefore, that from general considerations there is nothing to choose between a diagram constructed with p and v as co-ordinates and that constructed with τ and ϕ; the work and quantity of heat being represented on the former in a manner strictly analogous to that in which the heat and work are represented in the latter. This also appears from the general equations

$$d\mathrm{U} = d\mathrm{Q} - d\mathrm{W}, \quad d\mathrm{W} = pdv, \quad d\mathrm{Q} = \tau d\phi,$$

for these are unaltered when for v, p, W we write ϕ, $-\tau$, $-\mathrm{Q}$ respectively. Hence in our choice of co-ordinates we must be guided by considerations of convenience and simplicity in drawing the particular lines necessary to the problem in hand, as well as for the representation of W and Q. For one problem it may be most convenient to take p and v, while for another it may be much more simple [1] to take τ and ϕ, or v and ϕ, or some other pair, or perhaps some functions, of the quantities p, v, τ, ϕ, U.

When the substance passes through a complete cycle and returns to its initial condition, the whole external work done is represented by the area of the cycle, and the heat supplied is the equivalent of this (since the internal energy has not changed) on the pv diagram; while the whole heat supplied is represented by the area of the cycle on the $\tau\phi$ diagram, and the external work done is its equivalent. For this reason the pv and the $\tau\phi$ diagrams claim special attention. The importance of the $\tau\phi$ diagram is also indicated by the general consideration that, although work may be transferred by mechanical

---

[1] When τ and ϕ are used, Carnot's cycle takes the exceedingly simple form of a rectangle.

contrivances (levers, etc.) from systems at lower pressures to others at higher, yet by the second law of thermodynamics the transference of heat can only take place from bodies at higher to others at lower temperatures ; so that in the former case it is only necessary to ascertain the total quantity of work performed, but in the latter it is necessary to take into consideration the quantities of heat as well as the temperatures at which they are received. Hence, if in any particular problem several heat areas have to be considered, it is very important that these should be represented simply.

As an example of the use of the two systems we may take the simple case of a perfect gas. In this case we have $pv = R\tau$, and $U = C_v\tau$. Hence the isodynamic lines coincide with the isothermals whatever system of co-ordinates be chosen. If p and v be taken, then the isothermals and isentropics are given respectively by the equations $pv = $ const. and $pv^\gamma = $ const. ; but if τ and ϕ be taken as co-ordinates, the curves which we require are the isometrics and isopiestics. Now, by Example 7, p. 698, we have

$$\phi = C_v \log \tau + R \log v + \text{const.} \quad . \quad . \quad . \quad (1)$$

and consequently if the volume is constant this gives for the equation of the isometrics on the $\tau\phi$ diagram

$$\phi = C_v \log \tau + \text{const.} \quad . \quad . \quad . \quad \text{(isometrics)}$$

so that they are a system of similar logarithmic curves. So also equation (1) may be written in the form

$$\phi = C_p \log \tau - R \log p + \text{const.} \quad . \quad . \quad . \quad (2)$$

and therefore the isopiestics are given by the equation

$$\phi = C_p \log \tau + \text{const.} \quad . \quad . \quad . \quad \text{(isopiestics)}$$

These are consequently a similar family of logarithmic curves. The isodynamics (as in this case they coincide with the isothermals) are a system of right lines parallel to the axis of temperature.

Examples

1. In the case of a perfect gas, if any pair of the quantities $\log v$, $\log p$, $\log \tau$, $\log U$, ϕ, be chosen as co-ordinates, show that the isothermals, isentropics, isometrics, etc., are all right lines.[1]

{In the case of a perfect gas we have

$$\log p + \log v - \log \tau = \text{const.},$$
$$\log U - \log \tau = \text{const.},$$
$$\phi - C_v \log \tau - R \log v = \text{const.},$$

and these equations are each linear in the quantities mentioned in the question.}

2. If v and ϕ be taken as co-ordinates, show that if a series of isodynamic lines

---

[1] Professor J. W. Gibbs, *Trans. Connecticut Academy of Arts and Sciences*, vol. ii. p. 325, 1871–73.

be drawn for equal infinitesimal differences of energy, then any series of right lines parallel to the axis of volume are divided into segments inversely proportional to the pressure, while any series of lines parallel to the axis of entropy are divided into segments inversely proportional to the temperature.

{This follows from the equations

$$p = -\left(\frac{dU}{dv}\right)_\phi, \quad \tau = \left(\frac{dU}{d\phi}\right)_v.\}$$

358. Characteristic Surfaces.—When a plane diagram is constructed with any two variables which determine the condition of a body as co-ordinates, then every point in the plane of the diagram corresponds to a perfectly definite state of the body, and the indicator point is constrained to move along some definite curve only when the substance is forced to change its condition under some fixed law (for example, under constant temperature, or pressure, etc.). Now if any pair of the quantities p, v, τ, ϕ, U be taken as rectangular co-ordinates (or any two functions of these quantities which determine the state of the body), which for generality we shall call x and y, then at any given point on the plane diagram x and y will have given values corresponding to a definite state of the substance, so that the remaining three of the above five quantities will be perfectly determinate. Consequently, if a perpendicular be drawn to the plane of the diagram at the point xy, and if a length z be measured along it to represent any one of the other quantities, the locus of the extremity of this perpendicular in space will be a surface of some kind depending on the nature of the substance. In other words, if any three of the quantities p, v, τ, ϕ, U be taken as the rectangular co-ordinates x, y, z of a point P in space, then as the substance passes through all possible conditions of equilibrium, the point x, y, z will describe a surface which will possess certain geometrical properties and peculiarities depending on the nature of the substance. Such a surface will consequently exhibit the characteristic properties of the substance, and may be termed a *characteristic surface*.

The particular case in which the pressure, volume, and temperature are taken as co-ordinates has been already noticed (p. 88), and the functional relation $f(p, v, \tau) = 0$, already termed the characteristic equation of the substance, is the equation of this surface. For example, in the case of a perfect gas the equation of this surface is $xy = Rz$, viz. a rectangular hyperbolic paraboloid asymptotic to the planes xz and yz. The quantities p, v, τ, being those which are directly measured in any case, are naturally the quantities which would be first chosen as co-ordinates in any geometrical representation of the properties of a substance; but it by no means follows that the surface determined by these co-ordinates will afford the most comprehensive and elegant representation of the properties of the substance.   In addition, we possess no general equations connecting p, v, τ, or their differential coefficients, whereas, by means of the fundamental principles of thermodynamics, we have been led to general differential equations connecting certain other quantities.   For example, we have the fundamental equation

$$dU = \tau d\phi - p dv. \qquad \qquad (1)$$

connecting the differentials of v, ϕ, U, so that if these three quantities be chosen as co-ordinates, this equation is the differential equation of some surface of the form

$$U = f(v, \phi) \qquad \qquad (2)$$

The v, ϕ, U surface.

concerning which we possess at once certain valuable information. For by (1) we have

$$\left(\frac{dU}{d\phi}\right)_v = \tau, \text{ and } \left(\frac{dU}{dv}\right)_\phi = -p \qquad (3)$$

but by (2) it follows that the direction cosines of the normal to the surface at any point are proportional to $\dfrac{dU}{d\phi}, \dfrac{dU}{dv}$, -1, and consequently by (3) it follows that the direction cosines of the normal at any point of the surface are proportional to τ, $-p$, -1 respectively.   Hence, with this surface the volume, entropy, and internal energy are given directly by the co-ordinates of a point on the surface, and the remaining pair of quantities, viz. the pressure and temperature, are given by the direction of the normal to the surface at the same point.   The whole five quantities p, v, τ, ϕ, U are thus clearly represented in an exceedingly simple manner.

Another advantage of the v, ϕ, U co-ordinates lies in the fact that each of them possesses the additive property.   Thus, in a system the volume of the whole is the sum of the volumes of the separate parts into which it may be divided; the energy of the whole is the sum of the energies of its separate parts, and similarly for the entropy.   For this reason it follows that when such surfaces are constructed for different masses in the same condition, these surfaces will be similar to each other, and their linear dimensions will be simply proportional to the masses which they represent.

Additive property.

The surface obtained by using v, ϕ, U as co-ordinates has been brought into prominence by Gibbs,[1] and its properties will be considered briefly in the following article.   At present it may be mentioned in passing that any one of the equivalent forms of the equation $dU = \tau d\phi - p dv$, viz. with the notation of Art. 344,

---

[1] J. W. Gibbs, *Trans. Connecticut Academy of Arts and Sciences*, vol. ii. p. 382, 1871-73.

$$d\mathcal{F} = -\phi d\tau - pdv \quad . \quad . \quad . \quad . \quad (4)$$
$$d\mathcal{F}' = \tau d\phi + vdp \quad . \quad . \quad . \quad . \quad (5)$$
$$d\Phi = vdp - \phi d\tau \quad . \quad . \quad . \quad . \quad (6)$$

yields a surface which possesses properties characteristic of the sub stance, and which yields definite information as to its condition. Thus using (4), if v, τ, $\mathcal{F}$ be taken as co-ordinates, it follows that the entropy and pressure corresponding to any point are determined by the direction of the normal to the surface, and similarly in (5), when p, ϕ, $\mathcal{F}'$ are taken as co-ordinates, the direction of the normal determines τ and v, while in (6), with p, τ, Φ as co-ordinates, the volume and entropy are determined by the normal.

We are thus furnished with a considerable choice of surfaces, and that employed for any particular purpose can be selected to suit the problem in hand. Of course other surfaces may be constructed with any three functions of the quantities p, v, τ, ϕ, U as co-ordinates as may be found convenient.

359. Gibbs's Model.—The characteristic surface or thermo-dynamic model obtained by taking v, ϕ, U for co-ordinates has been carefully investigated by Gibbs.[1] It may be remarked at once that in constructing such a surface with regard to three mutually rectangular planes—viz. the plane of zero volume, the plane of zero entropy, and the plane of zero energy—that of zero volume alone is definite, while those of zero entropy and energy are arbitrary, for both of these quantities include an arbitrary constant. However, when the planes of reference are chosen, any point on this surface corresponds to a definite condition of the substance, and as the co-ordinates of the point represent the volume, entropy, and internal energy of the mass, it follows that any plane perpendicular to the axis of volume cuts the surface in a line of constant volume or iso-metric curve. Similarly the isentropics and isodynamics are the curves in which the surface is cut by planes perpendicular to the axes of entropy and energy respectively. Two systems of lines still remain for representation, viz. the isothermals and the isopiestics, and these can be very simply obtained from the conditions

$$\left(\frac{dU}{d\phi}\right)_v = \tau, \quad \left(\frac{dU}{dv}\right)_\phi = -p.$$

For if $U = f(v, \phi)$ be the equation of the surface, then if v be regarded as a constant, the relation between U and ϕ will be the equation of the isometric curve in which the surface is cut by a plane perpendicular to the axis of volume, and if a tangent line be drawn to this curve at

[1] J. W. Gibbs, *Trans. Connecticut Academy of Arts and Sciences*, vol. ii. p. 382, 1871-73.

any point, the trigonometrical tangent of the inclination of this line to the axis of entropy will be $\left(\dfrac{dU}{d\phi}\right)_v$. Hence if we refer to this as the *slope* of the curve at the point in question, we can say that the temperature at any point P (Fig. 234) is measured by the slope of the isometric passing through that point, and in the same way the pressure is measured by the slope of the isentropic.

The isothermal curves on the model are consequently such that if a tangent line be drawn to the surface at any point of one of them, and in such a direction that it is perpendicular to the axis of volume,

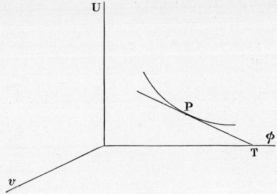

Fig. 234.

then the inclination of this line to the axis of entropy is the same at all points of the isothermal curve. The whole system of such tangent lines to any isothermal forms a system of lines, or a cylinder of rays, parallel to a line in the plane ϕU, and this cylinder obviously has ring-contact with the surface, the curve of contact being the isothermal curve. Hence we are led to Maxwell's [1] method of representing the isothermal curves on this surface, viz. place the model in the sunshine and turn it so that the sun's rays are parallel to the plane of entropy and energy, and make an angle with the axis of entropy whose tangent is proportional to the temperature. Then if we trace on the surface the boundary of light and shadow, the temperature at all points of this line will be the same.

The iso-thermals and iso-piestics.

Similarly the lines of constant pressure are found by drawing tangent lines to the surface in such a direction that they all are parallel to the plane of energy and volume, and make an angle with the axis of volume whose trigonometrical tangent measures the pressure. This system of parallel lines forms a cylinder whose line of contact with the surface is an isopiestic.

[1] J. C. Maxwell, *Theory of Heat.*

Of the various parts of a complete thermodynamic model one region consists of points which refer to the body when altogether in the solid state, another to the liquid condition, and a third to the gaseous. Besides these three parts of the surface, there are other tracts which refer to the body when it is changing state and exists as a mixture of the solid and liquid, or liquid and vapour, or solid and vapour, or finally as a mixture of the three states—solid, liquid, and vapour. We shall now consider the general character of these various parts, and for the sake of brevity we shall refer to those portions which represent the solid, liquid, and vapour as the parts S, L, and V of the surface respectively, while we shall refer to that portion which represents a mixture of solid and liquid as the part SL, to that which represents the mixture of liquid and vapour as LV, to that representing the solid and vapour as SV, and to that representing a mixture of all three states as SLV.

Every point on the part S represents a definite condition of the body when altogether in the solid state, and this portion is bounded partly by a line at every point of which fusion is about to occur, and partly by a line at each point of which the substance is about to sublime. The portion S may not, however, be completely enclosed by these lines, for if anything like continuity of state exists between the liquid and solid conditions, such as Andrews proved to exist between the liquid and gaseous, then the part S will be united to the part L of the surface by a neck or isthmus in which no discontinuity of curvature exists.

Similarly the portion L of the surface will be bounded partly by a line along which solidification is about to take place, and partly by a line at every point of which the substance is about to vaporise. These two lines do not completely enclose L, for in one region this part forms a continuation of the portion V which represents the condition of the substance when it is completely vaporised, in accordance with the experiments of Andrews. The part L is thus united to V by a neck of surface presenting no discontinuity, so that through this neck V may be regarded as a continuation of L, and it is probable that it is united to S by a similar neck, and that V is united to S in the same way.

The regions between S, L, and V are filled up by those parts of the surface (SL, LV, etc.) which represent the condition of the substance when changing state. The portion LV stretches from the fringe of L to the fringe of V, and its lines of junction with L and V are the lines already referred to, along one of which vaporisation is about to begin, and on the other of which it is completed. These two lines form what we call the LV *couple*, and along these lines the curvature of the surface suddenly changes so that they form lines of discontinuity of curvature on the surface regarded as a whole.   For the sake of distinction we may refer to these two lines as the L line and the V line respectively of the LV couple.   Similarly the part of the surface which applies to the change of state from solid to liquid is enclosed by a pair of lines, the SL couple, while the part representing sublimation is bounded by another pair, viz. the SV couple.

With this notation we can say that to any point A on the L line of the LV couple there is a corresponding point B on the V line of the same couple.   At A vaporisation under certain conditions is about to begin, and at B it is completed.   Now change of state takes place in such a way that the pressure and temperature remain the same throughout the operation, and consequently the plane which touches the part L of Gibbs's model at the point A also touches the part V at the point B, since the direction of this plane is determined by p and τ. Further, this plane touches the LV tract of the surface all along the line AB, for at every point of this line the pressure and temperature have the same values.   Thus, if a plane be drawn to touch L, and also to touch V, this plane will have line-contact with LV, and the line of contact AB (Fig. 235) will be such that any point P on it represents a definite mixture of the liquid and vapour, and the point P divides AB into segments such that P is the centre of gravity of the liquid portion of the mass placed at A and the gaseous portion placed at B.

As A moves along the L line of the LV couple B moves along the V line, and the line AB sweeps out the LV part of the surface.   This part of the surface is a portion of what is called a developable surface, and may be regarded as developed in the following manner.   Let a tangent plane be drawn to touch both L and V (this will be a double tangent plane), and let this plane roll on L and V, maintaining contact with both, then this plane as it passes through its consecutive positions will envelop a developable surface, viz. the surface LV.

Similar remarks apply to the tracts which represent the mixtures of solid and liquid and solid and vapour.   Each of these tracts (Fig. 235) is a developable surface, the tangent plane touches it along a line, and any point on one of them represents a definite mixture of two states in the manner already described.

Finally, there is a portion of the surface which possesses no curvature.   This portion is a plane triangle and corresponds to the triple point (Art. 349), or that condition in which the substance can exist simultaneously in the solid, liquid, and gaseous states.   For if a plane be drawn to touch S and also to touch L, then as this plane rolls

on S and L, it is possible that in one position it may also come into
contact with V.   In this position the three points of contact will form a
plane triangle SLV (Fig. 235) such that its vertices are points which
represent conditions of the substance, at one of which it is altogether
solid, at another liquid, and at the third vapour.   Any point on one
side of this triangle represents a definite mixture of solid and liquid,

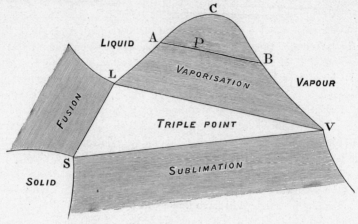

Fig. 235.

any point on another liquid and vapour, and any point on the third
solid and vapour, whereas any point within the triangle represents a
definite mixture of the three states, such that the point in question is
the centre of gravity of the masses of solid, liquid, and vapour placed
at the corresponding vertices of the triangle.

The plane of this triangle might be supposed to start rolling on
any pair of the parts S, L, V, so that if it begins to roll round a
certain side of the triangle it will generate the SL developable region,
starting round another edge it will develop the LV region, and round
the third the SV region.   However, as the two lines of the LV couple
approach each other and ultimately unite so as to form a continuous
curve (Andrews), it follows that as the tangent plane rolls on L and
V, the points of contact A and B approach each other and ultimately
coincide at a point C where the two lines of the LV couple unite.
The point C (Fig. 235) is the critical point for the fluid state, and if
the tangent plane be allowed to roll beyond this point it will touch
the surface in a single point.   The substance is here homogeneous and
belongs to the neck of continuity connecting L and V.

Similar remarks apply to the SL couple and the SV couple, and
if the lines of these couples unite so that each couple forms a con-

tinuous curve, then the points of junction are the critical points for the SL and SV conditions. Further, the vertices of the triangle formed by the points of contact of the triple tangent plane SLV are points at which the substance is all solid, all liquid, and all vapour respectively, and they are consequently points in which the lines of the three couples meet in pairs. Thus the S line of the SL couple and the S line of the SV couple intersect at one vertex, and the other corresponding pairs of lines intersect at the other vertices.

360. Surface of Stability.—When any thermodynamic model is constructed with three chosen co-ordinates, the values of any pair may be chosen arbitrarily, but when these are given the value of the third is completely determined. It may happen that for given values of two there may be more than one corresponding value of the third, but in this case the corresponding values of the third are perfectly definite. The points of any such surface consequently represent all conditions of the substance which are possible and consistent with equilibrium. To fix our ideas let us suppose that the quantities p, v, τ are taken as co-ordinates, then when values of p and v are chosen corresponding to any point in the plane pv we say that there is some value (or values) of τ corresponding to equilibrium, and by erecting a perpendicular to the plane pv at the point in question, and measuring off a length which represents this temperature, a definite point is obtained, which is a point on the surface of the model. Now when we say that to given values of p and v there is a corresponding value of τ, we merely state that there is a definite condition p, v, τ of the substance, in which it is in equilibrium, or that when the pressure and volume have values p and v then the temperature must have a certain value τ and no other. For given values of p and v and a varying value of τ the point p, v, τ is constrained to move along a right line perpendicular to the plane pv, and the point (or points) where this line meets the surface of the model is the point which represents the condition of equilibrium of the substance when its pressure is p and its volume v. If the substance were supposed to be in a state represented by any other point on this line equilibrium would not exist until the point moved to the surface.

The surface described in the preceding article, or a corresponding surface constructed with other co-ordinates, is such that the condition of the substance at every point of it is one of stable equilibrium, and it may be regarded as the surface of stability. If the condition of the substance be imagined to be represented by any point in the space inside or outside the surface, this condition will not be one of equi-

3 C

librium, or if the substance happened to exist in such a state the
equilibrium in this state would be unstable.   Such cases of unstable
equilibrium are presented in superheated globules of liquids and
supersaturated solutions of salts, or over-cooled liquids and vapours,
and the points representing them will not lie on the model we have
constructed, but will constitute a locus outside the surface of the
model similar to the theoretic part of the isothermal line conceived
by James Thomson (BMND, Fig. 149).   The substance at any
point of this line is in unstable equilibrium, and if disturbed will
rapidly change its condition till the indicator point reaches the line of
stability BD.   Thus we might imagine the portions S, L, V of the
thermodynamic model to be parts of one continuous surface so as to
be united, not by the developable sheets SL, LV, SV already described,
but by portions similar to the James Thomson part of the isothermal
BMND (Fig. 149).   These new tracts, together with the portions
S, L, V, constitute one continuous surface which exhibits no discontinuity of curvature along the line couples SL, LV, and SV ; but the
points of these tracts, although they represent conditions of equilibrium
which may be realised under certain circumstances, are nevertheless
states of unstable equilibrium.[1]

Thus the portions S, L, V of the model, together with the developable sheets SL, LV, and VS, represent all possible conditions of stable
equilibrium, from the very manner in which they are constructed, and
all other points of space represent conditions (a) in which change is
taking place, or (β) in which, if equilibrium exists, it is essentially
unstable.

In the case of an isolated body, or system, thermal and mechanical
equilibrium must always be established during any spontaneous changes
in such a way that the point representing the state of the system
moves in a plane perpendicular to the axis of energy, for since the
system is isolated its energy must remain constant (the term energy
here including all forms under which it appears in the system).
Hence if a body, or system, be left to itself—that is, if it neither
gives energy to nor receives energy from other bodies—then the path
described by the system in passing from one condition to another must
be an isodynamic line.   This line may lie on the surface of the model,

Isolated
system.

[1] The equilibrium of a system may be stable for very small disturbances and unstable for displacements of any considerable magnitude—that is, equilibrium may
exist and will not be broken by disturbances below a certain limit.   It is the existence of such a limit that renders possible the existence of those states which we term
unstable, such as superheated drops or supersaturated vapours, and it is probably
determined by such magnitudes as the size of a molecule and the distance through
which molecular forces are sensible.

or it may not, but if the initial and final conditions are states of equilibrium, the extremities of the line must be situated on the surface, whereas if the whole line lies on the surface every state passed through during the transformation is one of equilibrium, and the path is an *equilibrium path*.

Hence, as far as considerations of energy alone guide us, the system may pass of itself from any condition A to any other B, if A and B are on the same isodynamic line, but thermal equilibrium is always established by conduction of heat from the warmer to the colder parts of the system, and this entails an increase of entropy, so that the system cannot pass of itself from A to B, even though these points are on the same isodynamic line, unless the entropy at B is greater than the entropy at A. This consideration consequently determines the direction in which the transformation must take place, viz. in the direction of increasing entropy.

In reasoning about a system passing from one condition to another " of itself " we mean that during the transformation it is isolated from other systems, and consequently neither receives nor parts with energy. Now the whole energy of a system may be allocated under several heads, such as the *vis viva* of its constituent masses, the molecular energy which in part constitutes the sensible heat of the body, and the so-called potential energy which depends on its configuration, etc. The mode or portion of the whole energy with regard to these various constituents probably determines whether the condition of the system is one of equilibrium, and also whether the equilibrium is stable or unstable. Thus when a system is in stable equilibrium the energy is probably divided in such a way that an average is struck between kinetic and potential, as in the case of a vibrating elastic solid in which the energy is half kinetic and half potential. If, however, the energy happens to be distributed in any other manner so that the portion existing in one department is too small, while that in another is too great, as compared with this average, then the equilibrium, if it exists under such conditions, will be unstable. *Partition of the energy.*

Some such partition of the energy as this would appear to exist in those unstable conditions of superheated liquid globules, etc., which are represented by the James Thomson part of the isothermal (Fig. 149). Thus at a point M the temperature is too high for the conditions of pressure and volume under which the substance exists —that is, too large a share of the energy is apportioned to the sensible heat department, and the explosion of the globule to a condition on the line BD is merely the result of the redistribution of the energy in the average manner. Similarly at N the temperature is too low, and too small a portion of the energy exists as sensible heat.   At this point the vapour is over-cooled, and collapse takes place until the sensible heat has obtained its proper share.

According to this view, then, a condition of stable equilibrium of a substance is one in which the whole energy is divided into its several constituents in such a way that some average is struck in its partition, and all the states of stable equilibrium are represented by the surface of the model which consists of parts S, L, V, referring to the condition of the substance when homogeneous throughout, together with three developable tracts SL, LV, VS, and the plane triangle SLV, referring to conditions of heterogeneity in which the substance exists in two or three different states simultaneously.   On this surface there is a discontinuity of curvature where S, L, V join the developable sheets, but the surface may be made continuous if the energy is apportioned among its several constituents in a different manner.   The parts S, L, V can thus be joined by sheets SL, LV, VS, which form, with S, L, V, a continuous surface exhibiting no discontinuity of curvature, but the points of these new sheets correspond to a partition of energy which is inconsistent with stability.

In conclusion, we give the following example (after Gibbs) in illustration of the manner in which the model may be employed in the deduction of thermodynamic formulæ.   Let L and V (Fig. 236) be two corresponding points on the LV couple—at L the substance is entirely liquid, and at V it is all vapour, the change of state taking place along the line LV.   Through L and V draw planes perpendicular to the axes of volume and entropy respectively. These planes will meet in a line AB parallel to the axis of energy.   Further, let the tangent plane to the surface along the line LV be ALV, and let A'LV be the consecutive tangent plane.   Then if LB and VC be drawn perpendicular to AB, these lines will be parallel to the axes of ϕ and v respectively. But since p and τ are represented in the manner already described (p. 746), it follows that

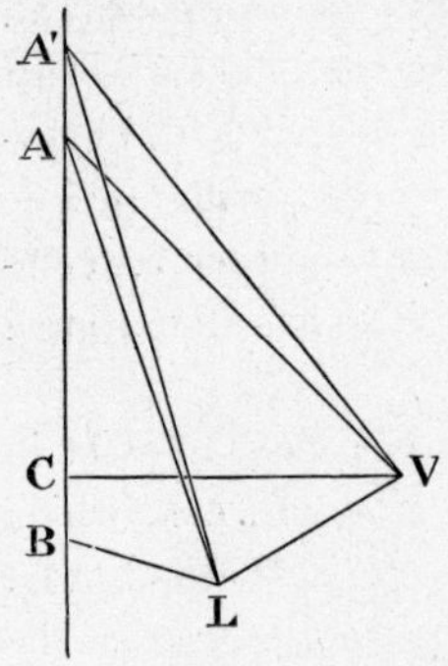

$$p = \frac{AC}{CV}, \quad \text{and} \quad \tau = \frac{AB}{BL},$$

therefore

$$dp = \frac{AA'}{CV}, \quad \text{and} \quad d\tau = \frac{AA'}{BL},$$

and consequently

$$\frac{dp}{d\tau} = \frac{BL}{CV} = \frac{\phi_2 - \phi_1}{v_2 - v_1}.$$

Fig. 236.

But $\phi_2 - \phi_1$ is the change of entropy, is passing from L to V, and is consequently equal to L/τ where L is the latent heat of vaporisation, so that we have the fundamental equation

$$\frac{dp}{d\tau} = \frac{L}{\tau(v_2 - v_1)}.$$

SECTION VIII

ON THE ABSOLUTE SCALE OF TEMPERATURE

361. Introduction.—The idea of an absolute scale of temperature, independent of the properties of any particular substance, has been briefly introduced in Art. 329, and this scale must be carefully distinguished from any other founded arbitrarily on the effects of heat on a property of some particular substance chosen for the sake of convenience. In the scale of temperature proposed in Art. 17, equal differences of temperature are measured by equal increments of volume of a fluid enclosed in a glass measuring-flask, and the number representing the temperature of a body on such an instrument will depend on the nature of the particular fluid employed. Each fluid will furnish a scale possessing a zero determined by the minimum volume of the fluid, and the scales furnished by different instruments will agree neither in their zero nor throughout their length. For this reason some particular substance had to be chosen for the construction of a standard thermometer, and for this purpose a permanent gas was found to possess special advantages.

On the other hand, the system of thermometry, proposed by Lord Kelvin from thermodynamic considerations (Art. 329), is independent of the properties of any substance (and in this sense *absolute*), and we have seen that if we possessed a substance which rigorously obeyed the laws of a perfect gas,[1] then a thermometer constructed with this substance so as to measure equal changes of temperature by equal changes of volume under constant pressure, or by equal changes of pressure at constant volume, would give a scale such that the ratio of any two temperatures on it (measured from the zero of the instrument) is equal to the ratio of the quantities of heat taken in and ejected by a perfect thermodynamic engine working between these limits of temperature. Consequently, if we possessed a substance which behaved

---

[1] That is Boyle's law, and has R constant and γ constant, or the two specific heats constant.

as a so-called perfect gas even for some limited range of temperature, then by constructing a thermometer with this substance and graduating it within this range into degrees of any arbitrary length, the scale could be extended in both directions outside this range, and the position of the absolute zero of temperature could be determined.

Thus if air obeyed the gaseous laws rigorously between the freezing point and the boiling point of water, and if this interval of temperature be represented by 100, and if a be the expansion for $1°$, then the absolute temperature of the freezing point would be $1/a$, and that of the boiling point $100 + 1/a$. But since air obeys the gaseous laws only approximately between these limits, the position of the absolute zero determined from the expansion of air in this manner is only approximate, and its true position can be determined only by observing the manner in which air deviates from these laws. When this has been determined, the corresponding correction can be applied to the previous approximate scale of the air thermometer, and the instrument may be graduated according to the absolute scale.

362. First Example.[1]—Before proceeding to the description of the experiments by which Lord Kelvin and Joule determined this correction and reduced the indications of the air thermometer to the absolute scale, it may be advantageous to mention some general methods by which the absolute temperature τ may be deduced in terms of quantities which are capable of being determined without the aid of any previously constructed scale of temperature. For this purpose it is evident that if we possess any thermodynamic relation or any equation involving τ and other quantities which can be expressed in terms of p and v, then each such relation furnishes a means of estimating τ when the other quantities are known.

Thus, for example, if we take the equation of Art. 346, viz.—

$$\frac{d\tau}{\tau} = \frac{v_2 - v_1}{L} dp,$$

in which v_1 and v_2 are expressible in terms of p, and where L is a quantity of heat expressed in dynamical units, and requires for its estimation no previously constructed scale of temperature, we see that τ is here expressed in terms of quantities which are capable of measurement, and which are independent of all methods of reckoning temperature. Integrating this equation we obtain

$$\log \frac{\tau}{\tau_0} = \int_{p_0}^{p} \frac{v_2 - v_1}{L} dp.$$

---

[1] See Lord Kelvin's article "Heat," *Ency. Brit.*, 9th edition.

This furnishes the absolute temperature corresponding to any pressure (v_1, v_2, and L being expressible in terms of p) of the mixture of liquid and saturated vapour, and the same pressure will correspond to some determinate temperature on the centigrade scale, or any other scale, and a comparison of the absolute scale with any other may be effected.

In no case, however, has the specific volume of a saturated vapour been determined with sufficient accuracy to admit of the graduation of a steam thermometer (Art. 93) in this manner, and the foregoing equation has been employed so far rather for the calculation of saturated vapour densities than as the basis of a system of absolute thermometry, and until the necessary experimental data have been obtained with much greater accuracy, the steam thermometer cannot compete with any permanent gas thermometer in furnishing an approximate estimation of temperature on the absolute scale.[1]

In the same manner we might have employed for the expression of τ any one of the thermodynamic relations of Art. 344, or any other equation involving τ, and quantities which can be measured without reference to a scale of temperature. The foregoing is the case of the steam thermometer, and the substance exists simultaneously in two distinct states. When the state is uniform, the second thermodynamic relation may be applied, and the latent heat of isothermal expansion replaces the latent heat of change of state.

363. Second Example.—As a further illustration we may show how the absolute scale may be experimentally established by calorimetric observations on a gas combined with measurements of pressure and volume, but without using any measurement of temperature. Suppose that we are able, with sufficient accuracy, to make observations of—

(1) The quantity of heat required, in work units, to produce a given change of pressure when the volume is kept constant.

(2) The quantity of heat required, in work units, to produce a given change of pressure (or volume) when the temperature is kept constant.

(3) The relation between pressure and volume when the temperature is kept constant.

It is to be borne in mind that in carrying out (2) and (3) thermometers may be used to ensure constancy of temperature, since no scale

---

[1] It would be possible to modify the method here described in such a way as to avoid the necessity for knowing the latent heat or the specific volume of the saturated vapour or Joule's equivalent, and thus render the results' precise (see *Phil. Mag.* vol. vi. p. 318, 1928).

of temperature is required for this. The experiments required for (3) are those which have already been made by Amagat and others (Art. 248), but each isothermal is supposed to be defined, not by its temperature, but by the pressure corresponding to some given volume.

Now, if γ is the ratio of the specific heats at constant pressure and volume respectively, we have by Ex. 26, p. 713,

$$\gamma - 1 = \left(-\frac{dQ}{dp} \right)_\tau \div \left(\frac{dQ}{dp} \right)_v,$$

and therefore we can find γ from observations (1) and (2). But since $\gamma = E_\phi \div E_\tau$ (Ex. 2, p. 707), we have also

$$\left(\frac{dp}{dv} \right)_\phi = \gamma \left(\frac{dp}{dv} \right)_\tau,$$

and since $\left(\frac{dp}{dv} \right)_\tau$ is known from observations (3), we can find the value of $\left(\frac{dp}{dv} \right)_\phi$ for any given values of p and v, i.e. we can find the direction of the adiabatic curve at any point of the p-v diagram. If now in

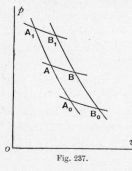

Fig. 237.

this way we plot any two adiabatics A_0A_1, B_0B_1 (Fig. 237), and also use observations (3) to plot a number of isothermals A_0B_0, AB, A_1B_1, etc., two of which, say A_0B_0 and A_1B_1, correspond to the temperatures of the normal freezing and boiling points τ_0 and τ_1, then we shall know from observations (2) the quantities of heat Q_0, Q, Q_1, etc. (in work units), required to cause unit mass of the gas to undergo the isothermal transformations A_0B_0, AB, A_1B_1, etc.

Then we have (Art. 327)

$$\frac{Q_1}{Q_0} = \frac{\tau_1}{\tau_0},$$

hence

$$\frac{\tau_1 - \tau_0}{\tau_0} = \frac{Q_1 - Q_0}{Q_0};$$

but $\tau_1 - \tau_0 = 100$, by definition, therefore

$$\tau_0 = \frac{100 Q_0}{Q_1 - Q_0},$$

which gives us the temperature τ_0 of the normal freezing point on the absolute scale. Then the temperature τ corresponding to any other isothermal AB is given by the equation

$$\tau = \tau_0 \frac{Q}{Q_0}.$$

The best gas to use for this purpose would be a monatomic gas such as argon or helium, for which $\gamma - 1$ is comparatively large, but as gas calorimetry is not susceptible of a high degree of accuracy, the method here outlined possesses only a theoretical interest.

Lord Kelvin seems to have come to the conclusion that the most promising course would be to use some method which avoids calorimetric measurements as much as possible, and he adopted that described in the following article. This method requires a knowledge of the specific heat of a gas, but the specific heat enters into the equations in such a way that a small error in its estimation would not appreciably affect the accuracy of the calculations.

364. The Porous Plug Experiment. — The investigation proposed by Lord Kelvin for the graduation of the constant-pressure air thermometer depends in principle on the determination of the heating or cooling effect produced in a fluid when forced through a porous plug or small orifice. When a fluid is forced through a small orifice the issuing jet possesses a certain *vis viva* which gradually subsides at some

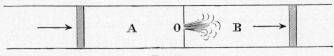

Fig. 238.

distance from the orifice, and is converted into heat through fluid friction. Thus if Fig. 238 represents a tube stopped at one part of its length by a diaphragm pierced by a small orifice O, and if a fluid be forced through this orifice from the side A to the side B by a piston M, which is urged forward by a pressure p, and if the fluid, as it escapes into B, pushes another piston N before it with a pressure p' ; then if M and N move with the same velocity,[1] the kinetic energy of translation of the fluid moving towards A will be the same as that moving away from it when we consider regions removed some distance from the aperture. Near the orifice, however, in the region of the rapids, the *vis viva* of the escaping jet has not subsided, and a large part of the internal energy of the fluid exists as this *vis viva* of the mass. It might reasonably be expected, therefore, that near the orifice the temperature of the fluid would be decidedly lower than at some distance from the orifice where the *vis viva* of the issuing jet has subsided and has been converted into heat.

In an experiment made with a thermometer held near an orifice through which air was escaping under a pressure of about 8 atmos.,

----

[1] In the case of compressible fluids, this can be arranged by making the diameter of the tube on the side B larger than that on the side A.

Joule and Thomson found a depression of temperature amounting to 13°·42 C. At a distance from the orifice, however, in the region of the tube where the motion has subsided into a uniform flow, the temperature of the stream on the side B may be either higher or lower than that on the side A, according to the nature of the escaping fluid.

Thus if U be the internal energy per unit mass on the side A, and p and v the pressure and volume, while U′, p', v' refer to the side B, then the decrease of internal energy is U – U′, and if no heat is supplied from without during the operation, $i.e.$ if the tube and pistons are non-conductors, then U – U′ must be equal to the work done by the fluid. Now in the compartment B the work done by unit mass of the fluid in pushing forward the piston N is $p'v'$, and similarly, on the other side, the work done on the fluid per unit mass by the piston M is pv. Consequently we have

$$U - U' = p'v' - pv,$$

that is

$$U + pv = U' + p'v'$$

or the quantity U + pv is the same before and after transit. Consequently if the product pv has not changed we must have U = U′, and if the internal energy depends only on the temperature, then the temperature of the stream leaving the diaphragm will be the same as that approaching it. Hence if the temperature is found to be the same on both sides, and if the fluid obeys Boyle's law, it follows that U = U′, even though the pressure and specific volume vary, and hence the internal energy must be a function of the temperature only. But if the temperature changes in passing from one side to the other, then it follows that U must depend on p and v as well as on the temperature ; or, in other words, Mayer's hypothesis (p. 276) will not be true. We have here, then, a test of the applicability of this hypothesis to the permanent gases which is very much more delicate than the calorimetric method adopted by Joule as explained in Art. 159. We must, however, give due allowance for deviations from Boyle's law, and the foregoing remarks are made on the supposition that this law is obeyed.[1]

[1] It is a fact of observation that those gases which most nearly obey Boyle's law exhibit the least change of temperature in the porous plug experiment. But we cannot infer from this that Mayer's hypothesis implies Boyle's law. Van der Waals's equation suggests that deviations from Boyle's law are due to two causes, the actual size of the molecules and their mutual attraction. If the temperature of a gas is determined only by the mean kinetic energy of the molecules, then Mayer's hypothesis would be true if the mutual attraction were zero, though Boyle's law would not. In this case we should expect a heating effect in the porous plug experiment.

In the experiments conducted by Joule and Lord Kelvin [1] the gas under examination was passed at a slow uniform rate through a long copper spiral tube immersed in a bath which was constantly stirred and kept at a uniform temperature.   To the upright end, *aa* (Fig. 239), of this copper pipe a short tube of boxwood, *bb*, was secured, and in this boxwood piece a plug of cotton-wool (or filaments of silk when high pressures were used) was fixed by means of two perforated brass plates shown as dotted lines at the extremities of the plug.   This plug was 2·72 inches long and 1·5 inch diameter.   A tin can, *d*, filled with cotton-wool, was attached to the brass casting *aa*, and served to keep the water of the bath from coming in contact with the boxwood piece enclosing the plug.   A ther-mometer was placed in the exit tube, with its bulb at a short dis-tance above the plug, and in order to permit of the reading of the temperature this part of the tube (*ee*) was made of glass.

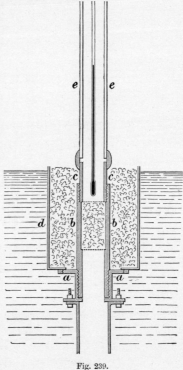

Among the difficulties met with during this investigation was the fluctuation of temperature which occurred when the stop-cock was opened in order to allow the gas to flow through the tube.   This arose from the initial adiabatic expansion of the gas and the compression of the air in the tube, and although this disturbance soon ceased on account of the stream of gas being in con-tact with the good-conducting copper spiral, still further fluctuations were produced by its contact with the surface of the badly-conducting boxwood piece enclosing the plug.

Fig. 239.

This effect lasted for a much longer time, and it was necessary to allow the stream to flow through the plug for a considerable period (one hour before the result could be depended on) before any observations were recorded.   The cooling effect was, besides, exaggerated at first on account of the necessary drying of the material of the plug by the

[1] *Phil. Mag.*, 4th series, vol. iv., 1852 ; *Phil. Trans.*, 1853, 1854, 1862 ; Joule's *Scientific Papers*, vol. ii.

current of gas, and oscillations of temperature were caused by the intermittent action of the pump (causing adiabatic expansion or compression),
so that it was very necessary to secure as uniform a flow as possible.
Further, after passing through the plug, if there is any change of

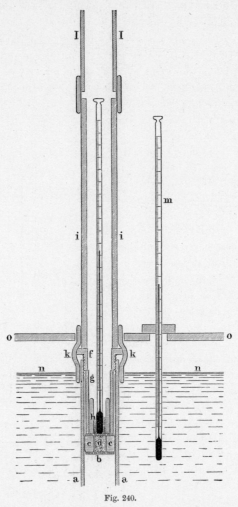

Fig. 240.

temperature there will be conduction of heat through the walls of the
tube, and a correction in this respect becomes necessary. This correction was determined by an experiment in which the difference of
temperature between the gas and the bath was large, and it was found
to be directly proportional to the difference of temperature, and inversely proportional to the quantity of gas transmitted in a given time.

In the experiments at high temperatures, however, it was found necessary to increase the length of the copper spiral in order to make certain that the gas acquired the temperature of the bath. With air and carbon dioxide, which could be obtained in large quantities, the delay occasioned by the initial fluctuations of temperature caused no serious difficulty, and the nozzle depicted in Fig. 239 was considered the best. In the case of hydrogen, which could be obtained only in a limited supply, the nozzle was altered as shown in Fig. 240. The plug d was enclosed in a short piece of india-rubber tubing, and a cork tube, h, was placed within the copper tubing, in order to protect the bulb of the thermometer from the effects of a too rapid conduction of heat from the bath, and cotton-wool was loosely packed round the bulb so as to distribute the current of gas as evenly as possible. The top of the glass tube ii was attached to a metallic tube II, which carried the gas to a reservoir in which it was preserved.

In the case of all the gases examined a thermal effect was experienced after passing through the plug, and this in the case of air, oxygen, and carbon dioxide was a cooling effect. Each of these gases showed a temperature sensibly lower than the bath after passing through the plug; but in the case of hydrogen, although the first experiments appeared to give a cooling effect, a later and more accurate investigation proved that the temperature of the stream issuing from the plug was higher than that of the bath. With this gas there was therefore a heating effect, so that it stands out from the others in this respect also, as it does in regard to deviations from Boyle's law. A heating effect would be expected from this gas on account of the manner in which it deviates from Boyle's law, but that this effect should more than counterbalance the cooling which must arise from residual molecular attraction, if any, or as to whether in hydrogen this latter effect should be a heating rather than a cooling, could not be predicted *a priori*.

The thermal effect in all cases was found to be proportional to the difference of pressure on the two sides of the plug, even for differences of 5 or 6 atmos., and in the case of hydrogen it amounted to a heating of $0°·039$ C. per atmosphere difference of pressure on the two sides. The law of variation of the effect with temperature was not fully determined in this case, and the foregoing number is taken as the mean of the heating effects at temperatures between $0°$ and $100°$ C.

$\delta\theta$ proportional to δp.

We shall now consider how this result may be applied to the graduation of a hydrogen thermometer according to the absolute scale. For this purpose we must base the investigation on the condition which controls the experiment, viz. that the quantity $U + pv$ remains unaltered.   Now the general equation $\tau\delta\phi = \delta U + p\delta v$ may be written in the form

$$\delta(U + pv) = \tau\delta\phi + v\delta p \quad . \quad . \quad . \quad . \quad . \quad (1)$$

and consequently, since $U + pv$ does not vary, we must have

$$\tau\delta\phi + v\delta p = 0 \quad . \quad . \quad . \quad . \quad . \quad (2)$$

and if p and θ (the temperature registered by an ordinary centigrade thermometer) be taken as independent variables this becomes

$$\tau\left(\frac{d\phi}{d\theta}\delta\theta + \frac{d\phi}{dp}\delta p\right) + v\delta p = 0 \quad . \quad . \quad . \quad . \quad (3)$$

But by the fourth thermodynamic relation

$$\left(\frac{d\phi}{dp}\right)_\theta = -\left(\frac{dv}{d\tau}\right)_p,$$

therefore (3) becomes

$$\tau\left(\frac{d\phi}{d\theta}\right)_p \delta\theta - \tau\left(\frac{dv}{d\tau}\right)_p \delta p + v\delta p = 0,$$

or

$$\tau\frac{dv}{d\tau} - v = \tau\frac{d\phi}{d\theta}\frac{\delta\theta}{\delta p} ;$$

now [1] in this equation

$$\tau\frac{d\phi}{d\theta} = \left(\frac{dQ}{d\theta}\right)_p = C_p,$$

therefore

$$\tau\frac{dv}{d\tau} - v = C_p\frac{\delta\theta}{\delta p} \quad . \quad . \quad . \quad . \quad . \quad (4)$$

Here C_p is measured in dynamical units as a quantity of work, and its measurement does not necessarily involve the idea of a scale of temperature, being merely the quantity of work required to be spent in raising a unit mass of the gas through a range indicated by two marks on a thermoscope, which if desirable might be taken as the interval of temperature between the freezing point and boiling point of water.   Further, $\delta\theta/\delta p$ is the cooling (or heating) effect per unit difference of pressure on the two sides of the plug, and $\delta\theta$ may be measured in terms of the same interval of temperature as unit.   Thus we now require an interval of temperature in terms of which the absolute temperature is to be expressed, and in the preceding investigation this is represented by a degree on the ordinary centigrade scale. Now for hydrogen $\delta\theta$ was found proportional to δp, and for one atmo-

---

[1] If there is neither heating nor cooling $\delta\theta$ is zero, and we have

$$\frac{d\tau}{\tau} = \frac{dv}{v},$$

so that

$$\log\tau = \log v + C$$

where C is a function of p alone.   Consequently the characteristic equation of the substance is of the form $\tau = vf(p).$

sphere difference of pressure Π we have $\delta p = -\Pi$ and $\delta\theta = 0\cdot039$, therefore

$$\frac{\delta\theta}{\delta p} = -\frac{0\cdot039}{\Pi},$$

and the equation becomes

$$\tau\frac{dv}{d\tau} - v = -\frac{0\cdot039}{\Pi}C_p,$$

or

$$\frac{d\tau}{\tau} = \frac{dv}{v - 0\cdot039C_p/\Pi} \qquad \cdots \qquad (5)$$

Consequently, if we assume C_p to be constant within the range of the experiment (and its variation is undoubtedly very small), so that the effect of this variation is negligible in the small term in which C_p appears, we have by integration

$$\log \tau = \log (v - 0\cdot039C_p/\Pi) + \text{const.},$$

or

$$\tau = a(v - 0\cdot039C_p/\Pi) \qquad \cdots \qquad (6)$$

where a is an arbitrary constant which depends upon the unit of temperature adopted.

If τ_0 and v_0 correspond to the freezing point of water, while τ_{100} and v_{100} correspond to the boiling point, and if this interval of temperature be represented by 100, as on the centigrade scale, then (6) gives

$$\frac{\tau_0}{\tau_{100} - \tau_0} = \frac{\tau_0}{100} = \frac{v_0 - 0\cdot039C_p/\Pi}{v_{100} - v_0},$$

or

$$\tau_0 = \frac{100}{a}(1 - 0\cdot039C_p/\Pi v_0) \qquad \cdots \qquad (7)$$

where a is the expansion of unit volume of hydrogen between the freezing and the boiling points of water.

Now v_0 is the volume of unit mass at the freezing point under the pressure p, and if V_0 be the volume per unit mass under the pressure of one atmosphere Π, then (7) may be written in the form

$$\tau_0 = \frac{100}{a}\left(1 - \frac{V_0}{v_0}\cdot039C_p/\Pi V_0\right).$$

Now, Regnault found that the quantity $C_p/\Pi V_0$ for hydrogen agrees with that for air to $\frac{1}{2}$ per cent, and for air he found ΠV_0 (height of homogeneous atmosphere) $= 7990$, whereas the specific heat expressed in thermal units is $0\cdot238$. Hence if we take the number 427 for J the equation may be written in the form

$$\tau_0 = \frac{100}{a}\left(1 + c\frac{V_0}{v_0}\right),$$

where for hydrogen $c = -\cdot00049$, and for this gas expanding under a constant pressure of one atmosphere $a = \cdot36613$, which gives $100/a = 273\cdot13$, therefore with $v_0 = V_0$ we find

$$\tau_0 = 273.$$

The temperature of melting ice is consequently $273°$ on the absolute scale when the interval between the freezing point and the boiling point of water is denoted by 100.

Numbers agreeing very closely with this were deduced from the experiments on air, and a fairly concordant figure was obtained from those on carbon dioxide. For each of these gases the thermal effect was a lowering of temperature, which in the case of carbon dioxide was very decided. This cooling effect was also found to be sensibly independent of the pressure, but to vary considerably with temperature, and this variation was found to be very approximately as the inverse square of the quantity $273 + \theta$ where θ is the temperature centigrade on the mercury thermometer; and consequently it will be sufficiently accurate to write in the small term in the denominator of (5) the cooling effect per atmosphere in the form

$$A\left(\frac{273}{\tau}\right)^2,$$

and we then have

$$\frac{\delta\theta}{\delta p} = \frac{A}{\Pi}\left(\frac{\tau_0}{\tau}\right)^2,$$

where $\tau_0 = 273$. The value of A for air was found to be $0\cdot275$, and for carbon dioxide $1\cdot388$.

Returning to equation (4) we have

$$\tau\frac{dv}{d\tau} - v = C_p\frac{\delta\theta}{\delta p} = \frac{C_p A}{\Pi}\left(\frac{\tau_0}{\tau}\right)^2;$$

that is

$$\frac{d}{d\tau}\left(\frac{v}{\tau}\right) = \frac{C_p A}{\Pi}\frac{\tau_0^2}{\tau^4},$$

consequently

$$\frac{v}{\tau} - \frac{v_0}{\tau_0} = \int_{\tau_0}^{\tau}\frac{C_p A}{\Pi}\frac{\tau_0^2 d\tau}{\tau^4};$$

and therefore, if we regard C_p as constant, we have

$$\frac{v}{\tau} - \frac{v_0}{\tau_0} = -\frac{C_p A \tau_0^2}{3\Pi}\left(\frac{1}{\tau^3} - \frac{1}{\tau_0^3}\right);$$

consequently we deduce at once

$$\frac{v - v_0}{v_0} = \frac{\tau - \tau_0}{\tau_0}\left\{1 + \tfrac{1}{3}A\frac{C_p}{\Pi v_0}\left(1 + \frac{\tau_0}{\tau} + \frac{\tau_0^2}{\tau^2}\right)\right\},$$

or if the interval $\tau - \tau_0$ be reckoned 100, then a denoting the expansion of unit volume between the freezing point and the boiling point of water, we have

$$\tau_0 = \frac{100}{a}\left(1 + c\frac{V_0}{v_0}\right),$$

where

$$c = \frac{C_p}{\Pi V_0}\tfrac{1}{3}A\left\{1 + \frac{\tau_0}{\tau_0 + 100} + \frac{\tau_0^2}{(\tau_0 + 100)^2}\right\} = \frac{C_p}{\Pi V_0} \times \cdot 756A \,;$$

and the latter factor differs so little from

$$\tfrac{1}{2}\left\{1 + \frac{1}{(1\cdot3663)^2}\right\}A = \cdot769A,$$

the mean of the cooling effects at $0°$ and $100°$ C., that if this mean had been used, as was done in the case of hydrogen in absence of anything better, the effect on the result would be scarcely perceptible.

Regnault found $C_p/\Pi V_0$ greater for carbon dioxide than for air in the ratio $1\cdot39$ to 1 for the average of temperatures between $0°$ and $210°$, but he also found that the specific heat of this gas varies largely with temperature, and taking the mean of its value at $0°$ C. and $100°$ C. as the proper mean in this investigation, we find that $C_p/\Pi V_0$ for this gas is $1\cdot29$ times the value of this quantity for air. This latter we have already found to be $\cdot0126$. Hence in the formula

$$\tau_0 = \frac{100}{a}\left(1 + c\frac{V_0}{v_0}\right)$$

the quantity c has the value $- \cdot00049$ for hydrogen, $+ \cdot0026$ for air, and $+ \cdot0163$ for carbonic acid. The following table of results is extracted from Lord Kelvin's article :—

Name of Gas.	Expansion at One Atmo. between Freezing and Boiling Points, Regnault, a.	Proper Mean Cooling Effect per Atmo., M.	Uncorrected Estimate of Temperature of Melting Ice, $100/a$.	Correction calculated from Cooling Effect, $\frac{100}{a}\frac{C_p}{\Pi V_0}$M.	Absolute Temperature of Melting Ice, τ_0.
Hydrogen	$\cdot36613$	$-0°\cdot039$	$273\cdot13$	$-0°\cdot13$	273
Air	$\cdot36706$	$+0°\cdot208$	$272\cdot44$	$+0°\cdot70$	$273\cdot14$
Carbonic acid . . .	$\cdot37100$	$+1°\cdot005$	$269\cdot5$	$+4°\cdot4$	$273\cdot9$

As the experiments on air were more trustworthy than those on hydrogen, the number $273\cdot14$ obtained from them was regarded as the most reliable approximation to the absolute temperature of melting ice.

The following method[1] of calculating the absolute temperature from the observations seems more satisfactory. The equation for the cooling effect is

---

[1] *The Principles of Thermodynamics*, by G. Birtwistle, p. 82, 2nd ed., 1927.

$$C_p \frac{d\tau}{dp} = \tau \left(\frac{dv}{d\tau}\right)_p - v,$$

where C_p is the true specific heat at constant pressure based on the absolute scale. Let θ be the temperature as given by the uncorrected air (or gas) thermometer, and C_p' the corresponding specific heat at constant pressure. Then

$$C_p = \frac{dQ}{d\tau}, \ C_p' = \frac{dQ}{d\theta}, \ \therefore \ C_p = C_p' \frac{d\theta}{d\tau}.$$

The equation for the cooling effect becomes

$$C_p' \frac{d\theta}{d\tau} \left(\frac{d\tau}{d} \cdot \frac{d\theta}{dp}\right) = \tau \left(\frac{dv}{d\theta}\right)_p \frac{d\theta}{d\tau} - v,$$

or

$$C_p' \frac{d\theta}{dp} + v = \tau \left(\frac{dv}{d\theta}\right)_p \frac{d\theta}{d\tau};$$

therefore

$$\int \frac{d\tau}{\tau} = \int \left\{ \left(\frac{dv}{d\theta}\right)_p d\theta \right\} \Big/ \left\{ C_p' \frac{d\theta}{dp} + v \right\};$$

therefore

$$\log \frac{\tau_{100}}{\tau_0} = \int_{\theta_0}^{\theta_{100}} \left\{ \left(\frac{dv}{d\theta}\right)_p d\theta \right\} \Big/ \left\{ C_p' \frac{d\theta}{dp} + v \right\};$$

whence $\frac{\tau_{100}}{\tau_0}$ is obtained by plotting the values of the integrand on the left from observations based on the air or gas thermometer, and finding the integral as an area. Combining this result with $\tau_{100} - \tau_0 = 100$, we deduce the value of τ_0. By similarly integrating from θ_0 to any temperature θ, we may find the corresponding absolute temperature τ.

Mixtures.   The cooling effect was also investigated in the case of mixtures of different gases, and it was found that the cooling of the mixture on passing through the plug was not the corresponding mean of the cooling effects of the constituent gases. Thus oxygen and nitrogen taken separately showed almost the same deviations from the condition of a perfect gas, the deviation of nitrogen being slightly less than that of oxygen ; but a mixture of oxygen and nitrogen appeared to deviate less than nitrogen. In the same way a mixture of carbon dioxide and air would be expected to show a smaller cooling effect than pure carbon dioxide, and a larger cooling effect than air. This was found to be the case, but the cooling effect of the mixture was not that which would take place if each constituent produced its own proportion of the effect independently of the other. This evidently points to some intermolecular action between the constituents of the mixture, or to diffusion effects in passing through the plug.

365. Later Experiments and Calculations.—The porous plug experiment for air was repeated by Hoxton [1] and also by Eumorfopoulos and Rai.[2] A possible source of uncertainty in the original form of apparatus used by Joule and Thomson is that the

[1] *Phys. Review*, vol. xiii. p. 438, 1919.
[2] *Phil. Mag.* vol. ii. p. 961, 1926.

plug itself is at a lower temperature than either the entering or issuing gas, because the gas possesses kinetic energy which is afterwards converted into heat. The plug, therefore, tends to gain heat from its walls. To avoid this effect as much as possible, Hoxton used a plug in which the flow was radial,[1] that is, he used a porous cylindrical vessel, closed at one end (a porcelain filter), and forced the air to flow inward through the walls into the vessel, whence it issued from the open end. The air, after being freed from carbon dioxide and moisture, was passed through an oil thermostat, and then through the plug, which was also enclosed in the thermostat. The bath temperature was varied between 15° and 90° C., and the mean pressure between 4·5 and 6·4 metres of mercury. The temperature-drop was measured by platinum resistance thermometers differentially connected. Hoxton found that the cooling effect could be represented by the equation

$$\frac{\delta\theta}{\delta p} = -0\cdot2599 + 182\cdot0\left(\frac{1}{\tau}\right) - 552\cdot4\left(\frac{p}{\tau^2}\right),$$

where τ is absolute temperature, and p the pressure in metres of mercury. The result obtained for the absolute zero was $-273°\cdot36$, which is lower than any other estimates.

Eumorfopoulos and Rai used a porous plug of alundum. They found that for air the cooling effect was given by the equations

$$\frac{\delta\theta}{\delta p} = 0\cdot2492(P_2 - P_1) - 0\cdot00128(P_2^2 - P_1^2) \quad \text{(at 20° C.)}$$

and

$$\frac{\delta\theta}{\delta p} = 0\cdot1453(P_2 - P_1) - 0\cdot00095(P_2^2 - P_1^2) \quad \text{(at 100° C.)},$$

where P_2 and P_1 are the pressures (in atmospheres) of the entering and issuing air.

The exact position of the absolute zero on the centigrade thermodynamic scale is still in doubt to the extent of about $0°\cdot1$. Berthelot[2] in 1903 obtained the figure $-273°\cdot13$ from calculations based on Joule and Thomson's experiments, and in 1907 various figures ranging from $-273°\cdot04$ to $-273°\cdot10$ based on Chappuis' observations on the pressure coefficients of hydrogen and nitrogen between 0° and 100°, combined with the slopes of the pv diagrams at 0° and 100°. By a similar method Onnes and Clay[3] found the value $-273°\cdot08$, which was afterwards corrected to $-273°\cdot10$.

Absolute zero.

---

[1] The radial flow method was first suggested by Regnault (*Relation des expériences*, iii. p. 700).

[2] *Travaux et Mémoires du Bureau Int. des Poids et Mesures*, vol. xiii., 1907.

[3] *Proc. R. Acad. of Amsterdam*, vol. x. p. 589.

Henning and Heuse [1] also, from observations of pressure coefficients, found the value $-273°\cdot20$. Buckingham obtained $-273°\cdot13$ by calculations based on Joule and Thomson's experiments; and Keyes,[2] using his own equation of state and the results of Amagat's experiments, obtained $-273°\cdot135$.

Correction of gas thermometer. Numerous calculations have been made of the corrections to be applied to the gas thermometer to reduce the readings to the thermodynamic scale. The following table is given by Buckingham [3] of the thermodynamic correction to the constant pressure nitrogen scale according to various authors :—

Degrees, N-scale C.	Rose-Innes 1901.	Callendar 1903.	Berthelot 1903.	Buckingham 1907.	Mean of Foregoing.
10	0·0120	0·0109	0·010	0·0078	0·010
20	0·0205	0·0188	0·017	0·0137	0·017
30	0·0261	0·0236	0·022	0·0179	0·022
40	0·0288	0·0260	0·024	0·0203	0·025
50	0·0289	0·0260	0·024	0·0209	0·025
60	0·0269	0·0240	0·022	0·0198	0·023
70	0·0228	0·0204	0·019	0·0172	0·020
80	0·0168	0·0151	0·014	0·0129	0·015
90	0·0092	0·0081	0·007	0·0071	0·008

366. Temperature of Inversion of the Cooling Effect.—The experiments of Joule and Lord Kelvin show that the cooling effect diminishes with rise of temperature. It would naturally then be expected that at a certain temperature the effect would vanish, and above this temperature the gas would be warmed after passing through the porous plug. This is found to be actually the case. For air the temperature at which the cooling effect vanishes appears to be somewhat below 100° C. In the case of hydrogen it is far below the freezing point. Thus hydrogen no longer occupies an anomalous position in this respect; it differs from other gases merely in possessing a lower temperature of inversion. At a sufficiently low temperature hydrogen also is cooled by free expansion (Art. 240).

The temperature of inversion of the Joule-Kelvin effect for hydrogen has been experimentally determined by Olszewski.[4] The

---

[1] *Zeit. für Physik*, vol. v. p. 285, 1921.

[2] *Journ. Amer. Chem. Soc.* vol. xliii. p. 1452, 1921.

[3] *Phil. Mag.* vol. xv. p. 526, 1908. The method of applying the corrections adopted by Callendar is described in the 2nd and 3rd editions of this book, and was taken from an article in *Phil. Mag.*, Jan. 1903.

[4] See *Nature*, vol. lxv. p. 576, 1902. As the pressure of the gas after expansion was 1 atmo., Olszewski only found the mean cooling effect over a wide range of pressure.

apparatus is shown in Fig. 241.   Hydrogen, carefully purified, entered under high pressure by the tube a and, after passing through the coil b, escaped at the valve c, which is of the same type as that used in the apparatus for liquefying the gas.   The valve c was enclosed in a thin metal box hh, and the gas issued from this box by the vertical tube p, through which also an electric resistance thermometer was introduced.   The electric connections were made by means of binding screws at f and g.

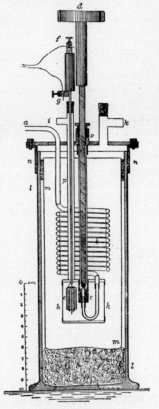

So as to be able to surround the coil b and the metal box with different refrigerants, the metal cap nn was cemented to the top of a thick-walled glass vessel ll.   This in turn contained a thin glass vessel mm, insulated from the former at the top and bottom.   The temperature of the coil and jet could be roughly determined from the readings of a mercury manometer attached to the apparatus.

Using liquid air as a refrigerant, considerable cooling was observed on opening the valve c, and the same effect was obtained in a less degree with liquid ethylene, boiling at $-103°$ C.   A series of experiments was then made with solid carbon dioxide and ether, beginning

Fig. 241.

at $-78°$ C. and gradually reducing the temperature by means of an exhaust pump connected to the cover of the apparatus at k.   At $-78°$ there was a slight heating effect, and at $-83°$ a decided cooling took place.   By numerous trials it was found that the temperature at which the Joule-Kelvin effect became zero was about $-80°·5$ C.   The pressure of the gas before expansion was between 117 and 110 atmospheres.

To every temperature τ of a gas there should correspond some pressure p for which

$$\tau \left(\frac{dv}{d\tau} \right)_p - v = 0,$$

i.e. so that at this temperature and pressure the Joule-Thomson

cooling effect is zero, the difference of pressure on the two sides of
the plug being very small. Jakob[1] has adopted the following
ingenious method of finding the curve of inversion :—

Since
$$\frac{d}{d\tau}\left(\frac{pv}{\tau}\right)_p = \frac{p}{\tau^2}\left\{\tau\left(\frac{dv}{d\tau}\right)_p - v\right\}$$

it follows that when the cooling effect is zero, the left-hand side of
this equation vanishes, so that pv/τ is constant for small changes in
τ. By inspecting tables of isotherms and isobars of gases, he found
many places where this condition was satisfied, and thus could mark
these points on a diagram in which the co-ordinates represent tempera-

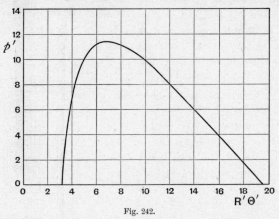

Fig. 242.

ture and pressure. These points lie on the same curve for all gases,
if the units of temperature and pressure refer to corresponding states
(Art. 253). Writing $p' = p/p_c$, $\Theta' = \Theta/\Theta_c$, $R' = R\Theta_c/p_c v_c$, where p_c, v_c,
and Θ_c are the critical pressure, volume, and temperature, then if
$R'\Theta'$ and p' are taken as the co-ordinates, the curve is that represented in Fig. 242. Jakob used the tables of Mack (for ethyl
ether), of Witkowski (for hydrogen), and of Amagat (for ethylene,
carbon dioxide, oxygen, and nitrogen). The curve is represented by
the equation

$$p' = 23\cdot37 - 1\cdot174\,R'\Theta' - \frac{178\cdot6}{(R'\Theta')^2}.$$

The region within the curve corresponds to states of the gas in
which cooling would occur. If Van der Waals's equation were exact,
then the curve would also be a parabola, but its axis would be
parallel to the axis of pressure, and the curve would pass through
the origin.[2]

---

[1] *Phys. Zeitschr.* vol. xxii. p. 65, 1921.
[2] A figure is given in Birtwistle's *Thermodynamics*, p. 80.

367. Nernst's Heat Theorem.[1]—The theorem propounded by Nernst, which is sometimes referred to as the Third Law of Thermodynamics, is described by Nernst as the principle of the unattainability of the absolute zero. It is a statement concerning the behaviour of bodies in the neighbourhood of the absolute zero of temperature, which cannot be proved, but which, like the second law of thermodynamics, yields deductions which are verified in a remarkable way by experimental facts. Starting from equation (4) of Art. 350, we have

$$U = \mathscr{F} - \tau \left(\frac{d\mathscr{F}}{d\tau} \right)_v \qquad . \quad . \quad . \quad . \quad (1)$$

where U is the internal energy, and $\mathscr{F}$ is the free energy. The specific heat at constant volume is $C_v = \left(\dfrac{dU}{d\tau} \right)_v$ and is known by experiment to be a continuous function of the temperature for all bodies which do not change their state (*e.g.* by passing from solid to liquid, or from one allotropic state to another). For such bodies C_v and therefore U must be capable of expansion as a series in powers of the temperature. We therefore put

$$U = U_0 + a\tau + \beta\tau^2 + \gamma\tau^3 + \delta\tau^4 + \qquad . \quad . \quad . \quad (2)$$

$$C_v = a + 2\beta\tau + 3\gamma\tau^2 + 4\delta\tau^3 + \qquad . \quad . \quad . \quad (3)$$

where the coefficients a, β, γ, etc., can be found by experiments determining the specific heat C_v at various temperatures. Now equation (1) may be written

$$\frac{U}{\tau^2} = - \left\{ \frac{d}{d\tau} \left(\frac{\mathscr{F}}{\tau} \right) \right\}_v ;$$

therefore, by integration, the volume being supposed to remain constant,

$$\left[\frac{\mathscr{F}}{\tau} \right]_{\tau_1}^{\tau} = - \int_{\tau_1}^{\tau} \frac{U d\tau}{\tau^2} = \left[\frac{U_0}{\tau} - a \log \tau - \beta\tau - \tfrac{1}{2}\gamma\tau^2 - \cdots \right]_{\tau_1}^{\tau},$$

where τ_1 is any fixed temperature. Hence

$$\frac{\mathscr{F}}{\tau} - \frac{\mathscr{F}_1}{\tau_1} = \frac{U_0}{\tau} - \frac{U_0}{\tau_1} - a \log \frac{\tau}{\tau_1} - \beta\tau(\tau - \tau_1) - \tfrac{1}{2}\gamma\tau(\tau^2 - \tau_1^2) - \cdots$$

or

$$\mathscr{F} = U_0 + (\mathscr{F}_1 - U_0)\frac{\tau}{\tau_1} - a\tau \log \frac{\tau}{\tau_1} - \beta\tau(\tau - \tau_1) - \tfrac{1}{2}\gamma\tau(\tau^2 - \tau_1^2) \quad . \quad (4)$$

From this equation we see that when $\tau = 0$, $\mathscr{F} = U_0$, that is, that the internal energy and the free energy are equal at absolute zero. Nernst now makes the assumption that *the internal energy and the free*

---

[1] *The New Heat Theorem*, by W. Nernst, English translation, 1926.

energy vary in the same way in the neighbourhood of the absolute zero.
From equation (2) $\dfrac{dU}{d\tau}$ is finite however small τ may be; therefore,
by Nernst's principle, $\dfrac{d\mathcal{F}}{d\tau}$ remains finite as τ tends to zero. But if
we differentiate equation (4) we get a term $-\alpha \log\dfrac{\tau}{\tau_1}$ on the right-
hand side, and as this tends to infinity as τ tends to zero, it follows
that α must vanish. If we put $\alpha = 0$ in (4) and differentiate, we get

$$\frac{d\mathcal{F}}{d\tau} = \frac{\mathcal{F}_1 - U_0}{\tau_1} - \beta(2\tau - \tau_1) - \tfrac{1}{2}\gamma(3\tau^2 - \tau_1{}^2) - \ldots$$

but since $\alpha = 0$, $\dfrac{dU}{d\tau} = 0$ when $\tau = 0$, from (2), therefore, by Nernst's
principle, $\dfrac{d\mathcal{F}}{d\tau} = 0$ when $\tau = 0$, so that

$$\frac{\mathcal{F}_1 - U_0}{\tau_1} + \beta\tau_1 + \tfrac{1}{2}\gamma\tau_1{}^2 + \tfrac{1}{3}\delta\tau_1{}^3 + \ldots = 0.$$

Since τ may be any finite temperature, we may remove the sub-
scripts and write

$$\mathcal{F} = U_0 - \beta\tau^2 - \tfrac{1}{2}\gamma\tau^3 - \tfrac{1}{3}\delta\tau^4 - \quad . \quad . \quad . \quad . \quad (5)$$

As shown in Art. 350, when τ and v are taken as independent
variables, all other quantities pertaining to the condition of the body
can be expressed in terms of $\mathcal{F}$ and its partial derivatives, so that if
we know the coefficients β, γ, etc., we know $\mathcal{F}$, and can derive various
properties of substances, even for temperatures far removed from
the absolute zero.[1]

It can be shown from Debye's theory of specific heats (Art.
168) that at very low temperatures the specific heat of a pure metal
should vary as the cube of the absolute temperature, and this has
been confirmed for copper by Onnes and Keesom.[2] In this case,
not only does the coefficient α vanish in equation (2) but also β and
γ, so that

$$U = U_0 + \delta\tau^4 + \ldots \; ; \quad \mathcal{F} = U - \tfrac{1}{4}\delta\tau^4 \ldots$$

From Art. 150, equation (3),

$$\phi = -\left(\frac{d\mathcal{F}}{d\tau}\right),$$

---

[1] Most of the results derived by Nernst from his theorem belong to the domain
of physical chemistry, and the reader is referred to his book for an account of them.

[2] The experiments of Keesom and Andrews (*Comm. No. 185a, Phys. Lab. of
Leiden*, 1927) indicate that lead exhibits a departure from the cube law.

therefore Nernst's theorem implies that the entropy vanishes at absolute zero. The area of a Carnot's cycle, one of whose isothermals is the absolute zero, may be written $\tau(\phi_2 - \phi_1)$ where ϕ_1 and ϕ_2 are the entropies corresponding to the two adiabatics. But as τ, ϕ_1, and ϕ_2 all tend to zero together, the area, when τ is small, is a small quantity of a higher order. We infer that all processss designed to reduce the temperature of a body by making it do work tend to become infinitely slow as the absolute zero is approached.

CHAPTER IX

KINETIC THEORY OF GASES

SECTION I

GAS IN EQUILIBRIUM

368. Kinetic Theory of Matter. — In the third and following sections of the first chapter of this book a full account has been
given of the researches which have led physicists to reject the caloric
theory of heat and to adopt the view that heat is a form of energy,
and, further, that the heat-energy of matter is kinetic, being due
to the agitation of the molecules or atoms of which the matter is
constituted. According to this theory, the motion of any one
molecule or atom is continually being modified by the presence of its
neighbours, and when two molecules approach each other sufficiently
closely a limiting position is reached in which further approach is
impossible, and the molecules begin to recede from each other.
Such an occurrence is generally referred to as an *encounter* between
two molecules, and the statement that such encounters take place
involves the assumption that when the distance between two
molecules is very small, certain forces of repulsion are called into
play which cause the relative velocity to be reversed. We have at
present no precise knowledge of the constitution of a molecule or of
the nature of the forces which they exert on each other, and even
if we possessed such knowledge it is almost certain that the
mathematical difficulties of the investigation would prevent us from
making full use of it. We know, however, that though the molecules
of different forms of matter are differently constituted, yet there are
certain general properties in which all forms of matter resemble
each other, and we may infer that these properties do not depend
on the particular molecular constitution of the kind of matter which
may be the subject of investigation. We have a right, then, to
expect that any reasonable assumptions as to the form of a molecule
and the nature of an encounter will lead to useful results, even

778

although the data with which we start our inquiry are far simpler than those which the modern theory of molecular and atomic structure would suggest (see p. 76). Some general theorems have indeed been obtained by treating the molecule as a mechanical system possessing n degrees of freedom, without specifying definitely either its structure or the forces which act during an encounter. In what follows, those data will, however, be assumed which, from the physical point of view, appear to be the simplest.

As the properties of gases are simpler than those of liquids or solids, so the assumptions which are made in dealing with gases on the kinetic theory are simpler than those which would have to be made in the other cases. The path of a molecule in a gas between two successive encounters is assumed to be a straight line, and this greatly simplifies the investigation. Many of the results given in this chapter strictly apply only to a monatomic gas, viz. one in which the molecule contains only one atom.

369. Gas in Equilibrium—Data Postulated.—In Arts. 53-55 a short account has been given of the molecular theory of matter, and it has there been shown that Boyle's law for a gas in equilibrium is expressed according to this theory by the equation [1]

$$pv = \frac{1}{3}\overline{c^2} \qquad . \qquad . \qquad . \qquad . \qquad . \qquad (1)$$

when p is the pressure, v the volume of unit mass, and $\overline{c^2}$ the mean square of the molecular velocity of the gas. We shall now investigate more fully the consequences of the dynamical theory in the case of gases. The first step is to determine the way in which the velocities are distributed amongst the molecules in a gas when a steady state is attained.

At first sight it might appear that in a state of equilibrium the velocities of the molecules would be all equal. A little consideration will, however, convince us that this is not the case, for even if the velocities were originally equal, the encounters between the molecules would soon produce an inequality. For instance, if two equal smooth elastic spheres, moving with velocities of equal magnitude collide, they will not have equal velocities after separating, except under special conditions of impact. Maxwell [2] first enunciated the theorem that *the components of molecular velocity are distributed amongst the molecules according to the same law as the errors are distributed amongst the observations in the theory of errors of observation.* This is

---

[1] The notation here adopted is more convenient for our present purpose than that of Art. 55.

[2] *Scientific Papers*, vol. i. p. 377 ; vol. ii. p. 43.

Maxwell's law of distribution of molecular velocities. Maxwell's original proof of this theorem is open to objection, but was afterwards improved both by Maxwell himself and by others. A method of proof by L. Boltzmann [1] is here adopted.

Since the velocity of a given molecule is constantly changing both in direction and magnitude owing to encounters with other molecules, we do not attempt to study the path of a single molecule, but adopt a statistical mode of treatment, *i.e.* we consider the molecules as divided into classes according to their velocities, and estimate the number belonging to any given class. In the case of a gas at rest and in thermal equilibrium, the number of molecules in any class will be some function (as yet unknown) of the velocity characteristic of that class. When two molecules of any two classes collide, they will in general, after separating, belong to two new classes. Hence each class is continually losing molecules belonging to it, and at the same time continually gaining fresh recruits from the other classes. The condition for stability of distribution of velocities is that each class should in any period gain as many members as it loses. In order to obtain this condition in the form of a mathematical equation, it will be convenient to make the following assumptions :—

(1) The molecular velocities are without any regularity of distribution in space, *i.e.* the probability that a particular molecule should belong to a particular class is quite independent of the classes to which its immediate neighbours may belong.[2]

(2) The molecules are so small and so sparsely distributed, and the time occupied by an encounter is so brief compared to the period between two encounters, that encounters between three or more molecules are very infrequent, and their effects may be neglected. Thus only binary encounters need be considered.

(3) The law of conservation of energy holds for the kinetic energy of molecules during encounters.[3]

----

[1] *Vorlesungen über Gastheorie*, vol. i. chap. i.

[2] This assumption has been objected to by S. H. Burbury (*Phil. Mag.*, 1900, 1901) on the ground that the mutual influence of the molecules would tend to produce equality of velocity in neighbouring molecules, so that a kind of *molecular drift* would be going on even in a gas at rest, that is, a gas having no sensible currents through it. See also the preface to Burbury's *Kinetic Theory of Gases*. A proof of Maxwell's law of distribution of velocities has, however, been given by J. H. Jeans, which is not based on the assumption of molecular chaos (*Dynamical Theory of Gases*, 2nd ed., chap. iii.).

[3] It is obvious that any *irreversible* transformation of energy, such as takes place during the collision of imperfectly elastic bodies, would be inconsistent with a steady state since a loss of kinetic energy would then be continually going on

(4) The molecules are hard, smooth, and perfectly elastic spheres which rebound on collision according to the ordinary laws of mechanics.

The last assumption is frankly made for the purpose of simplifying the investigation and avoiding the difficulties inherent in a general mathematical treatment.[1] We do not, of course, believe that the molecules of any gas are elastic spheres. But, according to the modern theory of atomic structure (p. 77), the mass of the atom is almost entirely resident in the central nucleus, which is extremely small, so that, since the atoms are not broken up or ionised by ordinary collisions, it is probable that the energy of rotation of the atom of a monatomic gas, in so far as it is communicable between atom and atom, is negligible compared with its energy of translation. Such an atom may be regarded as very approximately a body possessing only three degrees of freedom like the smooth sphere which we take as its model. The supposition that the exchanges of energy and momentum which occur during a collision are the same as for perfectly elastic spheres is probably neither very exact nor very widely divergent from the truth. As we have already indicated, we may expect that any convenient hypothesis as to the shape of a molecule and the mechanism of an encounter which conforms with our other assumptions will lead to those properties which all gases have in common, in spite of the diversity which they exhibit in their chemical constitution, spectral lines, etc. Maxwell, for instance, investigated the properties of a gas whose molecules are supposed to repel each other with a force varying inversely as the fifth power of the distance, an assumption which also simplifies the mathematical treatment. At the same time it must be borne in mind that in calculating relations between the specific heats, viscosity, conductivity, and other constants which are different for different gases, we cannot expect to obtain accurate numerical coefficients in all cases.

---

without possibility of recovery. But a conversion of energy of translation into potential energy (as when gravity is supposed to act) or into internal energy of the molecule (provided this is reconvertible into energy of translation) may take place. Thus, to take a simple case, if the molecules are supposed to be smooth ellipsoids of revolution, the law of distribution of velocities would not apply to the velocities of rotation about their axes of revolution, but would apply to the velocities of rotation about axes perpendicular to these. We may observe that though each individual encounter is assumed to be reversible in character, the aggregate result, or the process by which a gas attains a state of thermal equilibrium, is as irreversible as the mixing of two fine powders.

[1] For the more general discussion, in which the molecules are regarded as dynamical systems of n degrees of freedom specified by generalised co-ordinates, the reader is referred to treatises on the kinetic theory, *e.g.* Jeans' *Dynamical Theory of Gases*.

370. Velocity Diagram — Encounters between Molecules of Different Classes.—The simplest case which we can consider is that of a single gas whose molecules are spheres all of mass m and diameter σ. The gas is supposed to be at rest as a whole, and in thermal equilibrium with the walls of the containing vessel. This means that no energy is gained or lost by collisions with the boundary, a condition which may be secured by supposing the molecules to rebound from the walls as from a perfectly smooth elastic surface. External forces such as gravity will, for the present, be considered absent. If a given small volume is taken in any part of the vessel— this volume being yet large enough to contain a great many molecules —it will, owing to the homogeneity of the gas, contain the same number of molecules, whose velocities are distributed according to the same law, in whatever part of the gas the small volume is taken; and further, the total energy will be the same. While we suppose the state of the gas to be uniform throughout, we need not at present assume it to be steady, *i.e.* the distribution of velocities will be regarded as a function of the time as well as of the velocities.

It will be found very helpful to represent the velocity of a molecule in direction and magnitude by means of a *velocity-diagram*

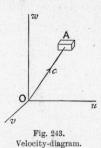

Fig. 243.
Velocity-diagram.

(Fig. 243). Take any point O as origin, and let the line OA represent the velocity of a molecule in direction and magnitude. Then the point A may be called the velocity-point corresponding to that particular molecule. If we suppose the velocity-points of all the molecules in a unit volume of the gas to be thus marked on the diagram, then we must think of the whole space (in three dimensions) as closely dotted with a multitude of points, each one representing by its position relative to O the velocity of the corresponding molecule. The density of the points, viz. the number per unit volume of the diagram-space, will vary with the distance from O, but, since a molecule is just as likely to be moving in one direction as another, the density will be the same in all regions equidistant from O; in other words, the diagram will be sensibly symmetrical round the point O. It must be remembered that the point A represents only the velocity of the molecule, and gives no indication of its position in space. Thus two molecules whose velocity-points are close together may themselves be far apart in the gas, and *vice versa*.

If we take any set of rectangular axes through O, then the components of velocity u, v, w of a molecule A can be represented by lengths u, v, w measured along these axes.   We shall call all molecules whose velocity-components lie within the limits

$$u \text{ and } u + du, \quad v \text{ and } v + dv, \quad w \text{ and } w + dw$$

"molecules of class (u, v, w)" or, when referring to the diagram, "molecules of class A". Similarly, the expression "molecules of class (c)" will be used to denote all molecules whose absolute velocity, regardless of direction, lies between the limits c and $c + dc$, that is, all molecules whose velocity-points lie within a thin spherical shell of radius c and thickness dc with its centre at O on the velocity-diagram. The velocity-points of molecules of class A all lie within a small parallelepiped of volume $du\, dv\, dw = d\omega$ say (Fig. 243).   Also, if c is the length of OA, $c^2 = u^2 + v^2 + w^2$.

Consider now the effect of a collision between two molecules whose velocities are represented by the vectors OA and OA′ respectively (Fig. 244).   Then the middle point M of AA′ is the velocity-point of the centre of gravity of the two, because A′A represents the velocity of the molecule A relative to the molecule A′, and its velocity relative to their centre of gravity must be half A′A.   The velocity of the centre of gravity is unaltered by collision, so that the point M is the same after collision.   If B and B′ are the new velocity-points after collision, M must be the middle point of BB′.   If we draw OK parallel to the line joining the centres of the spheres at the moment of impact, and LN through M parallel to OK, then we may, if we choose, take OK as our axis of u, the axes of v and w being any two axes perpendicular to OK and to each other.   If u', v', w' are the components of velocity of the molecule A′, and the components after collision are U, V, W and U′, V′, W′ for the two molecules respectively; then, since v, w, v', w' are all unchanged by collision, we have

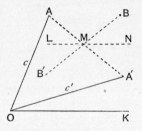

Fig. 244.—Velocity-diagram.

$$V = v, \quad W = w, \quad V' = v', \quad W' = w' \qquad . \qquad . \qquad . \qquad (1)$$

Also the total momentum along the u-axis is unaltered, and the total kinetic energy is unaltered.   These two conditions furnish the equations

$$U + U' = u + u', \quad U^2 + U'^2 = u^2 + u'^2,$$

the only applicable solution of which is $U = u'$, $U' = u$.   Referring to the diagram, we see from equations (1) that AB and A′B′ are parallel to OK or LN, and, from the values obtained for U and U′ that AB′

and A′B are perpendicular to OK or LN. Thus, being given the velocities OA, OA′ of any two colliding molecules and the direction OK of their line of centres at the moment of impact, we get the following simple construction for B, B′, the new velocity-points after collision : through the middle point M of AA′ draw LN parallel to OK, and through A, A′ draw parallels and perpendiculars to LN ; these will intersect in B, B′. In short, B and B′ are the reflections of A′ and A in the line LN.

We can now prove the following theorem, which will be required immediately : if, of two colliding molecules whose line of centres at impact is given in direction, the velocity-point of the one lies in the small parallel-epiped A (Fig. 245) of volume $du\, dv\, dw = d\omega$, and the velocity-point of the other lies in the small parallelepiped A′ of volume $du'\, dv'\, dw' = d\omega'$; then, after collision, the velocity-points of the two molecules will lie within parallelepipeds B, B′, whose volumes $d\Omega$, $d\Omega'$ are connected with $d\omega$, $d\omega'$ by the relation

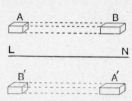

Fig. 245.—Velocity-diagram.

$$d\Omega\, d\Omega' = d\omega\, d\omega' \qquad . \qquad . \qquad . \qquad . \qquad (2)$$

For, from what has just been said, A and B are elements of the same long thin prism parallel to LN, and similarly A′ and B′, while the length of B (measured parallel to LN) is equal to that of A′, and similarly the lengths of B′ and A are equal ; the theorem then immediately follows.[1]

371. Number of Collisions of a given Type—Total Gain of Molecules of a given Class.—Our next step is to find an expression for the number of collisions of the type discussed in the last article which occur in a given small interval of time dt. Since the velocity-diagram is symmetrical about the point O, the density of the velocity-points is a function of c and t only,[2] where c is the distance from O. Let this density be denoted by $f(c)$, then the number of molecules in class A is $f(c)d\omega$. Similarly, the number of molecules in class A′ is $f(c')d\omega'$. We shall, for shortness, call a collision which conforms with the subjoined conditions a " collision of type a."

(1) One of the colliding molecules belongs to class A and the other to class A′.

---

[1] Or, algebraically, since $U = u'$, $V = v$, $W = w$, $U' = u$, $V' = v'$, $W' = w'$, therefore $d\Omega\, d\Omega' = dU\, dV\, dW\, dU'\, dV'\, dW' = du'\, dv\, dw\, du\, dv'\, dw' = d\omega\, d\omega'$.

[2] According to what was said in the last article, the density $f(c)$ is, for the present, to be regarded as a function of the time t as well as of the velocity c. It might be written $f(c, t)$, but this is unnecessary.

(2) The direction of the line of centres of the spheres at the moment of impact, drawn from a fixed point (OK, Fig. 244), lies within a very thin cone of solid angle $d\lambda$.

To find the number of collisions of type a which occur in the interval of time dt, imagine a sphere of radius σ (the diameter of a molecule) to be drawn concentrically round every molecule of class A (Fig. 246). From the centre C of the molecule draw lines describing the small cone CD whose solid angle is $d\lambda$. The portion of surface of the sphere enclosed by the cone will have an area $\sigma^2 d\lambda$. On this area as base erect an oblique cylinder DE, whose generators are parallel to the line AA′ and are equal in length to qdt, where q is the scalar magnitude of the velocity represented by AA′ (Fig. 244). Imagine every molecule of class A to carry with it the sphere so described with the little cylinder attached, the direction of the cone and cylinder remaining always the same; then a collision of type a will occur whenever, at the beginning of the interval dt, the centre of a molecule of class A′ finds itself within one of these small cylinders. For the velocity of a molecule of class A′ relative to one of class A is represented by AA′ in direction and magnitude; it will therefore be able to travel a distance qdt in time dt, so that if its centre lies anywhere within the small cylinder it will reach the base within the interval dt. The spheres will then be in contact and their line of centres within the cone.

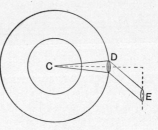

Fig. 246.

If θ is the angle (which must be acute) between the axis of the cylinder and the axis of the cone produced, the height of the cylinder is $qdt \cos\theta$ and its volume is $q\sigma^2 \cos\theta\, d\lambda\, dt$, so that the total volume of all the cylinders is $f(c)d\omega . q\sigma^2 \cos\theta\, d\lambda\, dt$. Since the number of molecules of class A′ in unit volume of the gas is $f(c')d\omega'$, the number contained within the space occupied by the cylinders is $f(c)f(c')q\sigma^2 \cos\theta\, d\omega\, d\omega'\, d\lambda\, dt$. Thus we get

Number of collisions of type a in time $dt = f(c)f(c')q\sigma^2 \cos\theta\, d\omega\, d\omega'\, d\lambda\, dt,$

which therefore gives the number of molecules lost by class A in time dt owing to collisions of type a.

We shall now consider a collision of the opposite type—one which furnishes a gain to class A. Let a collision be called a "collision of type β" if it fulfils the following conditions:—

3 E

(1) *After* collision one of the molecules is of class A and the other of class A′.

(2) The direction of the line of centres at the moment of impact, drawn from a fixed point, lies within the thin cone of solid angle $d\lambda$.

Referring to Fig. 244, we see readily that before collision the molecules must belong to classes B and B′ respectively, but the direction of the line OK is that from the centre of the B′ molecule to the centre of the B molecule, not *vice versa*.[1] Consequently, just as in the case of a collision of type a, we get

Number of collisions of type β in time $dt = f(C)f(C')q\sigma^2 \cos\theta\, d\Omega\, d\Omega'\, d\lambda\, dt,$

where $C^2 = U^2 + V^2 + W^2$, $C'^2 = U'^2 + V'^2 + W'^2$; and this is the number of molecules gained by class A in time dt owing to collisions of type β.

Now, since we proved in Art. 370 that $d\Omega\, d\Omega' = d\omega\, d\omega'$, we find that

The net gain in numbers to class A in time dt due to collisions of types a and β is algebraically equal to

$$\{f(C)f(C') - f(c)f(c')\}q\sigma^2 \cos\theta\, d\omega\, d\omega'\, d\lambda\, dt.$$

To find the net gain to class A, in the interval dt, due to collisions of all possible types, we must integrate with respect to $d\omega'$ and $d\lambda$, that is, for all classes to which the other colliding molecule may belong, and for all directions of centres at impact. The total number of molecules gained by class A in time dt is thus [2]

$$\sigma^2 d\omega\, dt \iint \{f(C)f(C') - f(c)f(c')\}q \cos\theta\, d\omega'\, d\lambda \quad . \quad . \quad (1)$$

The number of molecules in class A at the beginning of the time is $f(c)d\omega$, therefore the increase in the number during the interval is

$$\frac{\partial}{\partial t}f(c)d\omega\, dt \quad . \quad . \quad . \quad . \quad (2)$$

Equating (1) and (2) we get

$$\frac{\partial}{\partial t}f(c) = \sigma^2 \iint \{f(C)f(C') - f(c)f(c')\}q \cos\theta\, d\omega'\, d\lambda \quad . \quad (3)$$

---

[1] Fig. 244 has been drawn so that the line OK is from the centre of the A molecule to the centre of the A′ molecule. If, after a collision of type a, the velocities of both molecules were simultaneously reversed, they would retrace their paths, and their final velocities after re-impact would be their original velocities reversed. But to reverse the velocities without reversing the line of centres gives the same diagram (turned through 180°) as if we reversed the line of centres and left the velocities unchanged.

[2] Strictly speaking, five integral signs should be written here, since $d\omega'$ is a differential of the third order, and $d\lambda$ one of the second order (see Art. 378, where the integration is carried out). No ambiguity can, however, arise from the use of the above abbreviated notation. It is of course understood that when we replace $d\Omega\, d\Omega'$ by $d\omega\, d\omega'$ we must suppose that, before integrating, C and C′ (as well as $q \cos\theta$) are expressed in terms of u, v, w, u', v', w'; u, v, w being treated as constants in effecting the integrations.

This is the statistical equation for a gas at rest in which the molecular velocities are equally distributed in all directions; and it is from this equation that the function f, whose form we are seeking, is to be determined.

When the gas is in a steady state, the left-hand side of this equation vanishes, therefore the right-hand side vanishes also. This condition is evidently secured if the function f is of such a form that

$$f(C)f(C') - f(c)f(c') = 0 \qquad . \qquad . \qquad . \qquad . \qquad (4)$$

for every type of collision. In the next article is given Boltzmann's proof[1] that this is the only possible solution; after which the determination of the form of the function f is proceeded with.

372. Boltzmann's H - Theorem. — We shall use the following notation: Let $f(c_0)$ be the value of $f(c)$ when any arbitrary value c_0 is given to c and any value, say $t = 0$, to the time, so that $f(c_0)$ is a constant of the same dimensions[2] as $f(c)$; and put

$$\psi = \frac{f(c)}{f(c_0)}, \quad \psi' = \frac{f(c')}{f(c_0)}, \quad \Psi = \frac{f(C)}{f(c_0)}, \quad \Psi' = \frac{f(C')}{f(c_0)} \quad . \qquad . \qquad . \qquad (1)$$

Let us now consider the variation in time of a quantity H defined by the equation

$$\mathrm{H} = \int \psi \log \psi \, d\omega,$$

the integral being taken over the whole space in the velocity-diagram. Differentiating under the integral sign, we have

$$\frac{d\mathrm{H}}{dt} = \int (1 + \log \psi) \frac{\partial \psi}{\partial t} \, d\omega.$$

Now, since $\dfrac{\partial \psi}{\partial t} = \dfrac{1}{f(c_0)} \dfrac{\partial f(c)}{\partial t}$, we get, by equation (3) of the last article,

$$\frac{d\mathrm{H}}{dt} = \frac{\sigma^2}{f(c_0)} \int \int \int (1 + \log \psi)\{f(C)f(C') - f(c)f(c')\} q \cos \theta \, d\lambda \, d\omega \, d\omega'.$$

It is obvious that we could also put

$$\mathrm{H} = \int \psi' \log \psi' d\omega'$$

and, proceeding as before, get the same value for $d\mathrm{H}/dt$, except that ψ' would be written for ψ. Adding the two expressions for $d\mathrm{H}/dt$ and halving, we get the more symmetrical result

$$\frac{d\mathrm{H}}{dt} = \tfrac{1}{2}\frac{\sigma^2}{f(c_0)} \int \int \int (2 + \log \psi\psi')\{f(C)f(C') - f(c)f(c')\} q \cos \theta \, d\lambda \, d\omega \, d\omega'.$$

---

[1] *Loc. cit.* p. 32.

[2] The quantity $f(c_0)$ is introduced in order to avoid writing $\log f(c)$ (as is usually done) when $f(c)$ is not of zero dimensions, as quantities of mixed dimensions do not occur in physics.

Again, we may write $H = \int \Psi \log \Psi d\Omega$ or $\int \Psi' \log \Psi' d\Omega'$ and obtain the last result with small letters and capitals interchanged, that is

$$\frac{dH}{dt} = \frac{1}{2}\frac{\sigma^2}{f(c_0)}\iiint (2 + \log \Psi\Psi')\{f(c)f(c') - f(C)f(C')\}q \cos\theta\, d\lambda\, d\Omega\, d\Omega',$$

and if we put $d\omega\, d\omega'$ for $d\Omega\, d\Omega'$ according to equation (2), Art. 370, and again add the two expressions and halve, we get finally

$$\frac{dH}{dt} = \frac{1}{4}\frac{\sigma^2}{f(c_0)}\iiint \log\frac{f(c)f(c')}{f(C)f(C')}\{f(C)f(C') - f(c)f(c')\}q \cos\theta\, d\lambda\, d\omega\, d\omega',$$

where we have replaced ψ, ψ', Ψ, Ψ' by their values given by equations (1).

The expression under the integral signs cannot be positive, for we have seen that θ is always acute, so that $\cos\theta$ is positive, and in fact that $q\cos\theta d\lambda$ is the volume of a small cylinder in the gas-space, which must always be positive; while the sign of the logarithm must always be opposite to that of the expression in brackets. Thus dH/dt is always negative, unless $f(C)f(C') - f(c)f(c')$ vanishes for all types of collision, when dH/dt also vanishes. But if the gas is in a steady state, H will be constant in time and dH/dt must vanish; this condition can therefore only be fulfilled if

$$f(C)f(C') - f(c)f(c') = 0.$$

373. Deduction of Maxwell's Law.—The equation

$$f(C)\, f(C') - f(c)\, f(c') = 0 \quad . \qquad . \qquad . \qquad . \qquad . \qquad (1)$$

has now been shown to be a necessary and sufficient condition for a steady state of the gas. The four quantities c, c', C, C' are not independent, for the kinetic energy of a colliding pair of molecules is unaltered by collision, so that

$$mC^2 + mC'^2 = mc^2 + mc'^2 \quad . \qquad . \qquad . \qquad . \qquad . \qquad (2)$$

Put $mc^2 = x$, $mc'^2 = y$, $mC^2 = X$, $mC'^2 = Y$, and write

$$\phi(x) = \phi(mc^2) = \log\psi = \log\frac{f(c)}{f(c_0)} \qquad\qquad \text{(Art. 372)},$$

then $f(c) = f(c_0)e^{\phi(x)}$, and (1) and (2) become

$$\phi(X) + \phi(Y) = \phi(x) + \phi(y); \quad X + Y = x + y.$$

Eliminating Y, we get

$$\phi(X) + \phi(x + y - X) = \phi(x) + \phi(y).$$

Now this is not an equation connecting X, x, and y, which are obviously independent; it is an equation which demands that the function ϕ shall be of such a form that it is true for all values of

X, x, and y.   We may therefore differentiate partially with respect to X, x, and y, obtaining the equations

$$\phi'(X) - \phi'(x+y-X) = 0,$$
$$\phi'(x+y-X) = \phi'(x),$$
$$\phi'(x+y-X) = \phi'(y),$$

whence

$$\phi'(x) = \phi'(y) = \phi'(X) = -h \text{ (say)},$$

where h is a constant which is the same for all classes of molecules. Integrating, we get

$$\phi(x) = -hx + \text{const.}$$

or

$$f(c) = Ae^{-hmc^2} \qquad . \quad . \quad . \quad . \quad . \quad (3)$$

where A is a constant.   This is the mathematical expression of Maxwell's law of distribution of velocities. · It states that the density of the velocity-points in the velocity-space is proportional to e^{-hmc^2}, where c is the magnitude of the velocity and hm a constant.

The proof of Maxwell's law can be extended to the case of a mixture of two gases, the masses and diameters of their molecules being m, m_1 and σ, σ_1 respectively.   This is the case considered by Boltzmann.   If $f(c)$ and $F(c_1)$ are the corresponding functions representing the density of distribution of the velocity-points, the result arrived at is

$$f(c) = Ae^{-hmc^2}, \quad F(c_1) = A_1 e^{-hm_1 c_1^2},$$

where A, A_1, and h are constants.[1]

It is important to note that the same constant h occurs in the formula for each gas.   It can also be shown that if the gases are not mixed, but are in thermal equilibrium, i.e. energy is free to pass from one to the other, then the constant h is still the same for both.[2]

374. Definite Integrals. — Before proceeding to deduce the physical consequences of Maxwell's law, it will be convenient to evaluate certain definite integrals which are of frequent occurrence.

Consider the integral

$$I_a = \int_0^a e^{-\lambda x^2} dx.$$

We may write

$$I_a^2 = \int_0^a e^{-\lambda x^2} dx \times \int_0^a e^{-\lambda y^2} dy = \int_0^a \int_0^a e^{-\lambda(x^2+y^2)} dx\, dy.$$

---

[1] Boltzmann, *loc. cit.* chap. i.   The theorem (2) of Art. 370 does not apply, but Jacobi's method of transforming integrals can be used instead (see Williamson's *Integral Calculus*, chap. ix.).   See also Ex. 4 at the end of this section.

[2] Jeans, *Dynamical Theory of Gases*, 2nd ed., p. 125.

If we regard x and y as co-ordinates of a point referred to rectangular axes OX, OY (Fig. 247), then $dx\,dy$ is an element of area, and I_a^2 is the surface-integral of $e^{-\lambda(x^2+y^2)}$ taken over the square OACB, where $OA = OB = a$. Transforming to polar co-ordinates, we see that the integrals

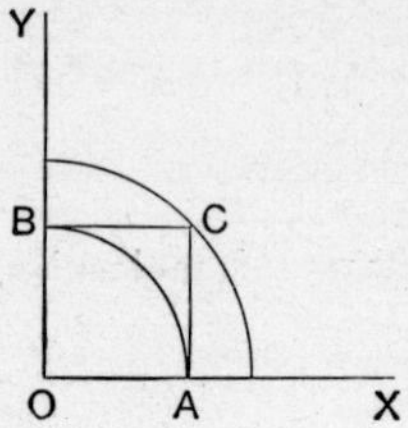

Fig. 247.

$$\int_0^a \int_0^{\frac{\pi}{2}} e^{-\lambda r^2} r\,d\theta dr \text{ and } \int_0^{a\sqrt{2}} \int_0^{\frac{\pi}{2}} e^{-\lambda r^2} r\,d\theta dr$$

represent the same surface-integral taken over quadrants of circles through A, B, and through C respectively. Since the integrand is always positive, the value of I_a^2 is intermediate between the values of the two integrals just written. These are immediately integrable, their values being

$$\frac{\pi}{4\lambda}\left(1 - e^{-\lambda a^2}\right) \text{ and } \frac{\pi}{4\lambda}\left(1 - e^{-2\lambda a^2}\right)$$

respectively. Both integrals converge to the value $\pi/4\lambda$ when a tends to infinity; we have therefore

$$I_\infty = \int_0^\infty e^{-\lambda x^2} dx = \tfrac{1}{2}\sqrt{\frac{\pi}{\lambda}} \qquad \dots \qquad (1)$$

Also, by direct integration

$$\int_0^\infty x e^{-\lambda x^2} dx = \frac{1}{2\lambda} \qquad \dots \qquad (2)$$

If we differentiate k times with respect to λ, we get the general formulæ [1] (c being written for x, and hm for λ)

$$\int_0^\infty c^{2k} e^{-hmc^2} dc = \frac{1.3.5\dots(2k-1)\sqrt{\pi}}{2^{k+1}(hm)^{k+\frac{1}{2}}} \qquad \dots \qquad (3)$$

$$\int_0^\infty c^{2k+1} e^{-hmc^2} dc = \frac{k!}{2(hm)^{k+1}} \qquad \dots \qquad (4)$$

If these integrals are taken from $-\infty$ to $+\infty$, instead of from 0 to ∞, then, since e^{-hmc^2} is an even function of c, the right-hand side of the equation would be doubled in (3) and would be zero in (4).

Another integral which we shall require is

$$\int_0^\infty x^2 \left\{ e^{-(x-a)^2} - e^{-(x+a)^2} \right\} dx \qquad \dots \qquad (5)$$

---

[1] The formulæ (3) and (4) can be written in the single form

$$\int_0^\infty c^n e^{-hmc^2} dc = \frac{\Gamma\left(\dfrac{n+1}{2}\right)}{2(hm)^{\frac{n+1}{2}}}.$$

Putting $\mu = x - a$

$$\int_0^\infty x^2 e^{-(x-a)^2} dx = \int_{-a}^\infty (\mu + a)^2 e^{-\mu^2} d\mu,$$

but

$$\int (\mu + a)^2 e^{-\mu^2} d\mu = \int \mu^2 e^{-\mu^2} d\mu + 2a \int \mu e^{-\mu^2} d\mu + a^2 \int e^{-\mu^2} d\mu$$

$$= -(\tfrac{1}{2}\mu + a) e^{-\mu^2} + (a^2 + \tfrac{1}{2}) \int e^{-\mu^2} d\mu,$$

therefore

$$\int_0^\infty x^2 e^{-(x-a)^2} dx = \tfrac{1}{2} a e^{-a^2} + (a^2 + \tfrac{1}{2}) \int_{-a}^\infty e^{-\mu^2} d\mu.$$

Changing the sign of a in this, we get

$$\int_0^\infty x^2 e^{-(x+a)^2} dx = -\tfrac{1}{2} a e^{-a^2} + (a^2 + \tfrac{1}{2}) \int_a^\infty e^{-\mu^2} d\mu,$$

therefore (5) is equal to

$$a e^{-a^2} + (a^2 + \tfrac{1}{2}) \int_{-a}^a e^{-\mu^2} d\mu.$$

In this expression we may write $2\int_0^a e^{-\mu^2} d\mu$ instead of $\int_{-a}^a e^{-\mu^2} d\mu$, since $e^{-\mu^2}$ is an even function of μ. We obtain the formula in a more general form by writing $x = q \sqrt{\lambda}$, $a = c \sqrt{\lambda}$, viz.

$$\int_0^\infty q^2 \left\{ e^{-\lambda(q-c)^2} - e^{-\lambda(q+c)^2} \right\} dq = \frac{1}{\lambda} \left\{ c e^{-\lambda c^2} + \frac{2\lambda c^2 + 1}{\sqrt{\lambda}} \int_0^{c\sqrt{\lambda}} e^{-\mu^2} d\mu \right\} . \quad (6)$$

375. Velocity of Mean Square—Temperature.—We have now to determine the meaning of the constants A and h in the formula

$$f(c) = A e^{-hmc^2}.$$

The number of molecules whose velocities lie between the values c and $c + dc$ is

$$f(c) d\omega = A e^{-hmc^2} d\omega,$$

and, since $f(c)$ depends on the magnitude of the velocity and not on its direction, this number is got by summing the number in all the elements of volume on the velocity-diagram which make up the thin spherical shell whose internal and external radii are c and $c + dc$. The volume of this shell is $4\pi c^2 dc$; substituting this for $d\omega$, we get, if $d\nu$ is the number of molecules whose velocities lie between the given limits,

$$d\nu = 4\pi A e^{-hmc^2} c^2 dc,$$

therefore

$$\nu = 4\pi A \int_0^\infty e^{-hmc^2} c^2 dc,$$

where ν is the total number of molecules in unit volume of the gas. Integrating with the aid of formula (3), we have

$$\nu = A\left(\frac{\pi}{hm}\right)^{\frac{3}{2}};$$

therefore

$$A = \nu\left(\frac{hm}{\pi}\right)^{\frac{3}{2}},$$

and

$$f(c) = \nu\left(\frac{hm}{\pi}\right)^{\frac{3}{2}} e^{-hmc^2} \qquad . \qquad . \qquad . \qquad . \qquad . \qquad 1)$$

To find $\overline{c^2}$, the mean square velocity, we have

$$\overline{c^2} = \frac{1}{\nu}\int_0^\infty c^2 d\nu = \frac{\displaystyle\int_0^\infty c^4 e^{-hmc^2} dc}{\displaystyle\int_0^\infty c^2 e^{-hmc^2} dc} = \frac{3}{2hm};$$

therefore

$$mc^2 = \frac{3}{2h}.$$

The value of the mean velocity $\overline{c}$ is less important ; it is

$$\overline{c} = \frac{1}{\nu}\int_0^\infty c \, d\nu = \frac{2}{\sqrt{\pi hm}}.$$

We may observe that $\overline{c^2} = \frac{3\pi}{8}\left(\overline{c}\right)^2$, so that the velocity of mean square is somewhat greater than the mean velocity.

If we put $hmc^2 = x^2$ in the formula

$$d\nu = 4\pi\nu\left(\frac{hm}{\pi}\right)^{\frac{3}{2}} e^{-hmc^2} c^2 dc$$

we get

$$\frac{d\nu}{\nu} = \frac{4}{\sqrt{\pi}} x^2 e^{-x^2} dx.$$

In Fig. 248 the curve $y = \frac{4}{\sqrt{\pi}} x^2 e^{-x^2}$ is traced ; since $y\,dx = d\nu/\nu$, it follows that the area of the narrow strip between two ordinates whose abscissæ are x and $x + dx$ is equal in numerical value to the ratio of the number of molecules whose velocities lie between c and $c + dc$ to the whole number, and therefore, by summing the areas of any number of successive strips, we see that the area between any two ordinates gives the proportionate number of molecules which possess velocities between the corresponding limits. The area between the whole curve and the axis of x is of course equal to unity. The maximum ordinate corresponds to a velocity equal to $(hm)^{-\frac{1}{2}}$, which may be called the most probable velocity.

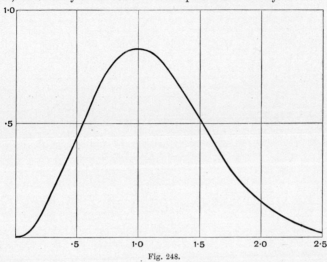

Fig. 248.

In the case of a mixture of two gases, or two gases in thermal equilibrium (see Art. 373), since h is the same constant for each, we have

$$m\overline{c^2} = m_1\overline{c_1^2} = \frac{3}{2h} \qquad . \quad . \quad . \quad . \quad . \quad (2)$$

so that the mean kinetic energy of molecular translation is the same for both. Hence the condition for equality of temperature on the kinetic theory is that the mean kinetic energy of molecular agitation should be the same for the two gases. The temperature of a gas is therefore a function of the molecular kinetic energy only. We shall now show that if the temperature of a gas be defined as *a quantity proportional to the mean molecular kinetic energy of translation*, then the gas of the kinetic theory will obey the ordinary laws of gases. Referring to the equation of a perfect gas given in Art. 89, viz.

$$pv = R\Theta \qquad . \quad . \quad . \quad . \quad . \quad . \quad (3)$$

put $R = NR_0$, where N is the number of molecules in volume v when the gas is at standard temperature and pressure ; so that

$$pv = NR_0\Theta.$$

If v is the volume of unit mass, then $Nm = 1$, and

$$mpv = R_0\Theta.$$

Here R_0 is a constant which is the same for every gas ;[1] thus the

---

[1] To calculate R_0, suppose the gas to be at standard temperature and pressure, *i.e.* put $p = 1\cdot0132 \times 10^6$, $\Theta = 273\cdot1$, and $mv = m/\rho$ which is the same for all gases by

temperature of a gas on the ordinary gas-scale is proportional to mpv, the ratio being the same for every gas.

Now equation (1), Art. 369, may be written

$$mpv = \frac{1}{3} m\overline{c^2} = \frac{1}{2h} \qquad\qquad \text{by (2),}$$

and this equation shows that, on the kinetic theory also, mpv is the same for all gases at the same temperature. Thus we may define temperature on the kinetic theory by the equation

$$2h\mathrm{R}_0\Theta = 1 \quad . \quad . \quad . \quad . \quad . \quad (4)$$

where R_0 is a universal constant, and the gas of the kinetic theory will obey all the laws implied by equation (3).

In addition, Avogadro's law is shown to hold, for if the two gases are at the same temperature and pressure

$$m\overline{c^2} = m_1\overline{c_1}^2 \; ; \quad \nu m\overline{c^2} = \nu_1 m_1 \overline{c_1}^2 \qquad\qquad \text{(see Art. 55),}$$

therefore

$$\nu = \nu_1,$$

or, if two gases are at the same temperature and pressure, the number of molecules in unit volume is the same for both.

The simple form of molecule we have been so far considering has only three degrees of freedom and its kinetic energy is wholly translational. In the more general theory, in which the molecules are not supposed to be uniform spheres, they may possess rotational energy and may also be capable of executing internal vibrations. It has been shown that in such cases *the energy is equally divided among all the degrees of freedom*.[1] This is called the law of equipartition of energy. For the simple spherical molecule we have

$$\tfrac{1}{2}m\overline{u^2} = \tfrac{1}{2}m\overline{v^2} = \tfrac{1}{2}m\overline{w^2} = \frac{1}{4h} = \tfrac{1}{2}\mathrm{R}_0\Theta.$$

If we had a mixture of two gases, in one of which the molecules were spheres such as we have been considering, and in the other

---

Avogadro's law. For oxygen, $\rho = 0\cdot001429$, $m = 52\cdot83 \times 10^{-24}$ grammes, which gives $\mathrm{R}_0 = mp/\rho\Theta = 1\cdot372 \times 10^{-16}$. The quantity which is usually taken as the universal gas-constant is not R_0 but $\mu\mathrm{R}_0/m$, where μ is the molecular weight. This has the advantage that its calculation does not require a knowledge of m, which is the most uncertain of the above numbers. In the case of oxygen, putting $\mu = 32$, we get $\mu\mathrm{R}_0/m = 83\cdot08 \times 10^6$. The value given in Kaye and Laby's *Tables of Physical and Chemical Constants* is $83\cdot15 \times 10^6$ ergs per gramme, and Henning (*Zeit. für Physik*, vol. vi. p. 69, 1921) gives $83\cdot13 \times 10^6$.

[1] See Jeans, *loc. cit.* pp. 80, 123. The kinetic energy is supposed to be expressed in terms of the principal co-ordinates of the system (see Routh's *Rigid Dynamics*, vol. i. p. 367), *i.e.* as a sum of squares of differential coefficients of the independent co-ordinates, each co-ordinate representing one degree of freedom. The law of equipartition of energy cannot be universally true (see Art. 288).

were, say, smooth ellipsoids of revolution, the latter would have five degrees of freedom; then the mean energy corresponding to each of these eight degrees of freedom would be the same for each, and equal to $1/4h$. Thus the definition of temperature applies also to gases with more complex molecular systems. The principle of equipartition of energy is a *statistical* one, and in general applies only to the mean energy of a large number.

It will be noticed that the *size* of the molecules does not enter into the final results of the foregoing investigation. In fact, as Jeans has shown,[1] Maxwell's law holds even for large molecules. But the calculation of the pressure (Art. 55) holds only for infinitely small molecules, since the centres of molecules cannot come into contact with each other or with the walls of the vessel. For molecules of appreciable size the actual pressure will be greater[2] than that given by the formula $pv = \frac{1}{3}\bar{c^2}$.

376. Specific Heats.—It may be inferred from the example given in the last article that if we have two gases, the molecules of the one having more degrees of freedom than those of the other, and if we increase the temperature of each gas by the same amount, the former will require more energy to be communicated to it than the latter ; in other words, the specific heat is greater when the molecules have more degrees of freedom. Let us suppose that the molecule of a gas has n degrees of freedom. For a smooth rigid sphere $n = 3$, for a smooth rigid figure of revolution $n = 5$, and for a rigid body in general $n = 6$. In what follows all the quantities are supposed to be expressed in dynamical units. Let U be the molecular kinetic energy of unit mass, then, since the kinetic energy of translation of unit mass is $\frac{1}{2}\bar{c^2}$, and this accounts for three degrees of freedom,

$$U = \frac{n}{6}\bar{c^2} = \tfrac{1}{2}npv = \tfrac{1}{2}nR\Theta.$$

If we give a small amount of heat dQ to the gas,

$$dQ = dU + pdv = \tfrac{1}{2}nRd\Theta + pdv \qquad \text{(Art. 321)}.$$

Let C_p and C_v be the specific heats at constant pressure and constant volume respectively, then

$$C_v = \left(\frac{dQ}{d\Theta}\right)_v = \tfrac{1}{2}nR,$$

$$C_p = \left(\frac{dQ}{d\Theta}\right)_p = \tfrac{1}{2}nR + p\left(\frac{dv}{d\Theta}\right)_p,$$

---

[1] *Loc. cit.* p. 54.

[2] If p' is the actual pressure, then, to a first approximation, $pv = p'(v - b)$, where b is a constant, and $b = \frac{2}{3}\nu\pi\sigma^3 =$ four times the volume of the molecules in the gas, v being the volume of unit mass (see note, p. 480).

but

$$\left(\frac{dv}{d\Theta}\right)_p = \frac{d}{d\Theta}\left(\frac{R\Theta}{p}\right) - \frac{R}{p},$$

therefore

$$C_p = \tfrac{1}{2}(n+2)R.$$

The ratio of the specific heats is given by

$$\gamma = \frac{C_p}{C_v} = \frac{n+2}{n}.$$

The value of γ for mercury vapour, and the inert gases helium, argon, etc., is $\frac{5}{3}$ (slightly less for helium). These gases behave like the simple gas of our theory. The inert gases are held to be monatomic for this reason together with the evidence of their positions in the series of the elements, and the fact that mercury vapour is known on other grounds to be monatomic. For oxygen, nitrogen, and hydrogen, $\gamma = \frac{7}{5}$ very nearly, so that the molecules of these gases behave like smooth figures of revolution.

The values of the specific heats in thermal units may be calculated from the formulæ

$$\frac{C_p}{J} = \tfrac{1}{2}(n+2)\frac{R'_0}{J\mu}, \quad \frac{C_v}{J} = \tfrac{1}{2}n\frac{R'_0}{J\mu},$$

where R'_0 is the gas-constant (note, p. 793). Putting $J = 4\cdot184 \times 10^7$, $R'_0 = 83\cdot15 \times 10^6$, $n = 5$, we get the following values :—

Gas.	$\dfrac{C_p}{J}$.		$\dfrac{C_v}{J}$.	
	Calc.	Obs.	Calc.	Obs.
Air . . .	0·2403	0·2374	0·1719	0·1721
Hydrogen . .	3·4778	3·4090	2·484	2·402
Oxygen . .	0·2174	0·2175	...	...
Nitrogen . .	0·2484	0·2438	...	...

The experimental values, taken from Regnault's and Joly's tables (pp. 268, 256), are reproduced for comparison. A very close agreement cannot be expected, since the formulæ make the specific heats independent of temperature and pressure, which is known not to be strictly true (Arts. 156, 167, 168).

The observed value of γ for chlorine is about $\frac{4}{3}$, corresponding to $n = 6$. Many compound gases and vapours give values of γ not corresponding to integral values of n.

377. Gas subject to Gravitation—Atmosphere.—In order to find the law of distribution of velocities in a column of gas which is under the action of gravity, we may proceed as follows. Suppose we have two similar columns of the same gas in equilibrium at the same temperature and pressure, and under the action of no forces, then the distribution of velocities will be that which we have already determined. Call the two columns (of which one is represented in Fig. 249) P and Q respectively, and let ν_0 be the number of molecules per unit volume. Consider the distribution of velocities in a thin horizontal stratum X_0Y_0 in each, X_0Y_0 being taken as the plane $z = 0$. The number of molecules of class (u, v, w) is, by Art. 375,

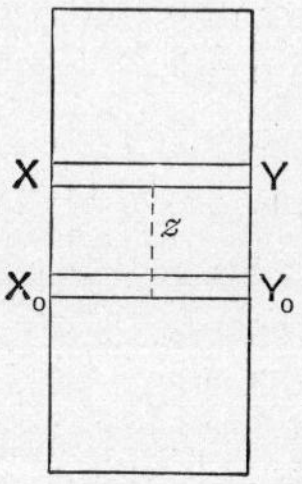

$$\nu_0\left(\frac{hm}{\pi}\right)^{\frac{3}{2}} e^{-hm(u^2+v^2+w^2)} du\, dv\, dw \qquad . \qquad . \qquad (1)$$

Now suppose gravity to act on Q but not on P.

Fig. 249.

The velocities of molecules in X_0Y_0 will be initially the same in both columns, but if a molecule from a stratum XY whose height above X_0Y_0 is z enters X_0Y_0, its vertical component of velocity will be $\sqrt{w^2 + 2gz}$ in Q instead of w as in P. Thus differences will appear in the distribution in the two columns. But if the number of molecules of class (u, v, w) in the stratum XY were

$$\nu_0\left(\frac{hm}{\pi}\right)^{\frac{3}{2}} e^{-hm(u^2+v^2+w^2+2gz)} du\, dv\, dw \qquad . \qquad . \qquad . \qquad (2)$$

in Q, then the number of class $(u, v, \sqrt{w^2 - 2gz})$ would by the same rule be

$$\nu_0\left(\frac{hm}{\pi}\right)^{\frac{3}{2}} e^{-hm(u^2+v^2+w^2)} du\, dv\, dw,$$

which is the same as (1), and the same number would therefore enter X_0Y_0 as in P, and they would there have the appropriate component of velocity w, just as in P. Thus, by altering the distribution of the molecules in the manner indicated, we can make the stratum X_0Y_0 in Q correspond to the state of equilibrium in P. Moreover, every other stratum such as XY would be in equilibrium also, for the law of distribution expressed by (2) is the same as (1), the factor e^{-2hmgz} (which does not involve the velocities) meaning that the number of molecules per unit volume in the stratum XY is

$$\nu = \nu_0 e^{-2hmgz} \qquad . \qquad . \qquad . \qquad . \qquad . \qquad (3)$$

If then, in a column of gas under gravity, ν varies with height according to equation (3), while Maxwell's distribution of velocities holds in every stratum, and the temperature (which depends on h) is the same throughout, the column will be in equilibrium.[1]

---

[1] The mode of argument is general, and applies equally to a gas under any system of conservative forces. If $E = \frac{1}{2}m(u^2+v^2+w^2)$ and χ is the potential energy

If ρ_0 is the density at the plane of reference, and ρ the density at the plane whose vertical co-ordinate is z, then, since ρ is proportional to ν,

$$\rho = \rho_0 e^{-2hmgz} \qquad . \qquad . \qquad . \qquad . \qquad . \qquad (4)$$

We may arrive at the same result by another method, if we assume that, on thermodynamical grounds, the temperature must be the same throughout. Consider first the total amount of momentum, measured in the positive direction of the z-axis, which flows across any horizontal plane whose area is S. Let there be in unit volume ν_1 molecules of class (u_1, v_1, w_1), ν_2 of class (u_2, v_2, w_2), and so on, so that

$$\nu = \nu_1 + \nu_2 + \nu_3 + \text{etc.}$$

The number of molecules of class (u_1, v_1, w_1) which cross S in the positive direction in time dt is the number contained within an oblique cylinder (cf. Fig. 246) with base S and of height $w_1 dt$, the generators of the cylinder being parallel to the resultant velocity c_1 and of length $c_1 dt$. This number is $\nu_1 w_1 S dt$, and the momentum carried by them across S is $m\nu_1 w_1^2 S dt$, so that the total momentum carried across by all classes is

$$\tfrac{1}{2} m S dt \cdot \Sigma \nu_n w_n^2 \qquad . \qquad . \qquad . \qquad . \qquad (5)$$

for all values of n, the factor $\tfrac{1}{2}$ being introduced because the negative values of w, which are equal in number to the positive values, belong to molecules which do not cross S. But expression (5) also gives the total negative momentum carried across S in the opposite direction, and since the withdrawal of negative momentum is equivalent to the addition of positive momentum, we see that the total gain of momentum of the gas above the horizontal plane is

$$m S dt \cdot \Sigma \nu_n w_n^2,$$

but

$$\frac{1}{\nu} \Sigma \nu_n w_n^2 = \overline{w^2},$$

therefore the total positive momentum passing upward through S in time dt is, since $m\nu = \rho$, equal to

$$\rho S \overline{w^2} dt.$$

Returning now to the consideration of the column of gas under gravity, the total momentum, measured upwards, contained within a

---

of a molecule in any equipotential stratum, while ν_0 is the value of ν for the equipotential surface $\chi = 0$, then the number of molecules of class (u, v, w) in the stratum χ is

$$\nu_0 \left(\frac{hm}{\pi}\right)^{\frac{3}{2}} e^{-2h(E+\chi)} du\, dv\, dw.$$

horizontal stratum of thickness dz must be constant, and is in fact zero for a gas at rest. The momentum entering the lower surface is $\rho S \overline{w^2} dt$, and the momentum leaving the upper surface is $(\rho + d\rho) S \overline{w^2} dt$, $\overline{w^2}$ being the same for both, as the temperature is uniform. The molecules in the stratum, being under the action of gravity, lose momentum $g\rho S dz dt$ in time dt. Equating then the total loss of momentum to zero, we get the equation

$$S\overline{w^2} d\rho + g\rho S dz = 0,$$

therefore

$$\overline{w^2} \log \frac{\rho}{\rho_0} = -gz,$$

or, since $2hm\overline{w^2} = 1$,

$$\rho = \rho_0 e^{-2hmgz}$$

as before.   This method of proof is equivalent to the ordinary hydro-static method, but, when we regard a gas as consisting of a number of discrete molecules, we cannot directly speak of the pressure which one portion of gas exerts on another. We may, however, define the pressure at a point in a gas as the total momentum per second which passes perpendicularly through a plane of unit area at the point.   If the gas is in motion, the point must be supposed to move with it, *i.e.* in such a way that the total mass passing through a small plane at the point is zero, however the plane may be oriented.   The momentum is then measured relative to this plane.

If the column consists of a mixture of two or more gases, then the above method of investigation shows that the distribution of each gas is quite independent of the others, the lighter gases tending to predominate at the top of the column, since the exponential factor, which involves m, differs for different gases.

The Atmosphere.[1]—Owing to solar radiation the earth's atmosphere is very far from being in a state of thermal equilibrium.   The temperature of the earth's surface varies greatly in different latitudes and at different seasons, and is also modified by the presence of large land-masses in different quarters of the globe.   The greatest annual extremes of temperature occur in the interior of continents in high latitudes, the diurnal variations being also considerable over land. The direction of the prevailing winds is affected by the rotation of the earth.   Clouds have a marked influence on the temperature of the earth's surface and of the air in the lower parts of the atmosphere. The temperature of the air at different levels has been studied by means of sounding balloons, provided with apparatus for registering

[1] W. L. Moore, *Descriptive Meteorology*, chap. viii. ; Jeans, *loc. cit.* chap. xv. ; S. Chapman and E. A. Milne, *Quart. Journ. R. Meteorological Soc.* vol. xlvi. p. 357, 1920.

the temperature and elevation.   The temperature of the atmosphere
in general diminishes with height, at first irregularly and then nearly
uniformly up to a height of about 10 kilometres or more, above
which it is nearly constant.   The atmosphere may be conveniently
divided into three regions ; the first, extending from the surface up
to about 3 kilometres, is the region of strong disturbances and of
clouds.   The temperature diminishes with height on the whole, but
inversions of the temperature gradient are frequent, especially in the
early morning.   The second region, extending roughly from about 3
kilometres to 10 kilometres, is generally free from dense clouds, the
cirri floating in its uppermost layers.   In this region the temperature diminishes.   If mixing were perfect, the rate of diminution
would be according to the adiabatic law : that is to say, the variation
of temperature would be such that a mass of air brought from one
level to another, and allowed to alter in volume adiabatically till its
pressure were equal to that at the new level, would be at the same
temperature as the surrounding air.   Lord Kelvin has called this a
state of *convective equilibrium*.[1]   But owing to heat exchanges due to
radiation and conduction, the rate of fall of temperature is not much
more than half the adiabatic gradient.   The temperature at the top
of this second region varies from $-40°$ C. to $-70°$ C.   These two
regions are often regarded as one, the region in which the temperature
on the whole diminishes upward, which is called the *troposphere*.
The mean gradient in the troposphere is about 6° C. per kilometre.
The third region, the existence of which was first discovered by
Teisserenc de Bort, begins at about 10 kilometres.   It is usually
referred to as the *isothermal layer* or the *stratosphere*.   The temperature is not quite uniform in this layer ; it usually increases slightly
with elevation, up to the limits of observation—about 26 kilometres.
At a height of 18 or 20 kilometres, the pressure is nearly the same
everywhere and there is no wind.

The separation of the constituent gases of the atmosphere by
gravity indicated by the kinetic theory does not occur in the troposphere, owing to mixing, and would not be appreciable except at
great heights, even if the air were in equilibrium.   The variation
in the proportions of oxygen and nitrogen ought, however, to be
quite measurable at the greatest heights attained in the isothermal
layer by sounding balloons.   If hydrogen exists at all in the upper
atmosphere, then at 60 kilometres the air should contain several per
cent of hydrogen, and at 100 kilometres it would be nearly all
hydrogen.   Of course, the absolute amount of the hydrogen would

[1] J. Clerk Maxwell, *Theory of Heat*, p. 321.

be excessively small, since at the surface, where it is greatest, it forms only about 0·01 per cent by volume of the air. Chapman and Milne think it probable that hydrogen produced at the surface disappears in the upper atmosphere, owing to recombination with oxygen. The next lightest gas, helium, does not combine, and at a height of 100 kilometres the proportionate volume of helium should be nearly three times that of the oxygen and one-tenth that of the nitrogen.

Auroræ occur at heights of 100 to 130 kilometres.

It has been suggested by G. J. Stoney that, in the highest parts of the earth's atmosphere, the swifter molecules of a light gas such as hydrogen would have sufficient velocity to escape from the earth's attraction and pass away into space. Later calculations,[1] however, indicate that the earth should be able to retain hydrogen and all other gases. The retention of an atmosphere by other members of the solar system should depend partly on their masses and partly on their temperatures. Thus the absence of an atmosphere on the moon can be accounted for by its small mass. Mercury, which is a small planet and nearest to the sun, is believed to be devoid of atmosphere. Mars could not retain hydrogen, and perhaps not even

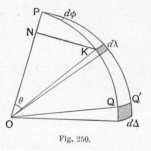

Fig. 250.

helium, but should be able to retain water vapour and heavier gases. It is known to have an atmosphere, though not a dense one. All the larger planets have dense atmospheres.

378. Number of Collisions.—The number of collisions which occur in one second in unit volume of a gas can be calculated from Maxwell's formula. The number of collisions per second which take place between pairs of molecules of classes (u, v, w) and (u', v', w') whose line of centres, drawn from a fixed point, lies within a small solid angle $d\lambda$ is, by Arts. 371, 373, equal to

$$A^2 e^{-hm(c^2+c'^2)} q\sigma^2 \cos\theta \, d\lambda \, d\omega \, d\omega' \quad . \quad . \quad . \quad (1)$$

and we have to integrate this for all possible lines of centres and for all values of c and c'. We shall require the following theorem :—

Let OP be a fixed radius of a unit sphere drawn round O as centre (Fig. 250), and let PQ, PQ' be neighbouring arcs of great circles, and the shaded area $d\Lambda$ an element of the surface of the sphere included between the arcs PQ, PQ' and between arcs of small

[1] Jeans, *loc. cit.* p. 357.

circles drawn round OP as axis. Let $d\phi$ be the angle between PQ
and PQ′, and 2θ the angle POQ. Then, if the extremity of a radius
vector from O traces out the area $d\Lambda$, the bisector of the angle
between this radius vector and OP will trace out a corresponding
area $d\lambda$. From the extremity of the bisector OK of the angle POQ
draw KN perpendicular to OP. If $d\theta$ is the angle subtended at O by
$d\lambda$ in the plane POQ, then the area of $d\lambda$ is NK $d\phi\, d\theta = \sin \theta\, d\phi\, d\theta$.
Similarly the area of $d\Lambda$ is $\sin 2\theta\, d\phi\, d(2\theta) = 2 \sin 2\theta\, d\phi\, d\theta$. We may
therefore write

$$d\lambda = \sin \theta\, d\phi\, d\theta \; ; \quad d\Lambda = 2 \sin 2\theta\, d\phi\, d\theta,$$

whence

$$\cos \theta\, d\lambda = \tfrac{1}{4} d\Lambda.$$

Now, referring to Figs. 244, 246, θ is the angle between the line of
centres at impact and the direction of the relative velocity, *i.e.* the
angle NMA′ (Fig. 244). The angle BMA′ is 2θ. Regarding A and
A′ as fixed points, when the line MN (which is parallel to OK) traces
out the solid angle $d\lambda$, the line MB′ traces out a solid angle $d\Lambda$.
Since θ may have any value up to a right angle, the point B may lie
anywhere on the surface of a sphere round M as centre. That is to
say, we have to integrate $\cos \theta d\lambda$ over a hemisphere of the unit
sphere, or $\tfrac{1}{4} d\Lambda$ over the whole sphere ; thus the integral is π.

The total number of collisions per second between molecules of
classes $(u,\ v,\ w)$ and $(u',\ v',\ w')$ is therefore

$$\pi \mathrm{A}^2 e^{-hm(c^2+c'^2)} q \sigma^2 d\omega\, d\omega' \ . \qquad . \qquad . \qquad . \qquad (2)$$

We have now, while keeping c fixed in magnitude and direction,
to integrate for all possible values of c', that is, to find the total number
of collisions per second of class $(u,\ v,\ w)$ with
all other classes. Let OA (Fig. 251) represent
the vector c, and OA′ the vector c'. With
centre A draw a sphere of radius q (which
will pass through A′) and another of radius
$q + dq$. Let θ' be the angle OAA′, then if we
draw another radius close to AA′, in the plane
OAA′, the small shaded area on the diagram
may be represented by $q dq d\theta'$. If the plane
OAA′ is turned through a small angle $d\phi'$
round OA as axis, the shaded area will sweep
out a small volume $q \sin \theta' d\phi' \cdot q dq d\theta'$ on the
velocity-diagram. We shall take this small

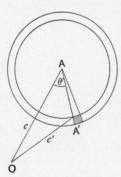

Fig. 251.—Velocity-diagram.

volume as $d\omega'$ instead of $du'\, dv'\, dw'$. The expression (2) may now
be written

$$\pi\sigma^2 A^2 e^{-hm(c^2+c'^2)}d\omega \,.\, q^3dq \sin \theta'd\theta'd\phi'.$$

Integrating with respect to ϕ', that is, along a ring-element of volume on the diagram whose axis is OA, we get

$$2\pi^2\sigma^2 A^2 e^{-hm(c^2+c'^2)}d\omega \, q^3dq \sin \theta'd\theta' \quad . \qquad . \qquad . \qquad (3)$$

We next integrate with respect to θ', that is, for all ring-elements which make up the thin spherical shell of radius q. Both c and q are still kept constant, but c' now varies. We have

$$c'^2 = q^2 + c^2 - 2qc \cos \theta',$$

therefore

$$c'dc' = qc \sin \theta'd\theta'.$$

Changing the variable from θ' to c', (3) becomes

$$2\pi^2\sigma^2 A^2 \frac{1}{c} e^{-hmc^2}d\omega \,.\, q^2dq \,.\, e^{-hmc'^2}c'dc'.$$

As we are integrating over a sphere with A as centre, the limiting values of c' are $c + q$ for the upper limit and $c - q$ for the lower. If $q > c$, that is, if O lies within the sphere, the lower limit will be $q - c$ instead of $c - q$, but this makes no difference, since only an even function of c' is involved. We have

$$\int_{c-q}^{c+q} e^{-hmc'^2}c'dc' = \frac{1}{2hm}\left[-e^{-hmc'^2}\right]_{c-q}^{c+q}$$
$$= \frac{1}{2hm}\left\{e^{-hm(q-c)^2} - e^{-hm(q+c)^2}\right\},$$

therefore the integration of (3) gives the expression

$$\frac{\pi^2\sigma^2 A^2}{hmc} e^{-hmc^2}d\omega \,.\, q^2\left\{e^{-hm(q-c)^2} - e^{-hm(q+c)^2}\right\}dq \quad . \qquad . \qquad (4)$$

and this is the number of collisions per second between molecules of class (u, v, w) and all other classes for which the relative velocity lies between q and $q + dq$.

Now q may be supposed to take all values from 0 to ∞; integrating therefore between these limits, we get, by (6) Art. 374,

$$\frac{\pi^2\sigma^2 A^2}{h^2m^2} e^{-hmc^2}d\omega\left\{e^{-hmc^2} + \frac{2hmc^2+1}{c\sqrt{hm}}\int_0^{c\sqrt{hm}} e^{-\mu^2}d\mu\right\}. \quad . \qquad . \qquad (5)$$

as the total number of collisions between molecules of class (u, v, w) and all other classes.

We may remark here that the rate of wastage of class (u, v, w), that is, the ratio of the number lost per second to the whole number, is got by dividing (5) by $Ae^{-hmc^2}d\omega$. If k is this quantity, then, putting for A its value $\nu(hm/\pi)^{\frac{3}{2}}$,

$$k = \nu\sigma^2 \sqrt{\frac{\pi}{hm}} \left\{ e^{-hmc^2} + \frac{2hmc^2+1}{c\sqrt{hm}} \int_0^{c\sqrt{hm}} e^{-\mu^2}d\mu \right\} \qquad . \qquad . \quad (6)$$

The last step in the calculation is to integrate (5) with respect to c from 0 to ∞. Putting $4\pi c^2 dc$ for $d\omega$ as in Art. 375, and changing the variable from c to a, where $a = c\sqrt{hm}$, we get the integral

$$\frac{4\pi^3\sigma^2 A^2}{\sqrt{h^7 m^7}} \int_0^\infty \left\{ a^3 e^{-2a^2} + a(2a^2+1)e^{-a^2} \int_0^a e^{-\mu^2}d\mu \right\} da \qquad . \qquad . \quad (7)$$

This can be integrated by parts, for since

$$\int a(2a^2+1)e^{-a^2}da = -(a^2+\tfrac{3}{2})e^{-a^2},$$

the integral of the term involving $\int_0^a e^{-\mu^2}d\mu$ is

$$-(a^2+\tfrac{3}{2})e^{-a^2}\int_0^a e^{-\mu^2}d\mu + \int(a^2+\tfrac{3}{2})e^{-2a^2}da,$$

so that (7) is equal to

$$\frac{4\pi^3\sigma^2 A^2}{\sqrt{h^7 m^7}}\left\{ \left[-(a^2+\tfrac{3}{2})e^{-a^2}\int_0^a e^{-\mu^2}d\mu \right]_0^\infty + \int_0^\infty (2a^2+\tfrac{3}{2})e^{-2a^2}da \right\}.$$

The expression in square brackets vanishes at both limits, and the value of the integral is got from formula (3), Art. 374. The expression reduces to

$$\frac{4\pi^3\sigma^2 A^2}{\sqrt{h^7 m^7}}\sqrt{\frac{\pi}{2}} = 2\nu^2\sigma^2\sqrt{\frac{2\pi}{hm}}.$$

This is the number of molecules lost by all classes in one second owing to collisions. Each collision means the loss of *two* molecules, one to each class. The whole number of collisions per second occurring in unit volume of the gas is therefore half the above expression, that is

$$\nu^2\sigma^2\sqrt{\frac{2\pi}{hm}} \qquad . \qquad . \qquad . \qquad . \quad (8)$$

This number is proportional to the square of the density and to the square root of the absolute temperature. For a given mass of gas at a given temperature the pressure varies as the density, so that the number of collisions per second is proportional to the square of the density.

As the molecules of a gas are not elastic spheres, it is difficult to assign a meaning to σ for any gas. Jeans[1] estimates the effective diameter of the hydrogen molecule at $2\cdot4 \times 10^{-8}$ centimetre. Writing (8) in the form

---

[1] *Loc. cit.* pp. 9, 342.

$$2\nu^2\sigma^2 \sqrt{\frac{\pi p}{\rho}},$$

and putting $\nu = 2\cdot7 \times 10^{19}$ (see p. 568), $p = 10^6$ and $\rho = 9 \times 10^{-5}$, we get $1\cdot6 \times 10^{29}$ as the number of collisions per second in one cubic centimetre of hydrogen at standard temperature and pressure.

379. Mean Free Path.—The average distance described by a molecule between two successive collisions is called the *mean free path*. The term is somewhat ambiguous, because the average can be calculated in different ways.

If $\bar{c}$ is the mean velocity of a molecule, then the distance traversed in one second by all the molecules in unit volume is $\nu\bar{c}$. If n is the number of collisions which occur in one second, then, since each collision terminates two free paths, the mean free path λ is given by the equation

$$\lambda = \frac{\nu\bar{c}}{2n},$$

but

$$\bar{c} = \frac{2}{\sqrt{\pi hm}}, \quad n = \nu^2\sigma^2 \sqrt{\frac{2\pi}{hm}},$$

by Art. 375 and (8) of the last article, therefore

$$\lambda = \frac{1}{\pi\nu\sigma^2\sqrt{2}} \quad . \quad . \quad . \quad . \quad . \quad . \quad (1)$$

This is Maxwell's mean free path. Tait determines the mean free path in a different way. He considers a particular instant of time, and calculates the mean distance described by each molecule before its next collision. Tait's mean free path is somewhat less than Maxwell's. This is because, as Boltzmann points out, in Tait's method one free path is assigned to each molecule. In Maxwell's method a given interval of time is taken, and the swifter molecules, whose paths are longer, describe more paths in that interval, hence the average calculated in Maxwell's way is greater. For Tait's mean free path see Ex. 7 below.

As should obviously be the case, the mean free path in a given gas depends on the density and on nothing else. Using the data given in the last article, the mean free path of hydrogen under standard conditions is found to be about $1\cdot4 \times 10^{-5}$ centimetre.

Examples

1. Find the number of molecules of class (c, w) in a gas at rest, that is, the number whose velocity lies between the limits c and $c + dc$, and whose component of velocity parallel to the axis of w lies between the limits w and $w + dw$.

{In the expression $Ae^{-hmc^2}d\omega$ substitute for $d\omega$ the volume of the ring-element of space on the velocity-diagram, bounded by spheres of radii c and $c+dc$, and by planes whose co-ordinates are w and $w+dw$. This volume is found to be $2\pi cdwdc$.}

2. Find the number of molecules which cross unit area of any plane per second.

{Taking the plane to be perpendicular to the z-axis, the number of molecules of class (u, v, w) contained in an oblique cylinder whose base is unit area of the plane, and whose generators are parallel to the direction of c and of length cdt, is $Ae^{-hmc^2}wdudvdwdt$. All these will cross the plane in time dt. Putting $u^2+v^2+w^2$ for c^2, and integrating for u and v from $-\infty$ to $+\infty$, and for w from 0 to ∞, we find the number crossing in one direction to be $\nu/2\sqrt{\pi hm}$ or $\frac{1}{4}\bar{\nu}c$. The number crossing in both directions is $\frac{1}{2}\bar{\nu}c$.}

3. Show that a gas will be in equilibrium if the law of distribution of velocities is $f(c)=Ae^{-\lambda c^2}$, where A and λ are constants.

{If A and A' (Fig. 244) are any two points on the velocity-diagram, the velocity-points after collision of the corresponding molecules will be situated at opposite ends of a diameter of the sphere drawn on AA' as diameter. The number of collisions is clearly proportional to the product of the densities of velocity-points at A and A', that is, to $f(c)f(c')$. If, then, we can determine the form of $f(c)$ so as to make this product a constant for all pairs of extremities of diameters of any sphere, no class can gain molecules at the expense of any other class. Now, geometrically, $OA^2+OA'^2=2(OM^2+MA^2)$, which is a constant for each sphere, therefore the theorem follows immediately. Boltzmann's H-theorem is required to prove that this solution is the only one.}

4. Extend the theorem of Ex. (3) to the case of a mixture of two gases.

{In this case the point M divides AA_1 inversely as the masses m, m_1. After collision, B lies on the same sphere as A, and B_1 on the same sphere as A_1. If we can determine $f(c)$ and $F(c_1)$ so as to make $f(c) F(c_1)$ a constant for all pairs of opposite points, one on one sphere and one on the other, and also satisfy the condition of Ex. (3), we shall have a solution of the problem. But in this case $mOA^2+m_1OA_1^2=mMA^2+m_1MA_1^2+(m+m_1)OM^2=$ const. (see Casey's *Sequel to Euclid*, p. 24), therefore the necessary conditions are fulfilled by putting

$$f(c)=Ae^{-hmc^2}, \quad F(c_1)=A_1e^{-hm_1c_1^2},$$

where A, A_1, and h are arbitrary constants.}

5. In an experiment of Berthollet's, two equal globes, one filled with a light gas, and the other with a heavy gas at the same temperature and pressure, were placed with the light gas uppermost. When communication was opened by means of a stop-cock, the gases were found to be completely mixed in a short time. Assuming the gases to be monatomic, find the diminution of temperature, if D is the vertical distance between the centres of the globes.

Ans. $\dfrac{(\rho-\rho')g\mathrm{D\Theta}}{3p}$.

6. If n_1 molecules of class (u, v, w) start from the plane $z=z_1$, find how many of them will reach the plane $z=z_2$ without collision.

{The time taken to pass through any stratum of thickness dz is dz/w, and if n is the number reaching this stratum, $kndz/w$ of these are lost by collision in the stratum (6, Art. 378). We have therefore

$$-dn=kn\frac{dz}{w},$$

whence

$$\int_{n_1}^{n_2}\frac{dn}{n}=-\frac{k}{w}\int_{z_1}^{z_2}dz,$$

so that

$$n_2=n_1e^{-\frac{k}{w}(z_2-z_1)}.\Big\}$$

7. Find the mean free path of molecules of class (c).

{The aggregate distance travelled by n molecules of this class in one second is nc, and the number of collisions is kn, therefore $\lambda_o=c/k$. If we integrate to get the mean for all values of c, we get Tait's mean free path

$$\lambda=\frac{4}{\pi\nu\sigma^2}\int_0^\infty\frac{x^3e^{-x^2}dx}{\psi(x)},$$

$$\psi(x)=e^{-x^2}+\frac{2x^2+1}{x}\int_0^x e^{-\mu^2}d\mu.\Big\}$$

SECTION II

GAS NOT IN EQUILIBRIUM

380. Irreversible Processes.—It has been already pointed out (p. 780 footnote) that the encounters of molecules are dynamically strictly reversible. One of the most remarkable results of the kinetic theory is that it enables us to account for processes which are found in practice to be irreversible. To take a particular instance, let us suppose that a mass of gas, not in equilibrium, is enclosed in a rigid envelope and left to itself. The molecules are assumed to rebound from the walls of the envelope in the manner explained in Art. 370, so that the total energy remains constant. Since the gas is not in equilibrium, the quantity H (Art. 372) will initially have a value greater than the minimum value, but according to the theorem of that article, H will steadily diminish till it attains the minimum value, when the gas will be in equilibrium. It may now be argued that, since a molecule is just as likely to be moving in one direction as another, we may conclude that if, at any stage of the transformation, the velocity of every molecule were reversed in direction, the gas would be in a state which is just as likely to occur as the state in which it actually is. The value of H is not affected by reversing the velocities, and, as the gas will obviously revert to its original condition (with velocities reversed), H will *increase* till it attains its initial value when all the collisions have occurred in the reverse order. This argument is perfectly valid, though it is clearly contradictory to Boltzmann's H-theorem. On referring to Art. 371, we see that such a possibility is not absolutely excluded. The argument there given is really based on the theory of probability, for we have assumed that the number of molecules of class A contained in a given space is proportional to the magnitude of that space, and we can easily conceive a special distribution of molecules to exist which does not fulfil this condition. Such a distribution would, however, be extremely improbable, as Boltzmann has shown.[1] His argument, in outline, is substantially as follows.

---

[1] *Loc. cit.* pp. 38-47.

The whole space on the velocity-diagram may be supposed to be divided into a number of small cells, all equal to one another. Subject to the condition that the total energy of the gas is given, it is regarded as equally probable that the velocity-point of a given molecule should fall in any one cell or in any other. We can construct a very large (though finite) number of possible arrangements by distributing the velocity-points among the cells in different ways. Each of these arrangements is then equally likely to occur. We may, for instance, assign all the velocity-points to a given cell; this can be done only in one way. Or we may assign half the points to one cell and half to another; this can be done in as many ways as we can select $\frac{1}{2}n$ out of n things (n being the whole number of molecules), and this is a very large number. We infer that it is very much more probable that half the molecules have one velocity and half another velocity (in direction and magnitude) than that all should have the same velocity. It is then shown that the greatest possible number of arrangements corresponds to the case in which H is a minimum, i.e. that in which Maxwell's law holds. Small oscillations of the value of H about its minimum value are not improbable and in fact will occur, but any appreciable deviation from Maxwell's distribution will be extremely improbable. We may summarise the result of this argument by saying that the process by which a gas initially not in equilibrium attains a state of equilibrium is dynamically reversible but statistically irreversible.[1]

We may even devise conditions in which Maxwell's distribution is never attained. Thus if a gas is contained in a perfectly smooth cylindrical vessel and is initially in rotation, the moment of momentum round the axis of the cylinder will persist throughout.

There are three irreversible processes which are especially important; these are diffusion, viscous dissipation of energy, and conduction of heat. If a vessel contains two gases, originally separated, as in Berthollet's experiment, it is clear that the molecules of each gas will penetrate into the space occupied by the other gas, until the two gases are uniformly mixed. This process is called *diffusion*. Again, if a mass of gas is set in motion and left to itself, the currents will rapidly die out and the gas will come to rest, the mass-energy appearing finally as molecular energy. In fact, if two neighbouring strata of gas are moving with different velocities, the exchanges which take place between them will tend to equalise their velocities. This effect is the same as if the strata exerted a

[1] Boltzmann shows that the entropy of a monatomic gas may be taken as proportional to − H (see Art. 331).

tangential stress on each other, so that a gas behaves as a medium possessing *viscosity*. Thirdly, if different portions of a gas are at different temperatures, the interpenetration of molecules tends to produce equality of temperature throughout the mass. Thus a gas possesses *conductivity* for heat. These three phenomena correspond, as Maxwell points out, to exchanges of matter, of momentum, and of energy respectively between different parts of a gas. In the case of a gas consisting of molecules of the kind which we have been considering, no rigorous mathematical calculation of the coefficients of diffusion, viscosity, or heat-conductivity has yet been given. The elementary method of discussion adopted in the following articles, though instructive, is open to grave objections, which will be pointed out in due course.

381. Viscosity.—Let the gas under consideration be regarded as made up of parallel plane strata, all moving in the same direction with velocities proportional to their distances from a fixed plane corresponding to the stratum at rest. The direction of motion is supposed to be parallel to the fixed plane, so that each stratum moves in its own plane. The temperature and pressure are assumed to be uniform throughout. This is the case of a gas subjected to a uniform shearing stress. Let the fixed plane be taken as the plane of xy, the direction of motion being parallel to the x-axis. Then the velocity of a stratum whose co-ordinate is z is az, where a is a constant which will be assumed to be small. If we draw any plane parallel to the strata, then, as explained in the last article, we may regard the gas on one side of this plane as exerting a tangential stress on the gas on the other side. Let this stress be F dynes per square centimetre. Then, by the definition of viscosity, if η is the coefficient of viscosity,

$$F = \eta \frac{du_0}{dz},$$

where u_0 is the mass-velocity of the stratum whose co-ordinate is z. But $u_0 = az$, therefore we get

$$\eta = \frac{F}{a} \qquad . \qquad . \qquad . \qquad . \qquad . \qquad . \qquad (1)$$

We shall assume that the distribution of velocities in every stratum is Maxwell's distribution, except that the whole stratum is moving with a uniform velocity az in its own plane. Consider a stratum of thickness dz at a distance z from the plane of reference, and let us calculate the total momentum per unit area per second which is carried across the plane $z = 0$ by molecules from the stratum reaching that plane. The number of molecules of class (c, w) per unit area of the stratum is

$$2\nu \sqrt{\frac{h^3 m^3}{\pi}} e^{-hmc^2} c\, dw\, dc\, dz \qquad \text{(Ex. 1, p. 805)},$$

so that the number of this class created per second in unit area of the stratum is, by (6) p. 804,

$$2\nu \sqrt{\frac{h^3 m^3}{\pi}} ke^{-hmc^2} c\, dw\, dc\, dz,$$

and the number which reach the plane $z = 0$ is

$$2\nu \sqrt{\frac{h^3 m^3}{\pi}} ke^{-hmc^2} c\, dw\, dc \cdot e^{\frac{kz}{w}} dz \qquad \text{(Ex. 6, p. 806)}.$$

Each of these molecules carries a momentum maz across the plane $z = 0$, therefore the momentum carried across unit area of the plane $z = 0$ per second is

$$2\rho a \sqrt{\frac{h^3 m^3}{\pi}} ke^{-hmc^2} c\, dw\, dc \cdot ze^{\frac{kz}{w}} dz.$$

Integrating with respect to z from 0 to ∞, remembering that all the quantities are positive except w, which is necessarily negative, since it refers only to molecules which are travelling towards the plane of reference, we get

$$\frac{2\rho a}{k} \sqrt{\frac{h^3 m^3}{\pi}} e^{-hmc^2} cw^2\, dw\, dc.$$

We have now to integrate with respect to w from $-c$ to 0, and with respect to c from 0 to ∞. This gives

$$\tfrac{2}{3}\rho a \sqrt{\frac{h^3 m^3}{\pi}} \int_0^\infty \frac{c^4 e^{-hmc^2} dc}{k}.$$

Putting x for $c\sqrt{hm}$, this transforms into

$$\frac{2a\rho}{3\pi\nu\sigma^2 \sqrt{hm}} \int_0^\infty \frac{x^4 e^{-x^2} dx}{\psi(x)},$$

where $\psi(x)$ has the same meaning as in Ex. 7, p. 807. This last expression represents the total momentum parallel to the axis of x which crosses unit area of the plane $z = 0$ per second from the positive to the negative side. The negative momentum crossing in the opposite direction has the same value; these have to be added together, so that the tangential stress F is got by doubling the last expression. Equation (1) then gives us

$$\eta = \frac{4\rho}{3\pi\nu\sigma^2 \sqrt{hm}} \int_0^\infty \frac{x^4 e^{-x^2} dx}{\psi(x)}.$$

Again, putting $1/\pi v \sigma^2 \sqrt{2} = \lambda$ (Maxwell's mean free path, p. 805), and $2/\sqrt{\pi h m} = \bar{c}$ (the mean velocity corresponding to the temperature, p. 792), we get the formula

$$\eta = B\rho\lambda\bar{c} \quad . \quad . \quad . \quad . \quad . \quad (2)$$

where

$$B = \frac{2\sqrt{2\pi}}{3} \int_0^\infty \frac{x^4 e^{-x^2} dx}{\psi(x)}.$$

B is a numerical coefficient, which has been calculated by Boltzmann and Tait, the value obtained being 0·305...

Since $\bar{c}$ depends only on the temperature, and λ is inversely proportional to the density ρ, the viscosity is independent of the density. This law was predicted by Maxwell and has since been experimentally confirmed. At very low pressures, when the mean free path is comparable with the dimensions of the vessel enclosing the gas, the viscosity falls suddenly and rapidly as the density is reduced.

The formula (2) indicates that the viscosity is proportional to the square root of the absolute temperature. Experiment shows that it varies with temperature rather faster than this, and that η is proportional approximately to Θ^n, where n is 0·68 for hydrogen and helium and 0·98 for carbon dioxide, with intermediate values for other gases.[1] It may be inferred from this that the molecules of an actual gas do not rebound like very hard spheres.

For reasons given below, the numerical factor B occurring in the formula is to be regarded with suspicion. We cannot directly test the formula by experiment, as we do not know the value of σ, which is required to evaluate λ. Jeans,[2] quoting Chapman, gives 0·499 as the most reliable value of B, obtained by a series of successive approximations. Assuming this value for B, the formula may be used to calculate σ from the observed value of the viscosity. In this way the value $2·68 \times 10^{-8}$ cm. is obtained for hydrogen.[3] This may be compared with the figures $2·4 \times 10^{-8}$ (Art. 378) obtained by calculations based chiefly on the deviation from Boyle's law.

In the foregoing investigation we have made three assumptions : (1) that Maxwell's distribution holds in every stratum, (2) that the gas is in a steady state at uniform temperature, and (3) that the number of molecules gained or lost by any class is unaffected by the relative motion of the strata through which the molecules pass. When the velocity gradient is small, i.e. when a is small, the third assumption is justified, because the path of a molecule is in general extremely short. The first assumption is the most open to objection,

---

[1] Jeans, *loc. cit.* p. 302.   [2] Jeans, *loc. cit.* p. 293.   [3] Jeans, *loc. cit.* p. 342.

for it is clear that Maxwell's law cannot hold strictly in a stratum which is continually acquiring new members from other strata which are in motion. It is also obvious that the conversion of mass-motion into molecular motion tends to cause a rise in temperature. We might suppose the gas to be in a steady state if it were enclosed between parallel planes moving with the gas and maintained both at the same temperature. But in this case there would be a steady temperature gradient from the middle stratum to each boundary, so that conduction of heat would occur from the interior to the bounding planes. As we shall see in Art. 383, there is a close connection between viscosity and conductivity, and that Maxwell's law cannot be assumed for a gas which is conducting heat.

382. Coefficient of Self-Diffusion.—It will be convenient to make the following preliminary investigation :[1] Suppose we have a column of gas, which we shall take to be vertical, in which some property of the molecules is the same for all molecules in the same horizontal stratum, but varies with the height of the stratum. We may suppose that this property is measured by the magnitude of some quantity G, which is carried along by the molecule in its flight. If z is the vertical distance from some fixed horizontal plane, then G is to be considered as a function of z, but not of the velocities. We propose to calculate the amount of this quantity which is carried in one second across unit area of any horizontal plane whose co-ordinate is z. We shall assume that the density of the gas is uniform throughout, and that Maxwell's law holds for every stratum.

If $d\mathrm{N}$ is the number of molecules of class (c, w) which cross unit area of the plane in unit time, then, by Exs. (1) and (2), pp. 805-6,

$$d\mathrm{N} = 2\nu \sqrt{\frac{h^3 m^3}{\pi}} e^{-hmc^2} wc \, dw \, dc \quad . \quad . \quad . \quad (1)$$

If λ' is the distance travelled by a molecule since its last encounter till it reaches the plane z, then this molecule must have come from a stratum whose co-ordinate is $z - \dfrac{w}{c}\lambda'$. Now

$$\mathrm{G}\left(z - \frac{w}{c}\lambda'\right) = \mathrm{G}(z) - \frac{w}{c}\lambda' \frac{d\mathrm{G}(z)}{dz}$$

approximately, since λ' is small, and therefore this latter expression may be taken as the amount of the required quantity carried across the plane by the molecule. Summing for all the molecules, $d\mathrm{N}$ in number, we get as the amount carried across by all molecules of this class

---

[1] Boltzmann, *loc. cit.* p. 74.

$$\text{G}d\text{N} - \frac{w}{c}\frac{d\text{G}}{dz}\Sigma\lambda' \quad . \quad . \quad . \quad . \quad . \quad (2)$$

where $\Sigma\lambda'$ is the sum of all the paths of the molecules. Putting $\Sigma\lambda' = \lambda_c d\text{N}$, λ_c will, owing to our assumption of Maxwell's law, be a function of c only, and its value will be c/k (Ex. 7, p. 807). The expression (2) is therefore equal to

$$\cdot \left(\text{G} - \frac{w}{k}\frac{d\text{G}}{dz}\right)d\text{N}.$$

Substituting for $d\text{N}$ its value as given in equation (1), and integrating with respect to w from $-c$ to $+c$, we get, if $d\text{Q}$ is the amount of the quantity sought due to all molecules of class (c),

$$d\text{Q} = \frac{4\nu}{3}\frac{d\text{G}}{dz}\sqrt{\frac{h^3m^3}{\pi}}\frac{c^4e^{-hmc^2}dc}{k}.$$

Putting x for $c\sqrt{hm}$, and integrating from 0 to ∞, we get the whole quantity Q, due to molecules of all classes, in the form (see Ex. 7, p. 807)

$$\text{Q} = \frac{4}{3\pi\sigma^2\sqrt{hm}}\frac{d\text{G}}{dz}\int_0^\infty \frac{x^4e^{-x^2}dx}{\psi(x)}.$$

With the notation of the last article, this may be written

$$\text{Q} = \text{B}\nu\lambda\bar{c}\frac{d\text{G}}{dz} \quad . \quad . \quad . \quad . \quad . \quad (3)$$

If we suppose the horizontal strata to move relatively to each other as in the last article, and put $\text{G} = maz$, so that G is the horizontal momentum per molecule in the stratum z, we get the same result for the viscosity as before.

The coefficient of diffusion of one gas into another may be defined as follows. Let the vertical column consist of two gases A_1 and A_2 which may be supposed to have been originally separated by a horizontal partition, which has been withdrawn. At any stage of the mixing process let there be in a stratum whose co-ordinate is z a number ν_1 molecules per unit volume of the gas A_1 and ν_2 of the gas A_2. If N_1 is the number of molecules of the gas A_1 (supposed uppermost) which cross unit area of the plane z downwards per second, then if we write

$$N_1 = D_{12}\frac{d\nu_1}{dz},$$

D_{12} is the coefficient of diffusion of the gas A_1 into the gas A_2. The simplest example which we can take is the case of the diffusion of a gas into itself. To fix our ideas, let us suppose that the column consists of a single gas, the molecules in the upper half having been originally coloured red and those in the lower half blue. Then if N_1 and ν_1 refer to the red molecules, and if we write

$$N_1 = D\frac{d\nu_1}{dz},$$

D is the coefficient of self-diffusion. In formula (3) G is equal to unity for a red molecule and equal to zero for a blue one, so that we may put G equal to the ratio of the number of red molecules to the sum of the numbers of red and blue in the stratum. Thus if $\nu = \nu_1 + \nu_2$,

$$G = \frac{\nu_1}{\nu_1 + \nu_2} = \frac{\nu_1}{\nu},$$

therefore

$$\frac{dG}{dz} = \frac{1}{\nu}\frac{d\nu_1}{dz}.$$

Also $Q = N_1$, the formula then becomes

$$N_1 = B\lambda\bar{c}\,\frac{d\nu_1}{dz},$$

and we get

$$D = B\lambda\bar{c}.$$

The viscosity and self-diffusion are then connected by the simple relation

$$\eta = D\rho.$$

A more rigorous calculation [1] gives the result

$$1\cdot366\eta = D\rho.$$

In this case Maxwell's law holds, of course, for the mixture as a whole. If f_1 and f_2 are the densities of distribution on the velocity-diagram for the red and blue molecules respectively (Art. 373), we have

$$f_1 + f_2 = Ae^{-hmc^2}.$$

The error we have made is in tacitly assuming that f_1 and f_2 are each proportional to e^{-hmc^2}, whereas they are functions of w as well as of c. The red molecules in the stratum are, in fact, on the whole, moving downward and the blue upward. This is due to the fact that the gas is supposed to have come to the given state from a previous state in which the mixing was less complete. Thus the value obtained for D is too low.

383. Conduction of Heat.—To apply formula (3) of the last article to the calculation of the conductivity, we suppose that there is a vertical temperature gradient in the column of gas, and attribute

---

[1] Jeans, *loc. cit.* p. 333.

to each molecule the *mean* energy of all the molecules of the stratum from which it is supposed to come, that is, we put

$$G = \tfrac{1}{2}m\bar{c}^2 = \frac{3}{4h} = mC_v\Theta \qquad\qquad \text{(pp. 793-795).}$$

Equation (3), Art. 382, then becomes

$$Q = B\rho\lambda\bar{c}C_v\frac{d\Theta}{dz}. \qquad \cdot \qquad \cdot \qquad \cdot \qquad \cdot \qquad (1)$$

where Q is the transmission of heat per second per unit area of the plane. But if κ is the conductivity for heat, κ is defined by the equation

$$Q = \kappa\frac{d\Theta}{dz} \qquad \cdot \qquad \cdot \qquad \cdot \qquad \cdot \qquad (2)$$

thus, comparing (1) and (2), we obtain the result

$$\kappa = B\rho\lambda\bar{c}C_v.$$

The conductivity and viscosity, according to this equation and (2) of Art. 381, are connected by the simple relation

$$\kappa = C_v\eta \qquad \cdot \qquad \cdot \qquad \cdot \qquad \cdot \qquad (3)$$

Before criticising this result, we may at once state the conclusions which have been arrived at by more rigorous methods. Maxwell, by assuming that the molecules are point centres of force repelling each other with a force proportional to the fifth power of the distance, obtained the relation

$$\kappa = \tfrac{5}{2}C_v\eta \qquad \cdot \qquad \cdot \qquad \cdot \qquad \cdot \qquad (4)$$

and it has been found by Chapman[1] that this relation is nearly correct when the force of repulsion varies as any higher power of the distance. This includes the hard spherical molecule as a limiting case, the force of repulsion varying as an infinite power of the distance. The numerical factor in (4) is supported by experimental evidence. Measurements quoted by Jeans[2] show that for the monatomic gases helium and argon the factor is nearly 2·5. For diatomic and other gases the factor is much less. A formula has been given by Jeans[2] which agrees extremely well with experiment for diatomic and compound gases. This is obtained as follows: Adopting a suggestion of Eucken's, that formula (3) may apply to the *rotational* energy transmission, he writes the numerical coefficient with a mean value between that of (3) and (4) according to the number of degrees of freedom corresponding to the rotational and internal energy and to the translational energy respectively. Thus if the molecule has

---

[1] *Phil. Trans.*, 1916, p. 337.   [2] Jeans, *loc. cit.* p. 317.

n degrees of freedom, three of these belong to the translational energy, so that the numerical factor is

$$\frac{3 \times \frac{5}{2} + (n-3)}{n} = \frac{9(n+2) - 5n}{4n} = \tfrac{1}{4}(9\gamma - 5) \qquad \text{(Art. 376)},$$

which gives the relation

$$\kappa = \tfrac{1}{4}(9\gamma - 5)C_v\eta.$$

The following table (after Jeans) gives the values of the conductivity and the viscosity (at $0°$ C.) of a number of gases:—

Gas.	Conductivity. κ	Viscosity. η	$\kappa/\eta C_v$ (observed).	$\tfrac{1}{4}(9\gamma - 5)$.
Hydrogen . . .	·0003970	·0000867	1·89	1·90
Helium	·0003360	·000189	2·38	2·44
Air	·0000566	·000172	1·91	1·91
Oxygen . . .	·0000570	·000189	1·93	1·90
Nitrogen	·0000566	·000166	1·91	1·91
Argon	·0000389	·000210	2·49	2·44
Carbon monoxide . .	·00005425	·000163	1·88	1·91
Carbon dioxide . .	·0000337	·000142	1·52	1·72
Nitrous oxide . . .	·0000351	·000138	1·72	1·73
Nitric oxide . . .	·0000555	·000179	1·86	1·88
Ethylene	·0000407	·0000961	1·55	1·55

The formula connecting conductivity and viscosity leads us to expect that the conductivity, like the viscosity, is independent of the density. This was also predicted by Maxwell, and was verified by Stefan and by Kundt and Warburg. Maxwell stated that the conductivity varies directly as the absolute temperature. This would be strictly true for a gas composed of molecules repelling each other according to the fifth-power law, but is not in good agreement with experiment for actual gases. For the gas composed of hard spherical molecules the conductivity varies as the square root of the absolute temperature.

Returning now to the calculation by which formula (3) was arrived at, we can see that it is still more open to objection than the calculation of viscosity. We have assumed that the density is uniform, whereas it diminishes with temperature when the pressure is constant. This probably does not matter very much, as the mean free path increases in proportion. We have also attributed to each molecule, not its own proper energy, but a mean value; this also ought not to introduce a large error. Much the most serious objection to the method is the assumption that Maxwell's law holds for each stratum. We may conceive a column of gas to be built up of very thin strata, each with Maxwell's distribution of velocities, and

3 G

all at the same pressure, the temperature and density varying according to the proper laws for a steady state of conduction, whatever those laws may be. If the upper and lower boundaries of the column are kept at their appropriate temperatures and the gas otherwise left to itself, it will not be in a steady state, for each stratum is initially in a state in which there is no heat transmission. The mode of calculation is, in fact, designed rather to find how a gas so constituted will begin to conduct heat than to determine the conductivity in a column with an established temperature gradient. We may also use some of our previous results to show that the column is not in a steady state. For the pressure is given by the equation $p = v/2h$ (Eq. 2, p. 793, and 1, p. 779), while the number of molecules passing out of unit area of one side of a stratum per second is $\frac{1}{4}vc$ (Ex. 2, p. 806). Comparing two neighbouring strata, we see that

$$2p = \frac{v_1}{h_1} = \frac{v_2}{h_2},$$

which requires that the density varies inversely as the temperature. But for equality in the number of molecules exchanged, we require

$$v_1\bar{c}_1 = v_2\bar{c}_2, \text{ or } \frac{v_1}{\sqrt{h_1}} = \frac{v_2}{\sqrt{h_2}},$$

which is inconsistent with the equation first written.

384. Thermal Transpiration of Gases.—The passage of gases through narrow tubes and through porous septa was studied by Graham. He found that the rates of flow of gases through a porous diaphragm, such as a thin plate of graphite, are inversely as the square roots of their densities, if their temperatures and pressures are the same. This is Graham's law of diffusion, and, according to the kinetic theory, is equivalent to saying that the rate of flow is proportional to the molecular velocity. Graham found, however, that the passage of gases through capillary tubes or thick porous walls did not follow any such simple law ; in fact, he obtained different laws of motion with plates of different coarseness and with plates and capillary tubes. To the motion of a gas in such cases the name *transpiration* has been given. In Graham's experiments transpiration was produced by a difference of pressure in the gas on each side of the porous partition ; he does not seem to have suspected that a difference of temperature might have a similar effect. That such is the case was discovered by Professor Osborne Reynolds, who designated the phenomenon by the name of *thermal transpiration.*[1]

---

[1] Osborne Reynolds, *Phil. Trans.* A, 1879. *Scientific Papers*, vol. i.

For instance, in one experiment Professor Reynolds enclosed hydrogen in a vessel divided in the middle by a plate of meerschaum, the temperatures of the portions of gas on the two sides being maintained at 11° and 100° C. respectively, while the pressures were initially equal. In this case hydrogen was found to pass from the cold to the hot side of the partition until, when equilibrium was established, the pressure on the hot side was greater than that on the cold side by nearly 1 inch of mercury. The same effect was observed with air, but the difference of pressure was less.

To understand why this difference of pressure exists, let us consider the simplest case, that of a cylindrical vessel HC (Fig. 252), one end of which, H, is kept hot and the other, C, kept cold. Suppose, in the first instance, that the gas is sufficiently rarefied for mutual en-

Fig. 252.

counters to be infrequent compared with the impacts of molecules with the walls of the vessel. Let a molecule strike the end H perpendicularly with a velocity u' and rebound with a velocity u, these velocities being those characteristic of the temperatures of the two ends. The change of momentum is $m(u + u')$, if m is the mass of the molecule. If now the molecule arrives at C with the velocity u and rebounds with the velocity u', the change of momentum is again $m(u + u')$. In such a case, then, it would seem at first sight as though the molecules would be equally distributed throughout the space and would exert equal pressures on H and C. But if the molecules should strike the sides of the cylinder on their way, so as to give up part of their momentum to these sides when travelling in the direction HC and receive increased momentum when travelling in the direction CH— or, in other words, if the cooling and heating of the gas is effected, in part or in whole, by the side walls—then the molecules will arrive at H with a velocity greater than u', and at C with a velocity less than u, so that the pressure on H will be greater than that on C, and the excess of pressure on H over that on C will be exactly balanced by a tangential stress over the curved surface of the cylinder. The molecules would no longer be equally distributed, for they would spend more time at the cold end owing to their slower speed, and thus the density would be greatest at the cold end.

Let us now consider the effect of altering the dimensions of the cylinder. An increase in diameter would diminish the proportion of collisions with the sides as compared with those at the ends, so that the difference of pressure between the ends would be lessened. An increase of length beyond that necessary to ensure the complete heating or cooling of the molecules as they pass from end to end would have no effect in augmenting the difference of pressure. If the density were increased, the frequency of mutual collisions would be increased also—in other words, conduction of heat would take place chiefly through the gas, and this would tend to equalise the pressure, the more violent collisions with the hot end of the tube being made up for by the greater number of collisions with the cold end. Thus the difference of pressure would be most marked in a fine capillary tube. In a wide tube at ordinary pressures the effect would be quite inappreciable, not only because the transfer of heat would be almost entirely by mutual collisions, but also because it would be impossible to avoid convection currents due to gravitation. In the case of a porous plate separating two portions of gas at different temperatures, we may regard the plate as equivalent to a system of fine capillary tubes.

An important result established by Professor Reynolds is that gases transpiring through different plates behave in the same manner, provided that their densities are in a fixed ratio, depending on the

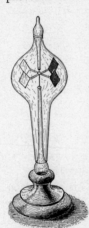

nature of the plates. Thus in the case of transpiration of air caused by pressure, similar results were obtained with stucco and meerschaum when the densities were in the ratio 1 : 5·6. Also, in the case of thermal transpiration, similar results were obtained with the stucco and meerschaum plates when the densities were in the ratio 1 : 6·5. The same ratios were obtained when hydrogen was used instead of air. This fact forms a valuable confirmation of the kinetic theory of gases, according to which we should expect that with passages of different sizes the distances separating the molecules would be proportional to the diameters of the respective passages when the results are similar. The discrepancy between the numbers 5·6 and 6·5 in the two cases is probably due to the altered condition of the plates when heated.

Fig. 253.

The same phenomenon was investigated by Knudsen.[1] In some of his experiments he used two vessels containing rarefied hydrogen, and connected by a tube consisting of alternately narrow and wide sections. The alternate junctions of the narrow and wide portions were heated. In this way a pressure gradient was set up in the narrow tubes, while the pressure gradient in the wider tubes (which would be in the reverse direction) was inappreciable, so that the total difference of pressure between the two vessels was the sum of the differences for all the narrow tubes. When the mean pressure of

[1] *Ann. der Physik*, vol. xxxi. pp. 205, 633, 1910; vol. lxxxiii. p. 797, 1927.

the gas in the apparatus was very small, then, as might be expected, the difference of pressure was also small.   As the mean pressure was gradually increased, the difference of pressure increased to a maximum and then diminished.   Thus for a tube whose internal diameter was $\frac{1}{3}$ mm. and the difference of temperature between the ends about 500° C., the pressure at the hot end was ten times that at the cold end when the mean pressure was $\frac{1}{4}$ mm. of mercury ; when the mean pressure was $3\frac{1}{2}$ mm., the difference of pressure was almost 3 mm. ; and when the mean pressure was about $\frac{1}{3}$ atmo., the difference was less than $\frac{1}{10}$ mm.

Knudsen found that if the diameter of the tube is very small compared with the mean free path of the gas, then the ratio of the pressures is proportional to the square root of the ratio of the absolute temperatures, a result which had also been obtained theoretically by Reynolds.

385. Crookes's Radiometer.—This instrument, invented by Sir W. Crookes, is represented in Fig. 253.   It consists of a very light vane constructed of thin mica discs or lozenges fastened at the ends of four arms of aluminium wire, the whole arranged to turn very freely about a vertical axis and enclosed in a glass vessel which is highly exhausted.   Each of the mica discs is blackened on one side.   On exposing the radiometer to sunlight or any convenient source of radiant heat, the vane revolves in such a direction that the blackened faces are always receding.

The explanation of this phenomenon will be readily understood from the reasoning in the preceding article.   The black faces absorb the rays which they receive more readily than the reflecting faces, and are consequently the hotter of the two.   The pressure is greater on the hotter black faces than on the others, owing to the greater velocity with which the gas molecules rebound.   In this case the tangential reaction is on the fixed walls of the containing vessel. It has been already remarked that the difference in pressure due to a difference of temperature between the ends of a tube containing gas at ordinary pressures would not be appreciable unless the tube were very narrow.   In the radiometer the spaces occupied by the gas are not narrow, but the gas is highly rarefied, so that the distribution of molecules is proportionate to the size of the vessel.   At higher pressures the vane revolves in the opposite direction owing to convection currents.   With smaller vanes the rarefaction need not be pushed so far.   Professor Reynolds obtained a repulsion effect at a pressure of half an atmosphere by using a silk fibre instead of a mica disc.

Professor Reynolds also obtained radiometer motion in a vessel filled with saturated water vapour at ordinary temperatures. A vessel of hot water repelled the wings of the vane and a piece of ice attracted them. In this case the effect was caused by condensation taking place on the sides which were cooled by radiation and by evaporation from the heated sides.

Maxwell[1] was the first to show that in an unequally heated gas the pressure is not the same in all directions, and that if the gas is rarefied, the differences of pressure would be sufficient to account for radiometer motion. Calculations of the amount of stress to be expected were given both by Maxwell and Reynolds, but the results differed, Reynolds obtaining a much smaller stress than Maxwell. Later investigations by J. E. Jones[2] confirm Maxwell's calculation.

[1] J. C. Maxwell, *Sci. Papers*, vol. ii. p. 681.
[2] J. E. Jones, *Phil. Trans.* vol. ccxxiii. (A) p. 1, 1922.

INDEX OF SUBJECTS

The numbers refer to pages

INDEX OF NAMES

The numbers refer to pages

Love, A. E. H., 483
Lucretius, 59
Lüdin, 323
Lummer, O., 283, 536, 542, 546, 550, 558, 575, 582
Lundquist, G., 546, 652
Lupin, H. von, 107

Mack, E., 774
Magnus, A., 289
Magnus, G., 197, 200, 202, 383, 390, 415, 521, 656
Mallory, F., 308
Marcet, F., 289, 350
Marchis, L., 112
Marignac, C. de, 219
Marshall, D., 372
Martine, 497
Mason, J. A., 429
Massieu, F., 732
Mathews, J. H., 374
Mathias, E., 452, 716, 724
Matteucci, C., 641
Matthiessen, A., 144, 185, 526
Maxwell, J. C., 48, 392, 459, 551, 622, 660, 674, 679, 749, 779, 781, 788, 800, 805, 812, 816, 817, 822
Mayer, J. R., 83, 276, 325, 671, 762
M'Connel, J. C., 337
Meissner, W., 574
Melloni, M., 492, 509, 526, 545
Mendeléeff, D., 62, 472
Mendenhall, C. E., 573, 583
Meyer, Lothar, 62, 287
Meyer, Victor, 401
M'Farlane, D., 505
Michel, G., 563, 568
Michelson, A. A., 559
Miculescu, C., 308, 325
Millikan, R. A., 568
Milne, E. A., 799
Milner, S. R., 652
Mitscherlich, E., 212
Monnier, 428
Montgolfier, J. M., 83
Moorby, W. H., 309, 325
Moore, W. L., 799
Morse, H. N., 580
Moseley, Canon H. (not Mosley), 338
Moseley, H. G. J., 77
Moss, H., 135, 179
Moss, R. J., 355
Mousson, A., 334
Moutier, J., 726, 739
Mueller, E. F., 147
Murray, M., 651
Muschenbroeck, P. van, 25, 33, 154, 429, 463

Natterer, J., 440, 466
Negretti, 107
Nernst, W., 244, 258, 289, 396, 775
Neumann, F. E., 288, 320
Neville, F. H., 148

Newlands, J.,
Newton, Sir I., 48,
Nichols, E. F., 560
Nicolson, J. T., 613, 615
Nobili, L., 526
Northmore, T., 440

Oersted, H. C., 463
Olszewski, K., 158, 441, 772
Onnes, H. Kamerlingh, 149, 150, 158, 207, 294, 441, 443, 473, 771
Orr, W. M'F., 555, 663, 679
Ostwald, W., 234, 281
Otto, J., 473

Paalzow, A., 652
Parker, A., 280
Partington, J. R., 284
Paschen, F., 550, 560, 582
Pawlewski, Br., 450
Péclet, E., 606
Pernter, J. M., 522
Perot, A., 326, 407, 716
Person, C. C., 231, 340
Petit, A. T., 27, 168, 171, 172, 181, 197, 207, 247, 286, 288, 498
Pfaff, F., 213
Pfaundler, L., 320
Phillips, J., 108
Pictet, R., 7, 493, 594
Pierre, Is., 183, 188
Pirani, M., 584
Planck, M., 77, 291, 561, 563, 565
Plateau, J. A. F., 329
Platter, H., 320
Playfair, L., 188
Plempius, 493
Poggendorf, J. C., 353
Poisson, S. D., 70, 631
Poole, H. H., 634
Pouillet, C. S. M., 154, 440, 464
Poynting, J. H., 282, 588
Prévost, P., 493
Pringsheim, E., 283, 546, 550, 558, 575, 582
Prinsep, J., 95, 157
Prout, W., 61
Provostaye, F. de la, 340, 504, 511
Puluj, J., 325

Rai, J., 770
Ramsay, Sir Wm., 206, 281, 356, 372, 387, 395, 412, 433, 450, 460
Ramsden, J., 163
Rankine, W. J. M., 7, 69, 84, 394, 721
Rayleigh, Lord, 441, 486, 561, 565, 569
Réaumur, R. A. F. de, 102
Regnault, H. V., 27, 120, 125, 127, 130, 153, 170, 174, 198, 202, 207, 231, 240, 247, 248, 264, 268, 271, 286, 287, 289, 320, 361, 365, 376, 383, 389, 394, 400, 411, 415, 422, 428, 464, 477, 720, 725, 767, 769, 771, 796

THE END

Printed in Great Britain by R. & R. CLARK, LIMITED, *Edinburgh.*